Australian Biological Resources Study

ZOOLOGICAL CATALOGUE OF AUSTRALIA

Volume 10

HYMENOPTERA: APOIDEA

An AGPS Press Publication
Australian Government Publishing Service
Canberra

ISBN for Series: 0 644 02840 8
ISBN for Volume 10: 0 644 29080 3

Zoological Catalogue of Australia

The compilation of the *Zoological Catalogue of Australia* is conducted under the auspices of the Australian Biological Resources Study, J. Just, Director (Fauna), W.W.K. Houston, Executive Editor.

Volume Editor: W.W.K. Houston
Assistant Editor: G.V. Maynard

Vol. 10

HYMENOPTERA: APOIDEA

Josephine C. Cardale
Australian National Insect Collection
CSIRO Division of Entomology
Canberra, ACT

This work may be cited as:

Cardale, J.C. (1993). Hymenoptera: Apoidea. *In* Houston, W.W.K. & Maynard, G.V. (eds) *Zoological Catalogue of Australia*. Canberra : AGPS Vol. 10 x 406 pp.

Printed for AGPS Press by State Print

CONTENTS

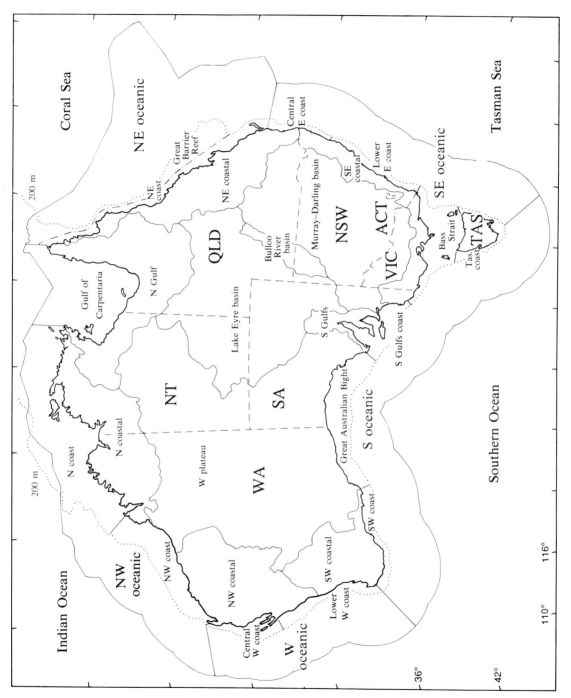

Map 1. States, standard drainage divisions, coastal zones within the 200 m bathymetric contour, and the 200 nautical mile Australian fishing zones. Simple conic projection with two standard parallels (18°S and 36°S)

EDITORIAL PREFACE

INTRODUCTION

An objective of the Australian Biological Resources Study is to stimulate research and publications on the taxonomy and distribution of the Australian fauna and flora. Consistent with this aim, the *Zoological Catalogue of Australia* was conceived as a concise, computer database consisting of current taxonomic and biological knowledge of the Australian fauna, accessible to all interested in such information. The database, and publications derived from it, provide a substantial assessment of current knowledge and should stimulate interest and provide a foundation for future investigations.

The database is an innovative five file structure which can be readily updated. The five files are: a genus taxonomic arrangement file, a species taxonomic arrangement file, a genus available name file, a species available name file and a bibliographic file. A computer program is used to automate the preparation of suitably typeset and indexed books derived from the database. This method yields a standard format and will provide consistency in the presentation of the data in the published *Catalogue*. The format and style of presentation are, therefore, the responsibility of the Australian Biological Resources Study. The authors are responsible only for the information content.

Each volume of the *Catalogue*, treating specific taxa, will cite by name and original reference all species known to occur in Australia. Australia is defined as including Lord Howe Is., Norfolk Is., Cocos (Keeling) Ils, Christmas Is., Ashmore and Cartier Ils, Macquarie Is., Australian Antarctic Territory, Heard and McDonald Ils, and the waters associated with these land areas of Australian political responsibility. Families may be placed in alphabetical or phylogenetic order. Genera and species are in alphabetical order within family, subfamily or tribe, but nominate subgenera and subspecies that occur in Australia are placed first. Information for each species includes synonymy, literature citation, location and status of the type material and type locality for each available name, a brief summary of geographical distribution and ecological attributes, and important references on various aspects, especially biology. The *Catalogue* is designed to serve as a bibliographic directory to the most comprehensive and recent information available on each species.

TAXONOMIC INFORMATION

Nomenclature in the *Catalogue* adheres to the provisions established in the *International Code of Zoological Nomenclature*, 3rd edn (1985). The author and date of all names appearing in the *Catalogue* are presented so that the user may understand the nature and relationships of the names. All names appear in their current legitimate form, which may differ from the form in their original presentation. The valid genus and species group names and their allocation to families are determined by the contributors. No new taxa are described in the *Catalogue* although new combinations, new replacement names, *stat. rev., stat. nov.,* synonymy and lectotype designations may be proposed. New distributional and other biological information may be included. Synonymies do not include combinational changes. Treatment of the nomenclature of family group names is not included.

A useful overview of nomenclature, for both the specialist and the non-specialist, may be found in Cogger, H.G. (1987). Classification and Nomenclature. pp. 266–286 *in* Dyne, G.R. & Walton, D.W. (eds) *Fauna of Australia. General Articles.* Canberra : Australian Government Publishing Service Vol. 1A.

FORMAT OF THE CATALOGUE

An example of the basic format used in the *Catalogue*, based on data from Vol. 4 Coleoptera, is given below. The numbers in the left margin refer to brief explanatory notes which follow the example.

1.   **Hypharpax** W.S. Macleay, 1825

2. *Hypharpax* Macleay, W.S. (1825). *Annulosa Javanica,* or an attempt to illustrate the natural affinities and analogies of the insects. London : Kingsbury, Parbury & Allen 52 pp. [22]

3. [proposed with subgeneric rank in *Harpalus* Latreille, 1802].

4. Type species: *Harpalus (Hypharpax) lateralis* Macleay, 1825 by monotypy.

2. *Sagraemerus* Redtenbacher, L. (1867). Coleopteren. *In, Reise der österreichischen Frigatte* Novara *um die Erde in den Jahren 1857, 1858, 1859,* unter den Befehlen des Commodore B. von Wüllerstorf-Urbair. Zoologischer Theil. Wien : Karl Gerold's Sohn Vol. 2 249 pp. 5 pls [13].

4. Type species: *Sagraemerus javanus* Redtenbacher, 1867 (=*Hypharpax dentipes* Wiedemann, 1823) by monotypy.

5. Taxonomic decision for synonymy: Andrewes, H.E. (1924). On the Oriental Carabidae of the "Reise Novara". *Trans. Entomol. Soc. Lond.* **1923**: 459–468 [467] [15 April 1924].

6. Extralimital distribution: New Guinea, Sulawesi, Java, Sumatra and New Zealand, see Noonan, G.R. (1976). Synopsis of the supra-specific taxa of the tribe Harpalini (Coleoptera : Carabidae). *Quaest. Entomol.* **13**: 3–87 [9].

7. *Hypharpax aereus* (Dejean, 1829)

8. *Harpalus aereus* Dejean, P.F.M.A. (1829). *Species général des Coléoptères, de la Collection de M. le Comte Dejean.* Paris : Méquignon-Marvis Vol. IV vii 520 pp. [384].

9. Type data: holotype, MNHP ♂.

10. Type locality: Australia (as Nouvelle Hollande).

8. *Harpalus boisduvalii* Castelnau, F.L. Laporte de (1867). *Notes on Australian Coleoptera.* Melbourne : R. Soc. Vict. 139 pp. [110]

3. [separates available prior to publication in *Trans. R. Soc. Vict.* **8:** 30–38 (1867), 95–225 (1868)].

9. Type data: syntypes, MCG*

10. Type locality: Swan River, WA

5. Taxonomic decision for synonymy: Chaudoir, M. de (1878). Les Harpaliens d'Australia d'après la collection de M. le Compte de Castelnau et la mienne. *Ann. Mus. Civ. Stor. Nat. Genova* **12**: 475–517 [487].

11. Distribution: NW coastal, SW coastal, S Gulfs, Murray-Darling basin, WA, SA, NSW.
Ecology: terrestrial, volant, (granivore), omnivore.

12. Reference: Blackburn, T. (1888). Further notes on Australian Coleoptera, with descriptions of new species. *Trans. R. Soc. S. Aust.* **10**: 177–287 [183].

Explanatory Notes

1. Genus Valid Name, Author and year of publication. Genus and subgenus names are given in full, with subgenus names in parentheses. Author's initials are used only where there may be ambiguity. Where there are subgenera, the nominate subgenus, if it occurs in Australia, is given first.

2. Genus Available Name, Author, year of publication, and work and page where the name was first made available. Genus Available Names, in synonymy, are listed in chronological order. Each name is given in its legitimate form, without diacritic marks or hyphenation. Published names judged to be not available may be included in the synonymies where clarification is needed to preclude future confusion on the status of these names.

3. Qualifications, if any, concerning the name are given in brackets after the bibliographic citation.

4. Type species of the genus available name, given in its original combination, followed if necessary by the form used by the nominator, and followed by the method of designation. If no type species was designated or indicated, the names of all originally included species are listed in chronological order.

5. Bibliographic Reference to the Synonymy adopted by the author of the volume or an appropriate statement if the synonymy is new and by the author.

6. Extralimital distribution. If species contained in the genus occur outside Australia, a brief descriptive phrase of that distribution and a bibliographic reference to a work, which leads the reader to literature defining that distribution, is given.

7. Species Valid Name, Author and year of publication. A subgeneric name, if present, is given in parentheses. If the valid name of the species is a changed combination, the author and year of publication of the species are in parentheses. Where there are subspecies, the nominate subspecies, if it occurs in Australia, is given first.

8. Species Available Name, Author, year of publication, and work and page where the name was first made available. Species available names, in synonymy, are listed in chronological order. Each name is given in its legitimate form, without diacritic marks, capitalization or hyphenation. Published names judged to be not available may be included in the synonymies where clarification is needed to preclude future confusion on the status of these names.

9. Type data includes nature of type specimen(s) and institution(s) in which the type(s) is held. An asterisk indicates that the type(s) has not been examined and its identity established personally by the author. The museum acronyms, and the institutions to which they refer, are listed in Appendix II. If the primary type is a lectotype or neotype, a reference to the subsequent designation follows.

10. Type locality is the place(s) where the primary type(s) (includes lectotype and neotype) was collected.

11. Distribution and Ecology. The known distribution and ecology of each species is given according to standardized lists of descriptors established by the Australian Biological Resources Study. These descriptors also serve as computer search terms for the *Zoological Catalogue of Australia* database. Descriptors in parentheses imply that the information is unconfirmed but, in the opinion of the author, likely to be correct. If the author qualifies the distribution or ecological data, that additional information is separated from the keywords by a semicolon.

The political and geographic region descriptors are given in the map on p. vi. Political areas include the adjacent waters. Terrestrial geographical terms are based on the drainage systems of continental Australia, while marine terms are self explanatory except as follows: the boundary between the coastal and oceanic zones is the 200 m contour; the Arafura Sea extends from Cape York to 124°E; and the boundary between the Tasman and Coral Seas is considered to be the latitude of Fraser Island, also regarded as the southern terminus of the Great Barrier Reef.

Ecological descriptors are general terms taken from the lists below. Terms for terrestrial habitat or vegetation type follow Specht, R.L. (1970). Vegetation. pp. 44–67 *in* Leeper, G.W. (ed.) *The Australian Environment.* 4th edn Melbourne : CSIRO-Melbourne Univ. Press.

Life History Characteristics

aerial	crepuscular	gregarious	peridomestic
amphibious	cryptozoic	interstitial	planktonic
anadromous	diurnal	migratory	sedentary
aquatic	endocommensal	nectonic	sessile
arboreal	eurybathic	noctidiurnal	terrestrial
burrowing	fossorial	nocturnal	territorial
catadromous	glider	nomadic	volant

Feeding Habit

algal-feeder	filter-feeder	herbivore	predator
arthropod-feeder	florivore	mellivore	omnivore
bacteria-feeder	folivore	miner	root-feeder
coprophagous	frugivore	necrophagous	sanguinivore
detritus-feeder	fungivore	non-feeder	sap-feeder
ectoparasite	gall-former	parasitoid	wood-borer
endoparasite	granivore	piscivore	

Community or Habitat Descriptors
Marine

abyssal	continental slope	mud bottom	sand bottom
abyssopelagic	coral reef	neritic	silt bottom
bathypelagic	estuarine	oceanic	sublittoral
benthic	littoral	pelagic	supralittoral
coastal salt marsh	mangrove	rock bottom	
continental shelf	mesopelagic	rock reef	

Freshwater

inland salt marsh	lotic freshwater	sand bottom	thermal springs
interstitial waters	mud bottom	silt bottom	torrent dweller
lake	permanent pond	springs	underground water
lentic freshwater	profundal	swamp	vegetation-held water
limnetic	rock bottom	temporary pond	
littoral	salt lake	temporary pools	

Vegetation Growth forms

tall closed forest	tall woodland	closed scrub	closed heath
closed forest	woodland	open scrub	open heath
low closed forest	low woodland	tall shrubland	hummock grassland
tall open forest	tall open woodland	low shrubland	tussock grassland
open forest	open woodland	tall open shrubland	
low open forest	low open woodland	low open shrubland	

Terrestrial and Miscellaneous

alpine	desert sand dunes	rocky desert	subtropical
caves	host (taxon)	rotting wood	temperate
coastal	litter	sand plain desert	tree hole
coastal sand dunes	montane	saxicoline	tropical
crops	riparian	soil	under bark

12. References, where entered, are selected to provide a useful lead into the literature on the species. Each reference may be followed with a word or words in parentheses indicating the nature of the content, if this is not obvious from the title.

13. Miscellaneous Items. Common abbreviations, contractions and symbols are listed in Appendix I. Taxonomic decisions made in this volume, such as new combinations, are indicated by the term "this work" and are also listed in Appendix III.

Literature citations throughout the *Catalogue* are given in full. Older works with extended subtitles may have been shortened, but only if their identity is preserved. Serial titles are abbreviated in a manner designed to facilitate library research. References or titles originally issued in script other then Roman and lacking a Romanized translation are transliterated with the original language shown in brackets.

14. Index. All valid and available names are indexed and in each appropriate combination, even though they may appear in the text in only one combination. Thus a quadrinominal used once will be indexed four times. Taxa of all names above the genus level are indexed also and are given in bold type; families and subfamilies with Australian taxa in the volume are given in upper case, others in lower case. The page(s) on which entries to unplaced taxa commence are listed also in the index against 'Unplaced taxa'.

ACKNOWLEDGEMENTS

The editors wish to thank staff of the Australian Biological Resources Study for assistance with the preparation of this volume. Particular thanks are due to Ha Diep and Alice Wells for editorial assistance, and to Wayne Murray for typesetting and database management. We also wish to acknowledge the support we have received from other sections of the Australian National Parks and Wildlife Service.

W.W.K. Houston

APOIDEA

Josephine C. Cardale

INTRODUCTION

The Apoidea, or bees, are represented in Australia by over 1500 species. Excluding the Formicidae, they are the largest group of aculeate Hymenoptera in Australia. They are closely related to the sphecoid wasps but exhibit a major biological difference: bees feed their larvae on pollen and nectar; sphecoids feed their larvae on insect or spider prey (Michener & Houston 1991). Brothers (1975), in a review of the aculeate Hymenoptera, placed the bees with the sphecids in the superfamily Sphecoidea. Lomholdt (1982) and the detailed cladistic analysis of Alexander (1992) support this arrangement. None of these works, however, support Lanham (1980) who postulated a closer relationship between bees and the Vespoidea of Brothers, than between bees and sphecoids.

The taxonomic arrangement of Michener & Houston (1991), treating Sphecoidea and Apoidea as separate superfamilies, is used in the *Catalogue*. Ten families of bees are recognised, of which seven are found in Australia. The species in the families that are found in Australia or its external territories (Lord Howe Is., Norfolk Is., Cocos (Keeling) Ils, Christmas Is., Ashmore Is., Cartier Is.) are treated in the *Catalogue*. The three families not recorded from Australia are the Andrenidae, known from all continents except Australia and Antarctica; the Oxaeidae, from the Nearctic and Neotropical Regions; and the Melittidae, from the Holarctic and Afrotropical Regions (Hurd 1979).

Michener (1965) revised the Apoidea of Australia and the South Pacific, listed the species and erected many new genera and subgenera. There have been three changes at the family level since 1965: Michener's Stenotritinae (Colletidae) have been raised to the family Stenotritidae (McGinley, 1980); the Ctenoplectrinae (previously in the Melittidae) have been raised to family rank also (Michener & Greenberg 1980); and the Fideliidae are now treated as a subfamily in the Megachilidae (Rozen 1977). Recent comparative morphological studies on Apoidea have confirmed the arrangement of the families and subfamilies used here (*e.g.* Cane 1979; De Lello 1971a, 1971b; Michener 1981a, 1985; Michener & Brooks 1984; Michener & Fraser 1978; Michener & Greenberg 1980; Wille 1979; Winston 1979).

Michener (1986) listed family-group names for all taxa of bees, and raised the problem of the status of some of the family-group names. Later he stated (Michener 1991) "the use of some of the best known family-group names of bees is not in strict accord with the Principle of Priority" and put forward a proposal to the *International Commission for Zoological Nomenclature* for the conservation of established names. In order to retain nomenclatural stability, those established family-group names in current usage are used in the *Catalogue*.

Michener (1979) examined the distributions of families of Apoidea. He found that bees reach their greatest abundance and diversity in warm temperate, and contiguous desertic regions, as in the Mediterranean basin, the Californian area and in Australia. Cool temperate areas in Australia have markedly few bees; only 18 genera have been recorded from Tasmania. The bee fauna of the moist tropics varies considerably. The fauna of the Afrotropical Region is richer than the Oriental Region and the fauna becomes poorer eastwards towards New Guinea and the northeast of Australia.

Australia is unique in having about half its species, and the greatest diversity of genera, in the primitive family Colletidae. As well, there is an extraordinary dependence of Australian bees on one family of plants, the Myrtaceae (Michener 1965; Armstrong 1979).

TAXONOMIC STUDIES

Fabricius (1775) published the first descriptions of Australian bees, based on the specimens collected by Joseph Banks and others on the eastern coast of Australia in 1770. Smith (1853, 1854, 1879), Cockerell (numerous papers from 1904 to 1939) and Rayment (numerous papers from 1927 to 1961) were responsible for most of the names published before 1965. Australian bees were catalogued by Froggatt (1892), Dalla Torre (1896), Hacker (1921) and Cockerell (1930–1934). Sandhouse (1943) listed the type species of genera and subgenera for the world. Type specimens of almost all species known from Australia before 1920 were deposited in overseas museums.

Since 1960, C.D. Michener has been the major worker on the Apoidea of Australia. He revised the entire fauna (Michener 1965), organised and integrated old information with his own biological and taxonomic studies, and placed our knowledge of Australian bees in a world context. Since 1967, T.F. Houston has made major contributions on the biology and taxonomy of Australian Apoidea, while E.M. Exley has published major revisions of genera of Euryglossinae (*e.g.* Exley 1968, 1976a, 1976b). Taxonomic revisions of several groups of bees are in progress and theses by Houston (1969), King (1986, 1991) and Maynard (1992) have been published in part.

Rayment (1935) published the first book on Australian bees. This book included many biological observations and descriptions of a large number of new species. He was a considerable artist, providing a large number of illustrations for his scientific papers, and he was a most prolific author. In addition to his taxonomic papers on bees, wasps and thrips, he wrote on apiculture, published three novels and numerous articles, and gave radio broadcasts on a wide variety of topics (Young 1967). Correspondents from all around Australia sent him specimens of native bees, particularly after an appeal in the *Australasian Beekeeper* for specimens.

Rayment's papers on Anthophoridae, submitted to the journal *Treubia*, were caught up in World War 2 when the Japanese invaded Java. Part I was published by the Japanese in 1944 (Rayment 1944, but it has the date 1942 printed on it) and Part II was published in 1947 (Rayment 1947; Young 1947). The split publication has caused taxonomic problems, as some new names were used in Part I but formal descriptions were not published until Part II. A qualification to the use of each of these names is given where they are used in the *Catalogue*. A number of Rayment names published in other papers have not been matched to formal descriptions; these are listed in Appendix III.

Before Rayment died, his personal collection, which contained a large number of genuine holotypes, was purchased by CSIRO Division of Entomology, Canberra. This collection is now in the Australian National Insect Collection (ANIC). When the specimens were transferred from Rayment's cabinet, over 30 of the type specimens which were described from his collection were not found: these types are listed in the *Catalogue* as "whereabouts unknown". Some of these types may be present in the ANIC or in other Australian collections but unlabelled, or it is possible that they were among specimens given away by Rayment before the collection left his possession.

K. Walker (*in litt.*, pers. comm. A. Neboiss and E. Matheson) provided a further insight into the problems associated with Rayment's types. Rayment did not collect extensively outside of the Melbourne environs. Instead he received material from a number of collectors.

Recognition of these collectors is important as most label data includes only their initials. The main collectors for Rayment were:

JK: Dr J. Kerr (medical practitioner), Brisbane, SE QLD (whose initials could be confused with NMV material of J. Kershaw);

RT: R. Trebilcock (solicitor), NW VIC;

AS: A. Snell (sheep shearer), WA;

ANB: A.N. Burns (Curator of Entomology, NMV), VIC; and

EM: E. Matheson (technician in Entomology, NMV), VIC.

Rayment had an indiscriminate (occasionally casual) attitude towards type labelling. He would sometimes place a red, type label on a specimen to indicate that he had examined the specimen and had identified it as the correct type for the species. In this sense, the word type and a red label was not meant to indicate holotype or paratype status of the specimens, but simply a correct identification. He often described the opposite sex of a described species years after the original description and called such specimens allotypes. He was known to give away small boxes of specimens with copies of his stories and these boxes would sometimes contain specimens labelled as types.

SOLITARY AND SOCIAL BEES

To the layman, the word "bee" generally means the introduced honeybee, *Apis mellifera* Linnaeus, a species of the comparatively small family of social bees, the Apidae. *Apis mellifera* occurs over much of Australia, in beehives or feral, and is highly visible on crops, garden plants and native vegetation. The painful sting it can inflict is well known. The honeybee is of considerable economic importance and its honey is a part of our diet. There are very few species of truly social bees in Australia and the great majority of native species, including all species of our largest family, the Colletidae, are solitary.

All bees visit flowers for nectar and almost all females gather pollen as food for their larvae. One Australian species, *Ctenoplectra australica* Cockerell, probably uses floral oils. The females of cleptoparasitic species, however, lay their eggs on the provisions that their host (another species of bee) has gathered for her own larvae.

Solitary bees do not cooperate in nest construction or provisioning. Each female makes her own nest, constructs a cell, mass provisions it with enough pollen and nectar to feed a larva to maturity, lays an egg in the cell and then closes that cell before starting the next cell or nest. There is no cooperation with or behavioural or morphological differentiation from other females of the same species. There is usually no contact between generations as the larvae develop in closed cells and the mother normally dies before her offspring emerge.

The most highly social bees, on the other hand, live in colonies where numerous individuals and adults of more than one generation coexist. There is cooperation and division of labour among individuals in the construction of the nest and the feeding of the larvae; there is contact between adults and larvae as the larvae are fed progressively; and the egg-laying caste is physically differentiated from the other females.

Between the extremes of solitary and fully social behaviour, there are various intermediates (Michener 1974): solitary species which nest in aggregations without interaction in nest building; communal species with several females sharing a nest but with each female constructing, provisioning and laying eggs in her own cells; communal species which cooperate in construction and provisioning of cells but each female has fully developed ovaries; and communal species where there are females that do not lay eggs but they differ from the egg-layers only in the lack of ovarian development.

3

A colony is described as subsocial when it consists of one female who protects and feeds her immature offspring before they reach maturity. In this case, there is no cooperation with or division of labour among the adults. Colonies of primitively social bees do have cooperation between and division of labour among the adults. Contact between two or more generations of adults occurs but the adults are not physically differentiated.

BIOLOGICAL STUDIES

Studies of bees have been hampered by problems associated with the identification of individuals to species. Very few Australian bees have been studied in the laboratory and, for most groups, field observations on biology are fragmentary. The best source of information is Michener (1965) and the most important references are listed under the family headings. McGinley (1989) catalogued references to immature Apoidea of the world.

Many of the solitary bees build nests in the soil, some in rotten wood. Others use pre-existing holes or hollows in wood or the soil, dig out the centre of a pithy stem, or re-use a mud-nest built by other Hymenoptera. Bees nesting in wood, rather than soil, are more likely to be successful migrants to another country; two such species of Australian Colletidae, *Euryglossina (Euryglossina) proctotrypoides* Cockerell and *Hyleoides concinna* (Fabricius) have become established in New Zealand (Donovan 1980, 1983; Fordham 1989).

The discovery of polymorphic males in some communally nesting Halictidae (Houston 1970) and work on the relatedness of nest-sharers in Allodapini (Schwarz 1988) have led to continuing research on the development of insect social behaviour (Knerer & Schwarz 1976, 1978; Knerer 1980; Kukuk & Schwarz 1987, 1988; Sugden 1989; Kukuk & Crozier 1990; O'Keefe & Schwarz 1990; Schwarz & Blows 1991; Schwarz & O'Keefe 1991).

FLOWER RELATIONSHIPS AND POLLINATION

Bees obtain their food (pollen, nectar, or in a few groups, oil), from the flowers of angiosperms. In turn, many plants depend on Apoidea to effect pollination. Polylectic species gather pollen from a wide range of plants while oligolectic species are restricted to a few species of related flowers. Many species of Australian bees, especially in the Colletidae, appear to be oligolectic on the family Myrtaceae. Where pollen is carried internally, as by Hylaeinae, Euryglossinae and at least one species of Colletinae (Houston 1981), it is difficult to confirm oligolecty.

Michener (1965) and Armstrong (1979) provide the most comprehensive information on the flower visiting records of Australian native bees but Australian flower visiting records for *A. mellifera* are scattered through the botanical and agricultural literature (*e.g.* Blake & Roff 1958; Collins & Rebelo 1987; Goebel 1984; Heard *et al.* 1990; Ramsey 1988; Vithanage & Ironside 1986). Many records of pollination by native bees do not identify the bees to species (*e.g.* Bernhardt 1986, 1987; Dafni & Calder 1987; Beardsell *et al.* 1986; Anderson & Symon 1988; House 1989; Gross 1992), so these records could not be included in the *Catalogue*.

BEES AND HUMANS

The majority of native bees are seldom noticed even though their nests may be conspicuous, especially those of species which nest in aggregations. Many bees that nest in pre-existing hollows, burrows or nests, *e.g.* those of Megachilidae (Rayment 1935), may be found also in locations around houses. However, they are seldom recorded as pests.

Xylocopini, or carpenter bees, excavate burrows in sound wood but no Australian species have been recorded as pests of structural timber. Blue-banded bees (*Amegilla (Zonamegilla)* spp.) are sometimes found nesting in adobe walls or in mortar between bricks or stones in house walls (Rayment 1944; Cardale 1968) and possibly cause damage to aboriginal rock art sites (Naumann & Watson 1987; Wylie *et al.* 1987). In the wild, both native and introduced honeybees build nests in hollow trees, in hollows among rocks and sometimes in cavities in houses. Native bees have been known to collect fresh paint or putty from buildings for use in their nests (Michener 1981b; Wagner & Dollin 1982).

Worldwide, Apidae are managed by humans for honey production and pollination of plants. Australian Aboriginals have been recorded eating the larvae of the large, solitary, soil-nesting anthophorid, *Amegilla dawsoni* (Douglas 1980) and use the honey of the stingless honeybees, *Trigona (Heterotrigona)* spp. and *Austroplebeia* spp. (McKenzie 1975; Dollin & Dollin 1983, 1986). The Australian native bees otherwise have been largely neglected but there is now interest in their potential as pollinators (Heard 1988; Velthuis 1990).

The honeybee, *A. mellifera*, was introduced into Australia early in the 19th century. The honey industry in Australia produces significant domestic and export income and, in addition, *A. mellifera* is the most important insect pollinator of crop plants as well as a very significant pollinator of native plants. It has been suspected of deleterious effects: it may "rob" native flowers without pollinating them or compete with native bees for floral resources (Douglas 1980; Pyke 1983; Pyke & Balzer 1985; Sugden & Pyke 1991; Wapshere 1988). The apiarists' point of view has been put, for example, Winner (1983), Burking & Kessell (1987) and in papers in Rhodes (1988).

Other species of bees were brought into Australia in the 1930's to pollinate specific introduced crops. Bumblebees were brought into Australia from England (Young 1967). They were also introduced from New Zealand where they had been established for the same purpose. The first introductions into Australia failed, but in 1992 one species, *Bombus terrestris* (Linnaeus), was found to be established. The alfalfa leafcutting bee, *Megachile rotundata* (Fabricius), was released in South Australia in 1987 in an attempt to improve the production of lucerne seed (Anon. 1987). Its establishment and success have yet to be assessed. Pollination of lucerne by honeybees and native bees was studied by Doull (1961) and Bray (1973).

Females of the larger, solitary, native bees can sting humans. These bees are not aggressive in defence of their nests and such stings are rare and usually involve the bee being trapped in clothing. Recorded cases of allergic reaction to stings from native bees are few (Morris *et al.* 1988).

A. mellifera is aggressive in defence of its colony and is relatively more likely to sting people. Pain and swelling at the site of the sting are a normal reaction. Medical treatment may be necessary if a person is stung by a large number of bees or on certain areas of the body, such as near the eyes or on the tongue. Serious medical problems may arise in individuals who have become sensitized to honeybee venom: they may suffer a severe allergic reaction to subsequent stings (Southcott 1988). The risk from bee stings is generally exaggerated (Schmidt 1986).

FOSSIL BEES

Houston (1987) described the fossil brood cells of Stenotritidae from Australia. Publications on fossil bees described from other parts of the world include Zeuner & Manning (1976), Wille (1977), Burnham (1979), Michener & Grimaldi (1988a, 1988b) and Rasnitsyn & Michener (1991).

NOMINA NUDA

The following names are recorded in the literature but there is no indication to which taxa they refer; they are not included elsewhere in the *Catalogue*. They do not satisfy the criteria of availability according to the *International Code of Zoological Nomenclature* and they are listed here as *nomina nuda* decision of J.C. Cardale. A full list of names designated as *nomina nuda* is given in Appendix III.

Anthophora duttiella Rayment, 1944: 15 (fig. only)
Anthophora engganensis Rayment, 1944: 15 (fig. only), p. 32 (as carrier of a small insect)
Anthophora engannensis Rayment, 1946: 65 (as carrier of a small insect)
Anthophora sybilae glauca Rayment, 1944: 21 (name only)
Euryglossa nigrocyanea Rayment, 1935: 23 pl. 2 fig. 18 (caption only); Michener 1965: 87
Exoneura roddi Rayment, 1949: 250 fig. 3 (caption only to fig. of larva)
Exoneura subholmesi Rayment, 1949: 248, 250 fig. 2, 253 (name only)
Halictus darlingensis Rayment, 1954: 31 (listed as host of mite)
Halictus paradimorphus Rayment, 1955: 152 (name only)
Hylaeus dorothae Erickson, 1951: 64 (name only); Erickson, 1965: 63 (repeats 1951 remarks)
Hylaeus nigrojugata Rayment, 1951: 305 (listed as host to mite)
Hylaeus nigrojugatus Rayment, 1954: 28 (nest, host to parasitic wasp)
Paracolletes paradoxus Rayment, 1955: 88 (explanation for Text-Fig. 4, fig. 2, on p. 102)
Prosopis ruficornis Rayment, 1929: 60 (name only)

NOTES ON THE CATALOGUE

Families are listed in the phylogenetic order of Michener & Houston (1991) but the subfamilies, genera and species are listed in alphabetical order, with nominate subgenera and subspecies, if they occur in Australia, first.

Type information is given almost exclusively for primary types; details of paratypes, including "allotypes", will be found by consulting the references. The term "syntypes (probable)" is given where the original description does not indicate how many specimens were in front of the describer. Some of the specimens accepted as holotypes by several workers, (*e.g.* Michener 1965) do not have this status. For example, some species of Cockerell were described from more than one specimen and in the original publication a holotype was not selected. Later authors examining Cockerell's material have found one specimen from each series is labelled 'type', and they have treated this specimen as the holotype. Under Art. 73, 1985 of the *International Code of Zoological Nomenclature*, all of such specimens from the original series are syntypes, unless a holotype has been inferred in subsequent literature, and thus the specimen is a lectotype by holotype inference (Art. 74).

The zoogeographic terms used for extralimital distribution follow Cranston & Naumann (1991). New Guinea is used in the zoogeographic sense; many of the references to distribution pre-date the formation of Papua New Guinea and West Irian. Non-Australian localities have been given their modern names (or spelling) but it was not possible to check all cases.

The distributions of species are mainly from published data and all localities are listed where five or fewer localities are published. There are few published distribution records from the Australian Capital Territory but many of the species recorded from the Murray-Darling basin, NSW, also occur in the ACT. Labels which read "National Park NSW" are assumed to refer to Royal National Park, south of Sydney, NSW, and "National Park QLD" to Lamington National Park, S QLD.

Comparatively little is known of the ecology of the Australian bees except for a few well-studied species. For most species, all relevant references are listed but catalogue references and those repeating information are not included. References are qualified when it seems likely that the species has been misidentified.

The records of flowers visited by each species, where known, are listed in the *Catalogue*. No attempt has been made to distinguish between pollen and nectar sources as this information was not given for most records. Plant names follow Chapman (1991).

ACKNOWLEDGEMENTS

Preparation of this volume of the *Catalogue* formed part of the research conducted by the CSIRO Division of Entomology, Canberra, and the Division's resources and facilities were made available to me. Compilation of the volume was supported by a grant from the Australian Biological Resources Study.

The illustrations used in the family introductions, except for Ctenoplectridae, are from Michener & Houston (1991). They were kindly provided by and are reproduced with permission from the CSIRO Division of Entomology and the Melbourne University Press. The illustration of Ctenoplectridae was prepared for ABRS by Mr G. Thompson of the Queensland Museum.

The author wishes to thank the following people for assistance, information and encouragement: Dr I.D. Naumann, ANIC and the Computing Section, CSIRO Division of Entomology, Canberra, ACT; the librarians at CSIRO Black Mountain Library, Canberra, ACT; Dr T.F. Houston, Western Australian Museum, Perth, WA; Dr J. King, Department of Primary Industries, Brisbane, QLD; Dr A. Dollin, North Richmond, NSW; Dr M.P. Schwarz, Monash University, Melbourne, VIC; Mr K. Walker, Museum of Victoria, Melbourne, VIC; Professor C.D. Michener and Dr R. Brooks, University of Kansas, Lawrence, Kansas, USA; and staff of the Australian Biological Resources Study, especially Dr W.W.K. Houston and Dr G. Maynard.

J.C.C.

REFERENCES

Alexander, B.A. (1992). An exploratory analysis of cladistic relationships within the superfamily Apoidea, with special reference to sphecid wasps (Hymenoptera). *J. Hymenoptera Res.* **1**: 25–61

Anderson, G.J. & Symon, D. (1988). Insect foragers on *Solanum* flowers in Australia. *Ann. M. Bot. Gard.* **75**: 842–852

Anon. (1987). Leafcutter bees released in S.A. *Australas. Beekpr* **88**: 175

Armstrong, J.A. (1979). Biotic pollination mechanisms in the Australian flora—a review. *N.Z. J. Bot.* **17**: 467–508

Beardsell, D.V., Clements, M.A., Hutchinson, J.F. & Williams, E.G. (1986). Pollination of *Diuris maculata* R.Br. (Orchidaceae) by floral mimicry of the native legumes *Daviesia* spp. and *Pultenaea scabra* R.Br. *Aust. J. Bot.* **34**: 165–173

Bernhardt, P. (1986). Bee-pollination in *Hibbertia fasciculata* (Dilleniaceae). *Plant Syst. Evol.* **152**: 231–241

Bernhardt, P. (1987). A comparison of the diversity, density, and foraging behavior of bees and wasps on Australian *Acacia. Ann. M. Bot. Gard.* **74**: 42–50

Blake, S.T. & Roff, C. (1958). *The Honey Flora of South-eastern Queensland.* Brisbane : Dept. Agriculture & Stock 199 pp.

Bray, R.A. (1973). Characteristics of some bees of the family Megachilidae in southeast Queensland and their potential as lucerne pollinators. *J. Aust. Entomol. Soc.* **12**: 99–102

Brothers, D.J. (1975). Phylogeny and classification of the aculeate Hymenoptera, with special reference to the Mutillidae. *Univ. Kans. Sci. Bull.* **50**: 483–648

Burking, R.C. & Kessell, A.C. (1987). The effects of the diminishing flora resource on the Western Australian beekeeping industry. *Australas. Beekpr* **88**: 184–188

Burnham, L. (1979). Survey of social insects in the fossil record. *Psyche (Camb.)* **85**: 85–133

Cane, J.H. (1979). The hind tibiotarsal and tibial spur articulations in bees (Hymenoptera : Apoidea). *J. Kansas Entomol. Soc.* **52**: 123–137

Cardale, J. (1968). Nests and nesting behaviour of *Amegilla (Amegilla) pulchra* (Smith) (Hymenoptera : Apoidea : Anthophorinae). *Aust. J. Zool.* **16**: 689–707

Chapman, A.D. (1991). *Australian Plant Name Index.* Australian Flora and Fauna Series Nos 12–15. Canberra : AGPS xxii 3055 pp.

Cockerell, T.D.A. (1930). The bees of Australia. *Aust. Zool.* **6**: 137–156, 205–236

Cockerell, T.D.A. (1931). The bees of Australia. *Aust. Zool.* **7**: 34–54

Cockerell, T.D.A. (1932). The bees of Australia. *Aust. Zool.* **7**: 206–218

Cockerell, T.D.A. (1933). The bees of Australia. *Aust. Zool.* **7**: 291–324

Cockerell, T.D.A. (1934). The bees of Australia. *Aust. Zool.* **8**: 2–38

Collins, B.G. & Rebelo, T. (1987). Pollination biology of the Proteaceae in Australia and southern Africa. *Aust. J. Ecol.* **12**: 387–421

Cranston, P.S. & Naumann, I.D. (1991). Biogeography. pp. 180–197 *in* CSIRO (sponsor) *The Insects of Australia.* A textbook for students and research workers. Melbourne : Melbourne University Press Vol. II 2nd Edn

Dafni, A. & Calder, D.M. (1987). Pollination by deceit and floral mimesis in *Thelymitra antennifera* (Orchidaceae). *Plant Syst. Evol.* **158**: 11–22

Dalla Torre, K.W. (1896). *Catalogus Hymenopterorum Hucusque Descriptorum Systematicus et Synonymicus.* Apidae (Anthophila). Lipsiae : G. Engelmann Vol. x 643 pp.

De Lello, E. (1971a). Adnexal glands of the sting apparatus of bees: anatomy and histology, I (Hymenoptera : Colletidae and Andrenidae). *J. Kansas Entomol. Soc.* **44**: 5–13

De Lello, E. (1971b). Adnexal glands of the sting apparatus of bees: anatomy and histology, II (Hymenoptera : Halictidae). *J. Kansas Entomol. Soc.* **44**: 14–20

Dollin, A. & Dollin, L. (1986). Tracing aboriginal apiculture of Australian native bees in the far north-west. *Australas. Beekpr* **88**: 118–122

Dollin, L. & Dollin, A. (1983). Honeymooning in far north Queensland with Australian native bees. *Australas. Beekpr* **85**: 104–107

Donovan, B.J. (1980). Interactions between native and introduced bees in New Zealand. *N.Z. J. Ecol.* **3**: 104–116

Donovan, B.J. (1983). Occurrence of the Australian bee *Hyleoides concinna* (Hymenoptera : Colletidae) in New Zealand. *N.Z. J. Zool.* **10**: 345–348

Douglas, A.M. (1980). *Our Dying Fauna.* A personal perspective on a changing environment. Perth : Creative Research, in association with Biological Services 170 pp.

Doull, K.M. (1961). Insect problems of lucerne seed production in South Australia. *J. Aust. Inst. Agric. Sci.* **27**: 11–15

Erickson, R. (1951). *Orchids of the West.* Perth : Paterson Brokensha 109 pp.

Erickson, R. (1965). *Orchids of the West.* Perth : Paterson Brokensha 107 pp. 2nd edn

Exley, E.M. (1968). Revision of the genus *Euryglossina* Cockerell (Apoidea : Colletidae). *Aust. J. Zool.* **16**: 915–1020

Exley, E.M. (1976a). New species and records of *Pachyprosopis* Perkins (Apoidea : Colletidae : Euryglossinae). *J. Aust. Entomol. Soc.* **14**: 399–407

Exley, E.M. (1976b). Revision of the subgenus *Euryglossa* Smith (Apoidea : Colletidae : Euryglossinae). *Aust. J. Zool. Suppl. Ser.* **41**: 1–72

Fabricius, J.C. (1775). *Systema Entomologiae,* sistens insectorum classes, ordines, genera, species, adiectis synonymis, locis, descriptionibus, observationibus. Korte : Flensburgi et Lipsiae xxvii 832 pp.

Fordham, R.A. (1989). Further New Zealand records of the new immigrant Australian bee *Hyleoides concinna* (Hymenoptera: Colletidae; Hylaeinae). *N.Z. Entomol.* **12**: 65–67

Froggatt, W.W. (1892). Catalogue of the described Hymenoptera of Australia. Part II. *Proc. Linn. Soc. N.S.W. (2)***7**: 205–248

Goebel, R. (1984). Honey bees for pollination. *Qd Agric. J.* **110**: 317–321

Gross, C.L. (1992). Floral traits and pollinator constancy: foraging by native bees among three sympatric legumes. *Aust. J. Ecol.* **17**: 67–74

Hacker, H. (1921). Catalogue of Australian bees. *Mem. Qd Mus.* **7**: 99–163

Heard, T.A. (1988). Propagation of hives of *Trigona carbonaria* Smith (Hymenoptera: Apidae). *J. Aust. Entomol. Soc.* **27**: 303–304

Heard, T.A., Vithanage, V. & Chacko, E.K. (1990). Pollination biology of cashew in the Northern Territory of Australia. *Aust. J. Agric. Res.* **41**: 1101–1114

House, S.M. (1989). Pollen movement to flowering canopies of pistillate individuals of three rain forest tree species in tropical Australia. *Aust. J. Ecol.* **14**: 77–94

Houston, T.F. (1969). The systematics and biology of Australian hylaeine bees (Hymenoptera : Colletidae). Unpubl. PhD Thesis. Brisbane : University of Queensland 423 pp.

Houston, T.F. (1970). Discovery of an apparent male soldier caste in a nest of a halictine bee (Hymenoptera : Halictidae), with notes on the nest. *Aust. J. Zool.* **18**: 345–351

Houston, T.F. (1981). Alimentary transport of pollen in a paracolletine bee (Hymenoptera : Colletidae). *Aust. Entomol. Mag.* **8**: 57–59

Houston, T.F. (1987). Fossil brood cells of stenotritid bees (Hymenoptera : Apoidea) from the Pleistocene of South Australia. *Trans. R. Soc. S. Aust.* **111**: 93–97

Hurd, P.D. (1979). Superfamily Apoidea. pp. 1741–2209 *in* Krombein, K.V., Hurd, P.D., Smith, D.R. & Burks, B.D. (eds) (1979). *Catalog of Hymenoptera in America North of Mexico.* Washington : Smithsonian Institution Vol. 2

International Commission on Zoological Nomenclature (1985). *International Code of Zoological Nomenclature Third Edition* adopted by the XX General Assembly of the International Union of Biological Sciences. London : Int. Trust Zool. Nom. in association with Br. Mus. Nat. Hist. 338 pp.

King, J. (1986). The systematics of some Australian Megachilidae (Hymenoptera : Apoidea). Unpubl. PhD Thesis. Brisbane : University of Queensland 439 pp.

King, J. (1991). Studies on the Genus *Austrochile* Michener *N. Stat.* in Australia (Megachilidae: Hymenoptera). Unpubl. MSc Thesis. Brisbane : University of Queensland 135 pp.

Knerer, G. (1980). Evolution of halictine castes. *Naturwissensch.* **67**: 133–135

Knerer, G. & Schwarz, M. (1976). Halictine social evolution: the Australian enigma. *Science* **194**: 445–448

Knerer, G. & Schwarz, M. (1978). Beobachtungen an australischen Furchenbienen (Hymenopteren; Halictinae). *Zool. Anz.* **200**: 321–333

Kukuk, P.F. & Crozier, R.H. (1990). Trophallaxis in a communal halictine bee *Lasioglossum (Chilalictus) erythrurum. Proc. Natl Acad. Sci. U.S.A.* **87**: 5402–5404

Kukuk, P.F. & Schwarz, M. (1987). Intranest behavior of the communal sweat bee *Lasioglossum (Chilalictus) erythrurum* (Hymenoptera : Halictidae). *J. Kansas Entomol. Soc.* **60**: 58–64

Kukuk, P.F. & Schwarz, M. (1988). Macrocephalic male bees as functional reproductives and probable guards. *Pan-Pac. Entomol.* **64**: 131–137

Lanham, U.N. (1980). Evolutionary origin of bees (Hymenoptera : Apoidea). *J. N.Y. Entomol. Soc.* **88**: 199–209

Lomholdt, O. (1982). On the origin of the bees (Hymenoptera: Apidae, Sphecidae). *Ent. Scand.* **13**: 185-190

Maynard, G.V. (1992). Systematic Studies on Australian *Leioproctus* Smith (Hymenoptera: Colletidae). Unpubl. PhD Thesis. Brisbane : University of Queensland 429 pp.

McGinley, R.J. (1980). Glossal morphology of the Colletidae and recognition of the Stenotritidae at the family level (Hymenoptera : Apoidea). *J. Kansas Entomol. Soc.* **53**: 539–552

McGinley, R.J. (1989). A catalog and review of immature Apoidea (Hymenoptera). *Smithson. Contrib. Zool.* **494**: 1–24

McKenzie, E. (1975). Growing up with aborigines. *Qd Nat.* **21**: 46–51

Michener, C.D. (1965). A classification of the bees of the Australian and South Pacific regions. *Bull. Am. Mus. Nat. Hist.* **130**: 1–362

Michener, C.D. (1974). *The Social Behaviour of the Bees.* A comparative study. Cambridge : Belknap Press of Harvard University Press 404 pp.

Michener, C.D. (1979). Biogeography of the bees. *Ann. M. Bot. Gard.* **66**: 277–347

Michener, C.D. (1981a). Comparative morphology of the middle coxae of Apoidea. *J. Kansas Entomol. Soc.* **54**: 319–326

Michener, C.D. (1981b). Paint for nest construction. *Bee World* **62**: 34

Michener, C.D. (1985). A comparative study of the mentum and lorum of bees (Hymenoptera : Apoidea). *J. Kansas Entomol. Soc.* **57**: 705–714

Michener, C.D. (1986). Family-group names among bees. *J. Kansas Entomol. Soc.* **59**: 219–234

Michener, C.D. (1991). Case 2535. Proposed precedence of some bee family-group names (Insecta, Hymenoptera): names based on *Colletes* Latreille, 1802, on *Paracolletes* Smith, 1853, on *Halictus* Latreille, 1804, on *Anthidium* Fabricius, 1804 and on *Anthophora* Latreille, 1803 to have precedence over some senior names. *Bull. Zool. Nomen.* **48**: 227–235

Michener, C.D. & Brooks, R.W. (1984). A comparative study of the glossae of bees (Apoidea). *Contrib. Am. Entomol. Inst.* **22**: 1–73

Michener, C.D. & Fraser, A. (1978). A comparative anatomical study of mandibular structure in bees. *Univ. Kansas Sci. Bull.* **51**: 463–482

Michener, C.D. & Greenberg, L. (1980). Ctenoplectridae and the origin of long-tongued bees. *Zool. J. Linn. Soc.* **69**: 183–203

Michener, C.D. & Grimaldi, D.A. (1988a). The oldest fossil bee: apoid history, evolutionary stasis, and antiquity of social behavior. *Proc. Natl Acad. Sci. U.S.A.* **85**: 6424–6426

Michener, C.D. & Grimaldi, D.A. (1988b). A *Trigona* from Late Cretaceous amber of New Jersey (Hymenoptera: Apidae: Meliponinae). *Am. Mus. Novit.* **2917**: 1–10

Michener, C.D. & Houston, T.F. (1991). Apoidea. pp. 993–1000 *in* CSIRO (sponsor) *The Insects of Australia*. A textbook for students and research workers. Melbourne : Melbourne University Press Vol. II 2nd Edn

Morris, B., Southcott, R.V. & Gale, A.E. (1988). Effects of stings of Australian native bees. *Med. J. Aust.* **149**: 707–709

Naumann, I.D. & Watson, J.A.L. (1987). Appendix 1. Wasps and bees (Hymenoptera) on rock faces at Koolburra. *Rock Art Research* **4**: 17–28

O'Keefe, K.J. & Schwarz, M.P. (1990). Pheromones are implicated in reproductive differentiation in a primitively social bee. *Naturwissensch.* **77**: 83–86

Pyke, G. (1983). Australian Museum Report. Section 13. Page 45. Management of honeybees in Kosciusko National Park. *Australas. Beekpr* **84**: 249–251

Pyke, G.H. & Balzer, L. (1985). The effects of the introduced honeybee (*Apis mellifera*) on Australian native bees. A report prepared for NSW National Parks and Wildlife Service. *Occ. Pap. N.S.W. Natl Parks Wldlf. Serv.* **7**: 1–48

Ramsey, M.W. (1988). Differences in pollinator effectiveness of birds and insects visiting *Banksia menziesii* (Proteaceae). *Oecologia* **76**: 119–124

Rasnitsyn, A.P. & Michener, C.D. (1991). Miocene fossil bumble bee from the Soviet Far East with comments on the chronology and distribution of fossil bees (Hymenoptera: Apidae). *Ann. Entomol. Soc. Am.* **84**: 583–589

Rayment, T. (1929). The cuckoo-bees, *Coelioxys frogatti* Cockerell. *Vict. Nat.* **46**: 58–61

Rayment, T. (1935). *A Cluster of Bees*. Sixty essays on the life-histories of Australian bees, with specific descriptions of over 100 new species, and an introduction by Professor E.F. Phillips, D.Ph., Cornell University, U.S.A. Sydney : Endeavour Press 752 pp.

Rayment, T. (1944). A critical revision of species in the *zonata* group of *Anthophora* by new characters (Part I). *Treubia* (Japanese edition) **1**: 1–30 [dated 1942, actual date of issue 1944]

Rayment, T. (1946). New bees and wasps—Part III. Another new *Exoneura*; also notes on the biology of *E. hamulata*. *Vict. Nat.* **63**: 63–68

Rayment, T. (1947). A critical revision of species in the *zonata* group of *Anthophora* by new characters (Part II). *Treubia* **19**: 46–73

Rayment, T. (1949). New bees and wasps—Part IX. Four undescribed species of *Exoneura*, with notes on their collection, and description of new parasites discovered on the genus. *Vict. Nat.* **65**: 247–254

Rayment, T. (1951). Biology of the reed-bees. With descriptions of three new species and two allotypes of *Exoneura. Aust. Zool.* **11**: 285–313

Rayment, T. (1954). Incidence of acarid mites on the biology of bees. *Aust. Zool.* **12**: 26–38

Rayment, T. (1955). Dimorphism and parthenogenesis in halictine bees. *Aust. Zool.* **12**: 142–153

Rhodes, J.W. (ed.) (1988). *Bee Keeping in the Year 2000.* Second Australian and International Beekeeping Congress. Surfers Paradise, Gold Coast, Queensland, Australia. July 21–26, 1988. Brisbane : Dept Primary Industries 288 pp.

Rozen, J.G. (1977). The ethology and systematic relationships of fideliine bees, including a description of the mature larva of *Parafidelia* (Hymenoptera, Apoidea). *Am. Mus. Novit.* **2637**: 1–15

Sandhouse, G.A. (1943). The type species of the genera and subgenera of bees. *Proc. U.S. Natl Mus.* **92**(3156): 519–619

Schmidt, J.O. (1986). Allergy to Hymenoptera venoms. pp. 509–546 *in* Piek, T. (ed.) *Venoms of the Hymenoptera. Biochemical, Pharmacological and Behavioural Aspects.* London : Academic Press

Schwarz, M.P. (1988). Local resource enhancement and sex ratios in a primitively social bee. *Nature* **331**: 346–348

Schwarz, M.P. & Blows, M.W. (1991). Kin association during nest founding in the bee *Exoneura bicolor*: active discrimination, philopatry and familiar landmarks. *Psyche (Camb.)* **98**: 241–250

Schwarz, M.P. & O'Keefe, K.J. (1991). Cooperative nesting and ovarian development in females of the predominantly social bee *Exoneura bicolor* Smith (Hymenoptera: Anthophoridae) after forced solitary eclosion. *J. Aust. Entomol. Soc.* **30**: 251–255

Smith, F. (1853). *Catalogue of Hymenopterous Insects in the Collection of the British Museum.* Part I. Andrenidae and Apidae. London : British Museum 197 pp.

Smith, F. (1854). *Catalogue of Hymenopterous Insects in the Collection of the British Museum.* Part II. Apidae. London : British Museum pp. 199–465

Smith, F. (1879). *Descriptions of New Species of Hymenoptera in the Collection of the British Museum.* London : British Museum xxi 240 pp.

Southcott, R.V. (1988). Some harmful Australian insects. *Med. J. Aust.* **149**: 656-662

Sugden, E.A. (1989). A semi-natural, manipular observation nest for *Exoneura* spp. and other allodapine bees (Hymenoptera: Anthophoridae). *Pan-Pac. Entomol.* **65**: 17–24

Sugden, E.A. & Pyke, G.H. (1991). Effects of honey bees on colonies of *Exoneura asimillima*, an Australian native bee. *Aust. J. Ecol.* **16**: 171–181

Velthuis, H.H.W. (1990). The biology and the economic value of the stingless bees, compared to the honeybees. *Apiacta* **25**: 68–74

Vithanage, V. & Ironside, D.A. (1986). The insect pollinators of *Macadamia* and their relative importance. *J. Aust. Inst. Agric. Sci.* **52**: 155–160

Wagner, A. & Dollin, L. (1982). North Queensland's native bees—the little Aussie battlers. *Australas. Beekpr* **84**: 70–72

Wapshere, A.J. (1988). Hypotheses concerning the effects of honey bees on native fauna and flora in national parks and the possibility of experimental confirmation. pp. 166–168 *in* Rhodes, J.W. (ed.) *Bee Keeping in the Year 2000.* Second Australian and International Beekeeping Congress. Surfers Paradise, Gold Coast, Queensland, Australia. July 21–26, 1988. Brisbane : Dept Primary Industries 288 pp.

Wille, A. (1977). A general review of the fossil stingless bees. *Rev. Biol. Trop.* **25**: 43–46

Wille, A. (1979). A comparative study of the pollen press and nearby structures in the bees of the family Apidae. *Rev. Biol. Trop.* **27**: 217–221

Winner, W.G. (1983). Introduced bees in conservation parks. *Australas. Beekpr* **84**: 213–214

Winston, M.L. (1979). The proboscis of the long-tongued bees: a comparative study. *Univ. Kansas Sci. Bull.* **51**: 631–667

Wylie, F.R., Walsh, G.L. & Yule, R.A. (1987). Insect damage to aboriginal relics at burial and rock-art sites near Carnarvon in central Queensland. *J. Aust. Entomol. Soc.* **26**: 335–345

Young, L. (1947). Wartime adventures of a science paper. *Vict. Nat.* **64**: 147

Young, L. (1967). *The Melody Lingers On.* Biography of Tarlton Rayment. Melbourne : Hawthorne Press 123 pp.

Zeuner, F.E. & Manning, F.J. (1976). A monograph on fossil bees (Hymenoptera: Apoidea). *Bull. Br. Mus. (Nat. Hist.) Geol.* **27**: 149–268

COLLETIDAE

INTRODUCTION

The Colletidae are short-tongued bees, characterized by a short, broad glossa which is truncate, emarginate or bifid apically except in a few male Hylaeinae (McGinley 1980; Michener & Brooks 1984). In Australia, this family includes about half of the described species of bees. The species are more numerous and there is a greater diversity in Australia than in other parts of the world (Michener 1979).

The Colletidae are divided into five subfamilies: Colletinae and Hylaeinae which have cosmopolitan distributions; Euryglossinae which are endemic to Australia; and Diphaglossinae and Xeromelissinae which are not known to occur in Australia (Michener 1965).

Euryglossa depressa   [by M. Quick]

The females of this family line their brood cells with a transparent, cellophane-like material (Michener & Houston 1991)—a behaviour that is unique amongst bees. All Colletidae are thought to be solitary and there are no parasitic species recorded from Australia. Rayment (1935) and Michener (1960) described the nests of several species and McGinley (1981) described larvae.

Short-tongued bees are not normally able to obtain nectar from flowers with deeply recessed nectaries but Houston (1983) described elongate palpi in Colletidae which are used to access such nectaries. Flower visiting records are given in Michener (1965), Armstrong (1979) and Bernhardt (1987).

The Colletinae are cosmopolitan in distribution but only the pan-austral tribe Paracolletini, with seven genera, occurs in Australia (Michener 1989). Adults are hairy bees of medium size (5–15 mm). The females transport pollen externally on the scopa on the hind legs, although Houston (1981b) recorded the alimentary transport of pollen in one species of *Leioproctus*. The forewing usually has three, sometimes two, submarginal cells. Females have a pygidial plate which is broadest basally; the basitibial plate is usually defined by a carina. Females construct nests in soil or occasionally in rotting wood. Houston (1989, 1990, 1991) described and gave information on the behaviour of some distinctive bees from Western Australia. Maynard (1991, 1992) revised two subgenera of *Leioproctus*.

The Euryglossinae are endemic to Australia and contain 18 genera, five of which occur in Tasmania; one species, *Euryglossina (Euryglossina) proctotrypoides* Cockerell, was accidentally introduced into New Zealand (Donovan 1980). Adults are minute to medium in size (2–10 mm), usually sparsely haired and often with pale markings. A scopa is lacking and pollen is transported in the crop. The forewing usually has two submarginal cells, sometimes one. The pygidial plate of females is slender and parallel sided; the basitibial plate is recognisable, though often only outlined by a few tubercles. Adults usually nest in the soil but a few species nest in holes in dead wood (Houston 1969). Exley revised most of the genera, including *Euryglossina* (Exley 1968), *Pachyprosopis* (Exley 1976a) and *Euryglossa* (Exley 1976b).

The Hylaeinae are cosmopolitan in distribution, but only in Australia do they constitute a major element of the bee fauna. In addition, the Australian Hylaeinae are more diverse than those of other biogeographic regions. There are nine genera, of which two have been recorded from Tasmania; one species, *Hyleoides concinna* (Fabricius), was accidentally introduced into New Zealand (Donovan 1983). Adults are minute to medium in size (3–13 mm), often slender, sparsely haired and usually dark coloured with pale markings on the face and thorax. Hylaeinae lack pollen-carrying scopae and the females carry pollen provisions for larvae in the crop. The forewing usually has two submarginal cells and the females usually lack pygidial and basitibial plates. Males of some Australian species have an acute glossa (Michener 1992). Most species nest in pithy stems or in pre-existing holes in dead wood but a few nest in the soil. Houston (1975, 1981a) revised many of the genera.

References

Armstrong, J.A. (1979). Biotic pollination mechanisms in the Australian flora—a review. *N.Z. J. Bot.* **17**: 467–508

Bernhardt, P. (1987). A comparison of the diversity, density, and foraging behavior of bees and wasps on Australian *Acacia* *Ann. M. Bot. Gard.* **74**: 42–50

Donovan, B.J. (1980). Interactions between native and introduced bees in New Zealand. *N.Z. J. Ecol.* **3**: 104–116

Donovan, B.J. (1983). Occurrence of the Australian bee *Hyleoides concinna* (Hymenoptera : Colletidae) in New Zealand. *N.Z. J. Zool.* **10**: 345–348

Exley, E.M. (1968). Revision of the genus *Euryglossina* Cockerell (Apoidea : Colletidae). *Aust. J. Zool.* **16**: 915–1020

Exley, E.M. (1976a). New species and records of *Pachyprosopis* Perkins (Apoidea : Colletidae : Euryglossinae). *J. Aust. Entomol. Soc.* **14**: 399–407

Exley, E.M. (1976b). Revision of the subgenus *Euryglossa* Smith (Apoidea : Colletidae : Euryglossinae). *Aust. J. Zool. Suppl. Ser.* **41**: 1–72

Houston, T.F. (1969). The systematics and biology of Australian hylaeine bees (Hymenoptera : Colletidae). Unpubl. PhD Thesis. Brisbane : University of Queensland 423 pp.

Houston, T.F. (1975). A revision of the Australian hylaeine bees (Hymenoptera : Colletidae). I. Introductory material and the genera *Heterapoides* Sandhouse, *Gephyrohylaeus* Michener, *Hyleoides* Smith, *Pharohylaeus* Michener, *Hemirhiza* Michener, *Amphylaeus* Michener and *Meroglossa* Smith. *Aust. J. Zool. Suppl. Ser.* **36**: 1–135

Houston, T.F. (1981a). A revision of the Australian hylaeine bees (Hymenoptera : Colletidae). II. Genus *Hylaeus* Fabricius : Subgenera *Analastoroides* Rayment, *Edriohylaeus* Michener, *Euprosopellus* Michener, *Euprosopis* Perkins, *Euprosopoides* Michener, *Gnathoprosopis* Perkins, *Gnathoprosopoides* Michener, *Hylaeorhiza* Michener, *Hylaeteron* Michener, *Laccohylaeus*, subgen. nov., *Macrohylaeus* Michener, *Meghylaeus* Cockerell, *Planihylaeus*, subgen. nov., *Sphaerhylaeus* Cockerell and *Xenohylaeus* Michener. *Aust. J. Zool. Suppl. Ser.* **80**: 1–128

Houston, T.F. (1981b). Alimentary transport of pollen in a paracolletine bee (Hymenoptera : Colletidae). *Aust. Entomol. Mag.* **8**: 57–59

Houston, T.F. (1983). An extraordinary new bee and adaptation of palpi for nectar-feeding in some Australian Colletidae and Pergidae (Hymenoptera). *J. Aust. Entomol. Soc.* **22**: 263–270

Houston, T.F. (1989). *Leioproctus* bees associated with Western Australian smoke bushes (*Conospermum* spp.) and their adaptations for foraging and concealment (Hymenoptera: Colletidae: Paracolletini). *Rec. West. Aust. Mus.* **14**: 275–292

Houston, T.F. (1990). Descriptions of new paracolletine bees associated with flowers of *Eremophila* (Hymenoptera: Colletidae). *Rec. West. Aust. Mus.* **14**: 583–621

Houston, T.F. (1991). Two new and unusual species of the bee genus *Leioproctus* Smith (Hymenoptera: Colletidae), with notes on their behaviour. *Rec. West. Aust. Mus.* **15**: 83–96

Maynard, G.V. (1991). Revision of *Leioproctus (Protomorpha)* Rayment (Hymenoptera: Colletidae) with description of two new species. *J. Aust. Entomol. Soc.* **30**: 67–75

Maynard, G.V. (1992). Revision of *Leioproctus (Cladocerapis)* Cockerell (Hymenoptera: Colletidae). *J. Aust. Entomol. Soc.* **31**: 1–11

McGinley, R.J. (1980). Glossal morphology of the Colletidae and recognition of the Stenotritidae at the family level (Hymenoptera : Apoidea). *J. Kansas Entomol. Soc.* **53**: 539–552

McGinley, R.J. (1981). Systematics of the Colletidae based on mature larvae with phenetic analysis of apoid larvae (Insecta, Hymenoptera, Apoidea). *Univ. Calif. Publ. Entomol.* **91**: 1–309

Michener, C.D. (1960). Notes on the behavior of Australian colletid bees. *J. Kansas Entomol. Soc.* **33**: 22–31

Michener, C.D. (1965). A classification of the bees of the Australian and South Pacific regions. *Bull. Am. Mus. Nat. Hist.* **130**: 1–362

Michener, C.D. (1979). Biogeography of the bees. *Ann. M. Bot. Gard.* **66**: 277–347

Michener, C.D. (1989). Classification of American Colletinae (Hymenoptera, Apoidea). *Univ. Kansas Sci. Bull.* **53**: 622–703

Michener, C.D. (1992). Sexual dimorphism in the glossa of Colletidae (Hymenoptera, Apoidea). *J. Kansas Entomol. Soc.* **65**: 1–9

Michener, C.D. & Brooks, R.W. (1984). A comparative study of the glossae of bees (Apoidea). *Contrib. Am. Entomol. Inst.* **22**: 1–73

Michener, C.D. & Houston, T.F. (1991). Apoidea. pp. 993–1000 *in* CSIRO (sponsor) *The Insects of Australia*. A textbook for students and research workers. Melbourne : Melbourne University Press Vol. II 2nd Edn

Rayment, T. (1935). *A Cluster of Bees*. Sixty essays on the life-histories of Australian bees, with specific descriptions of over 100 new species, and an introduction by Professor E.F. Phillips, D.Ph., Cornell University, U.S.A. Sydney : Endeavour Press 752 pp.

COLLETINAE

Callomelitta Smith, 1853

Callomelitta Smith, F. (1853). *Catalogue of Hymenopterous Insects in the Collection of the British Museum. Part I. Andrenidae and Apidae.* London : British Museum 197 pp. [85]. Type species: *Callomelitta picta* Smith, 1853 by monotypy.

Binghamiella Cockerell, T.D.A. (1907). On a collection of Australian and Asiatic bees. *Bull. Am. Mus. Nat. Hist.* **23**: 221–236 [235]. Type species: *Sphecodes antipodes* Smith, 1853 by monotypy.

Pachyodonta Rayment, T. (1954). Remarkable bees from a rain forest. *Aust. Zool.* **12**: 46–56 [48] [proposed with subgeneric rank in *Binghamiella* Cockerell, 1907]. Type species: *Binghamiella (Pachyodonta) fulvicornis* Rayment, 1954 by monotypy.

Taxonomic decision for synonymy: Michener, C.D. (1965). A classification of the bees of the Australian and South Pacific regions. *Bull. Am. Mus. Nat. Hist.* **130**: 1–362 [37].

Callomelitta antipodes (Smith, 1853)

Sphecodes antipodes Smith, F. (1853). *Catalogue of Hymenopterous Insects in the Collection of the British Museum. Part I. Andrenidae and Apidae.* London : British Museum 197 pp. [37].
Type data: holotype, BMNH Hym.17.a.558 ♀.
Type locality: Sydney, NSW.

Sphecodes antipus Sichel, J. (1865). Révision monographique, critique et synonymique du genre mellifère *Sphecodes* Latr., basé sur la méthode numérique; avec des remarques sur les moeurs des Sphécodes comme insectes nidifiants et non parasites. *Ann. Soc. Entomol. Fr. (4)*5: 397–466 [451] [unjustified emendation and junior objective synonym of *Sphecodes antipodes* Smith, 1853].

Distribution: NE coastal, SE coastal, Murray-Darling basin, SW coastal, QLD, NSW, VIC, WA.
Ecology: larva—sedentary : adult—volant; melliferous, solitary, nest in rotting wood, flower visiting record: aster, *Bursaria* Cav. [Pittosporaceae], *Leptospermum* Forster & G.Forster [Myrtaceae].
References: Cockerell, T.D.A. (1907). On a collection of Australian and Asiatic bees. *Bull. Am. Mus. Nat. Hist.* **23**: 221–236 (taxonomy, as *Binghamiella antipodes* (Smith, 1853)); Rayment, T. (1929). Studies of Australian bees. The red bees. *Vict. Nat.* **45**: 240–243 (biology); Rayment, T. (1935). *A Cluster of Bees.* Sixty essays on the life-histories of Australian bees, with specific descriptions of over 100 new species, and an introduction by Professor E.F. Phillips, D.Ph., Cornell University, U.S.A. Sydney : Endeavour Press 752 pp. (biology); Rayment, T. (1953). *Bees of the Portland District.* Victoria : Portland Field Naturalist's Club 39 pp. (distribution); Rayment, T. (1954). Remarkable bees from a rain forest. *Aust. Zool.* **12**: 46–56 (illustration); Michener, C.D. (1965). A classification of the bees of the Australian and South Pacific regions. *Bull. Am. Mus. Nat. Hist.* **130**: 1–362 (distribution); Michener, C.D. & Fraser,

A. (1978). A comparative anatomical study of mandibular structure in bees. *Univ. Kansas Sci. Bull.* **51**: 463–482 (mandible); Michener, C.D. (1992). Sexual dimorphism in the glossa of Colletidae (Hymenoptera, Apoidea). *J. Kansas Entomol. Soc.* **65**: 1–9 (glossa).

Callomelitta chlorura Cockerell, 1929

Callomelitta picta chlorura Cockerell, T.D.A. (1929). Bees, chiefly Australian species, described or determined by Dr. H. Friese. *Am. Mus. Novit.* **343**: 1–20 [9].
Type data: holotype, AMNH ♀*.
Type locality: Adelaide, SA.

Distribution: S Gulfs, SA; known only from type locality.
Ecology: Adult—volant; melliferous, solitary, nest in rotting wood.
Reference: Michener, C.D. (1965). A classification of the bees of the Australian and South Pacific regions. *Bull. Am. Mus. Nat. Hist.* **130**: 1–362 [38] (taxonomy).

Callomelitta fulvicornis (Rayment, 1954)

Binghamiella (Pachyodonta) fulvicornis Rayment, T. (1954). Remarkable bees from a rain forest. *Aust. Zool.* **12**: 46–56 [49].
Type data: holotype, ANIC ♀.
Type locality: Jamberoo, NSW.

Distribution: SE coastal, NSW; known only from type locality.
Ecology: adult—volant; melliferous, nests in rotting wood, flower visiting record: *Prostanthera* Labill. [Lamiaceae].
Reference: Michener, C.D. (1965). A classification of the bees of the Australian and South Pacific regions. *Bull. Am. Mus. Nat. Hist.* **130**: 1–362 [38] (taxonomy).

Callomelitta insularis (Cockerell, 1914)

Binghamiella insularis Cockerell, T.D.A. (1914). New Australian bees. *Entomologist* **47**: 197–201 [199].
Type data: syntypes, BMNH 2♂ (a male specimen is labelled 'type' and has registration number Hym.17.a.608).
Type locality: Eaglehawk Neck, TAS.

Distribution: SE coastal, VIC, TAS; only published localities Portland, George Town, Eaglehawk Neck.
Ecology: adult—volant; melliferous, solitary, nest in rotting wood, flower visiting record: aster, *Dahlia* Cav. [Asteraceae], *Eucalyptus* L'Hérit. [Myrtaceae].
References: Cockerell, T.D.A. (1916). Some bees from Australia, Tasmania, and the New Hebrides. *Proc. Acad. Nat. Sci. Philad.* **68**: 360–375 (as subspecies of *Binghamiella antipodes* (Smith, 1853)); Rayment, T. (1953). *Bees of the Portland District.* Victoria : Portland Field Naturalist's Club 39 pp. (flower record).

Callomelitta littleri Cockerell, 1914

Callomelitta littleri Cockerell, T.D.A. (1914). Some Tasmanian bees. *Entomologist* **47**: 305–308 [305].
Type data: holotype, BMNH Hym.17.a.544 ♀.
Type locality: Launceston, TAS.

Callomelitta nigrofasciata Cockerell, T.D.A. (1918). Descriptions and records of bees. LXXIX. *Ann. Mag. Nat. Hist. (9)* **1**: 158–167 [164].
Type data: holotype, AMNH ♀*.
Type locality: Launceston, TAS.

Callomelitta nigriventris Friese, H. (1924). Ueber die Bienen Australiens. *Konowia* **3**: 216–249 [231].
Type data: syntypes (probable), AMNH ♀* (location of other specimen(s) unknown).
Type locality: Adelaide, SA (probably incorrect, possibly from Sydney area), see Cockerell, T.D.A. (1929). Bees, chiefly Australian species, described or determined by Dr. H. Friese. *Am. Mus. Novit.* **343**: 1–20 [8].

Taxonomic decision for synonymy: Cockerell, T.D.A. (1921). Australian bees in the Queensland Museum. *Mem. Qd Mus.* **7**: 81–98 [88] (for *Callomelitta nigrofasciata* Cockerell, 1918); Cockerell, T.D.A. (1929). Bees, chiefly Australian species, described or determined by Dr. H. Friese. *Am. Mus. Novit.* **343**: 1–20 [8] (for *Callomellitta nigriventris* Friese, 1924).

Distribution: NE coastal, SE coastal, (S Gulfs), QLD, NSW, VIC, (SA).
Ecology: adult—volant; melliferous, solitary, nest in rotting wood.
References: Cockerell, T.D.A. (1922). Australian bees in the Queensland Museum. *Mem. Qd Mus.* **7**: 257–279 (distribution); Cockerell, T.D.A. (1929). Bees, chiefly Australian species, described or determined by Dr. H. Friese. *Am. Mus. Novit.* **343**: 1–20 (taxonomy, distribution).

Callomelitta nigra (Rayment, 1929)

Binghamiella antipodes nigra Rayment, T. (1929). Bees from East Gippsland. *Vict. Nat.* **46**: 124–129 [124].
Type data: syntypes, NMV 5♀.
Type locality: Cann River, VIC.

Distribution: SE coastal, VIC; known only from type locality.
Ecology: adult—volant; melliferous, solitary, nest in rotting wood, flower visiting record: *Leptospermum* Forster & G.Forster [Myrtaceae].
Reference: Michener, C.D. (1965). A classification of the bees of the Australian and South Pacific regions. *Bull. Am. Mus. Nat. Hist.* **130**: 1–362 [39] (taxonomy).

Callomelitta perpicta Cockerell, 1910

Callomelitta picta perpicta Cockerell, T.D.A. (1910). Some Australian bees in the Berlin Museum. *J. N.Y. Entomol. Soc.* **18**: 98–114 [100].
Type data: holotype, ZMB ♂*.
Type locality: Ararat, VIC.

Callomelitta cyanescens Friese, H. (1924). Ueber die Bienen Australiens. *Konowia* **3**: 216–249 [231].
Type data: holotype (probable), AMNH ♂*.
Type locality: "Central Australia".

Taxonomic decision for synonymy: Cockerell, T.D.A. (1929). Bees, chiefly Australian species, described or determined by Dr. H. Friese. *Am. Mus. Novit.* **343**: 1–20 [9].

Distribution: SE coastal, VIC; only published localities Ararat, Portland, Emerald, south Gippsland and "Central Australia".
Ecology: adult—volant; melliferous, solitary, nest in rotting wood, flower visiting record: aster, *Acacia* Miller [Mimosaceae], *Eucalyptus* L'Hérit. [Myrtaceae].
References: Rayment, T. (1949). New bees and wasps—Part XII. A new blue bee and an old whiteant. *Vict. Nat.* **66**: 147–151 (nest); Rayment, T. (1953). *Bees of the Portland District*. Victoria : Portland Field Naturalist's Club 39 pp. (flower record); Michener, C.D. (1965). A classification of the bees of the Australian and South Pacific regions. *Bull. Am. Mus. Nat. Hist.* **130**: 1–362 [39] (taxonomy); Bernhardt, P. (1987). A comparison of the diversity, density, and foraging behavior of bees and wasps on Australian *Acacia*. *Ann. M. Bot. Gard.* **74**: 42–50 (flower record).

Callomelitta picta Smith, 1853

Callomelitta picta Smith, F. (1853). *Catalogue of Hymenopterous Insects in the Collection of the British Museum. Part I. Andrenidae and Apidae*. London : British Museum 197 pp. [85].
Type data: holotype, BMNH ♂♀ (female specimen is labelled 'type' and has registration number Hym.17.a.540).
Type locality: TAS (as Van Diemen's Land).

Distribution: SE coastal, Murray-Darling basin, NSW, VIC, TAS.
Ecology: adult—volant; melliferous, solitary, nest in rotting wood, flower visiting record: *Callistemon* R.Br. [Myrtaceae], *Eucalyptus* L'Hérit. [Myrtaceae], *Leptospermum* Forster & G.Forster [Myrtaceae], *Prostanthera* Labill. [Lamiaceae].
References: Cockerell, T.D.A. (1905). Notes on some bees in the British Museum. *Trans. Am. Entomol. Soc.* **31**: 309–364 (redescription); Cockerell, T.D.A. (1905). Descriptions and records of bees. II. *Ann. Mag. Nat. Hist. (7)* **16**: 292–301 (distribution); Cockerell, T.D.A. (1929). Bees, chiefly Australian species, described or determined by Dr. H. Friese. *Am. Mus. Novit.* **343**: 1–20 (taxonomy); Rayment, T. (1935). *A Cluster of Bees*. Sixty essays on the life-histories of Australian bees, with specific descriptions of over 100 new species, and an introduction by Professor E.F. Phillips, D.Ph., Cornell University, U.S.A. Sydney : Endeavour Press 752 pp. (flower record); Rayment, T. (1954). Remarkable bees from a rain forest. *Aust. Zool.* **12**: 46–56 (distribution); Ashton, D. (1975). Studies of flowering behaviour in *Eucalyptus regnans* F. Muell. *Aust. J. Bot.* **23**: 399–411 (flower record).

Callomelitta rugosa Cockerell, 1915

Callomelitta rugosa Cockerell, T.D.A. (1915). Descriptions and records of bees. LXVI. *Ann. Mag. Nat. Hist. (8)*15: 341–350 [345].
Type data: holotype, BMNH Hym.17.a.543 ♀.
Type locality: QLD.

Distribution: QLD; known only from type locality, exact locality unknown.
Ecology: adults—volant; melliferous, solitary.

Callomelitta turnerorum Cockerell, 1910

Callomelitta turnerorum Cockerell, T.D.A. (1910). Descriptions and records of bees. XXXIII. *Ann. Mag. Nat. Hist. (8)*6: 356–366 [356].
Type data: holotype, BMNH Hym.17.a.545 ♀.
Type locality: Kuranda (as Cairns Kuranda), QLD.

Distribution: NE coastal, QLD; known only from type locality.
Ecology: adults—volant; melliferous, solitary.

Callomelitta wilsoni Cockerell, 1929

Callomelitta picta wilsoni Cockerell, T.D.A. (1929). Bees from the Australian region. *Am. Mus. Novit.* 346: 1–18 [9].
Type data: holotype, AMNH ♀*.
Type locality: Eltham, VIC.

Distribution: SE coastal, VIC; known only from type locality.
Ecology: adults—volant; melliferous, solitary.
References: Rayment, T. (1935). *A Cluster of Bees.* Sixty essays on the life-histories of Australian bees, with specific descriptions of over 100 new species, and an introduction by Professor E.F. Phillips, D.Ph., Cornell University, U.S.A. Sydney : Endeavour Press 752 pp. (illustation); Michener, C.D. (1965). A classification of the bees of the Australian and South Pacific regions. *Bull. Am. Mus. Nat. Hist.* 130: 1–362 (taxonomy).

Hesperocolletes Michener, 1965

Hesperocolletes Michener, C.D. (1965). A classification of the bees of the Australian and South Pacific regions. *Bull. Am. Mus. Nat. Hist.* 130: 1–362 [75]. Type species: *Hesperocolletes douglasi* Michener, 1965 by original designation.

Hesperocolletes douglasi Michener, 1965

Hesperocolletes douglasi Michener, C.D. (1965). A classification of the bees of the Australian and South Pacific regions. *Bull. Am. Mus. Nat. Hist.* 130: 1–362 [262].
Type data: holotype, WAM 38–2607 ♂.
Type locality: Rottnest Is., WA.

Distribution: SW coastal, WA; known only from type locality.
Ecology: adults—volant; melliferous, solitary.

Leioproctus Smith, 1853

Taxonomic decision for subgeneric arrangement: Michener, C.D. (1965). A classification of the bees of the Australian and South Pacific regions. *Bull. Am. Mus. Nat. Hist.* 130: 1–362 [39].

Species now known not to occur in Australia: *Leioproctus (Hoplocolletes) ventralis* (Friese, 1924) (described as *Dasycolletes ventralis* Friese, 1924, from "Sydney, Australia" is from Brazil) and *Leioproctus (Nesocolletes) waterhousei* (Cockerell, 1905) (described as *Paracolletes waterhousei* Cockerell, 1905, was based on a specimen assumed to be from Australia but this subgenus is known only from New Zealand), see Michener, C.D. (1965). A classification of the bees of the Australian and South Pacific regions. *Bull. Am. Mus. Nat. Hist.* 130: 1–362 [41, 42, 53].

Leioproctus (Leioproctus) Smith, 1853

Leioproctus Smith, F. (1853). *Catalogue of Hymenopterous Insects in the Collection of the British Museum.* Part I. Andrenidae and Apidae. London : British Museum 197 pp. [8]. Type species: *Leioproctus imitatus* Smith, 1853 by subsequent designation, see Cockerell, T.D.A. (1905). Notes on some bees in the British Museum. *Trans. Am. Entomol. Soc.* 31: 309–364 [348].

Lamprocolletes Smith, F. (1853). *Catalogue of Hymenopterous Insects in the Collection of the British Museum.* Part I. Andrenidae and Apidae. London : British Museum 197 pp. [10]. Type species: *Andrena chalybeata* Erichson, 1842 by subsequent designation, see Cockerell, T.D.A. (1905). Notes on some bees in the British Museum. *Trans. Am. Entomol. Soc.* 31: 309–364 [345].

Dasycolletes Smith, F. (1853). *Catalogue of Hymenopterous Insects in the Collection of the British Museum.* Part I. Andrenidae and Apidae. London : British Museum 197 pp. [14]. Type species: *Dasycolletes metallicus* Smith, 1853 by subsequent designation, see Cockerell, T.D.A. (1905). Notes on some bees in the British Museum. *Trans. Am. Entomol. Soc.* 31: 309–364 [347].

Lioproctus Smith, F. (1879). *Descriptions of New Species of Hymenoptera in the Collection of the British Museum.* London : British Museum xxi 240 pp. [6] [incorrect subsequent spelling for *Leioproctus* Smith, 1853, name not available].

Heterocolletes Rayment, T. (1935). *A Cluster of Bees.* Sixty essays on the life-histories of Australian bees, with specific descriptions of over 100 new species, and an introduction by Professor E.F. Phillips, D.Ph., Cornell University, U.S.A. Sydney : Endeavour Press 752 pp. [184] [proposed with subgeneric rank in *Paracolletes* Smith, 1853]. Type species: *Paracolletes (Heterocolletes) capillatus* Rayment, 1935 by original designation.

Taxonomic decision for synonymy: Michener, C.D. (1965). A classification of the bees of the Australian and South Pacific regions. *Bull. Am. Mus. Nat. Hist.* 130: 1–362 [47].

Extralimital distribution: New Zealand, New Guinea and Misool, see Michener, C.D. (1965). A classification of the bees of the Australian and South Pacific regions. *Bull. Am. Mus. Nat. Hist.* **130**: 1–362 [50].

Species now known not to occur in Australia: *Leioproctus (Leioproctus) maorium* (Cockerell, 1913), described as *Paracolletes maorium* Cockerell, 1913, is known only from New Zealand, the record from Australia was in error, see Cockerell, T.D.A. (1934). The bees of Australia. *Aust. Zool.* **8**: 2–38 [29].

Leioproctus (Leioproctus) abnormis (Cockerell, 1916)

Paracolletes abnormis Cockerell, T.D.A. (1916). Descriptions and records of bees. LXXIII. *Ann. Mag. Nat. Hist. (8)***18**: 44–53 [46].
Type data: holotype, BMNH Hym.17.a.462 ♂.
Type locality: Alexandria, NT.

Distribution: Murray-Darling basin, N Gulf, NSW, VIC, NT.
Ecology: adult—volant; melliferous, solitary.
References: Cockerell, T.D.A. (1934). The bees of Australia. *Aust. Zool.* **8**: 2–38 (taxonomy); Maynard, G.V. (1992). Systematic Studies on Australian *Leioproctus* Smith (Hymenoptera: Colletidae). Unpubl. PhD Thesis. Brisbane : Univ. of Queensland 429 pp. (distribution).

Leioproctus (Leioproctus) advena (Smith, 1862)

Andrena advena Smith, F. (1862). Descriptions of new species of Australian Hymenoptera, and of a species of *Formica* from New Zealand. *Trans. Entomol. Soc. Lond. (3)***1**: 53–62 [60].
Type data: holotype, BMNH Hym.17.a.500 ♀.
Type locality: Australia.

Distribution: NE coastal, SE coastal, S Gulfs, SW coastal, NW coastal, QLD, NSW, VIC, SA, WA.
Ecology: larva—sedentary : adult—volant; melliferous, solitary, flower visiting record: *Boronia* Sm. [Rutaceae], *Daviesia* Sm. [Fabaceae], *Dillwynia* Sm. [Fabaceae], *Hibbertia* Andrews [Dilleniaceae], *Leptospermum* Forster & G.Forster [Myrtaceae], *Leucopogon* R.Br. [Epacridaceae], *Pultenaea* Sm. [Fabaceae].
References: Alfken, J.D. (1907). Apidae. pp. 259–261 *in* Michaelsen, W. & Hartmeyer, R. (eds) *Die Fauna Südwest-Australiens.* Jena : G. Fischer Bd 1 Lfg 6 (taxonomy); Cockerell, T.D.A. (1909). Descriptions and records of bees. XXII. *Ann. Mag. Nat. Hist. (8)***4**: 309–317 (redescription); Cockerell, T.D.A. (1929). Bees in the Queensland Museum. *Mem. Qd Mus.* **9**: 298–323 (taxonomy); Cockerell, T.D.A. (1929). Bees in the Australian Museum collection. *Rec. Aust. Mus.* **17**: 199–243 (distribution); Rayment, T. (1931). Bees in the collections of the Western Australian Museum and the Agricultural Department, Perth. *J. Proc. R. Soc. West. Aust.* **17**: 157–190 (biology); Rayment, T. (1935). *A Cluster of Bees.* Sixty essays on the life-histories of Australian bees, with specific descriptions of over 100 new species, and an introduction by Professor E.F. Phillips, D.Ph., Cornell University, U.S.A. Sydney : Endeavour Press 752 pp. (taxonomy); Rayment, T. (1953). *Bees of the Portland District.* Victoria : Portland Field Naturalist's Club 39 pp. (flower record); Michener, C.D. (1965). A classification of the bees of the Australian and South Pacific regions. *Bull. Am. Mus. Nat. Hist.* **130**: 1–362 (flower records).

Leioproctus (Leioproctus) alienus (Smith, 1853)

Andrena aliena Smith, F. (1853). *Catalogue of Hymenopterous Insects in the Collection of the British Museum.* Part I. Andrenidae and Apidae. London : British Museum 197 pp. [113].
Type data: holotype, BMNH Hym.17.a.1375 ♀.
Type locality: Australia (as St John's Bluff [USA] in description), see Michener, C.D. (1965). A classification of the bees of the Australian and South Pacific regions. *Bull. Am. Mus. Nat. Hist.* **130**: 1–362 [50].

Distribution: Australia; known only from type locality, exact locality unknown.
Ecology: adult—volant; melliferous, solitary.

Leioproctus (Leioproctus) alleynae (Rayment, 1935)

Paracolletes alleynae Rayment, T. (1935). *A Cluster of Bees.* Sixty essays on the life-histories of Australian bees, with specific descriptions of over 100 new species, and an introduction by Professor E.F. Phillips, D.Ph., Cornell University, U.S.A. Sydney : Endeavour Press 752 pp. [668].
Type data: holotype (probable), ANIC ♂.
Type locality: Croydon, VIC.

Distribution: SE coastal, NSW, VIC.
Ecology: adult—volant; melliferous, solitary, flower visiting record: *Leptospermum* Forster & G.Forster [Myrtaceae].
Reference: Rayment, T. (1954). Remarkable bees from a rain forest. *Aust. Zool.* **12**: 46–56 (description of ?male).

Leioproctus (Leioproctus) amabilis (Smith, 1879)

Lamprocolletes amabilis Smith, F. (1879). *Descriptions of New Species of Hymenoptera in the Collection of the British Museum.* London : British Museum xxi 240 pp. [9].
Type data: holotype, BMNH Hym.17.a.515 ♀.
Type locality: Australia (as New Holland).
Lamprocolletes metallicus Smith, F. (1879). *Descriptions of New Species of Hymenoptera in the Collection of the British Museum.* London : British Museum xxi 240 pp. [8] [junior secondary homonym of *Dasycolletes metallicus* Smith, 1853].
Type data: holotype, BMNH Hym.17.a.513 ♂.
Type locality: Australia.

Taxonomic decision for synonymy: Cockerell, T.D.A. (1905). Notes on some bees in the British Museum. *Trans. Am. Entomol. Soc.* **31**: 309–364 [346].

Distribution: NE coastal, SE coastal, SW coastal, Murray-Darling basin, QLD, NSW, ACT, VIC, SA, WA.

Ecology: adult—volant; melliferous, solitary.

References: Cockerell, T.D.A. (1905). Descriptions and records of bees. VI. *Ann. Mag. Nat. Hist. (7)*16: 477–486 (taxonomy); Cockerell, T.D.A. (1929). Bees in the Australian Museum collection. *Rec. Aust. Mus.* 17: 199–243 (distribution); Rayment, T. (1934). Contributions to the fauna of Rottnest Island. VIII. Apoidea. With description of new species. *J. Proc. R. Soc. West. Aust.* 20: 201–212 (distribution); Maynard, G.V. (1992). Systematic Studies on Australian *Leioproctus* Smith (Hymenoptera: Colletidae). Unpubl. PhD Thesis. Brisbane : Univ. of Queensland 429 pp. (distribution).

Leioproctus (Leioproctus) apicalis (Cockerell, 1921)

Paracolletes apicalis Cockerell, T.D.A. (1921). Australian bees in the Queensland Museum. *Mem. Qd Mus.* 7: 81–98 [94].
Type data: holotype, QM T2399 ♀.
Type locality: Swan River, WA.

Distribution: SW coastal, WA; known only from type locality.

Ecology: adult—volant; melliferous, solitary.

Leioproctus (Leioproctus) atronitens (Cockerell, 1914)

Paracolletes atronitens Cockerell, T.D.A. (1914). Descriptions and records of bees. LXI. *Ann. Mag. Nat. Hist. (8)*14: 39–49 [48].
Type data: syntypes, BMNH 2♂ (a male specimen is labelled 'type' and has registration number Hym.17.a.461).
Type locality: Yallingup, WA.

Distribution: SW coastal, WA; known only from type locality.

Ecology: adult—volant; melliferous, solitary.

Leioproctus (Leioproctus) bacchalis (Cockerell, 1914)

Paracolletes providellus bacchalis Cockerell, T.D.A. (1914). Descriptions and records of bees. LVI. *Ann. Mag. Nat. Hist. (8)*13: 136–146 [138].
Type data: holotype, BMNH Hym.17.a.428 ♂.
Type locality: Bacchus Marsh, VIC.

Distribution: SE coastal, Murray-Darling basin, NSW, VIC, TAS.

Ecology: adult—volant; melliferous, solitary, flower visiting record: garden ivy, *Leptospermum* Forster & G.Forster [Myrtaceae].

References: Cockerell, T.D.A. (1915). Descriptions and records of bees. LXVII. *Ann. Mag. Nat. Hist. (8)*15: 529–537 (variety); Rayment, T. (1935). *A Cluster of Bees.* Sixty essays on the life-histories of Australian bees, with specific descriptions of over 100 new species, and an introduction by Professor E.F. Phillips, D.Ph., Cornell University, U.S.A. Sydney : Endeavour Press 752 pp. (taxonomy); Rayment, T. (1939). Bees from the high lands of New South Wales and Victoria. *Aust. Zool.* 9: 263–294 (distribution); Rayment, T. (1953). *Bees of the Portland District.* Victoria : Portland Field Naturalist's Club 39 pp. (distribution); Rayment, T. (1957). Closer than a brother. *Proc. R. Zool. Soc. N.S.W.* 1955–56: 87–90 (as host); Michener, C.D. (1965). A classification of the bees of the Australian and South Pacific regions. *Bull. Am. Mus. Nat. Hist.* 130: 1–362 (taxonomy).

Leioproctus (Leioproctus) bicristatus (Cockerell, 1929)

Paracolletes bicristatus Cockerell, T.D.A. (1929). Bees in the Queensland Museum. *Mem. Qd Mus.* 9: 298–323 [307].
Type data: syntypes, QM 2♀ (location of second female is unknown; a female specimen is labelled 'type' and has the registration number T4098).
Type locality: Tooloom, NSW.

Distribution: NE coastal, SE coastal, QLD, NSW; known only from Tooloom, Gympie and Ma Ma Creek.

Ecology: adult—volant; melliferous, solitary.

Reference: Maynard, G.V. (1992). Systematic Studies on Australian *Leioproctus* Smith (Hymenoptera: Colletidae). Unpubl. PhD Thesis. Brisbane : Univ. of Queensland 429 pp. (distribution).

Leioproctus (Leioproctus) boroniae (Cockerell, 1921)

Paracolletes boroniae Cockerell, T.D.A. (1921). Australian bees in the Queensland Museum. *Mem. Qd Mus.* 7: 81–98 [92].
Type data: holotype, QM T2408 ♀.
Type locality: Birkdale, near Brisbane, QLD.

Distribution: NE coastal, QLD; known only from type locality.

Ecology: adult—volant; melliferous, solitary, flower visiting record: *Boronia* Sm. [Rutaceae].

Leioproctus (Leioproctus) caerulescens (Cockerell, 1929)

Paracolletes providellus caerulescens Cockerell, T.D.A. (1929). Bees, chiefly Australian species, described or determined by Dr. H. Friese. *Am. Mus. Novit.* 343: 1–20 [2] [junior secondary homonym of *Pasiphae caerulescens* Spinola, 1851].
Type data: holotype, AMNH ♂*.
Type locality: Como, NSW.

Distribution: SE coastal, NSW; known only from type locality.

Ecology: adult—volant; melliferous, solitary.

Reference: Michener, C.D. (1965). A classification of the bees of the Australian and South Pacific regions. *Bull. Am. Mus. Nat. Hist.* 130: 1–362 (taxonomy).

Leioproctus (Leioproctus) canutus Houston, 1990

Leioproctus (Leioproctus) canutus Houston, T.F. (1990). Descriptions of new paracolletine bees associated with flowers of *Eremophila* (Hymenoptera: Colletidae). *Rec. West. Aust. Mus.* **14**: 583–621 [592].
Type data: holotype, WAM 89/385 ♂*.
Type locality: 10 km ESE Meedo Homestead, WA.

Distribution: NW coastal, WA; known only from type locality.
Ecology: adult—volant; melliferous, solitary, flower visiting record: *Eremophila* R.Br. [Myoporaceae].

Leioproctus (Leioproctus) capillatus (Rayment, 1935)

Paracolletes (Heterocolletes) capillatus Rayment, T. (1935). *A Cluster of Bees.* Sixty essays on the life-histories of Australian bees, with specific descriptions of over 100 new species, and an introduction by Professor E.F. Phillips, D.Ph., Cornell University, U.S.A. Sydney : Endeavour Press 752 pp. [678].
Type data: holotype, ANIC ♂.
Type locality: Wilsons Promontory, VIC.

Distribution: Murray-Darling basin, SE coastal, NSW, VIC; only published localities Mt Canobolas, Wilsons Promontory, Emerald and Mt Buffalo.
Ecology: adult—volant; melliferous, solitary, flower visiting record: *Leptospermum* Forster & G.Forster [Myrtaceae].
References: Rayment, T. (1939). Bees from the high lands of New South Wales and Victoria. *Aust. Zool.* **9**: 263–294 (distribution); Rayment, T. (1947). Bees from the Victorian Alps. *Vict. Nat.* **64**: 103–107 (distribution); Rayment, T. (1954). Incidence of acarid mites on the biology of bees. *Aust. Zool.* **12**: 26–38 (as host).

Leioproctus (Leioproctus) capito Houston, 1990

Leioproctus (Leioproctus) capito Houston, T.F. (1990). Descriptions of new paracolletine bees associated with flowers of *Eremophila* (Hymenoptera: Colletidae). *Rec. West. Aust. Mus.* **14**: 583–621 [595].
Type data: holotype, WAM 82/474 ♂*.
Type locality: 9.5 km SE Banjiwarn Homestead, WA.

Distribution: Lake Eyre basin, SW coastal, W plateau, SA, WA.
Ecology: adult—volant; melliferous, solitary, flower visiting record: *Dipteracanthus* Nees [Acanthaceae], *Eremophila* R.Br. [Myoporaceae].

Leioproctus (Leioproctus) carinatulus (Cockerell, 1905)

Paracolletes carinatulus Cockerell, T.D.A. (1905). Descriptions and records of bees. VI. *Ann. Mag. Nat. Hist.* **(7)16**: 477–486 [481].
Type data: holotype, BMNH Hym.17.a.425 ♂.
Type locality: Mackay, QLD (as Queensland, Ridg.11.91 in description).

Distribution: NE coastal, SE coastal, QLD, NSW; only published localities Mackay, Halifax and Sydney.
Ecology: adult—volant; melliferous, solitary.
References: Cockerell, T.D.A. (1907). On a collection of Australian and Asiatic bees. *Bull. Am. Mus. Nat. Hist.* **23**: 221–236 (description of female); Cockerell, T.D.A. (1930). Australian bees in the Museum of Comparative Zoology. *Psyche (Camb.)* **37**: 141–154 (variety).

Leioproctus (Leioproctus) carinatus (Smith, 1853)

Lamprocolletes carinatus Smith, F. (1853). *Catalogue of Hymenopterous Insects in the Collection of the British Museum.* Part I. Andrenidae and Apidae. London : British Museum 197 pp. [11].
Type data: holotype, BMNH Hym.17.a.488 ♀.
Type locality: Australia (as New Holland).

Distribution: NE coastal, SE coastal, Murray-Darling basin, QLD, NSW, VIC, TAS.
Ecology: adult—volant; melliferous, solitary.
References: Cockerell, T.D.A. (1913). A small collection of bees from Tasmania. *Proc. Linn. Soc. N.S.W.* **37**: 596–599 (description of male); Cockerell, T.D.A. (1934). The bees of Australia. *Aust. Zool.* **8**: 2–38 (distribution).

Leioproctus (Leioproctus) castaneipes (Cockerell, 1914)

Paracolletes castaneipes Cockerell, T.D.A. (1914). Descriptions and records of bees. LXI. *Ann. Mag. Nat. Hist.* **(8)14**: 39–49 [47].
Type data: syntypes, BMNH 2♂ (a specimen is labelled 'type' and has registration number Hym.17.a.450).
Type locality: Yallingup, WA.

Distribution: SW coastal, WA; known only from type locality.
Ecology: adult—volant; melliferous, solitary.

Leioproctus (Leioproctus) chalcurus (Cockerell, 1921)

Paracolletes chalcurus Cockerell, T.D.A. (1921). Australian bees in the Queensland Museum. *Mem. Qd Mus.* **7**: 81–98 [92].
Type data: holotype, QM T2400 ♀.
Type locality: Cunderdin, WA.

Distribution: W plateau, WA; known only from type locality.
Ecology: adult—volant; melliferous, solitary.

Leioproctus (Leioproctus) chalybeatus (Erichson, 1842)

Andrena chalybeata Erichson, W.F. (1842). Beitrag zur Fauna von Vandiemensland mit besonderer Rücksicht auf die geographische Verbreitung der Insekten. *Arch. Naturg.* **8**: 83–287 [268].
Type data: holotype, ZMB ♀* (G. Maynard, pers. comm.).
Type locality: TAS.

Distribution: SE coastal, Murray-Darling basin, NSW, VIC, TAS; only published localities Jindabyne, Mt Victoria, Jamberoo, Mt Buffalo and TAS.
Ecology: adult—volant; melliferous, solitary, flower visiting record: *Kunzea* Reichb. [Myrtaceae].
References: Cockerell, T.D.A. (1934). The bees of Australia. *Aust. Zool.* **8**: 2–38 (taxonomy); Rayment, T. (1948). Some bees from the Victorian Alps. *Vict. Nat.* **65**: 201–202 (distribution); Rayment, T. (1954). Remarkable bees from a rain forest. *Aust. Zool.* **12**: 46–56 (distribution).

Leioproctus (Leioproctus) cinereus (Smith, 1853)

Lamprocolletes cinereus Smith, F. (1853). *Catalogue of Hymenopterous Insects in the Collection of the British Museum.* Part I. Andrenidae and Apidae. London : British Museum 197 pp. [12].
Type data: holotype, BMNH Hym.17.a.508 ♀.
Type locality: SA.

Distribution: SA; known only from type locality, exact locality unknown.
Ecology: adult—volant; melliferous, solitary.

Leioproctus (Leioproctus) clarki (Cockerell, 1929)

Paracolletes melbournensis clarki Cockerell, T.D.A. (1929). Bees in the Queensland Museum. *Mem. Qd Mus.* **9**: 298–323 [308].
Type data: holotype, QM T4089 ♀.
Type locality: Perth, WA.

Distribution: SE coastal, Murray-Darling basin, S Gulfs, SW coastal, NSW, VIC, ACT, SA, WA, TAS.
Ecology: adult—volant; melliferous, solitary.
References: Rayment, T. (1931). Bees in the collections of the Western Australian Museum and the Agricultural Department, Perth. *J. Proc. R. Soc. West. Aust.* **17**: 157–190 (distribution); Maynard, G.V. (1992). Systematic Studies on Australian *Leioproctus* Smith (Hymenoptera: Colletidae). Unpubl. PhD Thesis. Brisbane : Univ. of Queensland 429 pp. (distribution).

Leioproctus (Leioproctus) concavus Houston, 1990

Leioproctus (Leioproctus) concavus Houston, T.F. (1990). Descriptions of new paracolletine bees associated with flowers of *Eremophila* (Hymenoptera: Colletidae). *Rec. West. Aust. Mus.* **14**: 583–621 [599].
Type data: holotype, WAM 87/1448 ♀*.
Type locality: 70–75 km ENE Norseman, WA.

Distribution: W plateau, WA; only published localities near Norseman and near Kalgoorlie.
Ecology: adult—volant; melliferous, solitary, flower visiting record: *Eremophila* R.Br. [Myoporaceae].

Leioproctus (Leioproctus) confusus Cockerell, 1904

Leioproctus confusus Cockerell, T.D.A. (1904). New and little known bees in the collection of the British Museum. *Ann. Mag. Nat. Hist. (7)***14**: 203–208 [204].

Type data: holotype, BMNH Hym.17.a.529 ♀.
Type locality: Australia (New Holland on label, New Zealand in published description), see Michener, C.D. (1965). A classification of the bees of the Australian and South Pacific regions. *Bull. Am. Mus. Nat. Hist.* **130**: 1–362 [50].

Distribution: Australia; known only from type locality, exact locality unknown.
Ecology: adult—volant; melliferous, solitary.

Leioproctus (Leioproctus) conospermi Houston, 1989

Leioproctus (Leioproctus) conospermi Houston, T.F. (1989). *Leioproctus* bees associated with Western Australian smoke bushes (*Conospermum* spp.) and their adaptations for foraging and concealment (Hymenoptera: Colletidae: Paracolletini). *Rec. West. Aust. Mus.* **14**: 275–292 [277].
Type data: holotype, WAM 88/974 ♂*.
Type locality: 48 km SW Mt Ragged, WA.

Distribution: SW coastal, WA.
Ecology: adult—volant; melliferous, solitary, flower visiting record: *Conospermum* Sm. [Proteaceae].

Leioproctus (Leioproctus) cristatus (Smith, 1853)

Lamprocolletes cristatus Smith, F. (1853). *Catalogue of Hymenopterous Insects in the Collection of the British Museum.* Part I. Andrenidae and Apidae. London : British Museum 197 pp. [11].
Type data: holotype, OUM ♀.
Type locality: Australia (as New Holland).

Distribution: NE coastal, SE coastal, QLD, VIC.
Ecology: adult—volant; melliferous, solitary.
References: Cockerell, T.D.A. (1925). Descriptions and records of bees. CIV. *Ann. Mag. Nat. Hist. (9)***15**: 489–496 (taxonomy); Maynard, G.V. (1992). Systematic Studies on Australian *Leioproctus* Smith (Hymenoptera: Colletidae). Unpubl. PhD Thesis. Brisbane : Univ. of Queensland 429 pp. (distribution).

Leioproctus (Leioproctus) cupreus (Smith, 1853)

Lamprocolletes cupreus Smith, F. (1853). *Catalogue of Hymenopterous Insects in the Collection of the British Museum.* Part I. Andrenidae and Apidae. London : British Museum 197 pp. [13].
Type data: holotype, BMNH Hym.17.a.489 ♀.
Type locality: Adelaide, SA.

Distribution: NE coastal, SE coastal, Murray-Darling basin, S Gulfs, Bulloo River basin, Lake Eyre basin, QLD, NSW, VIC, SA, NT.
Ecology: adult—volant; melliferous, solitary, flower visiting record: *Eucalyptus* L'Hérit. [Myrtaceae].
References: Friese, H. (1924). Ueber die Bienen Australiens. *Konowia* **3**: 216–249 (description of male); Rayment, T. (1953). *Bees of the Portland District.* Victoria : Portland Field Naturalist's Club 39 pp. (distribution); Maynard, G.V. (1992). Systematic

Studies on Australian *Leioproctus* Smith (Hymenoptera: Colletidae). Unpubl. PhD Thesis. Brisbane : Univ. of Queensland 429 pp. (distribution).

Leioproctus (Leioproctus) cyaneorufus (Cockerell, 1930)

Paracolletes cyaneorufus Cockerell, T.D.A. (1930). New Australian bees. *Mem. Qd Mus.* **10**: 37–50 [47].
Type data: holotype, QM T4028 ♀.
Type locality: Bribie Is., QLD.

Distribution: NE coastal, QLD.
Ecology: adult—volant; melliferous, solitary.
Reference: Maynard, G.V. (1992). Systematic Studies on Australian *Leioproctus* Smith (Hymenoptera: Colletidae). Unpubl. PhD Thesis. Brisbane : Univ. of Queensland 429 pp. (distribution).

Leioproctus (Leioproctus) cyanurus (Cockerell, 1914)

Paracolletes humerosus cyanurus Cockerell, T.D.A. (1914). Descriptions and records of bees. LVI. *Ann. Mag. Nat. Hist. (8)* **13**: 136–146 [140].
Type data: holotype, BMNH Hym.17.a.522 ♀.
Type locality: Oakley (probably Oakleigh), VIC.

Distribution: SE coastal, VIC; only published localities Oakleigh (as Oakley), Emerald and Croydon.
Ecology: adult—volant; melliferous, solitary.
References: Rayment, T. (1947). Bees from the Victorian Alps. *Vict. Nat.* **64**: 103–107 (distribution); Michener, C.D. (1965). A classification of the bees of the Australian and South Pacific regions. *Bull. Am. Mus. Nat. Hist.* **130**: 1–362 [50] (taxonomy).

Leioproctus (Leioproctus) eremites Houston, 1990

Leioproctus (Leioproctus) eremites Houston, T.F. (1990). Descriptions of new paracolletine bees associated with flowers of *Eremophila* (Hymenoptera: Colletidae). *Rec. West. Aust. Mus.* **14**: 583–621 [601].
Type data: holotype, WAM 88/1047 ♂*.
Type locality: Coppin Pool area, 30 km S Mt Bruce, WA.

Distribution: NW coastal, WA.
Ecology: adult—volant; melliferous, solitary, nest in aggregations in soil, flower visiting record: *Eremophila* R.Br. [Myoporaceae], *Ptilotus* R.Br. [Amaranthaceae].

Leioproctus (Leioproctus) eremitulus Houston, 1990

Leioproctus (Leioproctus) eremitulus Houston, T.F. (1990). Descriptions of new paracolletine bees associated with flowers of *Eremophila* (Hymenoptera: Colletidae). *Rec. West. Aust. Mus.* **14**: 583–621 [603].
Type data: holotype, SAMA ♂*.
Type locality: 45 km ENE Dalhousie Homestead, SA.

Distribution: Lake Eyre basin, SA, NT.
Ecology: adult—volant; melliferous, solitary, flower visiting record: *Dipteracanthus* Nees [Acanthaceae], *Eremophila* R.Br. [Myoporaceae].

Leioproctus (Leioproctus) eucalypti (Cockerell, 1916)

Paracolletes eucalypti Cockerell, T.D.A. (1916). Descriptions and records of bees. LXXIII. *Ann. Mag. Nat. Hist. (8)* **18**: 44–53 [51].
Type data: holotype, BMNH Hym.17.a.433 ♂.
Type locality: Mt Yule, Healesville, VIC.

Distribution: SE coastal, VIC; only published localities Mt Yule, Healesville and Beaconsfield.
Ecology: adult—volant; melliferous, solitary, flower visiting record: *Eucalyptus* L'Hérit. [Myrtaceae].
Reference: Cockerell, T.D.A. (1929). Bees in the Queensland Museum. *Mem. Qd Mus.* **9**: 298–323 (description of female).

Leioproctus (Leioproctus) euphenax (Cockerell, 1913)

Paracolletes euphenax Cockerell, T.D.A. (1913). Descriptions and records of bees. L. *Ann. Mag. Nat. Hist. (8)* **11**: 273–283 [279].
Type data: holotype, QM T4083 ♂.
Type locality: Brisbane, QLD.

Distribution: NE coastal, SE coastal, QLD, VIC; only published localities Brisbane, Cleveland and Sandringham.
Ecology: adult—volant; melliferous, solitary.
References: Cockerell, T.D.A. (1926). Descriptions and records of bees. CX. *Ann. Mag. Nat. Hist. (9)* **17**: 510–519 (taxonomy); Rayment, T. (1931). Bees in the collections of the Western Australian Museum and the Agricultural Department, Perth. *J. Proc. R. Soc. West. Aust.* **17**: 157–190 (taxonomy); Rayment, T. (1954). Incidence of acarid mites on the biology of bees. *Aust. Zool.* **12**: 26–38 (taxonomy).

Leioproctus (Leioproctus) excubitor Houston, 1991

Leioproctus (Leioproctus) excubitor Houston, T.F. (1991). Two new and unusual species of the bee genus *Leioproctus* Smith (Hymenoptera: Colletidae), with notes on their behaviour. *Rec. West. Aust. Mus.* **15**: 83–96 [84].
Type data: holotype, WAM 89/520 ♂*.
Type locality: East Yuna Reserve, 34 km WNW Mullewa, WA.

Distribution: Lake Eyre basin, W plateau, NW coastal, NT, WA.
Ecology: adult—volant; melliferous, solitary, flower visiting record: *Acacia* Miller [Mimosaceae], *Asphodelus* L. [Liliaceae], *Comesperma* Labill. [Polygalaceae], *Dampiera* R.Br. [Goodeniaceae], *Eucalyptus* L'Hérit. [Myrtaceae], *Ptilotus* R.Br. [Amaranthaceae], *Schoenia* Steetz [Cyperaceae].

Leioproctus (Leioproctus) facialis (Cockerell, 1921)

Paracolletes facialis Cockerell, T.D.A. (1921). Australian bees in the Queensland Museum. *Mem. Qd Mus.* **7**: 81–98 [93].

Type data: holotype, QM T2404 ♂.
Type locality: Coolangatta, QLD.

Distribution: NE coastal, SE coastal, QLD, NSW, VIC; only published localities Coolangatta to Sandringham.

Ecology: larva—sedentary : adult—volant; melliferous, solitary, flower visiting record: capeweed, climbing lignum, gaillardia, rosemary, *Veronica* L. [Scrophulariaceae], *Bursaria* Cav. [Pittosporaceae], *Scirpus* L. [Cyperaceae].

References: Cockerell, T.D.A. (1926). Descriptions and records of bees. CX. *Ann. Mag. Nat. Hist. (9)17*: 510–519 (distribution); Rayment, T. (1935). *A Cluster of Bees*. Sixty essays on the life-histories of Australian bees, with specific descriptions of over 100 new species, and an introduction by Professor E.F. Phillips, D.Ph., Cornell University, U.S.A. Sydney : Endeavour Press 752 pp. (biology).

Leioproctus (Leioproctus) festivus (Cockerell, 1929)

Paracolletes festivus Cockerell, T.D.A. (1929). Bees, chiefly Australian species, described or determined by Dr. H. Friese. *Am. Mus. Novit.* **343**: 1–20 [6].
Type data: holotype, AMNH ♂*.
Type locality: Sydney, NSW.

Distribution: SE coastal, NSW; known only from type locality.
Ecology: adult—volant; melliferous, solitary.

Leioproctus (Leioproctus) flavomaculatus (Cockerell, 1905)

Paracolletes flavomaculatus Cockerell, T.D.A. (1905). Descriptions and records of bees. VI. *Ann. Mag. Nat. Hist. (7)16*: 477–486 [479].
Type data: holotype, BMNH Hym.17.a.435 ♂.
Type locality: Australia.

Distribution: NE coastal, SE coastal, QLD, VIC; only published localities Kuranda, Cairns, Stradbroke Is. and Wallaby Creek.

Ecology: adult—volant; melliferous, solitary, flower visiting record: *Eucalyptus* L'Hérit. [Myrtaceae].

References: Cockerell, T.D.A. (1910). New and little-known bees. *Trans. Am. Entomol. Soc.* **36**: 199–249 (description of female); Cockerell, T.D.A. (1914). Descriptions and records of bees. LX. *Ann. Mag. Nat. Hist. (8)14*: 1–13 (distribution); Cockerell, T.D.A. (1930). Australian bees in the Museum of Comparative Zoology. *Psyche (Camb.)* **37**: 141–154 (distribution); Ashton, D. (1975). Studies of flowering behaviour in *Eucalyptus regnans* F. Muell. *Aust. J. Bot.* **23**: 399–411 (flower record).

Leioproctus (Leioproctus) frankiellus Michener, 1965

Paracolletes franki Cockerell, T.D.A. (1929). Bees, chiefly Australian species, described or determined by Dr. H. Friese. *Am. Mus. Novit.* **343**: 1–20 [5] [junior secondary homonym of *Bicolletes franki* Friese, 1908].
Type data: holotype, AMNH ♀*.
Type locality: Adelaide, SA.

Leioproctus (Leioproctus) frankiellus Michener, C.D. (1965). A classification of the bees of the Australian and South Pacific regions. *Bull. Am. Mus. Nat. Hist.* **130**: 1–362 [50] [*nom. nov.* for *Paracolletes franki* Cockerell, 1929].

Distribution: S Gulfs, SA; known only from type locality.
Ecology: adult—volant; melliferous, solitary.

Leioproctus (Leioproctus) frenchi (Cockerell, 1929)

Paracolletes semipurpureus frenchi Cockerell, T.D.A. (1929). Bees, chiefly Australian species, described or determined by Dr. H. Friese. *Am. Mus. Novit.* **343**: 1–20 [1].
Type data: holotype, BMNH Hym.17.a.491 ♀.
Type locality: Rutherglen, VIC.

Distribution: SE coastal, Murray-Darling basin, VIC; only published localities Portland and Rutherglen.
Ecology: adult—volant; melliferous, solitary, flower visiting record: *Eucalyptus* L'Hérit. [Myrtaceae].

References: Rayment, T. (1953). *Bees of the Portland District*. Victoria : Portland Field Naturalist's Club 39 pp. (distribution); Michener, C.D. (1965). A classification of the bees of the Australian and South Pacific regions. *Bull. Am. Mus. Nat. Hist.* **130**: 1–362 [50] (taxonomy).

Leioproctus (Leioproctus) friesellus Michener, 1965

Paracolletes fervidus Friese, H. (1924). Ueber die Bienen Australiens. *Konowia* **3**: 216–249 [220] [junior primary homonym of *Paracolletes fervidus* Smith, 1879].
Type data: holotype (probable), AMNH ♀*.
Type locality: Fremantle (as Freemantle), WA.

Paracolletes friesei Cockerell, T.D.A. (1929). Bees, chiefly Australian species, described or determined by Dr. H. Friese. *Am. Mus. Novit.* **343**: 1–20 [2] [junior secondary homonym of *Bicolletes friesei* Ducke, 1912]. Publication date established from Cockerell, T.D.A. (1929). Bees in the Australian Museum collection. *Rec. Aust. Mus.* **17**: 199–243 [211].
Type data: holotype, QM T4027 ♀.
Type locality: King George Sound, WA.

Leioproctus (Leioproctus) friesellus Michener, C.D. (1965). A classification of the bees of the Australian and South Pacific regions. *Bull. Am. Mus. Nat. Hist.* **130**: 1–362 [50] [*nom. nov.* for *Paracolletes friesei* Cockerell, 1929].

Taxonomic decision for synonymy: Cockerell, T.D.A. (1929). Bees, chiefly Australian species, described or determined by Dr. H. Friese. *Am. Mus. Novit.* **343**: 1–20 [2].

Distribution: SE coastal, Murray-Darling basin, SW coastal, NSW, VIC, WA.
Ecology: adult—volant; melliferous, solitary.

References: Cockerell, T.D.A. (1929). Bees in the Queensland Museum. *Mem. Qd Mus.* **9**: 298–323; Rayment, T. (1934). Contributions to the fauna of Rottnest Island. VIII. Apoidea. With description of new species. *J. Proc. R. Soc. West. Aust.* **20**: 201–212 (description of male); Maynard, G.V. (1992). Systematic Studies on Australian *Leioproctus* Smith (Hymenoptera: Colletidae). Unpubl. PhD Thesis. Brisbane : Univ. of Queensland 429 pp. (distribution).

Leioproctus (Leioproctus) hackeri (Cockerell, 1918)

Paracolletes hackeri Cockerell, T.D.A. (1918). Some bees collected in Queensland. *Mem. Qd Mus.* **6**: 112–120 [112].
Type data: holotype, QM T4115 ♀.
Type locality: Birkdale, Brisbane, QLD.

Distribution: NE coastal, SE coastal, QLD, NSW; only published localities Birkdale, Brisbane to Sydney.
Ecology: adult—volant; melliferous, solitary.
References: Cockerell, T.D.A. (1930). Australian bees in the Museum of Comparative Zoology. *Psyche (Camb.)* **37**: 141–154 (distribution); Rayment, T. (1935). *A Cluster of Bees*. Sixty essays on the life-histories of Australian bees, with specific descriptions of over 100 new species, and an introduction by Professor E.F. Phillips, D.Ph., Cornell University, U.S.A. Sydney : Endeavour Press 752 pp. (illustration, as *Anthoglossa hackeri* (Cockerell, 1918)).

Leioproctus (Leioproctus) hardyi (Cockerell, 1929)

Paracolletes nigroclypeatus hardyi Cockerell, T.D.A. (1929). Bees in the Queensland Museum. *Mem. Qd Mus.* **9**: 298–323 [310].
Type data: holotype, QM T4088 ♀.
Type locality: Perth, WA.

Distribution: SW coastal, WA; known only from type locality.
Ecology: adult—volant; melliferous, solitary.
Reference: Michener, C.D. (1965). A classification of the bees of the Australian and South Pacific regions. *Bull. Am. Mus. Nat. Hist.* **130**: 1–362 [51] (taxonomy).

Leioproctus (Leioproctus) helmsi (Cockerell, 1929)

Paracolletes helmsi Cockerell, T.D.A. (1929). Bees in the Australian Museum collection. *Rec. Aust. Mus.* **17**: 199–243 [209].
Type data: holotype, AM K48303 ♂.
Type locality: Kosciusko (5,000 ft), NSW.

Distribution: Murray-Darling basin, NSW; known only from type locality.
Ecology: adult—volant; melliferous, solitary.

Leioproctus (Leioproctus) hobartensis (Cockerell, 1906)

Paracolletes hobartensis Cockerell, T.D.A. (1906). Descriptions and records of bees. VII. *Ann. Mag. Nat. Hist. (7)***17**: 23–29 [23].
Type data: holotype, BMNH Hym.17.a.446 ♀.
Type locality: Hobart, TAS.

Distribution: TAS; known only from type locality.
Ecology: adult—volant; melliferous, solitary.

Leioproctus (Leioproctus) humerosus (Smith, 1879)

Dasycolletes humerosus Smith, F. (1879). *Descriptions of New Species of Hymenoptera in the Collection of the British Museum*. London : British Museum xxi 240 pp. [11].
Type data: holotype, BMNH Hym.17.a.521 ♀.
Type locality: Melbourne, VIC.

Distribution: SE coastal, Murray-Darling basin, VIC; only published localities Melbourne and Mt Buffalo.
Ecology: adult—volant; melliferous, solitary.
References: Cockerell, T.D.A. (1926). Descriptions and records of bees. CXI. *Ann. Mag. Nat. Hist. (9)***17**: 657–665 (taxonomy); Rayment, T. (1947). Bees from the Victorian Alps. *Vict. Nat.* **64**: 103–107 (distribution).

Leioproctus (Leioproctus) ibex (Cockerell, 1914)

Paracolletes ibex Cockerell, T.D.A. (1914). Descriptions and records of bees. LVI. *Ann. Mag. Nat. Hist. (8)***13**: 136–146 [138].
Type data: holotype, BMNH Hym.17.a.480 ♂.
Type locality: Windsor, VIC.

Distribution: SE coastal, SW coastal, VIC, WA; only published localities Windsor and Wyalkatchem.
Ecology: adult—volant; melliferous, solitary.
Reference: Cockerell, T.D.A. (1929). Bees in the Australian Museum collection. *Rec. Aust. Mus.* **17**: 199–243 (distribution).

Leioproctus (Leioproctus) illawarraensis (Rayment, 1954)

Paracolletes subviridis illawarraensis Rayment, T. (1954). Remarkable bees from a rain forest. *Aust. Zool.* **12**: 46–56 [48].
Type data: syntypes, ANIC 2♀.
Type locality: Jamberoo, NSW.

Distribution: SE coastal, NSW; known only from type locality.
Ecology: adult—volant; melliferous, solitary, flower visiting record: *Leptospermum* Forster & G.Forster [Myrtaceae].
Reference: Michener, C.D. (1965). A classification of the bees of the Australian and South Pacific regions. *Bull. Am. Mus. Nat. Hist.* **130**: 1–362 [51] (taxonomy).

Leioproctus (Leioproctus) incomptus (Cockerell, 1921)

Paracolletes incomptus Cockerell, T.D.A. (1921). Australian bees in the Queensland Museum. *Mem. Qd Mus.* **7**: 81–98 [94].
Type data: holotype, QM T2407 ♀.
Type locality: Mundaring, WA.

Distribution: SW coastal, WA; known only from type locality.

Ecology: adult—volant; melliferous, solitary.

Leioproctus (Leioproctus) insularis (Cockerell, 1913)

Paracolletes tuberculatus insularis Cockerell, T.D.A. (1913). Descriptions and records of bees. L. *Ann. Mag. Nat. Hist. (8)***11**: 273–283 [275].
Type data: holotype, QM T4082 ♀.
Type locality: Stradbroke Is., QLD.

Distribution: NE coastal, SE coastal, QLD, VIC.
Ecology: larva—sedentary : adult—volant; melliferous, solitary, flower visiting record: *Acacia* Miller [Mimosaceae], *Boronia* Sm. [Rutaceae], *Hibbertia* Andrews [Dilleniaceae], *Muehlenbeckia* Meissner [Polygonaceae].
References: Rayment, T. (1935). *A Cluster of Bees.* Sixty essays on the life-histories of Australian bees, with specific descriptions of over 100 new species, and an introduction by Professor E.F. Phillips, D.Ph., Cornell University, U.S.A. Sydney : Endeavour Press 752 pp. (biology); Michener, C.D. (1965). A classification of the bees of the Australian and South Pacific regions. *Bull. Am. Mus. Nat. Hist.* **130**: 1–362 [51] (flower records, taxonomy); De Lello, E. (1971). Adnexal glands of the sting apparatus of bees : anatomy and histology, I (Hymenoptera : Colletidae and Andrenidae). *J. Kansas Entomol. Soc.* **44**: 5–13 (sting glands, as *Leioproctus insulares,* incorrect subsequent spelling); Maynard, G.V. (1992). Systematic Studies on Australian *Leioproctus* Smith (Hymenoptera: Colletidae). Unpubl. PhD Thesis. Brisbane : Univ. of Queensland 429 pp. (distribution).

Leioproctus (Leioproctus) irroratus (Smith, 1853)

Lamprocolletes irroratus Smith, F. (1853). *Catalogue of Hymenopterous Insects in the Collection of the British Museum.* Part I. Andrenidae and Apidae. London : British Museum 197 pp. [12].
Type data: holotype, OUM ♀.
Type locality: VIC.

Distribution: NE coastal, SE coastal, Murray-Darling basin, QLD, NSW, VIC.
Ecology: adult—volant; melliferous, solitary, flower visiting record: *Lomatia* R.Br. [Proteaceae].
References: Cockerell, T.D.A. (1925). Descriptions and records of bees. CIV. *Ann. Mag. Nat. Hist. (9)***15**: 489–496 (taxonomy); Cockerell, T.D.A. (1926). Descriptions of records of bees. CXI. *Ann. Mag. Nat. Hist. (9)***17**: 657–665 (taxonomy); Rayment, T. (1939). Bees from the high lands of New South Wales and Victoria. *Aust. Zool.* **9**: 263–294 (distribution); Rayment, T. (1947). Bees from the Victorian Alps. *Vict. Nat.* **64**: 103–107 (distribution); Maynard, G.V. (1992). Systematic Studies on Australian *Leioproctus* Smith (Hymenoptera: Colletidae). Un-

publ. PhD Thesis. Brisbane : Univ. of Queensland 429 pp. (distribution).

Leioproctus (Leioproctus) kumarina Houston, 1990

Leioproctus (Leioproctus) kumarina Houston, T.F. (1990). Descriptions of new paracolletine bees associated with flowers of *Eremophila* (Hymenoptera: Colletidae). *Rec. West. Aust. Mus.* **14**: 583–621 [604].
Type data: holotype, WAM 89/386 ♀*.
Type locality: 83 miles S Newman, WA.

Distribution: NW coastal, WA; known only from type locality.
Ecology: adult—volant; melliferous, solitary, flower visiting record: *Scaevola* L. [Goodeniaceae].

Leioproctus (Leioproctus) lanceolatus Houston, 1990

Leioproctus (Leioproctus) lanceolatus Houston, T.F. (1990). Descriptions of new paracolletine bees associated with flowers of *Eremophila* (Hymenoptera: Colletidae). *Rec. West. Aust. Mus.* **14**: 583–621 [605].
Type data: holotype, WAM 82/479 ♂*.
Type locality: 11 km W Banjiwarn Homestead, WA.

Distribution: Lake Eyre basin, W plateau, SA, WA, NT.
Ecology: adult—volant; melliferous, solitary, flower visiting record: *Dipteracanthus* Nees [Acanthaceae], *Eremophila* R.Br. [Myoporaceae].

Leioproctus (Leioproctus) launcestonensis (Cockerell, 1914)

Paracolletes launcestonensis Cockerell, T.D.A. (1914). Some Tasmanian bees. *Entomologist* **47**: 305–308 [305].
Type data: holotype, BMNH Hym.17.a.485 ♀.
Type locality: Launceston, TAS.

Distribution: NE coastal, SE coastal, QLD, NSW, VIC, TAS.
Ecology: adult—volant; melliferous, solitary.
Reference: Maynard, G.V. (1992). Systematic Studies on Australian *Leioproctus* Smith (Hymenoptera: Colletidae). Unpubl. PhD Thesis. Brisbane : Univ. of Queensland 429 pp. (distribution).

Leioproctus (Leioproctus) leai (Cockerell, 1913)

Paracolletes leai Cockerell, T.D.A. (1913). A small collection of bees from Tasmania. *Proc. Linn. Soc. N.S.W.* **37**: 596–599 [597].
Type data: holotype, USNM ♀*.
Type locality: Ulverstone, TAS.

Distribution: NE coastal, SE coastal, Murray-Darling basin, SW coastal, QLD, NSW, VIC, SA, WA, TAS.
Ecology: adult—volant; melliferous, solitary.
References: Cockerell, T.D.A. (1913). Descriptions and records of bees. LIV. *Ann. Mag. Nat. Hist. (8)***12**: 368–376 (redescription); Cockerell, T.D.A. (1914). Descriptions and records of bees. LVI. *Ann. Mag. Nat. Hist. (8)***13**: 136–146 (distribution); Cockerell,

T.D.A. (1929). Bees in the Australian Museum collection. *Rec. Aust. Mus.* **17**: 199–243 (distribution); Rayment, T. (1947). Bees from the Victorian Alps. *Vict. Nat.* **64**: 103–107 (taxonomy); Maynard, G.V. (1992). Systematic Studies on Australian *Leioproctus* Smith (Hymenoptera: Colletidae). Unpubl. PhD Thesis. Brisbane : Univ. of Queensland 429 pp. (distribution).

Leioproctus (Leioproctus) longipalpus Houston, 1990

Leioproctus (Leioproctus) longipalpus Houston, T.F. (1990). Descriptions of new paracolletine bees associated with flowers of *Eremophila* (Hymenoptera: Colletidae). *Rec. West. Aust. Mus.* **14**: 583–621 [607].
Type data: holotype, WAM 88/1058 ♂*.
Type locality: 12 km E Marandoo Camp, WA.

Distribution: NW coastal, WA; only published localities near Marandoo Camp and near Mt Bruce.
Ecology: adult—volant; melliferous, solitary, flower visiting record: *Eremophila* R.Br. [Myoporaceae].

Leioproctus (Leioproctus) lucanus Houston, 1990

Leioproctus (Leioproctus) lucanus Houston, T.F. (1990). Descriptions of new paracolletine bees associated with flowers of *Eremophila* (Hymenoptera: Colletidae). *Rec. West. Aust. Mus.* **14**: 583–621 [609].
Type data: holotype, SAMA ♂*.
Type locality: 2 km S Hamilton Homestead, SA.

Distribution: Lake Eyre basin, W plateau, SA, WA, NT.
Ecology: adult—volant; melliferous, solitary, flower visiting record: *Eremophila* R.Br. [Myoporaceae], *Scaevola* L. [Goodeniaceae].

Leioproctus (Leioproctus) lucidicinctus Houston, 1990

Leioproctus (Leioproctus) lucidicinctus Houston, T.F. (1990). Descriptions of new paracolletine bees associated with flowers of *Eremophila* (Hymenoptera: Colletidae). *Rec. West. Aust. Mus.* **14**: 583–621 [610].
Type data: holotype, WAM 88/1045 ♂*.
Type locality: 57 km ENE Carnarvon, WA.

Distribution: Lake Eyre basin, NW coastal, SA, WA, NT; only published localities near Hamilton Homestead, near Carnarvon and Plenty River.
Ecology: adult—volant; melliferous, solitary, flower visiting record: *Eremophila* R.Br. [Myoporaceae].

Leioproctus (Leioproctus) macmillani Houston, 1991

Leioproctus (Leioproctus) macmillani Houston, T.F. (1991). Two new and unusual species of the bee genus *Leioproctus* Smith (Hymenoptera: Colletidae), with notes on their behaviour. *Rec. West. Aust. Mus.* **15**: 83–96 [88].
Type data: holotype, WAM 87/1452 ♂*.
Type locality: Gnangara (State Forest), *ca*. 20 km NNE Perth, WA.

Distribution: SW coastal, WA.
Ecology: adult—volant; melliferous, solitary, flower visiting record: *Andersonia* R.Br. [Epacridaceae], *Astroloma* R.Br. [Epacridaceae].

Leioproctus (Leioproctus) maculatus (Rayment, 1930)

Paracolletes maculatus Rayment, T. (1930). New and remarkable bees. *Proc. R. Soc. Vict.* **43**: 42–61 [48].
Type data: syntypes, ANIC 1♂1♀.
Type locality: Sandringham, VIC.

Distribution: SE coastal, Murray-Darling basin, S Gulfs, SW coastal, VIC, SA, WA.
Ecology: adult—volant; melliferous, solitary, flower visiting record: *Arctotheca* Wendl. [Asteraceae], *Leucopogon* R.Br. [Epacridaceae], *Myoporum* Banks & Sol. ex G.Forster [Myoporaceae].
References: Rayment, T. (1935). *A Cluster of Bees*. Sixty essays on the life-histories of Australian bees, with specific descriptions of over 100 new species, and an introduction by Professor E.F. Phillips, D.Ph., Cornell University, U.S.A. Sydney : Endeavour Press 752 pp. (illustration); Maynard, G.V. (1992). Systematic Studies on Australian *Leioproctus* Smith (Hymenoptera: Colletidae). Unpubl. PhD Thesis. Brisbane : Univ. of Queensland 429 pp. (distribution).

Leioproctus (Leioproctus) megachalcoides Michener, 1965

Leioproctus (Leioproctus) megachalcoides Michener, C.D. (1965). A classification of the bees of the Australian and South Pacific regions. *Bull. Am. Mus. Nat. Hist.* **130**: 1–362 [246].
Type data: holotype, WAM 65–724 ♀.
Type locality: Mullewa, WA.

Distribution: NW coastal, WA; only published localities Mullewa and Dongara.
Ecology: adult—volant; melliferous, solitary.
Reference: Michener, C.D. & Houston, T.F. (1991). Apoidea. pp. 993–1000 *in* CSIRO (sponsor) *The Insects of Australia*. A textbook for students and research workers. Melbourne : Melbourne University Press Vol. II 2nd Edn (illustration).

Leioproctus (Leioproctus) melanoproctus Michener, 1965

Paracolletes melanurus Cockerell, T.D.A. (1930). New Australian bees. *Mem. Qd Mus.* **10**: 37–50 [47] [junior secondary homonym of *Pasiphae cyanea melanura* Cockerell, 1917].
Type data: holotype, QM T4029 ♀.
Type locality: Tooloom, NSW.

Leioproctus (Leioproctus) melanoproctus Michener, C.D. (1965). A classification of the bees of the Australian and South Pacific regions. *Bull. Am. Mus. Nat. Hist.* **130**: 1–362

[51] [*nom. nov.* for *Paracolletes melanurus* Cockerell, 1930].

Distribution: SE coastal, NSW; known only from type locality.
Ecology: adult—volant; melliferous, solitary.

Leioproctus (Leioproctus) melbournensis (Cockerell, 1910)

Paracolletes melbournensis Cockerell, T.D.A. (1910). New and little-known bees. *Trans. Am. Entomol. Soc.* **36**: 199–249 [205].
Type data: syntypes (probable), ZMB ♀*, BMNH ♀*.
Type locality: Melbourne, VIC.

Distribution: SE coastal, Murray-Darling basin, NSW, VIC, (WA), TAS.
Ecology: adult—volant; melliferous, solitary, flower visiting record: aster, *Eucalyptus* L'Hérit. [Myrtaceae].
References: Cockerell, T.D.A. (1913). A small collection of bees from Tasmania. *Proc. Linn. Soc. N.S.W.* **37**: 596–599 (distribution); Rayment, T. (1935). *A Cluster of Bees*. Sixty essays on the life-histories of Australian bees, with specific descriptions of over 100 new species, and an introduction by Professor E.F. Phillips, D.Ph., Cornell University, U.S.A. Sydney : Endeavour Press 752 pp. (illustration); Rayment, T. (1953). *Bees of the Portland District*. Victoria : Portland Field Naturalist's Club 39 pp. (distribution).

Leioproctus (Leioproctus) metallescens (Cockerell, 1914)

Paracolletes metallescens Cockerell, T.D.A. (1914). Descriptions and records of bees. LXI. *Ann. Mag. Nat. Hist.* (8)**14**: 39–49 [44].
Type data: holotype (probable), BMNH Hym.17.a.449 ♀.
Type locality: Yallingup, WA.

Distribution: SE coastal, SW coastal, NW coastal, VIC, WA; only published localities Cape Schanck, Yallingup, King George Sound and Eradu.
Ecology: adult—volant; melliferous, solitary, flower visiting record: *Acacia* Miller [Mimosaceae], *Eucalyptus* L'Hérit. [Myrtaceae], *Lycium* L. [Solanaceae], *Melaleuca* L. [Myrtaceae].
References: Cockerell, T.D.A. (1929). Bees in the Australian Museum collection. *Rec. Aust. Mus.* **17**: 199–243 (distribution); Bernhardt, P., Kenrick, J. & Knox, R.B. (1984). Pollination biology and the breeding system of *Acacia retinodes* (Leguminosae: Mimosoideae). *Ann. M. Bot. Gard.* **71**: 17–29 (distribution, flower records); Bernhardt, P. (1987). A comparison of the diversity, density, and foraging behavior of bees and wasps on Australian *Acacia*. *Ann. M. Bot. Gard.* **74**: 42–50 (flower record).

Leioproctus (Leioproctus) mimulus (Cockerell, 1910)

Paracolletes mimulus Cockerell, T.D.A. (1910). New and little-known bees. *Trans. Am. Entomol. Soc.* **36**: 199–249 [206].
Type data: holotype, BMNH Hym.17.a.442 ♀.
Type locality: VIC.

Distribution: SE coastal, S Gulfs, VIC, SA; only published localities Gorae West, Emerald and Adelaide.
Ecology: adult—volant; melliferous, solitary, flower visiting record: aster, *Eucalyptus* L'Hérit. [Myrtaceae].
References: Cockerell, T.D.A. (1929). Bees, chiefly Australian species, described or determined by Dr. H. Friese. *Am. Mus. Novit.* **343**: 1–20 (taxonomy); Rayment, T. (1953). *Bees of the Portland District*. Victoria : Portland Field Naturalist's Club 39 pp. (distribution).

Leioproctus (Leioproctus) moniliformis (Cockerell, 1916)

Paracolletes moniliformis Cockerell, T.D.A. (1916). Descriptions and records of bees. LXXIII. *Ann. Mag. Nat. Hist.* (8)**18**: 44–53 [51].
Type data: holotype, BMNH Hym.17.a.465 ♂.
Type locality: Yallingup, WA.

Distribution: SW coastal, WA; known only from type locality.
Ecology: adult—volant; melliferous, solitary.

Leioproctus (Leioproctus) nanus (Smith, 1879)

Lamprocolletes nanus Smith, F. (1879). *Descriptions of New Species of Hymenoptera in the Collection of the British Museum*. London : British Museum xxi 240 pp. [9].
Type data: holotype, BMNH Hym.17.a.514 ♀.
Type locality: WA.

Distribution: WA; known only from type locality, exact locality unknown.
Ecology: adult—volant; melliferous, solitary.

Leioproctus (Leioproctus) nasutus Houston, 1990

Leioproctus (Leioproctus) nasutus Houston, T.F. (1990). Descriptions of new paracolletine bees associated with flowers of *Eremophila* (Hymenoptera: Colletidae). *Rec. West. Aust. Mus.* **14**: 583–621 [612].
Type data: holotype, WAM 89/345 ♂*.
Type locality: Meleya Well, Thundelarra Station, WA.

Distribution: SW coastal, Murray-Darling basin, S Gulfs, QLD, SA, WA.
Ecology: adult—volant; melliferous, solitary, flower visiting record: *Eremophila* R.Br. [Myoporaceae], *Scaevola* L. [Goodeniaceae].
Reference: Maynard, G.V. (1992). Systematic Studies on Australian *Leioproctus* Smith (Hymenoptera: Colletidae). Unpubl. PhD Thesis. Brisbane : Univ. of Queensland 429 pp. (distribution).

Leioproctus (Leioproctus) nicholsoni (Cockerell, 1929)

Paracolletes nicholsoni Cockerell, T.D.A. (1929). Bees in the Australian Museum collection. *Rec. Aust. Mus.* **17**: 199–243 [203].
Type data: syntypes, AM 5♀.
Type locality: Kojarena, WA.

Distribution: NW coastal, WA; only published localities Kojarena, Eradu and Geraldton.
Ecology: adult—volant; melliferous, solitary, flower visiting record: *Caladenia* R.Br. [Orchidaceae].
References: Erickson, R. (1951). *Orchids of the West.* Perth : Paterson Brokensha 109 pp. (flower record); Erickson, R. (1965). *Orchids of the West.* Perth : Paterson Brokensha 107 pp. 2nd edn (flower record).

Leioproctus (Leioproctus) nigritulus (Cockerell, 1916)

Paracolletes nigritulus Cockerell, T.D.A. (1916). Descriptions and records of bees. LXXIII. *Ann. Mag. Nat. Hist. (8)***18**: 44–53 [48].
Type data: syntypes, BMNH 2♀ (a specimen is labelled 'type' and has registration number Hym.17.a.482).
Type locality: Yallingup, WA.

Distribution: SW coastal, WA; known only from type locality.
Ecology: adult—volant; melliferous, solitary.

Leioproctus (Leioproctus) nigroclypeatus (Cockerell, 1910)

Paracolletes nigroclypeatus Cockerell, T.D.A. (1910). New and little-known bees. *Trans. Am. Entomol. Soc.* **36**: 199–249 [204].
Type data: holotype, BMNH Hym.17.a.441 ♀.
Type locality: VIC.

Distribution: SE coastal, VIC; only published localities Elsternwick, Bunyip, Sandringham, Eltham and Gorae West.
Ecology: adult—volant; melliferous, solitary, flower visiting record: *Eucalyptus* L'Hérit. [Myrtaceae].
References: Rayment, T. (1935). *A Cluster of Bees.* Sixty essays on the life-histories of Australian bees, with specific descriptions of over 100 new species, and an introduction by Professor E.F. Phillips, D.Ph., Cornell University, U.S.A. Sydney : Endeavour Press 752 pp. (distribution); Rayment, T. (1953). *Bees of the Portland District.* Victoria : Portland Field Naturalist's Club 39 pp. (distribution).

Leioproctus (Leioproctus) nigrofulvus (Cockerell, 1914)

Paracolletes nigrofulvus Cockerell, T.D.A. (1914). Descriptions and records of bees. LVI. *Ann. Mag. Nat. Hist. (8)***13**: 136–146 [137].
Type data: holotype, BMNH Hym.17.a.479 ♂.
Type locality: Shoalhaven, NSW.

Distribution: SE coastal, Murray-Darling basin, NSW, ACT.
Ecology: adult—volant; melliferous, solitary.
Reference: Maynard, G.V. (1992). Systematic Studies on Australian *Leioproctus* Smith (Hymenoptera: Colletidae). Unpubl. PhD Thesis. Brisbane : Univ. of Queensland 429 pp. (distribution).

Leioproctus (Leioproctus) nigropurpureus (Rayment, 1935)

Paracolletes nigropurpureus Rayment, T. (1935). *A Cluster of Bees.* Sixty essays on the life-histories of Australian bees, with specific descriptions of over 100 new species, and an introduction by Professor E.F. Phillips, D.Ph., Cornell University, U.S.A. Sydney : Endeavour Press 752 pp. [140].
Type data: holotype (probable), ANIC ♂.
Type locality: Heathmont, near Melbourne, VIC.

Distribution: SE coastal, VIC; known only from type locality.
Ecology: adult—volant; melliferous, solitary, flower visiting record: *Diuris* Sm. [Orchidaceae], *Hardenbergia* Benth. [Fabaceae].

Leioproctus (Leioproctus) nitidulus (Cockerell, 1916)

Paracolletes nitidulus Cockerell, T.D.A. (1916). Descriptions and records of bees. LXXIII. *Ann. Mag. Nat. Hist. (8)***18**: 44–53 [46].
Type data: holotype (probable), BMNH Hym.17.a.463 ♀.
Type locality: Yallingup, WA.

Distribution: SE coastal, SW coastal, VIC, WA; only published localities Gorae West and Yallingup.
Ecology: adult—volant; melliferous, solitary, flower visiting record: *Eucalyptus* L'Hérit. [Myrtaceae], *Leptospermum* Forster & G.Forster [Myrtaceae].
Reference: Rayment, T. (1953). *Bees of the Portland District.* Victoria : Portland Field Naturalist's Club 39 pp. (distribution).

Leioproctus (Leioproctus) nomadiformis (Cockerell, 1921)

Paracolletes nomadiformis Cockerell, T.D.A. (1921). Australian bees in the Queensland Museum. *Mem. Qd Mus.* **7**: 81–98 [95].
Type data: holotype, QM T2406 ♂.
Type locality: Kuranda, QLD.

Distribution: NE coastal, QLD; known only from type locality.
Ecology: adult—volant; melliferous, solitary.

Leioproctus (Leioproctus) obscuripennis (Cockerell, 1905)

Paracolletes obscuripennis Cockerell, T.D.A. (1905). Descriptions and records of bees. VI. *Ann. Mag. Nat. Hist. (7)***16**: 477–486 [484].
Type data: syntypes (probable), BMNH 2♂ (specimen is

labelled 'type' and has registration number Hym.17.a.436).
Type locality: TAS.

Distribution: SW coastal, WA, TAS; only published localities Great Lake, Launceston and Bolgart.
Ecology: adult—volant; melliferous, solitary, flower visiting record: *Bursaria* Cav. [Pittosporaceae], *Hakea* Schrader [Proteaceae], *Helichrysum* Miller *s.lat.* [Asteraceae].
Reference: Rayment, T. (1953). New bees and wasps, Part XX. *Vict. Nat.* **70**: 68–71 (distribution).

Leioproctus (Leioproctus) obscurus (Smith, 1853)

Lamprocolletes obscurus Smith, F. (1853). *Catalogue of Hymenopterous Insects in the Collection of the British Museum.* Part I. Andrenidae and Apidae. London : British Museum 197 pp. [11].
Type data: lectotype, BMNH ♀ Hym.17.a.499.
Subsequent designation: Cockerell, T.D.A. (1926). Descriptions and records of bees. CX. *Ann. Mag. Nat. Hist.* (9)**17**: 510–519 [516]; Cardale J.C., this work, interprets Cockerell's incorrect inference of holotype as a lectotype designation (Art. 74, ICZN 1985).
Type locality: TAS (as Van Diemens Land).

Distribution: Murray-Darling basin, NSW, VIC, (WA), TAS; only published localities Mt Kosciusko, Mt Buffalo, Mt Wellington, Russell Falls and WA.
Ecology: adult—volant; melliferous, solitary.
References: Cockerell, T.D.A. (1905). Descriptions and records of bees. III. *Ann. Mag. Nat. Hist.* (7)**16**: 301–308 (taxonomy); Cockerell, T.D.A. (1921). Australian bees in the Queensland Museum. *Mem. Qd Mus.* **7**: 81–98 (distribution); Cockerell, T.D.A. (1929). Bees in the Queensland Museum. *Mem. Qd Mus.* **9**: 298–323 (taxonomy); Rayment, T. (1947). Bees from the Victorian Alps. *Vict. Nat.* **64**: 103–107 (distribution).

Leioproctus (Leioproctus) opaculus (Cockerell, 1929)

Paracolletes opaculus Cockerell, T.D.A. (1929). Bees in the Australian Museum collection. *Rec. Aust. Mus.* **17**: 199–243 [211].
Type data: holotype, AM ♀.
Type locality: Geraldton, WA.

Distribution: NW coastal, WA; known only from type locality.
Ecology: adult—volant; melliferous, solitary.

Leioproctus (Leioproctus) ornatissimus (Cockerell, 1916)

Paracolletes ornatissimus Cockerell, T.D.A. (1916). A collection of bees from Queensland. *Mem. Qd Mus.* **5**: 197–204 [200].
Type data: holotype, BMNH Hym.17.a.483 ♀.
Type locality: Oxley, Brisbane, QLD.

Distribution: NE coastal, QLD; only published localities Oxley (Brisbane) and Ipswich.
Ecology: adult—volant; melliferous, solitary, flower

visiting record: *Eucalyptus* L'Hérit. [Myrtaceae].
Reference: Michener, C.D. (1965). A classification of the bees of the Australian and South Pacific regions. *Bull. Am. Mus. Nat. Hist.* **130**: 1–362 (flower record).

Leioproctus (Leioproctus) pallidicinctus (Rayment, 1953)

Paracolletes pallidicinctus Rayment, T. (1953). *Bees of the Portland District.* Victoria : Portland Field Naturalist's Club 39 pp. [4].
Type data: holotype, ANIC ♂.
Type locality: Emu Hill, W of Gorae, VIC.

Distribution: SE coastal, VIC; known only from type locality.
Ecology: adult—volant; melliferous, solitary, flower visiting record: *Eucalyptus* L'Hérit. [Myrtaceae].

Leioproctus (Leioproctus) pappus Houston, 1989

Leioproctus (Leioproctus) pappus Houston, T.F. (1989). *Leioproctus* bees associated with Western Australian smoke bushes (*Conospermum* spp.) and their adaptations for foraging and concealment (Hymenoptera: Colletidae: Paracolletini). *Rec. West. Aust. Mus.* **14**: 275–292 [281].
Type data: holotype, WAM 88/991 ♂*.
Type locality: Boorabbin Rock, WA.

Distribution: SW coastal, NW coastal, W plateau, WA.
Ecology: adult—volant; melliferous, solitary, flower visiting record: *Conospermum* Sm. [Proteaceae].

Leioproctus (Leioproctus) pavonellus (Cockerell, 1929)

Paracolletes pavonellus Cockerell, T.D.A. (1929). Bees in the Australian Museum collection. *Rec. Aust. Mus.* **17**: 199–243 [208].
Type data: holotype, AM K37276 ♀.
Type locality: King George Sound, WA.

Distribution: SW coastal, WA; known only from type locality.
Ecology: adult—volant; melliferous, solitary.

Leioproctus (Leioproctus) phillipensis (Rayment, 1953)

Paracolletes advena phillipensis Rayment, T. (1953). *Bees of the Portland District.* Victoria : Portland Field Naturalist's Club 39 pp. [2].
Type data: syntypes, ANIC 3♀.
Type locality: Sandringham, VIC.

Distribution: SE coastal, VIC; known only from type locality.
Ecology: adult—volant; melliferous, solitary, flower visiting record: *Cryptostemma* R.Br. [Asteraceae], *Leucopogon* R.Br. [Epacridaceae].
References: Rayment, T. (1954). Incidence of acarid mites on the biology of bees. *Aust. Zool.* **12**: 26–38 (as host); Michener, C.D. (1965). A classification of the bees of the Australian and South Pacific regions.

Bull. Am. Mus. Nat. Hist. **130**: 1–362 [51] (taxonomy).

Leioproctus (Leioproctus) philonesus (Cockerell, 1929)

Paracolletes philonesus Cockerell, T.D.A. (1929). Bees in the Australian Museum collection. *Rec. Aust. Mus.* **17**: 199–243 [201].
Type data: holotype, AM K45346 ♀.
Type locality: Mt Gower, Lord Howe Is.

Distribution: Lord Howe Is.; known only from type locality.
Ecology: adult—volant; melliferous, solitary.

Leioproctus (Leioproctus) platycephalus (Cockerell, 1912)

Paracolletes platycephalus Cockerell, T.D.A. (1912). Descriptions and records of bees. XLIII. *Ann. Mag. Nat. Hist. (8)9*: 377–387 [379].
Type data: holotype, BMNH Hym.17.a.476 ♀.
Type locality: VIC.

Distribution: SE coastal, Murray-Darling basin, S Gulfs, NSW, ACT, VIC, SA.
Ecology: adult—volant; melliferous, solitary, flower visiting record: *Leucopogon* R.Br. [Epacridaceae], *Pultenaea* Sm. [Fabaceae].
References: Cockerell, T.D.A. (1913). Descriptions and records of bees. L. *Ann. Mag. Nat. Hist. (8)11*: 273–283 (description of male); Rayment, T. (1953). *Bees of the Portland District.* Victoria : Portland Field Naturalist's Club 39 pp. (distribution); Maynard, G.V. (1992). Systematic Studies on Australian *Leioproctus* Smith (Hymenoptera: Colletidae). Unpubl. PhD Thesis. Brisbane : Univ. of Queensland 429 pp. (distribution).

Leioproctus (Leioproctus) plebeius (Cockerell, 1921)

Paracolletes plebeius Cockerell, T.D.A. (1921). Australian bees in the Queensland Museum. *Mem. Qd Mus.* **7**: 81–98 [94].
Type data: holotype, QM T2403 ♀.
Type locality: Bright, VIC.

Distribution: SE coastal, Murray-Darling basin, NSW, VIC.
Ecology: adult—volant; melliferous, solitary, flower visiting record: blackberry, *Eucalyptus* L'Hérit. [Myrtaceae], *Leptospermum* Forster & G.Forster [Myrtaceae].
References: Rayment, T. (1935). *A Cluster of Bees.* Sixty essays on the life-histories of Australian bees, with specific descriptions of over 100 new species, and an introduction by Professor E.F. Phillips, D.Ph., Cornell University, U.S.A. Sydney : Endeavour Press 752 pp. (description of male); Rayment, T. (1939). Bees from the high lands of New South Wales and Victoria. *Aust. Zool.* **9**: 263–294 (distribution); Ray-

ment, T. (1953). *Bees of the Portland District.* Victoria : Portland Field Naturalist's Club 39 pp. (distribution).

Leioproctus (Leioproctus) plumosellus (Cockerell, 1905)

Paracolletes plumosellus Cockerell, T.D.A. (1905). Descriptions and records of bees. VI. *Ann. Mag. Nat. Hist. (7)16*: 477–486 [480].
Type data: holotype, BMNH Hym.17.a.426 ♂.
Type locality: Australia (as New Holland).

Distribution: SW coastal, WA; only published locality Perth.
Ecology: adult—volant; melliferous, solitary.
Reference: Rayment, T. (1930). Notes on a collection of bees from Western Australia. *J. Proc. R. Soc. West. Aust.* **16**: 45–56 (distribution).

Leioproctus (Leioproctus) plumosus (Smith, 1853)

Lamprocolletes plumosus Smith, F. (1853). *Catalogue of Hymenopterous Insects in the Collection of the British Museum.* Part I. Andrenidae and Apidae. London : British Museum 197 pp. [12].
Type data: holotype, BMNH Hym.17.a.493 ♀.
Type locality: Swan River, WA.

Lamprocolletes bicolor Smith, F. (1879). *Descriptions of New Species of Hymenoptera in the Collection of the British Museum.* London : British Museum xxi 240 pp. [10].
Type data: syntypes, BMNH Hym.17.a.494a,b 2♂ (one male described as female).
Type locality: Swan River, WA.

Taxonomic decision for synonymy: Cockerell, T.D.A. (1916). A collection of bees from Queensland. *Mem. Qd Mus.* **5**: 197–204 [200].

Distribution: Murray-Darling basin, SE coastal, S Gulfs, SW coastal, NW coastal, QLD, NSW, VIC, SA, WA.
Ecology: adult—volant; melliferous, solitary, flower visiting record: *Acacia* Miller [Mimosaceae], *Daviesia* Sm. [Fabaceae], *Eucalyptus* L'Hérit. [Myrtaceae], *Leucopogon* R.Br. [Epacridaceae], *Salpichroa* Miers [Solanaceae].
References: Cockerell, T.D.A. (1910). New and little-known bees. *Trans. Am. Entomol. Soc.* **36**: 199–249 (description of male); Rayment, T. (1929). The plumed bees. *Vict. Nat.* **46**: 155–162 (illustration); Cockerell, T.D.A. (1929). Bees in the Australian Museum collection. *Rec. Aust. Mus.* **17**: 199–243 (taxonomy); Cockerell, T.D.A. (1930). New Australian bees. *Mem. Qd Mus.* **10**: 37–50 (variety); Rayment, T. (1931). Bees in the collections of the Western Australian Museum and the Agricultural Department, Perth. *J. Proc. R. Soc. West. Aust.* **17**: 157–190 (taxonomy); Rayment, T. (1935). *A Cluster of Bees.* Sixty essays on the life-histories of Australian bees, with specific descriptions of over 100 new species, and an introduction by Professor E.F. Phillips, D.Ph.,

Cornell University, U.S.A. Sydney : Endeavour Press 752 pp. (biology); Rayment, T. (1953). *Bees of the Portland District.* Victoria : Portland Field Naturalist's Club 39 pp. (distribution); Bernhardt, P., Kenrick, J. & Knox, R.B. (1984). Pollination biology and the breeding system of *Acacia retinodes* (Leguminosae: Mimosoideae). *Ann. M. Bot. Gard.* **71**: 17–29 (flower record); Bernhardt, P. (1987). A comparison of the diversity, density, and foraging behavior of bees and wasps on Australian *Acacia. Ann. M. Bot. Gard.* **74**: 42–50 (flower record); Maynard, G.V. (1992). Systematic Studies on Australian *Leioproctus* Smith (Hymenoptera: Colletidae). Unpubl. PhD Thesis. Brisbane : Univ. of Queensland 429 pp. (distribution).

Leioproctus (Leioproctus) providellus (Cockerell, 1905)

Paracolletes providellus Cockerell, T.D.A. (1905). Descriptions and records of bees, VI. *Ann. Mag. Nat. Hist.* *(7)***16**: 477–486 [483].
Type data: holotype (probable), BMNH Hym.17.a.427 ♂.
Type locality: Australia.

Distribution: SE coastal, Murray-Darling basin, VIC; only published localities Windsor, Emerald, Gorae West and Mt Buffalo.
Ecology: adult—volant; melliferous, solitary, flower visiting record: *Eucalyptus* L'Hérit. [Myrtaceae], *Leptospermum* Forster & G.Forster [Myrtaceae].
References: Cockerell, T.D.A. (1914). Descriptions and records of bees. LVI. *Ann. Mag. Nat. Hist.* (8)**13**: 136–146 (varieties); Rayment, T. (1947). Bees from the Victorian Alps. *Vict. Nat.* **64**: 103–107 (distribution); Rayment, T. (1953). *Bees of the Portland District.* Victoria : Portland Field Naturalist's Club 39 pp. (distribution); Rayment, T. (1957). Closer than a brother. *Proc. R. Zool. Soc. N.S.W.* **1955–56**: 87–90 (as host).

Leioproctus (Leioproctus) providus (Smith, 1879)

Lamprocolletes providus Smith, F. (1879). *Descriptions of New Species of Hymenoptera in the Collection of the British Museum.* London : British Museum xxi 240 pp. [8].
Type data: holotype, BMNH Hym.17.a.510 ♀.
Type locality: Australia.

Distribution: Murray-Darling basin, SE coastal, SW coastal, QLD, NSW, VIC, WA, TAS.
Ecology: adult—volant; melliferous, solitary, flower visiting record: *Eucalyptus* L'Hérit. [Myrtaceae].
References: Cockerell, T.D.A. (1910). New and little-known bees. *Trans. Am. Entomol. Soc.* **36**: 199–249 (variety); Cockerell, T.D.A. (1915). Descriptions and records of bees. LXIX. *Ann. Mag. Nat. Hist.* (8)**16**: 96–104 (description of male); Cockerell, T.D.A. (1929). Bees in the Australian Museum collection. *Rec. Aust. Mus.* **17**: 199–243 (taxonomy); Cockerell, T.D.A. (1930). New Australian bees. *Mem. Qd Mus.* **10**: 37–50 (taxonomy); Rayment, T.

(1931). Bees in the collections of the Western Australian Museum and the Agricultural Department, Perth. *J. Proc. R. Soc. West. Aust.* **17**: 157–190 (distribution); Rayment, T. (1953). *Bees of the Portland District.* Victoria : Portland Field Naturalist's Club 39 pp. (flower record).

Leioproctus (Leioproctus) punctatus (Smith, 1853)

Lamprocolletes punctatus Smith, F. (1853). *Catalogue of Hymenopterous Insects in the Collection of the British Museum.* Part I. Andrenidae and Apidae. London : British Museum 197 pp. [14].
Type data: holotype, BMNH Hym.17.a.512 ♀.
Type locality: Adelaide, SA.

Distribution: S Gulfs, SA; known only from type locality.
Ecology: adult—volant; melliferous, solitary.

Leioproctus (Leioproctus) recusus (Cockerell, 1921)

Paracolletes recusus Cockerell, T.D.A (1921). Australian bees in the Queensland Museum. *Mem. Qd Mus.* **7**: 81–98 [94].
Type data: holotype, QM T2398 ♀.
Type locality: Mt Tamborine (as Tambourine), QLD.

Distribution: NE coastal, QLD; known only from type locality.
Ecology: adult—volant; melliferous, solitary.

Leioproctus (Leioproctus) regalis (Cockerell, 1921)

Paracolletes regalis Cockerell, T.D.A. (1921). Australian bees in the Queensland Museum. *Mem. Qd Mus.* **7**: 81–98 [93].
Type data: holotype, QM T2395 ♂.
Type locality: Kuranda, QLD.

Distribution: NE coastal, QLD; known only from type locality.
Ecology: adult—volant; melliferous, solitary.

Leioproctus (Leioproctus) rhodopus (Cockerell, 1914)

Paracolletes rhodopus Cockerell, T.D.A. (1914). Descriptions and records of bees. LXI. *Ann. Mag. Nat. Hist.* (8)**14**: 39–49 [46].
Type data: holotype, BMNH Hym.17.a.419 ♀.
Type locality: Yallingup, WA.

Distribution: SW coastal, WA; known only from type locality.
Ecology: adult—volant; melliferous, solitary.

Leioproctus (Leioproctus) roseoviridis (Cockerell, 1905)

Paracolletes roseoviridis Cockerell, T.D.A. (1905). New Australian bees, in the collection of the British Museum. *Entomologist* **38**: 270–273, 302–304 [270].

Type data: holotype, BMNH Hym.17.a.438 ♂.
Type locality: WA.

Distribution: WA; known only from type locality, exact locality unknown.
Ecology: adult—volant; melliferous, solitary.

Leioproctus (Leioproctus) rubellus (Smith, 1862)

Dasycolletes rubellus Smith, F. (1862). Descriptions of new species of Australian Hymenoptera, and of a species of *Formica* from New Zealand. *Trans. Entomol. Soc. Lond.* (3)**1**: 53–62 [58].
Type data: holotype, BMNH Hym.17.a.524 ♀.
Type locality: Lower Plenty, VIC (as Lower Plenty, SA).

Distribution: SE coastal, VIC; known only from type locality.
Ecology: adult—volant; melliferous, solitary.

Leioproctus (Leioproctus) rudis (Cockerell, 1906)

Paracolletes rudis Cockerell, T.D.A. (1906). Descriptions and records of bees. VII. *Ann. Mag. Nat. Hist.* (7)**17**: 23–29 [25].
Type data: holotype (probable), BMNH Hym.17.a.439 ♀.
Type locality: Swan River, WA.

Distribution: SW coastal, WA; known only from type locality.
Ecology: adult—volant; melliferous, solitary.
Reference: Cockerell, T.D.A. (1929). Bees in the Queensland Museum. *Mem. Qd Mus.* **9**: 298–323 (taxonomy).

Leioproctus (Leioproctus) ruficornis (Smith, 1879)

Lamprocolletes ruficornis Smith, F. (1879). *Descriptions of New Species of Hymenoptera in the Collection of the British Museum*. London : British Museum xxi 240 pp. [10].
Type data: holotype, BMNH Hym.17.a.516 ♂.
Type locality: WA.

Distribution: SW coastal, WA; only published locality Southern Cross.
Ecology: adult—volant; melliferous, solitary.
References: Cockerell, T.D.A. (1907). On a collection of Australian and Asiatic bees. *Bull. Am. Mus. Nat. Hist.* **23**: 221–236 (taxonomy); Rayment, T. (1935). *A Cluster of Bees*. Sixty essays on the life-histories of Australian bees, with specific descriptions of over 100 new species, and an introduction by Professor E.F. Phillips, D.Ph., Cornell University, U.S.A. Sydney : Endeavour Press 752 pp. (description of male).

Leioproctus (Leioproctus) rufipes (Cockerell, 1929)

Paracolletes amabilis rufipes Cockerell, T.D.A. (1929). Bees in the Australian Museum collection. *Rec. Aust. Mus.* **17**: 199–243 [199].

Type data: holotype, AM K50213 ♂.
Type locality: Berowra, near Hawkesbury River, NSW.

Distribution: SE coastal, NSW; known only from type locality.
Ecology: adult—volant; melliferous, solitary.
Reference: Michener, C.D. (1965). A classification of the bees of the Australian and South Pacific regions. *Bull. Am. Mus. Nat. Hist.* **130**: 1–362 [52] (taxonomy).

Leioproctus (Leioproctus) rufoaeneus (Friese, 1924)

Dasycolletes rufoaeneus Friese, H. (1924). Ueber die Bienen Australiens. *Konowia* **3**: 216–249 [219].
Type data: syntypes (probable), AMNH 4♂*.
Type locality: Adelaide, SA.

Distribution: S Gulfs, SA; known only from type locality.
Ecology: adult—volant; melliferous, solitary.
Reference: Cockerell, T.D.A. (1929). Bees, chiefly Australian species, described or determined by Dr. H. Friese. *Am. Mus. Novit.* **343**: 1–20 (redescription).

Leioproctus (Leioproctus) scitulus (Cockerell, 1921)

Paracolletes scitulus Cockerell, T.D.A. (1921). Australian bees in the Queensland Museum. *Mem. Qd Mus.* **7**: 81–98 [97].
Type data: holotype, QM T2397 ♂.
Type locality: Brisbane, QLD.

Distribution: NE coastal, QLD; known only from type locality.
Ecology: adult—volant; melliferous, solitary.

Leioproctus (Leioproctus) semilautus (Cockerell, 1905)

Paracolletes semilautus Cockerell, T.D.A. (1905). Descriptions and records of bees. VI. *Ann. Mag. Nat. Hist.* (7)**16**: 477–486 [485].
Type data: holotype, BMNH Hym.17.a.420 ♂.
Type locality: Australia.

Distribution: Australia; known only from type locality, exact locality unknown.
Ecology: adult—volant; melliferous, solitary.

Leioproctus (Leioproctus) semilucens (Cockerell, 1929)

Paracolletes semilucens Cockerell, T.D.A. (1929). Bees in the Queensland Museum. *Mem. Qd Mus.* **9**: 298–323 [309].
Type data: holotype, QM Hy/4097 ♀.
Type locality: Perth, WA.

Distribution: SW coastal, WA; only published localities Perth and Swan River.
Ecology: adult—volant; melliferous, solitary.

Leioproctus (Leioproctus) semipurpureus (Cockerell, 1905)

Paracolletes cupreus semipurpureus Cockerell, T.D.A. (1905). Descriptions and records of bees. VI. *Ann. Mag. Nat. Hist.* (7)**16**: 477–486 [479].
Type data: holotype, BMNH Hym.17.a.490 ♀.
Type locality: Mackay, QLD.

Lamprocolletes cupreus minor Friese, H. (1924). Ueber die Bienen Australiens. *Konowia* **3**: 216–249 [221].
Type data: holotype (probable), AMNH ♀*.
Type locality: Sydney, NSW.

Taxonomic decision for synonymy: Cockerell, T.D.A. (1929). Bees, chiefly Australian species, described or determined by Dr. H. Friese. *Am. Mus. Novit.* **343**: 1–20 [1].

Distribution: NE coastal, SE coastal, QLD, NSW.
Ecology: adult—volant; melliferous, solitary, flower visiting record: *Eucalyptus* L'Hérit. [Myrtaceae].
References: Cockerell, T.D.A. (1907). On a collection of Australian and Asiatic bees. *Bull. Am. Mus. Nat. Hist.* **23**: 221–236 (distribution); Cockerell, T.D.A. (1910). New and little-known bees. *Trans. Am. Entomol. Soc.* **36**: 199–249 (variety); Cockerell, T.D.A. (1930). Australian bees in the Museum of Comparative Zoology. *Psyche (Camb.)* **37**: 141–154 (distribution); Michener, C.D. (1965). A classification of the bees of the Australian and South Pacific regions. *Bull. Am. Mus. Nat. Hist.* **130**: 1–362 (flower record, taxonomy).

Leioproctus (Leioproctus) semiviridis (Cockerell, 1930)

Paracolletes semiviridis Cockerell, T.D.A. (1930). New Australian bees. *Mem. Qd Mus.* **10**: 37–50 [48].
Type data: holotype, QM Hy/4080 ♂.
Type locality: Charleville, QLD.

Distribution: Murray-Darling basin, QLD; known only from type locality.
Ecology: adult—volant; melliferous, solitary.

Leioproctus (Leioproctus) sexmaculatus (Cockerell, 1914)

Paracolletes sexmaculatus Cockerell, T.D.A. (1914). Descriptions and records of bees. LXI. *Ann. Mag. Nat. Hist.* (8)**14**: 39–49 [43].
Type data: holotype (probable), BMNH Hym.17.a.452 ♀.
Type locality: Yallingup, WA.

Distribution: SW coastal, WA; known only from type locality.
Ecology: adult—volant; melliferous, solitary.
Reference: Cockerell, T.D.A. (1934). The bees of Australia. *Aust. Zool.* **8**: 2–38 (taxonomy, as *Nodocolletes sexmaculatus* (Cockerell, 1914)).

Leioproctus (Leioproctus) sigillatus (Cockerell, 1914)

Paracolletes sigillatus Cockerell, T.D.A. (1914). Descriptions and records of bees. LVI. *Ann. Mag. Nat. Hist.* (8)**13**: 136–146 [139].
Type data: holotype, BMNH Hym.17.a.477 ♀.
Type locality: SA.

Distribution: SA; known only from type locality, exact locality unknown.
Ecology: adult—volant; melliferous, solitary.

Leioproctus (Leioproctus) simulator Michener, 1965

Paracolletes simillimus Cockerell, T.D.A. (1916). Descriptions and records of bees. LXXIII. *Ann. Mag. Nat. Hist.* (8)**18**: 44–53 [48] [junior secondary homonym of *Euryglossa simillimus* Smith, 1879].
Type data: syntypes, BMNH 2♂ (a specimen is labelled 'type' and has registration number Hym.17.a.464).
Type locality: Yallingup, WA.

Leioproctus (Leioproctus) simulator Michener, C.D. (1965). A classification of the bees of the Australian and South Pacific regions. *Bull. Am. Mus. Nat. Hist.* **130**: 1–362 [52] [*nom. nov.* for *Paracolletes simillimus* Cockerell, 1916].

Distribution: SW coastal, WA; known only from type locality.
Ecology: adult—volant; melliferous, solitary.

Leioproctus (Leioproctus) stewarti (Rayment, 1947)

Paracolletes stewarti Rayment, T. (1947). New bees and wasps—Part VI. An undescribed *Paracolletes* from the Victorian Alps. *Vict. Nat.* **64**: 102–103 [102].
Type data: holotype, ANIC ♂.
Type locality: Mt Buffalo, VIC.

Distribution: Murray-Darling basin, VIC; known only from type locality.
Ecology: adult—volant; melliferous, solitary, nest in soil, flower visiting record: *Kunzea* Reichb. [Myrtaceae], *Microseris* D. Don [Asteraceae].
Reference: Rayment, T. (1948). Some bees from the Victorian Alps. *Vict. Nat.* **65**: 201–202 (flower record).

Leioproctus (Leioproctus) subdolus (Cockerell, 1913)

Paracolletes fervidus subdolus Cockerell, T.D.A. (1913). Descriptions and records of bees. L. *Ann. Mag. Nat. Hist.* (8)**11**: 273–283 [279].
Type data: holotype, BMNH Hym.17.a.415 ♀.
Type locality: Cheltenham, VIC.

Distribution: SE coastal, VIC; only published localities Cheltenham, Highett, Watsonia, Tooradin and Clyde.
Ecology: adult—volant; melliferous, solitary.
References: Rayment, T. (1947). New bees and wasps—Part V. The male of *Paracolletes fervidus*, subsp. *subdolus* Cockerell. *Vict. Nat.* **64**: 13–14 (description of male); Rayment, T. (1949). New bees and wasps—Part XI. Two confusing earth-digging bees. *Vict. Nat.* **66**: 33–36 (distribution, subspecies to species).

Leioproctus (Leioproctus) subminutus (Rayment, 1934)

Paracolletes subminutus Rayment, T. (1934). Contributions to the fauna of Rottnest Island. VIII. Apoidea. With description of new species. *J. Proc. R. Soc. West. Aust.* **20**: 201–212 [206].
Type data: holotype (probable), ANIC ♀.
Type locality: Swan River, WA.

Distribution: SW coastal, WA; only published localities Swan River and Rottnest Is.
Ecology: adult—volant; melliferous, solitary.

Leioproctus (Leioproctus) subpunctatus (Rayment, 1935)

Paracolletes subpunctatus Rayment, T. (1935). *A Cluster of Bees.* Sixty essays on the life-histories of Australian bees, with specific descriptions of over 100 new species, and an introduction by Professor E.F. Phillips, D.Ph., Cornell University, U.S.A. Sydney : Endeavour Press 752 pp. [675].
Type data: holotype, ANIC ♂.
Type locality: Swan River, WA.

Distribution: SW coastal, WA; known only from type locality.
Ecology: adult—volant; melliferous, solitary.

Leioproctus (Leioproctus) subviridis (Cockerell, 1915)

Paracolletes subviridis Cockerell, T.D.A. (1915). Descriptions and records of bees. LXIX. *Ann. Mag. Nat. Hist. (8)***16**: 96–104 [103].
Type data: holotype, BMNH Hym.17.a.418 ♀.
Type locality: Bridport, TAS.

Distribution: TAS; known only from type locality.
Ecology: adult—volant; melliferous, solitary.

Leioproctus (Leioproctus) thornleighensis (Cockerell, 1906)

Paracolletes thornleighensis Cockerell, T.D.A. (1906). Descriptions and records of bees. VII. *Ann. Mag. Nat. Hist. (7)***17**: 23–29 [27].
Type data: syntypes, BMNH 2♂ (a specimen is labelled 'type' and has registration number Hym.17.a.432).
Type locality: Thornleigh, NSW.

Lamprocolletes nigriventris Friese, H. (1924). Ueber die Bienen Australiens. *Konowia* **3**: 216–249 [221].
Type data: syntypes (probable), AMNH ♂* (number of specimens unknown).
Type locality: Thornleigh, NSW.

Taxonomic decision for synonymy: Cockerell, T.D.A. (1929). Bees, chiefly Australian species, described or determined by Dr. H. Friese. *Am. Mus. Novit.* **343**: 1–20 [1].

Distribution: NE coastal, SE coastal, QLD, NSW; only published localities Kuranda, Caloundra, Brisbane and Thornleigh.
Ecology: adult—volant; melliferous, solitary.
References: Cockerell, T.D.A. (1913). Descriptions and records of bees. L. *Ann. Mag. Nat. Hist. (8)***11**: 273–283 (taxonomy); Cockerell, T.D.A. (1914). Descriptions and records of bees. LXI. *Ann. Mag. Nat. Hist. (8)***14**: 39–49 (description of female); Rayment, T. (1935). *A Cluster of Bees.* Sixty essays on the life-histories of Australian bees, with specific descriptions of over 100 new species, and an introduction by Professor E.F. Phillips, D.Ph., Cornell University, U.S.A. Sydney : Endeavour Press 752 pp. (distribution).

Leioproctus (Leioproctus) tomentosus Houston, 1989

Leioproctus (Leioproctus) tomentosus Houston, T.F. (1989). *Leioproctus* bees associated with Western Australian smoke bushes (*Conospermum* spp.) and their adaptations for foraging and concealment (Hymenoptera: Colletidae: Paracolletini). *Rec. West. Aust. Mus.* **14**: 275–292 [286].
Type data: holotype, WAM 88/959 ♂*.
Type locality: 8.4 km NNW Cataby, WA.

Distribution: SW coastal, WA; only published localities near Cataby and Badgingarra National Park.
Ecology: adult—volant; melliferous, solitary, flower visiting record: *Conospermum* Sm. [Proteaceae].

Leioproctus (Leioproctus) truncatulus (Cockerell, 1913)

Paracolletes truncatulus Cockerell, T.D.A. (1913). Descriptions and records of bees. L. *Ann. Mag. Nat. Hist. (8)***11**: 273–283 [275].
Type data: holotype, BMNH Hym.17.a.484 ♀.
Type locality: "Blackwood, Australia" (probably VIC or SA).

Distribution: NE coastal, QLD; only published localities Beerwah, Dunwich, Stradbroke Is. and Blackwood (probably VIC or SA).
Ecology: adult—volant; melliferous, solitary, flower visiting record: *Aotus* Smith [Fabaceae], *Dillwynia* Sm. [Fabaceae], *Pultenaea* Sm. [Fabaceae].
References: Cockerell, T.D.A. (1921). Australian bees in the Queensland Museum. *Mem. Qd Mus.* **7**: 81–98 (distribution); Michener, C.D. (1965). A classification of the bees of the Australian and South Pacific regions. *Bull. Am. Mus. Nat. Hist.* **130**: 1–362 (flower records, distribution).

Leioproctus (Leioproctus) unguidentatus Michener, 1965

Leioproctus (Leioproctus) unguidentatus Michener, C.D. (1965). A classification of the bees of the Australian and South Pacific regions. *Bull. Am. Mus. Nat. Hist.* **130**: 1–362 [247].
Type data: holotype, ANIC ♀.
Type locality: Dunwich, QLD.

Distribution: NE coastal, QLD; known only from type locality.

Ecology: adult—volant; melliferous, solitary, flower visiting record: *Dillwynia* Sm. [Fabaceae].

Leioproctus (Leioproctus) versicolor (Smith, 1853)

Lamprocolletes versicolor Smith, F. (1853). *Catalogue of Hymenopterous Insects in the Collection of the British Museum.* Part I. Andrenidae and Apidae. London : British Museum 197 pp. [14].
Type data: holotype, BMNH Hym.17.a.511 ♀.
Type locality: Adelaide, SA.
Paracolletes spatulatus Cockerell, T.D.A. (1905). Descriptions and records of bees. VI. *Ann. Mag. Nat. Hist.* (7)**16**: 477–486 [483].
Type data: holotype, BMNH Hym.17.a.430 ♂.
Type locality: Blackheath, NSW.

Taxonomic decision for synonymy: Cockerell, T.D.A. (1915). Descriptions and records of bees. LXVII. *Ann. Mag. Nat. Hist.* (8)**15**· 529–537 [529].

Distribution: SE coastal, S Gulfs, NSW, VIC, SA, TAS; only published localities Blackheath, Lebra (probably Leura), Portland, Mt Wellington and Adelaide.
Ecology: adult—volant; melliferous, solitary, flower visiting record: *Eucalyptus* L'Hérit. [Myrtaceae].
References: Cockerell, T.D.A. (1929). Bees, chiefly Australian species, described or determined by Dr. H. Friese. *Am. Mus. Novit.* **343**: 1–20 (distribution); Rayment, T. (1953). *Bees of the Portland District.* Victoria : Portland Field Naturalist's Club 39 pp. (distribution).

Leioproctus (Leioproctus) viridicinctus (Cockerell, 1905)

Paracolletes viridicinctus Cockerell, T.D.A. (1905). Descriptions and records of bees. VI. *Ann. Mag. Nat. Hist.* (7)**16**: 477–486 [482].
Type data: holotype (probable), BMNH Hym.17.a.437 ♀.
Type locality: TAS.

Distribution: SE coastal, VIC, TAS; only published localities Portland, Black Rock, Croydon and Eaglehawk Neck.
Ecology: adult—volant; melliferous, solitary, flower visiting record: chrysanthemum, *Casuarina* L. [Casuarinaceae].
References: Cockerell, T.D.A. (1914). Descriptions and records of bees. LVI. *Ann. Mag. Nat. Hist.* (8)**13**: 136–146 (distribution); Cockerell, T.D.A. (1915). Descriptions and records of bees. LXVII. *Ann. Mag. Nat. Hist.* (8)**15**: 529–537 (distribution); Rayment, T. (1948). Notes on remarkable wasps and bees. With specific descriptions. *Aust. Zool.* **11**: 238–254 (description of male); Rayment, T. (1953). *Bees of the Portland District.* Victoria : Portland Field Naturalist's Club 39 pp. (distribution).

Leioproctus (Leioproctus) worsfoldi (Cockerell, 1906)

Paracolletes worsfoldi Cockerell, T.D.A. (1906). Descriptions and records of bees. VII. *Ann. Mag. Nat. Hist.* (7)**17**: 23–29 [24].
Type data: holotype, BMNH Hym.17.a.423 ♀.
Type locality: WA.

Distribution: SW coastal, WA; only published locality King George Sound.
Ecology: adult—volant; melliferous, solitary.
Reference: Cockerell, T.D.A. (1929). Bees in the Queensland Museum. *Mem. Qd Mus.* **9**: 298–323 (taxonomy).

Leioproctus (Anacolletes) Michener, 1965

Anacolletes Michener, C.D. (1965). A classification of the bees of the Australian and South Pacific regions. *Bull. Am. Mus. Nat. Hist.* **130**: 1–362 [59] [proposed with subgeneric rank in *Leioproctus* Smith, 1853]. Type species: *Lamprocolletes bimaculatus* Smith, 1879 by original designation.

Leioproctus (Anacolletes) bimaculatus (Smith, 1879)

Lamprocolletes bimaculatus Smith, F. (1879). *Descriptions of New Species of Hymenoptera in the Collection of the British Museum.* London : British Museum xxi 240 pp. [10].
Type data: holotype, BMNH Hym.17.a.492 ♀.
Type locality: Swan River, WA.

Distribution: SW coastal, WA; only published localities Swan River, Perth, Yallingup and Smiths Mill.
Ecology: adult—volant; melliferous, solitary.
References: Cockerell, T.D.A. (1905). Descriptions and records of bees. VI. *Ann. Mag. Nat. Hist.* (7)**16**: 477–486 (description of male); Cockerell, T.D.A. (1914). Descriptions and records of bees. LXI. *Ann. Mag. Nat. Hist.* (8)**14**: 39–49 (distribution); Rayment, T. (1931). Bees in the collections of the Western Australian Museum and the Agricultural Department, Perth. *J. Proc. R. Soc. West. Aust.* **17**: 157–190 (redescription).

Leioproctus (Anacolletes) callurus (Cockerell, 1914)

Paracolletes callurus Cockerell, T.D.A. (1914). Descriptions and records of bees. LXI. *Ann. Mag. Nat. Hist.* (8)**14**: 39–49 [40].
Type data: syntypes, BMNH 2♀ (a specimen is labelled 'type' and has registration number Hym.17.a.451).
Type locality: Yallingup, WA.

Distribution: SW coastal, WA; known only from type locality.
Ecology: adults—volant; melliferous, solitary.

Leioproctus (Anacolletes) nigrior (Cockerell, 1929)

Paracolletes callurus nigrior Cockerell, T.D.A. (1929). Bees in the Australian Museum collection. *Rec. Aust. Mus.* **17**: 199–243 [203].
Type data: holotype, AM ♀.
Type locality: King George Sound, WA.

Distribution: SW coastal, WA; known only from type locality.
Ecology: adults—volant; melliferous, solitary.
Reference: Michener, C.D. (1965). A classification of the bees of the Australian and South Pacific regions. *Bull. Am. Mus. Nat. Hist.* **130**: 1–362 [59] (taxonomy).

Leioproctus (Anacolletes) pachyodontus (Cockerell, 1915)

Paracolletes pachyodontus Cockerell, T.D.A. (1915). Descriptions and records of bees. LXVII. *Ann. Mag. Nat. Hist.* (8)**15**: 529–537 [529].
Type data: syntypes, BMNH 3♂ (a specimen is labelled 'type' and has registration number Hym.17.a.454).
Type locality: Yallingup, WA.

Distribution: SW coastal, WA; known only from type locality.
Ecology: adults—volant; melliferous, solitary.

Leioproctus (Andrenopsis) Cockerell, 1905

Andrenopsis Cockerell, T.D.A. (1905). Notes on some bees in the British Museum. *Trans. Am. Entomol. Soc.* **31**: 309–364 [363]. Type species: *Andrenopsis flavorufus* Cockerell, 1905 by monotypy.

Leioproctus (Andrenopsis) douglasiellus Michener, 1965

Leioproctus (Andrenopsis) douglasiellus Michener, C.D. (1965). A classification of the bees of the Australian and South Pacific regions. *Bull. Am. Mus. Nat. Hist.* **130**: 1–362 [259].
Type data: holotype, WAM 54–128 ♀.
Type locality: Pearce, WA.

Distribution: SW coastal, WA; known only from type locality.
Ecology: adults—volant; melliferous, solitary.

Leioproctus (Andrenopsis) flavorufus (Cockerell, 1905)

Andrenopsis flavorufus Cockerell, T.D.A. (1905). Notes on some bees in the British Museum. *Trans. Am. Entomol. Soc.* **31**: 309–364 [364].
Type data: holotype, BMNH Hym.17.a.411 ♂.
Type locality: Australia.

Distribution: SE coastal, NSW; only published locality Sydney.
Ecology: adult—volant; melliferous, solitary.
Reference: Cockerell, T.D.A. (1929). Bees in the Australian Museum collection. *Rec. Aust. Mus.* **17**: 199–243 (distribution).

Leioproctus (Andrenopsis) nigrifrons Michener, 1965

Leioproctus (Andrenopsis) nigrifrons Michener, C.D. (1965). A classification of the bees of the Australian and South Pacific regions. *Bull. Am. Mus. Nat. Hist.* **130**: 1–362 [260].
Type data: holotype, QM T6233 ♂.
Type locality: Sunnybank, QLD.

Distribution: NE coastal, QLD; known only from type locality.
Ecology: adults—volant; melliferous, solitary.

Leioproctus (Andrenopsis) wilsoni (Rayment, 1930)

Andrenopsis wilsoni Rayment, T. (1930). New and remarkable bees. *Proc. R. Soc. Vict.* **43**: 42–61 [51].
Type data: holotype, NMV 1403 ♂.
Type locality: Bogong High Plains, VIC.

Distribution: Murray-Darling basin, VIC; known only from type locality.
Ecology: adults—volant; melliferous, solitary, flower visiting record: *Eucalyptus* L'Hérit. [Myrtaceae].
Reference: Rayment, T. (1935). *A Cluster of Bees.* Sixty essays on the life-histories of Australian bees, with specific descriptions of over 100 new species, and an introduction by Professor E.F. Phillips, D.Ph., Cornell University, U.S.A. Sydney : Endeavour Press 752 pp. (illustration).

Leioproctus (Baeocolletes) Michener, 1965

Baeocolletes Michener, C.D. (1965). A classification of the bees of the Australian and South Pacific regions. *Bull. Am. Mus. Nat. Hist.* **130**: 1–362 [70] [proposed with subgeneric rank in *Leioproctus* Smith, 1853]. Type species: *Leioproctus (Baeocolletes) calcaratus* Michener, 1965 by original designation.

Leioproctus (Baeocolletes) calcaratus Michener, 1965

Leioproctus (Baeocolletes) calcaratus Michener, C.D. (1965). A classification of the bees of the Australian and South Pacific regions. *Bull. Am. Mus. Nat. Hist.* **130**: 1–362 [257].
Type data: holotype, WAM 52–3071 ♀.
Type locality: Belele, WA.

Distribution: W plateau, WA; known only from type locality.
Ecology: adults—volant; melliferous, solitary.

Leioproctus (Baeocolletes) mas Michener, 1965

Leioproctus (Baeocolletes) mas Michener, C.D. (1965). A classification of the bees of the Australian and South Pacific regions. *Bull. Am. Mus. Nat. Hist.* **130**: 1–362 [258].
Type data: holotype, ANIC ♂.
Type locality: 5 miles N Nocatunga, QLD.

Distribution: Bulloo River basin, QLD; known only from type locality.
Ecology: adults—volant; melliferous, solitary.

Leioproctus (Baeocolletes) minimus Michener, 1965

Leioproctus (Baeocolletes) minimus Michener, C.D. (1965). A classification of the bees of the Australian and South Pacific regions. *Bull. Am. Mus. Nat. Hist.* **130**: 1–362 [258].
Type data: holotype, MCZ ♂*.
Type locality: Meekatharra, WA.

Distribution: W plateau, WA; known only from type locality.
Ecology: adults—volant; melliferous, solitary.

Leioproctus (Ceratocolletes) Michener, 1965

Ceratocolletes Michener, C.D. (1965). A classification of the bees of the Australian and South Pacific regions. *Bull. Am. Mus. Nat. Hist.* **130**: 1–362 [63] [proposed with subgeneric rank in *Leioproctus* Smith, 1853]. Type species: *Lamprocolletes antennatus* Smith, 1879 by original designation.

Leioproctus (Ceratocolletes) andreniformis (Cockerell, 1915)

Paracolletes andreniformis Cockerell, T.D.A. (1915). Descriptions and records of bees. LXVI. *Ann. Mag. Nat. Hist. (8)***15**: 341–350 [344].
Type data: syntypes, BMNH 3♀ (a female specimen is labelled 'type' and has registration number Hym.17.a.460).
Type locality: Yallingup, WA.

Distribution: SW coastal, WA; known only from type locality.
Ecology: adults—volant; melliferous, solitary.

Leioproctus (Ceratocolletes) antennatus (Smith, 1879)

Lamprocolletes antennatus Smith, F. (1879). *Descriptions of New Species of Hymenoptera in the Collection of the British Museum.* London : British Museum xxi 240 pp. [10].
Type data: holotype, BMNH Hym.17.a.518 ♂.
Type locality: Swan River, WA.

Distribution: SW coastal, WA; known only from type locality.
Ecology: adults—volant; melliferous, solitary.
Reference: Rayment, T. (1931). Bees in the collections of the Western Australian Museum and the Agricultural Department, Perth. *J. Proc. R. Soc. West. Aust.* **17**: 157–190 (taxonomy).

Leioproctus (Chrysocolletes) Michener, 1965

Chrysocolletes Michener, C.D. (1965). A classification of the bees of the Australian and South Pacific regions. *Bull. Am. Mus. Nat. Hist.* **130**: 1–362 [71] [proposed with subgeneric rank in *Leioproctus* Smith, 1853]. Type species: *Paracolletes moretonianus* Cockerell, 1905 by original designation.

Leioproctus (Chrysocolletes) crenulatus Michener, 1965

Leioproctus (Chrysocolletes) crenulatus Michener, C.D. (1965). A classification of the bees of the Australian and South Pacific regions. *Bull. Am. Mus. Nat. Hist.* **130**: 1–362 [261].
Type data: holotype, ANIC ♂.
Type locality: Wallangarra, QLD.

Distribution: Murray-Darling basin, QLD; known only from type locality.
Ecology: adults—volant; melliferous, solitary, flower visiting record: *Pultenaea* Sm. [Fabaceae].

Leioproctus (Chrysocolletes) moretonianus (Cockerell, 1905)

Paracolletes moretonianus Cockerell, T.D.A. (1905). Descriptions and records of bees. V. *Ann. Mag. Nat. Hist. (7)***16**: 465–477 [477].
Type data: syntypes, BMNH 2♂ (a specimen is labelled 'type' and has registration number Hym.17.a.429).
Type locality: Moreton Bay, QLD.

Distribution: NE coastal, SE coastal, QLD, NSW; only published localities Moreton Bay, Capalaba, Jimboomba, Beenleigh and Woy Woy.
Ecology: adult—volant; melliferous, solitary, flower visiting record: *Goodenia* Sm. [Goodeniaceae], *Velleia* Sm. [Goodeniaceae].
References: Rayment, T. (1935). *A Cluster of Bees.* Sixty essays on the life-histories of Australian bees, with specific descriptions of over 100 new species, and an introduction by Professor E.F. Phillips, D.Ph., Cornell University, U.S.A. Sydney : Endeavour Press 752 pp. (redescription); Michener, C.D. (1965). A classification of the bees of the Australian and South Pacific regions. *Bull. Am. Mus. Nat. Hist.* **130**: 1–362 (flower records); Michener, C.D. (1992). Sexual dimorphism in the glossa of Colletidae (Hymenoptera, Apoidea). *J. Kansas Entomol. Soc.* **65**: 1–9 (glossa).

Leioproctus (Cladocerapis) Cockerell, 1904

Cladocerapis Cockerell, T.D.A. (1904). New genera of bees. *Entomol. News* **15**: 292 [292]. Type species: *Lamprocolletes cladocerus* Smith, 1862 (=*Lamprocolletes bipectinatus* Smith, 1857) by original designation.

Leioproctus (Cladocerapis) bipectinatus (Smith, 1857)

Lamprocolletes bipectinatus Smith, F. (1857). [Description of a most extraordinary aculeate hymenopterous insect recently received from Australia.] *Trans. Entomol. Soc. Lond. Proc. (ns)***4**: 31 [31] [senior objective synonym of *Lamprocolletes cladocerus* Smith, 1862].
Type data: holotype, BMNH Hym.17.a.504 ♂.
Type locality: Australia, between Sydney and Moreton Bay (as Moreton).

Lamprocolletes cladocerus Smith, F. (1862). Descriptions of new species of Australian Hymenoptera, and of a species

of *Formica* from New Zealand. *Trans. Entomol. Soc. Lond.* *(3)***1**: 53–62 [57] [junior objective synonym of *Lamprocolletes bipectinatus* Smith, 1857].
Type data: holotype, BMNH Hym.17.a.504 ♂.
Type locality: Sydney, NSW.

Distribution: NE coastal, SE coastal, Murray-Darling basin, QLD, NSW.
Ecology: adult—volant; melliferous, solitary, nest in ground, flower visiting record: *Persoonia* Sm. [Proteaceae].
References: Cockerell, T.D.A. (1905). Descriptions and records of bees. IV. *Ann. Mag. Nat. Hist.* *(7)***16**: 392–403 [393] (taxonomy); Rayment, T. (1935). *A Cluster of Bees.* Sixty essays on the life-histories of Australian bees, with specific descriptions of over 100 new species, and an introduction by Professor E.F. Phillips, D.Ph., Cornell University, U.S.A. Sydney : Endeavour Press 752 pp. (illustration); Rayment, T. (1950). New bees and wasps—Part XIV. Three new bees in the genus *Cladocerapis*, and their role in the pollination of several *Persoonia* species ("Geebungs"). *Vict. Nat.* **67**: 101–111 (distribution); Rayment, T. (1957). Closer than a brother. *Proc. R. Zool. Soc. N.S.W.* **1955–56**: 87–90 (illustration); Michener, C.D. (1960). Notes on the behavior of Australian colletid bees. *J. Kansas Entomol. Soc.* **33**: 22–31 (flower record); Maynard, G.V. (1992). Revision of *Leioproctus (Cladocerapis)* Cockerell (Hymenoptera: Colletidae). *J. Aust. Entomol. Soc.* **31**: 1–11 (redescription).

Leioproctus (Cladocerapis) carinatifrons (Cockerell, 1929)

Paracolletes carinatifrons Cockerell, T.D.A. (1929). Bees in the Australian Museum collection. *Rec. Aust. Mus.* **17**: 199–243 [209].
Type data: holotype, AM K49023 ♀.
Type locality: Sydney, NSW.

Cladocerapis colmani Rayment, T. (1950). New bees and wasps—Part XIV. Three new bees in the genus *Cladocerapis*, and their role in the pollination of several *Persoonia* species ("Geebungs"). *Vict. Nat.* **67**: 101–111 [101].
Type data: holotype (probable), ANIC ♀.
Type locality: Narrabeen, NSW.

Cladocerapis goraeensis Rayment, T. (1953). *Bees of the Portland District.* Victoria : Portland Field Naturalist's Club 39 pp. [6].
Type data: holotype, ANIC ♀.
Type locality: Gorae West, VIC.

Taxonomic decision for synonymy: Maynard, G.V. (1992). Revision of *Leioproctus (Cladocerapis)* Cockerell (Hymenoptera: Colletidae). *J. Aust. Entomol. Soc.* **31**: 1–11 [4].

Distribution: SE coastal, S Gulfs, NSW, VIC, SA.
Ecology: adult—volant; melliferous, solitary, nest in ground, flower visiting record: *Persoonia* Sm. [Proteaceae].

Leioproctus (Cladocerapis) clypeatus (Cockerell, 1916)

Paracolletes clypeatus Cockerell, T.D.A. (1916). Descriptions and records of bees. LXXIII. *Ann. Mag. Nat. Hist. (8)***18**: 44–53 [52].
Type data: holotype, BMNH Hym.17.a.457 ♂.
Type locality: Yallingup, WA.

Distribution: SW coastal, WA; only published localities Yallingup and Fitzgerald River National Park.
Ecology: adult—volant; melliferous, solitary, nest in ground, flower visiting record: *Persoonia* Sm. [Proteaceae].
Reference: Maynard, G.V. (1992). Revision of *Leioproctus (Cladocerapis)* Cockerell (Hymenoptera: Colletidae). *J. Aust. Entomol. Soc.* **31**: 1–11 (redescription).

Leioproctus (Cladocerapis) floccosus Maynard, 1992

Leioproctus (Cladocerapis) floccosus Maynard, G.V. (1992). Revision of *Leioproctus (Cladocerapis)* Cockerell (Hymenoptera: Colletidae). *J. Aust. Entomol. Soc.* **31**: 1–11 [6] [name misspelled as *floccossus* in key, p. 2].
Type data: holotype, WAM 90/529 ♀*.
Type locality: The Dell, nr Mundaring (Perth), WA.

Distribution: SW coastal, WA; known only from type locality.
Ecology: adults—volant; melliferous, solitary.

Leioproctus (Cladocerapis) ignicolor Maynard, 1992

Leioproctus (Cladocerapis) ignicolor Maynard, G.V. (1992). Revision of *Leioproctus (Cladocerapis)* Cockerell (Hymenoptera: Colletidae). *J. Aust. Entomol. Soc.* **31**: 1–11 [6].
Type data: holotype, WAM 90/920 ♂*.
Type locality: Boorabbin Rock, WA.

Distribution: SW coastal, NW coastal, WA.
Ecology: adult—volant; melliferous, solitary, nest in ground, flower visiting record: *Persoonia* Sm. [Proteaceae].

Leioproctus (Cladocerapis) incanescens (Cockerell, 1913)

Paracolletes incanescens Cockerell, T.D.A. (1913). Descriptions and records of bees. L. *Ann. Mag. Nat. Hist. (8)***11**: 273–283 [277].
Type data: holotype, QM Hy/4084 ♀.
Type locality: Stradbroke Is., QLD.

Paracolletes punctiventris Cockerell, T.D.A. (1929). Bees, chiefly Australian species, described or determined by Dr. H. Friese. *Am. Mus. Novit.* **343**: 1–20 [4].
Type data: holotype, AMNH ♂*.
Type locality: Sydney, NSW.

Cladocerapis persooniae Rayment, T. (1950). New bees and wasps—Part XIV. Three new bees in the genus *Cladocerapis*, and their role in the pollination of several *Persoonia* species ("Geebungs"). *Vict. Nat.* **67**: 101–111 [102].

Type data: lectotype, ANIC ♀ (number of specimens unknown).
Subsequent designation: Maynard, G.V. (1992). Revision of *Leioproctus (Cladocerapis)* Cockerell (Hymenoptera: Colletidae). *J. Aust. Entomol. Soc.* **31**: 1–11; Cardale J.C., this work, interprets Maynard's incorrect inference of holotype as a lectotype designation (Art. 74, ICZN 1985).
Type locality: Jamberoo, NSW.

Taxonomic decision for synonymy: Maynard, G.V. (1992). Revision of *Leioproctus (Cladocerapis)* Cockerell (Hymenoptera: Colletidae). *J. Aust. Entomol. Soc.* **31**: 1–11 [7].

Distribution: NE coastal, SE coastal, QLD, NSW.

Ecology: larva—sedentary : adult—volant; melliferous, solitary, nest in ground, flower visiting record: *Claoxylon* A. Juss. [Euphorbiaceae], *Leptospermum* Forster & G.Forster [Myrtaceae], *Lomatia* R.Br. [Proteaceae], *Persoonia* Sm. [Proteaceae].
References: Rayment, T. (1954). Remarkable bees from a rain forest. *Aust. Zool.* **12**: 46–56 (biology, as *Cladocerapis persooniae* Rayment, 1950); Michener, C.D. (1960). Notes on the behavior of Australian colletid bees. *J. Kansas Entomol. Soc.* **33**: 22–31 (biology).

Leioproctus (Cladocerapis) perpolitus (Cockerell, 1916)

Paracolletes perpolitus Cockerell, T.D.A. (1916). Descriptions and records of bees. LXXIII. *Ann. Mag. Nat. Hist.* (8)**18**: 44–53 [49].
Type data: holotype, BMNH Hym.17.a.447 ♂.
Type locality: Yallingup, WA.

Distribution: SW coastal, WA; known only from type locality.

Ecology: adults—volant; melliferous, solitary.
Reference: Maynard, G.V. (1992). Revision of *Leioproctus (Cladocerapis)* Cockerell (Hymenoptera: Colletidae). *J. Aust. Entomol. Soc.* **31**: 1–11 (redescription).

Leioproctus (Cladocerapis) raymenti Michener, 1965

Cladocerapis plumosus Rayment, T. (1935). *A Cluster of Bees.* Sixty essays on the life-histories of Australian bees, with specific descriptions of over 100 new species, and an introduction by Professor E.F. Phillips, D.Ph., Cornell University, U.S.A. Sydney : Endeavour Press 752 pp. [688] [junior secondary homonym of *Lamprocolletes plumosus* Smith, 1853].
Type data: holotype, ANIC ♀.
Type locality: Monbulk, VIC.
Leioproctus (Cladocerapis) raymenti Michener, C.D. (1965). A classification of the bees of the Australian and South Pacific regions. *Bull. Am. Mus. Nat. Hist.* **130**: 1–362 [55] [*nom. nov.* for *Cladocerapis plumosus* Rayment, 1935].

Distribution: SE coastal, NSW, VIC.

Ecology: adult—volant; melliferous, solitary, nest in

ground, flower visiting record: *Persoonia* Sm. [Proteaceae].
Reference: Maynard, G.V. (1992). Revision of *Leioproctus (Cladocerapis)* Cockerell (Hymenoptera: Colletidae). *J. Aust. Entomol. Soc.* **31**: 1–11 (redescription, distribution).

Leioproctus (Cladocerapis) speculiferus (Cockerell, 1921)

Paracolletes speculiferus Cockerell, T.D.A. (1921). Australian bees in the Queensland Museum. *Mem. Qd Mus.* **7**: 81–98 [95].
Type data: holotype, QM T2405 ♂.
Type locality: [Lamington] National Park, QLD.
Cladocerapis heronii Rayment, T. (1935). *A Cluster of Bees.* Sixty essays on the life-histories of Australian bees, with specific descriptions of over 100 new species, and an introduction by Professor E.F. Phillips, D.Ph., Cornell University, U.S.A. Sydney : Endeavour Press 752 pp. [688].
Type data: holotype, ANIC ♂.
Type locality: Dorrigo, NSW.
Cladocerapis woyensis Rayment, T. (1935). *A Cluster of Bees.* Sixty essays on the life-histories of Australian bees, with specific descriptions of over 100 new species, and an introduction by Professor E.F. Phillips, D.Ph., Cornell University, U.S.A. Sydney : Endeavour Press 752 pp. [689].
Type data: holotype, ANIC ♀.
Type locality: Woy Woy, NSW.
Cladocerapis hackeri Rayment, T. (1950). New bees and wasps—Part XIV. Three new bees in the genus *Cladocerapis*, and their role in the pollination of several *Persoonia* species ("Geebungs"). *Vict. Nat.* **67**: 101–111 [102] [junior secondary homonym of *Paracolletes hackeri* Cockerell, 1918; not renamed].
Type data: holotype, ANIC ♀.
Type locality: Bribie Is., QLD.

Taxonomic decision for synonymy: Maynard, G.V. (1992). Revision of *Leioproctus (Cladocerapis)* Cockerell (Hymenoptera: Colletidae). *J. Aust. Entomol. Soc.* **31**: 1–11 [10].

Distribution: NE coastal, SE coastal, Murray-Darling basin, QLD, NSW, VIC, TAS.
Ecology: adult—volant; melliferous, solitary, nest in ground, flower visiting record: *Persoonia* Sm. [Proteaceae].
Reference: Michener, C.D. (1960). Notes on the behavior of Australian colletid bees. *J. Kansas Entomol. Soc.* **33**: 22–31 (flower record).

Leioproctus (Colletellus) Michener, 1965

Colletellus Michener, C.D. (1965). A classification of the bees of the Australian and South Pacific regions. *Bull. Am. Mus. Nat. Hist.* **130**: 1–362 [70] [proposed with subgeneric rank in *Leioproctus* Smith, 1853]. Type species: *Andrenopsis velutinus* Cockerell, 1929 (=*Leioproctus (Colletellus) velutinellus* Michener, 1965) by original designation.

Leioproctus (Colletellus) velutinellus Michener, 1965

Andrenopsis velutinus Cockerell, T.D.A. (1929). Bees in the Australian Museum collection. *Rec. Aust. Mus.* **17**: 199–243 [212] [junior secondary homonym of *Paracolletes velutinus* Cockerell, 1929: 208].
Type data: holotype, AM ♀.
Type locality: Kojarena, WA.

Leioproctus (Colletellus) velutinellus Michener, C.D. (1965). A classification of the bees of the Australian and South Pacific regions. *Bull. Am. Mus. Nat. Hist.* **130**: 1–362 [71] [*nom. nov.* for *Andrenopsis velutinus* Cockerell, 1929: 212].

Distribution: SW coastal, NW coastal, WA; only published localities Kojarena and SW Australia.
Ecology: adult—volant; melliferous, solitary, flower visiting record: *Stylidium* Willd. [Stylidiaceae].
References: Erickson, R. (1958). *Triggerplants*. Perth : Paterson Brokensha 229 pp. (flower record); Carlquist, S. (1969). Studies in Stylidiaceae : new taxa, field observations, evolutionary tendencies. *Aliso* **7**: 13–64 (flower record).

Leioproctus (Colletopsis) Michener, 1965

Colletopsis Michener, C.D. (1965). A classification of the bees of the Australian and South Pacific regions. *Bull. Am. Mus. Nat. Hist.* **130**: 1–362 [58] [proposed with subgeneric rank in *Leioproctus* Smith, 1853]. Type species: *Leioproctus (Colletopsis) contrarius* Michener, 1965 by original designation.

Leioproctus (Colletopsis) contrarius Michener, 1965

Leioproctus (Colletopsis) contrarius Michener, C.D. (1965). A classification of the bees of the Australian and South Pacific regions. *Bull. Am. Mus. Nat. Hist.* **130**: 1–362 [252].
Type data: holotype, WAM 54–55 ♀.
Type locality: Bullsbrook, WA.

Distribution: SW coastal, WA; only published localities Bullsbrook and Forrestdale.
Ecology: adult—volant; melliferous, solitary.

Leioproctus (Euryglossidia) Cockerell, 1910

Euryglossidia Cockerell, T.D.A. (1910). Descriptions and records of bees. XXXIII. *Ann. Mag. Nat. Hist. (8)***6**: 356–366 [358]. Type species: *Euryglossidia rectangulata* Cockerell, 1910 by original designation.

Lysicolletes Rayment, T. (1935). *A Cluster of Bees*. Sixty essays on the life-histories of Australian bees, with specific descriptions of over 100 new species, and an introduction by Professor E.F. Phillips, D.Ph., Cornell University, U.S.A. Sydney : Endeavour Press 752 pp. [208] [proposed with subgeneric rank in *Paracolletes* Smith, 1853]. Type species: *Paracolletes (Lysicolletes) singularis* Rayment, 1935 by original designation.

Taxonomic decision for synonymy: Michener, C.D. (1965). A classification of the bees of the Australian and South Pacific regions. *Bull. Am. Mus. Nat. Hist.* **130**: 1–362 [66].

Leioproctus (Euryglossidia) acaciae (Rayment, 1939)

Euryglossidia acaciae Rayment, T. (1939). Bees from the high lands of New South Wales and Victoria. *Aust. Zool.* **9**: 263–294 [274].
Type data: holotype, ANIC ♂.
Type locality: Emerald, VIC.

Distribution: SE coastal, VIC; known only from type locality.
Ecology: adult—volant; melliferous, solitary, flower visiting record: *Acacia* Miller [Mimosaceae].

Leioproctus (Euryglossidia) australiensis (Dalla Torre, 1896)

Scrapter bicolor Smith, F. (1862). Descriptions of new species of Australian Hymenoptera, and of a species of *Formica* from New Zealand. *Trans. Entomol. Soc. Lond. (3)***1**: 53–62 [61] [junior primary homonym of *Scrapter bicolor* Lepeletier, 1825].
Type data: holotype, BMNH Hym.17.a.291 ♀.
Type locality: Australia.

Macropis australiensis Dalla Torre, K.W. (1896). *Catalogus Hymenopterorum Hucusque Descriptorum Systematicus et Synonymicus*. Apidae (Anthophila). Lipsiae : G. Engelmann Vol. x 643 pp. [193] [*nom. nov.* for *Scrapter bicolor* Smith, 1862].

Distribution: Australia; known only from type locality, exact locality unknown.
Ecology: adult—volant; melliferous, solitary.
References: Cockerell, T.D.A. (1910). Descriptions and records of bees. XXXIII. *Ann. Mag. Nat. Hist. (8)***6**: 356–366 (taxonomy, as *Melittosmithia australiensis* (Dalla Torre, 1896)); Meade-Waldo, G. (1923). Hymenoptera. Fam. Apidae. Subfam. Prosopidinae. *Genera Insectorum* **181**: 1–45 (taxonomy, as *Euryglossidia bicolor* (Smith, 1862)).

Leioproctus (Euryglossidia) baeckeae (Rayment, 1948)

Euryglossa baeckeae Rayment, T. (1948). Notes on remarkable wasps and bees. With specific descriptions. *Aust. Zool.* **11**: 238–254 [248].
Type data: holotype, ANIC ♂.
Type locality: Bolgart, WA.

Distribution: SW coastal, WA; known only from type locality.
Ecology: adult—volant; melliferous, solitary, flower visiting record: *Baeckea* L. [Myrtaceae].
Reference: Michener, C.D. (1965). A classification of the bees of the Australian and South Pacific regions. *Bull. Am. Mus. Nat. Hist.* **130**: 1–362 (generic placement, as *Leioproctus (Euryglossidia) baeckiae*, incorrect subsequent spelling).

Leioproctus (Euryglossidia) cyanescens (Cockerell, 1929)

Euryglossidia cyanescens Cockerell, T.D.A. (1929). Bees in the Australian Museum collection. *Rec. Aust. Mus.* **17**: 199–243 [215].
Type data: holotype, AM ♀.
Type locality: Kojarena, WA.

Distribution: NW coastal, W plateau, SW coastal, WA; only published localities Kojarena, Cunderdin, Bullfinch and Emu Rock (53 km E Hyden).
Ecology: larva—sedentary : adult—volant; melliferous, solitary, flower visiting record: *Acacia* Miller [Mimosaceae], *Eucalyptus* L'Hérit. [Myrtaceae], *Muehlenbeckia* Meissner [Polygonaceae], *Thryptomene* Endl. [Myrtaceae].
References: Rayment, T. (1931). Bees in the collections of the Western Australian Museum and the Agricultural Department, Perth. *J. Proc. R. Soc. West. Aust.* **17**: 157–190 (distribution); Rayment, T. (1935). *A Cluster of Bees*. Sixty essays on the life-histories of Australian bees, with specific descriptions of over 100 new species, and an introduction by Professor E.F. Phillips, D.Ph., Cornell University, U.S.A. Sydney : Endeavour Press 752 pp. (illustration); Houston, T.F. (1981). Alimentary transport of pollen in a paracolletine bee (Hymenoptera : Colletidae). *Aust. Entomol. Mag.* **8**: 57–59 (biology).

Leioproctus (Euryglossidia) cygnellus (Cockerell, 1905)

Euryglossa cygnella Cockerell, T.D.A. (1905). Descriptions and records of bees. V. *Ann. Mag. Nat. Hist. (7)***16**: 465–477 [473].
Type data: holotype, BMNH Hym.17.a.263 ♂.
Type locality: Swan River, WA.

Distribution: SW coastal, WA; known only from type locality.
Ecology: adult—volant; melliferous, solitary.

Leioproctus (Euryglossidia) eraduensis (Cockerell, 1929)

Euryglossidia eraduensis Cockerell, T.D.A. (1929). Bees in the Australian Museum collection. *Rec. Aust. Mus.* **17**: 199–243 [217].
Type data: holotype, AM ♀.
Type locality: Eradu, WA.

Distribution: NW coastal, WA; known only from type locality.
Ecology: adult—volant; melliferous, solitary.

Leioproctus (Euryglossidia) halictiformis (Smith, 1879)

Euryglossa halictiformis Smith, F. (1879). *Descriptions of New Species of Hymenoptera in the Collection of the British Museum*. London : British Museum xxi 240 pp. [15].

Type data: holotype, BMNH Hym.17.a.249 ♀.
Type locality: Swan River, WA.

Distribution: SW coastal, WA; known only from type locality.
Ecology: adult—volant; melliferous, solitary.

Leioproctus (Euryglossidia) ichneumonoides (Cockerell, 1906)

Euryglossa ichneumonoides Cockerell, T.D.A. (1906). Four interesting Australian bees, in the collection of the British Museum. *Entomologist* **39**: 15–18 [17].
Type data: holotype, BMNH Hym.17.a.290 ♂.
Type locality: WA.

Distribution: WA; known only from type locality, exact locality unknown.
Ecology: adult—volant; melliferous, solitary.

Leioproctus (Euryglossidia) imitator (Rayment, 1959)

Lysicolletes imitator Rayment, T. (1959). A new genus of bees in the family Colletidae. *Aust. Zool.* **12**: 324–329 [327].
Type data: holotype, whereabouts unknown ♂* (not located in T. Rayment coll. transferred to ANIC).
Type locality: Engadine, NSW.

Distribution: SE coastal, NSW; known only from type locality.
Ecology: adult—volant; melliferous, solitary.

Leioproctus (Euryglossidia) mastersi (Cockerell, 1929)

Euryglossidia mastersi Cockerell, T.D.A. (1929). Bees in the Australian Museum collection. *Rec. Aust. Mus.* **17**: 199–243 [215].
Type data: holotype, AM 48327 ♀.
Type locality: King George Sound, WA.

Distribution: SW coastal, WA; known only from type locality.
Ecology: adult—volant; melliferous, solitary.

Leioproctus (Euryglossidia) nigrescens (Cockerell, 1929)

Euryglossidia nigrescens Cockerell, T.D.A. (1929). Bees in the Australian Museum collection. *Rec. Aust. Mus.* **17**: 199–243 [216].
Type data: holotype (probable), AM ♂.
Type locality: Geraldton, WA.

Distribution: NW coastal, WA; only published localities Geraldton and Eradu.
Ecology: adult—volant; melliferous, solitary.

Leioproctus (Euryglossidia) purpurascens (Cockerell, 1914)

Euryglossidia purpurascens Cockerell, T.D.A. (1914). New Australian bees. *Entomologist* **47**: 197–201 [197].
Type data: holotype, BMNH Hym.17.a.293 ♂.
Type locality: Yallingup, WA.

Distribution: SW coastal, WA; known only from type locality.

Ecology: adult—volant; melliferous, solitary.

Leioproctus (Euryglossidia) rectangulatus (Cockerell, 1910)

Euryglossidia rectangulata Cockerell, T.D.A. (1910). Descriptions and records of bees. XXXIII. *Ann. Mag. Nat. Hist.* (8)**6**: 356–366 [359].
Type data: holotype (probable), BMNH Hym.17.a.289 ♀.
Type locality: VIC.

Distribution: VIC; known only from type locality, exact locality unknown.

Ecology: adult—volant; melliferous, solitary.

References: Meade-Waldo, G. (1923). Hymenoptera. Fam. Apidae. Subfam. Prosopidinae. *Genera Insectorum* **181**: 1–45 (illustration); Rayment, T. (1935). *A Cluster of Bees.* Sixty essays on the life-histories of Australian bees, with specific descriptions of over 100 new species, and an introduction by Professor E.F. Phillips, D.Ph., Cornell University, U.S.A. Sydney : Endeavour Press 752 pp. (illustration).

Leioproctus (Euryglossidia) rejectus (Cockerell, 1905)

Euryglossa rejecta Cockerell, T.D.A. (1905). Descriptions and records of bees. V. *Ann. Mag. Nat. Hist.* (7)**16**: 465–477 [476].
Type data: holotype, BMNH Hym.17.a.269 ♂.
Type locality: Perth, WA.

Distribution: SW coastal, WA; only published localities Perth and Bolgart.

Ecology: adult—volant; melliferous, solitary, flower visiting record: *Caladenia* R.Br. [Orchidaceae].
References: Rayment, T. (1948). Notes on remarkable wasps and bees. With specific descriptions. *Aust. Zool.* **11**: 238–254 (redescription); Erickson, R. (1949). Notes on the leafless orchid *Caladenia aphylla* Bentham. *West. Aust. Nat.* **2**: 42–44 (flower record); Erickson, R. (1951). *Orchids of the West.* Perth : Paterson Brokensha 109 pp. (flower record); Erickson, R. (1965). *Orchids of the West.* 2nd edn Perth : Paterson Brokensha 107 pp. (flower record).

Leioproctus (Euryglossidia) rubiginosus (Dalla Torre, 1896)

Euryglossa rubricata Smith, F. (1879). *Descriptions of New Species of Hymenoptera in the Collection of the British Museum.* London : British Museum xxi 240 pp. [14] [junior primary homonym of *Euryglossa rubricata* Smith, 1879: 12].
Type data: holotype, BMNH Hym.17.a.2749 (note by C.D. Michener, pinned to specimen, states that the abdomen does not belong with the rest of the body).
Type locality: Swan River, WA.

Euryglossa rubiginosa Dalla Torre, K.W. (1896). *Catalogus Hymenopterorum Hucusque Descriptorum Systematicus et Synonymicus.* Apidae (Anthophila). Lipsiae : G. Engelmann Vol. x 643 pp. [50] [*nom. nov.* for *Euryglossa rubricata* Smith, 1879: 14].

Distribution: SW coastal, WA; known only from type locality.

Ecology: adult—volant; melliferous, solitary.

Leioproctus (Euryglossidia) simillimus (Smith, 1879)

Euryglossa simillima Smith, F. (1879). *Descriptions of New Species of Hymenoptera in the Collection of the British Museum.* London : British Museum xxi 240 pp. [12].
Type data: holotype, BMNH Hym.17.a.292 ♀.
Type locality: Swan River, WA.

Distribution: SW coastal, WA; known only from type locality.

Ecology: adult—volant; melliferous, solitary.

Leioproctus (Euryglossidia) singularis (Rayment, 1935)

Lysicolletes singularis Rayment, T. (1935). *A Cluster of Bees.* Sixty essays on the life-histories of Australian bees, with specific descriptions of over 100 new species, and an introduction by Professor E.F. Phillips, D.Ph., Cornell University, U.S.A. Sydney : Endeavour Press 752 pp. [684].
Type data: syntypes, ANIC ♂♀.
Type locality: Merredin, WA.

Distribution: SW coastal, WA; known only from type locality.

Ecology: adult—volant; melliferous, solitary.

Leioproctus (Euryglossidia) striatulus (Rayment, 1959)

Filiglossa striatulus Rayment, T. (1959). A new genus of bees in the family Colletidae. *Aust. Zool.* **12**: 324–329 [326].
Type data: holotype, ANIC ♀.
Type locality: Patonga, NSW.

Filiglossa proximus Rayment, T. (1959). A new genus of bees in the family Colletidae. *Aust. Zool.* **12**: 324–329 [326] [junior secondary homonym of *Goniocolletes proximus* Rayment, 1935].
Type data: holotype, ANIC ♀.
Type locality: Patonga, NSW.

Taxonomic decision for synonymy: Michener, C.D. (1965). A classification of the bees of the Australian and South Pacific regions. *Bull. Am. Mus. Nat. Hist.* **130**: 1–362 [69].

Distribution: SE coastal, NSW; known only from type locality.

Ecology: adult—volant; melliferous, solitary.

Leioproctus (Euryglossidia) viridescens (Cockerell, 1929)

Euryglossidia viridescens Cockerell, T.D.A. (1929). Bees in the Australian Museum collection. *Rec. Aust. Mus.* **17**: 199–243 [216].
Type data: syntypes, AM 3♀.
Type locality: Geraldton, WA.

Distribution: NW coastal, WA; known only from type locality.
Ecology: adult—volant; melliferous, solitary.

Leioproctus (Euryglossidia) vitrifrons (Smith, 1879)

Dasycolletes vitrifrons Smith, F. (1879). *Descriptions of New Species of Hymenoptera in the Collection of the British Museum.* London : British Museum xxi 240 pp. [11].
Type data: holotype, BMNH Hym.17.a.523 ♂.
Type locality: Swan River, WA.

Distribution: SW coastal, WA; known only from type locality.
Ecology: adult—volant; melliferous, solitary.
Reference: Rayment, T. (1935). *A Cluster of Bees.* Sixty essays on the life-histories of Australian bees, with specific descriptions of over 100 new species, and an introduction by Professor E.F. Phillips, D.Ph., Cornell University, U.S.A. Sydney : Endeavour Press 752 pp. (taxonomy).

Leioproctus (Excolletes) Michener, 1965

Excolletes Michener, C.D. (1965). A classification of the bees of the Australian and South Pacific regions. *Bull. Am. Mus. Nat. Hist.* **130**: 1–362 [56] [proposed with subgeneric rank in *Leioproctus* Smith, 1853]. Type species: *Leioproctus (Excolletes) impatellatus* Michener, 1965 by original designation.

Leioproctus (Excolletes) impatellatus Michener, 1965

Leioproctus (Excolletes) impatellatus Michener, C.D. (1965). A classification of the bees of the Australian and South Pacific regions. *Bull. Am. Mus. Nat. Hist.* **130**: 1–362 [251] [misspelled on label of holotype as *apatella*].
Type data: holotype, ANIC ♀.
Type locality: 95 miles N Tibooburra, NSW.

Distribution: Lake Eyre basin, Murray-Darling basin, QLD, NSW, NT.
Ecology: adult—volant; melliferous, solitary.
Reference: Maynard, G.V. (1992). Systematic Studies on Australian *Leioproctus* Smith (Hymenoptera: Colletidae). Unpubl. PhD Thesis. Brisbane : Univ. of Queensland 429 pp. (distribution).

Leioproctus (Filiglossa) Rayment, 1959

Filiglossa Rayment, T. (1959). A new genus of bees in the family Colletidae. *Aust. Zool.* **12**: 324–329 [324]. Type species: *Filiglossa filamentosa* Rayment, 1959 by original designation.

Leioproctus (Filiglossa) filamentosus (Rayment, 1959)

Filiglossa filamentosa Rayment, T. (1959). A new genus of bees in the family Colletidae. *Aust. Zool.* **12**: 324–329 [324].
Type data: holotype, ANIC ♂.
Type locality: Lane Cove, NSW.

Distribution: SE coastal, NSW; known only from type locality.
Ecology: adult—volant; melliferous, solitary.
Reference: Michener, C.D. (1965). A classification of the bees of the Australian and South Pacific regions. *Bull. Am. Mus. Nat. Hist.* **130**: 1–362 (taxonomy).

Leioproctus (Glossurocolletes) Michener, 1965

Glossurocolletes Michener, C.D. (1965). A classification of the bees of the Australian and South Pacific regions. *Bull. Am. Mus. Nat. Hist.* **130**: 1–362 [60] [proposed with subgeneric rank in *Leioproctus* Smith, 1853]. Type species: *Leioproctus (Glossurocolletes) bilobatus* Michener, 1965 by original designation.

Leioproctus (Glossurocolletes) bilobatus Michener, 1965

Leioproctus (Glossurocolletes) bilobatus Michener, C.D. (1965). A classification of the bees of the Australian and South Pacific regions. *Bull. Am. Mus. Nat. Hist.* **130**: 1–362 [253].
Type data: holotype, ANIC ♂.
Type locality: Stirling Range, WA.

Distribution: SW coastal, WA; known only from type locality.
Ecology: adult—volant; melliferous, solitary.

Leioproctus (Glossurocolletes) xenoceratus Michener, 1965

Leioproctus (Glossurocolletes) xenoceratus Michener, C.D. (1965). A classification of the bees of the Australian and South Pacific regions. *Bull. Am. Mus. Nat. Hist.* **130**: 1–362 [254].
Type data: holotype, WAM 65–725 ♂.
Type locality: Capel, WA.

Distribution: SW coastal, WA; known only from type locality.
Ecology: adult—volant; melliferous, solitary.

Leioproctus (Goniocolletes) Cockerell, 1907

Goniocolletes Cockerell, T.D.A. (1907). On a collection of Australian and Asiatic bees. *Bull. Am. Mus. Nat. Hist.* **23**: 221–236 [231]. Type species: *Goniocolletes morsus* Cockerell, 1907 by original designation.

Leioproctus (Goniocolletes) abdominalis (Smith, 1879)

Paracolletes abdominalis Smith, F. (1879). *Descriptions of New Species of Hymenoptera in the Collection of the British Museum.* London : British Museum xxi 240 pp. [5].

Type data: holotype, BMNH Hym.17.a.416 ♀.
Type locality: Geraldton (as Champion Bay), WA.

Distribution: Murray-Darling basin, NW coastal, VIC, WA; only published localities Bamawn and Champion Bay.
Ecology: adult—volant; melliferous, solitary.
Reference: Cockerell, T.D.A. (1929). Bees from the Australian region. *Am. Mus. Novit.* **346**: 1–18 (distribution).

Leioproctus (Goniocolletes) albopilosus (Rayment, 1930)

Paracolletes albopilosus Rayment, T. (1930). Notes on a collection of bees from Western Australia. *J. Proc. R. Soc. West. Aust.* **16**: 45–56 [50].
Type data: holotype, ANIC ♂.
Type locality: Perth, WA.

Distribution: SW coastal, WA; known only from type locality.
Ecology: adult—volant; melliferous, solitary, flower visiting record: *Stylidium* Willd. [Stylidiaceae].
References: Erickson, R. (1958). *Triggerplants*. Perth : Paterson Brokensha 229 pp. (flower record); Carlquist, S. (1969). Studies in Stylidiaceae : new taxa, field observations, evolutionary tendencies. *Aliso* **7**: 13–64 (flower record).

Leioproctus (Goniocolletes) argentifrons (Smith, 1879)

Lamprocolletes argentifrons Smith, F. (1879). *Descriptions of New Species of Hymenoptera in the Collection of the British Museum.* London : British Museum xxi 240 pp. [11].
Type data: holotype, BMNH Hym.17.a.517 ♂.
Type locality: Swan River, WA.

Distribution: SW coastal, WA; known only from type locality.
Ecology: adult—volant; melliferous, solitary.
References: Cockerell, T.D.A. (1910). New and little-known bees. *Trans. Am. Entomol. Soc.* **36**: 199–249 (variety); Cockerell, T.D.A. (1914). Descriptions and records of bees. LVI. *Ann. Mag. Nat. Hist. (8)***13**: 136–146 (variety).

Leioproctus (Goniocolletes) aurescens (Cockerell, 1921)

Paracolletes aurescens Cockerell, T.D.A. (1921). Australian bees in the Queensland Museum. *Mem. Qd Mus.* **7**: 81–98 [96].
Type data: holotype, QM T2402 ♂.
Type locality: Bribie Is., QLD.

Distribution: NE coastal, QLD; known only from type locality.
Ecology: adult—volant; melliferous, solitary.

Leioproctus (Goniocolletes) aurifrons (Smith, 1853)

Lamprocolletes aurifrons Smith, F. (1853). *Catalogue of Hymenopterous Insects in the Collection of the British Museum.* Part I. Andrenidae and Apidae. London : British Museum 197 pp. [13].
Type data: holotype, BMNH Hym.17.a.509 ♂.
Type locality: Adelaide, SA.

Distribution: S Gulfs, SA; known only from type locality.
Ecology: adult—volant; melliferous, solitary.

Leioproctus (Goniocolletes) clarus (Rayment, 1935)

Paracolletes clarus Rayment, T. (1935). *A Cluster of Bees.* Sixty essays on the life-histories of Australian bees, with specific descriptions of over 100 new species, and an introduction by Professor E.F. Phillips, D.Ph., Cornell University, U.S.A. Sydney : Endeavour Press 752 pp. [669].
Type data: holotype, ANIC ♀.
Type locality: Sea Lake, VIC.

Distribution: Murray-Darling basin, VIC; known only from type locality.
Ecology: adult—volant; melliferous, solitary.

Leioproctus (Goniocolletes) colletellus (Cockerell, 1905)

Paracolletes colletellus Cockerell, T.D.A. (1905). Descriptions and records of bees. VI. *Ann. Mag. Nat. Hist. (7)***16**: 477–486 [485].
Type data: holotype, BMNH 2♂ (a specimen is labelled 'type' and has registration number Hym.17.a.431).
Type locality: Adelaide River, NT.

Distribution: N coastal, NT; known only from type locality.
Ecology: adult—volant; melliferous, solitary.

Leioproctus (Goniocolletes) dolosus Michener, 1965

Leioproctus (Goniocolletes) dolosus Michener, C.D. (1965). A classification of the bees of the Australian and South Pacific regions. *Bull. Am. Mus. Nat. Hist.* **130**: 1–362 [256].
Type data: holotype, ANIC ♂.
Type locality: Tooradin, VIC.

Distribution: SE coastal, VIC; only published localities Tooradin, Sandringham, Highett and Watsonia.
Ecology: adult—volant; melliferous, solitary.

Leioproctus (Goniocolletes) eugeniarum (Cockerell, 1912)

Paracolletes eugeniarum Cockerell, T.D.A. (1912). Descriptions and records of bees. XLIII. *Ann. Mag. Nat. Hist. (8)***9**: 377–387 [380].
Type data: holotype, BMNH Hym.17.a.458 ♀.
Type locality: Mackay, QLD.

Distribution: NE coastal, QLD; known only from type locality.
Ecology: adult—volant; melliferous, solitary.

Leioproctus (Goniocolletes) fimbriatinus (Cockerell, 1910)

Paracolletes fimbriatinus Cockerell, T.D.A. (1910). New and little-known bees. *Trans. Am. Entomol. Soc.* **36**: 199–249 [202].
Type data: syntypes, BMNH 2♂ (a specimen is labelled 'type' and has registration number Hym.17.a.443).
Type locality: Ararat, VIC.

Distribution: Murray-Darling basin, SE coastal, QLD, NSW, VIC; only published localities Stanthorpe, White Swamp, Ararat and Melbourne.
Ecology: adult—volant; melliferous, solitary.
References: Cockerell, T.D.A. (1929). Bees from the Australian region. *Am. Mus. Novit.* **346**: 1–18 (distribution); Cockerell, T.D.A. (1929). Bees in the Queensland Museum. *Mem. Qd Mus.* **9**: 298–323 (description of female); Rayment, T. (1939). Bees from the high lands of New South Wales and Victoria. *Aust. Zool.* **9**: 263–294 (distribution).

Leioproctus (Goniocolletes) fimbriatus (Smith, 1879)

Leioproctus fimbriatus Smith, F. (1879). *Descriptions of New Species of Hymenoptera in the Collection of the British Museum.* London : British Museum xxi 240 pp. [6] [genus name misspelled as 'Lioproctus' in original description].
Type data: holotype (probable), BMNH Hym.17.a.501 ♀.
Type locality: Australia.

Distribution: NE coastal, SE coastal, S Gulfs, QLD, NSW, VIC, SA.
Ecology: adult—volant; melliferous, solitary.
Reference: Maynard, G.V. (1992). Systematic Studies on Australian *Leioproctus* Smith (Hymenoptera: Colletidae). Unpubl. PhD Thesis. Brisbane : Univ. of Queensland 429 pp. (distribution).

Leioproctus (Goniocolletes) gallipes (Cockerell, 1913)

Paracolletes gallipes Cockerell, T.D.A. (1913). Descriptions and records of bees. L. *Ann. Mag. Nat. Hist.* (8)**11**: 273–283 [280].
Type data: holotype, BMNH Hym.17.a.478 ♀.
Type locality: Poonarunna, SA.

Distribution: Lake Eyre basin, SA; known only from type locality.
Ecology: adult—volant; melliferous, solitary.

Leioproctus (Goniocolletes) hillieri (Cockerell, 1914)

Paracolletes fimbriatinus hillieri Cockerell, T.D.A. (1914). Descriptions and records of bees. LXI. *Ann. Mag. Nat. Hist.* (8)**14**: 39–49 [47].
Type data: holotype, BMNH Hym.17.a.444 ♂.
Type locality: Hermannsburg, NT.

Distribution: Lake Eyre basin, NT; known only from type locality.

Ecology: adult—volant; melliferous, solitary.
Reference: Michener, C.D. (1965). A classification of the bees of the Australian and South Pacific regions. *Bull. Am. Mus. Nat. Hist.* **130**: 1–362 [66] (taxonomy).

Leioproctus (Goniocolletes) microdontus (Cockerell, 1929)

Paracolletes microdontus Cockerell, T.D.A. (1929). Bees in the Queensland Museum. *Mem. Qd Mus.* **9**: 298–323 [309].
Type data: holotype, QM 2♀ (a specimen is labelled 'type' and has registration number Hy/4085).
Type locality: Perth, WA.

Distribution: SW coastal, WA; known only from type locality.
Ecology: adult—volant; melliferous, solitary.

Leioproctus (Goniocolletes) morsus (Cockerell, 1907)

Goniocolletes morsus Cockerell, T.D.A. (1907). On a collection of Australian and Asiatic bees. *Bull. Am. Mus. Nat. Hist.* **23**: 221–236 [231].
Type data: holotype, AMNH ♂*.
Type locality: NSW.
Dasycolletes curvipes Friese, H. (1924). Ueber die Bienen Australiens. *Konowia* **3**: 216–249 [217].
Type data: syntypes (probable), ZMB 3♂* (G. Maynard, pers. comm.).
Type locality: Adelaide, SA.

Taxonomic decision for synonymy: Cockerell, T.D.A. (1929). Descriptions and records of bees. CXV. *Ann. Mag. Nat. Hist.* (10)**3**: 354–360 [358].

Distribution: S Gulfs, NSW, SA; only published localities NSW and Adelaide.
Ecology: adult—volant; melliferous, solitary.

Leioproctus (Goniocolletes) pallidus (Cockerell, 1915)

Goniocolletes pallidus Cockerell, T.D.A. (1915). Descriptions and records of bees. LXVI. *Ann. Mag. Nat. Hist.* (8)**15**: 341–350 [345].
Type data: holotype, BMNH Hym.17.a.398 ♂.
Type locality: Hermannsburg, NT.

Distribution: Lake Eyre basin, NT; known only from type locality.
Ecology: adult—volant; melliferous, solitary.

Leioproctus (Goniocolletes) perfasciatus (Cockerell, 1906)

Paracolletes perfasciatus Cockerell, T.D.A. (1906). Descriptions and records of bees. VII. *Ann. Mag. Nat. Hist.* (7)**17**: 23–29 [25].
Type data: holotype, BMNH Hym.17.a.424 ♀.
Type locality: WA.

Distribution: Murray-Darling basin, S Gulfs, NW coastal.

Ecology: adult—volant; melliferous, solitary.

References: Montague, P.D. (1914). A report on the fauna of the Monte Bello islands. *Proc. Zool. Soc. Lond.* **1914**: 625–652 (distribution); Maynard, G.V. (1992). Systematic Studies on Australian *Leioproctus* Smith (Hymenoptera: Colletidae). Unpubl. PhD Thesis. Brisbane : Univ. of Queensland 429 pp. (distribution).

Leioproctus (Goniocolletes) proximus (Rayment, 1935)

Goniocolletes proximus Rayment, T. (1935). *A Cluster of Bees*. Sixty essays on the life-histories of Australian bees, with specific descriptions of over 100 new species, and an introduction by Professor E.F. Phillips, D.Ph., Cornell University, U.S.A. Sydney : Endeavour Press 752 pp. [687].
Type data: holotype, ANIC ♂.
Type locality: Swan River, WA.

Distribution: SW coastal, WA; known only from type locality.
Ecology: adult—volant; melliferous, solitary.

Leioproctus (Goniocolletes) ruficaudus Michener, 1965

Leioproctus rufiventris Friese, H. (1924). Ueber die Bienen Australiens. *Konowia* **3**: 216–249 [219] [junior secondary homonym of *Pasiphae rufiventris* Spinola, 1851].
Type data: syntypes (probable), AMNH ♀* (number of specimens unknown).
Type locality: Adelaide, SA.
Leioproctus (Goniocolletes) ruficaudus Michener, C.D. (1965). A classification of the bees of the Australian and South Pacific regions. *Bull. Am. Mus. Nat. Hist.* **130**: 1–362 [66] [*nom. nov.* for *Leioproctus rufiventris* Friese, 1924].

Distribution: S Gulfs, SA; known only from type locality.
Ecology: adult—volant; melliferous, solitary.

Leioproctus (Goniocolletes) similior Michener, 1965

Goniocolletes simillimus Rayment, T. (1935). *A Cluster of Bees*. Sixty essays on the life-histories of Australian bees, with specific descriptions of over 100 new species, and an introduction by Professor E.F. Phillips, D.Ph., Cornell University, U.S.A. Sydney : Endeavour Press 752 pp. [686] [junior secondary homonym of *Euryglossa simillima* Smith, 1879].
Type data: holotype, ANIC ♂.
Type locality: Wentworth, NSW.
Leioproctus (Goniocolletes) similior Michener, C.D. (1965). A classification of the bees of the Australian and South Pacific regions. *Bull. Am. Mus. Nat. Hist.* **130**: 1–362 [66] [*nom. nov.* for *Goniocolletes simillimus* Rayment, 1935].

Distribution: Murray-Darling basin, NSW; known only from type locality.
Ecology: adult—volant; melliferous, solitary.

Leioproctus (Goniocolletes) velutinus (Cockerell, 1929)

Paracolletes velutinus Cockerell, T.D.A. (1929). Bees in the Australian Museum collection. *Rec. Aust. Mus.* **17**: 199–243 [208].
Type data: holotype, AM ♂.
Type locality: Eradu, WA.

Distribution: NW coastal, WA; known only from type locality.
Ecology: adult—volant; melliferous, solitary.

Leioproctus (Nodocolletes) Rayment, 1931

Nodocolletes Rayment, T. (1931). Bees in the collections of the Western Australian Museum and the Agricultural Department, Perth. *J. Proc. R. Soc. West. Aust.* **17**: 157–190 [164]. Type species: *Nodocolletes dentatus* Rayment, 1931 by original designation.

Extralimital distribution: New Caledonia, see Michener, C.D. (1965). A classification of the bees of the Australian and South Pacific regions. *Bull. Am. Mus. Nat. Hist.* **130**: 1–362 [63].

Leioproctus (Nodocolletes) caeruleotinctus (Cockerell, 1905)

Paracolletes caeruleotinctus Cockerell, T.D.A. (1905). Descriptions and records of bees. VI. *Ann. Mag. Nat. Hist.* (7)**16**: 477–486 [480].
Type data: syntypes, BMNH 2♂ (a specimen is labelled 'type' and has registration number Hym.17.a.434).
Type locality: Mackay, QLD.
Paracolletes turneri Cockerell, T.D.A. (1910). New and little-known bees. *Trans. Am. Entomol. Soc.* **36**: 199–249 [203].
Type data: holotype, BMNH Hym.17.a.440 ♀.
Type locality: Mackay, QLD.
Paracolletes picta Rayment, T. (1930). New and remarkable bees. *Proc. R. Soc. Vict.* **43**: 42–61 [47].
Type data: holotype, ANIC ♀.
Type locality: Charleville, QLD.

Taxonomic decision for synonymy: Michener, C.D. (1965). A classification of the bees of the Australian and South Pacific regions. *Bull. Am. Mus. Nat. Hist.* **130**: 1–362 [63, 233].

Distribution: NE coastal, Murray-Darling basin, QLD, VIC.
Ecology: adult—volant; melliferous, solitary, flower visiting record: *Cassia* L. *s.lat.* [Caesalpiniaceae], *Eucalyptus* L'Hérit. [Myrtaceae], *Wahlenbergia* Roth [Campanulaceae].
References: Cockerell, T.D.A. (1910). New and little-known bees. *Trans. Am. Entomol. Soc.* **36**: 199–249 (description of male); Cockerell, T.D.A. (1914). Descriptions and records of bees. LVI. *Ann. Mag. Nat. Hist.* (8)**13**: 136–146 (distribution); Cockerell, T.D.A. (1914). Descriptions and records of bees. LX. *Ann. Mag. Nat. Hist.* (8)**14**: 1–13 (distribution).

Leioproctus (Nodocolletes) dentatus (Rayment, 1931)

Nodocolletes dentatus Rayment, T. (1931). Bees in the collections of the Western Australian Museum and the Agricultural Department, Perth. *J. Proc. R. Soc. West. Aust.* **17**: 157–190 [165].
Type data: holotype, WADA ♀.
Type locality: Moora, WA.

Distribution: SW coastal, WA; known only from type locality.
Ecology: adult—volant; melliferous, solitary, flower visiting record: *Eucalyptus* L'Hérit. [Myrtaceae].
Reference: Rayment, T. (1935). *A Cluster of Bees.* Sixty essays on the life-histories of Australian bees, with specific descriptions of over 100 new species, and an introduction by Professor E.F. Phillips, D.Ph., Cornell University, U.S.A. Sydney : Endeavour Press 752 pp. (illustration).

Leioproctus (Nodocolletes) dentiger (Cockerell, 1910)

Paracolletes dentiger Cockerell, T.D.A. (1910). New and little-known bees. *Trans. Am. Entomol. Soc.* **36**: 199–249 [199].
Type data: holotype, ZMB ♀*.
Type locality: Australia (as New Holland).

Distribution: SW coastal, WA; only published localities Yallingup and King George Sound.
Ecology: adult—volant; melliferous, solitary.
References: Cockerell, T.D.A. (1914). Descriptions and records of bees. LXI. *Ann. Mag. Nat. Hist.* (8)**14**: 39–49 (redescription); Cockerell, T.D.A. (1929). Bees in the Australian Museum collection. *Rec. Aust. Mus.* **17**: 199–243 (distribution).

Leioproctus (Nodocolletes) diodontus (Cockerell, 1929)

Paracolletes diodontus Cockerell, T.D.A. (1929). Bees in the Australian Museum collection. *Rec. Aust. Mus.* **17**: 199–243 [206].
Type data: holotype, AM ♀.
Type locality: Eradu, WA.

Distribution: NW coastal, WA; known only from type locality.
Ecology: adult—volant; melliferous, solitary.

Leioproctus (Nodocolletes) elegans (Smith, 1853)

Leioproctus elegans Smith, F. (1853). *Catalogue of Hymenopterous Insects in the Collection of the British Museum.* Part I. Andrenidae and Apidae. London : British Museum 197 pp. [9].
Type data: holotype, BMNH Hym.17.a.495 ♀.
Type locality: Adelaide, SA.

Distribution: NE coastal, SE coastal, S Gulfs, QLD, NSW, VIC, SA.
Ecology: adult—volant; melliferous, solitary.
Reference: Maynard, G.V. (1992). Systematic Stud-ies on Australian *Leioproctus* Smith (Hymenoptera: Colletidae). Unpubl. PhD Thesis. Brisbane : Univ. of Queensland 429 pp. (distribution).

Leioproctus (Nodocolletes) fulvus (Smith, 1879)

Lamprocolletes fulvus Smith, F. (1879). *Descriptions of New Species of Hymenoptera in the Collection of the British Museum.* London : British Museum xxi 240 pp. [9].
Type data: holotype, BMNH Hym.17.a.502 ♀.
Type locality: QLD.

Distribution: NE coastal, SE coastal, S Gulfs, QLD, NSW, SA.
Ecology: adult—volant; melliferous, solitary.
Reference: Maynard, G.V. (1992). Systematic Stud-ies on Australian *Leioproctus* Smith (Hymenoptera: Colletidae). Unpubl. PhD Thesis. Brisbane : Univ. of Queensland 429 pp. (distribution).

Leioproctus (Nodocolletes) macrodontus (Rayment, 1935)

Paracolletes macrodontus Rayment, T. (1935). *A Cluster of Bees.* Sixty essays on the life-histories of Australian bees, with specific descriptions of over 100 new species, and an introduction by Professor E.F. Phillips, D.Ph., Cornell University, U.S.A. Sydney : Endeavour Press 752 pp. [674].
Type data: holotype, ANIC ♂.
Type locality: Cottesloe, WA.

Distribution: SW coastal, WA; known only from type locality.
Ecology: adult—volant; melliferous, solitary.

Leioproctus (Nodocolletes) megachalceus (Cockerell, 1913)

Paracolletes megachalceus Cockerell, T.D.A. (1913). Descriptions and records of bees. LIV. *Ann. Mag. Nat. Hist.* (8)**12**: 368–376 [374].
Type data: holotype, BMNH Hym.17.a.470 ♀.
Type locality: Clarence River, NSW.

Distribution: SE coastal, NSW; only published localities Clarence River and Raymond Terrace.
Ecology: adult—volant; melliferous, solitary.
Reference: Cockerell, T.D.A. (1929). Bees in the Australian Museum collection. *Rec. Aust. Mus.* **17**: 199–243 (distribution).

Leioproctus (Nodocolletes) megadontus (Cockerell, 1913)

Paracolletes megadontus Cockerell, T.D.A. (1913). Descriptions and records of bees. LIV. *Ann. Mag. Nat. Hist.* (8)**12**: 368–376 [375].
Type data: holotype, QM Hy/4081 ♀.
Type locality: Caloundra, QLD.

Distribution: NE coastal, QLD.
Ecology: adult—volant; melliferous, solitary.
Reference: Maynard, G.V. (1992). Systematic Stud-

ies on Australian *Leioproctus* Smith (Hymenoptera: Colletidae). Unpubl. PhD Thesis. Brisbane : Univ. of Queensland 429 pp. (distribution).

Leioproctus (Nodocolletes) phanerodontus (Cockerell, 1929)

Paracolletes phanerodontus Cockerell, T.D.A. (1929). Bees in the Australian Museum collection. *Rec. Aust. Mus.* **17**: 199–243 [207].
Type data: holotype, AM K37281 ♀.
Type locality: King George Sound, WA.

Distribution: SW coastal, WA; known only from type locality.
Ecology: adult—volant; melliferous, solitary.

Leioproctus (Nodocolletes) subdentatus (Rayment, 1931)

Nodocolletes subdentatus Rayment, T. (1931). Bees in the collections of the Western Australian Museum and the Agricultural Department, Perth. *J. Proc. R. Soc. West. Aust.* **17**: 157–190 [166].
Type data: holotype, ANIC ♀.
Type locality: Quairading, WA.

Distribution: SW coastal, WA; known only from type locality.
Ecology: adult—volant; melliferous, solitary.
Reference: Rayment, T. (1935). *A Cluster of Bees.* Sixty essays on the life-histories of Australian bees, with specific descriptions of over 100 new species, and an introduction by Professor E.F. Phillips, D.Ph., Cornell University, U.S.A. Sydney : Endeavour Press 752 pp. (illustration).

Leioproctus (Nodocolletes) subvigilans (Cockerell, 1914)

Paracolletes subvigilans Cockerell, T.D.A. (1914). Descriptions and records of bees. LXI. *Ann. Mag. Nat. Hist.* (8)**14**: 39–49 [45].
Type data: syntypes, BMNH 3♀ (a specimen is labelled type and has registration number Hym.17.a.448).
Type locality: Yallingup, WA.

Distribution: SW coastal, WA; known only from type locality.
Ecology: adult—volant; melliferous, solitary.

Leioproctus (Nodocolletes) tuberculatus (Cockerell, 1913)

Paracolletes tuberculatus Cockerell, T.D.A. (1913). Descriptions and records of bees. L. *Ann. Mag. Nat. Hist.* (8)**11**: 273–283 [274].
Type data: holotype, USNM ♀*.
Type locality: Cheltenham, VIC.

Distribution: SE coastal, NE coastal, S Gulfs, QLD, NSW, VIC, SA.
Ecology: adult—volant; melliferous, solitary, nest in ground.
References: Cockerell, T.D.A. (1914). Descriptions

and records of bees. LVI. *Ann. Mag. Nat. Hist.* (8)**13**: 136–146 (distribution); Rayment, T. (1929). The plumed bees. *Vict. Nat.* **46**: 155–162 (illustration); Rayment, T. (1935). *A Cluster of Bees.* Sixty essays on the life-histories of Australian bees, with specific descriptions of over 100 new species, and an introduction by Professor E.F. Phillips, D.Ph., Cornell University, U.S.A. Sydney : Endeavour Press 752 pp. (biology); Maynard, G.V. (1992). Systematic Studies on Australian *Leioproctus* Smith (Hymenoptera: Colletidae). Unpubl. PhD Thesis. Brisbane : Univ. of Queensland 429 pp. (distribution).

Leioproctus (Nodocolletes) vigilans Smith, 1879

Leioproctus vigilans Smith, F. (1879). *Descriptions of New Species of Hymenoptera in the Collection of the British Museum.* London : British Museum xxi 240 pp. [7] [the genus name misspelled as *Lioproctus* in the original description].
Type data: holotype, BMNH Hym.17.a.496 ♀.
Type locality: Swan River, WA.

Distribution: SW coastal, WA; known only from type locality.
Ecology: adult—volant; melliferous, solitary.
References: Cockerell, T.D.A. (1910). New and little-known bees. *Trans. Am. Entomol. Soc.* **36**: 199–249 (taxonomy); Rayment, T. (1931). Bees in the collections of the Western Australian Museum and the Agricultural Department, Perth. *J. Proc. R. Soc. West. Aust.* **17**: 157–190 (illustration); Rayment, T. (1935). *A Cluster of Bees.* Sixty essays on the life-histories of Australian bees, with specific descriptions of over 100 new species, and an introduction by Professor E.F. Phillips, D.Ph., Cornell University, U.S.A. Sydney : Endeavour Press 752 pp. (illustration).

Leioproctus (Notocolletes) Cockerell, 1916

Notocolletes Cockerell, T.D.A. (1916). Descriptions and records of bees. LXXIII. *Ann. Mag. Nat. Hist.* (8)**18**: 44–53 [44]. Type species: *Notocolletes heterodoxus* Cockerell, 1916 by monotypy.

Leioproctus (Notocolletes) heterodoxus (Cockerell, 1916)

Notocolletes heterodoxus Cockerell, T.D.A. (1916). Descriptions and records of bees. LXXIII. *Ann. Mag. Nat. Hist.* (8)**18**: 44–53 [45].
Type data: holotype, BMNH Hym.17.a.399 ♂.
Type locality: Gawler District (as Gawter D.S. Austr.), SA, see Houston, T.F. (1974). Rediscovery and further description of the bee *Leioproctus (Notocolletes) heterodoxus* (Cockerell) (Hymenoptera : Colletidae). *Aust. Entomol. Mag.* **2**: 7–9 [7].

Distribution: S Gulfs, SA; only published localities in Gawler district, Lakes Albert and Alexandrina.
Ecology: adult—volant; melliferous, solitary, flower visiting record: *Arctotheca* Wendl. [Asteraceae].

Reference: Houston, T.F. (1974). Rediscovery and further description of the bee *Leioproctus (Notocolletes) heterodoxus* (Cockerell) (Hymenoptera : Colletidae). *Aust. Entomol. Mag.* **2**: 7–9 (redescription).

Leioproctus (Protomorpha) Rayment, 1959

Protomorpha Rayment, T. (1959). A new and remarkable colletid bee. *Aust. Zool.* **12**: 334–336 [334]. Type species: *Protomorpha tarsalis* Rayment, 1959 by original designation.

Microcolletes Michener, C.D. (1965). A classification of the bees of the Australian and South Pacific regions. *Bull. Am. Mus. Nat. Hist.* **130**: 1–362 [55] [proposed with subgeneric rank in *Leioproctus* Smith, 1853]. Type species: *Paracolletes halictiformis* Cockerell, 1916 (=*Leioproctus (Microcolletes) halictomimus* Michener, 1965) by original designation.

Taxonomic decision for synonymy: Maynard, G.V. (1991). Revision of *Leioproctus (Protomorpha)* Rayment (Hymenoptera: Colletidae) with description of two new species. *J. Aust. Entomol. Soc.* **30**: 67–75 [67].

Leioproctus (Protomorpha) alloeopus Maynard, 1991

Leioproctus (Protomorpha) alloeopus Maynard, G.V. (1991). Revision of *Leioproctus (Protomorpha)* Rayment (Hymenoptera: Colletidae) with description of two new species. *J. Aust. Entomol. Soc.* **30**: 67–75 [69].
Type data: holotype, CAS ♂*.
Type locality: 37 miles (59 km) S Leonora, WA.

Distribution: W plateau, WA; only published localities near Leonora, near Lake Throssel, near Neale Junction and near Banjawarn Homestead.
Ecology: adult—volant; melliferous, solitary, flower visiting record: *Scaevola* L. [Goodeniaceae], *Sida* L. [Malvaceae].

Leioproctus (Protomorpha) fallax (Cockerell, 1921)

Paracolletes fallax Cockerell, T.D.A. (1921). Australian bees in the Queensland Museum. *Mem. Qd Mus.* **7**: 81–98 [96].
Type data: holotype, QM T2396 ♀.
Type locality: Bribie Is., QLD.

Distribution: NE coastal, Murray-Darling basin, QLD, NSW; only published localities Bribie Is., Coolangatta and near Coonabarabran.
Ecology: adult—volant; melliferous, solitary.
Reference: Maynard, G.V. (1991). Revision of *Leioproctus (Protomorpha)* Rayment (Hymenoptera: Colletidae) with description of two new species. *J. Aust. Entomol. Soc.* **30**: 67–75 (redescription).

Leioproctus (Protomorpha) minutus (Cockerell, 1916)

Paracolletes minutus Cockerell, T.D.A. (1916). Descriptions and records of bees. LXXIII. *Ann. Mag. Nat. Hist.* (8)**18**: 44–53 [50].

Type data: holotype, BMNH Hym.17.a.445a ♂.
Type locality: Yallingup, WA.

Paracolletes halictiformis Cockerell, T.D.A. (1916). Some bees from Australia, Tasmania, and the New Hebrides. *Proc. Acad. Nat. Sci. Philad.* **68**: 360–375 [365] [junior secondary homonym of *Euryglossa halictiformis* Smith, 1879].
Type data: holotype, BMNH Hym.17.a.473 ♀.
Type locality: Yallingup, WA.

Leioproctus (Microcolletes) halictomimus Michener, C.D. (1965). A classification of the bees of the Australian and South Pacific regions. *Bull. Am. Mus. Nat. Hist.* **130**: 1–362 [55] [*nom. nov.* for *Paracolletes halictiformis* Cockerell, 1916].

Taxonomic decision for synonymy: Maynard, G.V. (1991). Revision of *Leioproctus (Protomorpha)* Rayment (Hymenoptera: Colletidae) with description of two new species. *J. Aust. Entomol. Soc.* **30**: 67–75 [72].

Distribution: SW coastal, WA; only published localities Yallingup and Rottnest Is.
Ecology: adult—volant; melliferous, solitary.
References: Cockerell, T.D.A. (1929). Bees, chiefly Australian species, described or determined by Dr. H. Friese. *Am. Mus. Novit.* **343**: 1–20 (taxonomy); Rayment, T. (1934). Contributions to the fauna of Rottnest Island. VIII. Apoidea. With description of new species. *J. Proc. R. Soc. West. Aust.* **20**: 201–212 (distribution).

Leioproctus (Protomorpha) plautus Maynard, 1991

Leioproctus (Protomorpha) plautus Maynard, G.V. (1991). Revision of *Leioproctus (Protomorpha)* Rayment (Hymenoptera: Colletidae) with description of two new species. *J. Aust. Entomol. Soc.* **30**: 67–75 [70].
Type data: holotype, WAM 87/1413 ♂*.
Type locality: 10–13 km NE Wanneroo, WA.

Distribution: SW coastal, WA; only published localities near Wanneroo.
Ecology: adult—volant; melliferous, solitary, flower visiting record: *Beaufortia* R.Br. [Myrtaceae], *Lechenaultia* R.Br. [Goodeniaceae], *Scholtzia* Schauer [Myrtaceae].

Leioproctus (Protomorpha) tarsalis (Rayment, 1959)

Protomorpha tarsalis Rayment, T. (1959). A new genus of bees in the family Colletidae. *Aust. Zool.* **12**: 324–329 [335].
Type data: holotype, ANIC ♂.
Type locality: Caldwell, NSW.

Distribution: N Gulf, Murray-Darling basin, Lake Eyre basin, S Gulfs, N coastal, QLD, NSW, SA, WA, NT.
Ecology: adult—volant; melliferous, solitary, males possibly form sleeping aggregations, flower visiting record: *Eucalyptus* L'Hérit. [Myrtaceae].
Reference: Maynard, G.V. (1991). Revision of *Leioproctus (Protomorpha)* Rayment (Hymenoptera: Colletidae) with description of two new species. *J.*

Aust. Entomol. Soc. **30**: 67–75 (redescription, description of female, biology).

Leioproctus (Urocolletes) Michener, 1965

Urocolletes Michener, C.D. (1965). A classification of the bees of the Australian and South Pacific regions. *Bull. Am. Mus. Nat. Hist.* **130**: 1–362 [58] [proposed with subgeneric rank in *Leioproctus* Smith, 1853]. Type species: *Leioproctus (Urocolletes) rhodurus* Michener, 1965 by original designation.

Leioproctus (Urocolletes) rhodurus Michener, 1965

Leioproctus (Urocolletes) rhodurus Michener, C.D. (1965). A classification of the bees of the Australian and South Pacific regions. *Bull. Am. Mus. Nat. Hist.* **130**: 1–362 [253].
Type data: holotype, WAM 37-3797 ♀.
Type locality: Midland, WA.

Distribution: SW coastal, WA; known only from type locality.
Ecology: adult—volant; melliferous, solitary, flower visiting record: *Leptospermum* Forster & G.Forster [Myrtaceae].

Leioproctus (Unplaced)

Leioproctus albovittatus (Cockerell, 1929)

Paracolletes albovittatus Cockerell, T.D.A. (1929). Bees in the Australian Museum collection. *Rec. Aust. Mus.* **17**: 199–243 [210].
Type data: holotype, AM ♀.
Type locality: Eradu, WA.

Distribution: NW coastal, WA; known only from type locality.
Ecology: adult—volant; melliferous, solitary.
Reference: Maynard, G.V. (1991). Revision of *Leioproctus (Protomorpha)* Rayment (Hymenoptera: Colletidae) with description of two new species. *J. Aust. Entomol. Soc.* **30**: 67–75 (taxonomy).

Leioproctus ferrisi (Rayment, 1935)

Paracolletes ferrisi Rayment, T. (1935). *A Cluster of Bees.* Sixty essays on the life-histories of Australian bees, with specific descriptions of over 100 new species, and an introduction by Professor E.F. Phillips, D.Ph., Cornell University, U.S.A. Sydney : Endeavour Press 752 pp. [671].
Type data: holotype, ANIC ♂.
Type locality: Gunbower, VIC.

Distribution: Murray-Darling basin, VIC; known only from type locality.
Ecology: adult—volant; melliferous, solitary.
Reference: Michener, C.D. (1965). A classification of the bees of the Australian and South Pacific regions. *Bull. Am. Mus. Nat. Hist.* **130**: 1–362 (taxonomy).

Leioproctus finkei Michener, 1965

Leioproctus (Microcolletes) finkei Michener, C.D. (1965). A classification of the bees of the Australian and South Pacific regions. *Bull. Am. Mus. Nat. Hist.* **130**: 1–362 [248].
Type data: holotype, ANIC ♀.
Type locality: Finke River, NT (as Finke Crossing, Central Australia).

Distribution: Lake Eyre basin, W plateau, QLD, SA, NT.
Ecology: adult—volant; melliferous, solitary.
References: Maynard, G.V. (1991). Revision of *Leioproctus (Protomorpha)* Rayment (Hymenoptera: Colletidae) with description of two new species. *J. Aust. Entomol. Soc.* **30**: 67–75 (taxonomy); Maynard, G.V. (1992). Systematic Studies on Australian *Leioproctus* Smith (Hymenoptera: Colletidae). Unpubl. PhD Thesis. Brisbane : Univ. of Queensland 429 pp. (distribution).

Leioproctus helichrysi (Cockerell, 1918)

Paracolletes helichrysi Cockerell, T.D.A. (1918). Some bees collected in Queensland. *Mem. Qd Mus.* **6**: 112–120 [112].
Type data: holotype, BMNH Hym.17.a.474 ♀.
Type locality: Mt Tamborine, QLD.

Distribution: NE coastal, QLD; known only from type locality.
Ecology: adult—volant; melliferous, solitary, flower visiting record: *Erigeron* L. [Asteraceae], *Helichrysum* Miller *s.lat.* [Asteraceae].
References: Michener, C.D. (1965). A classification of the bees of the Australian and South Pacific regions. *Bull. Am. Mus. Nat. Hist.* **130**: 1–362 (flower record); Maynard, G.V. (1991). Revision of *Leioproctus (Protomorpha)* Rayment (Hymenoptera: Colletidae) with description of two new species. *J. Aust. Entomol. Soc.* **30**: 67–75 (taxonomy).

Leioproctus microsomus Michener, 1965

Leioproctus (Microcolletes) microsomus Michener, C.D. (1965). A classification of the bees of the Australian and South Pacific regions. *Bull. Am. Mus. Nat. Hist.* **130**: 1–362 [248].
Type data: holotype, ANIC ♀.
Type locality: 17 miles S of Dalby, QLD.

Distribution: Murray-Darling basin, QLD; only published localities near Dalby and Jondaryan.
Ecology: adult—volant; melliferous, solitary, flower visiting record: *Wahlenbergia* Roth [Campanulaceae].
Reference: Maynard, G.V. (1991). Revision of *Leioproctus (Protomorpha)* Rayment (Hymenoptera: Colletidae) with description of two new species. *J. Aust. Entomol. Soc.* **30**: 67–75 (taxonomy).

Leioproctus nomiaeformis (Cockerell, 1930)

Paracolletes nomiaeformis Cockerell, T.D.A. (1930). New Australian bees. *Mem. Qd Mus.* **10**: 37–50 [48].
Type data: syntypes, QM 3♂ (a specimen is labelled 'type' and has registration number Hy/3746).
Type locality: Charleville, QLD.

Distribution: Murray-Darling basin, QLD; known only from type locality.
Ecology: adult—volant; melliferous, solitary.
Reference: Maynard, G.V. (1991). Revision of *Leioproctus (Protomorpha)* Rayment (Hymenoptera: Colletidae) with description of two new species. *J. Aust. Entomol. Soc.* **30**: 67–75 (taxonomy).

Leioproctus perminutus (Cockerell, 1929)

Lamprocolletes minutus Friese, H. (1924). Ueber die Bienen Australiens. *Konowia* **3**: 216–249 [221] [junior secondary homonym of *Paracolletes minutus* Cockerell, 1916].
Type data: holotype (probable), AMNH ♀*.
Type locality: Fremantle, WA.

Paracolletes perminutus Cockerell, T.D.A. (1929). Bees, chiefly Australian species, described or determined by Dr. H. Friese. *Am. Mus. Novit.* **343**: 1–20 [2] [*nom. nov.* for *Lamprocolletes minutus* Friese, 1924].

Distribution: SW coastal, WA; known only from type locality.
Ecology: adult—volant; melliferous, solitary.
Reference: Maynard, G.V. (1991). Revision of *Leioproctus (Protomorpha)* Rayment (Hymenoptera: Colletidae) with description of two new species. *J. Aust. Entomol. Soc.* **30**: 67–75 (taxonomy).

Leioproctus pusillus (Cockerell, 1929)

Paracolletes pusillus Cockerell, T.D.A. (1929). Bees in the Australian Museum collection. *Rec. Aust. Mus.* **17**: 199–243 [204].
Type data: holotype, AM ♂.
Type locality: Geraldton, WA.

Distribution: SW coastal, NW coastal, WA; only published localities Geraldton and Bolgart.
Ecology: adult—volant; melliferous, solitary, nest gregariously in ground.
References: Rayment, T. (1947). Biology and taxonomy of the solitary bee, *Parasphecodes fulviventris* (Friese). *Aust. Zool.* **11**: 76–95 (biology); Maynard, G.V. (1991). Revision of *Leioproctus (Protomorpha)* Rayment (Hymenoptera: Colletidae) with description of two new species. *J. Aust. Entomol. Soc.* **30**: 67–75 (taxonomy).

Leioproctus rudissimus (Cockerell, 1929)

Paracolletes rudissimus Cockerell, T.D.A. (1929). Bees in the Australian Museum collection. *Rec. Aust. Mus.* **17**: 199–243 [200].
Type data: holotype, AM ♂.
Type locality: Wyalkatchem (as Wyalcatchem), WA.

Distribution: SW coastal, WA; known only from type locality.
Ecology: adult—volant; melliferous, solitary.
Reference: Maynard, G.V. (1991). Revision of *Leioproctus (Protomorpha)* Rayment (Hymenoptera: Colletidae) with description of two new species. *J. Aust. Entomol. Soc.* **30**: 67–75 (taxonomy).

Leioproctus tropicalis (Cockerell, 1929)

Paracolletes tropicalis Cockerell, T.D.A. (1929). Bees from the Australian region. *Am. Mus. Novit.* **346**: 1–18 [1].
Type data: holotype, AMNH ♂* (the type is a male, but described as a female, G. Maynard, pers. comm.).
Type locality: Melville Is., NT.

Distribution: N coastal, NT; known only from type locality.
Ecology: adult—volant; melliferous, solitary.
Reference: Maynard, G.V. (1991). Revision of *Leioproctus (Protomorpha)* Rayment (Hymenoptera: Colletidae) with description of two new species. *J. Aust. Entomol. Soc.* **30**: 67–75 (taxonomy).

Leioproctus wahlenbergiae Michener, 1965

Leioproctus (Microcolletes) wahlenbergiae Michener, C.D. (1965). A classification of the bees of the Australian and South Pacific regions. *Bull. Am. Mus. Nat. Hist.* **130**: 1–362 [250].
Type data: holotype, ANIC ♀.
Type locality: 17 miles S of Dalby, QLD.

Distribution: Murray-Darling basin, QLD; only published localities Dalby, Clifton and Jondaryan.
Ecology: adult—volant; melliferous, solitary, flower visiting record: *Wahlenbergia* Roth [Campanulaceae].
Reference: Maynard, G.V. (1991). Revision of *Leioproctus (Protomorpha)* Rayment (Hymenoptera: Colletidae) with description of two new species. *J. Aust. Entomol. Soc.* **30**: 67–75 (taxonomy).

Neopasiphae Perkins, 1912

Neopasiphae Perkins, R.C.L. (1912). Notes, with descriptions of new species, on aculeate Hymenoptera of the Australian Region. *Ann. Mag. Nat. Hist.* (8)**9**: 96–121 [114]. Type species: *Neopasiphae mirabilis* Perkins, 1912 by monotypy.

Michener, C.D. (1965). A classification of the bees of the Australian and South Pacific regions. *Bull. Am. Mus. Nat. Hist.* **130**: 1–362.

Neopasiphae insignis Rayment, 1930

Neopasiphae insignis Rayment, T. (1930). New and remarkable bees. *Proc. R. Soc. Vict.* **43**: 42–61 [42].
Type data: holotype, NMV ♀.
Type locality: as "probably Victoria" (locality probably in error, specimen without locality label), see Michener, C.D. (1965). A classification of the bees of the Australian and South Pacific regions. *Bull. Am. Mus. Nat. Hist.* **130**: 1–362 [75].

Distribution: (VIC); known only from type locality.
Ecology: adult—volant; melliferous, solitary.
References: Rayment, T. (1935). *A Cluster of Bees*. Sixty essays on the life-histories of Australian bees, with specific descriptions of over 100 new species, and an introduction by Professor E.F. Phillips, D.Ph., Cornell University, U.S.A. Sydney : Endeavour Press 752 pp. (redescription); Rayment, T. (1954). Incidence of acarid mites on the biology of bees. *Aust. Zool.* **12**: 26–38 (as host); Michener, C.D. (1965). A classification of the bees of the Australian and South Pacific regions. *Bull. Am. Mus. Nat. Hist.* **130**: 1–362 (taxonomy).

Neopasiphae mirabilis Perkins, 1912

Neopasiphae mirabilis Perkins, R.C.L. (1912). Notes, with descriptions of new species, on aculeate Hymenoptera of the Australian Region. *Ann. Mag. Nat. Hist.* *(8)***9**: 96–121 [115].
Type data: holotype, BMNH Hym.17.a.227 ♂.
Type locality: Violet Range, WA.

Distribution: W plateau, WA; known only from type locality.
Ecology: adult—volant; melliferous, solitary.
References: Meade-Waldo, G. (1923). Hymenoptera. Fam. Apidae. Subfam. Prosopidinae. *Genera Insectorum* **181**: 1–45 (illustration); Cockerell, T.D.A. (1926). Descriptions and records of bees. CX. *Ann. Mag. Nat. Hist.* *(9)***17**: 510–519 (specimens from WA); Rayment, T. (1935). *A Cluster of Bees*. Sixty essays on the life-histories of Australian bees, with specific descriptions of over 100 new species, and an introduction by Professor E.F. Phillips, D.Ph., Cornell University, U.S.A. Sydney : Endeavour Press 752 pp. (illustration); Michener, C.D. (1965). A classification of the bees of the Australian and South Pacific regions. *Bull. Am. Mus. Nat. Hist.* **130**: 1–362 (illustration).

Neopasiphae simplicior Michener, 1965

Neopasiphae simplicior Michener, C.D. (1965). A classification of the bees of the Australian and South Pacific regions. *Bull. Am. Mus. Nat. Hist.* **130**: 1–362 [262].
Type data: holotype, WAM 65–726 ♂.
Type locality: Cannington (as Camington), WA.

Distribution: SW coastal, WA; known only from type locality.
Ecology: adult—volant; melliferous, solitary.

Paracolletes Smith, 1853

Taxonomic decision for subgeneric arrangement: Michener, C.D. (1965). A classification of the bees of the Australian and South Pacific regions. *Bull. Am. Mus. Nat. Hist.* **130**: 1–362 [76].

Paracolletes (Paracolletes) Smith, 1853

Paracolletes Smith, F. (1853). *Catalogue of Hymenopterous Insects in the Collection of the British*

Museum. Part I. Andrenidae and Apidae. London : British Museum 197 pp. [6]. Type species: *Paracolletes crassipes* Smith, 1853 by monotypy.

Paracolletes (Paracolletes) brevicornis (Smith, 1854)

Tetralonia brevicornis Smith, F. (1854). *Catalogue of Hymenopterous Insects in the Collection of the British Museum*. Part II. Apidae. London : British Museum pp. 199–465 [303].
Type data: holotype, BMNH Hym.17.a.498 ♂.
Type locality: Moreton Bay, QLD.

Distribution: NE coastal, QLD; known only from type locality.
Ecology: adult—volant; melliferous, solitary.
References: Cockerell, T.D.A. (1921). Australian bees in the Queensland Museum. *Mem. Qd Mus.* **7**: 81–98 (as *Reepenia brevicornis* (Smith, 1854)); Cockerell, T.D.A. (1926). Descriptions and records of bees. CXII. *Ann. Mag. Nat. Hist.* *(9)***18**: 216–227 (generic placement).

Paracolletes (Paracolletes) convictus (Cockerell, 1909)

Tetralonia convicta Cockerell, T.D.A. (1909). Descriptions and records of bees. XXII. *Ann. Mag. Nat. Hist.* *(8)***4**: 309–317 [310].
Type data: holotype, BMNH Hym.17.a.528 ♂.
Type locality: Australia.

Distribution: SE coastal, VIC; only published locality Port Phillip.
Ecology: adult—volant; melliferous, solitary.
Reference: Cockerell, T.D.A. (1910). Some Australian bees in the Berlin Museum. *J. N.Y. Entomol. Soc.* **18**: 98–114 (distribution).

Paracolletes (Paracolletes) crassipes Smith, 1853

Paracolletes crassipes Smith, F. (1853). *Catalogue of Hymenopterous Insects in the Collection of the British Museum*. Part I. Andrenidae and Apidae. London : British Museum 197 pp. [6].
Type data: holotype, BMNH Hym.17.a.422 ♀.
Type locality: Swan River, WA.
Paracolletes australis Friese, H. (1924). Ueber die Bienen Australiens. *Konowia* **3**: 216–249 [220].
Type data: syntypes (probable), AMNH ♂♀*.
Type locality: Sydney and Mittagong, NSW and Adelaide, SA.

Taxonomic decision for synonymy: Cockerell, T.D.A. (1929). Bees, chiefly Australian species, described or determined by Dr. H. Friese. *Am. Mus. Novit.* **343**: 1–20 [1].

Distribution: NE coastal, Murray-Darling basin, SE coastal, S Gulfs, SW coastal, QLD, NSW, SA, WA.
Ecology: adult—volant; melliferous, solitary, flower visiting record: *Eucalyptus* L'Hérit. [Myrtaceae], *Leptospermum* Forster & G.Forster [Myrtaceae].
References: Cockerell, T.D.A. (1907). On a collection of Australian and Asiatic bees. *Bull. Am. Mus.*

Nat. Hist. **23**: 221–236 (distribution); Cockerell, T.D.A. (1912). Descriptions and records of bees. XLIII. *Ann. Mag. Nat. Hist. (8)***9**: 377–387 (description of male); Cockerell, T.D.A. (1914). Descriptions and records of bees. LVI. *Ann. Mag. Nat. Hist. (8)***13**: 136–146 (distribution); Rayment, T. (1947). What of the *Planidia? Vict. Nat.* **64**: 31–32 (as host); Michener, C.D. (1965). A classification of the bees of the Australian and South Pacific regions. *Bull. Am. Mus. Nat. Hist.* **130**: 1–362 (flower record).

Paracolletes (Paracolletes) fervidus Smith, 1879

Paracolletes fervidus Smith, F. (1879). *Descriptions of New Species of Hymenoptera in the Collection of the British Museum.* London : British Museum xxi 240 pp. [4].
Type data: holotype, BMNH Hym.17.a.414 ♀.
Type locality: Australia (as New Holland).

Distribution: SE coastal, VIC; only published locality Tooradin
Ecology: adult—volant; melliferous, solitary.
Reference: Rayment, T. (1949). New bees and wasps—Part XI. Two confusing earth-digging bees. *Vict. Nat.* **66**: 33–36 (redescription).

Paracolletes (Paracolletes) leptospermi Cockerell, 1912

Paracolletes crassipes leptospermi Cockerell, T.D.A. (1912). Descriptions and records of bees. XLIII. *Ann. Mag. Nat. Hist. (8)***9**: 377–387 [378].
Type data: holotype, BMNH Hym.17.a.475 ♂.
Type locality: Mackay, QLD.

Distribution: NE coastal, SE coastal, QLD, NSW; only published localities Mackay and Jamberoo.
Ecology: adult—volant; melliferous, solitary.
References: Rayment, T. (1954). Remarkable bees from a rain forest. *Aust. Zool.* **12**: 46–56 (distribution); Michener, C.D. (1965). A classification of the bees of the Australian and South Pacific regions. *Bull. Am. Mus. Nat. Hist.* **130**: 1–362 [78] (taxonomy).

Paracolletes (Paracolletes) rebellis Cockerell, 1912

Paracolletes rebellis Cockerell, T.D.A. (1912). Descriptions and records of bees. XLIII. *Ann. Mag. Nat. Hist. (8)***9**: 377–387 [379].
Type data: holotype, BMNH Hym.17.a.469 ♂.
Type locality: Melbourne, VIC.

Distribution: SE coastal, NSW, VIC; only published localities Moonbar, Jindabyne, Melbourne, Healesville and Woodend.
Ecology: adult—volant; melliferous, solitary.
References: Cockerell, T.D.A. (1914). Descriptions and records of bees. LVI. *Ann. Mag. Nat. Hist. (8)***13**: 136–146 (distribution); Cockerell, T.D.A. (1929). Bees in the Queensland Museum. *Mem. Qd Mus.* **9**: 298–323 (distribution); Cockerell, T.D.A. (1929).

Bees in the Australian Museum collection. *Rec. Aust. Mus.* **17**: 199–243 (distribution).

Paracolletes (Paracolletes) subfuscus Cockerell, 1906

Paracolletes subfuscus Cockerell, T.D.A. (1906). Descriptions and records of bees. VII. *Ann. Mag. Nat. Hist. (7)***17**: 23–29 [26].
Type data: holotype, BMNH Hym.17.a.421 ♂.
Type locality: Adelaide, SA.

Distribution: S Gulfs, SA; known only from type locality.
Ecology: adult—volant; melliferous, solitary.

Paracolletes (Paracolletes) submacrodontus Rayment, 1934

Paracolletes submacrodontus Rayment, T. (1934). Contributions to the fauna of Rottnest Island. VIII. Apoidea. With description of new species. *J. Proc. R. Soc. West. Aust.* **20**: 201–212 [206]
Type data: holotype, WAM 33–528 ♂.
Type locality: Rottnest Is., WA.

Distribution: SE coastal, SW coastal, NSW, WA; only published localities White Swamp and Rottnest Is.
Ecology: adult—volant; melliferous, solitary.
References: Rayment, T. (1935). *A Cluster of Bees.* Sixty essays on the life-histories of Australian bees, with specific descriptions of over 100 new species, and an introduction by Professor E.F. Phillips, D.Ph., Cornell University, U.S.A. Sydney : Endeavour Press 752 pp. (description of female as new species); Rayment, T. (1939). Bees from the high lands of New South Wales and Victoria. *Aust. Zool.* **9**: 263–294 (redescription, as *Stenotritus submacrodontus* (Rayment, 1934)).

Paracolletes (Anthoglossa) Smith, 1853

Anthoglossa Smith, F. (1853). *Catalogue of Hymenopterous Insects in the Collection of the British Museum.* Part I. Andrenidae and Apidae. London : British Museum 197 pp. [16] [first proposed as a genus]. Type species: *Anthoglossa plumata* Smith, 1853 by monotypy.

Paracolletes (Anthoglossa) callander Cockerell, 1915

Paracolletes callander Cockerell, T.D.A. (1915). Descriptions and records of bees. LXVI. *Ann. Mag. Nat. Hist. (8)***15**: 341–350 [343].
Type data: syntypes, BMNH 2♀ (a specimen is labelled 'type' and has the registration number Hym.17.a.459).
Type locality: Yallingup, WA.

Distribution: SW coastal, WA; only published localities Yallingup and Perth.
Ecology: adult—volant; melliferous, solitary.

Paracolletes (Anthoglossa) cygni (Cockerell, 1904)

Anthoglossa cygni Cockerell, T.D.A. (1904). New and little known bees in the collection of the British Museum. *Ann. Mag. Nat. Hist. (7)***14**: 203–208 [203].
Type data: holotype, BMNH Hym.17.a.396 ♀.
Type locality: Swan River, WA.

Distribution: SW coastal, WA; known only from type locality.
Ecology: adult—volant; melliferous, solitary.

Paracolletes (Anthoglossa) frederici Cockerell, 1905

Lamprocolletes rubellus Smith, F. (1868). Descriptions of aculeate Hymenoptera from Australia. *Trans. Entomol. Soc. Lond.* **1868**: 231–258 [253] [junior secondary homonym of *Dasycolletes rubellus* Smith, 1862 replaced before 1961, permanently invalid].
Type data: holotype, BMNH Hym.17.a.497 ♂.
Type locality: WA.

Paracolletes frederici Cockerell, T.D.A. (1905). Notes on some bees in the British Museum. *Trans. Am. Entomol. Soc.* **31**: 309–364 [345] [*nom. nov.* for *Lamprocolletes rubellus* Smith, 1868].

Distribution: NSW, WA; exact localities unknown.
Ecology: adult—volant; melliferous, solitary.
Reference: Cockerell, T.D.A. (1907). On a collection of Australian and Asiatic bees. *Bull. Am. Mus. Nat. Hist.* **23**: 221–236 (description of female).

Paracolletes (Anthoglossa) montanus Rayment, 1935

Paracolletes montanus Rayment, T. (1935). *A Cluster of Bees*. Sixty essays on the life-histories of Australian bees, with specific descriptions of over 100 new species, and an introduction by Professor E.F. Phillips, D.Ph., Cornell University, U.S.A. Sydney : Endeavour Press 752 pp. [678].
Type data: holotype, ANIC ♀.
Type locality: Mt Macedon, VIC.

Distribution: SE coastal, VIC; known only from type locality.
Ecology: adult—volant; melliferous, solitary.

Paracolletes (Anthoglossa) nigrocinctus Cockerell, 1914

Paracolletes nigrocinctus Cockerell, T.D.A. (1914). Descriptions and records of bees. LX. *Ann. Mag. Nat. Hist. (8)***14**: 1–13 [6].
Type data: syntypes, BMNH 4♂ (a specimen is labelled 'type' and has registration number Hym.17.a.455).
Type locality: Yallingup, WA.

Paracolletes tenuicinctus Cockerell, T.D.A. (1914). Descriptions and records of bees. LXI. *Ann. Mag. Nat. Hist. (8)***14**: 39–49 [42].
Type data: syntypes, BMNH 3♀ (a specimen is labelled 'type' and has registration number Hym.17.a.453).
Type locality: Yallingup, WA.

Taxonomic decision for synonymy: Cockerell, T.D.A. (1915). Descriptions and records of bees. LXVI. *Ann. Mag. Nat. Hist. (8)***15**: 341–350 [344].

Distribution: SW coastal, NW coastal, WA; only published localities Yallingup and Kojarena.
Ecology: adult—volant; melliferous, solitary, flower visiting record: *Leptospermum* Forster & G.Forster [Myrtaceae].
Reference: Cockerell, T.D.A. (1929). Bees in the Queensland Museum. *Mem. Qd Mus.* **9**: 298–323 (distribution).

Paracolletes (Anthoglossa) plumatus (Smith, 1853)

Anthoglossa plumata Smith, F. (1853). *Catalogue of Hymenopterous Insects in the Collection of the British Museum*. Part I. Andrenidae and Apidae. London : British Museum 197 pp. [16].
Type data: syntypes, BMNH ♂♀ (female specimen is labelled 'type' and has the registration number Hym.17.a.394).
Type locality: WA.

Distribution: SW coastal, WA; only published localities Mundijong and Serpentine.
Ecology: adult—volant; melliferous, solitary.
Reference: Alfken, J.D. (1907). Apidae. pp. 259–261 in Michaelsen, W. & Hartmeyer, R. (eds) *Die Fauna Südwest-Australiens*. Jena : G. Fischer Bd 1 Lfg 6 (distribution).

Paracolletes (Anthoglossa) robustus Cockerell, 1929

Paracolletes robustus Cockerell, T.D.A. (1929). Bees in the Australian Museum collection. *Rec. Aust. Mus.* **17**: 199–243 [207].
Type data: syntypes, AM 2♀ (a specimen is labelled 'type' and has registration number K48304).
Type locality: King George Sound, WA.

Distribution: SW coastal, WA; known only from type locality.
Ecology: adult—volant; melliferous, solitary.

Paracolletes (Anthoglossa) vittatus (Rayment, 1931)

Anthoglossa vittata Rayment, T. (1931). Bees in the collections of the Western Australian Museum and the Agricultural Department, Perth. *J. Proc. R. Soc. West. Aust.* **17**: 157–190 [159].
Type data: holotype, WAM ♀* (not found by J.C.C. in 1986).
Type locality: Perth, WA.

Distribution: SW coastal, WA; known only from type locality.
Ecology: adult—volant; melliferous, solitary.
Reference: Rayment, T. (1935). *A Cluster of Bees*. Sixty essays on the life-histories of Australian bees, with specific descriptions of over 100 new species, and an introduction by Professor E.F. Phillips, D.Ph., Cornell University, U.S.A. Sydney : Endeavour Press 752 pp. (illustration).

Phenacolletes Cockerell, 1905

Phenacolletes Cockerell, T.D.A. (1905). Descriptions and records of bees. III. *Ann. Mag. Nat. Hist. (7)***16**: 301–308 [301]. Type species: *Phenacolletes mimus* Cockerell, 1905 by monotypy.

Generic reference: Michener, C.D. (1989). Classification of American Colletinae (Hymenoptera, Apoidea). *Univ. Kansas Sci. Bull.* **53**: 622–703.

Phenacolletes mimus Cockerell, 1905

Phenacolletes mimus Cockerell, T.D.A. (1905). Descriptions and records of bees. III. *Ann. Mag. Nat. Hist. (7)***16**: 301–308 [302]. Type data: syntypes, BMNH 3♂ (a specimen is labelled 'type' and has registration number Hym.17.a.531). Type locality: Turtle Bay, WA.

Distribution: NW coastal, WA; known only from type locality.
Ecology: adult—volant; melliferous, solitary
Reference: Michener, C.D. (1965). A classification of the bees of the Australian and South Pacific regions. *Bull. Am. Mus. Nat. Hist.* **130**: 1–362 (redescription, as *Leioproctus (Phenacolletes) mimus* (Cockerell, 1905)).

Trichocolletes Cockerell, 1912

Taxonomic decision for subgeneric arrangement: Michener, C.D. (1965). A classification of the bees of the Australian and South Pacific regions. *Bull. Am. Mus. Nat. Hist.* **130**: 1–362 [78].

Trichocolletes (Trichocolletes) Cockerell, 1912

Trichocolletes Cockerell, T.D.A. (1912). New and little-known bees. *Entomologist* **45**: 175–178 [176]. Type species: *Lamprocolletes venustus* Smith, 1862 by original designation.

Trichocolletes (Trichocolletes) aureotinctus (Cockerell, 1906)

Anthoglossa aureotincta Cockerell, T.D.A. (1906). Four interesting Australian bees, in the collection of the British Museum. *Entomologist* **39**: 15–18 [16]. Type data: holotype, BMNH Hym.17.a.397 ♀. Type locality: Perth, WA.

Distribution: SW coastal, WA; known only from type locality.
Ecology: adult—volant; melliferous, solitary.
Reference: Rayment, T. (1931). Bees in the collections of the Western Australian Museum and the Agricultural Department, Perth. *J. Proc. R. Soc. West. Aust.* **17**: 157–190 (additional female from type locality).

Trichocolletes (Trichocolletes) burnsi Michener, 1965

Trichocolletes (Trichocolletes) burnsi Michener, C.D. (1965). A classification of the bees of the Australian and South Pacific regions. *Bull. Am. Mus. Nat. Hist.* **130**: 1–362 [263]. Type data: holotype, NMV T–6265 ♀. Type locality: Wentworth Falls, NSW.

Distribution: SE coastal, NSW; known only from type locality.
Ecology: adult—volant; melliferous, solitary.

Trichocolletes (Trichocolletes) chrysostomus (Cockerell, 1929)

Paracolletes chrysostomus Cockerell, T.D.A. (1929). Bees in the Australian Museum collection. *Rec. Aust. Mus.* **17**: 199–243 [202]. Type data: syntypes, AM 2♂. Type locality: Eradu, WA.

Distribution: NW coastal, WA; known only from type locality.
Ecology: adult—volant; melliferous, solitary.

Trichocolletes (Trichocolletes) daviesiae Rayment, 1931

Trichocolletes daviesiae Rayment, T. (1931). Bees in the collections of the Western Australian Museum and the Agricultural Department, Perth. *J. Proc. R. Soc. West. Aust.* **17**: 157–190 [164]. Type data: holotype, ANIC ♂. Type locality: Heathmont, VIC.

Distribution: SE coastal, VIC; known only from type locality.
Ecology: adult—volant; melliferous, solitary, flower visiting record: *Daviesia* Sm. [Fabaceae], *Hardenbergia* Benth. [Fabaceae].
Reference: Rayment, T. (1935). *A Cluster of Bees. Sixty essays on the life-histories of Australian bees, with specific descriptions of over 100 new species, and an introduction by Professor E.F. Phillips, D.Ph., Cornell University, U.S.A.* Sydney : Endeavour Press 752 pp. (illustration).

Trichocolletes (Trichocolletes) dives (Cockerell, 1914)

Anthoglossa dives Cockerell, T.D.A. (1914). Descriptions and records of bees. LXI. *Ann. Mag. Nat. Hist. (8)***14**: 39–49 [39]. Type data: holotype, BMNH Hym.17.a.393 ♀. Type locality: Yallingup, WA.

Distribution: SW coastal, WA; known only from type locality.
Ecology: adult—volant; melliferous, solitary.

Trichocolletes (Trichocolletes) dowerinensis Rayment, 1931

Trichocolletes dowerinensis Rayment, T. (1931). Bees in the collections of the Western Australian Museum and the Agricultural Department, Perth. *J. Proc. R. Soc. West. Aust.* **17**: 157–190 [162].

Type data: holotype, ANIC ♂.
Type locality: Dowerin, WA.

Distribution: SW coastal, WA; known only from type locality.
Ecology: adult—volant; melliferous, solitary, flower visiting record: *Daviesia* Sm. [Fabaceae].
References: Rayment, T. (1934). Contributions to the fauna of Rottnest Island. VIII. Apoidea. With description of new species. *J. Proc. R. Soc. West. Aust.* **20**: 201–212 (illustration); Rayment, T. (1935). *A Cluster of Bees.* Sixty essays on the life-histories of Australian bees, with specific descriptions of over 100 new species, and an introduction by Professor E.F. Phillips, D.Ph., Cornell University, U.S.A. Sydney : Endeavour Press 752 pp. (illustration).

Trichocolletes *(Trichocolletes)* *eremophilae* Houston, 1990

Trichocolletes (Trichocolletes) eremophilae Houston, T.F. (1990). Descriptions of new paracolletine bees associated with flowers of *Eremophila* (Hymenoptera: Colletidae). *Rec. West. Aust. Mus.* **14**: 583–621 [615].
Type data: holotype, WAM 89/328 ♂*.
Type locality: East Yuna Reserve, 34 km WNW Mullewa, WA.

Distribution: SW coastal, NW coastal, WA; only published localities near Mullewa, near Meekatharra, near Mulline and near Nalbarra Homestead.
Ecology: adult—volant; melliferous, solitary, flower visiting record: *Eremophila* R.Br. [Myoporaceae].

Trichocolletes *(Trichocolletes)* *erythrurus* (Cockerell, 1914)

Paracolletes erythrurus Cockerell, T.D.A. (1914). Descriptions and records of bees. LX. *Ann. Mag. Nat. Hist.* (8)**14**: 1–13 [5].
Type data: holotype, BMNH Hym.17.a.456 ♀.
Type locality: Yallingup, WA.

Distribution: SW coastal, WA; known only from type locality.
Ecology: adult—volant; melliferous, solitary.

Trichocolletes (Trichocolletes) hackeri (Cockerell, 1913)

Anthoglossa hackeri Cockerell, T.D.A. (1913). Descriptions and records of bees. LIV. *Ann. Mag. Nat. Hist.* (8)**12**: 368–376 [373].
Type data: holotype, QM Hy/4080 ♀.
Type locality: Mt Tamborine (as Tambourine Mountain), QLD.

Distribution: NE coastal, Murray-Darling basin, QLD; only published localities Mt Tamborine and Bunya Mts.
Ecology: adult—volant; melliferous, solitary, flower visiting record: *Eucalyptus* L'Hérit. [Myrtaceae], *Solanum* L. [Solanaceae], *Verticordia* DC. [Myrtaceae].
References: Rayment, T. (1935). *A Cluster of Bees.*

Sixty essays on the life-histories of Australian bees, with specific descriptions of over 100 new species, and an introduction by Professor E.F. Phillips, D.Ph., Cornell University, U.S.A. Sydney : Endeavour Press 752 pp. (illustration); Michener, C.D. (1965). A classification of the bees of the Australian and South Pacific regions. *Bull. Am. Mus. Nat. Hist.* **130**: 1–362 (flower record).

Trichocolletes *(Trichocolletes)* *latifrons* (Cockerell, 1914)

Paracolletes latifrons Cockerell, T.D.A. (1914). Descriptions and records of bees. LXI. *Ann. Mag. Nat. Hist.* (8)**14**: 39–49 [41].
Type data: holotype, BMNH Hym.17.a.486 ♀.
Type locality: Coolangatta, QLD.

Distribution: NE coastal, QLD; known only from type locality.
Ecology: adult—volant; melliferous, solitary.

Trichocolletes *(Trichocolletes)* *lucidus* (Cockerell, 1929)

Paracolletes marginatus lucidus Cockerell, T.D.A. (1929). Bees in the Australian Museum collection. *Rec. Aust. Mus.* **17**: 199–243 [203].
Type data: holotype, AM ♀.
Type locality: Geraldton, WA.

Distribution: NW coastal, WA; known only from type locality.
Ecology: adult—volant; melliferous, solitary.
Reference: Michener, C.D. (1965). A classification of the bees of the Australian and South Pacific regions. *Bull. Am. Mus. Nat. Hist.* **130**: 1–362 [80] (taxonomy).

Trichocolletes *(Trichocolletes)* *marginatulus* Michener, 1965

Trichocolletes (Trichocolletes) marginatulus Michener, C.D. (1965). A classification of the bees of the Australian and South Pacific regions. *Bull. Am. Mus. Nat. Hist.* **130**: 1–362 [264].
Type data: holotype, ANIC ♂.
Type locality: Dunwich, QLD.

Distribution: NE coastal, QLD; known only from type locality.
Ecology: adult—volant; melliferous, solitary, flower visiting record: *Aotus* Smith [Fabaceae], *Dillwynia* Sm. [Fabaceae].

Trichocolletes *(Trichocolletes)* *marginatus* (Smith, 1879)

Paracolletes marginatus Smith, F. (1879). *Descriptions of New Species of Hymenoptera in the Collection of the British Museum.* London : British Museum xxi 240 pp. [4].
Type data: lectotype, BMNH Hym.17.a.417 ♂.
Subsequent designation: Cockerell, T.D.A. (1913). Descriptions and records of bees. L. *Ann. Mag. Nat. Hist.* (8)**11**: 273–283 [274]; Cardale, J.C., this work, interprets

Cockerell's incorrect inference of holotype as a lectotype designation (Art. 74, ICZN 1985).
Type locality: QLD.

Distribution: SE coastal, Murray-Darling basin, SW coastal, QLD, VIC, WA, TAS.
Ecology: adult—volant; melliferous, solitary.
References: Cockerell, T.D.A. (1913). Descriptions and records of bees. L. *Ann. Mag. Nat. Hist. (8)*11: 273–283 (taxonomy); Cockerell, T.D.A. (1914). Some Tasmanian bees. *Entomologist* 47: 305–308 (distribution); Rayment, T. (1931). Bees in the collections of the Western Australian Museum and the Agricultural Department, Perth. *J. Proc. R. Soc. West. Aust.* 17: 157–190 (distribution).

Trichocolletes (Trichocolletes) maximus (Cockerell, 1929)

Paracolletes maximus Cockerell, T.D.A. (1929). Bees from the Australian region. *Am. Mus. Novit.* 346: 1–18 [9].
Type data: holotype, AMNH ♂*.
Type locality: VIC.

Distribution: VIC; known only from type locality, exact locality unknown.
Ecology: adult—volant; melliferous, solitary.

Trichocolletes (Trichocolletes) multipectinatus Houston, 1990

Trichocolletes (Trichocolletes) multipectinatus Houston, T.F. (1990). Descriptions of new paracolletine bees associated with flowers of *Eremophila* (Hymenoptera: Colletidae). *Rec. West. Aust. Mus.* 14: 583–621 [618].
Type data: holotype, WAM 87/1459 ♂*.
Type locality: Meleya Well, Thundelarra Station, WA.

Distribution: S Gulfs, W plateau, SW coastal, NW coastal, SA, WA; only published localities North Middleback Range, Lake Gilles National Park, Thundelarra Station, near Mt Jackson and near Mulline.
Ecology: adult—volant; melliferous, solitary, flower visiting record: *Eremophila* R.Br. [Myoporaceae].

Trichocolletes (Trichocolletes) nigroclypeatus Rayment, 1929

Trichocolletes nigroclypeatus Rayment, T. (1929). The plumed bees. *Vict. Nat.* 46: 155–162 [160].
Type data: holotype, ANIC ♀.
Type locality: Daylesford, VIC.

Distribution: SE coastal, VIC; only published localities Daylesford and Mt Macedon.
Ecology: larva—sedentary : adult—volant; melliferous, solitary, flower visiting record: *Daviesia* Sm. [Fabaceae].
References: Rayment, T. (1931). Bees in the collections of the Western Australian Museum and the Agricultural Department, Perth. *J. Proc. R. Soc. West. Aust.* 17: 157–190 (taxonomy); Rayment, T. (1935). *A Cluster of Bees.* Sixty essays on the life-histories

of Australian bees, with specific descriptions of over 100 new species, and an introduction by Professor E.F. Phillips, D.Ph., Cornell University, U.S.A. Sydney : Endeavour Press 752 pp. (biology).

Trichocolletes (Trichocolletes) rufibasis (Cockerell, 1929)

Paracolletes rufibasis Cockerell, T.D.A. (1929). Bees in the Australian Museum collection. *Rec. Aust. Mus.* 17: 199–243 [204].
Type data: syntypes, AM 2♂.
Type locality: Eradu, WA.

Distribution: NW coastal, WA; known only from type locality.
Ecology: adult—volant; melliferous, solitary.

Trichocolletes (Trichocolletes) rufopilosus (Rayment, 1935)

Paracolletes rufopilosus Rayment, T. (1935). *A Cluster of Bees.* Sixty essays on the life-histories of Australian bees, with specific descriptions of over 100 new species, and an introduction by Professor E.F. Phillips, D.Ph., Cornell University, U.S.A. Sydney : Endeavour Press 752 pp. [673].
Type data: holotype, ANIC ♂.
Type locality: Yelbeni (as Telbeni), WA.

Distribution: SW coastal, WA; only published localities Yelbeni and Swan River.
Ecology: adult—volant; melliferous, solitary.

Trichocolletes (Trichocolletes) rufus (Rayment, 1930)

Paracolletes rufa Rayment, T. (1930). New and remarkable bees. *Proc. R. Soc. Vict.* 43: 42–61 [53].
Type data: holotype, ANIC ♂.
Type locality: Purnong, SA.

Distribution: Murray-Darling basin, SA; known only from type locality.
Ecology: adult—volant; melliferous, solitary.
Reference: Rayment, T. (1935). *A Cluster of Bees.* Sixty essays on the life-histories of Australian bees, with specific descriptions of over 100 new species, and an introduction by Professor E.F. Phillips, D.Ph., Cornell University, U.S.A. Sydney : Endeavour Press 752 pp. (illustration).

Trichocolletes (Trichocolletes) sericeus (Smith, 1862)

Anthoglossa sericea Smith, F. (1862). Descriptions of new species of Australian Hymenoptera, and of a species of *Formica* from New Zealand. *Trans. Entomol. Soc. Lond. (3)*1: 53–62 [59].
Type data: holotype, BMNH Hym.17.a.395 ♀.
Type locality: Australia.

Distribution: Murray-Darling basin, VIC; only published locality Grampians.
Ecology: adult—volant; melliferous, solitary.

Reference: Rayment, T. (1935). *A Cluster of Bees.* Sixty essays on the life-histories of Australian bees, with specific descriptions of over 100 new species, and an introduction by Professor E.F. Phillips, D.Ph., Cornell University, U.S.A. Sydney : Endeavour Press 752 pp. (description of male).

Trichocolletes (Trichocolletes) tenuiculus Rayment, 1931

Trichocolletes tenuiculus Rayment, T. (1931). Bees in the collections of the Western Australian Museum and the Agricultural Department, Perth. *J. Proc. R. Soc. West. Aust.* **17**: 157–190 [162].
Type data: holotype, ANIC ♂.
Type locality: Canowindra, NSW.

Distribution: Murray-Darling basin, NSW; known only from type locality.
Ecology: adult—volant; flower visiting record: *Daviesia* Sm. [Fabaceae], *Hardenbergia* Benth. [Fabaceae].
References: Rayment, T. (1934). Contributions to the fauna of Rottnest Island. VIII. Apoidea. With description of new species. *J. Proc. R. Soc. West. Aust.* **20**: 201–212 (illustration); Rayment, T. (1935). *A Cluster of Bees.* Sixty essays on the life-histories of Australian bees, with specific descriptions of over 100 new species, and an introduction by Professor E.F. Phillips, D.Ph., Cornell University, U.S.A. Sydney : Endeavour Press 752 pp. (illustration).

Trichocolletes (Trichocolletes) venustus (Smith, 1862)

Lamprocolletes venustus Smith, F. (1862). Descriptions of new species of Australian Hymenoptera, and of a species of *Formica* from New Zealand. *Trans. Entomol. Soc. Lond.* (3)**1**: 53–62 [57].
Type data: holotype, BMNH Hym.17.a.503 ♂.
Type locality: Lower Plenty, VIC (as Lower Plenty, SA).

Distribution: NE coastal, SE coastal, Murray-Darling basin, SW coastal, W plateau, QLD, NSW, VIC, SA, WA, TAS.
Ecology: larva—sedentary : adult—volant; melliferous, solitary, flower visiting record: *Aotus* Smith [Fabaceae], *Daviesia* Sm. [Fabaceae], *Dillwynia* Sm. [Fabaceae], *Hardenbergia* Benth. [Fabaceae], *Hovea* R.Br. [Fabaceae], *Leptospermum* Forster & G.Forster [Myrtaceae], *Mirbelia* Sm. [Fabaceae], *Pultenaea* Sm. [Fabaceae]
References: Cockerell, T.D.A. (1907). On a collection of Australian and Asiatic bees. *Bull. Am. Mus. Nat. Hist.* **23**: 221–236 (distribution); Cockerell, T.D.A. (1913). Descriptions and records of bees. L. *Ann. Mag. Nat. Hist.* (8)**11**: 273–283 (description of female); Hacker, H. (1918). Entomological contributions. *Mem. Qd Mus.* **6**: 106–111 pls 31–32 (flower record); Rayment, T. (1929). The plumed bees. *Vict. Nat.* **46**: 155–162 (biology); Rayment, T. (1931). Bees in the collections of the Western Australian

Museum and the Agricultural Department, Perth. *J. Proc. R. Soc. West. Aust.* **17**: 157–190 (distribution); Rayment, T. (1935). *A Cluster of Bees.* Sixty essays on the life-histories of Australian bees, with specific descriptions of over 100 new species, and an introduction by Professor E.F. Phillips, D.Ph., Cornell University, U.S.A. Sydney : Endeavour Press 752 pp. (biology); Rayment, T. (1939). Bees from the high lands of New South Wales and Victoria. *Aust. Zool.* **9**: 263–294 (flower record); Rayment, T. (1948). Notes on remarkable wasps and bees. With specific descriptions. *Aust. Zool.* **11**: 238–254 (illustration); Michener, C.D. (1965). A classification of the bees of the Australian and South Pacific regions. *Bull. Am. Mus. Nat. Hist.* **130**: 1–362 (flower record); De Lello, E. (1971). Adnexal glands of the sting apparatus of bees : anatomy and histology, I (Hymenoptera : Colletidae and Andrenidae). *J. Kansas Entomol. Soc.* **44**: 5–13 (sting glands).

Trichocolletes (Callocolletes) Michener, 1965

Callocolletes Michener, C.D. (1965). A classification of the bees of the Australian and South Pacific regions. *Bull. Am. Mus. Nat. Hist.* **130**: 1–362 [80] [proposed with subgeneric rank in *Trichocolletes* Cockerell, 1912]. Type species: *Trichocolletes (Callocolletes) pulcherrimus* Michener, 1965 by original designation.

Trichocolletes (Callocolletes) pulcherrimus Michener, 1965

Trichocolletes (Callocolletes) pulcherrimus Michener, C.D. (1965). A classification of the bees of the Australian and South Pacific regions. *Bull. Am. Mus. Nat. Hist.* **130**: 1–362 [265].
Type data: holotype, WAM 65–727 ♂.
Type locality: Narrogin, WA.

Distribution: SW coastal, WA; only published localities Narrogin, 10 miles S Perenjori and Beverley.
Ecology: adult—volant; melliferous, solitary.

Incertae sedis

Dasycolletes chalceus Friese, H. (1924). Ueber die Bienen Australiens. *Konowia* **3**: 216–249 [218] [types not seen, description inadequate for placement].
Type data: syntypes (probable) (number of specimens unknown), AMNH ♀*.
Type locality: Sydney, NSW.

Dasycolletes crassipes Friese, H. (1924). Ueber die Bienen Australiens. *Konowia* **3**: 216–249 [218] [types not seen, description inadequate for placement].
Type data: syntypes (probable) (number of specimens unknown), AMNH ♀*.
Type locality: Adelaide, SA.

Leioproctus frontalis Smith, F. (1853). *Catalogue of Hymenopterous Insects in the Collection of the British Museum.* Part I. Andrenidae and Apidae. London : British Museum 197 pp. [9] [types not seen, description inadequate for placement; Michener, C.D. (1965). A classification of the bees of the Australian and South Pacific regions. *Bull. Am. Mus. Nat. Hist.* **130**: 1–362 (37) states 'The "type" in

the BM is false and is in fact the type of *waterhousei* Cockerell.'].
Type data: syntypes, BMNH ♂♀*.
Type locality: Australia (as New Holland).

EURYGLOSSINAE

Argohesma Exley, 1969

Argohesma Exley, E.M. (1969). *Argohesma*—a new genus of Australian bees (Apoidea : Colletidae). *Aust. J. Zool.* **17**: 527–534 [528]. Type species: *Argohesma eremica* Exley, 1969 by original designation.

Argohesma clara Exley, 1974

Argohesma clara Exley, E.M. (1974). A contribution to our knowledge of the bee fauna (Colletidae : Euryglossinae) of remote areas of Australia with descriptions of new species. *Proc. R. Soc. Qd* **85**: 95–110 [100].
Type data: holotype, QM T7157 ♀.
Type locality: NW Coastal Highway, 7 miles NE Karratha, WA.

Distribution: NW coastal, WA; only published localities Karratha and vicinity.
Ecology: adult—volant; melliferous, solitary, flower visiting record: *Eucalyptus* L'Hérit. [Myrtaceae].

Argohesma deloschema Exley, 1969

Argohesma deloschema Exley, E.M. (1969). *Argohesma* —a new genus of Australian bees (Apoidea : Colletidae). *Aust. J. Zool.* **17**: 527–534 [530].
Type data: holotype, QM T7085 ♀.
Type locality: Oxenford, QLD.

Distribution: NE coastal, SE coastal, QLD, VIC; only published localities Oxenford and Mt Yule, Healesville.
Ecology: adult—volant; melliferous, solitary, flower visiting record: *Eucalyptus* L'Hérit. [Myrtaceae].

Argohesma eremica Exley, 1969

Argohesma eremica Exley, E.M. (1969). *Argohesma*—a new genus of Australian bees (Apoidea : Colletidae). *Aust. J. Zool.* **17**: 527–534 [529].
Type data: holotype, ANIC ♀.
Type locality: Macdonald Downs, NT.

Distribution: N Gulf, Murray-Darling basin, Lake Eyre basin, QLD, VIC, SA, NT; only published localities Mica Creek (near Mt Isa), Gunbower, Markaranka, Morgan and Macdonald Downs.
Ecology: adult—volant; melliferous, solitary, flower visiting record: *Eucalyptus* L'Hérit. [Myrtaceae].

Argohesma euxesta Exley, 1969

Argohesma euxesta Exley, E.M. (1969). *Argohesma*—a new genus of Australian bees (Apoidea : Colletidae). *Aust. J. Zool.* **17**: 527–534 [531].
Type data: holotype, QM T7084 ♀.

Type locality: Kimberley Research Station, Wyndham, WA.

Distribution: N coastal, WA; known only from type locality.
Ecology: adult—volant; melliferous, solitary.

Argohesma lucida Exley, 1974

Argohesma lucida Exley, E.M. (1974). A contribution to our knowledge of the bee fauna (Colletidae : Euryglossinae) of remote areas of Australia with descriptions of new species. *Proc. R. Soc. Qd* **85**: 95–110 [99].
Type data: holotype, QM T7155 ♀.
Type locality: 50 miles W Coolgardie, WA.

Distribution: W plateau, WA; only published localities Coolgardie area.
Ecology: adult—volant; melliferous, solitary, flower visiting record: *Eucalyptus* L'Hérit. [Myrtaceae].

Argohesma lukinsiana Exley, 1969

Argohesma lukinsiana Exley, E.M. (1969). *Argohesma*—a new genus of Australian bees (Apoidea : Colletidae). *Aust. J. Zool.* **17**: 527–534 [531].
Type data: holotype, QM T7086 ♀.
Type locality: Kimberley Research Station, Wyndham, WA.

Distribution: N coastal, WA; known only from type locality.
Ecology: adult—volant; melliferous, solitary, flower visiting record: *Eucalyptus* L'Hérit. [Myrtaceae].

Argohesma megacephala Exley, 1974

Argohesma megacephala Exley, E.M. (1974). A contribution to our knowledge of the bee fauna (Colletidae : Euryglossinae) of remote areas of Australia with descriptions of new species. *Proc. R. Soc. Qd* **85**: 95–110 [97].
Type data: holotype, QM T7151 ♀.
Type locality: NW Coastal Highway, 7 miles NE Karratha, WA.

Distribution: NW coastal, WA; known only from type locality.
Ecology: adult—volant; melliferous, solitary, flower visiting record: *Eucalyptus* L'Hérit. [Myrtaceae].

Argohesma nukarnensis Exley, 1974

Argohesma nukarnensis Exley, E.M. (1974). A contribution to our knowledge of the bee fauna (Colletidae : Euryglossinae) of remote areas of Australia with descriptions of new species. *Proc. R. Soc. Qd* **85**: 95–110 [98].
Type data: holotype, QM T7153 ♀.
Type locality: 10 miles S Coolgardie, WA.

Distribution: SW coastal, W plateau, WA; only published localities near Coolgardie, Kalgoorlie, Nukarni, Merredin and Southern Cross.
Ecology: adult—volant; melliferous, solitary, flower visiting record: *Eucalyptus* L'Hérit. [Myrtaceae].

Brachyhesma Michener, 1965

Taxonomic decision for subgeneric arrangement: Exley, E.M. (1977). The Australian genus *Brachyhesma* (Apoidea : Colletidae) revised and reviewed. *Aust. J. Zool. Suppl. Ser.* **53**: 1–54 [2].

Generic reference: Exley, E.M. (1968). Revision of the genus *Brachyhesma* Michener (Apoidea : Colletidae). *Aust. J. Zool.* **16**: 167–201.

Brachyhesma (Brachyhesma) Michener, 1965

Brachyhesma Michener, C.D. (1965). A classification of the bees of the Australian and South Pacific regions. *Bull. Am. Mus. Nat. Hist.* **130**: 1–362 [112]. Type species: *Euryglossina sulphurella* Cockerell, 1913 by original designation.

Brachyhesma (Brachyhesma) angularis Exley, 1977

Brachyhesma (Brachyhesma) angularis Exley, E.M. (1977). The Australian genus *Brachyhesma* (Apoidea : Colletidae) revised and reviewed. *Aust. J. Zool. Suppl. Ser.* **53**: 1–54 [24].
Type data: holotype, QM T7708 ♂.
Type locality: 9 km E Tennant Creek, NT.

Distribution: Lake Eyre basin, NT; only published locality near Tennant Creek.
Ecology: adult—volant; melliferous, solitary, flower visiting record: *Eucalyptus* L'Hérit. [Myrtaceae].

Brachyhesma (Brachyhesma) antennata Exley, 1977

Brachyhesma (Brachyhesma) antennata Exley, E.M. (1977). The Australian genus *Brachyhesma* (Apoidea : Colletidae) revised and reviewed. *Aust. J. Zool. Suppl. Ser.* **53**: 1–54 [25].
Type data: holotype, QM T7710 ♂.
Type locality: Great Northern Highway, 9 km N Newman turnoff, WA.

Distribution: NW coastal, WA; only published localities Newman and vicinity, and Millstream.
Ecology: adult—volant; melliferous, solitary, flower visiting record: *Eucalyptus* L'Hérit. [Myrtaceae].

Brachyhesma (Brachyhesma) apicalis Exley, 1969

Brachyhesma (Brachyhesma) apicalis Exley, E.M. (1969). A new species of *Brachyhesma* (Apoidea : Colletidae). *J. Aust. Entomol. Soc.* **8**: 134–136 [134].
Type data: holotype, QM T7307 ♂.
Type locality: Charleville, QLD.

Distribution: Murray-Darling basin, (NW coastal), QLD, (WA); only published localities Charleville and ?Millstream.
Ecology: adult—volant; melliferous, solitary, flower visiting record: *Eucalyptus* L'Hérit. [Myrtaceae].
Reference: Exley, E.M. (1974). A contribution to our knowledge of the bee fauna (Colletidae : Euryglossinae) of remote areas of Australia with de-

scriptions of new species. *Proc. R. Soc. Qd* **85**: 95–110 (distribution).

Brachyhesma (Brachyhesma) aurata Exley, 1977

Brachyhesma (Brachyhesma) aurata Exley, E.M. (1977). The Australian genus *Brachyhesma* (Apoidea : Colletidae) revised and reviewed. *Aust. J. Zool. Suppl. Ser.* **53**: 1–54 [26].
Type data: holotype, QM T7718 ♂.
Type locality: Newman, WA.

Distribution: NW coastal, WA; known only from type locality.
Ecology: adult—volant; melliferous, solitary, flower visiting record: *Eucalyptus* L'Hérit. [Myrtaceae].

Brachyhesma (Brachyhesma) barrowensis Exley, 1968

Brachyhesma (Brachyhesma) barrowensis Exley, E.M. (1968). Revision of the genus *Brachyhesma* Michener (Apoidea : Colletidae). *Aust. J. Zool.* **16**: 167–201 [184].
Type data: holotype, ANIC ♂.
Type locality: 14 miles N Barrow Creek, NT.

Distribution: Murray-Darling basin, Lake Eyre basin, NW coastal, NSW, NT, WA.
Ecology: adult—volant; melliferous, solitary, flower visiting record: *Eucalyptus* L'Hérit. [Myrtaceae].
References: Exley, E.M. (1974). A contribution to our knowledge of the bee fauna (Colletidae : Euryglossinae) of remote areas of Australia with descriptions of new species. *Proc. R. Soc. Qd* **85**: 95–110 (distribution); Exley, E.M. (1975). New species and records of *Brachyhesma* Michener (Apoidea : Colletidae : Euryglossinae). *J. Aust. Entomol. Soc.* **14**: 139–144 (distribution).

Brachyhesma (Brachyhesma) carnarvonensis Exley, 1977

Brachyhesma (Brachyhesma) carnarvonensis Exley, E.M. (1977). The Australian genus *Brachyhesma* (Apoidea : Colletidae) revised and reviewed. *Aust. J. Zool. Suppl. Ser.* **53**: 1–54 [28].
Type data: holotype, QM T7706 ♂.
Type locality: 16 km E Carnarvon, WA.

Distribution: NW coastal, WA; only published localities near Carnarvon and Newman.
Ecology: adult—volant; melliferous, solitary, flower visiting record: *Eucalyptus* L'Hérit. [Myrtaceae].

Brachyhesma (Brachyhesma) dedari Exley, 1968

Brachyhesma (Brachyhesma) dedari Exley, E.M. (1968). Revision of the genus *Brachyhesma* Michener (Apoidea : Colletidae). *Aust. J. Zool.* **16**: 167–201 [186].
Type data: holotype, WAM 54–736 ♂.
Type locality: Dedari, 40 miles W Coolgardie, WA.

Distribution: SW coastal, W plateau, NW coastal, WA.
Ecology: adult—volant; melliferous, solitary, flower

visiting record: *Eucalyptus* L'Hérit. [Myrtaceae].
Reference: Exley, E.M. (1974). A contribution to our knowledge of the bee fauna (Colletidae : Euryglossinae) of remote areas of Australia with descriptions of new species. *Proc. R. Soc. Qd* **85**: 95–110 (distribution).

Brachyhesma (Brachyhesma) femoralis Exley, 1977

Brachyhesma (Brachyhesma) femoralis Exley, E.M. (1977). The Australian genus *Brachyhesma* (Apoidea : Colletidae) revised and reviewed. *Aust. J. Zool. Suppl. Ser.* **53**: 1–54 [29].
Type data: holotype, QM T7712 ♂.
Type locality: 18 km S 'Cataby', via Dandaragan, WA.

Distribution: SW coastal, NW coastal, WA; only published localities near "Cataby" via Dandaragan and near Dongara.
Ecology: adult—volant; melliferous, solitary, flower visiting record: *Eucalyptus* L'Hérit. [Myrtaceae].

Brachyhesma (Brachyhesma) grossopedalis Exley, 1977

Brachyhesma (Brachyhesma) grossopedalis Exley, E.M. (1977). The Australian genus *Brachyhesma* (Apoidea : Colletidae) revised and reviewed. *Aust. J. Zool. Suppl. Ser.* **53**: 1–54 [31].
Type data: holotype, QM T7714 ♂.
Type locality: North-west Coastal Highway, 12 km N Murchison River Crossing, WA.

Distribution: NW coastal, WA; only published localities N of Murchison River Crossing and "Wannoo" via Carnarvon.
Ecology: adult—volant; melliferous, solitary, flower visiting record: *Eucalyptus* L'Hérit. [Myrtaceae].

Brachyhesma (Brachyhesma) houstoni Exley, 1968

Brachyhesma (Brachyhesma) houstoni Exley, E.M. (1968). Three new species of *Brachyhesma* (Apoidea : Colletidae). *J. Aust. Entomol. Soc.* **7**: 135–141 [138].
Type data: holotype, QM T7090 ♂.
Type locality: Kongal, SA.

Distribution: Murray-Darling basin, SA; known only from type locality.
Ecology: adult—volant; melliferous, solitary.
Reference: Exley, E.M. (1969). A new species of *Brachyhesma* (Apoidea : Colletidae). *J. Aust. Entomol. Soc.* **8**: 134–136 (taxonomy).

Brachyhesma (Brachyhesma) hypoxantha (Rayment, 1934)

Euryglossina hypoxantha Rayment, T. (1934). Contributions to the fauna of Rottnest Island. VIII. Apoidea. With description of new species. *J. Proc. R. Soc. West. Aust.* **20**: 201–212 [202] [misspelled as *Euryglossina hypozantha* on p. 203].
Type data: holotype, ANIC ♀.
Type locality: Rottnest Is., WA.

Brachyhesma (Microhesma) dichaeta Michener, C.D. (1965). A classification of the bees of the Australian and South Pacific regions. *Bull. Am. Mus. Nat. Hist.* **130**: 1–362 [287].
Type data: holotype, WAM 33–662 ♀.
Type locality: Rottnest Is., WA.

Taxonomic decision for synonymy: Exley, E.M. (1968). Revision of the genus *Brachyhesma* Michener (Apoidea : Colletidae). *Aust. J. Zool.* **16**: 167–201 [188].

Distribution: Murray-Darling basin, S Gulfs, SW coastal, SA, WA; only published localities Meningie, Purnong, North Beach (Wallaroo) and Rottnest Is.
Ecology: adult—volant; melliferous, solitary, flower visiting record: *Leptospermum* Forster & G.Forster [Myrtaceae], *Melaleuca* L. [Myrtaceae].
Reference: Michener, C.D. (1965). A classification of the bees of the Australian and South Pacific regions. *Bull. Am. Mus. Nat. Hist.* **130**: 1–362 [114] (as *Brachyhesma (Microhesma) hypoxantha* (Rayment, 1934)).

Brachyhesma (Brachyhesma) isae Exley, 1977

Brachyhesma (Brachyhesma) isae Exley, E.M. (1977). The Australian genus *Brachyhesma* (Apoidea : Colletidae) revised and reviewed. *Aust. J. Zool. Suppl. Ser.* **53**: 1–54 [34].
Type data: holotype, QM T7720 ♂.
Type locality: 6 km E Mt Isa, QLD.

Distribution: N Gulf, QLD; only published localities near Mt Isa.
Ecology: adult—volant; melliferous, solitary, flower visiting record: *Eucalyptus* L'Hérit. [Myrtaceae], *Tristania* R.Br. [Myrtaceae].

Brachyhesma (Brachyhesma) longicornis Exley, 1968

Brachyhesma (Brachyhesma) longicornis Exley, E.M. (1968). Revision of the genus *Brachyhesma* Michener (Apoidea : Colletidae). *Aust. J. Zool.* **16**: 167–201 [190].
Type data: holotype, ANIC ♂.
Type locality: Macdonald Downs, NT.

Distribution: Lake Eyre basin, NT; known only from type locality.
Ecology: adult—volant; melliferous, solitary.
Reference: Exley, E.M. (1974). A contribution to our knowledge of the bee fauna (Colletidae : Euryglossinae) of remote areas of Australia with descriptions of new species. *Proc. R. Soc. Qd* **85**: 95–110 (distribution).

Brachyhesma (Brachyhesma) matarankae Exley, 1977

Brachyhesma (Brachyhesma) matarankae Exley, E.M. (1977). The Australian genus *Brachyhesma* (Apoidea : Colletidae) revised and reviewed. *Aust. J. Zool. Suppl. Ser.* **53**: 1–54 [34].
Type data: holotype, QM T7716 ♂.
Type locality: 8 km N Mataranka, NT.

Distribution: N Gulf, Lake Eyre basin, NT; only published localities near Mataranka, Elsey Cemetery, Daly Waters and Barrow Creek.

Ecology: adult—volant; melliferous, solitary, flower visiting record: *Eucalyptus* L'Hérit. [Myrtaceae].

Brachyhesma (Brachyhesma) monteithae Exley, 1975

Brachyhesma (Brachyhesma) monteithae Exley, E.M. (1975). New species and records of *Brachyhesma* Michener (Apoidea : Colletidae : Euryglossinae). *J. Aust. Entomol. Soc.* **14**: 139–144 [143].
Type data: holotype, QM T7349 ♂.
Type locality: Gregory River at Gregory Downs, QLD.

Distribution: N Gulf, QLD; known only from type locality.

Ecology: adult—volant; melliferous, solitary.

Brachyhesma (Brachyhesma) morvenensis Exley, 1974

Brachyhesma (Brachyhesma) morvenensis Exley, E.M. (1974). A contribution to our knowledge of the bee fauna (Colletidae : Euryglossinae) of remote areas of Australia with descriptions of new species. *Proc. R. Soc. Qd* **85**: 95–110 [103].
Type data: holotype, QM T7159 ♂.
Type locality: 7 miles W Charleville, QLD.

Distribution: Murray-Darling basin, QLD; only published localities Charleville and vicinity, and Morven.

Ecology: adult—volant; melliferous, solitary, flower visiting record: *Eucalyptus* L'Hérit. [Myrtaceae].

Reference: Exley, E.M. (1977). The Australian genus *Brachyhesma* (Apoidea : Colletidae) revised and reviewed. *Aust. J. Zool. Suppl. Ser.* **53**: 1–54 (taxonomy).

Brachyhesma (Brachyhesma) nigricornis Exley, 1975

Brachyhesma (Brachyhesma) nigricornis Exley, E.M. (1975). New species and records of *Brachyhesma* Michener (Apoidea : Colletidae : Euryglossinae). *J. Aust. Entomol. Soc.* **14**: 139–144 [143].
Type data: holotype, SAMA ♂*.
Type locality: Billiatt National Park, SA.

Distribution: Murray-Darling basin, N Gulf, SA, NT; only published localities Billiatt National Park and Mataranka.

Ecology: adult—volant; melliferous, solitary, flower visiting record: *Eucalyptus* L'Hérit. [Myrtaceae].

Reference: Exley, E.M. (1977). The Australian genus *Brachyhesma* (Apoidea : Colletidae) revised and reviewed. *Aust. J. Zool. Suppl. Ser.* **53**: 1–54 (distribution).

Brachyhesma (Brachyhesma) perlutea (Cockerell, 1916)

Euryglossina sulphurella perlutea Cockerell, T.D.A. (1916). Descriptions and records of bees. LXXII. *Ann. Mag. Nat. Hist.* (8)**17**: 428–435 [434].
Type data: holotype, BMNH Hym.17.a.295 ♂.
Type locality: Kalamunda, WA.

Distribution: S Gulfs, SW coastal, W plateau, NW coastal, SA, WA.

Ecology: larva—sedentary : adult—volant; melliferous, solitary, nest in soil, flower visiting record: *Eucalyptus* L'Hérit. [Myrtaceae].

References: Michener, C.D. (1965). A classification of the bees of the Australian and South Pacific regions. *Bull. Am. Mus. Nat. Hist.* **130**: 1–362 [114] (taxonomy); Exley, E.M. (1968). Revision of the genus *Brachyhesma* Michener (Apoidea : Colletidae). *Aust.J.Zool.* **16**: 167–201 (redescription); Houston, T.F. (1969). Observations on the nests and behaviour of some euryglossine bees (Hymenoptera : Colletidae). *J. Aust. Entomol. Soc.* **8**: 1–10 (biology); Exley, E.M. (1974). A contribution to our knowledge of the bee fauna (Colletidae : Euryglossinae) of remote areas of Australia with descriptions of new species. *Proc. R. Soc. Qd* **85**: 95–110 (distribution).

Brachyhesma (Brachyhesma) renneri Exley, 1968

Brachyhesma (Brachyhesma) renneri Exley, E.M. (1968). Revision of the genus *Brachyhesma* Michener (Apoidea : Colletidae). *Aust. J. Zool.* **16**: 167–201 [194].
Type data: holotype, ANIC ♂.
Type locality: 23 miles N Renner Springs, NT.

Distribution: N Gulf, NT; known only from type locality.

Ecology: adult—volant; melliferous, solitary, flower visiting record: *Eucalyptus* L'Hérit. [Myrtaceae].

Reference: Exley, E.M. (1974). A contribution to our knowledge of the bee fauna (Colletidae : Euryglossinae) of remote areas of Australia with descriptions of new species. *Proc. R. Soc. Qd* **85**: 95–110 (distribution).

Brachyhesma (Brachyhesma) sulphurella (Cockerell, 1913)

Euryglossina sulphurella Cockerell, T.D.A. (1913). Descriptions and records of bees. LI. *Ann. Mag. Nat. Hist.* (8)**11**: 387–394 [389].
Type data: holotype, BMNH Hym.17.a.296 ♀.
Type locality: Purnong, near Murray River, SA.

Euryglossina bicolor Rayment, T. (1928). A new prosopoid bee. *Vict. Nat.* **45**: 97–98 [fig. 4 on p. 97] [name introduced and used only as a caption on p. 98 to fig. on p. 97; the illustration of *Euryglossina bicolor* Rayment, 1928 was published again in 1935, but with the caption as *Euryglossina sulphurella* var. *colorata*; Rayment, T. (1935). *A Cluster of Bees*. Sixty essays on the life-histories of Australian bees, with specific descriptions of over 100 new species, and an introduction by Professor E.F. Phillips,

D.Ph., Cornell University, U.S.A. Sydney : Endeavour Press 752 pp. states 'This variety of *sulphurella*, appeared in the "Victorian Naturalist" August, 1928, without the description.'; the holotype is labelled *Euryglossina sulphurella colorata*].
Type data: holotype, ANIC ♀.
Type locality: Purnong, SA.

Euryglossina sulphurella colorata Rayment, T. (1935). *A Cluster of Bees.* Sixty essays on the life-histories of Australian bees, with specific descriptions of over 100 new species, and an introduction by Professor E.F. Phillips, D.Ph., Cornell University, U.S.A. Sydney : Endeavour Press 752 pp. [651] [junior objective synonym of *Euryglossina bicolor* Rayment, 1928].

Taxonomic decision for synonymy: Exley, E.M. (1968). Revision of the genus *Brachyhesma* Michener (Apoidea : Colletidae). *Aust. J. Zool.* **16**: 167–201 [195].

Distribution: Murray-Darling basin, W plateau, SW coastal, NSW, VIC, SA, WA.
Ecology: adult—volant; melliferous, solitary, flower visiting record: *Eucalyptus* L'Hérit. [Myrtaceac].
Reference: Exley, E.M. (1977). The Australian genus *Brachyhesma* (Apoidea : Colletidae) revised and reviewed. *Aust. J. Zool. Suppl. Ser.* **53**: 1–54 (distribution).

Brachyhesma (Brachyhesma) triangularis Exley, 1977

Brachyhesma (Brachyhesma) triangularis Exley, E.M. (1977). The Australian genus *Brachyhesma* (Apoidea : Colletidae) revised and reviewed. *Aust. J. Zool. Suppl. Ser.* **53**: 1–54 [37].
Type data: holotype, QM T7705 ♂.
Type locality: 13 km S Carnarvon, WA.

Distribution: NW coastal, WA; known only from type locality.
Ecology: adult—volant; melliferous, solitary, flower visiting record: *Eucalyptus* L'Hérit. [Myrtaceae].

Brachyhesma (Brachyhesma) wyndhami Exley, 1968

Brachyhesma (Brachyhesma) wyndhami Exley, E.M. (1968). Revision of the genus *Brachyhesma* Michener (Apoidea : Colletidae). *Aust. J. Zool.* **16**: 167–201 [198].
Type data: holotype, QM T6664 ♂.
Type locality: Wyndham, Kimberley Research Station (as K.R.S.), WA.

Distribution: NW coastal, N coastal, WA; only published localities Wyndham, Newman and Carnarvon.
Ecology: adult—volant; melliferous, solitary, flower visiting record: *Eucalyptus* L'Hérit. [Myrtaceae].
References: Exley, E.M. (1974). A contribution to our knowledge of the bee fauna (Colletidae : Euryglossinae) of remote areas of Australia with descriptions of new species. *Proc. R. Soc. Qd* **85**: 95–110 (distribution); Exley, E.M. (1977). The Australian genus *Brachyhesma* (Apoidea : Colletidae) re-

vised and reviewed. *Aust. J. Zool. Suppl. Ser.* **53**: 1–54 (illustration).

Brachyhesma (Anomalohesma) Exley, 1977

Anomalohesma Exley, E.M. (1977). The Australian genus *Brachyhesma* (Apoidea : Colletidae) revised and reviewed. *Aust. J. Zool. Suppl. Ser.* **53**: 1–54 [39] [proposed with subgeneric rank in *Brachyhesma* Michener, 1965]. Type species: *Brachyhesma (Anomalohesma) scapata* Exley, 1977 by original designation.

Brachyhesma (Anomalohesma) scapata Exley, 1977

Brachyhesma (Anomalohesma) scapata Exley, E.M. (1977). The Australian genus *Brachyhesma* (Apoidea : Colletidae) revised and reviewed. *Aust. J. Zool. Suppl. Ser.* **53**: 1–54 [39].
Type data: holotype, QM T7721 ♂.
Type locality: Rainbow Beach Road about 30 miles NE Gympie, QLD.

Distribution: NE coastal, QLD; known only from type locality.
Ecology: adult—volant; melliferous, solitary, flower visiting record: *Eucalyptus* L'Hérit. [Myrtaceae].

Brachyhesma (Henicohesma) Exley, 1968

Henicohesma Exley, E.M. (1968). Revision of the genus *Brachyhesma* Michener (Apoidea : Colletidae). *Aust. J. Zool.* **16**: 167–201 [199] [proposed with subgeneric rank in *Brachyhesma* Michener, 1965]. Type species: *Brachyhesma (Henicohesma) macdonaldensis* Exley, 1968 by original designation.

Brachyhesma (Henicohesma) deserticola Exley, 1968

Brachyhesma (Henicohesma) deserticola Exley, E.M. (1968). Three new species of *Brachyhesma* (Apoidea : Colletidae). *J. Aust. Entomol. Soc.* **7**: 135–141 [139].
Type data: holotype, QM T6637 ♂.
Type locality: Mica Creek, 5 miles from Mt Isa, QLD.

Distribution: N Gulf, Lake Eyre basin, QLD, NT; only published localities Mt Isa and vicinity and Barrow Creek.
Ecology: adult—volant; melliferous, solitary, flower visiting record: *Eucalyptus* L'Hérit. [Myrtaceae].
References: Exley, E.M. (1974). A contribution to our knowledge of the bee fauna (Colletidae : Euryglossinae) of remote areas of Australia with descriptions of new species. *Proc. R. Soc. Qd* **85**: 95–110 (distribution); Exley, E.M. (1977). The Australian genus *Brachyhesma* (Apoidea : Colletidae) revised and reviewed. *Aust. J. Zool. Suppl. Ser.* **53**: 1–54 (redescription).

Brachyhesma (Henicohesma) macdonaldensis Exley, 1968

Brachyhesma (Henicohesma) macdonaldensis Exley, E.M. (1968). Revision of the genus *Brachyhesma* Michener (Apoidea : Colletidae). *Aust. J. Zool.* **16**: 167–201 [199].

Type data: holotype, ANIC ♂.
Type locality: Macdonald Downs, NT.

Distribution: N Gulf, Lake Eyre basin, QLD, NT; only published localities Lake Moondarra and Macdonald Downs.
Ecology: adult—volant; melliferous, solitary, flower visiting record: *Eucalyptus* L'Hérit. [Myrtaceae].
Reference: Exley, E.M. (1974). A contribution to our knowledge of the bee fauna (Colletidae : Euryglossinae) of remote areas of Australia with descriptions of new species. *Proc. R. Soc. Qd* **85**: 95–110 (distribution).

Brachyhesma (Microhesma) Michener, 1965

Microhesma Michener, C.D. (1965). A classification of the bees of the Australian and South Pacific regions. *Bull. Am. Mus. Nat. Hist.* **130**: 1–362 [113] [proposed with subgeneric rank in *Brachyhesma* Michener, 1965]. Type species: *Brachyhesma (Microhesma) incompleta* Michener, 1965 by original designation.

Brachyhesma (Microhesma) bitrichopedalis Exley, 1968

Brachyhesma (Microhesma) bitrichopedalis Exley, E.M. (1968). Revision of the genus *Brachyhesma* Michener (Apoidea : Colletidae). *Aust. J. Zool.* **16**: 167–201 [170].
Type data: holotype, QM T6666 ♂.
Type locality: Murphys Creek, QLD.

Distribution: NE coastal, Murray-Darling basin, N Gulf, N coastal, QLD, NSW, WA, NT.
Ecology: adult—volant; melliferous, solitary, flower visiting record: *Angophora* Cav. [Myrtaceae], *Eucalyptus* L'Hérit. [Myrtaceae], *Leptospermum* Forster & G.Forster [Myrtaceae].
Reference: Exley, E.M. (1974). A contribution to our knowledge of the bee fauna (Colletidae : Euryglossinae) of remote areas of Australia with descriptions of new species. *Proc. R. Soc. Qd* **85**: 95–110 (distribution).

Brachyhesma (Microhesma) cavagnari Exley, 1968

Brachyhesma (Microhesma) cavagnari Exley, E.M. (1968). Revision of the genus *Brachyhesma* Michener (Apoidea : Colletidae). *Aust. J. Zool.* **16**: 167–201 [172].
Type data: holotype, ANIC ♂.
Type locality: Macdonald Downs, NT.

Distribution: Lake Eyre basin, S Gulfs, W plateau, SA, WA, NT; only published localities Macdonald Downs, Adelaide and near Coolgardie.
Ecology: adult—volant; melliferous, solitary.
Reference: Exley, E.M. (1977). The Australian genus *Brachyhesma* (Apoidea : Colletidae) revised and reviewed. *Aust. J. Zool. Suppl. Ser.* **53**: 1–54 (taxonomy).

Brachyhesma (Microhesma) cooki Michener, 1965

Brachyhesma (Microhesma) cooki Michener, C.D. (1965). A classification of the bees of the Australian and South

Pacific regions. *Bull. Am. Mus. Nat. Hist.* **130**: 1–362 [287].
Type data: holotype, USNM ♂*.
Type locality: Botany Bay (near Sydney), NSW.

Distribution: Murray-Darling basin, SE coastal, QLD, NSW; only published localities Amiens, Stanthorpe and Botany Bay.
Ecology: adult—volant; melliferous, solitary, flower visiting record: *Eucalyptus* L'Hérit. [Myrtaceae], *Leptospermum* Forster & G.Forster [Myrtaceae].
Reference: Exley, E.M. (1968). Revision of the genus *Brachyhesma* Michener (Apoidea : Colletidae). *Aust. J. Zool.* **16**: 167–201 (redescription).

Brachyhesma (Microhesma) healesvillensis Exley, 1968

Brachyhesma (Microhesma) healesvillensis Exley, E.M. (1968). Revision of the genus *Brachyhesma* Michener (Apoidea : Colletidae). *Aust. J. Zool.* **16**: 167–201 [176].
Type data: holotype, ANIC ♀.
Type locality: Mt Yule, Healesville, VIC.

Distribution: SE coastal, NSW, VIC; only published localities Singleton and Mt Yule, Healesville.
Ecology: adult—volant; melliferous, solitary, flower visiting record: *Angophora* Cav. [Myrtaceae], *Eucalyptus* L'Hérit. [Myrtaceae].

Brachyhesma (Microhesma) incompleta Michener, 1965

Brachyhesma (Microhesma) incompleta Michener, C.D. (1965). A classification of the bees of the Australian and South Pacific regions. *Bull. Am. Mus. Nat. Hist.* **130**: 1–362 [288].
Type data: holotype, QM T6224 ♀.
Type locality: Tamborine, QLD.

Distribution: NE coastal, SE coastal, Murray-Darling basin, QLD, NSW.
Ecology: adult—volant; melliferous, solitary, flower visiting record: *Angophora* Cav. [Myrtaceae], *Eucalyptus* L'Hérit. [Myrtaceae], *Leptospermum* Forster & G.Forster [Myrtaceae], *Melaleuca* L. [Myrtaceae], *Tristania* R.Br. [Myrtaceae].
References: Cockerell, T.D.A. (1922). Australian bees in the Queensland Museum. *Mem. Qd Mus.* **7**: 257–279 (female, as *Euryglossa furcifera* Cockerell, 1913); Exley, E.M. (1968). Revision of the genus *Brachyhesma* Michener (Apoidea : Colletidae). *Aust. J. Zool.* **16**: 167–201 (redescription); Michener, C.D. & Brooks, R.W. (1984). A comparative study of the glossae of bees (Apoidea). *Contrib. Am. Entomol. Inst.* **22**: 1–73 (glossa); Michener, C.D. (1992). Sexual dimorphism in the glossa of Colletidae (Hymenoptera, Apoidea). *J. Kansas Entomol. Soc.* **65**: 1–9 (glossa).

Brachyhesma (Microhesma) josephinae Exley, 1968

Brachyhesma (Microhesma) josephinae Exley, E.M. (1968). Revision of the genus *Brachyhesma* Michener

(Apoidea : Colletidae). *Aust. J. Zool.* **16**: 167–201 [179].
Type data: holotype, QM T6668 ♂.
Type locality: Ross River, Townsville, QLD.

Distribution: NE coastal, QLD; only published localities Ross River (Townsville), Millaroo, Mt Molloy and Mareeba.
Ecology: adult—volant; melliferous, solitary, flower visiting record: *Eucalyptus* L'Hérit. [Myrtaceae], *Melaleuca* L. [Myrtaceae].
Reference: Exley, E.M. (1977). The Australian genus *Brachyhesma* (Apoidea : Colletidae) revised and reviewed. *Aust. J. Zool. Suppl. Ser.* **53**: 1–54 (distribution).

Brachyhesma (Microhesma) katherinensis Exley, 1974

Brachyhesma (Microhesma) katherinensis Exley, E.M. (1974). A contribution to our knowledge of the bee fauna (Colletidae : Euryglossinae) of remote areas of Australia with descriptions of new species. *Proc. R. Soc. Qd* **85**: 95–110 [104].
Type data: holotype, QM T7161 ♂.
Type locality: 15 miles E Katherine, NT.

Distribution: N Gulf, N coastal, QLD, NT.
Ecology: adult—volant; melliferous, solitary, flower visiting record: *Eucalyptus* L'Hérit. [Myrtaceae].
Reference: Exley, E.M. (1977). The Australian genus *Brachyhesma* (Apoidea : Colletidae) revised and reviewed. *Aust. J. Zool. Suppl. Ser.* **53**: 1–54 (distribution).

Brachyhesma (Microhesma) microxantha (Cockerell, 1914)

Euryglossina microxantha Cockerell, T.D.A. (1914). Descriptions and records of bees. LX. *Ann. Mag. Nat. Hist.* *(8)***14**: 1–13 [7].
Type data: holotype, BMNH Hym.17.a.303 ♀.
Type locality: Mackay, QLD.

Distribution: NE coastal, QLD; known only from type locality.
Ecology: adult—volant; melliferous, solitary, flower visiting record: *Leptospermum* Forster & G.Forster [Myrtaceae].
Reference: Exley, E.M. (1968). Revision of the genus *Brachyhesma* Michener (Apoidea : Colletidae). *Aust. J. Zool.* **16**: 167–201 (generic placement).

Brachyhesma (Microhesma) minya Exley, 1975

Brachyhesma (Microhesma) minya Exley, E.M. (1975). New species and records of *Brachyhesma* Michener (Apoidea : Colletidae : Euryglossinae). *J. Aust. Entomol. Soc.* **14**: 139–144 [141].
Type data: holotype, QM T7351 ♂.
Type locality: Gawler Ranges, SA.

Distribution: S Gulfs, SA; known only from type locality.
Ecology: adult—volant; melliferous, solitary.

Brachyhesma (Microhesma) nabarleki Exley, 1977

Brachyhesma (Microhesma) nabarleki Exley, E.M. (1977). The Australian genus *Brachyhesma* (Apoidea : Colletidae) revised and reviewed. *Aust. J. Zool. Suppl. Ser.* **53**: 1–54 [14] [misspelled as *narbarleki* in key on p. 10].
Type data: holotype, ANIC ♂.
Type locality: Nabarlek Dam, 14 km SSW Nimbuwah Rock, NT.

Distribution: N coastal, NT; only published localities Nabarlek Dam, Magela Creek, Oenpelli, Elizabeth River and Katherine.
Ecology: adult—volant; melliferous, solitary, flower visiting record: *Eucalyptus* L'Hérit. [Myrtaceae], *Eugenia* L. [Myrtaceae].

Brachyhesma (Microhesma) newmanensis Exley, 1977

Brachyhesma (Microhesma) newmanensis Exley, E.M. (1977). The Australian genus *Brachyhesma* (Apoidea : Colletidae) revised and reviewed. *Aust. J. Zool. Suppl. Ser.* **53**: 1–54 [16].
Type data: holotype, QM T7729 ♂.
Type locality: Great Northern Highway, 9 km N Newman turnoff, WA.

Distribution: NW coastal, WA; known only from type locality.
Ecology: adult—volant; melliferous, solitary, flower visiting record: *Eucalyptus* L'Hérit. [Myrtaceae].

Brachyhesma (Microhesma) paucivenata Exley, 1977

Brachyhesma (Microhesma) paucivenata Exley, E.M. (1977). The Australian genus *Brachyhesma* (Apoidea : Colletidae) revised and reviewed. *Aust. J. Zool. Suppl. Ser.* **53**: 1–54 [17].
Type data: holotype, QM T7725 ♂.
Type locality: 12 km SW Katherine, NT.

Distribution: N Gulf, N coastal, QLD, WA, NT.
Ecology: adult—volant; melliferous, solitary, flower visiting record: *Eucalyptus* L'Hérit. [Myrtaceae].

Brachyhesma (Microhesma) rossi Exley, 1968

Brachyhesma (Microhesma) rossi Exley, E.M. (1968). Revision of the genus *Brachyhesma* Michener (Apoidea : Colletidae). *Aust. J. Zool.* **16**: 167–201 [182].
Type data: holotype, ANIC ♂.
Type locality: Gregory Downs, QLD.

Distribution: N Gulf, N coastal, QLD, WA, NT.
Ecology: adult—volant; melliferous, solitary.
References: Exley, E.M. (1974). A contribution to our knowledge of the bee fauna (Colletidae : Euryglossinae) of remote areas of Australia with descriptions of new species. *Proc. R. Soc. Qd* **85**: 95–110 (distribution); Exley, E.M. (1977). The Australian genus *Brachyhesma* (Apoidea : Colletidae) revised and reviewed. *Aust. J. Zool. Suppl. Ser.* **53**: 1–54 (distribution).

Brachyhesma (Microhesma) storeyi Exley, 1977

Brachyhesma (Microhesma) storeyi Exley, E.M. (1977). The Australian genus *Brachyhesma* (Apoidea : Colletidae) revised and reviewed. *Aust. J. Zool. Suppl. Ser.* **53**: 1–54 [19].
Type data: holotype, QM T7723 ♂.
Type locality: 5 miles NW Mt Molloy, QLD.

Distribution: NE coastal, N Gulf, QLD; only published localities near Mt Molloy and Petford.
Ecology: adult—volant; melliferous, solitary, flower visiting record: *Eucalyptus* L'Hérit. [Myrtaceae].

Brachyhesma (Microhesma) trichopterota Exley, 1968

Brachyhesma (Microhesma) trichopterota Exley, E.M. (1968). Three new species of *Brachyhesma* (Apoidea : Colletidae). *J. Aust. Entomol. Soc.* 7: 135–141 [137].
Type data: holotype, QM T7088 ♂.
Type locality: Mt Isa, QLD.

Distribution: N Gulf, QLD; only published localities Mt Isa and vicinity, and Georgetown.
Ecology: adult—volant; melliferous, solitary.
References: Exley, E.M. (1974). A contribution to our knowledge of the bee fauna (Colletidae : Euryglossinae) of remote areas of Australia with descriptions of new species. *Proc. R. Soc. Qd* **85**: 95–110 (distribution); Exley, E.M. (1977). The Australian genus *Brachyhesma* (Apoidea : Colletidae) revised and reviewed. *Aust. J. Zool. Suppl. Ser.* **53**: 1–54 (distribution).

Brachyhesma (Microhesma) ventralis Exley, 1977

Brachyhesma (Microhesma) ventralis Exley, E.M. (1977). The Australian genus *Brachyhesma* (Apoidea : Colletidae) revised and reviewed. *Aust. J. Zool. Suppl. Ser.* **53**: 1–54 [21].
Type data: holotype, QM T7727 ♂.
Type locality: 20 miles (32 km) W Tenterfield, NSW.

Distribution: NE coastal, Murray-Darling basin, QLD, NSW; only published localities near Slacks Creek and near Tenterfield.
Ecology: adult—volant; melliferous, solitary, flower visiting record: *Angophora* Cav. [Myrtaceae], *Melaleuca* L. [Myrtaceae].

Chaetohesma Exley, 1978

Chaetohesma Exley, E.M. (1978). *Chaetohesma*—a new genus of Australian bees (Apoidea : Colletidae : Euryglossinae). *Aust. J. Zool.* **26**: 373–397 [373]. Type species: *Chaetohesma tuberculata* Exley, 1978 by original designation.

Chaetohesma baringa Exley, 1978

Chaetohesma baringa Exley, E.M. (1978). *Chaetohesma*—a new genus of Australian bees (Apoidea : Colletidae : Euryglossinae). *Aust. J. Zool.* **26**: 373–397 [394].
Type data: holotype, QM T8415 ♀.
Type locality: Barrow Creek, NT.

Distribution: Lake Eyre basin, NT; only published localities Barrow Creek and vicinity.
Ecology: adult—volant; melliferous, solitary, flower visiting record: *Eucalyptus* L'Hérit. [Myrtaceae].

Chaetohesma foveolata Exley, 1978

Chaetohesma foveolata Exley, E.M. (1978). *Chaetohesma*—a new genus of Australian bees (Apoidea : Colletidae : Euryglossinae). *Aust. J. Zool.* **26**: 373–397 [392].
Type data: holotype, ANIC ♀.
Type locality: 22 km WSW Borroloola, NT.

Distribution: N Gulf, N coastal, NT; only published localities near Borroloola and Elizabeth River.
Ecology: adult—volant; melliferous, solitary, flower visiting record: *Eucalyptus* L'Hérit. [Myrtaceae], *Eugenia* L. [Myrtaceae].

Chaetohesma infuscata Exley, 1978

Chaetohesma infuscata Exley, E.M. (1978). *Chaetohesma*—a new genus of Australian bees (Apoidea : Colletidae : Euryglossinae). *Aust. J. Zool.* **26**: 373–397 [389].
Type data: holotype, QM T8413 ♀.
Type locality: 2 km W St George, QLD.

Distribution: Murray-Darling basin, QLD, NSW; only published localities near St George, Cunnamulla, near Bourke and near Moree.
Ecology: adult—volant; melliferous, solitary, flower visiting record: *Angophora* Cav. [Myrtaceae], *Capparis* L. [Capparaceae], *Convolvulus* L. [Convolvulaceae], *Eucalyptus* L'Hérit. [Myrtaceae].

Chaetohesma isae Exley, 1978

Chaetohesma isae Exley, E.M. (1978). *Chaetohesma*—a new genus of Australian bees (Apoidea : Colletidae : Euryglossinae). *Aust. J. Zool.* **26**: 373–397 [390].
Type data: holotype, QM T8425 ♀.
Type locality: 20 km N Mt Isa, QLD.

Distribution: N Gulf, QLD; known only from type locality.
Ecology: adult—volant; melliferous, solitary, flower visiting record: *Eucalyptus* L'Hérit. [Myrtaceae].

Chaetohesma levis Exley, 1978

Chaetohesma levis Exley, E.M. (1978). *Chaetohesma*—a new genus of Australian bees (Apoidea : Colletidae : Euryglossinae). *Aust. J. Zool.* **26**: 373–397 [380].
Type data: holotype, QM T8411 ♀.
Type locality: Barrow Creek, NT.

Distribution: N Gulf, Lake Eyre basin, QLD, NT; only published localities Mt Isa, Lake Moondarra, Barrow Creek and Macdonald Downs.
Ecology: adult—volant; melliferous, solitary, flower visiting record: *Eucalyptus* L'Hérit. [Myrtaceae].

Chaetohesma megastigma Exley, 1978

Chaetohesma megastigma Exley, E.M. (1978). *Chaetohesma*—a new genus of Australian bees (Apoidea :

Colletidae : Euryglossinae). *Aust. J. Zool.* **26**: 373–397 [395].
Type data: holotype, QM T8417 ♀.
Type locality: 12 km N Murchison River Crossing on North West Coastal Highway, WA.

Distribution: NW coastal, WA; only published localities on North West Coastal Highway near Murchison River crossing and Nabawa.
Ecology: adult—volant; melliferous, solitary, flower visiting record: *Eucalyptus* L'Hérit. [Myrtaceae].

Chaetohesma newmanensis Exley, 1978

Chaetohesma newmanensis Exley, E.M. (1978). *Chaetohesma*—a new genus of Australian bees (Apoidea : Colletidae : Euryglossinae). *Aust. J. Zool.* **26**: 373–397 [379].
Type data: holotype, QM T8409 ♀.
Type locality: Great Northern Highway, 9 km N Newman turnoff, WA.

Distribution: NW coastal, WA; known only from type locality.
Ecology: adult—volant; melliferous, solitary, flower visiting record: *Eucalyptus* L'Hérit. [Myrtaceae].

Chaetohesma robusta Exley, 1978

Chaetohesma robusta Exley, E.M. (1978). *Chaetohesma*—a new genus of Australian bees (Apoidea : Colletidae : Euryglossinae). *Aust. J. Zool.* **26**: 373–397 [391].
Type data: holotype, QM T8423 ♀.
Type locality: 15 km E Forsayth, QLD.

Distribution: N Gulf, QLD; only published localities near Forsayth, near Georgetown and near Mt Surprise.
Ecology: adult—volant; melliferous, solitary, flower visiting record: *Eucalyptus* L'Hérit. [Myrtaceae].

Chaetohesma striolata Exley, 1978

Chaetohesma striolata Exley, E.M. (1978). *Chaetohesma*—a new genus of Australian bees (Apoidea : Colletidae : Euryglossinae). *Aust. J. Zool.* **26**: 373–397 [382].
Type data: holotype, QM T8419 ♀.
Type locality: 16 km W Mt Carbine, QLD.

Distribution: NE coastal, N Gulf, N coastal, QLD, WA, NT.
Ecology: adult—volant; melliferous, solitary, flower visiting record: *Eucalyptus* L'Hérit. [Myrtaceae].

Chaetohesma tuberculata Exley, 1978

Chaetohesma tuberculata Exley, E.M. (1978). *Chaetohesma*—a new genus of Australian bees (Apoidea : Colletidae : Euryglossinae). *Aust. J. Zool.* **26**: 373–397 [378].
Type data: holotype, QM T8421 ♀.
Type locality: 7 km E Kununurra, QLD.

Distribution: N Gulf, N coastal, QLD, WA, NT.
Ecology: adult—volant; melliferous, solitary, flower visiting record: *Eucalyptus* L'Hérit. [Myrtaceae].

References: Exley, E.M. (1969). *Argohesma*—a new genus of Australian bees (Apoidea : Colletidae). *Aust. J. Zool.* **17**: 527–534 (description of male, as *Argohesma* Male Species B); Exley, E.M. (1969). Revision of the subgenus *Xenohesma* Michener (Apoidea : Colletidae). *Aust. J. Zool.* **17**: 535–551 (description of female, as female of *Euryglossa (Xenohesma) stagei* Exley, 1969); Exley, E.M. (1974). A contribution to our knowledge of the bee fauna (Colletidae : Euryglossinae) of remote areas of Australia with descriptions of new species. *Proc. R. Soc. Qd* **85**: 95–110 (as *Xanthesma brachycera* (Cockerell, 1914)).

Dasyhesma Michener, 1965

Dasyhesma Michener, C.D. (1965). A classification of the bees of the Australian and South Pacific regions. *Bull. Am. Mus. Nat. Hist.* **130**: 1–362 [102]. Type species: *Dasyhesma robusta* Michener, 1965 by original designation.

Dasyhesma robusta Michener, 1965

Dasyhesma robusta Michener, C.D. (1965). A classification of the bees of the Australian and South Pacific regions. *Bull. Am. Mus. Nat. Hist.* **130**: 1–362 [284].
Type data: holotype, WAM 54–127 ♀.
Type locality: Pearce, WA.

Distribution: SW coastal, WA; only published localities Pearce, Capel and Bullsbrook.
Ecology: adult—volant; melliferous, solitary.

Euryglossa Smith, 1853

Taxonomic decision for subgeneric arrangement: Michener, C.D. (1965). A classification of the bees of the Australian and South Pacific regions. *Bull. Am. Mus. Nat. Hist.* **130**: 1–362 [87].

Euryglossa (Euryglossa) Smith, 1853

Euryglossa Smith, F. (1853). *Catalogue of Hymenopterous Insects in the Collection of the British Museum*. Part I. Andrenidae and Apidae. London : British Museum 197 pp. [17]. Type species: *Euryglossa cupreochalybea* Smith, 1853 by subsequent designation, see Meade-Waldo, G. (1923). Hymenoptera. Fam. Apidae. Subfam. Prosopidinae. *Genera Insectorum* **181**: 1–45 [7].
Euryglossimorpha Strand, E. (1910). Apidologisches aus dem Naturhistorischen Museum zu Wiesbaden. *Jahrb. Nassau. Ver. Naturk.* **63**: 35–52 [40] [proposed with subgeneric rank in *Euryglossa* Smith, 1853]. Type species: *Euryglossa nigra* Smith, 1879 by monotypy.

Taxonomic decision for synonymy: Michener, C.D. (1965). A classification of the bees of the Australian and South Pacific regions. *Bull. Am. Mus. Nat. Hist.* **130**: 1–362 [92].

Euryglossa (Euryglossa) adelaidae Cockerell, 1905

Euryglossa adelaidae Cockerell, T.D.A. (1905). Descriptions and records of bees. V. *Ann. Mag. Nat. Hist.* (7)**16**: 465–477 [475].

Type data: holotype, BMNH Hym.17.a.282 ♂ (described as ♀).
Type locality: Adelaide, SA.

Halictus oxleyi Cockerell, T.D.A. (1905). New Australian bees, in the collection of the British Museum. *Entomologist* **38**: 270–273, 302–304 [303].
Type data: holotype, BMNH Hym.17.a.953 ♂.
Type locality: Adelaide, SA.

Euryglossa chrysoceras Cockerell, T.D.A. (1910). Some Australian bees in the Berlin Museum. *J. N.Y. Entomol. Soc.* **18**: 98–114 [99].
Type data: holotype, ZMB ♂*.
Type locality: Adelaide, SA.

Euryglossa leptospermi Cockerell, T.D.A. (1910). Descriptions and records of bees. XXXI. *Ann. Mag. Nat. Hist. (8)***6**: 160–168 [167].
Type data: holotype, BMNH Hym.17.a.271 ♀.
Type locality: Mackay, QLD.

Euryglossa myrtacearum Cockerell, T.D.A. (1910). New and little-known bees. *Trans. Am. Entomol. Soc.* **36**: 199–249 [209].
Type data: holotype, BMNH Hym.17.a.276 ♀.
Type locality: Mackay, QLD.

Euryglossa variabilis Perkins, R.C.L. (1912). Notes, with descriptions of new species, on aculeate Hymenoptera of the Australian Region. *Ann. Mag. Nat. Hist. (8)***9**: 96–121 [110].
Type data: syntypes (probable), BMNH ♀ (number of specimens unknown, described as ♂, a specimen is labelled 'type' and has registration number Hym.17.a.2832).
Type locality: Bundaberg, QLD.

Euryglossa sanguinosa Cockerell, T.D.A. (1913). Some Australian bees. *Proc. Acad. Nat. Sci. Philad.* **65**: 28–44 [35].
Type data: holotype, BMNH Hym.17.a.260 ♀.
Type locality: Windsor, VIC.

Stilpnosoma variegatum Friese, H. (1924). Ueber die Bienen Australiens. *Konowia* **3**: 216–249 [232].
Type data: holotype, AMNH ♀*.
Type locality: Mackay, QLD.

Stilpnosoma laterale Friese, H. (1924). Ueber die Bienen Australiens. *Konowia* **3**: 216–249 [232].
Type data: holotype, AMNH ♀*.
Type locality: Mackay, QLD.

Stilpnosoma piceum Friese, H. (1924). Ueber die Bienen Australiens. *Konowia* **3**: 216–249 [234].
Type data: lectotype, AMNH 26860 ♂*.
Subsequent designation: Exley, E.M. (1976). Revision of the subgenus *Euryglossa* Smith (Apoidea : Colletidae : Euryglossinae). *Aust. J. Zool. Suppl. Ser.* **41**: 1–72; Cardale, J.C., this work, interprets Exley's incorrect inference of holotype as a lectotype designation (Art. 74, ICZN 1985).
Type locality: Colo (as Cola) Vale, NSW.

Euryglossa albosignata Cockerell, T.D.A. (1929). Bees from the Australian region. *Am. Mus. Novit.* **346**: 1–18 [10].
Type data: holotype, AMNH ♀*.
Type locality: Bamawn, VIC.

Euryglossa coventryi Rayment, T. (1935). *A Cluster of Bees.* Sixty essays on the life-histories of Australian bees, with specific descriptions of over 100 new species, and an introduction by Professor E.F. Phillips, D.Ph., Cornell University, U.S.A. Sydney : Endeavour Press 752 pp. [641].
Type data: holotype, ANIC ♂.
Type locality: Croydon, VIC.

Euryglossa ephippiata punctata Rayment, T. (1939). Bees from the high lands of New South Wales and Victoria. *Aust. Zool.* **9**: 263–294 [269] [junior secondary homonym of *Euryglossidia punctata* Rayment, 1935].
Type data: lectotype, ANIC ♀.
Subsequent designation: Exley, E.M. (1976). Revision of the subgenus *Euryglossa* (Apoidea : Colletidae : Euryglossinae). *Aust. J. Zool. Suppl. Ser.* **41**: 1–72 [45]; Cardale, J.C., this work, interprets Exley's incorrect inference of holotype as a lectotype designation (Art. 74, ICZN).
Type locality: Gunbower, VIC (Gosford, NSW in description), see Exley, E.M. (1976). Revision of the subgenus *Euryglossa* Smith (Apoidea : Colletidae : Euryglossinae). *Aust. J. Zool. Suppl. Ser.* **41**: 1–72 [45].

Taxonomic decision for synonymy: Exley, E.M. (1976). Revision of the subgenus *Euryglossa* Smith (Apoidea : Colletidae : Euryglossinae). *Aust. J. Zool. Suppl. Ser.* **41**: 1–72 [42].

Distribution: NE coastal, SE coastal, Murray-Darling basin, S Gulfs, QLD, NSW, ACT, VIC, SA.
Ecology: adult—volant; melliferous, solitary, flower visiting record: *Angophora* Cav. [Myrtaceae], *Callistemon* R.Br. [Myrtaceae], *Eucalyptus* L'Hérit. [Myrtaceae], *?Jacksonia* Smith [Fabaceae], *Leptospermum* Forster & G.Forster [Myrtaceae], *Melaleuca* L. [Myrtaceae], *Tristania* R.Br. [Myrtaceae].
References: Cockerell, T.D.A. (1916). A collection of bees from Queensland. *Mem. Qd Mus.* **5**: 197–204 (flower record, as *Euryglossa chrysoceras* Cockerell, 1910); Michener, C.D. (1965). A classification of the bees of the Australian and South Pacific regions. *Bull. Am. Mus. Nat. Hist.* **130**: 1–362 [234] (flower records, as *Euryglossa chrysoceras* Cockerell, 1910).

Euryglossa (Euryglossa) alincia Exley, 1976

Euryglossa (Euryglossa) alincia Exley, E.M. (1976). Revision of the subgenus *Euryglossa* Smith (Apoidea : Colletidae : Euryglossinae). *Aust. J. Zool. Suppl. Ser.* **41**: 1–72 [40].
Type data: holotype, QM T7476 ♂.
Type locality: Amiens, QLD.

Distribution: Murray-Darling basin, N coastal, QLD, NT; only published localities Amiens and Darwin.
Ecology: adult—volant; melliferous, solitary, flower visiting record: *Leptospermum* Forster & G.Forster [Myrtaceae].

Euryglossa (Euryglossa) angelesi Exley, 1976

Euryglossa (Euryglossa) angelesi Exley, E.M. (1976). Revision of the subgenus *Euryglossa* Smith (Apoidea : Colletidae : Euryglossinae). *Aust. J. Zool. Suppl. Ser.* **41**: 1–72 [36].
Type data: holotype, QM T7474 ♀.
Type locality: 15 miles E Katherine, NT.

Distribution: N coastal, NT; known only from type locality.

Ecology: adult—volant; melliferous, solitary, flower visiting record: *Eucalyptus* L'Hérit. [Myrtaceae].

Euryglossa (Euryglossa) antennata (Rayment, 1935)

Euryglossimorpha antennata Rayment, T. (1935). *A Cluster of Bees*. Sixty essays on the life-histories of Australian bees, with specific descriptions of over 100 new species, and an introduction by Professor E.F. Phillips, D.Ph., Cornell University, U.S.A. Sydney : Endeavour Press 752 pp. [665].
Type data: holotype, ANIC ♂.
Type locality: Wongan Hills, WA.

Distribution: SW coastal, NW coastal, WA; only published localities Wongan Hills and Mingenew.
Ecology: adult—volant; melliferous, solitary.
Reference: Exley, E.M. (1976). Revision of the subgenus *Euryglossa* Smith (Apoidea : Colletidae : Euryglossinae). *Aust. J. Zool. Suppl. Ser.* **41**: 1–72 (redescription).

Euryglossa (Euryglossa) aureopilosa Rayment, 1935

Euryglossa aureopilosa Rayment, T. (1935). *A Cluster of Bees*. Sixty essays on the life-histories of Australian bees, with specific descriptions of over 100 new species, and an introduction by Professor E.F. Phillips, D.Ph., Cornell University, U.S.A. Sydney : Endeavour Press 752 pp. [642].
Type data: holotype, ANIC ♀.
Type locality: Gosford, NSW.

Euryglossimorpha aureomaculata Rayment, T. (1949). New bees and wasps—Part XII. A new blue bee and an old white-ant. *Vict. Nat.* **66**: 147–151 [149].
Type data: holotype, AM ♀.
Type locality: Mt Keira, NSW.

Taxonomic decision for synonymy: Exley, E.M. (1976). Revision of the subgenus *Euryglossa* Smith (Apoidea : Colletidae : Euryglossinae). *Aust. J. Zool. Suppl. Ser.* **41**: 1–72 [10].

Distribution: SE coastal, NSW, VIC; only published localities Gosford, Mt Keira and Mt Macedon.
Ecology: adult—volant; melliferous, solitary, nest in base of termite mound, flower visiting record: *Angophora* Cav. [Myrtaceae].

Euryglossa (Euryglossa) calaina Exley, 1976

Euryglossa (Euryglossa) calaina Exley, E.M. (1976). Revision of the subgenus *Euryglossa* Smith (Apoidea : Colletidae : Euryglossinae). *Aust. J. Zool. Suppl. Ser.* **41**: 1–72 [9].
Type data: holotype, WAM 54–1417 ♀*.
Type locality: Cranbrook, WA.

Distribution: SW coastal, WA; only published localities Cranbrook, Dudinin and Borden National Park.
Ecology: adult—volant; melliferous, solitary.

Euryglossa (Euryglossa) capitata Exley, 1976

Euryglossa (Euryglossa) capitata Exley, E.M. (1976). Revision of the subgenus *Euryglossa* Smith (Apoidea : Colletidae : Euryglossinae). *Aust. J. Zool. Suppl. Ser.* **41**: 1–72 [26].
Type data: holotype, NMV ♀.
Type locality: Mt Wilson, NSW.

Distribution: SE coastal, Murray-Darling basin, NSW; only published localities Mt Wilson, Mt Victoria and Gosford.
Ecology: adult—volant; melliferous, solitary.

Euryglossa (Euryglossa) cupreochalybea Smith, 1853

Euryglossa cupreochalybea Smith, F. (1853). *Catalogue of Hymenopterous Insects in the Collection of the British Museum*. Part I. Andrenidae and Apidae. London : British Museum 197 pp. [17].
Type data: holotype, BMNH Hym.17.a.230 ♀.
Type locality: Australia (as New Holland).

Distribution: SW coastal, WA; only published localities Yallingup, Gnowangerup, Merredin and Cranbrook.
Ecology: adult—volant; melliferous, solitary.
Reference: Exley, E.M. (1976). Revision of the subgenus *Euryglossa* Smith (Apoidea : Colletidae : Euryglossinae). *Aust. J. Zool. Suppl. Ser.* **41**: 1–72 (redescription).

Euryglossa (Euryglossa) depressa Smith, 1853

Euryglossa depressa Smith, F. (1853). *Catalogue of Hymenopterous Insects in the Collection of the British Museum*. Part I. Andrenidae and Apidae. London : British Museum 197 pp. [18].
Type data: holotype, BMNH Hym.17.a.231 ♀.
Type locality: Australia (as New Holland).

Euryglossa bicolor Smith, F. (1862). Descriptions of new species of Australian Hymenoptera, and of a species of *Formica* from New Zealand. *Trans. Entomol. Soc. Lond.* (3)**1**: 53–62 [58].
Type data: holotype, BMNH Hym.17.a.265 ♀.
Type locality: Adelaide, SA.

Euryglossa occipitalis Cockerell, T.D.A. (1922). Australian bees in the Queensland Museum. *Mem. Qd Mus.* **7**: 257–279 [271].
Type data: holotype, QM T2451 ♀.
Type locality: Portland, VIC.

Euryglossa longicornis Cockerell, T.D.A. (1922). Australian bees in the Queensland Museum. *Mem. Qd Mus.* **7**: 257–279 [272].
Type data: holotype, QM T2681 ♂.
Type locality: Kelvin Grove, Brisbane, QLD.

Taxonomic decision for synonymy: Exley, E.M. (1976). Revision of the subgenus *Euryglossa* Smith (Apoidea : Colletidae : Euryglossinae). *Aust. J. Zool. Suppl. Ser.* **41**: 1–72 [7].

Distribution: NE coastal, SE coastal, Murray-Darling basin, S Gulfs, QLD, NSW, ACT, VIC, SA.

Ecology: adult—volant; melliferous, solitary, flower visiting record: *Eucalyptus* L'Hérit. [Myrtaceae], *Leptospermum* Forster & G.Forster [Myrtaceae].
Reference: Michener, C.D. & Houston, T.F. (1991). Apoidea. pp. 993–1000 *in* CSIRO (sponsor) *The Insects of Australia*. A textbook for students and research workers. Melbourne : Melbourne University Press Vol. II 2nd Edn (illustration).

Euryglossa (Euryglossa) edwardsii Cockerell, 1907

Euryglossa edwardsii Cockerell, T.D.A. (1907). On a collection of Australian and Asiatic bees. *Bull. Am. Mus. Nat. Hist.* **23**: 221–236 [230].
Type data: holotype, AMNH ♀*.
Type locality: NSW.

Euryglossa ruberrima Cockerell, T.D.A. (1913). Some Australian bees. *Proc. Acad. Nat. Sci. Philad.* **65**: 28–44 [36].
Type data: holotype, BMNH Hym.17.a.255 ♀.
Type locality: VIC.

Euryglossa apicalis Cockerell, T.D.A. (1913). Descriptions and records of bees. LV. *Ann. Mag. Nat. Hist.* *(8)***12**: 505–514 [511].
Type data: holotype, USNM ♂*.
Type locality: Croydon, VIC.

Euryglossa depressa sparsa Cockerell, T.D.A. (1916). Some bees from Australia, Tasmania, and the New Hebrides. *Proc. Acad. Nat. Sci. Philad.* **68**: 360–375 [363].
Type data: syntypes, BMNH 3♀ (a specimen is labelled 'type' and has registration number Hym.17.a.232).
Type locality: Mt Yule, Healesville, VIC.

Taxonomic decision for synonymy: Exley, E.M. (1976). Revision of the subgenus *Euryglossa* Smith (Apoidea : Colletidae : Euryglossinae). *Aust. J. Zool. Suppl. Ser.* **41**: 1–72 [37].

Distribution: NE coastal, SE coastal, Murray-Darling basin, QLD, NSW, ACT, VIC.
Ecology: adult—volant; melliferous, solitary, flower visiting record: *Eucalyptus* L'Hérit. [Myrtaceae], *Leptospermum* Forster & G.Forster [Myrtaceae], *Melaleuca* L. [Myrtaceae], *Tristania* R.Br. [Myrtaceae].

Euryglossa (Euryglossa) ephippiata Smith, 1862

Euryglossa ephippiata Smith, F. (1862). Descriptions of new species of Australian Hymenoptera, and of a species of *Formica* from New Zealand. *Trans. Entomol. Soc. Lond.* *(3)***1**: 53–62 [58].
Type data: holotype, BMNH Hym.17.a.235 ♀.
Type locality: Australia ("Adelaide" in description is believed erroneous, not otherwise known from SA), see Exley, E.M. (1976). Revision of the subgenus *Euryglossa* Smith (Apoidea : Colletidae : Euryglossinae). *Aust. J. Zool. Suppl. Ser.* **41**: 1–72 [53].
Euryglossa nigra Smith, F. (1879). *Descriptions of New Species of Hymenoptera in the Collection of the British Museum*. London : British Museum xxi 240 pp. [13].
Type data: holotype, BMNH Hym.17.a.2627 ♂ (described as ♀).
Type locality: Australia.

Euryglossa (Euryglossimorpha) cincticornis Cockerell, T.D.A. (1913). Descriptions and records of bees. LV. *Ann. Mag. Nat. Hist.* *(8)***12**: 505–514 [511].
Type data: holotype, BMNH Hym.17.a.259 ♂.
Type locality: Warburton, VIC.

Euryglossa polysticta Cockerell, T.D.A. (1922). Australian bees in the Queensland Museum. *Mem. Qd Mus.* **7**: 257–279 [270].
Type data: holotype, BMNH Hym.17.a.283 ♀.
Type locality: Dandenong, VIC.

Euryglossa aurescens obscura Cockerell, T.D.A. (1929). Bees in the Queensland Museum. *Mem. Qd Mus.* **9**: 298–323 [298].
Type data: holotype, QM T4035 ♀.
Type locality: Gosford, NSW.

Taxonomic decision for synonymy: Exley, E.M. (1976). Revision of the subgenus *Euryglossa* Smith (Apoidea : Colletidae : Euryglossinae). *Aust. J. Zool. Suppl. Ser.* **41**: 1–72 [53].

Distribution: NE coastal, SE coastal, Murray-Darling basin, QLD, NSW, ACT, VIC, TAS.
Ecology: larva—sedentary : adult—volant; melliferous, solitary, nest in soil, flower visiting record: *Angophora* Cav. [Myrtaceae], *Bursaria* Cav. [Pittosporaceae], *Callistemon* R.Br. [Myrtaceae], *Cotoneaster* Medikus [Rosaceae], *Eucalyptus* L'Hérit. [Myrtaceae], *Jacksonia* Smith [Fabaceae], *Leptospermum* Forster & G.Forster [Myrtaceae], *Leucopogon* R.Br. [Epacridaceae], *Melaleuca* L. [Myrtaceae].
References: Meade-Waldo, G. (1923). Hymenoptera. Fam. Apidae. Subfam. Prosopidinae. *Genera Insectorum* **181**: 1–45 (illustration); Rayment, T. (1948). Notes on remarkable wasps and bees. With specific descriptions. *Aust. Zool.* **11**: 238–254 (biology, as *Euryglossimorpha nigra* Smith, 1879); Rayment, T. (1954). Incidence of acarid mites on the biology of bees. *Aust. Zool.* **12**: 26–38 (as host, as *Euryglossa nigra* (Smith, 1879)); Michener, C.D. (1965). A classification of the bees of the Australian and South Pacific regions. *Bull. Am. Mus. Nat. Hist.* **130**: 1–362 (as *Euryglossa (Euryglossa) obscura* Cockerell, 1929, flower record); Houston, T.F. (1969). Observations on the nests and behaviour of some euryglossine bees (Hymenoptera : Colletidae). *J. Aust. Entomol. Soc.* **8**: 1–10 (biology, as *Euryglossa nigra* Smith, 1879); Ireland, J.C. & Griffin, A.R. (1984). Observations on the pollination ecology of *Eucalyptus muellerana* Howitt in East Gippsland. *Vict. Nat.* **101**: 207–211 (flower record).

Euryglossa (Euryglossa) frenchii Cockerell, 1910

Euryglossa frenchii Cockerell, T.D.A. (1910). Descriptions and records of bees. XXXI. *Ann. Mag. Nat. Hist.* *(8)***6**: 160–168 [167].
Type data: holotype, BMNH Hym.17.a.247 ♀.
Type locality: VIC (label on specimen "Mackay" believed incorrect, no other records from QLD), see Exley, E.M. (1976). Revision of the subgenus *Euryglossa* Smith

(Apoidea : Colletidae : Euryglossinae). *Aust. J. Zool. Suppl. Ser.* **41**: 1–72 [31].

Distribution: Murray-Darling basin, Lake Eyre basin, S Gulfs, NSW, VIC, SA; only published localities near Broken Hill, Wentworth, near Hattah, Mt Serle and near Golden Grove.

Ecology: adult—volant; melliferous, solitary, flower visiting record: *Eucalyptus* L'Hérit. [Myrtaceae].

Reference: Exley, E.M. (1976). Revision of the subgenus *Euryglossa* Smith (Apoidea : Colletidae : Euryglossinae). *Aust. J. Zool. Suppl. Ser.* **41**: 1–72 (redescription).

Euryglossa (Euryglossa) glabra Exley, 1976

Euryglossa (Euryglossa) glabra Exley, E.M. (1976). Revision of the subgenus *Euryglossa* Smith (Apoidea : Colletidae : Euryglossinae). *Aust. J. Zool. Suppl. Ser.* **41**: 1–72 [32].
Type data: holotype, QM T7472 ♀.
Type locality: Morven, QLD.

Distribution: Murray-Darling basin, QLD, NSW; only published localities Morven, Charleville, Mungallala and Bourke.

Ecology: adult—volant; melliferous, solitary, flower visiting record: *Eucalyptus* L'Hérit. [Myrtaceae].

Euryglossa (Euryglossa) haematura Cockerell, 1911

Euryglossa haematura Cockerell, T.D.A. (1911). Descriptions and records of bees. XXXVIII. *Ann. Mag. Nat. Hist. (8)***8**: 283–290 [289].
Type data: holotype, BMNH Hym.17.a.278 ♀.
Type locality: Walcha, NSW.

Distribution: SE coastal, Murray-Darling basin, (QLD), NSW; only published localities Walcha and Barrington Tops, records from Queensland doubtful.

Ecology: larva—sedentary : adult—volant; melliferous, solitary, nest in bank of creek.

References: Cockerell, T.D.A. (1913). Descriptions and records of bees. L. *Ann. Mag. Nat. Hist. (8)***11**: 273–283 (Brisbane; doubtful record); Hacker, H. (1918). Entomological contributions. *Mem. Qd Mus.* **6**: 106–111 pls 31–32 (biology, no locality stated, probably QLD); Rayment, T. (1935). *A Cluster of Bees.* Sixty essays on the life-histories of Australian bees, with specific descriptions of over 100 new species, and an introduction by Professor E.F. Phillips, D.Ph., Cornell University, U.S.A. Sydney : Endeavour Press 752 pp. (biology, doubtful record); Exley, E.M. (1976). Revision of the subgenus *Euryglossa* Smith (Apoidea : Colletidae : Euryglossinae). *Aust. J. Zool. Suppl. Ser.* **41**: 1–72 (redescription).

Euryglossa (Euryglossa) hardyi Exley, 1976

Euryglossa (Euryglossa) hardyi Exley, E.M. (1976). Revision of the subgenus *Euryglossa* Smith (Apoidea : Colletidae : Euryglossinae). *Aust. J. Zool. Suppl. Ser.* **41**: 1–72 [61].

Type data: holotype, QM T7486 ♀.
Type locality: 5 km E Mt Isa, QLD.

Distribution: N Gulf, N coastal, QLD, NT; only published localities near Mt Isa and Pine Creek.

Ecology: adult—volant; melliferous, solitary, flower visiting record: *Eucalyptus* L'Hérit. [Myrtaceae].

Euryglossa (Euryglossa) homora Exley, 1976

Euryglossa (Euryglossa) homora Exley, E.M. (1976). Revision of the subgenus *Euryglossa* Smith (Apoidea : Colletidae : Euryglossinae). *Aust. J. Zool. Suppl. Ser.* **41**: 1–72 [17].
Type data: holotype, QM T7470 ♀.
Type locality: Mt Isa, QLD.

Distribution: N Gulf, Lake Eyre basin, QLD, NT; only published localities Mt Isa, Lake Moondarra, Macdonald Downs, Devils Marbles and Barrow Creek.

Ecology: adult—volant; melliferous, solitary, flower visiting record; *Eucalyptus* L'Hérit. [Myrtaceae].

Euryglossa (Euryglossa) jucunda Smith, 1879

Euryglossa jucunda Smith, F. (1879). *Descriptions of New Species of Hymenoptera in the Collection of the British Museum.* London : British Museum xxi 240 pp. [13] [the type locality has not been resolved; locality on holotype label given as Australia].
Type data: holotype, BMNH Hym.17.a.244 ♀.
Type locality: Geraldton (as Champion Bay district) and Perth (as Swan River), WA.

Distribution: SW coastal, (NW coastal), W plateau, SA, WA; only published localities (Champion Bay and Swan River), Gnowangerup and near Eucla.

Ecology: adult—volant; melliferous, solitary, flower visiting record: *Eucalyptus* L'Hérit. [Myrtaceae].

References: Cockerell, T.D.A. (1910). New and little-known bees. *Trans. Am. Entomol. Soc.* **36**: 199–249 (Mackay; doubtful record); Cockerell, T.D.A. (1922). Australian bees in the Queensland Museum. *Mem. Qd Mus.* **7**: 257–279 (Ebor; doubtful record); Meade-Waldo, G. (1923). Hymenoptera. Fam. Apidae. Subfam. Prosopidinae. *Genera Insectorum* **181**: 1–45 (illustration); Exley, E.M. (1976). Revision of the subgenus *Euryglossa* Smith (Apoidea : Colletidae : Euryglossinae). *Aust. J. Zool. Suppl. Ser.* **41**: 1–72 (redescription).

Euryglossa (Euryglossa) limata Exley, 1976

Euryglossa (Euryglossa) limata Exley, E.M. (1976). Revision of the subgenus *Euryglossa* Smith (Apoidea : Colletidae : Euryglossinae). *Aust. J. Zool. Suppl. Ser.* **41**: 1–72 [47].
Type data: holotype, QM T7481 ♀.
Type locality: 7 miles NE Karratha, WA.

Distribution: NW coastal, WA; known only from type locality.

Ecology: adult—volant; melliferous, solitary, flower visiting record: *Eucalyptus* L'Hérit. [Myrtaceae].

Euryglossa (Euryglossa) liopa Exley, 1976

Euryglossa (Euryglossa) liopa Exley, E.M. (1976). Revision of the subgenus *Euryglossa* Smith (Apoidea : Colletidae : Euryglossinae). *Aust. J. Zool. Suppl. Ser.* **41**: 1–72 [31].
Type data: holotype, ANIC ♀.
Type locality: Millstream, WA.

Distribution: NW coastal, WA; known only from type locality.
Ecology: adult—volant; melliferous, solitary, flower visiting record: *Eucalyptus* L'Hérit. [Myrtaceae].

Euryglossa (Euryglossa) millstreamensis Exley, 1976

Euryglossa (Euryglossa) millstreamensis Exley, E.M. (1976). Revision of the subgenus *Euryglossa* Smith (Apoidea : Colletidae : Euryglossinae). *Aust. J. Zool. Suppl. Ser.* **41**: 1–72 [18].
Type data: holotype, ANIC ♀.
Type locality: Millstream, WA.

Distribution: NW coastal, WA; known only from type locality.
Ecology: adult—volant; melliferous, solitary, flower visiting record: *Eucalyptus* L'Hérit. [Myrtaceae].

Euryglossa (Euryglossa) myrrhina Exley, 1976

Euryglossa (Euryglossa) myrrhina Exley, E.M. (1976). Revision of the subgenus *Euryglossa* Smith (Apoidea : Colletidae : Euryglossinae). *Aust. J. Zool. Suppl. Ser.* **41**: 1–72 [45].
Type data: holotype, QM T7479 ♀.
Type locality: Macdonald Downs, NT.

Distribution: Lake Eyre basin, NT; known only from type locality.
Ecology: adult—volant; melliferous, solitary.

Euryglossa (Euryglossa) nigrocaerulea Cockerell, 1913

Euryglossa nigrocaerulea Cockerell, T.D.A. (1913). Some Australian bees. *Proc. Acad. Nat. Sci. Philad.* **65**: 28–44 [33].
Type data: syntypes, USNM 2♀*.
Type locality: Croydon, VIC.
Euryglossa nubilipennis Cockerell, T.D.A. (1914). Descriptions and records of bees. LXII. *Ann. Mag. Nat. Hist. (8)***14**: 49–57 [56].
Type data: holotype, BMNH Hym.17.a.251 ♀.
Type locality: Mt Wellington, TAS.
Euryglossa depressa extrema Rayment, T. (1935). *A Cluster of Bees*. Sixty essays on the life-histories of Australian bees, with specific descriptions of over 100 new species, and an introduction by Professor E.F. Phillips, D.Ph., Cornell University, U.S.A. Sydney : Endeavour Press 752 pp. [641].
Type data: holotype, ANIC ♀.
Type locality: Wilsons Promontory, VIC.
Euryglossimorpha proxima Rayment, T. (1935). *A Cluster of Bees*. Sixty essays on the life-histories of Australian

bees, with specific descriptions of over 100 new species, and an introduction by Professor E.F. Phillips, D.Ph., Cornell University, U.S.A. Sydney : Endeavour Press 752 pp. [665].
Type data: holotype, ANIC ♂.
Type locality: Croydon, VIC (no locality given in original description), see Exley, E.M. (1976). Revision of the subgenus *Euryglossa* Smith (Apoidea : Colletidae : Euryglossinae). *Aust. J. Zool. Suppl. Ser.* **41**: 1–72 [25].
Euryglossidia punctata Rayment, T. (1935). *A Cluster of Bees*. Sixty essays on the life-histories of Australian bees, with specific descriptions of over 100 new species, and an introduction by Professor E.F. Phillips, D.Ph., Cornell University, U.S.A. Sydney : Endeavour Press 752 pp. [682].
Type data: holotype, ANIC ♀.
Type locality: Botanic Gardens, Melbourne, VIC.

Taxonomic decision for synonymy: Exley, E.M. (1976). Revision of the subgenus *Euryglossa* Smith (Apoidea : Colletidae : Euryglossinae). *Aust. J. Zool. Suppl. Ser.* **41**: 1–72 [23].

Distribution: NE coastal, SE coastal, Murray-Darling basin, S Gulfs, QLD, NSW, ACT, VIC, SA, TAS.
Ecology: adult—volant; melliferous, solitary, flower visiting record: *Eucalyptus* L'Hérit. [Myrtaceae], *Leptospermum* Forster & G.Forster [Myrtaceae], *Melaleuca* L. [Myrtaceae].

Euryglossa (Euryglossa) noosae Exley, 1976

Euryglossa (Euryglossa) noosae Exley, E.M. (1976). Revision of the subgenus *Euryglossa* Smith (Apoidea : Colletidae : Euryglossinae). *Aust. J. Zool. Suppl. Ser.* **41**: 1–72 [41].
Type data: holotype, QM T7477 ♀.
Type locality: Noosa, QLD.

Distribution: NE coastal, QLD; known only from type locality.
Ecology: adult—volant; melliferous, solitary, flower visiting record: *Eucalyptus* L'Hérit. [Myrtaceae], *Eugenia* L. [Myrtaceae].

Euryglossa (Euryglossa) pammicta Exley, 1976

Euryglossa (Euryglossa) pammicta Exley, E.M. (1976). Revision of the subgenus *Euryglossa* Smith (Apoidea : Colletidae : Euryglossinae). *Aust. J. Zool. Suppl. Ser.* **41**: 1–72 [63].
Type data: holotype, QM T7488 ♀.
Type locality: 9 miles NE Oodla Wirra, SA.

Distribution: Lake Eyre basin, W plateau, SA, WA; only published localities near Oodla Wirra, near Eucla, near Coolgardie and Booanya.
Ecology: adult—volant; melliferous, solitary, flower visiting record: *Eucalyptus* L'Hérit. [Myrtaceae].

Euryglossa (Euryglossa) pavonura Cockerell, 1910

Euryglossa pavonura Cockerell, T.D.A. (1910). New and little-known bees. *Trans. Am. Entomol. Soc.* **36**: 199–249 [211].
Type data: syntypes, BMNH 2♀ (one specimen is labelled

'type' and has the registration number Hym.17.a.2639).
Type locality: Cooktown, QLD.

Distribution: NE coastal, QLD; only published localities Cooktown and Prince of Wales Is.
Ecology: adult—volant; melliferous, solitary.
Reference: Exley, E.M. (1976). Revision of the subgenus *Euryglossa* Smith (Apoidea : Colletidae : Euryglossinae). *Aust. J. Zool. Suppl. Ser.* **41**: 1–72 (redescription, as *Euryglossa (Euryglossa) parvonura,* incorrect subsequent spelling).

Euryglossa (Euryglossa) politifrons Cockerell, 1922

Euryglossa politifrons Cockerell, T.D.A. (1922). Australian bees in the Queensland Museum. *Mem. Qd Mus.* **7**: 257–279 [271].
Type data: holotype, QM T2452 ♀.
Type locality: Emerald, QLD.

Distribution: NE coastal, Murray-Darling basin, N Gulf, QLD, NSW.
Ecology: adult—volant; melliferous, solitary, flower visiting record: *Eucalyptus* L'Hérit. [Myrtaceae], *Melaleuca* L. [Myrtaceae], *Tristania* R.Br. [Myrtaceae].
Reference: Exley, E.M. (1976). Revision of the subgenus *Euryglossa* Smith (Apoidea : Colletidae : Euryglossinae). *Aust. J. Zool. Suppl. Ser.* **41**: 1–72 (redescription).

Euryglossa (Euryglossa) rhodochlora Cockerell, 1914

Euryglossa rhodochlora Cockerell, T.D.A. (1914). Descriptions and records of bees. LXIV. *Ann. Mag. Nat. Hist. (8)***14**: 464–472 [470].
Type data: holotype, BMNH Hym.17.a.261 ♀.
Type locality: Yarrawin (Brewarrina), NSW.

Distribution: Murray-Darling basin, QLD, NSW.
Ecology: adult—volant; melliferous, solitary, flower visiting record: *Eucalyptus* L'Hérit. [Myrtaceae].
Reference: Exley, E.M. (1976). Revision of the subgenus *Euryglossa* Smith (Apoidea : Colletidae : Euryglossinae). *Aust. J. Zool. Suppl. Ser.* **41**: 1–72 (redescription).

Euryglossa (Euryglossa) rubricata Smith, 1879

Euryglossa rubricata Smith, F. (1879). *Descriptions of New Species of Hymenoptera in the Collection of the British Museum.* London : British Museum xxi 240 pp. [12].
Type data: holotype, BMNH Hym.17.a.246 ♀.
Type locality: Swan River, WA.

Euryglossa tricolor Smith, F. (1879). *Descriptions of New Species of Hymenoptera in the Collection of the British Museum.* London : British Museum xxi 240 pp. [15].
Type data: holotype, BMNH Hym.17.a.264 ♀.
Type locality: Swan River, WA.

Taxonomic decision for synonymy: Exley, E.M. (1976). Revision of the subgenus *Euryglossa* Smith (Apoidea : Col-

letidae : Euryglossinae). *Aust. J. Zool. Suppl. Ser.* **41**: 1–72 [12].

Distribution: Murray-Darling basin, Lake Eyre basin, W plateau, SW coastal, VIC, SA, WA.
Ecology: adult—volant; melliferous, solitary, flower visiting record: *Eucalyptus* L'Hérit. [Myrtaceae].
References: Cockerell, T.D.A. (1905). Description and records of bees II. *Ann. Mag. Nat. Hist. (7)***16**: 292–301 (QLD, doubtful record); Rayment, T. (1939). Bees from the high lands of New South Wales and Victoria. *Aust. Zool.* **9**: 263–294 (White Swamp, doubtful record).

Euryglossa (Euryglossa) salaris Cockerell, 1910

Euryglossa salaris Cockerell, T.D.A. (1910). New and little-known bees. *Trans. Am. Entomol. Soc.* **36**: 199–249 [210].
Type data: holotype, BMNH Hym.17.a.268 ♀.
Type locality: Mackay, QLD.

Distribution: NE coastal, Murray-Darling basin, Lake Eyre basin, QLD, NSW, SA.
Ecology: adult—volant; melliferous, solitary, flower visiting record: *Eucalyptus* L'Hérit. [Myrtaceae], *Tristania* R.Br. [Myrtaceae].
Reference: Exley, E.M. (1976). Revision of the subgenus *Euryglossa* Smith (Apoidea : Colletidae : Euryglossinae). *Aust. J. Zool. Suppl. Ser.* **41**: 1–72 (redescription).

Euryglossa (Euryglossa) schomburgki Cockerell, 1910

Euryglossa schomburgki Cockerell, T.D.A. (1910). Some Australian bees in the Berlin Museum. *J. N.Y. Entomol. Soc.* **18**: 98–114 [99].
Type data: holotype, ZMB 22116 ♀*.
Type locality: Adelaide, SA.

Euryglossa tenuicornis Cockerell, T.D.A. (1913). Some Australian bees. *Proc. Acad. Nat. Sci. Philad.* **65**: 28–44 [34].
Type data: syntypes, BMNH 3♂.
Type locality: Purnong, SA.

Taxonomic decision for synonymy: Exley, E.M. (1976). Revision of the subgenus *Euryglossa* Smith (Apoidea : Colletidae : Euryglossinae). *Aust. J. Zool. Suppl. Ser.* **41**: 1–72 [21].

Distribution: Murray-Darling basin, S Gulfs, SW coastal, W plateau, SA, WA.
Ecology: adult—volant; melliferous, solitary, flower visiting record: *Eucalyptus* L'Hérit. [Myrtaceae].
References: Rayment, T. (1939). Bees from the high lands of New South Wales and Victoria. *Aust. Zool.* **9**: 263–294 (Sydney; doubtful record).

Euryglossa (Euryglossa) subfusa Cockerell, 1910

Euryglossa subfusa Cockerell, T.D.A. (1910). New and little-known bees. *Trans. Am. Entomol. Soc.* **36**: 199–249 [210].

Type data: holotype, BMNH Hym.17.a.270 ♀.
Type locality: Darwin, NT.

Distribution: NE coastal, N coastal, QLD, NT; only published localities Herberton, Darwin, Rapid Creek, Berrimah and Nourlangie Creek.

Ecology: adult—volant; melliferous, solitary, flower visiting record: *Eucalyptus* L'Hérit. [Myrtaceae], *Tristania* R.Br. [Myrtaceae].

References: Meade-Waldo, G. (1923). Hymenoptera. Fam. Apidae. Subfam. Prosopidinae. *Genera Insectorum* **181**: 1–45 (as *Euryglossa subfusca*, incorrect subsequent spelling); Exley, E.M. (1976). Revision of the subgenus *Euryglossa* Smith (Apoidea : Colletidae : Euryglossinae). *Aust. J. Zool. Suppl. Ser.* **41**: 1–72 (redescription).

Euryglossa (Euryglossa) subsericea Cockerell, 1905

Euryglossa subsericea Cockerell, T.D.A. (1905). Descriptions and records of bees. II. *Ann. Mag. Nat. Hist. (7)***16**: 292–301 [293].
Type data: holotype, BMNH Hym.17.a.245 ♀.
Type locality: QLD.

Euryglossa reginae Cockerell, T.D.A. (1905). Descriptions and records of bees. V. *Ann. Mag. Nat. Hist. (7)***16**: 465–477 [475].
Type data: holotype, BMNH Hym.17.a.287 ♂.
Type locality: Mackay, QLD.

Stilpnosoma turneri Baker, C.F. (1906). The bee genus *Pasiphae* in North America. pp. 141–142 *in* Baker, C.F. (ed.) *Invertebrata Pacifica*. Hampton : Classey Vol. 1 (Reprinted 1969) [141] [publication validated a manuscript name of Friese who published it as a new species in 1924].
Type data: syntypes, AMNH ♀* (number of specimens unknown).
Type locality: Mackay, QLD.

Euryglossa aurescens Cockerell, T.D.A. (1913). Descriptions and records of bees. LV. *Ann. Mag. Nat. Hist. (8)***12**: 505–514 [509].
Type data: holotype, BMNH Hym.17.a.266 ♀.
Type locality: Mackay, QLD.

Stilpnosoma thoracicum Friese, H. (1924). Ueber die Bienen Australiens. *Konowia* **3**: 216–249 [233].
Type data: syntypes, AMNH ♀* (number of specimens unknown).
Type locality: Mackay, QLD.

Stilpnosoma ventrale Friese, H. (1924). Ueber die Bienen Australiens. *Konowia* **3**: 216–249 [233].
Type data: syntypes, whereabouts unknown 3♀*.
Type locality: Mackay, QLD.

Stilpnosoma turneri Friese, H. (1924). Ueber die Bienen Australiens. *Konowia* **3**: 216–249 [234] [junior primary homonym and junior objective synonym of *Stilpnosoma turneri* Baker, 1906; junior primary homonym of *Stilpnosoma turneri* Friese, 1917].

Taxonomic decision for synonymy: Exley, E.M. (1976). Revision of the subgenus *Euryglossa* Smith (Apoidea : Colletidae : Euryglossinae). *Aust. J. Zool. Suppl. Ser.* **41**: 1–72 [49].

Distribution: NE coastal, Murray-Darling basin, SE coastal, QLD, NSW, VIC.

Ecology: larva—sedentary : adult—volant; melliferous, solitary, nest in soil, flower visiting record: *Angophora* Cav. [Myrtaceae], *Dendrobium* Sw. [Orchidaceae], *Eucalyptus* L'Hérit. [Myrtaceae], *Eugenia* L. [Myrtaceae], *Leptospermum* Forster & G.Forster [Myrtaceae], *Melaleuca* L. [Myrtaceae], *Tristania* R.Br. [Myrtaceae].

References: Cockerell, T.D.A. (1929). Bees, chiefly Australian species, described or determined by Dr. H. Friese. *Am. Mus. Novit.* **343**: 1–20 (taxonomy); MacPherson, K. & Rupp, H.M.R. (1936). Further notes on orchid pollination. *N. Qd Nat.* **4**(43): 25–26 (flower record); Michener, C.D. (1960). Notes on the behavior of Australian colletid bees. *J. Kansas Entomol. Soc.* **33**: 22–31 (biology); McGinley, R.J. (1981). Systematics of the Colletidae based on mature larvae with phenetic analysis of apoid larvae (Insecta, Hymenoptera, Apoidea). *Univ. Calif. Publ. Entomol.* **91**: 1–309 (larva); Michener, C.D. & Brooks, R.W. (1984). A comparative study of the glossae of bees (Apoidea). *Contrib. Am. Entomol. Inst.* **22**: 1–73 (glossa); Michener, C.D. (1992). Sexual dimorphism in the glossa of Colletidae (Hymenoptera, Apoidea). *J. Kansas Entomol. Soc.* **65**: 1–9 (glossa).

Euryglossa (Euryglossa) terminata Smith, 1853

Euryglossa terminata Smith, F. (1853). *Catalogue of Hymenopterous Insects in the Collection of the British Museum. Part I. Andrenidae and Apidae.* London : British Museum 197 pp. [18].
Type data: holotype, OUM ♀.
Type locality: Australia (as New Holland).

Euryglossimorpha ruficauda Rayment, T. (1948). Notes on remarkable wasps and bees. With specific descriptions. *Aust. Zool.* **11**: 238–254 [245].
Type data: holotype, ANIC ♀.
Type locality: Patonga, NSW.

Taxonomic decision for synonymy: Exley, E.M. (1976). Revision of the subgenus *Euryglossa* Smith (Apoidea : Colletidae : Euryglossinae). *Aust. J. Zool. Suppl. Ser.* **41**: 1–72 [59].

Distribution: NE coastal, Murray-Darling basin, SE coastal, QLD, NSW; only published localities Brisbane, near Emu Vale and Patonga.

Ecology: adult—volant; melliferous, solitary, flower visiting record: *Eucalyptus* L'Hérit. [Myrtaceae].

Reference: McGinley, R.J. (1980). Glossal morphology of the Colletidae and recognition of the Stenotritidae at the family level (Hymenoptera : Apoidea). *J. Kansas Entomol. Soc.* **53**: 539–552 (glossa).

Euryglossa (Euryglossa) tolgae Exley, 1976

Euryglossa (Euryglossa) tolgae Exley, E.M. (1976). Revision of the subgenus *Euryglossa* Smith (Apoidea : Colletidae : Euryglossinae). *Aust. J. Zool. Suppl. Ser.* **41**: 1–72 [55].

Type data: holotype, QM T7484 ♀.
Type locality: 5 miles N Tolga, QLD.

Distribution: NE coastal, QLD; only published localities near Tolga, Kuranda, Mareeba, Meringa and Hervey Range.
Ecology: adult—volant; melliferous, solitary, flower visiting record: *Eucalyptus* L'Hérit. [Myrtaceae], *Melaleuca* L. [Myrtaceae], *Tristania* R.Br. [Myrtaceae].

Euryglossa (Euryglossa) trichoda Exley, 1976

Euryglossa (Euryglossa) trichoda Exley, E.M. (1976). Revision of the subgenus *Euryglossa* Smith (Apoidea : Colletidae : Euryglossinae). *Aust. J. Zool. Suppl. Ser.* **41**: 1–72 [20].
Type data: holotype, QM T7471 ♂.
Type locality: 3 miles SW Warwick, QLD.

Distribution: Murray-Darling basin, QLD; only published localities near Warwick and Amiens.
Ecology: adult—volant; melliferous, solitary, flower visiting record: *Leptospermum* Forster & G.Forster [Myrtaceae].

Euryglossa (Euryglossa) victoriae Cockerell, 1910

Euryglossa victoriae Cockerell, T.D.A. (1910). New and little-known bees. *Trans. Am. Entomol. Soc.* **36**: 199–249 [207].
Type data: holotype, BMNH Hym.17.a.286 ♀.
Type locality: VIC.

Euryglossidia murrayensis Rayment, T. (1935). *A Cluster of Bees*. Sixty essays on the life-histories of Australian bees, with specific descriptions of over 100 new species, and an introduction by Professor E.F. Phillips, D.Ph., Cornell University, U.S.A. Sydney : Endeavour Press 752 pp. [681].
Type data: holotype, ANIC ♀.
Type locality: Gunbower, VIC.

Euryglossa rhodochlora scutellata Rayment, T. (1939). Bees from the high lands of New South Wales and Victoria. *Aust. Zool.* **9**: 263–294 [269].
Type data: holotype, ANIC ♀.
Type locality: Gunbower, VIC.

Taxonomic decision for synonymy: Exley, E.M. (1976). Revision of the subgenus *Euryglossa* Smith (Apoidea : Colletidae : Euryglossinae). *Aust. J. Zool. Suppl. Ser.* **41**: 1–72 [14].

Distribution: Murray-Darling basin, W plateau, VIC, SA; only published localities Gunbower, Wyperfeld National Park and near Eucla.
Ecology: adult—volant; melliferous, solitary, flower visiting record: *Eucalyptus* L'Hérit. [Myrtaceae].

Euryglossa (Callohesma) Michener, 1965

Callohesma Michener, C.D. (1965). A classification of the bees of the Australian and South Pacific regions. *Bull. Am. Mus. Nat. Hist.* **130**: 1–362 [95] [proposed with subgeneric rank in *Euryglossa* Smith, 1853]. Type species: *Euryglossa calliopsiformis* Cockerell, 1905 by original designation.

Generic reference: Exley, E.M. (1974). A contribution to our knowledge of Australia's smallest bees with descriptions of new species (Hymenoptera : Colletidae : Euryglossinae). *J. Aust. Entomol. Soc.* **13**: 1–9.

Euryglossa (Callohesma) albiceris Exley, 1974

Euryglossa (Callohesma) albiceris Exley, E.M. (1974). Revision of the subgenus *Callohesma* Michener (Apoidea : Colletidae). *Aust. J. Zool. Suppl. Ser.* **26**: 1–58 [35].
Type data: holotype, QM T7358 ♀.
Type locality: Lake Moondarra, Mt Isa, QLD.

Distribution: N Gulf, QLD; only published localities Mt Isa and vicinity.
Ecology: adult—volant; melliferous, solitary, flower visiting record: *Eucalyptus* L'Hérit. [Myrtaceae].

Euryglossa (Callohesma) aurantifera Cockerell, 1912

Euryglossa aurantifera Cockerell, T.D.A. (1912). Descriptions and records of bees. XLI. *Ann. Mag. Nat. Hist. (8)***9**: 139–149 [143].
Type data: holotype (probable), USNM ♀*.
Type locality: Sydney, NSW.

Euryglossa cambournii Rayment, T. (1939). Bees from the high lands of New South Wales and Victoria. *Aust. Zool.* **9**: 263–294 [270].
Type data: holotype, ANIC ♀.
Type locality: Gosford, NSW.

Taxonomic decision for synonymy: Exley, E.M. (1974). Revision of the subgenus *Callohesma* Michener (Apoidea : Colletidae). *Aust. J. Zool. Suppl. Ser.* **26**: 1–58 [30].

Distribution: NE coastal, SE coastal, QLD, NSW, VIC.
Ecology: adult—volant; melliferous, solitary, flower visiting record: *Leptospermum* Forster & G.Forster [Myrtaceae], *Melaleuca* L. [Myrtaceae].
Reference: Rayment, T. (1953). *Bees of the Portland District*. Victoria : Portland Field Naturalist's Club 39 pp. (flower record).

Euryglossa (Callohesma) aureopicta Cockerell, 1929

Euryglossa aureopicta Cockerell, T.D.A. (1929). Bees in the Australian Museum collection. *Rec. Aust. Mus.* **17**: 199–243 [214].
Type data: holotype, AM K48295 ♀.
Type locality: King George Sound, WA.

Distribution: SW coastal, W plateau, WA.
Ecology: adult—volant; melliferous, solitary, flower visiting record: *Eucalyptus* L'Hérit. [Myrtaceae].
Reference: Exley, E.M. (1974). Revision of the subgenus *Callohesma* Michener (Apoidea : Colletidae). *Aust. J. Zool. Suppl. Ser.* **26**: 1–58 (redescription, distribution).

Euryglossa (Callohesma) calliopsella Cockerell, 1910

Euryglossa calliopsella Cockerell, T.D.A. (1910). New and little-known bees. *Trans. Am. Entomol. Soc.* **36**: 199–249 [208].
Type data: lectotype, BMNH Hym.17.a.284 ♀.
Subsequent designation: Exley, E.M. (1974). Revision of the subgenus *Callohesma* Michener (Apoidea : Colletidae). *Aust. J. Zool. Suppl. Ser.* **26**: 1–58 [42]; Cardale, J.C., this work, interprets Exley's incorrect inference of holotype as a lectotype designation (Art. 74, ICZN 1985).
Type locality: VIC.

Distribution: NE coastal, SE coastal, Murray-Darling basin, S Gulfs, QLD, NSW, VIC, SA.
Ecology: adult—volant; melliferous, solitary, flower visiting record: *Angophora* Cav. [Myrtaceae]; *Eucalyptus* L'Hér. [Myrtaceae]; *Leptospermum* Forster & G.Forster [Myrtaceae].
References: Cockerell, T.D.A. (1911). Descriptions and records of bees. XXXVIII. *Ann. Mag. Nat. Hist.* *(8)***8**: 283–290 (description of male); Rayment, T. (1935). *A Cluster of Bees*. Sixty essays on the life-histories of Australian bees, with specific descriptions of over 100 new species, and an introduction by Professor E.F. Phillips, D.Ph., Cornell University, U.S.A. Sydney : Endeavour Press 752 pp. (illustration); Exley, E.M. (1974). Revision of the subgenus *Callohesma* Michener (Apoidea : Colletidae). *Aust. J. Zool. Suppl. Ser.* **26**: 1–58 (redescription).

Euryglossa (Callohesma) calliopsiformis Cockerell, 1905

Euryglossa calliopsiformis Cockerell, T.D.A. (1905). Descriptions and records of bees. II. *Ann. Mag. Nat. Hist.* *(7)***16**: 292–301 [293].
Type data: holotype, BMNH Hym.17.a.288 ♀.
Type locality: Mackay, QLD.

Distribution: NE coastal, SE coastal, Murray-Darling basin, SW coastal, QLD, NSW, ACT, VIC, WA.
Ecology: adult—volant; melliferous, solitary, flower visiting record: *Angophora* Cav. [Myrtaceae], *Eucalyptus* L'Hér. [Myrtaceae], *Eugenia* L. [Myrtaceae], *Jacksonia* Smith [Fabaceae], *Leptospermum* Forster & G.Forster [Myrtaceae], *Melaleuca* L. [Myrtaceae].
References: Cockerell, T.D.A. (1914). Australian bees of the genus *Euryglossa*. *Entomologist* **47**: 213–215 (description of male); Michener, C.D. (1965). A classification of the bees of the Australian and South Pacific regions. *Bull. Am. Mus. Nat. Hist.* **130**: 1–362 (flower records); Exley, E.M. (1974). Revision of the subgenus *Callohesma* Michener (Apoidea : Colletidae). *Aust. J. Zool. Suppl. Ser.* **26**: 1–58 (redescription).

Euryglossa (Callohesma) campbelli Cockerell, 1929

Euryglossa campbelli Cockerell, T.D.A. (1929). Bees in the Australian Museum collection. *Rec. Aust. Mus.* **17**: 199–243 [213].

Type data: holotype, AM ♀.
Type locality: Almaden, QLD.

Distribution: N Gulf, QLD; known only from type locality.
Ecology: adult—volant; melliferous, solitary.
Reference: Exley, E.M. (1974). Revision of the subgenus *Callohesma* Michener (Apoidea : Colletidae). *Aust. J. Zool. Suppl. Ser.* **26**: 1–58 (redescription).

Euryglossa (Callohesma) chlora Exley, 1974

Euryglossa (Callohesma) chlora Exley, E.M. (1974). Revision of the subgenus *Callohesma* Michener (Apoidea : Colletidae). *Aust. J. Zool. Suppl. Ser.* **26**: 1–58 [14].
Type data: holotype, ANIC ♀.
Type locality: 14 miles N Barrow Creek, NT.

Distribution: Lake Eyre basin, NT; known only from type locality.
Ecology: adult—volant; melliferous, solitary.

Euryglossa (Callohesma) coolgardensis Exley, 1974

Euryglossa (Callohesma) coolgardensis Exley, E.M. (1974). Revision of the subgenus *Callohesma* Michener (Apoidea : Colletidae). *Aust. J. Zool. Suppl. Ser.* **26**: 1–58 [11].
Type data: holotype, QM T7372 ♂.
Type locality: 10 miles S Coolgardie, WA.

Distribution: W plateau, WA; known only from type locality.
Ecology: adult—volant; melliferous, solitary, flower visiting record: *Eucalyptus* L'Hérit. [Myrtaceae].

Euryglossa (Callohesma) eustonensis Exley, 1974

Euryglossa (Callohesma) eustonensis Exley, E.M. (1974). Revision of the subgenus *Callohesma* Michener (Apoidea : Colletidae). *Aust. J. Zool. Suppl. Ser.* **26**: 1–58 [9].
Type data: holotype, QM T7373 ♀.
Type locality: 20 miles E Euston, NSW.

Distribution: Murray-Darling basin, NSW, VIC, SA; only published localities near Euston, Wyperfeld National Park and Hartley.
Ecology: adult—volant; melliferous, solitary, flower visiting record: *Eucalyptus* L'Hérit. [Myrtaceae].

Euryglossa (Callohesma) euxantha Perkins, 1912

Euryglossa euxantha Perkins, R.C.L. (1912). Notes, with descriptions of new species, on aculeate Hymenoptera of the Australian Region. *Ann. Mag. Nat. Hist.* *(8)***9**: 96–121 [111].
Type data: holotype, BMNH Hym.17.a.2620 ♀.
Type locality: Darwin, NT.

Distribution: NE coastal, Murray-Darling basin, N coastal, QLD, SA, NT.
Ecology: adult—volant; melliferous, solitary, flower visiting record: *Eucalyptus* L'Hérit. [Myrtaceae].
Reference: Exley, E.M. (1974). Revision of the subgenus *Callohesma* Michener (Apoidea : Colletidae). *Aust. J. Zool. Suppl. Ser.* **26**: 1–58 (redescription).

Euryglossa (Callohesma) flava Exley, 1974

Euryglossa (Callohesma) flava Exley, E.M. (1974). Revision of the subgenus *Callohesma* Michener (Apoidea : Colletidae). *Aust. J. Zool. Suppl. Ser.* **26**: 1–58 [50].
Type data: holotype, QM T7377 ♀.
Type locality: Mt Isa, QLD.

Distribution: N Gulf, Lake Eyre basin, QLD, NT; only published localities Mt Isa, Lake Moondarra and Macdonald Downs.
Ecology: adult—volant; melliferous, solitary, flower visiting record: *Eucalyptus* L'Hérit. [Myrtaceae].

Euryglossa (Callohesma) flavopicta Smith, 1879

Euryglossa flavopicta Smith, F. (1879). *Descriptions of New Species of Hymenoptera in the Collection of the British Museum.* London : British Museum xxi 240 pp. [14].
Type data: holotype, BMNH Hym.17.a.243 ♀.
Type locality: Geraldton (as Champion Bay), WA.

Euryglossa tridentifrons Cockerell, T.D.A. (1913). Descriptions and records of bees. LV. *Ann. Mag. Nat. Hist. (8)***12**: 505–514 [510].
Type data: holotype, BMNH Hym.17.a.238 ♂.
Type locality: Nagambie, VIC.

Euryglossa strigosa Rayment, T. (1935). *A Cluster of Bees.* Sixty essays on the life-histories of Australian bees, with specific descriptions of over 100 new species, and an introduction by Professor E.F. Phillips, D.Ph., Cornell University, U.S.A. Sydney : Endeavour Press 752 pp. [638].
Type data: holotype, ANIC ♀.
Type locality: Sandringham, VIC.

Euryglossa raffae Rayment, T. (1935). *A Cluster of Bees.* Sixty essays on the life-histories of Australian bees, with specific descriptions of over 100 new species, and an introduction by Professor E.F. Phillips, D.Ph., Cornell University, U.S.A. Sydney : Endeavour Press 752 pp. [639].
Type data: holotype, ANIC ♀.
Type locality: Mallacoota, Gippsland, VIC.

Taxonomic decision for synonymy: Exley, E.M. (1974). Revision of the subgenus *Callohesma* Michener (Apoidea : Colletidae). *Aust. J. Zool. Suppl. Ser.* **26**: 1–58 [45].

Distribution: NE coastal, SE coastal, Murray-Darling basin, S Gulfs, SW coastal, NW coastal, QLD, NSW, ACT, VIC, SA, WA.
Ecology: adult—volant; melliferous, solitary, flower visiting record: *Angophora* Cav. [Myrtaceae], *Eucalyptus* L'Hérit. [Myrtaceae], *Leptospermum* Forster & G.Forster [Myrtaceae], *Melaleuca* L. [Myrtaceae].

Euryglossa (Callohesma) geminata Cockerell, 1911

Euryglossa geminata Cockerell, T.D.A. (1911). Descriptions and records of bees. XXXVIII. *Ann. Mag. Nat. Hist. (8)***8**: 283–290 [289].
Type data: holotype, BMNH Hym.17.a.257 ♀.
Type locality: Cheltenham, VIC.

Distribution: SE coastal, VIC; only published localities Cheltenham, Tooradin, Mt Yule (Healesville) and Cranbourne.
Ecology: adult—volant; melliferous, solitary, flower visiting record: *Eucalyptus* L'Hérit. [Myrtaceae].
Reference: Exley, E.M. (1974). Revision of the subgenus *Callohesma* Michener (Apoidea : Colletidae). *Aust. J. Zool. Suppl. Ser.* **26**: 1–58 (redescription).

Euryglossa (Callohesma) karratha Exley, 1974

Euryglossa (Callohesma) karratha Exley, E.M. (1974). Revision of the subgenus *Callohesma* Michener (Apoidea : Colletidae). *Aust. J. Zool. Suppl. Ser.* **26**: 1–58 [14].
Type data: holotype, QM T7371 ♀.
Type locality: NW Coastal Highway, 7 miles NE Karratha, WA.

Distribution: NW coastal, WA; known only from type locality.
Ecology: adult—volant; melliferous, solitary, flower visiting record: *Eucalyptus* L'Hérit. [Myrtaceae].

Euryglossa (Callohesma) lacteipennis Michener, 1965

Euryglossa (Callohesma) lacteipennis Michener, C.D. (1965). A classification of the bees of the Australian and South Pacific regions. *Bull. Am. Mus. Nat. Hist.* **130**: 1–362 [276].
Type data: holotype, BMNH Hym.17.a.2824 ♀.
Type locality: Yanchep, WA.

Distribution: SW coastal, WA; known only from type locality.
Ecology: adult—volant; melliferous, solitary.

Euryglossa (Callohesma) lucida Exley, 1974

Euryglossa (Callohesma) lucida Exley, E.M. (1974). Revision of the subgenus *Callohesma* Michener (Apoidea : Colletidae). *Aust. J. Zool. Suppl. Ser.* **26**: 1–58 [49].
Type data: holotype, QM T7379 ♀.
Type locality: 4–14 miles W Coolgardie, WA.

Distribution: W plateau, WA; only published localities near Coolgardie and Dedari.
Ecology: adult—volant; melliferous, solitary, flower visiting record: *Eucalyptus* L'Hérit. [Myrtaceae].

Euryglossa (Callohesma) matthewsi Exley, 1974

Euryglossa (Callohesma) matthewsi Exley, E.M. (1974). Revision of the subgenus *Callohesma* Michener (Apoidea : Colletidae). *Aust. J. Zool. Suppl. Ser.* **26**: 1–58 [12].
Type data: holotype, QM T7384 ♀.
Type locality: Wyperfeld National Park, VIC.

Distribution: Murray-Darling basin, W plateau, SW coastal, VIC, WA; only published localities Wyperfeld National Park, Kukerin, Dedari and Lake King.
Ecology: adult—volant; melliferous, solitary.
Reference: Evans, H.E. & Matthews, R.W. (1973). Systematics and nesting behavior of Australian

Bembix sand wasps (Hymenoptera, Sphecidae). *Mem. Am. Entomol. Inst.* **20**: 1–387 (as prey, as *Euryglossa (Callohesma)* sp.).

Euryglossa (Callohesma) megachlora Exley, 1974

Euryglossa (Callohesma) megachlora Exley, E.M. (1974). Revision of the subgenus *Callohesma* Michener (Apoidea : Colletidae). *Aust. J. Zool. Suppl. Ser.* **26**: 1–58 [16].
Type data: holotype, BMNH Hym.17.a.2844 ♀.
Type locality: Spargoville, 28 miles W Coolgardie, WA.

Distribution: W plateau, WA; known only from type locality.
Ecology: adult—volant; melliferous, solitary.

Euryglossa (Callohesma) nigripicta Exley, 1974

Euryglossa (Callohesma) nigripicta Exley, E.M. (1974). Revision of the subgenus *Callohesma* Michener (Apoidea : Colletidae). *Aust. J. Zool. Suppl. Ser.* **26**: 1–58 [22].
Type data: holotype, QM T7385 ♀.
Type locality: Gnowangerup, WA.

Distribution: SW coastal, WA; only published localities Gnowangerup and Cranbrook.
Ecology: adult—volant; melliferous, solitary.

Euryglossa (Callohesma) occidentalis Exley, 1974

Euryglossa (Callohesma) occidentalis Exley, E.M. (1974). Revision of the subgenus *Callohesma* Michener (Apoidea : Colletidae). *Aust. J. Zool. Suppl. Ser.* **26**: 1–58 [52].
Type data: holotype, ANIC ♀.
Type locality: Bunbury, WA.

Distribution: SW coastal, WA; only published localities Bunbury and vicinity, and Perth.
Ecology: adult—volant; melliferous, solitary.

Euryglossa (Callohesma) ornatula Cockerell, 1929

Euryglossa flavopicta ornatula Cockerell, T.D.A. (1929). Bees in the Australian Museum collection. *Rec. Aust. Mus.* **17**: 199–243 [213].
Type data: holotype, BMNH Hym.17.a.267 ♀.
Type locality: Brisbane, QLD.

Distribution: NE coastal, SE coastal, QLD, NSW, VIC; only published localities Brisbane, Lugano, Sydney and Mt Yule.
Ecology: adult—volant; melliferous, solitary, flower visiting record: *Eucalyptus* L'Hérit. [Myrtaceae].
References: Cockerell, T.D.A. (1916). A collection of bees from Queensland. *Mem. Qd Mus.* **5**: 197–204 (as *Euryglossa flavopicta* Smith, 1879); Cockerell, T.D.A. (1929). Bees in the Queensland Museum. *Mem. Qd Mus.* **9**: 298–323 (distribution); Michener, C.D. (1965). A classification of the bees of the Australian and South Pacific regions. *Bull. Am. Mus. Nat. Hist.* **130**: 1–362 [96] (taxonomy); Exley, E.M. (1974). Revision of the subgenus *Callohesma* Michener (Apoidea : Colletidae). *Aust. J. Zool. Suppl. Ser.* **26**: 1–58 (redescription).

Euryglossa (Callohesma) pedalis Exley, 1974

Euryglossa (Callohesma) pedalis Exley, E.M. (1974). Revision of the subgenus *Callohesma* Michener (Apoidea : Colletidae). *Aust. J. Zool. Suppl. Ser.* **26**: 1–58 [38].
Type data: holotype, QM T7362 ♀.
Type locality: Glenmorgan, QLD.

Distribution: NE coastal, Murray-Darling basin, QLD, VIC; only published localities Glenmorgan, near Bowen and Gunbower.
Ecology: adult—volant; melliferous, solitary, flower visiting record: *Eucalyptus* L'Hérit. [Myrtaceae].

Euryglossa (Callohesma) picta (Smith, 1854)

Allodape picta Smith, F. (1854). *Catalogue of Hymenopterous Insects in the Collection of the British Museum.* Part II. Apidae. London : British Museum pp. 199–465 [231].
Type data: holotype, BMNH Hym.17.a.425 ♀ (described as ♂).
Type locality: Australia (as New Holland).

Distribution: Australia; known only from type locality, exact locality unknown.
Ecology: adult—volant; melliferous, solitary.
Reference: Exley, E.M. (1974). Revision of the subgenus *Callohesma* Michener (Apoidea : Colletidae). *Aust. J. Zool. Suppl. Ser.* **26**: 1–58 (redescription).

Euryglossa (Callohesma) quadrimaculata Smith, 1879

Euryglossa quadrimaculata Smith, F. (1879). *Descriptions of New Species of Hymenoptera in the Collection of the British Museum.* London : British Museum xxi 240 pp. [12].
Type data: holotype, BMNH Hym.17.a.275 ♀.
Type locality: QLD.

Distribution: NE coastal, QLD; only published locality Helidon.
Ecology: adult—volant; melliferous, solitary, flower visiting record: *Angophora* Cav. [Myrtaceae].
Reference: Exley, E.M. (1974). Revision of the subgenus *Callohesma* Michener (Apoidea : Colletidae). *Aust. J. Zool. Suppl. Ser.* **26**: 1–58 (redescription).

Euryglossa (Callohesma) queenslandensis Exley, 1974

Euryglossa (Callohesma) queenslandensis Exley, E.M. (1974). Revision of the subgenus *Callohesma* Michener (Apoidea : Colletidae). *Aust. J. Zool. Suppl. Ser.* **26**: 1–58 [36].
Type data: holotype, QM T7364 ♀.
Type locality: 7 miles W Charleville, QLD.

Distribution: Murray-Darling basin, QLD; only published localities near Charleville and Morven.
Ecology: adult—volant; melliferous, solitary, flower visiting record: *Eucalyptus* L'Hérit. [Myrtaceae].

Euryglossa (Callohesma) recta Exley, 1974

Euryglossa (Callohesma) recta Exley, E.M. (1974). Revision of the subgenus *Callohesma* Michener (Apoidea : Colletidae). *Aust. J. Zool. Suppl. Ser.* **26**: 1–58 [56].
Type data: holotype, QM T7383 ♀.
Type locality: 7 miles W Coolgardie, WA.

Distribution: Murray-Darling basin, SW coastal, W plateau, NSW, WA; only published localities Hay, near Coolgardie, Spargoville and Gnowangerup.
Ecology: adult—volant; melliferous, solitary, flower visiting record: *Eucalyptus* L'Hérit. [Myrtaceae].

Euryglossa (Callohesma) rieki Exley, 1974

Euryglossa (Callohesma) rieki Exley, E.M. (1974). Revision of the subgenus *Callohesma* Michener (Apoidea : Colletidae). *Aust. J. Zool. Suppl. Ser.* **26**: 1–58 [26].
Type data: holotype, ANIC ♀.
Type locality: Canberra, ACT.

Distribution: Murray-Darling basin, SE coastal, ACT, VIC; only published localities Canberra, Cotter River and Mt Yule, Healesville.
Ecology: adult—volant; melliferous, solitary, flower visiting record: *Eucalyptus* L'Hérit. [Myrtaceae].

Euryglossa (Callohesma) setula Exley, 1974

Euryglossa (Callohesma) setula Exley, E.M. (1974). Revision of the subgenus *Callohesma* Michener (Apoidea : Colletidae). *Aust. J. Zool. Suppl. Ser.* **26**: 1–58 [28].
Type data: holotype, BMNH Hym.17.a.2845 ♀.
Type locality: Southern Cross, WA.

Distribution: SW coastal, W plateau, WA; only published localities Southern Cross and Dedari.
Ecology: adult—volant; melliferous, solitary.

Euryglossa (Callohesma) sinapipes Cockerell, 1910

Euryglossa sinapipes Cockerell, T.D.A. (1910). Some Australian bees in the Berlin Museum. *J. N.Y. Entomol. Soc.* **18**: 98–114 [99].
Type data: holotype, ZMB ♂*.
Type locality: Adelaide, SA.
Euryglossa carnosa Cockerell, T.D.A. (1913). Some Australian bees. *Proc. Acad. Nat. Sci. Philad.* **65**: 28–44 [33].
Type data: holotype, BMNH Hym.17.a.236 ♀.
Type locality: Purnong, SA.
Euryglossa sinapina Cockerell, T.D.A. (1913). Some Australian bees. *Proc. Acad. Nat. Sci. Philad.* **65**: 28–44 [35].
Type data: holotype, USNM ♂*.
Type locality: Purnong, SA.
Euryglossa melanothorax Rayment, T. (1935). *A Cluster of Bees*. Sixty essays on the life-histories of Australian bees, with specific descriptions of over 100 new species, and an introduction by Professor E.F. Phillips, D.Ph., Cornell University, U.S.A. Sydney : Endeavour Press 752 pp. [637].
Type data: holotype, ANIC ♂.
Type locality: Purnong, SA.

Taxonomic decision for synonymy: Exley, E.M. (1974). Revision of the subgenus *Callohesma* Michener (Apoidea : Colletidae). *Aust. J. Zool. Suppl. Ser.* **26**: 1–58 [18].

Distribution: Murray-Darling basin, S Gulfs, W plateau, SW coastal, VIC, SA, WA.
Ecology: adult—volant; melliferous, solitary, flower visiting record: *Eucalyptus* L'Hérit. [Myrtaceae].

Euryglossa (Callohesma) skermani Exley, 1974

Euryglossa (Callohesma) skermani Exley, E.M. (1974). Revision of the subgenus *Callohesma* Michener (Apoidea : Colletidae). *Aust. J. Zool. Suppl. Ser.* **26**: 1–58 [33].
Type data: holotype, QM T7360 ♀.
Type locality: Karratha, WA.

Distribution: NW coastal, WA; only published localities Karratha and near Dampier.
Ecology: adult—volant; melliferous, solitary, flower visiting record: *Eucalyptus* L'Hérit. [Myrtaceae].

Euryglossa (Callohesma) splendens Exley, 1974

Euryglossa (Callohesma) splendens Exley, E.M. (1974). Revision of the subgenus *Callohesma* Michener (Apoidea : Colletidae). *Aust. J. Zool. Suppl. Ser.* **26**: 1–58 [10].
Type data: holotype, WAM ♀*.
Type locality: Merredin, WA.

Distribution: SW coastal, WA; only published localities Merredin, Yellowdine (as Yellodine) and Southern Cross.
Ecology: adult—volant; melliferous, solitary.

Euryglossa (Callohesma) sulphurea Michener, 1965

Euryglossa (Callohesma) sulphurea Michener, C.D. (1965). A classification of the bees of the Australian and South Pacific regions. *Bull. Am. Mus. Nat. Hist.* **130**: 1–362 [276].
Type data: holotype, ANIC ♀.
Type locality: Gnowangerup, WA.

Distribution: Murray-Darling basin, SW coastal, SA, WA.
Ecology: adult—volant; melliferous, solitary, flower visiting record: *Eucalyptus* L'Hérit. [Myrtaceae].
Reference: Exley, E.M. (1974). Revision of the subgenus *Callohesma* Michener (Apoidea : Colletidae). *Aust. J. Zool. Suppl. Ser.* **26**: 1–58 (description of male).

Euryglossa (Callohesma) tibialis Cardale, 1993

Euryglossa (Callohesma) tuberculata Exley, E.M. (1974). Revision of the subgenus *Callohesma* Michener (Apoidea : Colletidae). *Aust. J. Zool. Suppl. Ser.* **26**: 1–58 [20] [junior primary homonym of *Euryglossa maculata tuberculata* Rayment, 1939].
Type data: holotype, QM T7370 ♀.
Type locality: Yellowdine, WA.
Euryglossa (Callohesma) tibialis Cardale, J.C, this work [*nom. nov.* for *Euryglossa (Callohesma) tuberculata* Exley, 1974].

Distribution: SW coastal, W plateau, WA; only published localities Yellowdine, Southern Cross and Dedari.
Ecology: adult—volant; melliferous, solitary.

Euryglossa (Callohesma) townsvillensis Exley, 1974

Euryglossa (Callohesma) townsvillensis Exley, E.M. (1974). Revision of the subgenus *Callohesma* Michener (Apoidea : Colletidae). *Aust. J. Zool. Suppl. Ser.* **26**: 1–58 [40].
Type data: holotype, QM T7375 ♀.
Type locality: Castle Hill, Townsville, QLD.

Distribution: NE coastal, QLD; known only from type locality.
Ecology: adult—volant; melliferous, solitary, flower visiting record: *Eucalyptus* L'Hérit. [Myrtaceae].

Euryglossa (Dermatohesma) Michener, 1965

Dermatohesma Michener, C.D. (1965). A classification of the bees of the Australian and South Pacific regions. *Bull. Am. Mus. Nat. Hist.* **130**: 1–362 [91] [proposed with subgeneric rank in *Euryglossa* Smith, 1853]. Type species: *Euryglossimorpha abnormis* Rayment, 1935 by original designation.

Euryglossa (Dermatohesma) abnormis (Rayment, 1935)

Euryglossimorpha abnormis Rayment, T. (1935). *A Cluster of Bees*. Sixty essays on the life-histories of Australian bees, with specific descriptions of over 100 new species, and an introduction by Professor E.F. Phillips, D.Ph., Cornell University, U.S.A. Sydney : Endeavour Press 752 pp. [664].
Type data: holotype, ANIC ♀.
Type locality: Gnangara, WA.

Distribution: SW coastal, WA; known only from type locality.
Ecology: adult—volant; melliferous, solitary.

Euryglossa (Euhesma) Michener, 1965

Euhesma Michener, C.D. (1965). A classification of the bees of the Australian and South Pacific regions. *Bull. Am. Mus. Nat. Hist.* **130**: 1–362 [88] [proposed with subgeneric rank in *Euryglossa* Smith, 1853]. Type species: *Euryglossa (Euhesma) wahlenbergiae* Michener, 1965 by original designation.

Euryglossa (Euhesma) altitudinis Cockerell, 1914

Euryglossa altitudinis Cockerell, T.D.A. (1914). Australian bees of the genus *Euryglossa*. *Entomologist* **47**: 213–215 [213].
Type data: holotype, BMNH Hym.17.a.262 ♂.
Type locality: Mt Lofty, SA.

Distribution: S Gulfs, SA; known only from type locality.
Ecology: adult—volant; melliferous, solitary.

Euryglossa (Euhesma) anthracocephala Cockerell, 1914

Euryglossa anthracocephala Cockerell, T.D.A. (1914). Australian bees of the family Prosopidae. *Insecutor Inscit. Menstr.* **2**: 97–101 [99].
Type data: holotype, QM Hy/4132 ♀.
Type locality: Brisbane, QLD.

Distribution: NE coastal, QLD; known only from type locality.
Ecology: adult—volant; melliferous, solitary, flower visiting record: *Eugenia* L. [Myrtaceae].

Euryglossa (Euhesma) aureophila Houston, 1992

Euryglossa (Euhesma) aureophila Houston, T.F. (1992). Three new, monolectic species of *Euryglossa (Euhesma)* from Western Australia (Hymenoptera: Colletidae). *Rec. West. Aust. Mus.* **15**: 719–728 [723].
Type data: holotype, WAM 91/500 ♂*.
Type locality: 10.5 km S Eneabba, WA.

Distribution: SW coastal, WA; known only from type locality.
Ecology: adult—volant; melliferous, solitary, flower visiting record: *Pileanthus* Labill. [Myrtaceae], *Verticordia* DC. [Myrtaceae].

Euryglossa (Euhesma) australis Michener, 1965

Euryglossa (Euhesma) australis Michener, C.D. (1965). A classification of the bees of the Australian and South Pacific regions. *Bull. Am. Mus. Nat. Hist.* **130**: 1–362 [268].
Type data: holotype, ANIC ♀.
Type locality: Ooldea, SA.

Distribution: Murray-Darling basin, S Gulfs, W plateau, VIC, SA; only published localities Little Desert, Ooldea and Karoonda to Peebinga.
Ecology: adult—volant; melliferous, solitary.

Euryglossa (Euhesma) crabronica Cockerell, 1914

Euryglossa crabronica Cockerell, T.D.A. (1914). A bee resembling a wasp. *Entomologist* **47**: 142–143 [142].
Type data: holotype, QM Hy/4131 ♀.
Type locality: Brisbane, QLD.

Distribution: NE coastal, QLD; known only from type locality.
Ecology: adult—volant; melliferous, solitary.

Euryglossa (Euhesma) dolichocephala Rayment, 1953

Euryglossa dolichocephala Rayment, T. (1953). New bees and wasps, Part XX. *Vict. Nat.* **70**: 68–71 [68].
Type data: holotype, ANIC ♀.
Type locality: Lake Hattah, VIC.

Distribution: Murray-Darling basin, VIC; known only from type locality.
Ecology: adult—volant; melliferous, solitary.

Euryglossa (Euhesma) fasciatella Cockerell, 1907

Euryglossa fasciatella Cockerell, T.D.A. (1907). On a collection of Australian and Asiatic bees. *Bull. Am. Mus. Nat. Hist.* **23**: 221–236 [230].
Type data: holotype, AMNH ♀*.
Type locality: SA.

Stilpnosoma nigrum Friese, H. (1924). Ueber die Bienen Australiens. *Konowia* **3**: 216–249 [235] [junior secondary homonym of *Euryglossa nigra* Smith, 1879].
Type data: holotype (probable), whereabouts unknown ♀*.
Type locality: Adelaide, SA.

Taxonomic decision for synonymy: Cockerell, T.D.A. (1929). Bees, chiefly Australian species, described or determined by Dr. H. Friese. *Am. Mus. Novit.* **343**: 1–20 [19].

Distribution: SE coastal, VIC, SA, TAS; only published localities Cheltenham, Sandringham, Swan Point (Tamar River) and Adelaide.
Ecology: larva—sedentary : adult—volant; melliferous, solitary, flower visiting record: *Leptospermum* Forster & G.Forster [Myrtaceae].
References: Cockerell, T.D.A. (1913). Descriptions and records of bees. LV. *Ann. Mag. Nat. Hist. (8)***12**: 505–514 (description of male); Cockerell, T.D.A. (1915). Descriptions and records of bees. LXIX. *Ann. Mag. Nat. Hist. (8)***16**: 96–104 (distribution); Cockerell, T.D.A. (1926). Descriptions and records of bees. CX. *Ann. Mag. Nat. Hist. (9)***17**: 510–519 (distribution); Rayment, T. (1927). A new Australian cliff-bee. *Euryglossa asperithorax*, sp.n. *Vict. Nat.* **44**: 75 (illustration); Rayment, T. (1927). The cliff-bees. *Vict. Nat.* **44**: 76–84 (biology); Rayment, T. (1935). *A Cluster of Bees*. Sixty essays on the life-histories of Australian bees, with specific descriptions of over 100 new species, and an introduction by Professor E.F. Phillips, D.Ph., Cornell University, U.S.A. Sydney : Endeavour Press 752 pp. (biology); Rayment, T. (1945). Tea-tree (*Leptospermum myrsinivides*) bees (*Euryglossa fasciatella*) of Port Phillip. *Walkabout* **11**(10): 27–29 (biology).

Euryglossa (Euhesma) filicis Cockerell, 1926

Euryglossa nitidifrons filicis Cockerell, T.D.A. (1926). Descriptions and records of bees. CXII. *Ann. Mag. Nat. Hist. (9)***18**: 216–227 [217].
Type data: syntypes, NMV 2♀ (one specimen is labelled 'type' and has registration number T–4363).
Type locality: Fern Tree Gully, VIC.

Distribution: SE coastal, VIC; known only from type locality.
Ecology: adult—volant; melliferous, solitary.
Reference: Michener, C.D. (1965). A classification of the bees of the Australian and South Pacific regions. *Bull. Am. Mus. Nat. Hist.* **130**: 1–362 [91] (taxonomy).

Euryglossa (Euhesma) flavocuneata Cockerell, 1915

Euryglossa flavocuneata Cockerell, T.D.A. (1915). Descriptions and records of bees. LXVI. *Ann. Mag. Nat. Hist. (8)***15**: 341–350 [349].
Type data: holotype, BMNH Hym.17.a.277 ♀.
Type locality: Yallingup, WA.

Distribution: SW coastal, WA; known only from type locality.
Ecology: adult—volant; melliferous, solitary.

Euryglossa (Euhesma) goodeniae Cockerell, 1926

Euryglossa goodeniae Cockerell, T.D.A. (1926). Descriptions and records of bees. CX. *Ann. Mag. Nat. Hist. (9)***17**: 510–519 [515].
Type data: holotype, BMNH Hym.17.a.228 ♂.
Type locality: Sandringham, VIC.

Distribution: SE coastal, VIC; known only from type locality.
Ecology: larva—sedentary : adult—volant; melliferous, solitary, flower visiting record: *Goodenia* Sm. [Goodeniaceae].
References: Rayment, T. (1927). A new Australian cliff-bee. *Euryglossa asperithorax*, sp.n. *Vict. Nat.* **44**: 75 (illustration); Rayment, T. (1935). *A Cluster of Bees*. Sixty essays on the life-histories of Australian bees, with specific descriptions of over 100 new species, and an introduction by Professor E.F. Phillips, D.Ph., Cornell University, U.S.A. Sydney : Endeavour Press 752 pp. (biology); Houston, T.F. (1983). An extraordinary new bee and adaptation of palpi for nectar-feeding in some Australian Colletidae and Pergidae (Hymenoptera). *J. Aust. Entomol. Soc.* **22**: 263–270 (palps).

Euryglossa (Euhesma) grisea (Alfken, 1907)

Allodape grisea Alfken, J.D. (1907). Apidae. pp. 259–261 in Michaelsen, W. & Hartmeyer, R. (eds) *Die Fauna Südwest-Australiens*. Jena : G. Fischer Bd 1 Lfg 6 [260].
Type data: syntypes, ZMB 2♂*.
Type locality: Denham, WA.

Distribution: NW coastal, WA; known only from type locality.
Ecology: adult—volant; melliferous, solitary.
References: Michener, C.D. & Syed, I.H. (1962). Specific characters of the larvae and adults of *Allodapula* in the Australian region (Hymenoptera : Ceratinini). *J. Entomol. Soc. Qd* **1**: 30–41 (taxonomy); Michener, C.D. (1968). The generic placement of *"Allodape" grisea* Alfken (Hymenoptera : Apoidea). *J. Aust. Entomol. Soc.* **7**: 142 (taxonomy).

Euryglossa (Euhesma) halictina Cockerell, 1920

Euryglossa halictina Cockerell, T.D.A. (1920). Descriptions and records of bees. LXXXVIII. *Ann. Mag. Nat. Hist. (9)* **5**: 113–119 [117].

Type data: holotype, BMNH Hym.17.a.253 ♀.
Type locality: Bridport, TAS.

Distribution: TAS; known only from type locality.
Ecology: adult—volant; melliferous, solitary.

Euryglossa (Euhesma) halictoides Rayment, 1939

Euryglossa halictoides Rayment, T. (1939). Bees from the high lands of New South Wales and Victoria. *Aust. Zool.* **9**: 263–294 [268].
Type data: holotype, ANIC ♀.
Type locality: Frankston, VIC.

Distribution: SE coastal, VIC; known only from type locality.
Ecology: adult—volant; melliferous, solitary, nest in beach sand.

Euryglossa (Euhesma) hemichlora Cockerell, 1914

Euryglossa hemichlora Cockerell, T.D.A. (1914). Australian bees of the genus *Euryglossa*. *Entomologist* **47**: 213–215 [214].
Type data: holotype, BMNH Hym.17.a.274 ♂.
Type locality: Yallingup, WA.

Distribution: SW coastal, WA; known only from type locality.
Ecology: adult—volant; melliferous, solitary.

Euryglossa (Euhesma) hemixantha Cockerell, 1914

Euryglossa hemixantha Cockerell, T.D.A. (1914). Australian bees of the family Prosopididae. *Insecutor Inscit. Menstr.* **2**: 97–101 [99].
Type data: holotype, QM Hy/4133 ♂.
Type locality: Brisbane, QLD.

Distribution: NE coastal, QLD; known only from type locality.
Ecology: adult—volant; melliferous, solitary.

Euryglossa (Euhesma) hyphesmoides Michener, 1965

Euryglossa (Euhesma) hyphesmoides Michener, C.D. (1965). A classification of the bees of the Australian and South Pacific regions. *Bull. Am. Mus. Nat. Hist.* **130**: 1–362 [269].
Type data: holotype, QM T6229 ♀.
Type locality: Mutdapilly, QLD.

Distribution: NE coastal, QLD; known only from type locality.
Ecology: adult—volant; melliferous, solitary, flower visiting record: *Eucalyptus* L'Hérit. [Myrtaceae].

Euryglossa (Euhesma) inconspicua Cockerell, 1913

Euryglossa inconspicua Cockerell, T.D.A. (1913). Descriptions and records of bees. LV. *Ann. Mag. Nat. Hist.* (8)**12**: 505–514 [512].
Type data: holotype, BMNH Hym.17.a.240 ♀.
Type locality: Purnong, SA.

Distribution: SE coastal, Murray-Darling basin, NSW, VIC, SA; only published localities Sydney, Orange, Sandringham and Purnong.
Ecology: larva—sedentary : adult—volant; melliferous, solitary, flower visiting record: *Goodenia* Sm. [Goodeniaceae].
References: Rayment, T. (1930). New and remarkable bees. *Proc. R. Soc. Vict.* **43**: 42–61 (description of male); Rayment, T. (1934). Contributions to the fauna of Rottnest Island. VIII. Apoidea. With description of new species. *J. Proc. R. Soc. West. Aust.* **20**: 201–212 (illustration); Rayment, T. (1935). *A Cluster of Bees*. Sixty essays on the life-histories of Australian bees, with specific descriptions of over 100 new species, and an introduction by Professor E.F. Phillips, D.Ph., Cornell University, U.S.A. Sydney : Endeavour Press 752 pp. (biology); Rayment, T. (1939). Bees from the high lands of New South Wales and Victoria. *Aust. Zool.* **9**: 263–294 (distribution).

Euryglossa (Euhesma) latissima Cockerell, 1914

Euryglossa latissima Cockerell, T.D.A. (1914). Australian bees of the genus *Euryglossa*. *Entomologist* **47**: 213–215 [215].
Type data: holotype, BMNH Hym.17.a.2638 ♀.
Type locality: Eaglehawk Neck, TAS.

Distribution: TAS; known only from type locality.
Ecology: adult—volant; melliferous, solitary.
Reference: Cockerell, T.D.A. (1915). Descriptions and records of bees. LXVII. *Ann. Mag. Nat. Hist.* (8)**15**: 529–537 (description of male).

Euryglossa (Euhesma) lutea Rayment, 1934

Euryglossa inconspicua lutea Rayment, T. (1934). Contributions to the fauna of Rottnest Island. VIII. Apoidea. With description of new species. *J. Proc. R. Soc. West. Aust.* **20**: 201–212 [204].
Type data: holotype, WAM 32–563 ♀.
Type locality: Rottnest Is., WA.

Distribution: SW coastal, WA; known only from type locality.
Ecology: adult—volant; melliferous, solitary.
Reference: Michener, C.D. (1965). A classification of the bees of the Australian and South Pacific regions. *Bull. Am. Mus. Nat. Hist.* **130**: 1–362 [91] (taxonomy).

Euryglossa (Euhesma) maculifera Michener, 1965

Melittosmithia maculata Rayment, T. (1935). *A Cluster of Bees*. Sixty essays on the life-histories of Australian bees, with specific descriptions of over 100 new species, and an introduction by Professor E.F. Phillips, D.Ph., Cornell University, U.S.A. Sydney : Endeavour Press 752 pp. [653] [junior secondary homonym of *Euryglossa maculata* Smith, 1879].
Type data: holotype, ANIC ♀.
Type locality: Beaumaris, VIC.

Euryglossa (Euhesma) maculifera Michener, C.D. (1965). A classification of the bees of the Australian and South

Pacific regions. *Bull. Am. Mus. Nat. Hist.* **130**: 1–362 [91] [*nom. nov.* for *Melittosmithia maculata* Rayment, 1935].

Distribution: SE coastal, VIC; known only from type locality.

Ecology: adult—volant; melliferous, solitary, flower visiting record: *Leptospermum* Forster & G.Forster [Myrtaceae].

Euryglossa (Euhesma) malaris Michener, 1965

Euryglossa (Euhesma) malaris Michener, C.D. (1965). A classification of the bees of the Australian and South Pacific regions. *Bull. Am. Mus. Nat. Hist.* **130**: 1–362 [270].
Type data: holotype, ANIC ♀.
Type locality: Mt Lofty Range, SA.

Distribution: S Gulfs, SA; known only from type locality.

Ecology: adult—volant; melliferous, solitary.

Reference: Houston, T.F. (1983). An extraordinary new bee and adaptation ot palpi for nectar-feeding in some Australian Colletidae and Pergidae (Hymenoptera). *J. Aust. Entomol. Soc.* **22**: 263–270 (palps).

Euryglossa (Euhesma) maura Cockerell, 1927

Euryglossa nubifera maura Cockerell, T.D.A. (1927). Some Australian bees. *Entomologist* **60**: 101–102 [102].
Type data: holotype, USNM ♀*.
Type locality: Barellan, NSW.

Distribution: Murray-Darling basin, NSW; known only from type locality.

Ecology: adult—volant; melliferous, solitary, flower visiting record: *Leptospermum* Forster & G.Forster [Myrtaceae].
Reference: Michener, C.D. (1965). A classification of the bees of the Australian and South Pacific regions. *Bull. Am. Mus. Nat. Hist.* **130**: 1–362 [91] (taxonomy).

Euryglossa (Euhesma) melanosoma Cockerell, 1914

Euryglossa melanosoma Cockerell, T.D.A. (1914). Australian bees of the genus *Euryglossa. Entomologist* **47**: 213–215 [214].
Type data: syntytpes, BMNH 2♀.
Type locality: Yallingup, WA.

Distribution: SW coastal, WA; known only from type locality.

Ecology: adult—volant; melliferous, solitary.

Euryglossa (Euhesma) mica Cockerell, 1918

Euryglossa neglectula mica Cockerell, T.D.A. (1918). Some bees collected in Queensland. *Mem. Qd Mus.* **6**: 112–120 [116].
Type data: holotype, QM T4145 ♂.
Type locality: Brisbane, QLD.

Distribution: NE coastal, QLD; known only from type locality.

Ecology: adult—volant; melliferous, solitary.
References: Cockerell, T.D.A. (1913). Descriptions

and records of bees. L. *Ann. Mag. Nat. Hist. (8)***11**: 273–283 (as *Euryglossa neglectula* var. A Cockerell, 1905); Cockerell, T.D.A. (1922). Australian bees in the Queensland Museum. *Mem. Qd Mus.* **7**: 257–279 (♀ from type locality); Michener, C.D. (1965). A classification of the bees of the Australian and South Pacific regions. *Bull. Am. Mus. Nat. Hist.* **130**: 1–362 [91] (taxonomy).

Euryglossa (Euhesma) morrisoni Houston, 1992

Euryglossa (Euhesma) morrisoni Houston, T.F. (1992). Three new, monolectic species of *Euryglossa (Euhesma)* from Western Australia (Hymenoptera: Colletidae). *Rec. West. Aust. Mus.* **15**: 719–728 [720].
Type data: holotype, WAM 91/544 ♂*.
Type locality: Melaleuca Park, 11 km NE Wanneroo, WA.

Distribution: SW coastal, WA; only published localities near Wanneroo, near Harvey and Moore River National Park.

Ecology: adult—volant; melliferous, solitary, flower visiting record: *Verticordia* DC. [Myrtaceae].

Euryglossa (Euhesma) neglectula Cockerell, 1905

Euryglossa neglectula Cockerell, T.D.A. (1905). Descriptions and records of bees. V. *Ann. Mag. Nat. Hist. (7)***16**: 465–477 [474].
Type data: holotype, BMNH Hym.17.a.241 ♀.
Type locality: Australia.

Distribution: NE coastal, SE coastal, QLD, NSW.

Ecology: adult—volant; melliferous, solitary, flower visiting record: *Angophora* Cav. [Myrtaceae], *Eucalyptus* L'Hérit. [Myrtaceae], *Melaleuca* L. [Myrtaceae].
References: Cockerell, T.D.A. (1916). A collection of bees from Queensland. *Mem. Qd Mus.* **5**: 197–204 (distribution); Rayment, T. (1939). Bees from the high lands of New South Wales and Victoria. *Aust. Zool.* **9**: 263–294 (distribution); Michener, C.D. (1965). A classification of the bees of the Australian and South Pacific regions. *Bull. Am. Mus. Nat. Hist.* **130**: 1–362 (flower records).

Euryglossa (Euhesma) nitidifrons Smith, 1879

Euryglossa nitidifrons Smith, F. (1879). *Descriptions of New Species of Hymenoptera in the Collection of the British Museum.* London : British Museum xxi 240 pp. [14].
Type data: holotype, BMNH Hym.17.a.250 ♀.
Type locality: Australia.

Distribution: Australia; known only from type locality, exact locality unknown.

Ecology: adult—volant; melliferous, solitary.

Euryglossa (Euhesma) nubifera Cockerell, 1922

Euryglossa nubifera Cockerell, T.D.A. (1922). Australian bees in the Queensland Museum. *Mem. Qd Mus.* **7**: 257–279 [273].

Type data: holotype (probable), QM Hy/2682.
Type locality: Coolangatta, QLD.

Distribution: NE coastal, QLD; known only from type locality.
Ecology: adult—volant; melliferous, solitary.

Euryglossa (Euhesma) palpalis Michener, 1965

Euryglossa (Euhesma) palpalis Michener, C.D. (1965). A classification of the bees of the Australian and South Pacific regions. Bull. Am. Mus. Nat. Hist. 130: 1–362 [271].
Type data: holotype, NMV T–6268 ♀ (originally deposited in ANIC, in error).
Type locality: Hotham Heights, 5,000 ft, VIC.

Distribution: Murray-Darling basin, VIC; only published localities Hotham Heights and Mt Buffalo.
Ecology: adult—volant; melliferous, solitary.
Reference: Houston, T.F. (1983). An extraordinary new bee and adaptation of palpi for nectar-feeding in some Australian Colletidae and Pergidae (Hymenoptera). J. Aust. Entomol. Soc. 22: 263–270 (palps).

Euryglossa (Euhesma) perditiformis Cockerell, 1910

Euryglossa perditiformis Cockerell, T.D.A. (1910). New and little-known bees. Trans. Am. Entomol. Soc. 36: 199–249 [207].
Type data: holotype, BMNH Hym.17.a.272 ♀.
Type locality: Mackay, QLD.

Distribution: NE coastal, SE coastal, QLD, NSW; only published localities Mackay and Gosford.
Ecology: adult—volant; melliferous, solitary.
Reference: Rayment, T. (1939). Bees from the high lands of New South Wales and Victoria. Aust. Zool. 9: 263–294 (distribution).

Euryglossa (Euhesma) perkinsi Michener, 1965

Euryglossa (Euhesma) perkinsi Michener, C.D. (1965). A classification of the bees of the Australian and South Pacific regions. Bull. Am. Mus. Nat. Hist. 130: 1–362 [272].
Type data: holotype, QM T6226 ♀.
Type locality: 17 miles S Dalby, QLD.

Distribution: Murray-Darling basin, QLD; known only from type locality.
Ecology: adult—volant; melliferous, solitary, flower visiting record: Wahlenbergia Roth [Campanulaceae].

Euryglossa (Euhesma) pernana Cockerell, 1905

Euryglossa pernana Cockerell, T.D.A. (1905). Descriptions and records of bees. V. Ann. Mag. Nat. Hist. (7)16: 465–477 [474].
Type data: holotype, BMNH Hym.17.a.234 ♂.
Type locality: Fremantle, WA.

Distribution: SW coastal, WA; known only from type locality.
Ecology: adult—volant; melliferous, solitary.

Euryglossa (Euhesma) platyrhina Cockerell, 1915

Euryglossa platyrhina Cockerell, T.D.A. (1915). Descriptions and records of bees. LXVI. Ann. Mag. Nat. Hist. (8)15: 341–350 [350].
Type data: syntypes, BMNH 3♀ (a specimen is labelled type and has registration number Hym.17.a.248).
Type locality: Yallingup, WA.

Distribution: SW coastal, WA; known only from type locality.
Ecology: adult—volant; melliferous, solitary.
Reference: Houston, T.F. (1983). An extraordinary new bee and adaptation of palpi for nectar-feeding in some Australian Colletidae and Pergidae (Hymenoptera). J. Aust. Entomol. Soc. 22: 263–270 (palps).

Euryglossa (Euhesma) rainbowi Cockerell, 1929

Euryglossa rainbowi Cockerell, T.D.A. (1929). Bees in the Australian Museum collection. Rec. Aust. Mus. 17: 199–243 [214].
Type data: syntypes, AM 2♀ (described as ♂).
Type locality: Blackwood, SA.

Distribution: S Gulfs, SA; known only from type locality.
Ecology: adult—volant; melliferous, solitary.

Euryglossa (Euhesma) ricae Rayment, 1948

Euryglossa ricae Rayment, T. (1948). Notes on remarkable wasps and bees. With specific descriptions. Aust. Zool. 11: 238–254 [248].
Type data: holotype, ANIC ♀.
Type locality: Bolgart, WA.

Distribution: SW coastal, WA; known only from type locality.
Ecology: adult—volant; melliferous, solitary, flower visiting record: Baeckea L. [Myrtaceae].

Euryglossa (Euhesma) ridens Cockerell, 1913

Euryglossa ridens Cockerell, T.D.A. (1913). Descriptions and records of bees. LI. Ann. Mag. Nat. Hist. (8)11: 387–394 [388].
Type data: holotype, BMNH Hym.17.a.239 ♀.
Type locality: Blue Mtns, NSW.

Distribution: SE coastal, NSW; known only from type locality.
Ecology: adult—volant; melliferous, solitary.

Euryglossa (Euhesma) rufiventris Michener, 1965

Euryglossa (Euhesma) rufiventris Michener, C.D. (1965). A classification of the bees of the Australian and South Pacific regions. Bull. Am. Mus. Nat. Hist. 130: 1–362 [273].
Type data: holotype, ANIC ♀.
Type locality: Trayning, WA.

Distribution: SW coastal, WA; known only from type locality.
Ecology: adult—volant; melliferous, solitary.

Euryglossa (Euhesma) semaphore Houston, 1992

Euryglossa (Euhesma) semaphore Houston, T.F. (1992). Three new, monolectic species of *Euryglossa (Euhesma)* from Western Australia (Hymenoptera: Colletidae). *Rec. West. Aust. Mus.* **15**: 719–728 [725].
Type data: holotype, WAM 91/487 ♂*.
Type locality: 10.5 km S Eneabba, WA.

Distribution: SW coastal, WA; known only from type locality.
Ecology: adult—volant; melliferous, solitary, flower visiting record: *Pileanthus* Labill. [Myrtaceae].

Euryglossa (Euhesma) serrata Cockerell, 1927

Euryglossa nitidifrons serrata Cockerell, T.D.A. (1927). Some Australian bees. *Entomologist* **60**: 101–102 [101].
Type data: holotype, USNM ♀*.
Type locality: Beaumaris, VIC.

Distribution: SE coastal, VIC; known only from type locality.
Ecology: larva—sedentary : adult—volant; melliferous, solitary, nest in soil, flower visiting record: *Leptospermum* Forster & G.Forster [Myrtaceae].
References: Rayment, T. (1935). *A Cluster of Bees.* Sixty essays on the life-histories of Australian bees, with specific descriptions of over 100 new species, and an introduction by Professor E.F. Phillips, D.Ph., Cornell University, U.S.A. Sydney : Endeavour Press 752 pp. (biology); Michener, C.D. (1965). A classification of the bees of the Australian and South Pacific regions. *Bull. Am. Mus. Nat. Hist.* **130**: 1–362 [91] (taxonomy).

Euryglossa (Euhesma) subinconspicua Rayment, 1934

Euryglossa subinconspicua Rayment, T. (1934). Contributions to the fauna of Rottnest Island. VIII. Apoidea. With description of new species. *J. Proc. R. Soc. West. Aust.* **20**: 201–212 [204].
Type data: holotype (probable), ANIC ♀.
Type locality: Kiata, VIC.

Distribution: Murray-Darling basin, VIC; known only from type locality.
Ecology: adult—volant; melliferous, solitary, flower visiting record: *Bursaria* Cav. [Pittosporaceae].
Reference: Rayment, T. (1935). *A Cluster of Bees.* Sixty essays on the life-histories of Australian bees, with specific descriptions of over 100 new species, and an introduction by Professor E.F. Phillips, D.Ph., Cornell University, U.S.A. Sydney : Endeavour Press 752 pp. (description, as new species).

Euryglossa (Euhesma) tasmanica Cockerell, 1918

Euryglossa tasmanica Cockerell, T.D.A. (1918). Descriptions and records of bees. LXXIX. *Ann. Mag. Nat. Hist.* (9)**1**: 158–167 [164].
Type data: syntypes, BMNH 3♀ (a specimen is labelled 'type' and has registration number Hym.17.a.254).
Type locality: Launceston, TAS.

Distribution: TAS; known only from type locality.
Ecology: adult—volant; melliferous, solitary.
Reference: Cockerell, T.D.A. (1927). Some Australian bees. *Entomologist* **60**: 101–102 (as *Euryglossa nitidifrons tasmanica* Cockerell, 1918).

Euryglossa (Euhesma) tuberculata Rayment, 1939

Euryglossa maculata tuberculata Rayment, T. (1939). Bees from the high lands of New South Wales and Victoria. *Aust. Zool.* **9**: 263–294 [267].
Type data: syntypes, ANIC 6♀.
Type locality: Gosford, NSW.

Distribution: SE coastal, NSW; known only from type locality.
Ecology: adult—volant; melliferous, solitary.
Reference: Michener, C.D. (1965). A classification of the bees of the Australian and South Pacific regions. *Bull. Am. Mus. Nat. Hist.* **130**: 1–362 [91] (taxonomy).

Euryglossa (Euhesma) tubulifera Houston, 1983

Euryglossa (Euhesma) tubulifera Houston, T.F. (1983). An extraordinary new bee and adaptation of palpi for nectar-feeding in some Australian Colletidae and Pergidae (Hymenoptera). *J. Aust. Entomol. Soc.* **22**: 263–270 [263].
Type data: holotype, WAM 82/480 ♂*.
Type locality: Kenwick, 14 km SE Perth, WA.

Distribution: SW coastal, WA; only published localities Kenwick and Tutanning Reserve.
Ecology: adult—volant; melliferous, solitary, flower visiting record: *Calothamnus* Lab. [Myrtaceae].

Euryglossa (Euhesma) undulata Cockerell, 1914

Euryglossa undulata Cockerell, T.D.A. (1914). New Australian bees. *Entomologist* **47**: 197–201 [198].
Type data: holotype, BMNH Hym.17.a.233 ♀.
Type locality: Yallingup, WA.

Distribution: SW coastal, WA; known only from type locality.
Ecology: adult—volant; melliferous, solitary.

Euryglossa (Euhesma) wahlenbergiae Michener, 1965

Euryglossa (Euhesma) wahlenbergiae Michener, C.D. (1965). A classification of the bees of the Australian and South Pacific regions. *Bull. Am. Mus. Nat. Hist.* **130**: 1–362 [274].
Type data: holotype, QM T6227 ♀.
Type locality: Helidon, QLD.

Distribution: NE coastal, Murray-Darling basin, QLD, NSW, ACT; only published localities Helidon, Warwick, Stanthorpe, Glen Innes and Canberra.
Ecology: adult—volant; melliferous, solitary, flower visiting record: *Wahlenbergia* Roth [Campanulaceae].

Euryglossa (Euhesma) walkeriana Cockerell, 1905

Euryglossa walkeriana Cockerell, T.D.A. (1905). Descriptions and records of bees. V. *Ann. Mag. Nat. Hist.* *(7)***16**: 465–477 [473].
Type data: holotype, BMNH Hym.17.a.285 ♀.
Type locality: Launceston, TAS.

Distribution: NE coastal, QLD, TAS; only published localities Brisbane, Noosa, Launceston and Hobart.
Ecology: adult—volant; melliferous, solitary, flower visiting record: *Banksia* L.f. [Proteaceae].
References: Cockerell, T.D.A. (1922). Australian bees in the Queensland Museum. *Mem. Qd Mus.* **7**: 257–279 (distribution); Cockerell, T.D.A. (1926). Descriptions and records of bees. CXII. *Ann. Mag. Nat. Hist.* *(9)***18**: 216–227 (distribution); Rayment, T. (1934). Contributions to the fauna of Rottnest Island. VIII. Apoidea. With description of new species. *J. Proc. R. Soc. West. Aust.* **20**: 201–212 (illustration); Michener, C.D. (1965). A classification of the bees of the Australian and South Pacific regions. *Bull. Am. Mus. Nat. Hist.* **130**: 1–362 (flower record).

Euryglossa (Parahesma) Michener, 1965

Parahesma Michener, C.D. (1965). A classification of the bees of the Australian and South Pacific regions. *Bull. Am. Mus. Nat. Hist.* **130**: 1–362 [92] [proposed with subgeneric rank in *Euryglossa* Smith, 1853]. Type species: *Euryglossa (Parahesma) tuberculipes* Michener, 1965 by original designation.

Euryglossa (Parahesma) tuberculipes Michener, 1965

Euryglossa (Parahesma) tuberculipes Michener, C.D. (1965). A classification of the bees of the Australian and South Pacific regions. *Bull. Am. Mus. Nat. Hist.* **130**: 1–362 [275].
Type data: holotype, BMNH Hym.17.a.2825 ♀.
Type locality: VIC.

Distribution: VIC; known only from type locality, exact locality unknown.
Ecology: adult—volant; melliferous, solitary.

Euryglossa (Unplaced)

Euryglossa catanii Rayment, 1949

Euryglossa catanii Rayment, T. (1949). New bees and wasps—Part X. *Vict. Nat.* **65**: 271–272 [271].
Type data: holotype (probable), whereabouts unknown (T. Rayment, pers. coll. not found in ANIC) ♂*.
Type locality: Reed's Lookout, Mt Buffalo, VIC.

Distribution: Murray-Darling basin, VIC; known only from type locality.
Ecology: adult—volant; melliferous, solitary, flower visiting record: *Stylidium* Willd. [Stylidiaceae].

Euryglossa endeavouricola Strand, 1921

Euryglossa endeavouricola Strand, E. (1921). Apidologisches, insbesondere über paläarktische *Andrena*-Arten, auf Grund von Material des Deutschen Entomologischen Museums. *Arch. Naturg.* **87**(A)3: 266–304 [269].
Type data: holotype (probable), ?DEIB ♀*.
Type locality: Endeavour River, QLD (as Endeavour River, N.S.Wales).

Distribution: NE coastal, QLD; known only from type locality.
Ecology: adult—volant; melliferous, solitary.

Euryglossa tarsata Alfken, 1907

Euryglossa tarsata Alfken, J.D. (1907). Apidae. pp. 259–261 *in* Michaelsen, W. & Hartmeyer, R. (eds) *Die Fauna Südwest-Australiens*. Jena : G. Fischer Bd 1 Lfg 6 [260].
Type data: holotype, whereabouts unknown ♂*.
Type locality: Serpentine, WA.

Distribution: SW coastal, WA; known only from type locality.
Ecology: adult—volant; melliferous, solitary.

Euryglossella Cockerell, 1910

Euryglossella Cockerell, T.D.A. (1910). Some very small Australian bees. *Entomologist* **43**: 262–264 [263]. Type species: *Euryglossella minima* Cockerell, 1910 by monotypy.

Zalygus Cockerell, T.D.A. (1929). Bees in the Queensland Museum. *Mem. Qd Mus.* **9**: 298–323 [321]. Type species: *Zalygus cornutus* Cockerell, 1929 by monotypy.

Taxonomic decision for synonymy: Michener, C.D. (1965). A classification of the bees of the Australian and South Pacific regions. *Bull. Am. Mus. Nat. Hist.* **130**: 1–362 [111].

Euryglossella cornuta (Cockerell, 1929)

Zalygus cornutus Cockerell, T.D.A. (1929). Bees in the Queensland Museum. *Mem. Qd Mus.* **9**: 298–323 [321].
Type data: holotype, QM Hy/4044 ♀.
Type locality: Brisbane, QLD.

Distribution: NE coastal, QLD.
Ecology: adult—volant; melliferous, solitary, flower visiting record: *Angophora* Cav. [Myrtaceae], *Callistemon* R.Br. [Myrtaceae], *Eucalyptus* L'Hérit. [Myrtaceae], *Melaleuca* L. [Myrtaceae], *Tristania* R.Br. [Myrtaceae].
References: Michener, C.D. (1965). A classification of the bees of the Australian and South Pacific regions. *Bull. Am. Mus. Nat. Hist.* **130**: 1–362 [111] (illustration, flower record, as *Euryglossina (Euryglossella) cornuta* (Cockerell, 1929)); Exley, E.M. (1968). A revision of the genus *Euryglossella* Cockerell (Apoidea : Colletidae). *Aust. J. Zool.* **16**: 219–226 (redescription, generic placement); Exley, E.M. (1982). The genus *Euryglossella* Cockerell (Hymenoptera : Apoidea). *Int. J. Entomol.* **1**: 21–29 (distribution).

Euryglossella darwiniensis Exley, 1974

Euryglossella darwiniensis Exley, E.M. (1974). A contribution to our knowledge of Australia's smallest bees with descriptions of new species (Hymenoptera : Colletidae : Euryglossinae). *J. Aust. Entomol. Soc.* **13**: 1–9 [8].
Type data: holotype, QM T7494 ♂.
Type locality: Elizabeth River, 21 miles S Darwin, NT.

Distribution: NE coastal, N Gulf, N coastal, QLD, NT.
Ecology: adult—volant; melliferous, solitary, flower visiting record: *Eucalyptus* L'Hérit. [Myrtaceae], *Eugenia* L. [Myrtaceae], *Melaleuca* L. [Myrtaceae], *Pongamia* Vent. [Fabaceae], *Tristania* R.Br. [Myrtaceae].
Reference: Exley, E.M. (1982). The genus *Euryglossella* Cockerell (Hymenoptera : Apoidea). *Int. J. Entomol.* **1**: 21–29 (distribution).

Euryglossella incompleta Exley, 1974

Euryglossella incompleta Exley, E.M. (1974). A contribution to our knowledge of Australia's smallest bees with descriptions of new species (Hymenoptera : Colletidae : Euryglossinae). *J. Aust. Entomol. Soc.* **13**: 1–9 [9].
Type data: holotype, QM T7389 ♂.
Type locality: Mt Bundey Road, via Darwin, NT.

Distribution: NE coastal, N Gulf, N coastal, QLD, NT.
Ecology: adult—volant; melliferous, solitary, flower visiting record: *Eucalyptus* L'Hérit. [Myrtaceae], *Eugenia* L. [Myrtaceae].
Reference: Exley, E.M. (1982). The genus *Euryglossella* Cockerell (Hymenoptera : Apoidea). *Int. J. Entomol.* **1**: 21–29 (description of female).

Euryglossella minima Cockerell, 1910

Euryglossella minima Cockerell, T.D.A. (1910). Some very small Australian bees. *Entomologist* **43**: 262–264 [263].
Type data: holotype, BMNH Hym.17.a.305 ♀.
Type locality: Mackay, QLD.

Distribution: NE coastal, QLD; only published localities Mackay, Townsville, Shute Harbour and near Kuranda.
Ecology: adult—volant; melliferous, solitary, flower visiting record: *Eucalyptus* L'Hérit. [Myrtaceae].
References: Meade-Waldo, G. (1923). Hymenoptera. Fam. Apidae. Subfam. Prosopidinae. *Genera Insectorum* **181**: 1–45 (illustration); Rayment, T. (1935). *A Cluster of Bees*. Sixty essays on the life-histories of Australian bees, with specific descriptions of over 100 new species, and an introduction by Professor E.F. Phillips, D.Ph., Cornell University, U.S.A. Sydney : Endeavour Press 752 pp. (illustration); Exley, E.M. (1968). A revision of the genus *Euryglossella* Cockerell (Apoidea : Colletidae). *Aust. J. Zool.* **16**: 219–226 (redescription); Exley, E.M. (1982). The genus *Euryglossella* Cockerell (Hyme-noptera : Apoidea). *Int. J. Entomol.* **1**: 21–29 (taxonomy).

Euryglossella neominima Exley, 1974

Euryglossella neominima Exley, E.M. (1974). A contribution to our knowledge of Australia's smallest bees with descriptions of new species (Hymenoptera : Colletidae : Euryglossinae). *J. Aust. Entomol. Soc.* **13**: 1–9 [5].
Type data: holotype, QM T7381 ♂.
Type locality: Castle Hill, Townsville, QLD.

Distribution: NE coastal, N Gulf, QLD.
Ecology: adult—volant; melliferous, solitary, flower visiting record: *Eucalyptus* L'Hérit. [Myrtaceae], *Eugenia* L. [Myrtaceae], *Grevillea* R.Br. ex J. Knight [Proteaceae], *Melaleuca* L. [Myrtaceae].
Reference: Exley, E.M. (1982). The genus *Euryglossella* Cockerell (Hymenoptera : Apoidea). *Int. J. Entomol.* **1**: 21–29 (distribution).

Euryglossella oenpelli Exley, 1982

Euryglossella oenpelli Exley, E.M. (1982). The genus *Euryglossella* Cockerell (Hymenoptera : Apoidea). *Int. J. Entomol.* **1**: 21–29 [27].
Type data: holotype, whereabouts unknown ♀*.
Type locality: Birraduk Creek, 18 km E by N Oenpelli, NT.

Distribution: N coastal, NT; known only from type locality.
Ecology: adult—volant; melliferous, solitary, flower visiting record: *Eucalyptus* L'Hérit. [Myrtaceae].

Euryglossella perkinsi (Michener, 1965)

Euryglossina (Euryglossella) perkinsi Michener, C.D. (1965). A classification of the bees of the Australian and South Pacific regions. *Bull. Am. Mus. Nat. Hist.* **130**: 1–362 [287].
Type data: holotype, QM T6232 ♀.
Type locality: Binna Burra, near Lamington National Park, McPherson Range, QLD.

Distribution: NE coastal, QLD; only published localities Binna Burra, Tamborine and Noosa.
Ecology: adult—volant; melliferous, solitary, flower visiting record: *Angophora* Cav. [Myrtaceae], *Claoxylon* A. Juss. [Euphorbiaceae], *Eugenia* L. [Myrtaceae].
Reference: Exley, E.M. (1968). A revision of the genus *Euryglossella* Cockerell (Apoidea : Colletidae). *Aust. J. Zool.* **16**: 219–226 (redescription and generic placement).

Euryglossella weiri Exley, 1974

Euryglossella weiri Exley, E.M. (1974). A contribution to our knowledge of Australia's smallest bees with descriptions of new species (Hymenoptera : Colletidae : Euryglossinae). *J. Aust. Entomol. Soc.* **13**: 1–9 [8].
Type data: holotype, QM T7388 ♂.
Type locality: Coconut Grove, via Darwin, NT.

Distribution: NE coastal, N Gulf, N coastal, QLD, NT.

Ecology: adult—volant; melliferous, solitary, flower visiting record: *Eucalyptus* L'Hérit. [Myrtaceae], *Eugenia* L. [Myrtaceae], *Melaleuca* L. [Myrtaceae] *Tristania* R.Br. [Myrtaceae].

Reference: Exley, E.M. (1982). The genus *Euryglossella* Cockerell (Hymenoptera : Apoidea). *Int. J. Entomol.* **1**: 21–29 (description of female).

Euryglossina Cockerell, 1910

Taxonomic decision for subgeneric arrangement: Exley, E.M. (1968). Revision of the genus *Euryglossina* Cockerell (Apoidea : Colletidae). *Aust. J. Zool.* **16**: 915–1020 [915].

Generic reference: Michener, C.D. (1965). A classification of the bees of the Australian and South Pacific regions. *Bull. Am. Mus. Nat. Hist.* **130**: 1–362.

Euryglossina (Euryglossina) Cockerell, 1910

Euryglossina Cockerell, T.D.A. (1910). New and little-known bees. *Trans. Am. Entomol. Soc.* **36**: 199–249 [211] [proposed with subgeneric rank in *Euryglossa* Smith, 1853]. Type species: *Euryglossa semipurpurea* Cockerell, 1910 by monotypy.

Extralimital distribution: New Zealand (accidental introduction), see Callan, E.M. (1979). The Sphecidae (Hymenoptera) of New Zealand. *N.Z. Entomol.* **7**: 30–41 [39].

Euryglossina (Euryglossina) atra Exley, 1968

Euryglossina (Euryglossina) atra Exley, E.M. (1968). Revision of the genus *Euryglossina* Cockerell (Apoidea : Colletidae). *Aust. J. Zool.* **16**: 915–1020 [946]. Type data: holotype, QM T6639 ♀. Type locality: Sunnybank, QLD.

Distribution: NE coastal, QLD.
Ecology: adult—volant; melliferous, solitary, flower visiting record: wild parsley, *Leptospermum* Forster & G.Forster [Myrtaceae], *Melaleuca* L. [Myrtaceae].

Euryglossina (Euryglossina) bowenensis Exley, 1968

Euryglossina (Euryglossina) bowenensis Exley, E.M. (1968). Revision of the genus *Euryglossina* Cockerell (Apoidea : Colletidae). *Aust. J. Zool.* **16**: 915–1020 [951]. Type data: holotype, QM T6642 ♀. Type locality: 7 miles S Bowen, QLD.

Distribution: NE coastal, QLD; only published localities near Bowen, Proserpine and Townsville.
Ecology: adult—volant; melliferous, solitary, flower visiting record: *Melaleuca* L. [Myrtaceae].

Euryglossina (Euryglossina) clypearis Exley, 1976

Euryglossina (Euryglossina) clypearis Exley, E.M. (1976). New species and records of *Euryglossina* Cockerell (Apoidea : Colletidae : Euryglossinae). *J. Aust. Entomol. Soc.* **15**: 273–279 [275]. Type data: holotype, QM T7490 ♀. Type locality: Elsey Cemetery, 19 km S Mataranka, NT.

Distribution: NE coastal, N Gulf, N coastal, QLD, NT; only published localities near Mundubbera, Elsey Cemetery, Katherine Gorge and near Katherine.
Ecology: adult—volant; melliferous, solitary, flower visiting record: *Eucalyptus* L'Hérit. [Myrtaceae].

Euryglossina (Euryglossina) cockerelli Perkins, 1912

Euryglossina cockerelli Perkins, R.C.L. (1912). Notes, with descriptions of new species, on aculeate Hymenoptera of the Australian Region. *Ann. Mag. Nat. Hist. (8)***9**: 96–121 [113]. Type data: holotype, BMNH Hym.17.a.2621 ♀. Type locality: Bundaberg, QLD.

Euryglossina flaviventris personata Cockerell, T.D.A. (1929). Bees in the Queensland Museum. *Mem. Qd Mus.* **9**: 298–323 [317]. Type data: holotype, QM Hy/4045 ♀. Type locality: Brisbane, QLD.

Euryglossina semiflava Cockerell, T.D.A. (1929). Bees in the Queensland Museum. *Mem. Qd Mus.* **9**: 298–323 [318]. Type data: holotype, QM Hy/4041 ♂ (described as ♀). Type locality: Brisbane, QLD.

Taxonomic decision for synonymy: Exley, E.M. (1968). Revision of the genus *Euryglossina* Cockerell (Apoidea : Colletidae). *Aust. J. Zool.* **16**: 915–1020 [929].

Distribution: NE coastal, Murray-Darling basin, QLD.
Ecology: adult—volant; melliferous, solitary, flower visiting record: *Angophora* Cav. [Myrtaceae], *Callistemon* R.Br. [Myrtaceae], *Eucalyptus* L'Hérit. [Myrtaceae], *Eugenia* L. [Myrtaceae], *Leptospermum* Forster & G.Forster [Myrtaceae], *Melaleuca* L. [Myrtaceae], *Syncarpia* Ten. [Myrtaceae], *Tristania* R.Br. [Myrtaceae].
Reference: Michener, C.D. (1965). A classification of the bees of the Australian and South Pacific regions. *Bull. Am. Mus. Nat. Hist.* **130**: 1–362 (flower records, as *Euryglossina personata* Cockerell, 1929).

Euryglossina (Euryglossina) douglasi Exley, 1968

Euryglossina (Euryglossina) douglasi Exley, E.M. (1968). Revision of the genus *Euryglossina* Cockerell (Apoidea : Colletidae). *Aust. J. Zool.* **16**: 915–1020 [941]. Type data: holotype, WAM 54–678 ♀. Type locality: between Karalee and Dedari, WA.

Distribution: SW coastal, W plateau, WA.
Ecology: adult—volant; melliferous, solitary, flower visiting record: *Eucalyptus* L'Hérit. [Myrtaceae].
Reference: Exley, E.M. (1976). New species and records of *Euryglossina* Cockerell (Apoidea : Colletidae : Euryglossinae). *J. Aust. Entomol. Soc.* **15**: 273–279 (distribution).

Euryglossina (Euryglossina) flaviventris Cockerell, 1916

Euryglossina flaviventris Cockerell, T.D.A. (1916). Some bees from Australia, Tasmania, and the New Hebrides. *Proc. Acad. Nat. Sci. Philad.* **68**: 360–375 [362].
Type data: holotype, BMNH Hym.17.a.299 ♀.
Type locality: Mt Yule, Healesville, VIC.

Distribution: NE coastal, Murray-Darling basin, SE coastal, S Gulfs, (SW coastal), QLD, NSW, VIC, SA, (WA).
Ecology: adult—volant; melliferous, solitary, flower visiting record: *Angophora* Cav. [Myrtaceae], *Callistemon* R.Br. [Myrtaceae], *Eucalyptus* L'Hérit. [Myrtaceae], *Leptospermum* Forster & G.Forster [Myrtaceae], *Melaleuca* L. [Myrtaceae].
References: Rayment, T. (1934). Contributions to the fauna of Rottnest Island. VIII. Apoidea. With description of new species. *J. Proc. R. Soc. West. Aust.* **20**: 201–212 (Rottnest Is., doubtful record); Rayment, T. (1935). *A Cluster of Bees*. Sixty essays on the life-histories of Australian bees, with specific descriptions of over 100 new species, and an introduction by Professor E.F. Phillips, D.Ph., Cornell University, U.S.A. Sydney : Endeavour Press 752 pp. (illustration); Michener, C.D. (1965). A classification of the bees of the Australian and South Pacific regions. *Bull. Am. Mus. Nat. Hist.* **130**: 1–362 (illustration, flower records); Exley, E.M. (1968). Revision of the genus *Euryglossina* Cockerell (Apoidea : Colletidae). *Aust. J. Zool.* **16**: 915–1020 (redescription).

Euryglossina (Euryglossina) fuscescens Cockerell, 1929

Euryglossina flaviventris fuscescens Cockerell, T.D.A. (1929). Bees in the Queensland Museum. *Mem. Qd Mus.* **9**: 298–323 [317].
Type data: holotype, QM Hy/3731 ♀.
Type locality: Brisbane, QLD.

Distribution: NE coastal, Murray-Darling basin, QLD, NSW.
Ecology: adult—volant; melliferous, solitary, flower visiting record: *Angophora* Cav. [Myrtaceae], *Callistemon* R.Br. [Myrtaceae], *Eucalyptus* L'Hérit. [Myrtaceae], *Leptospermum* Forster & G.Forster [Myrtaceae], *Melaleuca* L. [Myrtaceae], *Syncarpia* Ten. [Myrtaceae], *Tristania* R.Br. [Myrtaceae].
References: Michener, C.D. (1965). A classification of the bees of the Australian and South Pacific regions. *Bull. Am. Mus. Nat. Hist.* **130**: 1–362 [109] (taxonomy); Exley, E.M. (1968). Revision of the genus *Euryglossina* Cockerell (Apoidea : Colletidae). *Aust. J. Zool.* **16**: 915–1020 (redescription).

Euryglossina (Euryglossina) gigantocephala Exley, 1968

Euryglossina (Euryglossina) gigantocephala Exley, E.M. (1968). Revision of the genus *Euryglossina* Cockerell (Apoidea : Colletidae). *Aust. J. Zool.* **16**: 915–1020 [943].
Type data: holotype, QM T6644 ♀.
Type locality: Fernvale, QLD.

Distribution: NE coastal, Murray-Darling basin, QLD; only published localities Fernvale, near Marlborough, Mundubbera, Rockhampton and near Warwick.
Ecology: adult—volant; melliferous, solitary, flower visiting record: *Angophora* Cav. [Myrtaceae], *Eucalyptus* L'Hérit. [Myrtaceae].
Reference: Exley, E.M. (1976). New species and records of *Euryglossina* Cockerell (Apoidea : Colletidae : Euryglossinae). *J. Aust. Entomol. Soc.* **15**: 273–279 (distribution).

Euryglossina (Euryglossina) glenmorganensis Exley, 1968

Euryglossina (Euryglossina) glenmorganensis Exley, E.M. (1968). Revision of the genus *Euryglossina* Cockerell (Apoidea : Colletidae). *Aust. J. Zool.* **16**: 915–1020 [951].
Type data: holotype, QM T6640 ♀.
Type locality: Glenmorgan, QLD.

Distribution: Murray-Darling basin, QLD; known only from type locality.
Ecology: adult—volant; melliferous, solitary, flower visiting record: *Eucalyptus* L'Hérit. [Myrtaceae].

Euryglossina (Euryglossina) haemodonta Exley, 1969

Euryglossina (Euryglossina) haemodonta Exley, E.M. (1969). A supplement to the revision of *Euryglossina* (Apoidea : Colletidae). *J. Aust. Entomol. Soc.* **8**: 139–144 [139].
Type data: holotype, QM T7356 ♀.
Type locality: Charleville, QLD.

Distribution: Murray-Darling basin, QLD; known only from type locality.
Ecology: adult—volant; melliferous, solitary, flower visiting record: *Eucalyptus* L'Hérit. [Myrtaceae].

Euryglossina (Euryglossina) healesvillensis Exley, 1968

Euryglossina (Euryglossina) healesvillensis Exley, E.M. (1968). Revision of the genus *Euryglossina* Cockerell (Apoidea : Colletidae). *Aust. J. Zool.* **16**: 915–1020 [939].
Type data: holotype, BMNH Hym.17.a.2848 ♀.
Type locality: Mt Yule, Healesville, VIC.

Distribution: SE coastal, Murray-Darling basin, NSW, VIC, TAS.
Ecology: adult—volant; melliferous, solitary, flower visiting record: *Bursaria* Cav. [Pittosporaceae], *Eucalyptus* L'Hérit. [Myrtaceae], *Melaleuca* L. [Myrtaceae] or *Cotoneaster* Medikus [Rosaceae].
Reference: Exley, E.M. (1976). New species and records of *Euryglossina* Cockerell (Apoidea : Colletidae : Euryglossinae). *J. Aust. Entomol. Soc.* **15**: 273–279 (distribution).

Euryglossina (Euryglossina) hypochroma Cockerell, 1916

Euryglossina hypochroma Cockerell, T.D.A. (1916). Some bees from Australia, Tasmania, and the New Hebrides. *Proc. Acad. Nat. Sci. Philad.* **68**: 360–375 [362].
Type data: syntypes, BMNH 2♀ (a specimen is labelled 'type' and has registration number Hym.17.a.300).
Type locality: Perth, WA.

Distribution: NE coastal, SE coastal, Murray-Darling basin, S Gulfs, SW coastal, QLD, NSW, ACT, VIC, SA, WA, TAS.
Ecology: larva—sedentary : adult—volant; melliferous, solitary, nest in wood, flower visiting record: *Angophora* Cav. [Myrtaceae], *Callistemon* R.Br. [Myrtaceae], *Eucalyptus* L'Hérit. [Myrtaceae], *Leptospermum* Forster & G.Forster [Myrtaceae], *Melaleuca* L. [Myrtaceae].
References: Rayment, T. (1954). Incidence of acarid mites on the biology of bees. *Aust. Zool.* **12**: 26–38 (as host); Michener, C.D. (1965). A classification of the bees of the Australian and South Pacific regions. *Bull. Am. Mus. Nat. Hist.* **130**: 1–362 (illustration, flower records); Exley, E.M. (1968). Revision of the genus *Euryglossina* Cockerell (Apoidea : Colletidae). *Aust. J. Zool.* **16**: 915–1020 (redescription); Houston, T.F. (1969). Observations on the nests and behaviour of some euryglossine bees (Hymenoptera : Colletidae). *J. Aust. Entomol. Soc.* **8**: 1–10 (biology).

Euryglossina (Euryglossina) intermedia Michener, 1965

Euryglossina (Euryglossina) intermedia Michener, C.D. (1965). A classification of the bees of the Australian and South Pacific regions. *Bull. Am. Mus. Nat. Hist.* **130**: 1–362 [285].
Type data: holotype, QM T6230 ♀.
Type locality: Wallangarra, QLD.

Distribution: NE coastal, Murray-Darling basin, QLD.
Ecology: adult—volant; melliferous, solitary, flower visiting record: *Leptospermum* Forster & G.Forster [Myrtaceae], *Melaleuca* L. [Myrtaceae], *Tristania* R.Br. [Myrtaceae].
Reference: Exley, E.M. (1968). Revision of the genus *Euryglossina* Cockerell (Apoidea : Colletidae). *Aust. J. Zool.* **16**: 915–1020 (redescription).

Euryglossina (Euryglossina) kellyi Exley, 1968

Euryglossina (Euryglossina) kellyi Exley, E.M. (1968). Revision of the genus *Euryglossina* Cockerell (Apoidea : Colletidae). *Aust. J. Zool.* **16**: 915–1020 [929].
Type data: holotype, QM T6641 ♀.
Type locality: Mt Yule, Healesville, VIC.

Distribution: SE coastal, S Gulfs, VIC, SA; only published localities Mt Yule (Healesville), Sandringham, Adelaide and Scotts Creek.

Ecology: adult—volant; melliferous, solitary, flower visiting record: *Banksia* L.f. [Proteaceae], *Eucalyptus* L'Hérit. [Myrtaceae].

Euryglossina (Euryglossina) lobiocula Exley, 1968

Euryglossina (Euryglossina) lobiocula Exley, E.M. (1968). Revision of the genus *Euryglossina* Cockerell (Apoidea : Colletidae). *Aust. J. Zool.* **16**: 915–1020 [943].
Type data: holotype, QM T6647 ♀.
Type locality: Mica Creek, 5 miles from Mt Isa, QLD.

Distribution: N Gulf, Murray-Darling basin, Lake Eyre basin, QLD, NSW, NT; only published localities Mica Creek, Mt Isa, Tenterfield and Alice Springs.
Ecology: adult—volant; melliferous, solitary, flower visiting record: *Angophora* Cav. [Myrtaceae], *Eucalyptus* L'Hérit. [Myrtaceae].
Reference: Exley, E.M. (1976). New species and records of *Euryglossina* Cockerell (Apoidea : Colletidae : Euryglossinae). *J. Aust. Entomol. Soc.* **15**: 273–279 (description of male).

Euryglossina (Euryglossina) lynettae (Rayment, 1955)

Pachyprosopis lynettae Rayment, T. (1955). Historic pole 346. *Proc. R. Zool. Soc. N.S.W.* **1953–54**: 63–67 [65].
Type data: holotype, ANIC ♀ (described as ♂).
Type locality: Toorak, VIC.

Distribution: SE coastal, Murray-Darling basin, S Gulfs, SW coastal, VIC, SA, WA, TAS.
Ecology: adult—volant; melliferous, solitary, nest in abandoned beetle galleries, flower visiting record: *Eucalyptus* L'Hérit. [Myrtaceae].
Reference: Exley, E.M. (1968). Revision of the genus *Euryglossina* Cockerell (Apoidea : Colletidae). *Aust. J. Zool.* **16**: 915–1020 (redescription).

Euryglossina (Euryglossina) mutica (Cockerell, 1912)

Euryglossa mutica Cockerell, T.D.A. (1912). Descriptions and records of bees. XLI. *Ann. Mag. Nat. Hist.* (8)**9**: 139–149 [143].
Type data: holotype, USNM ♂*.
Type locality: Sydney, NSW.

Distribution: NE coastal, SE coastal, Murray-Darling basin, QLD, NSW.
Ecology: adult—volant; melliferous, solitary, flower visiting record: *Angophora* Cav. [Myrtaceae], *Callistemon* R.Br. [Myrtaceae], *Tristania* R.Br. [Myrtaceae].
Reference: Exley, E.M. (1968). Revision of the genus *Euryglossina* Cockerell (Apoidea : Colletidae). *Aust. J. Zool.* **16**: 915–1020 (redescription).

Euryglossina (Euryglossina) narifera (Cockerell, 1915)

Euryglossa narifera Cockerell, T.D.A. (1915). Descriptions and records of bees. LXVI. *Ann. Mag. Nat. Hist. (8)***15**: 341–350 [348].
Type data: syntypes, BMNH 3♀ (a specimen is labelled 'type' and has registration number Hym.17.a.252).
Type locality: Yallingup, WA.

Distribution: SW coastal, WA; known only from type locality.
Ecology: adult—volant; melliferous, solitary.
Reference: Exley, E.M. (1968). Revision of the genus *Euryglossina* Cockerell (Apoidea : Colletidae). *Aust. J. Zool.* **16**: 915–1020 (redescription).

Euryglossina (Euryglossina) nigra Exley, 1968

Euryglossina (Euryglossina) nigra Exley, E.M. (1968). Revision of the genus *Euryglossina* Cockerell (Apoidea : Colletidae). *Aust. J. Zool.* **16**: 915–1020 [945].
Type data: holotype, QM T7073 ♀.
Type locality: Brisbane, QLD.

Distribution: NE coastal, Murray-Darling basin, QLD, NSW; only published localities Brisbane, Capalaba, Mt Pleasant, Beerwah and Wallangarra (as Wallangarra, NSW).
Ecology: adult—volant; melliferous, solitary, flower visiting record: wild parsley, *Callistemon* R.Br. [Myrtaceae], *Leptospermum* Forster & G.Forster [Myrtaceae], *Syncarpia* Ten. [Myrtaceae].

Euryglossina (Euryglossina) perpusilla (Cockerell, 1910)

Euryglossa perpusilla Cockerell, T.D.A. (1910). Some very small Australian bees. *Entomologist* **43**: 262–264 [263].
Type data: holotype, BMNH Hym.17.a.297 ♀.
Type locality: Mackay, QLD.

Euryglossina perpusilla nana Cockerell, T.D.A. (1916). Some bees from Australia, Tasmania, and the New Hebrides. *Proc. Acad. Nat. Sci. Philad.* **68**: 360–375 [363].
Type data: syntypes, BMNH 3♀ (a specimen is labelled 'type' and has registration number Hym.17.a.298).
Type locality: Kalamunda, WA.

Taxonomic decision for synonymy: Exley, E.M. (1968). Revision of the genus *Euryglossina* Cockerell (Apoidea : Colletidae). *Aust. J. Zool.* **16**: 915–1020 [947].

Distribution: NE coastal, SE coastal, SW coastal, QLD, NSW, WA, TAS.
Ecology: adult—volant; melliferous, solitary, flower visiting record: *Eucalyptus* L'Hérit. [Myrtaceae], *Tristania* R.Br. [Myrtaceae].
References: Cockerell, T.D.A. (1914). Australian bees of the family Prosopididae. *Insecutor Inscit. Menstr.* **2**: 97–101 (misidentification; see Exley, 1968); Cockerell, T.D.A. (1916). Some bees from Australia, Tasmania and the New Hebrides. *Proc.*

Acad. Nat. Sci. Philad. **68**: 360–375 (generic placement).

Euryglossina (Euryglossina) philoxantha Cockerell, 1929

Euryglossina philoxantha Cockerell, T.D.A. (1929). Bees in the Queensland Museum. *Mem. Qd Mus.* **9**: 298–323 [318].
Type data: holotype, QM Hy/3730 ♂.
Type locality: Brisbane, QLD.

Distribution: NE coastal, Murray-Darling basin, SW coastal, QLD, WA.
Ecology: adult—volant; melliferous, solitary, flower visiting record: wild parsley, *Eucalyptus* L'Hérit. [Myrtaceae], *Leptospermum* Forster & G.Forster [Myrtaceae], *Tristania* R.Br. [Myrtaceae].
Reference: Exley, E.M. (1968). Revision of the genus *Euryglossina* Cockerell (Apoidea : Colletidae). *Aust. J. Zool.* **16**: 915–1020 (redescription).

Euryglossina (Euryglossina) proctotrypoides Cockerell, 1913

Euryglossina proctotrypoides Cockerell, T.D.A. (1913). Descriptions and records of bees. LI. *Ann. Mag. Nat. Hist. (8)***11**: 387–394 [392].
Type data: holotype, USNM ♀*.
Type locality: Croydon, VIC.

Euryglossa minuta Rayment, T. (1935). *A Cluster of Bees.* Sixty essays on the life-histories of Australian bees, with specific descriptions of over 100 new species, and an introduction by Professor E.F. Phillips, D.Ph., Cornell University, U.S.A. Sydney : Endeavour Press 752 pp. [636].
Type data: holotype, ANIC ♂* (Exley, E.M. (1968). Revision of the genus *Euryglossina* Cockerell (Apoidea : Colletidae). *Aust. J. Zool.* **16**: 915–1020 [937], states holotype is a ♂ not a ♀ as published).
Type locality: Sandringham, VIC.

Taxonomic decision for synonymy: Exley, E.M. (1968). Revision of the genus *Euryglossina* Cockerell (Apoidea : Colletidae). *Aust. J. Zool.* **16**: 915–1020 [937].

Distribution: NE coastal, SE coastal, Murray-Darling basin, S Gulfs, QLD, NSW, VIC, SA, TAS; introduced into, and established in New Zealand by 1979.
Ecology: larva—sedentary : adult—volant; melliferous, solitary, nest in beetle burrows in wood, flower visiting record: *Angophora* Cav. [Myrtaceae], *Callistemon* R.Br. [Myrtaceae], *Eucalyptus* L'Hérit. [Myrtaceae], *Leptospermum* Forster & G.Forster [Myrtaceae], *Melaleuca* L. [Myrtaceae].
References: Callan, E.M. (1979). The Sphecidae (Hymenoptera) of New Zealand. *N.Z. Entomol.* **7**: 30–41 (N.Z. record); Donovan, B.J. (1980). Interactions between native and introduced bees in New Zealand. *N.Z. J. Ecol.* **3**: 104–116 (biology).

Euryglossina (Euryglossina) semipurpurea (Cockerell, 1910)

Euryglossa semipurpurea Cockerell, T.D.A. (1910). New and little-known bees. *Trans. Am. Entomol. Soc.* **36**: 199–249 [208].
Type data: holotype, BMNH Hym.17.a.294 ♀.
Type locality: Mackay, QLD.

Distribution: NE coastal, QLD; known only from type locality.
Ecology: adult—volant; melliferous, solitary, flower visiting record: *Eucalyptus* L'Hérit. [Myrtaceae].
Reference: Exley, E.M. (1968). Revision of the genus *Euryglossina* Cockerell (Apoidea : Colletidae). *Aust. J. Zool.* **16**: 915–1020 (redescription).

Euryglossina (Euryglossina) storeyi Exley, 1976

Euryglossina (Euryglossina) storeyi Exley, E.M. (1976). New species and records of *Euryglossina* Cockerell (Apoidea : Colletidae : Euryglossinae). *J. Aust. Entomol. Soc.* **15**: 273–279 [276].
Type data: holotype, QM T7492 ♀.
Type locality: Broome, WA.

Distribution: NE coastal, N coastal, N Gulf, QLD, WA, NT.
Ecology: adult—volant; melliferous, solitary, flower visiting record: *Eucalyptus* L'Hérit. [Myrtaceae].

Euryglossina (Euryglossina) stygica Exley, 1968

Euryglossina (Euryglossina) stygica Exley, E.M. (1968). Revision of the genus *Euryglossina* Cockerell (Apoidea : Colletidae). *Aust. J. Zool.* **16**: 915–1020 [939].
Type data: holotype, BMNH Hym.17.a.2847 ♀.
Type locality: Mt Yule, Healesville, VIC.

Distribution: Murray-Darling basin, SE coastal, ACT, VIC; only published localities Black Mtn and Mt Yule, Healesville.
Ecology: adult—volant; melliferous, solitary, flower visiting record: *Eucalyptus* L'Hérit. [Myrtaceae].

Euryglossina (Euryglossina) townsvillensis Exley, 1968

Euryglossina (Euryglossina) townsvillensis Exley, E.M. (1968). Revision of the genus *Euryglossina* Cockerell (Apoidea : Colletidae). *Aust. J. Zool.* **16**: 915–1020 [954].
Type data: holotype, QM T6643 ♀.
Type locality: Ross River, Townsville, QLD.

Distribution: NE coastal, QLD; known only from type locality.
Ecology: adult—volant; melliferous, solitary, flower visiting record: *Eucalyptus* L'Hérit. [Myrtaceae], *Melaleuca* L. [Myrtaceae].

Euryglossina (Microdontura) Cockerell, 1929

Microdontura Cockerell, T.D.A. (1929). Bees in the Queensland Museum. *Mem. Qd Mus.* **9**: 298–323 [322].
Type species: *Microdontura mellea* Cockerell, 1929 by monotypy.

Euryglossina (Microdontura) mellea (Cockerell, 1929)

Microdontura mellea Cockerell, T.D.A. (1929). Bees in the Queensland Museum. *Mem. Qd Mus.* **9**: 298–323 [322].
Type data: holotype, QM Hy/4046 ♀.
Type locality: Brisbane, QLD.

Distribution: NE coastal, Murray-Darling basin, QLD, NSW.
Ecology: adult—volant; melliferous, solitary, flower visiting record: *Callistemon* R.Br. [Myrtaceae], *Eucalyptus* L'Hérit. [Myrtaceae], *Leptospermum* Forster & G.Forster [Myrtaceae], *Melaleuca* L. [Myrtaceae], *Syncarpia* Ten. [Myrtaceae], *Tristania* R.Br. [Myrtaceae].
References: Michener, C.D. (1965). A classification of the bees of the Australian and South Pacific regions. *Bull. Am. Mus. Nat. Hist.* **130**: 1–362 (flower record); Exley, E.M. (1968). Revision of the genus *Euryglossina* Cockerell (Apoidea : Colletidae). *Aust. J. Zool.* **16**: 915–1020 (redescription).

Euryglossina (Turnerella) Cockerell, 1910

Turnerella Cockerell, T.D.A. (1910). Some very small Australian bees. *Entomologist* **43**: 262–264 [262]. Type species: *Turnerella gilberti* Cockerell, 1910 by monotypy.

Euryglossina (Turnerella) angulifacies Exley, 1968

Euryglossina (Turnerella) angulifacies Exley, E.M. (1968). Revision of the genus *Euryglossina* Cockerell (Apoidea : Colletidae). *Aust. J. Zool.* **16**: 915–1020 [968].
Type data: holotype, QM T6653 ♀.
Type locality: Amiens, QLD.

Distribution: Murray-Darling basin, SE coastal, QLD, NSW, TAS; only published localities Amiens, Wallangarra, Gosford and Eaglehawk Neck.
Ecology: adult—volant; melliferous, solitary, flower visiting record: *Leptospermum* Forster & G.Forster [Myrtaceae].

Euryglossina (Turnerella) argocephala Exley, 1968

Euryglossina (Turnerella) argocephala Exley, E.M. (1968). Revision of the genus *Euryglossina* Cockerell (Apoidea : Colletidae). *Aust. J. Zool.* **16**: 915–1020 [998].
Type data: holotype, QM T7074 ♀.,
Type locality: Greenmount, WA.

Distribution: Murray-Darling basin, S Gulfs, SW coastal, QLD, SA, WA; only published localities Glenmorgan, Charleville, Waite Institute (Adelaide), Greenmount and Bullsbrook.
Ecology: adult—volant; melliferous, solitary, flower visiting record: *Eucalyptus* L'Hérit. [Myrtaceae].
Reference: Exley, E.M. (1969). A supplement to the revision of *Euryglossina* (Apoidea : Colletidae). *J. Aust. Entomol. Soc.* **8**: 139–144 (description of male).

Euryglossina (Turnerella) atomaria (Cockerell, 1914)

Euryglossella atomaria Cockerell, T.D.A. (1914). Australian bees of the family Prosopididae. *Insecutor Inscit. Menstr.* **2**: 97–101 [100].
Type data: holotype, BMNH Hym.17.a.304 ♀.
Type locality: Brisbane, QLD.
Turnerella atomaria fusciventris Cockerell, T.D.A. (1929). Bees in the Queensland Museum. *Mem. Qd Mus.* **9**: 298–323 [319].
Type data: holotype, QM Hy/4043 ♀.
Type locality: Brisbane, QLD.

Taxonomic decision for synonymy: Exley, E.M. (1968). Revision of the genus *Euryglossina* Cockerell (Apoidea : Colletidae). *Aust. J. Zool.* **16**: 915–1020 [988].

Distribution: NE coastal, QLD.
Ecology: adult—volant; melliferous, solitary, flower visiting record: *Angophora* Cav. [Myrtaceae], *Callistemon* R.Br. [Myrtaceae], *Leptospermum* Forster & G.Forster [Myrtaceae], *Melaleuca* L. [Myrtaceae], *Tristania* R.Br. [Myrtaceae].
References: Cockerell, T.D.A. (1922). Descriptions and records of bees. XCVI. *Ann. Mag. Nat. Hist.* *(9)*10: 544–550 (description of male); Cockerell, T.D.A. (1929). Bees in the Queensland Museum. *Mem. Qd Mus.* **9**: 298–323 (taxonomy).

Euryglossina (Turnerella) aurantia Exley, 1969

Euryglossina (Turnerella) aurantia Exley, E.M. (1969). A supplement to the revision of *Euryglossina* (Apoidea : Colletidae). *J. Aust. Entomol. Soc.* **8**: 139–144 [141].
Type data: holotype, QM T7354 ♀.
Type locality: Charleville, QLD.

Distribution: Murray-Darling basin, QLD; only published localities Charleville and Glenmorgan.
Ecology: adult—volant; melliferous, solitary, flower visiting record: *Eucalyptus* L'Hérit. [Myrtaceae].
Reference: Exley, E.M. (1968). Revision of the genus *Euryglossina* Cockerell (Apoidea : Colletidae). *Aust. J. Zool.* **16**: 915–1020 (as *Euryglossina (Turnerella)* Species K).

Euryglossina (Turnerella) crococephala Exley, 1968

Euryglossina (Turnerella) crococephala Exley, E.M. (1968). Revision of the genus *Euryglossina* Cockerell (Apoidea : Colletidae). *Aust. J. Zool.* **16**: 915–1020 [971].
Type data: holotype, QM T6663 ♀.
Type locality: Waite Institute, Adelaide, SA.

Distribution: NE coastal, Murray-Darling basin, QLD, NSW, SA; only published localities Ipswich, Waite Institute (Adelaide), Kongal and NSW (label illegible).
Ecology: adult—volant; melliferous, solitary, flower visiting record: *Angophora* Cav. [Myrtaceae], *Eucalyptus* L'Hérit. [Myrtaceae], *Melaleuca* L. [Myrtaceae].

Euryglossina (Turnerella) doddi (Perkins, 1912)

Turnerella doddi Perkins, R.C.L. (1912). Notes, with descriptions of new species, on aculeate Hymenoptera of the Australian Region. *Ann. Mag. Nat. Hist.* (8)**9**: 96–121 [114].
Type data: holotype, BMNH Hym.17.a.2622 ♀.
Type locality: Darwin, NT.

Distribution: NE coastal, N Gulf, N coastal, QLD, NT; only published localities Barkly Highway between Camooweal and Mt Isa, near Mt Isa, Townsville and Darwin.
Ecology: adult—volant; melliferous, solitary, flower visiting record: *Eucalyptus* L'Hérit. [Myrtaceae].
Reference: Exley, E.M. (1968). Revision of the genus *Euryglossina* Cockerell (Apoidea : Colletidae). *Aust. J. Zool.* **16**: 915–1020 (redescription).

Euryglossina (Turnerella) flavolateralis Michener, 1965

Turnerella semiflava Cockerell, T.D.A. (1929). Bees in the Queensland Museum. *Mem. Qd Mus.* **9**: 298–323 [320] [junior secondary homonym of *Euryglossina semiflava* Cockerell, 1929: 318].
Type data: lectotype, QM Hy/3727 ♀.
Subsequent designation: Exley, E.M. (1968). Revision of the genus *Euryglossina* Cockerell (Apoidea : Colletidae). *Aust. J. Zool.* **16**: 915–1020 [965]; Cardale, J.C., this work, interprets Exley's incorrect inference of holotype as a lectotype designation (Art. 74, ICZN 1985).
Type locality: Brisbane, QLD.
Euryglossina (Turnerella) flavolateralis Michener, C.D. (1965). A classification of the bees of the Australian and South Pacific regions. *Bull. Am. Mus. Nat. Hist.* **130**: 1–362 [109] [*nom. nov.* for *Turnerella semiflava* Cockerell, 1929: 320].

Distribution: NE coastal, Murray-Darling basin, QLD, SA.
Ecology: adult—volant; melliferous, solitary, flower visiting record: *Angophora* Cav. [Myrtaceae], *Callistemon* R.Br. [Myrtaceae], *Eucalyptus* L'Hérit. [Myrtaceae], *Melaleuca* L. [Myrtaceae].
Reference: Exley, E.M. (1968). Revision of the genus *Euryglossina* Cockerell (Apoidea : Colletidae). *Aust. J. Zool.* **16**: 915–1020 (redescription).

Euryglossina (Turnerella) gilberti (Cockerell, 1910)

Turnerella gilberti Cockerell, T.D.A. (1910). Some very small Australian bees. *Entomologist* **43**: 262–264 [262].
Type data: holotype, BMNH Hym.17.a.306 ♂.
Type locality: Mackay, QLD.
Turnerella pachycephala Cockerell, T.D.A. (1929). Bees in the Queensland Museum. *Mem. Qd Mus.* **9**: 298–323 [319].
Type data: lectotype, QM Hy/3728 ♀, BMNH paralectotype ♀.
Subsequent designation: Exley, E.M. (1968). Revision of the genus *Euryglossina* Cockerell (Apoidea : Colletidae). *Aust. J. Zool.* **16**: 915–1020 [992]; Cardale, J.C., this work, interprets Exley's incorrect inference of holotype as a

lectotype designation (Art. 74, ICZN 1985).
Type locality: Brisbane, QLD.

Taxonomic decision for synonymy: Exley, E.M. (1968). Revision of the genus *Euryglossina* Cockerell (Apoidea : Colletidae). *Aust. J. Zool.* **16**: 915–1020 [992].

Distribution: NE coastal, Murray-Darling basin, N Gulf, QLD, NSW.
Ecology: adult—volant; melliferous, solitary, flower visiting record: wild parsley, *Angophora* Cav. [Myrtaceae], *Callistemon* R.Br. [Myrtaceae], *Eucalyptus* L'Hérit. [Myrtaceae], *Eugenia* L. [Myrtaceae], *Leptospermum* Forster & G.Forster [Myrtaceae], *Melaleuca* L. [Myrtaceae], *Tristania* R.Br. [Myrtaceae].
References: Meade-Waldo, G. (1923). Hymenoptera. Fam. Apidae. Subfam. Prosopidinae. *Genera Insectorum* **181**: 1–45 (illustration); Rayment, T. (1935). *A Cluster of Bees*. Sixty essays on the life-histories of Australian bees, with specific descriptions of over 100 new species, and an introduction by Professor E.F. Phillips, D.Ph., Cornell University, U.S.A. Sydney : Endeavour Press 752 pp. (illustration).

Euryglossina (Turnerella) glauerti (Rayment, 1934)

Turnerella glauerti Rayment, T. (1934). Contributions to the fauna of Rottnest Island. VIII. Apoidea. With description of new species. *J. Proc. R. Soc. West. Aust.* **20**: 201–212 [202].
Type data: holotype, WAM 33–816a ♂ (described as ♀).
Type locality: Rottnest [Is.], WA.

Distribution: SW coastal, WA; only published localities Rottnest Is. and Gnowangerup.
Ecology: adult—volant; melliferous, solitary.
Reference: Exley, E.M. (1968). Revision of the genus *Euryglossina* Cockerell (Apoidea : Colletidae). *Aust. J. Zool.* **16**: 915–1020 (redescription).

Euryglossina (Turnerella) globuliceps (Cockerell, 1918)

Euryglossella globuliceps Cockerell, T.D.A. (1918). Some bees collected in Queensland. *Mem. Qd Mus.* **6**: 112–120 [116].
Type data: holotype, QM Hy/4137 ♀.
Type locality: Brisbane, QLD.

Distribution: NE coastal, SE coastal, Murray-Darling basin, S Gulfs, QLD, NSW, VIC, SA.
Ecology: adult—volant; melliferous, solitary, flower visiting record: *Eucalyptus* L'Hérit. [Myrtaceae], *Leptospermum* Forster & G.Forster [Myrtaceae], *Lomatia* R.Br. [Proteaceae], *Melaleuca* L. [Myrtaceae], *Syncarpia* Ten. [Myrtaceae], *Tristania* R.Br. [Myrtaceae].
References: Cockerell, T.D.A. (1929). Bees in the Queensland Museum. *Mem. Qd Mus.* **9**: 298–323 (taxonomy); Michener, C.D. (1965). A classification of the bees of the Australian and South Pacific

regions. *Bull. Am. Mus. Nat. Hist.* **130**: 1–362 (flower record); Exley, E.M. (1968). Revision of the genus *Euryglossina* Cockerell (Apoidea : Colletidae). *Aust. J. Zool.* **16**: 915–1020 (redescription).

Euryglossina (Turnerella) gracilis Exley, 1968

Euryglossina (Turnerella) gracilis Exley, E.M. (1968). Revision of the genus *Euryglossina* Cockerell (Apoidea : Colletidae). *Aust. J. Zool.* **16**: 915–1020 [996].
Type data: holotype, QM T6654 ♀.
Type locality: Mt Pleasant, QLD.

Distribution: NE coastal, QLD; only published localities Mt Pleasant and Capalaba.
Ecology: adult—volant; melliferous, solitary, flower visiting record: *Eucalyptus* L'Hérit. [Myrtaceae], *Leptospermum* Forster & G.Forster [Myrtaceae].

Euryglossina (Turnerella) grandigena Exley, 1968

Euryglossina (Turnerella) grandigena Exley, E.M. (1968). Revision of the genus *Euryglossina* Cockerell (Apoidea : Colletidae). *Aust. J. Zool.* **16**: 915–1020 [967].
Type data: holotype, QM T6661 ♀.
Type locality: Tibrogargan Creek, QLD.

Distribution: NE coastal, QLD; only published localities Tibrogargan Creek, Isis River and Stradbroke Is.
Ecology: adult—volant; melliferous, solitary, flower visiting record: *Leptospermum* Forster & G.Forster [Myrtaceae], *Melaleuca* L. [Myrtaceae].

Euryglossina (Turnerella) leyburnensis Exley, 1983

Euryglossina (Turnerella) leyburnensis Exley, E.M. (1983). A remarkable bee from Eastern Australia (Hymenoptera : Apoidea : Colletidae). *J. Aust. Entomol. Soc.* **22**: 293–294 [293].
Type data: holotype, QM ♀*.
Type locality: 15 km S Leyburn, QLD.

Distribution: SE coastal, Murray-Darling basin, QLD, NSW; only published localities near Leyburn, near Nanango, Stanthorpe and Legume.
Ecology: adult—volant; melliferous, solitary, flower visiting record: *Angophora* Cav. [Myrtaceae], *Eucalyptus* L'Hérit. [Myrtaceae].
Reference: Exley, E.M. (1968). Revision of the genus *Euryglossina* Cockerell (Apoidea : Colletidae). *Aust. J. Zool.* **16**: 915–1020 (male, as *Euryglossina (Turnerella)* Species S).

Euryglossina (Turnerella) macrostoma (Cockerell, 1929)

Turnerella macrostoma Cockerell, T.D.A. (1929). Bees in the Queensland Museum. *Mem. Qd Mus.* **9**: 298–323 [320].
Type data: holotype, QM Hy/3726 ♀.
Type locality: Brisbane, QLD.

Distribution: NE coastal, SE coastal, QLD, NSW; only published localities Brisbane, Capalaba, Mt Pleasant and Ku-ring-gai Chase (as Kuringai).
Ecology: adult—volant; melliferous, solitary, flower

visiting record: *Leptospermum* Forster & G.Forster [Myrtaceae], *Melaleuca* L. [Myrtaceae].
References: Michener, C.D. (1965). A classification of the bees of the Australian and South Pacific regions. *Bull. Am. Mus. Nat. Hist.* **130**: 1–362 (flower record); Exley, E.M. (1968). Revision of the genus *Euryglossina* Cockerell (Apoidea : Colletidae). *Aust. J. Zool.* **16**: 915–1020 (redescription).

Euryglossina (Turnerella) megalocephala Exley, 1968

Euryglossina (Turnerella) megalocephala Exley, E.M. (1968). Revision of the genus *Euryglossina* Cockerell (Apoidea : Colletidae). *Aust. J. Zool.* **16**: 915–1020 [973].
Type data: holotype, QM T6660 ♀.
Type locality: Glass House Mtn, QLD.

Distribution: NE coastal, QLD; only published localities Glass House Mtn and near Nanango.
Ecology: adult—volant; melliferous, solitary, flower visiting record: *Angophora* Cav. [Myrtaceae], *Melaleuca* L. [Myrtaceae].

Euryglossina (Turnerella) melanocephala Exley, 1968

Euryglossina (Turnerella) melanocephala Exley, E.M. (1968). Revision of the genus *Euryglossina* Cockerell (Apoidea : Colletidae). *Aust. J. Zool.* **16**: 915–1020 [979].
Type data: holotype, QM T7462 ♀.
Type locality: Greenmount, WA.

Distribution: NE coastal, N Gulf, Murray-Darling basin, S Gulfs, SW coastal, QLD, NSW, SA, WA.
Ecology: adult—volant; melliferous, solitary, flower visiting record: *Angophora* Cav. [Myrtaceae], *Callistemon* R.Br. [Myrtaceae], *Eucalyptus* L'Hérit. [Myrtaceae], *Leptospermum* Forster & G.Forster [Myrtaceae], *Melaleuca* L. [Myrtaceae], *Syncarpia* Ten. [Myrtaceae], *Tristania* R.Br. [Myrtaceae].

Euryglossina (Turnerella) micheneri Exley, 1968

Euryglossina (Turnerella) micheneri Exley, E.M. (1968). Revision of the genus *Euryglossina* Cockerell (Apoidea : Colletidae). *Aust. J. Zool.* **16**: 915–1020 [991].
Type data: holotype, QM T7076 ♀.
Type locality: Castle Hill, Townsville, QLD.

Distribution: NE coastal, QLD.
Ecology: adult—volant; melliferous, solitary, flower visiting record: *Angophora* Cav. [Myrtaceae], *Eucalyptus* L'Hérit. [Myrtaceae], *Melaleuca* L. [Myrtaceae], *Tristania* R.Br. [Myrtaceae].

Euryglossina (Turnerella) nothula (Cockerell, 1922)

Euryglossella nothula Cockerell, T.D.A. (1922). Descriptions and records of bees. XCVI. *Ann. Mag. Nat. Hist.* (9)**10**: 544–550 [548].
Type data: lectotype, USNM ♀*.
Subsequent designation: Exley, E.M. (1968). Revision of the genus *Euryglossina* Cockerell (Apoidea : Colletidae). *Aust. J. Zool.* **16**: 915–1020 [979]; Cardale, J.C., this work,

interprets Exley's incorrect inference of holotype as a lectotype designation (Art. 74, ICZN 1985).
Type locality: Bribie Is., QLD.

Distribution: NE coastal, SE coastal, QLD, NSW; only published localities Bribie Is., Brisbane, Beerwah, Gordonvale and Buladelah.
Ecology: adult—volant; melliferous, solitary, flower visiting record: *Eucalyptus* L'Hérit. [Myrtaceae], *Eugenia* L. [Myrtaceae], *Syncarpia* Ten. [Myrtaceae].
References: Michener, C.D. (1965). A classification of the bees of the Australian and South Pacific regions. *Bull. Am. Mus. Nat. Hist.* **130**: 1–362 (flower record); Exley, E.M. (1968). Revision of the genus *Euryglossina* Cockerell (Apoidea : Colletidae). *Aust. J. Zool.* **16**: 915–1020 (redescription).

Euryglossina (Turnerella) polita Exley, 1968

Euryglossina (Turnerella) polita Exley, E.M. (1968). Revision of the genus *Euryglossina* Cockerell (Apoidea : Colletidae). *Aust. J. Zool.* **16**: 915–1020 [975].
Type data: holotype, QM T6656 ♀.
Type locality: Mica Creek, 5 miles from Mt Isa, QLD.

Distribution: N Gulf, QLD; only published localities Mt Isa and Mica Creek.
Ecology: adult—volant; melliferous, solitary, flower visiting record: *Eucalyptus* L'Hérit. [Myrtaceae].

Euryglossina (Turnerella) proserpinensis Exley, 1968

Euryglossina (Turnerella) proserpinensis Exley, E.M. (1968). Revision of the genus *Euryglossina* Cockerell (Apoidea : Colletidae). *Aust. J. Zool.* **16**: 915–1020 [999].
Type data: holotype, QM T6650 ♀.
Type locality: Proserpine, QLD.

Distribution: NE coastal, QLD; only published localities Proserpine, Bowen, Millaroo and Mt Carbine.
Ecology: adult—volant; melliferous, solitary, flower visiting record: *Callistemon* R.Br. [Myrtaceae], *Melaleuca* L. [Myrtaceae].

Euryglossina (Turnerella) pseudoatomaria Exley, 1968

Euryglossina (Turnerella) pseudoatomaria Exley, E.M. (1968). Revision of the genus *Euryglossina* Cockerell (Apoidea : Colletidae). *Aust. J. Zool.* **16**: 915–1020 [989].
Type data: holotype, QM T7463 ♀.
Type locality: Castle Hill, Townsville, QLD.

Distribution: NE coastal, Murray-Darling basin, SW coastal, QLD, NSW, SA, WA.
Ecology: adult—volant; melliferous, solitary, flower visiting record: *Angophora* Cav. [Myrtaceae], *Eucalyptus* L'Hérit. [Myrtaceae], *Melaleuca* L. [Myrtaceae], *Tristania* R.Br. [Myrtaceae].

Euryglossina (Turnerella) psilosoma Exley, 1968

Euryglossina (Turnerella) psilosoma Exley, E.M. (1968). Revision of the genus *Euryglossina* Cockerell (Apoidea :

Colletidae). *Aust. J. Zool.* **16**: 915–1020 [995].
Type data: holotype, QM T6655 ♀.
Type locality: Brisbane, QLD.

Distribution: NE coastal, QLD; known only from type locality.
Ecology: adult—volant; melliferous, solitary, flower visiting record: *Melaleuca* L. [Myrtaceae].

Euryglossina (Turnerella) pulcherrima Exley, 1968

Euryglossina (Turnerella) pulcherrima Exley, E.M. (1968). Revision of the genus *Euryglossina* Cockerell (Apoidea : Colletidae). *Aust. J. Zool.* **16**: 915–1020 [969].
Type data: holotype, QM T6659 ♀.
Type locality: Beerwah, QLD.

Distribution: NE coastal, QLD; only published localities Beerwah, Tewantin and Capalaba (record from Moonbi Range, NSW, considered doubtful).
Ecology: adult—volant; melliferous, solitary, flower visiting record: *(Angophora* Cav. [Myrtaceae]), *Syncarpia* Ten. [Myrtaceae], *Tristania* R.Br. [Myrtaceae].

Euryglossina (Turnerella) pulchra Exley, 1968

Euryglossina (Turnerella) pulchra Exley, E.M. (1968). Revision of the genus *Euryglossina* Cockerell (Apoidea : Colletidae). *Aust. J. Zool.* **16**: 915–1020 [966].
Type data: holotype, QM T6652 ♀.
Type locality: Brisbane, QLD.

Distribution: NE coastal, S Gulfs, QLD, SA; only published localities Brisbane, Fernvale, Ipswich, Moggill and Tusmore.
Ecology: larva—sedentary : adult—volant; melliferous, solitary, nest in wood, flower visiting record: *Angophora* Cav. [Myrtaceae], *Callistemon* R.Br. [Myrtaceae], *Eucalyptus* L'Hérit. [Myrtaceae].
Reference: Houston, T.F. (1969). Observations on the nests and behaviour of some euryglossine bees (Hymenoptera : Colletidae). *J. Aust. Entomol. Soc.* **8**: 1–10 (biology).

Euryglossina (Turnerella) subnothula (Cockerell, 1929)

Turnerella subnothula Cockerell, T.D.A. (1929). Bees in the Queensland Museum. *Mem. Qd Mus.* **9**: 298–323 [321].
Type data: holotype, QM Hy/4042 ♀.
Type locality: Oxley, Brisbane, QLD.

Distribution: NE coastal, Murray-Darling basin, QLD (as Wallangarra NSW).
Ecology: adult—volant; melliferous, solitary, flower visiting record: *Callistemon* R.Br. [Myrtaceae], *Leptospermum* Forster & G.Forster [Myrtaceae], *Melaleuca* L. [Myrtaceae].
References: Michener, C.D. (1965). A classification of the bees of the Australian and South Pacific regions. *Bull. Am. Mus. Nat. Hist.* **130**: 1–362 (flower record); Exley, E.M. (1968). Revision of the genus

Euryglossina Cockerell (Apoidea : Colletidae). *Aust. J. Zool.* **16**: 915–1020 (redescription).

Euryglossina (Turnerella) sulcata Exley, 1968

Euryglossina (Turnerella) sulcata Exley, E.M. (1968). Revision of the genus *Euryglossina* Cockerell (Apoidea : Colletidae). *Aust. J. Zool.* **16**: 915–1020 [974].
Type data: holotype, QM T6658 ♀.
Type locality: Glass House Mtn, QLD.

Distribution: NE coastal, SE coastal, Murray-Darling basin, QLD (as Wallangarra NSW), VIC.
Ecology: adult—volant; melliferous, solitary, flower visiting record: *Leptospermum* Forster & G.Forster [Myrtaceae], *Melaleuca* L. [Myrtaceae], *Syncarpia* Ten. [Myrtaceae].

Euryglossina (Turnerella) xanthocephala Exley, 1968

Euryglossina (Turnerella) xanthocephala Exley, E.M. (1968). Revision of the genus *Euryglossina* Cockerell (Apoidea : Colletidae). *Aust. J. Zool.* **16**: 915–1020 [970].
Type data: holotype, QM T6662 ♀.
Type locality: Capalaba, QLD.

Distribution: NE coastal, Murray-Darling basin, QLD; only published localities Capalaba, Amiens, Mt Pleasant, Mt May and Wallangarra (as Wallangarra NSW).
Ecology: adult—volant; melliferous, solitary, flower visiting record: *Leptospermum* Forster & G.Forster [Myrtaceae].

Euryglossina (Turnerella) xanthogena (Rayment, 1935)

Euryglossella bicolor Rayment, T. (1935). *A Cluster of Bees. Sixty essays on the life-histories of Australian bees, with specific descriptions of over 100 new species, and an introduction by Professor E.F. Phillips, D.Ph.,* Cornell University, U.S.A. Sydney : Endeavour Press 752 pp. [663] [junior secondary homonym of *Euryglossina bicolor* Rayment, 1928].
Type data: holotype, NMV T–1404 ♀.
Type locality: Melbourne, VIC.

Turnerella xanthogena Rayment, T. (1935). *A Cluster of Bees. Sixty essays on the life-histories of Australian bees, with specific descriptions of over 100 new species, and an introduction by Professor E.F. Phillips, D.Ph.,* Cornell University, U.S.A. Sydney : Endeavour Press 752 pp. [667].
Type data: holotype, whereabouts unknown ♀* (not located in T. Rayment coll. transferred to ANIC).
Type locality: Sandringham, VIC.

Taxonomic decision for synonymy: Exley, E.M. (1968). Revision of the genus *Euryglossina* Cockerell (Apoidea : Colletidae). *Aust. J. Zool.* **16**: 915–1020 [985].

Distribution: NE coastal, SE coastal, Murray-Darling basin, QLD, NSW, VIC.
Ecology: adult—volant; melliferous, solitary, flower visiting record: fennel, shirley poppies, *Eucalyptus*

L'Hérit. [Myrtaceae], *Eugenia* L. [Myrtaceae], *Melaleuca* L. [Myrtaceae], *Pongamia* Vent. [Fabaceae].

Euryglossula Michener, 1965

Euryglossula Michener, C.D. (1965). A classification of the bees of the Australian and South Pacific regions. *Bull. Am. Mus. Nat. Hist.* **130**: 1–362 [111]. Type species: *Euryglossina chalcosoma* Cockerell, 1913 by original designation.

Euryglossula carnarvonensis Exley, 1968

Euryglossula carnarvonensis Exley, E.M. (1968). Revision of the genus *Euryglossula* Michener (Apoidea : Colletidae). *Aust. J. Zool.* **16**: 203–217 [204].
Type data: holotype, WAM 67–1 ♀.
Type locality: Carnarvon, WA.

Distribution: NW coastal, WA; known only from type locality.
Ecology: adult—volant; melliferous, solitary.

Euryglossula chalcosoma (Cockerell, 1913)

Euryglossina chalcosoma Cockerell, T.D.A. (1913). Descriptions and records of bees. LI. *Ann. Mag. Nat. Hist.* *(8)***11**: 387–394 [391].
Type data: holotype, BMNH Hym.17.a.302 ♀.
Type locality: Croydon, VIC.

Euryglossina chalcosoma claristigma Rayment, T. (1935). *A Cluster of Bees.* Sixty essays on the life-histories of Australian bees, with specific descriptions of over 100 new species, and an introduction by Professor E.F. Phillips, D.Ph., Cornell University, U.S.A. Sydney : Endeavour Press 752 pp. [649].
Type data: holotype, ANIC ♀.
Type locality: Sandringham, VIC.

Taxonomic decision for synonymy: Exley, E.M. (1968). Revision of the genus *Euryglossula* Michener (Apoidea : Colletidae). *Aust. J. Zool.* **16**: 203–217 [206].

Distribution: NE coastal, SE coastal, Murray-Darling basin, QLD, NSW, VIC.
Ecology: larva—sedentary : adult—volant; melliferous, solitary, nest in soil in aggregations, flower visiting record: *Angophora* Cav. [Myrtaceae], *Callistemon* R.Br. [Myrtaceae], *Eucalyptus* L'Hérit. [Myrtaceae], *Jacksonia* Smith [Fabaceae], *Leptospermum* Forster & G.Forster [Myrtaceae], *Melaleuca* L. [Myrtaceae].
References: Michener, C.D. (1965). A classification of the bees of the Australian and South Pacific regions. *Bull. Am. Mus. Nat. Hist.* **130**: 1–362 (flower records); Houston, T.F. (1969). Observations on the nests and behaviour of some euryglossine bees (Hymenoptera : Colletidae). *J. Aust. Entomol. Soc.* **8**: 1–10 (biology); Michener, C.D. & Brooks, R.W. (1984). A comparative study of the glossae of bees (Apoidea). *Contrib. Am. Entomol. Inst.* **22**: 1–73 (glossa).

Euryglossula deserti Exley, 1968

Euryglossula deserti Exley, E.M. (1968). Revision of the genus *Euryglossula* Michener (Apoidea : Colletidae). *Aust. J. Zool.* **16**: 203–217 [210].
Type data: holotype, ANIC ♀.
Type locality: Macdonald Downs, NT.

Distribution: Lake Eyre basin, NT; known only from type locality.
Ecology: adult—volant; melliferous, solitary.

Euryglossula flava Exley, 1968

Euryglossula flava Exley, E.M. (1968). Revision of the genus *Euryglossula* Michener (Apoidea : Colletidae). *Aust. J. Zool.* **16**: 203–217 [212].
Type data: holotype, ANIC ♀.
Type locality: 14 miles N Barrow Creek, NT.

Distribution: N Gulf, Lake Eyre basin, QLD, NT; only published localities Barkly Tableland, near Cloncurry and near Barrow Creek.
Ecology: adult—volant; melliferous, solitary, flower visiting record: *Eucalyptus* L'Hérit. [Myrtaceae].

Euryglossula fultoni (Cockerell, 1913)

Euryglossina fultoni Cockerell, T.D.A. (1913). Descriptions and records of bees. LI. *Ann. Mag. Nat. Hist.* *(8)***11**: 387–394 [390].
Type data: holotype, USNM ♀*.
Type locality: Purnong, near Murray River, SA.

Distribution: Murray-Darling basin, S Gulfs, SW coastal, W plateau, SA, WA.
Ecology: adult—volant; melliferous, solitary, flower visiting record: *Eucalyptus* L'Hérit. [Myrtaceae], *Melaleuca* L. [Myrtaceae].
Reference: Exley, E.M. (1968). Revision of the genus *Euryglossula* Michener (Apoidea : Colletidae). *Aust. J. Zool.* **16**: 203–217 (redescription).

Euryglossula microdonta (Rayment, 1934)

Euryglossina microdonta Rayment, T. (1934). Contributions to the fauna of Rottnest Island. VIII. Apoidea. With description of new species. *J. Proc. R. Soc. West. Aust.* **20**: 201–212 [203].
Type data: holotype, WAM 33–824 ♀.
Type locality: Rottnest Is., WA.

Euryglossina parazantha Rayment, T. (1934). Contributions to the fauna of Rottnest Island. VIII. Apoidea. With description of new species. *J. Proc. R. Soc. West. Aust.* **20**: 201–212 [203] [misspelled as *Euryglossina paraxantha* in pl. 12 on p. 212].
Type data: holotype, ANIC ♂ (described as ♀).
Type locality: Rottnest Is., WA.

Taxonomic decision for synonymy: Exley, E.M. (1968). Revision of the genus *Euryglossula* Michener (Apoidea : Colletidae). *Aust. J. Zool.* **16**: 203–217 [215].

Distribution: Murray-Darling basin, S Gulfs, SW coastal, SA, WA; only published localities North Beach Wallaroo, Tintinara, Keith and Rottnest Is.

Ecology: adult—volant; melliferous, solitary, flower visiting record: *Eucalyptus* L'Hérit. [Myrtaceae], *Leptospermum* Forster & G.Forster [Myrtaceae].

Euryglossula variepicta Exley, 1969

Euryglossula variepicta Exley, E.M. (1969). A new species of *Euryglossula* (Apoidea : Colletidae). *J. Aust. Entomol. Soc.* **8**: 137–138 [137].
Type data: holotype, QM T7092 ♀.
Type locality: Blackall, QLD.

Distribution: Murray-Darling basin, QLD; known only from type locality.
Ecology: adult—volant; melliferous, solitary, flower visiting record: *Bauhinia* L. [Caesalpiniaceae], *?Eremophila* R.Br. [Myoporaceae].

Heterohesma Michener, 1965

Heterohesma Michener, C.D. (1965). A classification of the bees of the Australian and South Pacific regions. *Bull. Am. Mus. Nat. Hist.* **130**: 1–362 [97]. Type species: *Stilpnosoma clypeata* Rayment, 1954 by original designation.

Heterohesma clypeata (Rayment, 1954)

Stilpnosoma clypeata Rayment, T. (1954). Remarkable bees from a rain forest. *Aust. Zool.* **12**: 46–56 [50].
Type data: holotype, whereabouts unknown ♀* (not located in T. Rayment coll. transferred to ANIC).
Type locality: Jamberoo, NSW.

Distribution: SE coastal, NSW; only published localities Jamberoo, Barrington Tops and Mt Tomah.
Ecology: adult—volant; melliferous, solitary.
Reference: Exley, E.M. (1983). The genus *Heterohesma* Michener (Hymenoptera : Apoidea : Colletidae). *J. Aust. Entomol. Soc.* **22**: 219–221 (distribution).

Heterohesma weiri Exley, 1983

Heterohesma weiri Exley, E.M. (1983). The genus *Heterohesma* Michener (Hymenoptera : Apoidea : Colletidae). *J. Aust. Entomol. Soc.* **22**: 219–221 [219].
Type data: holotype, QM ♀*.
Type locality: New England National Park, via Ebor, NSW.

Distribution: SE coastal, NSW, VIC, TAS; only published localities New England National Park via Ebor, Granite Mtn, 9 km NW Buldan (as Buldah) and Mt Field National Park.
Ecology: adult—volant; melliferous, solitary.

Hyphesma Michener, 1965

Hyphesma Michener, C.D. (1965). A classification of the bees of the Australian and South Pacific regions. *Bull. Am. Mus. Nat. Hist.* **130**: 1–362 [103]. Type species: *Pachyprosopis atromicans* Cockerell, 1913 by original designation.

Hyphesma atromicans (Cockerell, 1913)

Pachyprosopis atromicans Cockerell, T.D.A. (1913). Some Australian bees. *Proc. Acad. Nat. Sci. Philad.* **65**: 28–44 [37].
Type data: holotype, MCZ ♀*.
Type locality: Purnong, Murray River, SA.

Pachyprosopis barbata Cockerell, T.D.A. (1914). Australian bees of the family Prosopididae. *Insecutor Inscit. Menstr.* **2**: 97–101 [101].
Type data: holotype, USNM ♂*.
Type locality: Brisbane, QLD.

Euryglossa oleariae Rayment, T. (1935). *A Cluster of Bees*. Sixty essays on the life-histories of Australian bees, with specific descriptions of over 100 new species, and an introduction by Professor E.F. Phillips, D.Ph., Cornell University, U.S.A. Sydney : Endeavour Press 752 pp. [640].
Type data: holotype, ANIC ♂ (described as ♀).
Type locality: Sandringham, VIC.

Euryglossa elthamensis Rayment, T. (1935). *A Cluster of Bees*. Sixty essays on the life-histories of Australian bees, with specific descriptions of over 100 new species, and an introduction by Professor E.F. Phillips, D.Ph., Cornell University, U.S.A. Sydney : Endeavour Press 752 pp. [643].
Type data: holotype, ANIC ♀.
Type locality: Eltham, VIC.

Pachyprosopis celmisiae Rayment, T. (1949). New bees and wasps—Part X. *Vict. Nat.* **65**: 271–272 [271].
Type data: holotype, ANIC ♀.
Type locality: Shore of Lake Catani, Mt Buffalo, VIC.

Taxonomic decision for synonymy: Exley, E.M. (1975). Revision of the genus *Hyphesma* Michener (Apoidea : Colletidae). *Aust. J. Zool.* **23**: 277–291 [281].

Distribution: NE coastal, SE coastal, Murray-Darling basin, S Gulfs, Lake Eyre basin, SW coastal, QLD, NSW, ACT, VIC, SA, WA, TAS.
Ecology: adult—volant; melliferous, solitary, flower visiting record: *Angophora* Cav. [Myrtaceae], *Bursaria* Cav. [Pittosporaceae], *Celmisia* Cass. [Asteraceae], *Eucalyptus* L'Hérit. [Myrtaceae], *Goodenia* Sm. [Goodeniaceae], *Jacksonia* Smith [Fabaceae], *Leptospermum* Forster & G.Forster [Myrtaceae], *Olearia* Moench [Asteraceae], *Tristania* R.Br. [Myrtaceae].
References: Exley, E.M. (1975). Revision of the genus *Hyphesma* Michener (Apoidea : Colletidae). *Aust. J. Zool.* **23**: 277–291 (biology); Cane, J.H. (1979). The hind tibiotarsal and tibial spur articulations in bees (Hymenoptera : Apoidea). *J. Kansas Entomol. Soc.* **52**: 123–137 (hind spur).

Hyphesma barrowensis Exley, 1975

Hyphesma barrowensis Exley, E.M. (1975). Revision of the genus *Hyphesma* Michener (Apoidea : Colletidae). *Aust. J. Zool.* **23**: 277–291 [290].
Type data: holotype, ANIC ♀.
Type locality: 14 miles N Barrow Creek, NT.

Distribution: Lake Eyre basin, NT; known only from type locality.
Ecology: adult—volant; melliferous, solitary.

Hyphesma cardaleae Exley, 1975

Hyphesma cardaleae Exley, E.M. (1975). Revision of the genus *Hyphesma* Michener (Apoidea : Colletidae). *Aust. J. Zool.* **23**: 277–291 [288].
Type data: holotype, ANIC ♀.
Type locality: Millstream, WA.

Distribution: NW coastal, WA; known only from type locality.
Ecology: adult—volant; melliferous, solitary, flower visiting record: *Eucalyptus* L'Hérit. [Myrtaceae].

Hyphesma cooba Exley, 1975

Hyphesma cooba Exley, E.M. (1975). Revision of the genus *Hyphesma* Michener (Apoidea : Colletidae). *Aust. J. Zool.* **23**: 277–291 [285].
Type data: holotype, QM T7353 ♂.
Type locality: Murphys Creek, near Helidon, QLD.

Distribution: NE coastal, QLD; known only from type locality.
Ecology: adult—volant; melliferous, solitary, flower visiting record: *Eucalyptus* L'Hérit. [Myrtaceae].

Hyphesma federalis Exley, 1975

Hyphesma federalis Exley, E.M. (1975). Revision of the genus *Hyphesma* Michener (Apoidea : Colletidae). *Aust. J. Zool.* **23**: 277–291 [286].
Type data: holotype, ANIC ♂.
Type locality: Black Mtn, ACT.

Distribution: Murray-Darling basin, ACT; known only from type locality.
Ecology: adult—volant; melliferous, solitary.

Hyphesma nitidiceps (Cockerell, 1912)

Pachyprosopis nitidiceps Cockerell, T.D.A. (1912). Descriptions and records of bees. XLIII. *Ann. Mag. Nat. Hist.* (8)**9**: 377–387 [384].
Type data: holotype, BMNH Hym.17.a.315 ♀.
Type locality: Mackay, QLD.

Distribution: NE coastal, QLD; known only from type locality.
Ecology: adult—volant; melliferous, solitary, flower visiting record: *Leptospermum* Forster & G.Forster [Myrtaceae].
Reference: Exley, E.M. (1975). Revision of the genus *Hyphesma* Michener (Apoidea : Colletidae). *Aust. J. Zool.* **23**: 277–291 (description of male).

Hyphesma nukarnensis Exley, 1975

Hyphesma nukarnensis Exley, E.M. (1975). Revision of the genus *Hyphesma* Michener (Apoidea : Colletidae). *Aust. J. Zool.* **23**: 277–291 [287].
Type data: holotype, QM T7347 ♀.
Type locality: Nukarni, WA.

Distribution: W plateau, SW coastal, SA, WA.
Ecology: adult—volant; melliferous, solitary, flower visiting record: *Eucalyptus* L'Hérit. [Myrtaceae].

Melittosmithia Schulz, 1906

Smithia Vachal, J. (1897). Éclaircissements sur le genre *Scrapter* et description d'une espèce nouvelle de *Dufourea* (Hymén.). *Bull. Soc. Entomol. Fr.* **1897**: 61–64 [63] [junior homonym of *Smithia* Milne-Edwards & Haime, 1851 (Coleoptera), *Smithia* Saussure, 1855 (Hymenoptera : Eumenidae), *Smithia* Mabille, 1880 (Lepidoptera), *Smithia* Maltzan, 1883 (Mollusca) and *Smithia* Monterosato, 1884 (Mollusca)]. Type species: *Scrapter carinata* Smith, 1862 by subsequent designation, see Cockerell, T.D.A. (1910). Descriptions and records of bees. XXXIII. *Ann. Mag. Nat. Hist.* (8)**6**: 356–366 [358].

Melittosmithia Schulz, W.A. (1906). *Spolia Hymenopterologica*. Paderborn : Pape iii 356 pp. 1 pl. [244] [*nom. nov.* for *Smithia* Vachal, 1897].

Generic reference: Michener, C.D. (1965). A classification of the bees of the Australian and South Pacific regions. *Bull. Am. Mus. Nat. Hist.* **130**: 1–362.

Melittosmithia adelaidae (Friese, 1924)

Stilpnosoma adelaidae Friese, H. (1924). Ueber die Bienen Australiens. *Konowia* **3**: 216–249 [235].
Type data: syntypes (probable), whereabouts unknown ♀*.
Type locality: Sydney, NSW.

Distribution: SE coastal, NSW; known only from type locality.
Ecology: adult—volant; melliferous, solitary.
Reference: Cockerell, T.D.A. (1926). Descriptions and records of bees. CXII. *Ann. Mag. Nat. Hist.* (9)**18**: 216–227 (generic placement).

Melittosmithia carinata (Smith, 1862)

Scrapter carinata Smith, F. (1862). Descriptions of new species of Australian Hymenoptera, and of a species of *Formica* from New Zealand. *Trans. Entomol. Soc. Lond.* (3)**1**: 53–62 [60].
Type data: holotype, BMNH Hym.17.a.307 ♀.
Type locality: Australia.

Distribution: Australia, known only from type locality, exact locality unknown.
Ecology: adult—volant; melliferous, solitary.
References: Cockerell, T.D.A. (1910). Descriptions and records of bees. XXXIII. *Ann. Mag. Nat. Hist.* (8)**6**: 356–366 (generic placement); Meade-Waldo, G. (1923). Hymenoptera. Fam. Apidae. Subfam. Prosopidinae. *Genera Insectorum* **181**: 1–45 (illustration); Rayment, T. (1935). *A Cluster of Bees.* Sixty essays on the life-histories of Australian bees, with specific descriptions of over 100 new species, and an introduction by Professor E.F. Phillips, D.Ph., Cornell University, U.S.A. Sydney : Endeavour Press 752 pp. (illustration).

Melittosmithia froggattiana (Cockerell, 1905)

Euryglossa froggattiana Cockerell, T.D.A. (1905). Descriptions and records of bees. V. *Ann. Mag. Nat. Hist. (7)***16**: 465–477 [472].
Type data: holotype, BMNH Hym.17.a.308 ♀.
Type locality: Shoalhaven, NSW.

Distribution: SE coastal, NSW; known only from type locality.
Ecology: adult—volant; melliferous, solitary.
Reference: Meade-Waldo, G. (1923). Hymenoptera. Fam. Apidae. Subfam. Prosopidinae. *Genera Insectorum* **181**: 1–45 (generic placement).

Melittosmithia subtilis Cockerell, 1926

Melittosmithia subtilis Cockerell, T.D.A. (1926). Descriptions and records of bees. CXII. *Ann. Mag. Nat. Hist. (9)***18**: 216–227 [216].
Type data: holotype, NMV ♀.
Type locality: "Oakley L." (probably Oakleigh), VIC.

Distribution: SE coastal, VIC; known only from type locality.
Ecology: adult—volant; melliferous, solitary.
Reference: Rayment, T. (1935). *A Cluster of Bees.* Sixty essays on the life-histories of Australian bees, with specific descriptions of over 100 new species, and an introduction by Professor E.F. Phillips, D.Ph., Cornell University, U.S.A. Sydney : Endeavour Press 752 pp. (illustration).

Pachyprosopis Perkins, 1908

Taxonomic decision for subgeneric arrangement: Exley, E.M. (1972). Revision of the genus *Pachyprosopis* Perkins (Apoidea : Colletidae). *Aust. J. Zool. Suppl. Ser.* **10**: 1–43 [1].

Generic reference: Michener, C.D. (1965). A classification of the bees of the Australian and South Pacific regions. *Bull. Am. Mus. Nat. Hist.* **130**: 1–362.

Pachyprosopis (Pachyprosopis) Perkins, 1908

Pachyprosopis Perkins, R.C.L. (1908). Some remarkable Australian Hymenoptera. *Proc. Hawaii. Entomol. Soc.* **2**: 27–35 [29]. Type species: *Pachyprosopis mirabilis* Perkins, 1908 by monotypy.

Pachyprosopis (Pachyprosopis) cornuta Exley, 1972

Pachyprosopis (Pachyprosopis) cornuta Exley, E.M. (1972). Revision of the genus *Pachyprosopis* Perkins (Apoidea : Colletidae). *Aust. J. Zool. Suppl. Ser.* **10**: 1–43 [13].
Type data: holotype, BMNH Hym.17.a.2846 ♀.
Type locality: Spargoville, 28 miles W Coolgardie, WA.

Distribution: W plateau, WA; only published localities Spargoville and Dedari.
Ecology: adult—volant; melliferous, solitary.

Pachyprosopis (Pachyprosopis) georgica Cockerell, 1929

Pachyprosopis georgica Cockerell, T.D.A. (1929). Bees in the Queensland Museum. *Mem. Qd Mus.* **9**: 298–323 [299].
Type data: holotype, QM T4034 ♀.
Type locality: King George Sound, WA.

Distribution: SW coastal, WA; known only from type locality.
Ecology: adult—volant; melliferous, solitary.
References: Michener, C.D. (1965). A classification of the bees of the Australian and South Pacific regions. *Bull. Am. Mus. Nat. Hist.* **130**: 1–362 (taxonomy); Exley, E.M. (1972). Revision of the genus *Pachyprosopis* Perkins (Apoidea : Colletidae). *Aust. J. Zool. Suppl. Ser.* **10**: 1–43 (redescription).

Pachyprosopis (Pachyprosopis) hackeri Cockerell, 1916

Pachyprosopis hackeri Cockerell, T.D.A. (1916). A collection of bees from Queensland. *Mem. Qd Mus.* **5**: 197–204 [199].
Type data: holotype, USNM ♀*.
Type locality: Oxley, Brisbane, QLD.

Distribution: NE coastal, Murray-Darling basin, QLD; only published localities Oxley (Brisbane) and Stanthorpe.
Ecology: adult—volant; melliferous, solitary.
References: Michener, C.D. (1965). A classification of the bees of the Australian and South Pacific regions. *Bull. Am. Mus. Nat. Hist.* **130**: 1–362 (taxonomy); Exley, E.M. (1972). Revision of the genus *Pachyprosopis* Perkins (Apoidea : Colletidae). *Aust. J. Zool. Suppl. Ser.* **10**: 1–43 (redescription).

Pachyprosopis (Pachyprosopis) haematostoma Cockerell, 1913

Pachyprosopis haematostoma Cockerell, T.D.A. (1913). Some Australian bees. *Proc. Acad. Nat. Sci. Philad.* **65**: 28–44 [36].
Type data: syntypes, USNM 2♀*.
Type locality: Croydon, VIC.

Pachyprosopis aurantipes Cockerell, T.D.A. (1913). Descriptions and records of bees. LV. *Ann. Mag. Nat. Hist. (8)***12**: 505–514 [513].
Type data: syntypes, BMNH Hym.17.a.317 2♂.
Type locality: Windsor, VIC.

Taxonomic decision for synonymy: Cockerell, T.D.A. (1915). Descriptions and records of bees. LXVI. *Ann. Mag. Nat. Hist. (8)***15**: 341–350 [347].

Distribution: NE coastal, SE coastal, Murray-Darling basin, S Gulfs, SW coastal, QLD, NSW, VIC, SA, WA.
Ecology: larva—sedentary : adult—volant; melliferous, solitary, nest in burrows in a tree stump, flower visiting record: *Angophora* Cav. [Myrtaceae], *Callistemon* R.Br. [Myrtaceae], *Eucalyptus* L'Hérit. [Myrtaceae], *Jacksonia* Smith [Fabaceae],

Leptospermum Forster & G.Forster [Myrtaceae], *Melaleuca* L. [Myrtaceae], *Tristania* R.Br. [Myrtaceae].

References: Rayment, T. (1935). *A Cluster of Bees. Sixty essays on the life-histories of Australian bees, with specific descriptions of over 100 new species, and an introduction by Professor E.F. Phillips, D.Ph., Cornell University, U.S.A.* Sydney : Endeavour Press 752 pp. (illustration); Michener, C.D. (1965). A classification of the bees of the Australian and South Pacific regions. *Bull. Am. Mus. Nat. Hist.* **130**: 1–362 (taxonomy, flower records); Houston, T.F. (1969). Observations on the nests and behaviour of some euryglossine bees (Hymenoptera : Colletidae). *J. Aust. Entomol. Soc.* **8**: 1–10 (biology); Exley, E.M. (1972). Revision of the genus *Pachyprosopis* Perkins (Apoidea · Colletidae). *Aust. J. Zool. Suppl. Ser.* **10**: 1–43 (redescription).

Pachyprosopis (Pachyprosopis) holoxanthopus Cockerell, 1914

Pachyprosopis holoxanthopus Cockerell, T.D.A. (1914). Descriptions and records of bees. LXIV. *Ann. Mag. Nat. Hist. (8)***14**: 464–472 [469].
Type data: holotype, BMNH Hym.17.a.312 ♂.
Type locality: Yarrawin (Brewarrina), NSW.

Distribution: Lake Eyre basin, Murray-Darling basin, QLD, NSW; only published localities Longreach, Charleville and Yarrawin (Brewarrina).
Ecology: adult—volant; melliferous, solitary, flower visiting record: *Eucalyptus* L'Hérit. [Myrtaceae], *Schinus* L. [Anacardiaceae].
References: Michener, C.D. (1965). A classification of the bees of the Australian and South Pacific regions. *Bull. Am. Mus. Nat. Hist.* **130**: 1–362 (taxonomy); Exley, E.M. (1972). Revision of the genus *Pachyprosopis* Perkins (Apoidea : Colletidac). *Aust. J. Zool. Suppl. Ser.* **10**: 1–43 (redescription).

Pachyprosopis (Pachyprosopis) mirabilis Perkins, 1908

Pachyprosopis mirabilis Perkins, R.C.L. (1908). Some remarkable Australian Hymenoptera. *Proc. Hawaii. Entomol. Soc.* **2**: 27–35 [30].
Type data: holotype, BMNH Hym.17.a.2829 ♀.
Type locality: QLD.

Distribution: NE coastal, Murray-Darling basin, S Gulfs, W plateau, N coastal, QLD, NSW, SA, WA, NT.
Ecology: adult—volant; melliferous, solitary, flower visiting record: *Angophora* Cav. [Myrtaceae], *Callistemon* R.Br. [Myrtaceae], *Eucalyptus* L'Hérit. [Myrtaceae], *Leptospermum* Forster & G.Forster [Myrtaceae], *Lomatia* R.Br. [Proteaceae], *Melaleuca* L. [Myrtaceae], *Tristania* R.Br. [Myrtaceae].
References: Michener, C.D. (1965). A classification of the bees of the Australian and South Pacific regions. *Bull. Am. Mus. Nat. Hist.* **130**: 1–362 (taxon-

omy); Exley, E.M. (1972). Revision of the genus *Pachyprosopis* Perkins (Apoidea : Colletidae). *Aust. J. Zool. Suppl. Ser.* **10**: 1–43 (redescription).

Pachyprosopis (Pachyprosopis) psilosomata Exley, 1972

Pachyprosopis (Pachyprosopis) psilosomata Exley, E.M. (1972). Revision of the genus *Pachyprosopis* Perkins (Apoidea : Colletidae). *Aust. J. Zool. Suppl. Ser.* **10**: 1–43 [15].
Type data: holotype, QM T7301 ♀.
Type locality: Brisbane, QLD.

Distribution: NE coastal, Murray-Darling basin, QLD.
Ecology: adult—volant; melliferous, solitary, flower visiting record: *Angophora* Cav. [Myrtaceae], *Eucalyptus* L'Hérit. [Myrtaceae], *Jacksonia* Smith [Fabaceae], *Leptospermum* Forster & G.Forster [Myrtaceae], *Melaleuca* L. [Myrtaceae].

Pachyprosopis (Pachyprosopina) Michener, 1965

Pachyprosopina Michener, C.D. (1965). A classification of the bees of the Australian and South Pacific regions. *Bull. Am. Mus. Nat. Hist.* **130**: 1–362 [108] [proposed with subgeneric rank in *Pachyprosopis* Perkins, 1908]. Type species: *Euryglossa paupercula* Cockerell, 1915 by original designation.

Pachyprosopis (Pachyprosopina) paupercula (Cockerell, 1915)

Euryglossa paupercula Cockerell, T.D.A. (1915). Descriptions and records of bees. LXVI. *Ann. Mag. Nat. Hist. (8)***15**: 341–350 [348].
Type data: holotype, BMNH Hym.17.a.256 ♀.
Type locality: Yallingup, WA.

Distribution: SW coastal, WA; known only from type locality.
Ecology: adult—volant; melliferous, solitary.
Reference: Exley, E.M. (1972). Revision of the genus *Pachyprosopis* Perkins (Apoidea : Colletidae). *Aust. J. Zool. Suppl. Ser.* **10**: 1–43 (generic placement uncertain).

Pachyprosopis (Pachyprosopula) Michener, 1965

Pachyprosopula Michener, C.D. (1965). A classification of the bees of the Australian and South Pacific regions. *Bull. Am. Mus. Nat. Hist.* **130**: 1–362 [106] [proposed with subgeneric rank in *Pachyprosopis* Perkins, 1908]. Type species: *Pachyprosopis kellyi* Cockerell, 1916 by original designation.

Pachyprosopis (Pachyprosopula) flava Exley, 1976

Pachyprosopis (Pachyprosopula) flava Exley, E.M. (1976). New species and records of *Pachyprosopis* Perkins (Apoidea : Colletidae : Euryglossinae). *J. Aust. Entomol. Soc.* **14**: 399–407 [406].
Type data: holotype, QM T7468 ♂.
Type locality: Lake Moondarra, QLD.

Distribution: N Gulf, N coastal, QLD, NT; only published localities Lake Moondarra and near Wave Hill.
Ecology: adult—volant; melliferous, solitary, flower visiting record: *Eucalyptus* L'Hérit. [Myrtaceae].

Pachyprosopis (Pachyprosopula) flavicauda Cockerell, 1912

Pachyprosopis flavicauda Cockerell, T.D.A. (1912). Descriptions and records of bees. XLI. *Ann. Mag. Nat. Hist. (8)***9**: 139–149 [141].
Type data: syntypes, BMNH Hym.17.a.319 2♀, QM ♀.
Type locality: Sydney, NSW.

Pachyprosopis humeralis Cockerell, T.D.A. (1912). Descriptions and records of bees. XLI. *Ann. Mag. Nat. Hist. (8)***9**: 139–149 [142].
Type data: holotype, USNM ♂*.
Type locality: Sydney, NSW.

Taxonomic decision for synonymy: Exley, E.M. (1972). Revision of the genus *Pachyprosopis* Perkins (Apoidea : Colletidae). *Aust. J. Zool. Suppl. Ser.* **10**: 1–43 [41].

Distribution: NE coastal, SE coastal, Murray-Darling basin, S Gulfs, QLD, NSW, ACT, VIC, SA, TAS.
Ecology: adult—volant; melliferous, solitary, flower visiting record: *Angophora* Cav. [Myrtaceae], *Callistemon* R.Br. [Myrtaceae], *Eucalyptus* L'Hérit. [Myrtaceae], *Melaleuca* L. [Myrtaceae].
Reference: Michener, C.D. (1965). A classification of the bees of the Australian and South Pacific regions. *Bull. Am. Mus. Nat. Hist.* **130**: 1–362 (flower records).

Pachyprosopis (Pachyprosopula) kellyi Cockerell, 1916

Pachyprosopis kellyi Cockerell, T.D.A. (1916). Descriptions and records of bees. LXXII. *Ann. Mag. Nat. Hist. (8)***17**: 428–435 [432].
Type data: holotype, BMNH Hym.17.a.316 ♀.
Type locality: Mt Yule, Healesville, VIC.

Pachyprosopis angulifera Cockerell, T.D.A. (1929). Bees in the Queensland Museum. *Mem. Qd Mus.* **9**: 298–323 [298].
Type data: syntypes, QM T3724 2♂.
Type locality: [Lamington] National Park, QLD.

Pachyprosopis strigata Rayment, T. (1935). *A Cluster of Bees*. Sixty essays on the life-histories of Australian bees, with specific descriptions of over 100 new species, and an introduction by Professor E.F. Phillips, D.Ph., Cornell University, U.S.A. Sydney : Endeavour Press 752 pp. [648].
Type data: syntypes, ANIC 2♂.
Type locality: Sandringham, VIC.

Pachyprosopis fulvescens Rayment, T. (1935). *A Cluster of Bees*. Sixty essays on the life-histories of Australian bees, with specific descriptions of over 100 new species, and an introduction by Professor E.F. Phillips, D.Ph., Cornell University, U.S.A. Sydney : Endeavour Press 752 pp. [648].
Type data: holotype (probable), ANIC ♀.
Type locality: Sandringham, VIC.

Taxonomic decision for synonymy: Exley, E.M. (1972). Revision of the genus *Pachyprosopis* Perkins (Apoidea : Colletidae). *Aust. J. Zool. Suppl. Ser.* **10**: 1–43 [33].

Distribution: NE coastal, SE coastal, QLD, VIC; only published localities National Park (QLD), Mt Yule, Healesville, Sandringham and Melbourne.
Ecology: adult—volant; melliferous, solitary, flower visiting record: *Eucalyptus* L'Hérit. [Myrtaceae].
Reference: Michener, C.D. (1965). A classification of the bees of the Australian and South Pacific regions. *Bull. Am. Mus. Nat. Hist.* **130**: 1–362 (generic placement, as *Pachyprosopis (Pachyprosopula) kelleyi* in fig. 335, incorrect subsequent spelling).

Pachyprosopis (Pachyprosopula) kununurra Exley, 1976

Pachyprosopis (Pachyprosopula) kununurra Exley, E.M. (1976). New species and records of *Pachyprosopis* Perkins (Apoidea : Euryglossinae). *J. Aust. Entomol. Soc.* **14**: 399–407 [405].
Type data: holotype, QM T7466 ♀.
Type locality: 15 miles SW Kununurra, WA.

Distribution: N Gulf, N coastal, QLD, WA, NT.
Ecology: adult—volant; melliferous, solitary, flower visiting record: *Eucalyptus* L'Hérit. [Myrtaceae].

Pachyprosopis (Pachyprosopula) purnongensis (Rayment, 1928)

Euryglossina purnongensis Rayment, T. (1928). A new prosopoid bee. *Vict. Nat.* **45**: 97–98 [figs 3, 11 & 13 on p. 97] [name introduced and used only as a caption on p. 98 to figs on p. 97].
Type data: syntypes, ANIC 2♂.
Type locality: Purnong, SA.

Distribution: Murray-Darling basin, S Gulfs, SW coastal, SA, WA; only published localities Purnong, Adelaide and Greenmount.
Ecology: adult—volant; melliferous, solitary, flower visiting record: *Eucalyptus* L'Hérit. [Myrtaceae].
References: Rayment, T. (1935). *A Cluster of Bees*. Sixty essays on the life-histories of Australian bees, with specific descriptions of over 100 new species, and an introduction by Professor E.F. Phillips, D.Ph., Cornell University, U.S.A. Sydney : Endeavour Press 752 pp. (description, as new species); Exley, E.M. (1972). Revision of the genus *Pachyprosopis* Perkins (Apoidea : Colletidae). *Aust. J. Zool. Suppl. Ser.* **10**: 1–43 (redescription).

Pachyprosopis (Pachyprosopula) trichopoda Exley, 1972

Pachyprosopis (Pachyprosopula) trichopoda Exley, E.M. (1972). Revision of the genus *Pachyprosopis* Perkins (Apoidea : Colletidae). *Aust. J. Zool. Suppl. Ser.* **10**: 1–43 [39].
Type data: holotype, QM T7296 ♂.
Type locality: 33 miles N Bowen, QLD.

Distribution: NE coastal, Murray-Darling basin, QLD, VIC.
Ecology: adult—volant; melliferous, solitary, flower visiting record: *Eucalyptus* L'Hérit. [Myrtaceae].

Pachyprosopis (Pachyprosopula) xanthodonta (Cockerell, 1913)

Euryglossina xanthodonta Cockerell, T.D.A. (1913). Descriptions and records of bees. LI. *Ann. Mag. Nat. Hist. (8)***11**: 387–394 [391].
Type data: holotype, BMNH Hym.17.a.301 ♂.
Type locality: Purnong, near Murray River, SA.
Pachyprosopis saturnina Cockerell, T.D.A. (1913). Descriptions and records of bees. LI. *Ann. Mag. Nat. Hist. (8)***11**: 387–394 [393].
Type data: syntypes, USNM 2♀*.
Type locality: Purnong, near Murray River, SA.

Taxonomic decision for synonymy: Exley, E.M. (1972). Revision of the genus *Pachyprosopis* Perkins (Apoidea : Colletidae). *Aust. J. Zool. Suppl. Ser.* **10**: 1–43 [37].

Distribution: N Gulf, Murray-Darling basin, S Gulfs, Lake Eyre basin, SW coastal, W plateau, QLD, NSW, SA, WA, NT.
Ecology: adult—volant; melliferous, solitary, flower visiting record: *Eucalyptus* L'Hérit. [Myrtaceae].
Reference: Michener, C.D. (1965). A classification of the bees of the Australian and South Pacific regions. *Bull. Am. Mus. Nat. Hist.* **130**: 1–362 (generic placement, incorrect subsequent spelling as *Pachyprosopis (Pachyprosopula) saturina* Cockerell, 1913).

Pachyprosopis (Parapachyprosopis) Exley, 1972

Parapachyprosopis Exley, E.M. (1972). Revision of the genus *Pachyprosopis* Perkins (Apoidea : Colletidae). *Aust. J. Zool. Suppl. Ser.* **10**: 1–43 [17] [proposed with subgeneric rank in *Pachyprosopis* Perkins, 1908]. Type species: *Pachyprosopis angophorae* Cockerell, 1912 by original designation.

Pachyprosopis (Parapachyprosopis) angophorae Cockerell, 1912

Pachyprosopis angophorae Cockerell, T.D.A. (1912). Descriptions and records of bees. XLI. *Ann. Mag. Nat. Hist. (8)***9**: 139–149 [141].
Type data: syntypes, USNM 2♂*.
Type locality: Sydney, NSW.
Pachyprosopis obesa Cockerell, T.D.A. (1912). Descriptions and records of bees. XLIII. *Ann. Mag. Nat. Hist. (8)***9**: 377–387 [383].
Type data: syntypes, BMNH Hym.17.a.318 2♀.
Type locality: Sydney, NSW.

Taxonomic decision for synonymy: Exley, E.M. (1972). Revision of the genus *Pachyprosopis* Perkins (Apoidea : Colletidae). *Aust. J. Zool. Suppl. Ser.* **10**: 1–43 [20].

Distribution: NE coastal, SE coastal, N coastal, QLD, NSW, NT.
Ecology: adult—volant; melliferous, solitary, nest in termite soil at base of or in hollow tree, flower visit-ing record: *Angophora* Cav. [Myrtaceae], *Eucalyptus* L'Hérit. [Myrtaceae], *Lomatia* R.Br. [Proteaceae].
References: Exley, E.M. (1976). New species and records of *Pachyprosopis* Perkins (Apoidea : Colletidae : Euryglossinae). *J. Aust. Entomol. Soc.* **14**: 399–407 (taxonomy); McGinley, R.J. (1981). Systematics of the Colletidae based on mature larvae with phenetic analysis of apoid larvae (Insecta, Hymenoptera, Apoidea). *Univ. Calif. Publ. Entomol.* **91**: 1–309 (larva).

Pachyprosopis (Parapachyprosopis) eucalypti Exley, 1972

Pachyprosopis (Parapachyprosopis) eucalypti Exley, E.M. (1972). Revision of the genus *Pachyprosopis* Perkins (Apoidea : Colletidae). *Aust. J. Zool. Suppl. Ser.* **10**: 1–43 [22].
Type data: holotype, QM T7300 ♂.
Type locality: McMillans Road, Berrimah, NT.

Distribution: N Gulf, N coastal, QLD, WA, NT.
Ecology: adult—volant; melliferous, solitary, flower visiting record: *Eucalyptus* L'Hérit. [Myrtaceae].
Reference: Exley, E.M. (1976). New species and records of *Pachyprosopis* Perkins (Apoidea : Colletidae : Euryglossinae). *J. Aust. Entomol. Soc.* **14**: 399–407 (distribution).

Pachyprosopis (Parapachyprosopis) eucyrta Exley, 1972

Pachyprosopis (Parapachyprosopis) eucyrta Exley, E.M. (1972). Revision of the genus *Pachyprosopis* Perkins (Apoidea : Colletidae). *Aust. J. Zool. Suppl. Ser.* **10**: 1–43 [24].
Type data: holotype, QM T7294 ♂.
Type locality: No. 496 Great Eastern Highway, Greenmount, WA.

Distribution: SW coastal, W plateau, WA.
Ecology: adult—volant; melliferous, solitary, flower visiting record: *Eucalyptus* L'Hérit. [Myrtaceae].

Pachyprosopis (Parapachyprosopis) grossoscapus Exley, 1976

Pachyprosopis (Parapachyprosopis) grossoscapus Exley, E.M. (1976). New species and records of *Pachyprosopis* Perkins (Apoidea : Colletidae : Euryglossinae). *J. Aust. Entomol. Soc.* **14**: 399–407 [401].
Type data: holotype, QM T7464 ♂.
Type locality: 15 miles SW Kununurra, WA.

Distribution: N Gulf, N coastal, QLD, WA, NT; only published localities Lake Moondarra, Mt Isa, near Kununurra and near Wave Hill.
Ecology: adult—volant; melliferous, solitary, flower visiting record: *Eucalyptus* L'Hérit. [Myrtaceae].

Pachyprosopis (Parapachyprosopis) indicans Cockerell, 1918

Pachyprosopis indicans Cockerell, T.D.A. (1918). Some bees collected in Queensland. *Mem. Qd Mus.* **6**: 112–120 [116].
Type data: holotype, QM Hy/4151 ♂.
Type locality: Brisbane, QLD.

Distribution: NE coastal, SE coastal, QLD, NSW; only published localities Brisbane, Acacia Ridge, Brown Plains, Fernvale and Como.
Ecology: larva—sedentary : adult—volant; melliferous, solitary, nest in earth in hollow tree, flower visiting record: *Angophora* Cav. [Myrtaceae].
References: Houston, T.F. (1969). Observations on the nests and behaviour of some euryglossine bees (Hymenoptera : Colletidae). *J. Aust. Entomol. Soc.* **8**: 1–10 (biology); Exley, E.M. (1972). Revision of the genus *Pachyprosopis* Perkins (Apoidea : Colletidae). *Aust. J. Zool. Suppl. Ser.* **10**: 1–43 (generic placement, redescription); McGinley, R.J. (1981). Systematics of the Colletidae based on mature larvae with phenetic analysis of apoid larvae (Insecta, Hymenoptera, Apoidea). *Univ. Calif. Publ. Entomol.* **91**: 1–309 (larva).

Pachyprosopis (Parapachyprosopis) melanognathus Exley, 1976

Pachyprosopis (Parapachyprosopis) melanognathus Exley, E.M. (1976). New species and records of *Pachyprosopis* Perkins (Apoidea : Colletidae : Euryglossinae). *J. Aust. Entomol. Soc.* **14**: 399–407 [402].
Type data: holotype, ANIC ♂.
Type locality: Nourlangie Creek, 8 km E Mt Cahill, NT.

Distribution: N coastal, NT; known only from type locality.
Ecology: adult—volant; melliferous, solitary, flower visiting record: *Eucalyptus* L'Hérit. [Myrtaceae].

Pachyprosopis (Parapachyprosopis) plebeia Cockerell, 1910

Pachyprosopis plebeia Cockerell, T.D.A. (1910). Descriptions and records of bees. XXXI. *Ann. Mag. Nat. Hist.* (8)**6**: 160–168 [166].
Type data: syntypes (probable), BMNH ♀ (number of specimens unknown, a specimen is labelled 'type' and has registration number Hym.17.a.314).
Type locality: Mackay, QLD.
Pachyprosopis doddi Cockerell, T.D.A. (1910). Descriptions and records of bees. XXXI. *Ann. Mag. Nat. Hist.* (8)**6**: 160–168 [167].
Type data: holotype, BMNH Hym.17.a.313 ♀.
Type locality: Townsville, QLD.

Taxonomic decision for synonymy: Exley, E.M. (1972). Revision of the genus *Pachyprosopis* Perkins (Apoidea : Colletidae). *Aust. J. Zool. Suppl. Ser.* **10**: 1–43 [28].

Distribution: NE coastal, QLD; only published localities Mackay, Townsville, Edungalba and Kuranda.

Ecology: adult—volant; melliferous, solitary, flower visiting record: *Eucalyptus* L'Hérit. [Myrtaceae], *Tristania* R.Br. [Myrtaceae].
References: Meade-Waldo, G. (1923). Hymenoptera. Fam. Apidae. Subfam. Prosopidinae. *Genera Insectorum* **181**: 1–45 (illustration); Rayment, T. (1935). *A Cluster of Bees.* Sixty essays on the life-histories of Australian bees, with specific descriptions of over 100 new species, and an introduction by Professor E.F. Phillips, D.Ph., Cornell University, U.S.A. Sydney : Endeavour Press 752 pp. (illustration).

Pachyprosopis (Parapachyprosopis) sternotricha Exley, 1972

Pachyprosopis (Parapachyprosopis) sternotricha Exley, E.M. (1972). Revision of the genus *Pachyprosopis* Perkins (Apoidea : Colletidae). *Aust. J. Zool. Suppl. Ser.* **10**: 1–43 [23].
Type data: holotype, QM T7303 ♂.
Type locality: Mt Bundey Road via Darwin, NT.

Distribution: N Gulf, N coastal, QLD, WA, NT; only published localities Lake Moondarra, near Mt Isa, Kununurra, near Darwin and Daly Waters.
Ecology: adult—volant; melliferous, solitary, flower visiting record: *Eucalyptus* L'Hérit. [Myrtaceae].
Reference: Exley, E.M. (1976). New species and records of *Pachyprosopis* Perkins (Apoidea : Colletidae : Euryglossinae). *J. Aust. Entomol. Soc.* **14**: 399–407 (distribution).

Pachyprosopis (Parapachyprosopis) xanthometopa Exley, 1972

Pachyprosopis (Parapachyprosopis) xanthometopa Exley, E.M. (1972). Revision of the genus *Pachyprosopis* Perkins (Apoidea : Colletidae). *Aust. J. Zool. Suppl. Ser.* **10**: 1–43 [29].
Type data: holotype, QM T7304 ♂.
Type locality: 8 miles Fernvale, QLD.

Distribution: NE coastal, N Gulf, N coastal, QLD, WA, NT.
Ecology: adult—volant; melliferous, solitary, flower visiting record: *Angophora* Cav. [Myrtaceae], *Eucalyptus* L'Hérit. [Myrtaceae].
Reference: Exley, E.M. (1976). New species and records of *Pachyprosopis* Perkins (Apoidea : Colletidae : Euryglossinae). *J. Aust. Entomol. Soc.* **14**: 399–407 (distribution).

Quasihesma Exley, 1968

Quasihesma Exley, E.M. (1968). *Quasihesma*—a new genus of Australian bees (Apoidea : Colletidae). *Aust. J. Zool.* **16**: 227–235 [228]. Type species: *Quasihesma moonbiensis* Exley, 1968 by original designation.

Quasihesma cardaleae Exley, 1968

Quasihesma cardaleae Exley, E.M. (1968). *Quasihesma*—a new genus of Australian bees (Apoidea : Colletidae). *Aust.*

J. Zool. **16**: 227–235 [233].
Type data: holotype, QM T6677 ♂.
Type locality: Harvey Range, 29 miles NW Townsville, QLD.

Distribution: NE coastal, Murray-Darling basin, N Gulf, N coastal, QLD, NT, (WA).
Ecology: adult—volant; melliferous, solitary, flower visiting record: *Eucalyptus* L'Hérit. [Myrtaceae], *Eugenia* L. [Myrtaceae], *Melaleuca* L. [Myrtaceae], *Tristania* R.Br. [Myrtaceae].
References: Exley, E.M. (1974). A contribution to our knowledge of Australia's smallest bees with descriptions of new species (Hymenoptera : Colletidae : Euryglossinae). *J. Aust. Entomol. Soc.* **13**: 1–9 (description of female); Exley, E.M. (1980). New species and records of *Quasihesma* Exley (Hymenoptera : Apoidea : Euryglossinae). *J. Aust. Entomol. Soc.* **19**: 161–170 (distribution).

Quasihesma clypearis Exley, 1980

Quasihesma clypearis Exley, E.M. (1980). New species and records of *Quasihesma* Exley (Hymenoptera : Apoidea : Euryglossinae). *J. Aust. Entomol. Soc.* **19**: 161–170 [166].
Type data: holotype, QM ♂.
Type locality: Cooktown, QLD.

Distribution: NE coastal, N Gulf, QLD; only published localities Cooktown and vicinity, near Coen and Laura.
Ecology: adult—volant; melliferous, solitary, flower visiting record: *Eucalyptus* L'Hérit. [Myrtaceae], *Melaleuca* L. [Myrtaceae].

Quasihesma doddi Exley, 1968

Quasihesma doddi Exley, E.M. (1968). *Quasihesma*—a new genus of Australian bees (Apoidea : Colletidae). *Aust. J. Zool.* **16**: 227–235 [233].
Type data: holotype, SAMA ♂*.
Type locality: Cairns district, QLD.

Distribution: NE coastal, QLD; known only from type locality.
Ecology: adult—volant; melliferous, solitary.
Reference: Exley, E.M. (1980). New species and records of *Quasihesma* Exley (Hymenoptera : Apoidea : Euryglossinae). *J. Aust. Entomol. Soc.* **19**: 161–170 (distribution).

Quasihesma gigantica Exley, 1974

Quasihesma gigantica Exley, E.M. (1974). A contribution to our knowledge of Australia's smallest bees with descriptions of new species (Hymenoptera : Colletidae : Euryglossinae). *J. Aust. Entomol. Soc.* **13**: 1–9 [4].
Type data: holotype, QM T7368 ♂.
Type locality: 129 miles S Darwin, NT.

Distribution: N coastal, NT; known only from type locality.
Ecology: adult—volant; melliferous, solitary, flower visiting record: *Eucalyptus* L'Hérit. [Myrtaceae].

Reference: Exley, E.M. (1980). New species and records of *Quasihesma* Exley (Hymenoptera : Apoidea : Euryglossinae). *J. Aust. Entomol. Soc.* **19**: 161–170 (distribution).

Quasihesma leucognatha Exley, 1974

Quasihesma leucognatha Exley, E.M. (1974). A contribution to our knowledge of Australia's smallest bees with descriptions of new species (Hymenoptera : Colletidae : Euryglossinae). *J. Aust. Entomol. Soc.* **13**: 1–9 [3].
Type data: holotype, QM T7366 ♂.
Type locality: 15 miles E Katherine, NT.

Distribution: NE coastal, N Gulf, N coastal, QLD, NT.
Ecology: adult—volant; melliferous, solitary, flower visiting record: *Eucalyptus* L'Hérit. [Myrtaceae], *Eugenia* L. [Myrtaceae], *Melaleuca* L. [Myrtaceae], *Tristania* R.Br. [Myrtaceae].
Reference: Exley, E.M. (1980). New species and records of *Quasihesma* Exley (Hymenoptera : Apoidea : Euryglossinae). *J. Aust. Entomol. Soc.* **19**: 161–170 (distribution).

Quasihesma melanognatha Exley, 1980

Quasihesma melanognatha Exley, E.M. (1980). New species and records of *Quasihesma* Exley (Hymenoptera : Apoidea : Euryglossinae). *J. Aust. Entomol. Soc.* **19**: 161–170 [164].
Type data: holotype, QM ♂.
Type locality: 4 km S Coen, QLD.

Distribution: NE coastal, N Gulf, QLD; only published localities near Cooktown, near Coen, Port Douglas, Mt Molloy and near Petford.
Ecology: adult—volant; melliferous, solitary, flower visiting record: *Eucalyptus* L'Hérit. [Myrtaceae], *Tristania* R.Br. [Myrtaceae].

Quasihesma moonbiensis Exley, 1968

Quasihesma moonbiensis Exley, E.M. (1968). *Quasihesma*—a new genus of Australian bees (Apoidea : Colletidae). *Aust. J. Zool.* **16**: 227–235 [230].
Type data: holotype, QM T6678 ♂.
Type locality: Moonbi Range, NSW.

Distribution: NE coastal, SE coastal, N Gulf, QLD, NSW, NT.
Ecology: adult—volant; melliferous, solitary, flower visiting record: *Angophora* Cav. [Myrtaceae], *Eucalyptus* L'Hérit. [Myrtaceae], *Eugenia* L. [Myrtaceae], *Melaleuca* L. [Myrtaceae], *Tristania* R.Br. [Myrtaceae].
Reference: Exley, E.M. (1980). New species and records of *Quasihesma* Exley (Hymenoptera : Apoidea : Euryglossinae). *J. Aust. Entomol. Soc.* **19**: 161–170 (distribution).

Quasihesma scapata Exley, 1980

Quasihesma scapata Exley, E.M. (1980). New species and records of *Quasihesma* Exley (Hymenoptera : Apoidea :

Euryglossinae). *J. Aust. Entomol. Soc.* **19**: 161–170 [169].
Type data: holotype, QM ♂.
Type locality: 8 km SE Cooktown, QLD.

Distribution: NE coastal, N Gulf, QLD; only published localities near Cooktown, near Coen and Upper Massey River Crossing.
Ecology: adult—volant; melliferous, solitary, flower visiting record: *Eucalyptus* L'Hérit. [Myrtaceae], *Eugenia* L. [Myrtaceae].

Quasihesma tuberculata Exley, 1980

Quasihesma tuberculata Exley, E.M. (1980). New species and records of *Quasihesma* Exley (Hymenoptera : Apoidea : Euryglossinae). *J. Aust. Entomol. Soc.* **19**: 161–170 [168].
Type data: holotype, QM ♂.
Type locality: airstrip, 27 km N Coen, QLD.

Distribution: N Gulf, QLD; only published localities near Coen and Pinnacle Creek.
Ecology: adult—volant; melliferous, solitary.

Quasihesma walkeri Exley, 1980

Quasihesma walkeri Exley, E.M. (1980). New species and records of *Quasihesma* Exley (Hymenoptera : Apoidea : Euryglossinae). *J. Aust. Entomol. Soc.* **19**: 161–170 [164].
Type data: holotype, QM ♂.
Type locality: Upper Massey River Crossing, 10 km N Silver Plains Homestead, 69 km E Coen, QLD.

Distribution: NE coastal, QLD; known only from type locality, Massey.
Ecology: adult—volant; melliferous, solitary, flower visiting record: *Eucalyptus* L'Hérit. [Myrtaceae].

Sericogaster Westwood, 1835

Sericogaster Westwood, J.O. (1835). Characters of new genera and species of hymenopterous insects. *Proc. Zool. Soc. Lond.* **3**: 51–54, 68–72 [71]. Type species: *Sericogaster fasciatus* Westwood, 1835 by monotypy.
Holohesma Michener, C.D. (1965). A classification of the bees of the Australian and South Pacific regions. *Bull. Am. Mus. Nat. Hist.* **130**: 1–362 [102]. Type species: *Stilpnosoma semisericea* Cockerell, 1905 by original designation.

Taxonomic decision for synonymy: Menke, A.S. & Michener, C.D. (1973). *Sericogaster* Westwood, a senior synonym of *Holohesma* Michener. *J. Aust. Entomol. Soc.* **12**: 173–174 [173].

Sericogaster fasciata Westwood, 1835

Sericogaster fasciatus Westwood, J.O. (1835). Characters of new genera and species of hymenopterous insects. *Proc. Zool. Soc. Lond.* **3**: 51–54, 68–72 [72].
Type data: holotype, OUM ♀.
Type locality: Australia (as New Holland).
Stilpnosoma semisericea Cockerell, T.D.A. (1905). Descriptions and records of bees. V. *Ann. Mag. Nat. Hist.* (7)**16**: 465–477 [476].
Type data: syntypes, BMNH 2♀ (a specimen is labelled 'type' and has registration number Hym.17.a.113).
Type locality: Mackay, QLD.

Stilpnosoma histrio Friese, H. (1924). Ueber die Bienen Australiens. *Konowia* **3**: 216–249 [232].
Type data: syntypes (probable), AMNH 1♀* (described from 3 females, location of other specimens unknown).
Type locality: Mackay, QLD.

Stilpnosoma cambournii Rayment, T. (1935). *A Cluster of Bees.* Sixty essays on the life-histories of Australian bees, with specific descriptions of over 100 new species, and an introduction by Professor E.F. Phillips, D.Ph., Cornell University, U.S.A. Sydney : Endeavour Press 752 pp. [Pl. e fig. 18 on p. 121, caption on p. 120].
Type data: holotype, ANIC ♀.
Type locality: Gosford, see Menke, A.S. & Michener, C.D. (1973). *Sericogaster* Westwood, a senior synonym of *Holohesma* Michener. *J. Aust. Entomol. Soc.* **12**: 173–174 [174].

Taxonomic decision for synonymy: Menke, A.S. & Michener, C.D. (1973). *Sericogaster* Westwood, a senior synonym of *Holohesma* Michener. *J. Aust. Entomol. Soc.* **12**: 173–174 [174].

Distribution: NE coastal, SE coastal, Murray-Darling basin, QLD, NSW; only published localities Mackay, Birkdale, near Stanthorpe and Gosford.
Ecology: adult—volant; melliferous, solitary, flower visiting record: *Leptospermum* Forster & G.Forster [Myrtaceae].
References: Cockerell, T.D.A. (1910). Descriptions and records of bees. XXXI. *Ann. Mag. Nat. Hist.* (8)**6**: 160–168 (as *Pachyprosopis semisericea* (Cockerell, 1905)); Michener, C.D. (1965). A classification of the bees of the Australian and South Pacific regions. *Bull. Am. Mus. Nat. Hist.* **130**: 1–362 (taxonomy, flower record, as *Holohesma semisericea* (Cockerell, 1905)).

Stenohesma Michener, 1965

Stenohesma Michener, C.D. (1965). A classification of the bees of the Australian and South Pacific regions. *Bull. Am. Mus. Nat. Hist.* **130**: 1–362 [99]. Type species: *Stenohesma nomadiformis* Michener, 1965 by original designation.

Stenohesma nomadiformis Michener, 1965

Stenohesma nomadiformis Michener, C.D. (1965). A classification of the bees of the Australian and South Pacific regions. *Bull. Am. Mus. Nat. Hist.* **130**: 1–362 [283].
Type data: holotype, NMV T-4367 ♀.
Type locality: Meringa, QLD.

Distribution: NE coastal, QLD; only published localities Mcringa, Herberton and Edungalba.
Ecology: adult—volant; melliferous, solitary.

Stilpnosoma Smith, 1879

Stilpnosoma Smith, F. (1879). *Descriptions of New Species of Hymenoptera in the Collection of the British Museum.* London : British Museum xxi 240 pp. [16]. Type species: *Stilpnosoma laevigatum* Smith, 1879 by monotypy.

Stilpnosoma laevigatum Smith, 1879

Stilpnosoma laevigatum Smith, F. (1879). *Descriptions of New Species of Hymenoptera in the Collection of the British Museum.* London : British Museum xxi 240 pp. [16].
Type data: holotype, BMNH Hym.17.a.112 ♀.
Type locality: QLD.
Stilpnosoma turneri Friese, H. (1917). Results of Dr. E. Mjöberg's Swedish Scientific Expeditions to Australia, 1910–1913. 13. Apidae. *Ark. Zool.* **11**(2): 1–9 [4] [junior primary homonym of *Stilpnosoma turneri* Baker, 1906].
Type data: syntypes (probable), AMNH ♂* (described as ♀, see Michener, C.D. (1965). A classification of the bees of the Australian and South Pacific regions. *Bull. Am. Mus. Nat. Hist.* **130**: 1–362 [102]).
Type locality: Mackay (as Makay) and Colosseum, QLD and Adelaide, SA.

Taxonomic decision for synonymy: Michener, C.D. (1965). A classification of the bees of the Australian and South Pacific regions. *Bull. Am. Mus. Nat. Hist.* **130**: 1–362 [102].

Distribution: NE coastal, S Gulfs, QLD, SA; only published localities Mackay, Colosseum and Adelaide.
Ecology: adult—volant; melliferous, solitary, flower visiting record: *Leptospermum* Forster & G.Forster [Myrtaceae].
References: Cockerell, T.D.A. (1905). Descriptions and records of bees. II. *Ann. Mag. Nat. Hist.* (7)**16**: 292–301 (redescription); Meade-Waldo, G. (1923). Hymenoptera. Fam. Apidae. Subfam. Prosopidinae. *Genera Insectorum* **181**: 1–45 (illustration); Friese, H. (1924). Ueber die Bienen Australiens. *Konowia* **3**: 216–249 (description of male); Rayment, T. (1935). *A Cluster of Bees.* Sixty essays on the life-histories of Australian bees, with specific descriptions of over 100 new species, and an introduction by Professor E.F. Phillips, D.Ph., Cornell University, U.S.A. Sydney : Endeavour Press 752 pp. (illustration).

Xanthesma Michener, 1965

Xanthesma Michener, C.D. (1965). A classification of the bees of the Australian and South Pacific regions. *Bull. Am. Mus. Nat. Hist.* **130**: 1–362 [97]. Type species: *Euryglossa furcifera* Cockerell, 1913 by original designation.

Xanthesma argosomata Exley, 1969

Xanthesma argosomata Exley, E.M. (1969). Revision of the genus *Xanthesma* Michener (Apoidea : Colletidae). *Aust. J. Zool.* **17**: 515–526 [522].
Type data: holotype, QM T7078 ♀.
Type locality: Tusmore, SA.

Distribution: Murray-Darling basin, S Gulfs, SA; only published localities Meningie and Tusmore.
Ecology: larva—sedentary : adult—volant; melliferous, solitary, nest in soil, flower visiting record: *Eucalyptus* L'Hérit. [Myrtaceae].
Reference: Houston, T.F. (1969). Observations on the nests and behaviour of some euryglossine bees (Hy-

menoptera : Colletidae). *J. Aust. Entomol. Soc.* **8**: 1–10 (biology, as *Xanthesma* sp.).

Xanthesma brachycera (Cockerell, 1914)

Euryglossa brachycera Cockerell, T.D.A. (1914). Descriptions and records of bees. LX. *Ann. Mag. Nat. Hist.* (8)**14**: 1–13 [7].
Type data: holotype, BMNH Hym.17.a.273 ♀.
Type locality: Townsville, QLD.

Distribution: NE coastal, (Murray-Darling basin), SW coastal, NW coastal, N Gulf, QLD, (NSW), WA, NT.
Ecology: adult—volant; melliferous, solitary, flower visiting record: *Eucalyptus* L'Hérit. [Myrtaceae].
References: Rayment, T. (1939). Bees from the high lands of New South Wales and Victoria. *Aust. Zool.* **9**: 263–294 (Wentworth; doubtful record); Exley, E.M. (1969). Revision of the genus *Xanthesma* Michener (Apoidea : Colletidae). *Aust. J. Zool.* **17**: 515–526 (distribution); Evans, H.E. & Matthews, R.W. (1973). Systematics and nesting behavior of Australian *Bembix* sand wasps (Hymenoptera, Sphecidae). *Mem. Am. Entomol. Inst.* **20**: 1–387 (Vic; ?this species, as prey); Exley, E.M. (1974). A contribution to our knowledge of the bee fauna (Colletidae : Euryglossinae) of remote areas of Australia with descriptions of new species. *Proc. R. Soc. Qd* **85**: 95–110; Exley, E.M. (1978). *Chaetohesma*—a new genus of Australian bees (Apoidea : Colletidae : Euryglossinae). *Aust. J. Zool.* **26**: 373–397 (supposed male, =*Chaetohesma tuberculata* Exley, 1978).

Xanthesma dasycephala Exley, 1969

Xanthesma dasycephala Exley, E.M. (1969). Revision of the genus *Xanthesma* Michener (Apoidea : Colletidae). *Aust. J. Zool.* **17**: 515–526 [519].
Type data: holotype, ANIC ♀.
Type locality: 14 miles N Barrow Creek, NT.

Distribution: Lake Eyre basin, NT; known only from type locality.
Ecology: adult—volant; melliferous, solitary, flower visiting record: *Eucalyptus* L'Hérit. [Myrtaceae].

Xanthesma flava Michener, 1965

Xanthesma flava Michener, C.D. (1965). A classification of the bees of the Australian and South Pacific regions. *Bull. Am. Mus. Nat. Hist.* **130**: 1–362 [281].
Type data: holotype, ANIC ♀* (lost, see Exley, E.M. (1969). Revision of the genus *Xanthesma* Michener (Apoidea : Colletidae). *Aust. J. Zool.* **17**: 515–526 [518]), paratype QM ♀.
Type locality: Turn-off Lagoons, N QLD.

Distribution: N Gulf, Lake Eyre basin, NW coastal, QLD, WA, NT.
Ecology: adult—volant; melliferous, solitary, flower visiting record: *Eucalyptus* L'Hérit. [Myrtaceae].
References: Exley, E.M. (1969). Revision of the genus *Xanthesma* Michener (Apoidea : Colletidae).

Aust. J. Zool. **17**: 515–526 (distribution); Exley, E.M. (1974). A contribution to our knowledge of the bee fauna (Colletidae : Euryglossinae) of remote areas of Australia with descriptions of new species. *Proc. R. Soc. Qd* **85**: 95–110 (description of male).

Xanthesma furcifera (Cockerell, 1913)

Euryglossa furcifera Cockerell, T.D.A. (1913). Descriptions and records of bees. LI. *Ann. Mag. Nat. Hist. (8)***11**: 387–394 [387].
Type data: holotype, USNM ♀*.
Type locality: Purnong, near Murray River, SA.

Distribution: Murray-Darling, basin, S Gulfs, NSW, VIC, SA.
Ecology: larva—sedentary : adult—volant; melliferous, solitary, nest in soil in aggregations, flower visiting record: *Eucalyptus* L'Hérit. [Myrtaceae].
References: Rayment, T. (1928). A new prosopoid bee. *Vict. Nat.* **45**: 97–98 (illustration); Rayment, T. (1935). *A Cluster of Bees.* Sixty essays on the life-histories of Australian bees, with specific descriptions of over 100 new species, and an introduction by Professor E.F. Phillips, D.Ph., Cornell University, U.S.A. Sydney : Endeavour Press 752 pp. (illustration); Houston, T.F. (1969). Observations on the nests and behaviour of some euryglossine bees (Hymenoptera : Colletidae). *J. Aust. Entomol. Soc.* **8**: 1–10 (biology); Exley, E.M. (1969). Revision of the genus *Xanthesma* Michener (Apoidea : Colletidae). *Aust. J. Zool.* **17**: 515–526 (distribution); Evans, H.E. & Matthews, R.W. (1973). Systematics and nesting behavior of Australian *Bembix* sand wasps (Hymenoptera, Sphecidae). *Mem. Am. Entomol. Inst.* **20**: 1–387 (?this species, as prey).

Xanthesma lasiosomata Exley, 1969

Xanthesma lasiosomata Exley, E.M. (1969). Revision of the genus *Xanthesma* Michener (Apoidea : Colletidae). *Aust. J. Zool.* **17**: 515–526 [523].
Type data: holotype, ANIC ♀.
Type locality: 23 miles N Renner Springs, NT.

Distribution: N Gulf, NT; known only from type locality.
Ecology: adult—volant; melliferous, solitary.

Xanthesma lutea Exley, 1969

Xanthesma lutea Exley, E.M. (1969). Revision of the genus *Xanthesma* Michener (Apoidea : Colletidae). *Aust. J. Zool.* **17**: 515–526 [525].
Type data: holotype, QM T7079 ♀.
Type locality: Mica Creek, 5 miles from Mt Isa, QLD.

Distribution: N Gulf, QLD; known only from type locality.
Ecology: adult—volant; melliferous, solitary, flower visiting record: *Eucalyptus* L'Hérit. [Myrtaceae].

Xanthesma merredensis Exley, 1974

Xanthesma merredensis Exley, E.M. (1974). A contribution to our knowledge of the bee fauna (Colletidae : Euryglossinae) of remote areas of Australia with descriptions of new species. *Proc. R. Soc. Qd* **85**: 95–110 [108].
Type data: holotype, QM T7173 ♀.
Type locality: 34 miles E Merredin, WA.

Distribution: SW coastal, NW coastal, WA; only published localities near Merredin and Dongara (as Dongarra).
Ecology: adult—volant; melliferous, solitary, flower visiting record: *Eucalyptus* L'Hérit. [Myrtaceae].

Xanthesma micheneri Exley, 1978

Xanthesma micheneri Exley, E.M. (1978). A new species of *Xanthesma* from Australia (Apoidea : Colletidae : Euryglossinae). *J. Kansas Entomol. Soc.* **51**: 781–786 [783].
Type data: holotype, QM ♀*.
Type locality: 7 km N Wannoo, via Carnarvon, WA.

Distribution: NW coastal, WA; only published localities near Wannoo and N of Murchison River.
Ecology: adult—volant; melliferous, solitary, flower visiting record: *Eucalyptus* L'Hérit. [Myrtaceae].

Xanthesma nigrior Michener, 1965

Xanthesma nigrior Michener, C.D. (1965). A classification of the bees of the Australian and South Pacific regions. *Bull. Am. Mus. Nat. Hist.* **130**: 1–362 [282].
Type data: holotype, WAM 54–564 ♂.
Type locality: between Karalee and Dedari, WA.

Distribution: SW coastal, W plateau, WA; only published localities between Karalee and Dedari, Yellowdine and Merredin.
Ecology: adult—volant; melliferous, solitary.
References: Exley, E.M. (1969). Revision of the genus *Xanthesma* Michener (Apoidea : Colletidae). *Aust. J. Zool.* **17**: 515–526 (distribution); Exley, E.M. (1974). A contribution to our knowledge of the bee fauna (Colletidae : Euryglossinae) of remote areas of Australia with descriptions of new species. *Proc. R. Soc. Qd* **85**: 95–110 (taxonomy, ♀ is not known; ♀ described by Michener, 1965 = *Xanthesma trisulca* Exley, 1969); Exley, E.M. (1978). A new species of *Xanthesma* from Australia (Apoidea : Colletidae : Euryglossinae). *J. Kansas Entomol. Soc.* **51**: 781–786 (illustration).

Xanthesma parva Exley, 1969

Xanthesma parva Exley, E.M. (1969). Revision of the genus *Xanthesma* Michener (Apoidea : Colletidae). *Aust. J. Zool.* **17**: 515–526 [522].
Type data: holotype, WAM 48–3082 ♀.
Type locality: Kukerin, WA.

Distribution: SW coastal, WA; known only from type locality.
Ecology: adult—volant; melliferous, solitary.

Xanthesma trisulca Exley, 1969

Xanthesma trisulca Exley, E.M. (1969). Revision of the genus *Xanthesma* Michener (Apoidea : Colletidae). *Aust. J. Zool.* **17**: 515–526 [524].
Type data: holotype, QM T7077 ♂.
Type locality: Yellowdine, WA.

Distribution: SW coastal, W plateau, WA.
Ecology: adult—volant; melliferous, solitary, flower visiting record: *Eucalyptus* L'Hérit. [Myrtaceae].
References: Michener, C.D. (1965). A classification of the bees of the Australian and South Pacific regions. *Bull. Am. Mus. Nat. Hist.* **130**: 1–362 (♀ described as *Xanthesma nigrior* Michener, 1965); Exley, E.M. (1974). A contribution to our knowledge of the bee fauna (Colletidae : Euryglossinae) of remote areas of Australia with descriptions of new species. *Proc. R. Soc. Qd* **85**: 95–110 (taxonomy); Exley, E.M. (1978). A new species of *Xanthesma* from Australia (Apoidea : Colletidae : Euryglossinae). *J. Kansas Entomol. Soc.* **51**: 781–786 (illustration).

Xanthesma vittata Exley, 1969

Xanthesma vittata Exley, E.M. (1969). Revision of the genus *Xanthesma* Michener (Apoidea : Colletidae). *Aust. J. Zool.* **17**: 515–526 [521].
Type data: holotype, ANIC ♀.
Type locality: 14 miles N Barrow Creek, NT.

Distribution: Lake Eyre basin, W plateau, NT, WA; only published localities near Barrow Creek, Dedari and Coolgardie.
Ecology: adult—volant; melliferous, solitary.
Reference: Exley, E.M. (1974). A contribution to our knowledge of the bee fauna (Colletidae : Euryglossinae) of remote areas of Australia with descriptions of new species. *Proc. R. Soc. Qd* **85**: 95–110 (distribution).

Xenohesma Michener, 1965

Xenohesma Michener, C.D. (1965). A classification of the bees of the Australian and South Pacific regions. *Bull. Am. Mus. Nat. Hist.* **130**: 1–362 [96] [proposed with subgeneric rank in *Euryglossa* Smith, 1853]. Type species: *Euryglossa (Xenohesma) flavicauda* Michener, 1965 by original designation.

Xenohesma blanda (Smith, 1879)

Euryglossa blanda Smith, F. (1879). *Descriptions of New Species of Hymenoptera in the Collection of the British Museum.* London : British Museum xxi 240 pp. [13].
Type data: holotype, BMNH Hym.17.a.280 ♂ (described as ♀).
Type locality: WA.

Distribution: WA; exact locality unknown.
Ecology: adult—volant; melliferous, solitary.
References: Michener, C.D. (1965). A classification of the bees of the Australian and South Pacific regions. *Bull. Am. Mus. Nat. Hist.* **130**: 1–362 (taxonomy, as *Euryglossa (Xenohesma) blanda* Smith, 1879); Exley, E.M. (1969). Revision of the subgenus *Xenohesma* Michener (Apoidea : Colletidae). *Aust. J. Zool.* **17**: 535–551 (redescription, as *Euryglossa (Xenohesma) blanda* Smith, 1879); Exley, E.M. (1978). A new species of *Xanthesma* from Australia (Apoidea : Colletidae : Euryglossinae). *J. Kansas Entomol. Soc.* **51**: 781–786 (generic placement).

Xenohesma chrysea (Exley, 1969)

Euryglossa (Xenohesma) chrysea Exley, E.M. (1969). Revision of the subgenus *Xenohesma* Michener (Apoidea : Colletidae). *Aust. J. Zool.* **17**: 535–551 [543].
Type data: holotype, ANIC (transferred from Waite Institute, Adelaide) ♂.
Type locality: Markaranka, Morgan, SA.

Distribution: Murray-Darling basin, SA; known only from type locality.
Ecology: adult—volant; melliferous, solitary, flower visiting record: *Eucalyptus* L'Hérit. [Myrtaceae].
Reference: Exley, E.M. (1978). A new species of *Xanthesma* from Australia (Apoidea : Colletidae : Euryglossinae). *J. Kansas Entomol. Soc.* **51**: 781–786 (generic placement).

Xenohesma clethrosema (Exley, 1969)

Euryglossa (Xenohesma) clethrosema Exley, E.M. (1969). Revision of the subgenus *Xenohesma* Michener (Apoidea : Colletidae). *Aust. J. Zool.* **17**: 535–551 [544].
Type data: holotype, ANIC ♂.
Type locality: 14 miles N Barrow Creek, NT.

Distribution: Lake Eyre basin, NT; known only from type locality.
Ecology: adult—volant; melliferous, solitary, flower visiting record: *Eucalyptus* L'Hérit. [Myrtaceae].
Reference: Exley, E.M. (1978). A new species of *Xanthesma* from Australia (Apoidea : Colletidae : Euryglossinae). *J. Kansas Entomol. Soc.* **51**: 781–786 (generic placement).

Xenohesma clypearis (Michener, 1965)

Euryglossa (Xenohesma) clypearis Michener, C.D. (1965). A classification of the bees of the Australian and South Pacific regions. *Bull. Am. Mus. Nat. Hist.* **130**: 1–362 [278].
Type data: holotype, WAM 44–559 ♀.
Type locality: Broomehill, WA.

Distribution: SW coastal, WA; known only from type locality.
Ecology: adult—volant; melliferous, solitary.
References: Exley, E.M. (1969). Revision of the subgenus *Xenohesma* Michener (Apoidea : Colletidae). *Aust. J. Zool.* **17**: 535–551 (description of male); Exley, E.M. (1978). A new species of *Xanthesma*

from Australia (Apoidea : Colletidae : Euryglossinae). *J. Kansas Entomol. Soc.* **51**: 781–786 (generic placement).

Xenohesma evansi (Michener, 1965)

Euryglossa (Xenohesma) evansi Michener, C.D. (1965). A classification of the bees of the Australian and South Pacific regions. *Bull. Am. Mus. Nat. Hist.* **130**: 1–362 [277].
Type data: holotype, AM K68420 ♂.
Type locality: Cunnamulla, QLD.

Distribution: Murray-Darling basin, QLD; known only from type locality.
Ecology: adult—volant; melliferous, solitary.
Reference: Exley, E.M. (1978). A new species of *Xanthesma* from Australia (Apoidea : Colletidae : Euryglossinae). *J. Kansas Entomol. Soc.* **51**: 781–786 (generic placement).

Xenohesma fasciata (Exley, 1969)

Euryglossa (Xenohesma) fasciata Exley, E.M. (1969). Revision of the subgenus *Xenohesma* Michener (Apoidea : Colletidae). *Aust. J. Zool.* **17**: 535–551 [546].
Type data: holotype, ANIC ♂.
Type locality: Macdonald Downs, NT.

Distribution: Lake Eyre basin, NT; known only from type locality.
Ecology: adult—volant; melliferous, solitary.
Reference: Exley, E.M. (1978). A new species of *Xanthesma* from Australia (Apoidea : Colletidae : Euryglossinae). *J. Kansas Entomol. Soc.* **51**: 781–786 (generic placement).

Xenohesma federalis (Michener, 1965)

Euryglossa (Xenohesma) federalis Michener, C.D. (1965). A classification of the bees of the Australian and South Pacific regions. *Bull. Am. Mus. Nat. Hist.* **130**: 1–362 [278].
Type data: holotype, ANIC ♀.
Type locality: Cotter (as Cutter) River, ACT.

Distribution: Murray-Darling basin, ACT; only published localities Cotter River and Black Mtn
Ecology: adult—volant; melliferous, solitary.
Reference: Exley, E.M. (1978). A new species of *Xanthesma* from Australia (Apoidea : Colletidae : Euryglossinae). *J. Kansas Entomol. Soc.* **51**: 781–786 (generic placement).

Xenohesma flavicauda (Michener, 1965)

Euryglossa (Xenohesma) flavicauda Michener, C.D. (1965). A classification of the bees of the Australian and South Pacific regions. *Bull. Am. Mus. Nat. Hist.* **130**: 1–362 [279].
Type data: holotype, ANIC ♂.
Type locality: 17 (miles) N Broken Hill, NSW.

Distribution: Murray-Darling basin, NSW; known only from type locality.
Ecology: adult—volant; melliferous, solitary.
References: Exley, E.M. (1969). Revision of the sub-

genus *Xenohesma* Michener (Apoidea : Colletidae). *Aust. J. Zool.* **17**: 535–551 (illustration); Exley, E.M. (1978). A new species of *Xanthesma* from Australia (Apoidea : Colletidae : Euryglossinae). *J. Kansas Entomol. Soc.* **51**: 781–786 (generic placement).

Xenohesma hirsutoscapa (Exley, 1969)

Euryglossa (Xenohesma) hirsutoscapa Exley, E.M. (1969). Revision of the subgenus *Xenohesma* Michener (Apoidea : Colletidae). *Aust. J. Zool.* **17**: 535–551 [547].
Type data: holotype, ANIC ♂.
Type locality: Langi Crossing, WA.

Distribution: N coastal, WA; known only from type locality.
Ecology: adult—volant; melliferous, solitary.
Reference: Exley, E.M. (1978). A new species of *Xanthesma* from Australia (Apoidea : Colletidae : Euryglossinae). *J. Kansas Entomol. Soc.* **51**: 781–786 (generic placement).

Xenohesma maculata (Smith, 1879)

Euryglossa maculata Smith, F. (1879). *Descriptions of New Species of Hymenoptera in the Collection of the British Museum.* London : British Museum xxi 240 pp. [13].
Type data: holotype, BMNH Hym.17.a.242 ♀.
Type locality: Swan River, WA.

Distribution: SW coastal, NW coastal, WA; only published localities Swan River, Northampton and Koorda.
Ecology: adult—volant; melliferous, solitary.
References: Cockerell, T.D.A. (1914). New Australian bees. *Entomologist* **47**: 197–201 (taxonomy); Rayment, T. (1953). *Bees of the Portland District.* Victoria : Portland Field Naturalist's Club 39 pp. (Portland; probable misidentification); Michener, C.D. (1965). A classification of the bees of the Australian and South Pacific regions. *Bull. Am. Mus. Nat. Hist.* **130**: 1–362 (taxonomy); Exley, E.M. (1969). Revision of the subgenus *Xenohesma* Michener (Apoidea : Colletidae). *Aust. J. Zool.* **17**: 535–551 (redescription); Exley, E.M. (1978). A new species of *Xanthesma* from Australia (Apoidea : Colletidae : Euryglossinae). *J. Kansas Entomol. Soc.* **51**: 781–786 (generic placement).

Xenohesma melanoclypearis (Exley, 1969)

Euryglossa (Xenohesma) melanoclypearis Exley, E.M. (1969). Revision of the subgenus *Xenohesma* Michener (Apoidea : Colletidae). *Aust. J. Zool.* **17**: 535–551 [545].
Type data: holotype, ANIC ♂.
Type locality: 23 miles N Renner Springs, NT.

Distribution: N Gulf, NT; known only from type locality.
Ecology: adult—volant; melliferous, solitary.
Reference: Exley, E.M. (1978). A new species of *Xanthesma* from Australia (Apoidea : Colletidae :

Euryglossinae). *J. Kansas Entomol. Soc.* **51**: 781–786 (generic placement).

Xenohesma perpulchra (Cockerell, 1916)

Euryglossa perpulchra Cockerell, T.D.A. (1916). Descriptions and records of bees. LXXII. *Ann. Mag. Nat. Hist. (8)***17**: 428–435 [434].
Type data: holotype, BMNH Hym.17.a.279 ♂.
Type locality: Kalamunda, WA.

Distribution: NE coastal, SW coastal, QLD, WA; only published localities near Bowen, Kalamunda, Nedlands and Crawley.
Ecology: adult—volant; melliferous, solitary.
References: Michener, C.D. (1965). A classification of the bees of the Australian and South Pacific regions. *Bull. Am. Mus. Nat. Hist.* **130**: 1–362 (taxonomy); Exley, E.M. (1969). Revision of the subgenus *Xenohesma* Michener (Apoidea : Colletidae). *Aust. J. Zool.* **17**: 535–551 (distribution); Exley, E.M. (1978). A new species of *Xanthesma* from Australia (Apoidea : Colletidae : Euryglossinae). *J. Kansas Entomol. Soc.* **51**: 781–786 (generic placement).

Xenohesma primaria (Michener, 1965)

Euryglossa (Xenohesma) primaria Michener, C.D. (1965). A classification of the bees of the Australian and South Pacific regions. *Bull. Am. Mus. Nat. Hist.* **130**: 1–362 [280].
Type data: holotype, ANIC ♂.
Type locality: "30m." (probably 30 miles) N Bunbury, WA.

Distribution: SW coastal, WA; known only from type locality.
Ecology: adult—volant; melliferous, solitary.
References: Exley, E.M. (1969). Revision of the subgenus *Xenohesma* Michener (Apoidea : Colletidae). *Aust. J. Zool.* **17**: 535–551 (illustration); Exley, E.M. (1978). A new species of *Xanthesma* from Australia (Apoidea : Colletidae : Euryglossinae). *J. Kansas Entomol. Soc.* **51**: 781–786 (generic placement).

Xenohesma scutellaris (Michener, 1965)

Euryglossa (Xenohesma) scutellaris Michener, C.D. (1965). A classification of the bees of the Australian and South Pacific regions. *Bull. Am. Mus. Nat. Hist.* **130**: 1–362 [280].
Type data: holotype, WAM 31–1255 ♀.
Type locality: Seabrook, WA.

Distribution: SW coastal, WA; known only from type locality.
Ecology: adult—volant; melliferous, solitary.
Reference: Exley, E.M. (1978). A new species of *Xanthesma* from Australia (Apoidea : Colletidae : Euryglossinae). *J. Kansas Entomol. Soc.* **51**: 781–786 (generic placement).

Xenohesma sigaloessa (Exley, 1969)

Euryglossa (Xenohesma) sigaloessa Exley, E.M. (1969). Revision of the subgenus *Xenohesma* Michener (Apoidea : Colletidae). *Aust. J. Zool.* **17**: 535–551 [548].
Type data: holotype, ANIC ♂.
Type locality: Macdonald Downs, NT.

Distribution: Lake Eyre basin, NT; known only from type locality.
Ecology: adult—volant; melliferous, solitary.
Reference: Exley, E.M. (1978). A new species of *Xanthesma* from Australia (Apoidea : Colletidae : Euryglossinae). *J. Kansas Entomol. Soc.* **51**: 781–786 (generic placement).

Xenohesma stagei (Exley, 1969)

Euryglossa (Xenohesma) stagei Exley, E.M. (1969). Revision of the subgenus *Xenohesma* Michener (Apoidea : Colletidae). *Aust. J. Zool.* **17**: 535–551 [549].
Type data: holotype, ANIC ♂.
Type locality: 40 miles SE Wyndham, WA.

Distribution: N Gulf, N coastal, QLD, NT, WA.
Ecology: adult—volant; melliferous, solitary, flower visiting record: *Eucalyptus* L'Hérit. [Myrtaceae].
References: Exley, E.M. (1978). *Chaetohesma*—a new genus of Australian bees (Apoidea : Colletidae : Euryglossinae). *Aust. J. Zool.* **26**: 373–397 (female of *Xenohesma stagei* is unknown; female described by Exley, 1969 =*Chaetohesma tuberculata* Exley 1978); Exley, E.M. (1978). A new species of *Xanthesma* from Australia (Apoidea : Colletidae : Euryglossinae). *J. Kansas Entomol. Soc.* **51**: 781–786 (generic placement).

Xenohesma villosula (Smith, 1879)

Euryglossa villosula Smith, F. (1879). *Descriptions of New Species of Hymenoptera in the Collection of the British Museum.* London : British Museum xxi 240 pp. [15].
Type data: holotype, BMNH Hym.17.a.281 ♂.
Type locality: Swan River, WA.

Distribution: SW coastal, WA; known only from type locality.
Ecology: adult—volant; melliferous, solitary.
References: Cockerell, T.D.A. (1914). New Australian bees. *Entomologist* **47**: 197–201 (taxonomy); Michener, C.D. (1965). A classification of the bees of the Australian and South Pacific regions. *Bull. Am. Mus. Nat. Hist.* **130**: 1–362 (taxonomy); Exley, E.M. (1969). Revision of the subgenus *Xenohesma* Michener (Apoidea : Colletidae). *Aust. J. Zool.* **17**: 535–551 (redescription); Exley, E.M. (1978). A new species of *Xanthesma* from Australia (Apoidea : Colletidae : Euryglossinae). *J. Kansas Entomol. Soc.* **51**: 781–786 (generic placement).

HYLAEINAE

Amphylaeus Michener, 1965

Taxonomic decision for subgeneric arrangement: Michener, C.D. (1965). A classification of the bees of the Australian and South Pacific regions. *Bull. Am. Mus. Nat. Hist.* **130**: 1–362 [147].

Generic reference: Houston, T.F. (1975). A revision of the Australian hylaeine bees (Hymenoptera : Colletidae). I. *Aust. J. Zool. Suppl. Ser.* **36**: 1–135.

Amphylaeus (Amphylaeus) Michener, 1965

Amphylaeus Michener, C.D. (1965). A classification of the bees of the Australian and South Pacific regions. *Bull. Am. Mus. Nat. Hist.* **130**: 1–362 [147]. Type species: *Prosopis morosa* Smith, 1879 by original designation.

Amphylaeus (Amphylaeus) morosus (Smith, 1879)

Prosopis morosa Smith, F. (1879). *Descriptions of New Species of Hymenoptera in the Collection of the British Museum.* London : British Museum xxi 240 pp. [26].
Type data: holotype, BMNH Hym.17.a.88 ♀.
Type locality: Australia.
Prosopis sculptifrons Cockerell, T.D.A. (1921). Australian bees in the Queensland Museum. *Mem. Qd Mus.* **7**: 81–98 [84].
Type data: holotype, BMNH Hym.17.a.102 ♂.
Type locality: [Lamington] National Park, QLD.
Meroglossa hardcastlei Rayment, T. (1939). Bees from the high lands of New South Wales and Victoria. *Aust. Zool.* **9**: 263–294 [273].
Type data: holotype, ANIC ♂.
Type locality: White Swamp, NSW.

Taxonomic decision for synonymy: Houston, T.F. (1975). A revision of the Australian hylaeine bees (Hymenoptera : Colletidae). I. *Aust. J. Zool. Suppl. Ser.* **36**: 1–135 [75].

Distribution: NE coastal, Murray-Darling basin, SE coastal, QLD, NSW, ACT, VIC.
Ecology: larva—sedentary : adult—volant; melliferous, solitary, though prereproductive adults of both sexes may be found in a nest, nests in dry *Xanthorrhoea* [Xanthorrhoeaceae] stems and in twigs of *Tristania* R.Br. [Myrtaceae], flower visiting record: *Acacia* Miller [Mimosaceae], *Aster* L. [Asteraceae], *Banksia* L.f. [Proteaceae], *Eucalyptus* L'Hérit. [Myrtaceae], *Gompholobium* Sm. [Fabaceae], *Melaleuca* L. [Myrtaceae], *Pultenaea* Sm. [Fabaceae], *Xanthorrhoea* Sm. [Xanthorrhoeaceae].
References: Meade-Waldo, G. (1923). Hymenoptera. Fam. Apidae. Subfam. Prosopidinae. *Genera Insectorum* **181**: 1–45 (as *Hylaeus (Koptogaster) morosus* (Smith, 1879) and *Hylaeus (Koptogaster) sculptifrons* (Cockerell, 1921)); Rayment, T. (1953). *Bees of the Portland District.* Victoria : Portland Field Naturalist's Club 39 pp. (flower record); Michener, C.D. (1960). Notes on the behavior of Australian colletid bees. *J. Kansas Entomol. Soc.* **33**: 22–31

(biology, as *Meroglossa sculptifrons* (Cockerell, 1921)); Michener, C.D. & Fraser, A. (1978). A comparative anatomical study of mandibular structure in bees. *Univ. Kansas Sci. Bull.* **51**: 463–482 (mandible); Cane, J.H. (1979). The hind tibiotarsal and tibial spur articulations in bees (Hymenoptera : Apoidea). *J. Kansas Entomol. Soc.* **52**: 123–137 (hind spur articulation); McGinley, R.J. (1980). Glossal morphology of the Colletidae and recognition of the Stenotritidae at the family level (Hymenoptera : Apoidea). *J. Kansas Entomol. Soc.* **53**: 539–552 (glossa); McGinley, R.J. (1981). Systematics of the Colletidae based on mature larvae with phenetic analysis of apoid larvae (Insecta, Hymenoptera, Apoidea). *Univ. Calif. Publ. Entomol.* **91**: 1–309 (larva); Michener, C.D. (1992). Sexual dimorphism in the glossa of Colletidae (Hymenoptera, Apoidea). *J. Kansas Entomol. Soc.* **65**: 1–9 (glossa).

Amphylaeus (Agogenohylaeus) Michener, 1965

Agogenohylaeus Michener, C.D. (1965). A classification of the bees of the Australian and South Pacific regions. *Bull. Am. Mus. Nat. Hist.* **130**: 1–362 [148] [proposed with subgeneric rank in *Amphylaeus* Michener, 1965]. Type species: *Prosopis nubilosella* Cockerell, 1910 by original designation.

Amphylaeus (Agogenohylaeus) flavicans Houston, 1975

Amphylaeus (Agogenohylaeus) flavicans Houston, T.F. (1975). A revision of the Australian hylaeine bees (Hymenoptera : Colletidae). I. *Aust. J. Zool. Suppl. Ser.* **36**: 1–135 [80].
Type data: holotype, QM T6887 ♂.
Type locality: 2 miles N Wallangarra, QLD.

Distribution: Murray-Darling basin, QLD; known only from type locality.
Ecology: adult—volant; melliferous, solitary, flower visiting record: *Amyema* Tieghem [Loranthaceae].

Amphylaeus (Agogenohylaeus) nubilosellus (Cockerell, 1910)

Prosopis nubilosella Cockerell, T.D.A. (1910). Descriptions and records of bees. XXXI. *Ann. Mag. Nat. Hist. (8)***6**: 160–168 [161].
Type data: lectotype, BMNH Hym.17.a.103 ♀.
Subsequent designation: Houston, T.F. (1975). A revision of the Australian hylaeine bees (Hymenoptera : Colletidae). I. *Aust. J. Zool. Suppl. Ser.* **36**: 1–135 [81]; Cardale, J.C., this work, interprets Houston's incorrect inference of holotype as a lectotype designation (Art. 74, ICZN 1985).
Type locality: Mackay, QLD.
Prosopis nubilosella mediosticta Cockerell, T.D.A. (1912). Descriptions and records of bees. XLI. *Ann. Mag. Nat. Hist. (8)***9**: 139–149 [145].
Type data: holotype, BMNH Hym.17.a.104 ♀.
Type locality: Botany, NSW.
Prosopis sydneyensis Friese, H. (1924). Ueber die Bienen Australiens. *Konowia* **3**: 216–249 [225].

Type data: holotype (probable), AMNH 26897 ♀*.
Type locality: Sydney, NSW.

Taxonomic decision for synonymy: Houston, T.F. (1975). A revision of the Australian hylaeine bees (Hymenoptera : Colletidae). I. *Aust. J. Zool. Suppl. Ser.* **36**: 1–135 [81].

Distribution: NE coastal, Murray-Darling basin, SE coastal, QLD, NSW.
Ecology: adult—volant; melliferous, solitary, nest in dead flower stalk (*Xanthorrhoea* Sm. [Xanthorrhoeaceae]), flower visiting record: *Banksia* L.f. [Proteaceae], *Boronia* Sm. [Rutaceae], *Daviesia* Sm. [Fabaceae], *Goodenia* Sm. [Goodeniaceae], *Jacksonia* Smith [Fabaceae], *Loranthus* Jacq. [Loranthaceae], *Melaleuca* L. [Myrtaceae], *Rubus* L. [Rosaceae], *Solanum* L. [Solanaceae].
References: Meade-Waldo, G. (1923). Hymenoptera. Fam. Apidae. Subfam. Prosopidinae. *Genera Insectorum* **181**: 1–45 (as *Hylaeus (Koptogaster) nubilosellus* (Cockerell, 1910)); Cockerell, T.D.A. (1929). Bees, chiefly Australian species, described or determined by Dr. H. Friese. *Am. Mus. Novit.* **343**: 1–20 (taxonomy); Michener, C.D. (1965). A classification of the bees of the Australian and South Pacific regions. *Bull. Am. Mus. Nat. Hist.* **130**: 1–362 (nest, flower record, as *Amphylaeus mediostictus* (Cockerell, 1912)).

Amphylaeus (Agogenohylaeus) obscuriceps (Friese, 1924)

Prosopis obscuriceps Friese, H. (1924). Ueber die Bienen Australiens. *Konowia* **3**: 216–249 [229].
Type data: lectotype, AMNH 26890 ♀*.
Subsequent designation: Houston, T.F. (1975). A revision of the Australian hylaeine bees (Hymenoptera : Colletidae). I. *Aust. J. Zool. Suppl. Ser.* **36**: 1–135 [84]; Cardale, J.C., this work, interprets Houston's incorrect inference of holotype as a lectotype designation (Art. 74, ICZN 1985).
Type locality: Australia (as New Holland).
Hylaeus longmani Cockerell, T.D.A. (1929). Bees in the Queensland Museum. *Mem. Qd Mus.* **9**: 298–323 [313].
Type data: holotype, QM Hy/4105 ♂.
Type locality: Brisbane, QLD.
Hylaeus arnoldi Rayment, T. (1939). Bees from the high lands of New South Wales and Victoria. *Aust. Zool.* **9**: 263–294 [263].
Type data: holotype, ANIC ♀.
Type locality: Emerald, VIC.

Taxonomic decision for synonymy: Houston, T.F. (1975). A revision of the Australian hylaeine bees (Hymenoptera : Colletidae). I. *Aust. J. Zool. Suppl. Ser.* **36**: 1–135 [83].

Distribution: NE coastal, Murray-Darling basin, SE coastal, QLD, NSW, ACT, VIC.
Ecology: adult—volant; melliferous, solitary, flower visiting record: *Banksia* L.f. [Proteaceae], *Callistemon* R.Br. [Myrtaceae], *Eucalyptus* L'Hérit. [Myrtaceae], *Eugenia* L. [Myrtaceae], *Hakea* Schrader [Proteaceae], *Loranthus* Jacq. [Loranthaceae], *Xanthorrhoea* Sm. [Xanthorrhoeaceae].

References: Michener, C.D. (1965). A classification of the bees of the Australian and South Pacific regions. *Bull. Am. Mus. Nat. Hist.* **130**: 1–362 (generic placement, for *Amphylaeus longmani* (Cockerell, 1929), *Amphylaeus arnoldi* (Rayment, 1939)); Michener, C.D. (1992). Sexual dimorphism in the glossa of Colletidae (Hymenoptera, Apoidea). *J. Kansas Entomol. Soc.* **65**: 1–9 (glossa).

Gephyrohylaeus Michener, 1965

Gephyrohylaeus Michener, C.D. (1965). A classification of the bees of the Australian and South Pacific regions. *Bull. Am. Mus. Nat. Hist.* **130**: 1–362 [138]. Type species: *Heterapis sandacanensis* Cockerell, 1919 by original designation.

Extralimital distribution: New Guinea, Borneo and Philippines, see Houston, T.F. (1975). A revision of the Australian hylaeine bees (Hymenoptera : Colletidae). I. *Aust. J. Zool. Suppl. Ser.* **36**: 1–135 [42].

Gephyrohylaeus sculptus (Cockerell, 1911)

Heterapis sculpta Cockerell, T.D.A. (1911). A new genus of Australian bees. *Entomologist* **44**: 140–142 [141].
Type data: holotype, BMNH Hym.17.a.310 ♀.
Type locality: Mackay, QLD.

Distribution: NE coastal, QLD; only published localities Mackay, Bamaga and Kuranda.
Ecology: adult—volant; melliferous, solitary.
References: Meade-Waldo, G. (1923). Hymenoptera. Fam. Apidae. Subfam. Prosopidinae. *Genera Insectorum* **181**: 1–45 (illustration); Rayment, T. (1935). *A Cluster of Bees*. Sixty essays on the life-histories of Australian bees, with specific descriptions of over 100 new species, and an introduction by Professor E.F. Phillips, D.Ph., Cornell University, U.S.A. Sydney : Endeavour Press 752 pp. (illustration); Michener, C.D. (1965). A classification of the bees of the Australian and South Pacific regions. *Bull. Am. Mus. Nat. Hist.* **130**: 1–362 (as *Heterapoides sculpta* (Cockerell, 1911)); Houston, T.F. (1975). A revision of the Australian hylaeine bees (Hymenoptera : Colletidae). I. *Aust. J. Zool. Suppl. Ser.* **36**: 1–135 (generic placement, redescription).

Hemirhiza Michener, 1965

Hemirhiza Michener, C.D. (1965). A classification of the bees of the Australian and South Pacific regions. *Bull. Am. Mus. Nat. Hist.* **130**: 1–362 [147]. Type species: *Palaeorhiza melliceps* Cockerell, 1918 by original designation.

Hemirhiza melliceps (Cockerell, 1918)

Palaeorhiza melliceps Cockerell, T.D.A. (1918). Some bees collected in Queensland. *Mem. Qd Mus.* **6**: 112–120 [115].
Type data: holotype, BMNH Hym.17.a.210 ♀.
Type locality: Brisbane, QLD.

Palaeorhiza hierogliphica Rayment, T. (1935). *A Cluster of Bees.* Sixty essays on the life-histories of Australian bees, with specific descriptions of over 100 new species, and an introduction by Professor E.F. Phillips, D.Ph., Cornell University, U.S.A. Sydney : Endeavour Press 752 pp. [666].
Type data: holotype, ANIC ♂.
Type locality: Mt Tamborine, QLD.

Taxonomic decision for synonymy: Michener, C.D. (1965). A classification of the bees of the Australian and South Pacific regions. *Bull. Am. Mus. Nat. Hist.* **130**: 1–362 [147].

Distribution: NE coastal, SE coastal, QLD, NSW.
Ecology: adult—volant; melliferous, solitary, flower visiting record: *Erigeron* L. [Asteraceae], *Prostanthera* Labill. [Lamiaceae], *Rubus* L. [Rosaceae], *Solanum* L. [Solanaceae].
References: Rayment, T. (1948). Notes on remarkable wasps and bees. With specific descriptions. *Aust. Zool.* **11**: 238–254 (flower record, as *Palaeorhiza hierogliphica* Rayment, 1935); Houston, T.F. (1975). A revision of the Australian hylaeine bees (Hymenoptera : Colletidae). I. *Aust. J. Zool. Suppl. Ser.* **36**: 1–135 (redescription); Michener, C.D. (1992). Sexual dimorphism in the glossa of Colletidae (Hymenoptera, Apoidea). *J. Kansas Entomol. Soc.* **65**: 1–9 (glossa).

Heterapoides Sandhouse, 1943

Heterapis Cockerell, T.D.A. (1911). A new genus of Australian bees. *Entomologist* **44**: 140–142 [140] [junior homonym of *Heterapis* Linston, 1889 (Nematoda)]. Type species: *Heterapis delicata* Cockerell, 1911 by original designation.
Heterapoides Sandhouse, G.A. (1943). The type species of the genera and subgenera of bees. *Proc. U.S. Natl Mus.* **92**(3156): 519–619 [557] [*nom. nov.* for *Heterapis* Cockerell, 1911].

Generic reference: Michener, C.D. (1965). A classification of the bees of the Australian and South Pacific regions. *Bull. Am. Mus. Nat. Hist.* **130**: 1–362.

Heterapoides bacillaria (Cockerell, 1914)

Prosopis bacillaria Cockerell, T.D.A. (1914). Australian bees of the family Prosopididae. *Insecutor Inscit. Menstr.* **2**: 97–101 [98].
Type data: neotype, QM T7251 ♂.
Subsequent designation: Houston, T.F. (1975). A revision of the Australian hylaeine bees (Hymenoptera : Colletidae). I *Aust. J. Zool. Suppl. Ser.* **36**: 1–135 [24].
Type locality: Brisbane, QLD.

Distribution: NE coastal, SE coastal, QLD, NSW.
Ecology: adult—volant; melliferous, solitary, flower visiting record: *Daviesia* Sm. [Fabaceae], *Jacksonia* Smith [Fabaceae], *Leptospermum* Forster & G.Forster [Myrtaceae], *Melaleuca* L. [Myrtaceae], *Tristania* R.Br. [Myrtaceae].
References: Meade-Waldo, G. (1923). Hymenoptera. Fam. Apidae. Subfam. Prosopidinae. *Genera In-*

sectorum **181**: 1–45 (as *Hylaeus (Koptogaster) bacillaria* (Cockerell, 1914)); Houston, T.F. (1975). A revision of the Australian hylaeine bees (Hymenoptera : Colletidae). I. *Aust. J. Zool. Suppl. Ser.* **36**: 1–135 (redescription).

Heterapoides delicata (Cockerell, 1911)

Heterapis delicata Cockerell, T.D.A. (1911). A new genus of Australian bees. *Entomologist* **44**: 140–142 [140].
Type data: holotype, BMNH Hym.17.a.309 ♀.
Type locality: Mackay, QLD.

Distribution: NE coastal, SE coastal, Murray-Darling basin, QLD, NSW, VIC.
Ecology: adult—volant; melliferous, solitary, flower visiting record: *Callistemon* R.Br. [Myrtaceae], *Eucalyptus* L'Hérit. [Myrtaceae], *Leptospermum* Forster & G.Forster [Myrtaceae], *Melaleuca* L. [Myrtaceae].
Reference: Houston, T.F. (1975). A revision of the Australian hylaeine bees (Hymenoptera : Colletidae). I. *Aust. J. Zool. Suppl. Ser.* **36**: 1–135 (redescription).

Heterapoides digitata Houston, 1975

Heterapoides digitata Houston, T.F. (1975). A revision of the Australian hylaeine bees (Hymenoptera : Colletidae). I. *Aust. J. Zool. Suppl. Ser.* **36**: 1–135 [27].
Type data: holotype, QM T6869 ♂.
Type locality: 3 miles SW Jimboomba, QLD.

Distribution: NE coastal, QLD.
Ecology: adult—volant; melliferous, solitary, flower visiting record: *Acacia* Miller [Mimosaceae], *Angophora* Cav. [Myrtaceae], *Eucalyptus* L'Hérit. [Myrtaceae], *Melaleuca* L. [Myrtaceae].

Heterapoides exleyae Houston, 1975

Heterapoides exleyae Houston, T.F. (1975). A revision of the Australian hylaeine bees (Hymenoptera : Colletidae). I. *Aust. J. Zool. Suppl. Ser.* **36**: 1–135 [29].
Type data: holotype, QM T6873 ♂.
Type locality: Noosa, QLD.

Distribution: NE coastal, QLD; only published localities Noosa, Tewantin and near Maidenwell.
Ecology: adult—volant; melliferous, solitary, flower visiting record: *Eugenia* L. [Myrtaceae], ?*Tristania* R.Br. [Myrtaceae].

Heterapoides extensa (Cockerell, 1916)

Prosopis extensa Cockerell, T.D.A. (1916). Some bees from Australia, Tasmania, and the New Hebrides. *Proc. Acad. Nat. Sci. Philad.* **68**: 360–375 [364].
Type data: holotype, BMNH Hym.17.a.91 ♀.
Type locality: Mt Yule, Healesville, VIC.

Distribution: NE coastal, Murray-Darling basin, SE coastal, QLD, NSW, ACT, VIC, SA.
Ecology: adult—volant; melliferous, solitary, flower visiting record: *Callistemon* R.Br. [Myrtaceae], *Daviesia* Sm. [Fabaceae], *Eucalyptus* L'Hérit. [Myrtaceae], *Jacksonia* Smith [Fabaceae],

Leptospermum Forster & G.Forster [Myrtaceae], *Melaleuca* L. [Myrtaceae], *Tristania* R.Br. [Myrtaceae], *Xanthorrhoea* Sm. [Xanthorrhoeaceae]. References: Meade-Waldo, G. (1923). Hymenoptera. Fam. Apidae. Subfam. Prosopidinae. *Genera Insectorum* **181**: 1–45 (as *Hylaeus (Koptogaster) extensus* (Cockerell, 1916)); Houston, T.F. (1975). A revision of the Australian hylaeine bees (Hymenoptera : Colletidae). I. *Aust. J. Zool. Suppl. Ser.* **36**: 1–135 (redescription); Alcock, J. & Houston, T.F. (1987). Resource defense and alternative mating tactics in the banksia bee, *Hylaeus alcyoneus* (Erichson). *Ethology* **76**: 177–188 (biology); Michener, C.D. (1992). Sexual dimorphism in the glossa of Colletidae (Hymenoptera, Apoidea). *J. Kansas Entomol. Soc.* **65**: 1–9 (glossa).

Heterapoides halictiformis Perkins, 1912

Heterapis halictiformis Perkins, R.C.L. (1912). Notes, with descriptions of new species, on aculeate Hymenoptera of the Australian Region. *Ann. Mag. Nat. Hist. (8)9*: 96–121 [112].
Type data: holotype, BMNH Hym.17.a.2826 ♂.
Type locality: Bundaberg, QLD.

Prosopis pulchripes Cockerell, T.D.A. (1914). Australian bees of the family Prosopididae. *Insecutor Inscit. Menstr.* **2**: 97–101 [97].
Type data: holotype, QM Hy/4150 ♂.
Type locality: Brisbane, QLD.

Heterapis hackeriella Cockerell, T.D.A. (1929). Bees in the Queensland Museum. *Mem. Qd Mus.* **9**: 298–323 [322].
Type data: holotype, QM Hy/3729 ♀.
Type locality: Brisbane, QLD.

Taxonomic decision for synonymy: Houston, T.F. (1975). A revision of the Australian hylaeine bees (Hymenoptera : Colletidae). I. *Aust. J. Zool. Suppl. Ser.* **36**: 1–135 [37].

Distribution: NE coastal, Murray-Darling basin, QLD, NSW.
Ecology: adult—volant; melliferous, solitary, flower visiting record: *Alphitonia* Reisseck ex Endl. [Rhamnaceae], *Angophora* Cav. [Myrtaceae], *Boronia* Sm. [Rutaceae], *Bursaria* Cav. [Pittosporaceae], *Callistemon* R.Br. [Myrtaceae], *Calytrix* Lab. [Myrtaceae], *Claoxylon* A. Juss. [Euphorbiaceae], *Jacksonia* Smith [Fabaceae], *Leptospermum* Forster & G.Forster [Myrtaceae], *Lomatia* R.Br. [Proteaceae], *Loranthus* Jacq. [Loranthaceae], *Melaleuca* L. [Myrtaceae], *Xanthorrhoea* Sm. [Xanthorrhoeaceae].
Reference: Michener, C.D. (1965). A classification of the bees of the Australian and South Pacific regions. *Bull. Am. Mus. Nat. Hist.* **130**: 1–362 (flower record, as *Heterapoides hackeriella* (Cockerell, 1929)).

Heterapoides leviceps Houston, 1975

Heterapoides leviceps Houston, T.F. (1975). A revision of the Australian hylaeine bees (Hymenoptera : Colletidae). I. *Aust. J. Zool. Suppl. Ser.* **36**: 1–135 [39].

Type data: holotype, QM T6879 ♂.
Type locality: Beerwah, QLD.

Distribution: NE coastal, Murray-Darling basin, SE coastal, QLD, NSW, VIC.
Ecology: adult—volant; melliferous, solitary, flower visiting record: wild parsley, *Angophora* Cav. [Myrtaceae], *Daviesia* Sm. [Fabaceae], *Eucalyptus* L'Hérit. [Myrtaceae], *Jacksonia* Smith [Fabaceae], *Leptospermum* Forster & G.Forster [Myrtaceae], *Melaleuca* L. [Myrtaceae], *Tristania* R.Br. [Myrtaceae].

Heterapoides nigriconcava Houston, 1975

Heterapoides nigriconcava Houston, T.F. (1975). A revision of the Australian hylaeine bees (Hymenoptera : Colletidae). I. *Aust. J. Zool. Suppl. Ser.* **36**: 1–135 [41].
Type data: holotype, QM T6884 ♂.
Type locality: S of Eukey (near Stanthorpe), QLD.

Distribution: NE coastal, Murray-Darling basin, SE coastal, QLD, NSW, VIC.
Ecology: adult—volant; melliferous, solitary, flower visiting record: wild parsley, *Daviesia* Sm. [Fabaceae], *Jacksonia* Smith [Fabaceae], *Leptospermum* Forster & G.Forster [Myrtaceae].

Hylaeus Fabricius, 1793

Hylaeus Fabricius, J.C. (1793). *Entomologia Systematica Emendata et Aucta.* secundum classes, ordines, genera, species. Adjectis synonimis, locis, observationibus, descriptionibus. Hafniae : C.G. Proft Vol. 2 viii 519 pp. [302]. Type species: *Apis annulata* Linnaeus, 1758 (=*Prosopis annulata* Fabricius, 1804) by subsequent designation, see Latreille, P.A. (1810). *Considérations Générales sur l'Ordre Naturel des Animaux Composant les Classes des Crustacès, des Arachnides, et des Insectes; avec un Tableau Méthodique de leurs Genres, Disposés en Familles.* Paris : F. Schoell 444 pp. [438].

Taxonomic decision for subgeneric arrangement: Houston, T.F. (1981). A revision of the Australian hylaeine bees (Hymenoptera : Colletidae). II. *Aust. J. Zool. Suppl. Ser.* **80**: 1–128 [4].

Extralimital distribution: Nearctic, Palaearctic, Oriental, Afrotropical, Holarctic and Neotropical Regions, see Hurd, P.D. (1979). Superfamily Apoidea. pp. 1741–2209 *in* Krombein, K.V., Hurd, P.D., Smith, D.R. & Burks, B.D. (eds) (1979). *Catalog of Hymenoptera in America North of Mexico* Vol. 2, Washington : Smithsonian Institution [1766].

Generic reference: Michener, C.D. (1965). A classification of the bees of the Australian and South Pacific regions. *Bull. Am. Mus. Nat. Hist.* **130**: 1–362.

Hylaeus (Analastoroides) Rayment, 1950

Analastoroides Rayment, T. (1950). New bees and wasps—Part XIII. *Analastoroides*, a new genus of wasp-like bees. *Vict. Nat.* **67**: 20–25 [20]. Type species: *Analastoroides foveata* Rayment, 1950 by original designation.

Hylaeus (Analastoroides) foveatus (Rayment, 1950)

Analastoroides foveata Rayment, T. (1950). New bees and wasps—Part XIII. *Analastoroides*, a new genus of wasp-like bees. *Vict. Nat.* **67**: 20–25 [20].
Type data: holotype, ANIC ♀.
Type locality: Jamberoo, NSW.

Distribution: SE coastal, NSW, VIC; only published localities Jamberoo and Lorne.
Ecology: adult—volant; melliferous, solitary, flower visiting record: *Eucalyptus* L'Hérit. [Myrtaceae], *Leptospermum* Forster & G.Forster [Myrtaceae].
References: Michener, C.D. (1965). A classification of the bees of the Australian and South Pacific regions. *Bull. Am. Mus. Nat. Hist.* **130**: 1–362 (redescription); Houston, T.F. (1981). A revision of the Australian hylaeine bees (Hymenoptera : Colletidae). II. *Aust. J. Zool. Suppl. Ser.* **80**: 1–128 (redescription, generic placement).

Hylaeus (Edriohylaeus) Michener, 1965

Edriohylaeus Michener, C.D. (1965). A classification of the bees of the Australian and South Pacific regions. *Bull. Am. Mus. Nat. Hist.* **130**: 1–362 [124] [proposed with subgeneric rank in *Hylaeus* Fabricius, 1793]. Type species: *Hylaeus (Edriohylaeus) ofarrelli* Michener, 1965 by original designation.

Hylaeus (Edriohylaeus) ofarrelli Michener, 1965

Hylaeus (Edriohylaeus) ofarrelli Michener, C.D. (1965). A classification of the bees of the Australian and South Pacific regions. *Bull. Am. Mus. Nat. Hist.* **130**: 1–362 [293].
Type data: holotype, QM T6738 ♂.
Type locality: Binna Burra, QLD.

Distribution: NE coastal, SE coastal, Murray-Darling basin, QLD, NSW, VIC.
Ecology: adult—volant; melliferous, solitary, nests in dead stem of *Verbena* L. [Verbenaceae] and in dead reed, flower visiting record: wild parsley, *Callistemon* R.Br. [Myrtaceae], *Claoxylon* A. Juss. [Euphorbiaceae], *Eucalyptus* L'Hérit. [Myrtaceae], *Jacksonia* Smith [Fabaceae], *Leptospermum* Forster & G.Forster [Myrtaceae], *Melaleuca* L. [Myrtaceae], *Syncarpia* Ten. [Myrtaceae].
Reference: Houston, T.F. (1981). A revision of the Australian hylaeine bees (Hymenoptera : Colletidae). II. *Aust. J. Zool. Suppl. Ser.* **80**: 1–128 (redescription and distribution).

Hylaeus (Euprosopellus) Michener, 1965

Euprosopellus Michener, C.D. (1965). A classification of the bees of the Australian and South Pacific regions. *Bull. Am. Mus. Nat. Hist.* **130**: 1–362 [132] [proposed with subgeneric rank in *Hylaeus* Fabricius, 1793]. Type species: *Prosopis dromedarius* Cockerell, 1910 by original designation.

Hylaeus (Euprosopellus) certus (Cockerell, 1921)

Prosopis certa Cockerell, T.D.A. (1921). Australian bees in the Queensland Museum. *Mem. Qd Mus.* **7**: 81–98 [85].
Type data: holotype, USNM ♂*.
Type locality: Brisbane, QLD.

Distribution: NE coastal, Murray-Darling basin, SE coastal, S Gulfs, QLD, NSW, SA.
Ecology: adult—volant; melliferous, solitary, flower visiting record: *Eucalyptus* L'Hérit. [Myrtaceae], *Leptospermum* Forster & G.Forster [Myrtaceae].
References: Meade-Waldo, G. (1923). Hymenoptera. Fam. Apidae. Subfam. Prosopidinae. *Genera Insectorum* **181**: 1–45 (as *Hylaeus (Koptogaster) certa* (Cockerell, 1921)); Houston, T.F. (1981). A revision of the Australian hylaeine bees (Hymenoptera : Colletidae). II. *Aust. J. Zool. Suppl. Ser.* **80**: 1–128 (redescription).

Hylaeus (Euprosopellus) chrysaspis (Cockerell, 1910)

Prosopis chrysaspis Cockerell, T.D.A. (1910). Some Australian bees in the Berlin Museum. *J. N.Y. Entomol. Soc.* **18**: 98–114 [102].
Type data: holotype, ZMB 19384 ♀*.
Type locality: Adelaide, SA.

Hylaeus perconstrictus Cockerell, T.D.A. (1929). Bees in the Queensland Museum. *Mem. Qd Mus.* **9**: 298–323 [311].
Type data: holotype, QM Hy/3723 ♂.
Type locality: Beaconsfield.

Hylaeus gracilicaudis Cockerell, T.D.A. (1929). Bees in the Australian Museum collection. *Rec. Aust. Mus.* **17**: 199–243 [222].
Type data: holotype, AM K48293 ♀.
Type locality: King George Sound, WA.

Taxonomic decision for synonymy: Houston, T.F. (1981). A revision of the Australian hylaeine bees (Hymenoptera : Colletidae). II. *Aust. J. Zool. Suppl. Ser.* **80**: 1–128 [13].

Distribution: SE coastal, Murray-Darling basin, S Gulfs, SW coastal, W plateau, NSW, VIC, SA, WA.
Ecology: adult—volant; melliferous, solitary, flower visiting record: *Eucalyptus* L'Hérit. [Myrtaceae], *Leptospermum* Forster & G.Forster [Myrtaceae], *Melaleuca* L. [Myrtaceae].
Reference: Meade-Waldo, G. (1923). Hymenoptera. Fam. Apidae. Subfam. Prosopidinae. *Genera Insectorum* **181**: 1–45 (as *Hylaeus (Koptogaster) chrysaspis* (Cockerell, 1910)).

Hylaeus (Euprosopellus) dromedarius (Cockerell, 1910)

Prosopis dromedarius Cockerell, T.D.A. (1910). Some Australian bees in the Berlin Museum. *J. N.Y. Entomol. Soc.* **18**: 98–114 [103].
Type data: holotype, ZMB 19386 ♂*.
Type locality: Adelaide, SA.

Prosopis indicator Cockerell, T.D.A. (1910). Some Australian bees in the Berlin Museum. *J. N.Y. Entomol. Soc.* **18**: 98–114 [103].
Type data: holotype, ZMB ♀* (described as ♂).
Type locality: Mallee, VIC.

Euprosopis elegans butleri Rayment, T. (1930). Notes on a collection of bees from Western Australia. *J. Proc. R. Soc. West. Aust.* **16**: 45–56 [47].
Type data: holotype (probable), ANIC ♀.
Type locality: Mt Macedon, VIC.

Taxonomic decision for synonymy: Houston, T.F. (1981). A revision of the Australian hylaeine bees (Hymenoptera : Colletidae). II. *Aust. J. Zool. Suppl. Ser.* **80**: 1–128 [15].

Distribution: Murray-Darling basin, S Gulfs, W plateau, SW coastal, VIC, SA, WA.
Ecology: adult—volant; melliferous, solitary, flower visiting record: *Eucalyptus* L'Hérit. [Myrtaceae], *Melaleuca* L. [Myrtaceae], *Pittosporum* Gaertner [Pittosporaceae].
Reference: Meade-Waldo, G. (1923). Hymenoptera. Fam. Apidae. Subfam. Prosopidinae. *Genera Insectorum* **181**: 1–45 (as *Hylaeus (Koptogaster) dromedarius* (Cockerell, 1910) and *Hylaeus (Koptogaster) indicator* (Cockerell, 1910)).

Hylaeus (Euprosopellus) pergibbosus Cockerell, 1926

Hylaeus pergibbosus Cockerell, T.D.A. (1926). Descriptions and records of bees. CXI. *Ann. Mag. Nat. Hist. (9)***17**: 657–665 [662].
Type data: holotype, NMV T3847 ♂.
Type locality: Kewell, VIC.

Distribution: Murray-Darling basin, S Gulfs, VIC, SA; only published localities Kewell, Mallee, Adelaide and Meningie.
Ecology: adult—volant; melliferous, solitary.
Reference: Houston, T.F. (1981). A revision of the Australian hylaeine bees (Hymenoptera : Colletidae). II. *Aust. J. Zool. Suppl. Ser.* **80**: 1–128 (redescription).

Hylaeus (Euprosopis) Perkins, 1912

Euprosopis Perkins, R.C.L. (1912). Notes, with descriptions of new species, on aculeate Hymenoptera of the Australian Region. *Ann. Mag. Nat. Hist. (8)***9**: 96–121 [106]. Type species: *Prosopis husela* Cockerell, 1910 by original designation.

Hylaeus (Euprosopis) disjunctus (Cockerell, 1905)

Prosopis disjuncta Cockerell, T.D.A. (1905). Descriptions and records of bees. IV. *Ann. Mag. Nat. Hist. (7)***16**: 392–403 [400].
Type data: syntypes, BMNH 2♂ (a specimen is labelled 'type' and has registration number Hym.17.a.170).
Type locality: Mackay, QLD.

Prosopis basalis Friese, H. (1924). Ueber die Bienen Australiens. *Konowia* **3**: 216–249 [223].

Type data: syntypes, AMNH 2♀1♂*.
Type locality: Mackay, QLD.

Taxonomic decision for synonymy: Houston, T.F. (1981). A revision of the Australian hylaeine bees (Hymenoptera : Colletidae). II. *Aust. J. Zool. Suppl. Ser.* **80**: 1–128 [19].

Distribution: NE coastal, Murray-Darling basin, N coastal, QLD, NT; record from SA (Orroroo) believed to be a labelling error.
Ecology: adult—volant; melliferous, solitary, flower visiting record: *Angophora* Cav. [Myrtaceae], *Callistemon* R.Br. [Myrtaceae], *Dendrobium* Sw. [Orchidaceae], *Eucalyptus* L'Hérit. [Myrtaceae], *Eugenia* L. [Myrtaceae], *Leptospermum* Forster & G.Forster [Myrtaceae], *Melaleuca* L. [Myrtaceae], *Tristania* R.Br. [Myrtaceae], *Xanthorrhoea* Sm. [Xanthorrhoeaceae].
References: Meade-Waldo, G. (1923). Hymenoptera. Fam. Apidae. Subfam. Prosopidinae. *Genera Insectorum* **181**: 1–45 (as *Hylaeus (Koptogaster) disjunctus* (Cockerell, 1905)); Michener, C.D. (1965). A classification of the bees of the Australian and South Pacific regions. *Bull. Am. Mus. Nat. Hist.* **130**: 1–362 (flower record); Slater, A.T. & Calder, D.M. (1988). The pollination biology of *Dendrobium speciosum* Smith: a case of false advertising? *Aust. J. Bot.* **36**: 145–158 (pollination).

Hylaeus (Euprosopis) elegans (Smith, 1853)

Prosopis elegans Smith, F. (1853). *Catalogue of Hymenopterous Insects in the Collection of the British Museum. Part I. Andrenidae and Apidae.* London : British Museum 197 pp. [28].
Type data: lectotype, BMNH Hym.17.a.188 ♀.
Subsequent designation: Houston, T.F. (1981). A revision of the Australian hylaeine bees (Hymenoptera : Colletidae). II. *Aust. J. Zool. Suppl. Ser.* **80**: 1–128 [22]; Cardale, J.C., this work, interprets Houston's incorrect inference of holotype as a lectotype designation (Art.74, ICZN 1985).
Type locality: Adelaide, SA.

Prosopis sydneyana Cockerell, T.D.A. (1905). Descriptions and records of bees. V. *Ann. Mag. Nat. Hist. (7)***16**: 465–477 [467].
Type data: holotype, BMNH Hym.17.a.173 ♂.
Type locality: Sydney, NSW.

Prosopis elegans huseloides Cockerell, T.D.A. (1910). Descriptions and records of bees. XXIX. *Ann. Mag. Nat. Hist. (8)***5**: 496–506 [498].'
Type data: syntypes, BMNH Hym.17.a.189 2♀.
Type locality: Townsville, QLD.

Prosopis rollei Cockerell, T.D.A. (1910). Some Australian bees in the Berlin Museum. *J. N.Y. Entomol. Soc.* **18**: 98–114 [105].
Type data: syntypes, ZMB 2♂*.
Type locality: Ararat, VIC.

Euprosopis nodosicornis Cockerell, T.D.A. (1913). Some Australian bees. *Proc. Acad. Nat. Sci. Philad.* **65**: 28–44 [43].
Type data: holotype, BMNH Hym.17.a.191 ♂.
Type locality: Australia.

Hylaeus rubripes Friese, H. (1924). Ueber die Bienen Australiens. *Konowia* 3: 216–249 [226].
Type data: syntypes, ZMB ♂* (number of specimens unknown).
Type locality: Ararat, VIC.

Prosopis flaviceps Friese, H. (1924). Ueber die Bienen Australiens. *Konowia* 3: 216–249 [227].
Type data: syntypes, AMNH ♂♀*.
Type locality: Ararat, VIC and Roebourne, WA.

Euprosopis elegans hillii Rayment, T. (1930). Notes on a collection of bees from Western Australia. *J. Proc. R. Soc. West. Aust.* 16: 45–56 [47].
Type data: holotype, whereabouts unknown ♀*.
Type locality: Horseshoe Bend, Finke River, NT.

Euprosopis elegans maculata Rayment, T. (1930). Notes on a collection of bees from Western Australia. *J. Proc. R. Soc. West. Aust.* 16: 45–56 [47].
Type data: holotype (probable), ANIC ♀.
Type locality: Sandringham, VIC.

Euprosopis elegans occidentalis Rayment, T. (1930). Notes on a collection of bees from Western Australia. *J. Proc. R. Soc. West. Aust.* 16: 45–56 [47].
Type data: syntypes (probable), ANIC ♀ (number of specimens unknown).
Type locality: Hampton, VIC.

Euprosopis elegans labiata Rayment, T. (1930). Notes on a collection of bees from Western Australia. *J. Proc. R. Soc. West. Aust.* 16: 45–56 [47].
Type data: holotype, whereabouts unknown ♀*.
Type locality: Mt Yule, Healesville, VIC.

Euprosopis elegans smithii Rayment, T. (1930). Notes on a collection of bees from Western Australia. *J. Proc. R. Soc. West. Aust.* 16: 45–56 [48].
Type data: holotype, whereabouts unknown ♂*.
Type locality: Adelaide, SA.

Taxonomic decision for synonymy: Houston, T.F. (1981). A revision of the Australian hylaeine bees (Hymenoptera : Colletidae). II. *Aust. J. Zool. Suppl. Ser.* 80: 1–128 [22].

Distribution: SE coastal, N Gulf, N coastal, NW coastal, SW coastal, W plateau, S Gulf, Murray-Darling basin, Bulloo River basin, Lake Eyre basin, QLD, NSW, ACT, VIC, SA, WA, NT.
Ecology: larva—sedentary : adult—volant; melliferous, solitary, nest in any suitable cavity in posts, plant-tubes, or the abandoned gallery of other bees or a longicorn beetle, flower visiting record: *Acacia* Miller [Mimosaceae], *Angophora* Cav. [Myrtaceae], *Atalaya* Blume [Sapindaceae], *Callistemon* R.Br. [Myrtaceae], *Calytrix* Lab. [Myrtaceae], *Eucalyptus* L'Hérit. [Myrtaceae], *Eucarya* T. Mitch. [Santalaceae], *Leptospermum* Forster & G.Forster [Myrtaceae], *Melaleuca* L. [Myrtaceae], *Schinus* L. [Anacardiaceae], *Tristania* R.Br. [Myrtaceae].
References: Meade-Waldo, G. (1923). Hymenoptera. Fam. Apidae. Subfam. Prosopidinae. *Genera Insectorum* 181: 1–45 (as *Hylaeus (Euprosopis) elegans* (Smith, 1853), *Hylaeus (Euprosopis) nodosicornis* (Cockerell, 1913) and *Hylaeus (Koptogaster) rollei* (Cockerell, 1910)); Rayment, T. (1935). *A Cluster of Bees*. Sixty essays on the life-histories of Australian bees, with specific descriptions of over 100 new species, and an introduction by Professor E.F. Phillips, D.Ph., Cornell University, U.S.A. Sydney : Endeavour Press 752 pp. (biology, illustration, as *Euprosopis elegans* (Smith, 1853)); Myers, J.G. (1935). Ethological observations on the citrus bee, *Trigona silvestriana* Vachal, and other Neotropical bees (Hym., Apoidea). *Trans. R. Entomol. Soc. Lond.* 83: 131–142 (biology, as *Prosopis rollei* Cockerell, 1910); Michener, C.D. (1965). A classification of the bees of the Australian and South Pacific regions. *Bull. Am. Mus. Nat. Hist.* 130: 1–362 (flower record); Michener, C.D. (1992). Sexual dimorphism in the glossa of Colletidae (Hymenoptera, Apoidea). *J. Kansas Entomol. Soc.* 65: 1–9 (glossa); Michener, C.D. & Houston, T.F. (1991). Apoidea. pp. 993–1000 *in* CSIRO (sponsor) *The Insects of Australia*. A textbook for students and research workers. Melbourne : Melbourne University Press Vol. II 2nd Edn (illustration).

Hylaeus (Euprosopis) honestus (Smith, 1879)

Prosopis honesta Smith, F. (1879). *Descriptions of New Species of Hymenoptera in the Collection of the British Museum*. London : British Museum xxi 240 pp. [19].
Type data: holotype, BMNH Hym.17.a.71 ♂.
Type locality: TAS.

Prosopis simillima Smith, F. (1879). *Descriptions of New Species of Hymenoptera in the Collection of the British Museum*. London : British Museum xxi 240 pp. [26].
Type data: holotype, BMNH Hym.17.a.46 ♀.
Type locality: Moreton Bay, QLD.

Prosopis chrysognatha Cockerell, T.D.A. (1910). Some Australian bees in the Berlin Museum. *J. N.Y. Entomol. Soc.* 18: 98–114 [102].
Type data: holotype, ZMB ♂*.
Type locality: Melbourne, VIC.

Prosopis leucosphaera Cockerell, T.D.A. (1913). Some Australian bees. *Proc. Acad. Nat. Sci. Philad.* 65: 28–44 [42].
Type data: holotype, BMNH Hym.17.a.94 ♀.
Type locality: Croydon, VIC.

Prosopis xanthosphaera Cockerell, T.D.A. (1913). Some Australian bees. *Proc. Acad. Nat. Sci. Philad.* 65: 28–44 [41].
Type data: holotype, BMNH Hym.17.a.98 ♀.
Type locality: King Is., TAS.

Prosopis daveyi Cockerell, T.D.A. (1921). Australian bees in the Queensland Museum. *Mem. Qd Mus.* 7: 81–98 [85].
Type data: holotype, QM Hy/2425 ♀.
Type locality: Bright, VIC.

Prosopis capitata Friese, H. (1924). Ueber die Bienen Australiens. *Konowia* 3: 216–249 [225] [described again as new on p. 227].
Type data: holotype (probable), AMNH ♂*.
Type locality: Ararat, VIC.

Prosopis maculiceps Friese, H. (1924). Ueber die Bienen Australiens. *Konowia* 3: 216–249 [229].
Type data: holotype (probable), AMNH ♀*.
Type locality: Australia (as New Holland).

Hylaeus honestus subhonestus Cockerell, T.D.A. (1929). Bees in the Queensland Museum. *Mem. Qd Mus.* **9**: 298–323 [312].
Type data: holotype, QM Hy/4031 ♂.
Type locality: Sheffield, TAS.

Taxonomic decision for synonymy: Houston, T.F. (1981). A revision of the Australian hylaeine bees (Hymenoptera : Colletidae). II. *Aust. J. Zool. Suppl. Ser.* **80**: 1–128 [26].

Distribution: NE coastal, SE coastal, Murray-Darling basin, S Gulfs, W plateau, SW coastal, QLD, NSW, ACT, VIC, SA, WA, TAS.
Ecology: adult—volant; melliferous, solitary, ?nest in *Acacia* Miller [Mimosaceae], flower visiting record: blackberry, *Aster* L. [Asteraceae], *Bursaria* Cav. [Pittosporaceae], *Calytrix* Lab. [Myrtaceae], *Eucalyptus* L'Hérit. [Myrtaceae], *Eugenia* L. [Myrtaceae], *Hypochaeris* L. [Asteraceae], *Jacksonia* Smith [Fabaceae], *Leptospermum* Forster & G.For ster [Myrtaceae], *Melaleuca* L. [Myrtaceae], *Pittosporum* Gaertner [Pittosporaceae].
References: Cockerell, T.D.A. (1912). Descriptions and records of bees. XLI. *Ann. Mag. Nat. Hist. (8)***9**: 139–149 (?nest, as *Prosopis chrysognatha* Cockerell, 1910); Meade-Waldo, G. (1923). Hymenoptera. Fam. Apidae. Subfam. Prosopidinae. *Genera Insectorum* **181**: 1–45 (as *Hylaeus (Koptogaster) honestus* (Smith, 1879), *Hylaeus (Koptogaster) simillimus* (Smith, 1879), *Hylaeus (Koptogaster) chrysognathus* (Cockerell, 1910), *Hylaeus (Koptogaster) leucosphaera* (Cockerell, 1913), *Hylaeus (Koptogaster) xanthosphaerus* (Cockerell, 1913) and *Hylaeus (Koptogaster) daveyi* (Cockerell, 1921)); Rayment, T. (1935). *A Cluster of Bees*. Sixty essays on the life-histories of Australian bees, with specific descriptions of over 100 new species, and an introduction by Professor E.F. Phillips, D.Ph., Cornell University, U.S.A. Sydney : Endeavour Press 752 pp. (flower record, as *Hylaeus chrysognatha* (Cockerell, 1910)); Rayment, T. (1953). *Bees of the Portland District*. Victoria : Portland Field Naturalist's Club 39 pp. (as host, as *Hylaeus honestus subhonestus* Cockerell, 1929).

Hylaeus (Euprosopis) huselus (Cockerell, 1910)

Prosopis husela Cockerell, T.D.A. (1910). Descriptions and records of bees. XXIX. *Ann. Mag. Nat. Hist. (8)***5**: 496–506 [498].
Type data: syntypes, BMNH 2♂♀ (a female specimen is labelled 'type' and has registration number Hym.17.a.180).
Type locality: Townsville, QLD.

Distribution: NE coastal, N Gulf, N coastal, Lake Eyre basin, QLD, NT, WA.
Ecology: adult—volant; melliferous, solitary.
References: Perkins, R.C.L. (1912). Notes, with descriptions of new species, on aculeate Hymenoptera of the Australian Region. *Ann. Mag. Nat. Hist. (8)***9**: 96–121 (as *Euprosopis husela* (Cockerell, 1910)); Meade-Waldo, G. (1923). Hymenoptera. Fam.

Apidae. Subfam. Prosopidinae. *Genera Insectorum* **181**: 1–45 (as *Hylaeus (Koptogaster) husela* (Cockerell, 1910)); Evans, H.E. & Matthews, R.W. (1973). Systematics and nesting behavior of Australian *Bembix* sand wasps (Hymenoptera, Sphecidae). *Mem. Am. Entomol. Inst.* **20**: 1–387 (as prey); Houston, T.F. (1981). A revision of the Australian hylaeine bees (Hymenoptera : Colletidae). II. *Aust. J. Zool. Suppl. Ser.* **80**: 1–128 (redescription).

Hylaeus (Euprosopis) violaceus (Smith, 1853)

Prosopis violacea Smith, F. (1853). *Catalogue of Hymenopterous Insects in the Collection of the British Museum*. Part I. Andrenidae and Apidae. London : British Museum 197 pp. [26].
Type data: lectotype, BMNH Hym.17.a.55 ♀.
Subsequent designation: Houston, T.F. (1981). A revision of the Australian hylaeine bees (Hymenoptera : Colletidae). II. *Aust. J. Zool. Suppl. Ser.* **80**: 1–128 [31]; Cardale, J.C., this work, interprets Houston's incorrect inference of holotype as a lectotype designation (Art. 74, ICZN 1985).
Type locality: Swan River, WA.

Prosopis cognata Smith, F. (1879). *Descriptions of New Species of Hymenoptera in the Collection of the British Museum*. London : British Museum xxi 240 pp. [18].
Type data: syntypes, BMNH Hym.17.a.54a,b 1♀1♂.
Type locality: Champion Bay (Geraldton) and Swan River, WA.

Hylaeus gosfordensis Rayment, T. (1939). Bees from the high lands of New South Wales and Victoria. *Aust. Zool.* **9**: 263–294 [266].
Type data: holotype, ANIC ♂.
Type locality: Gosford, NSW.

Taxonomic decision for synonymy: Houston, T.F. (1981). A revision of the Australian hylaeine bees (Hymenoptera : Colletidae). II. *Aust. J. Zool. Suppl. Ser.* **80**: 1–128 [31].

Distribution: SE coastal, Murray-Darling basin, S Gulfs, W plateau, SW coastal, NW coastal, NSW, VIC, SA, WA.
Ecology: adult—volant; melliferous, solitary, flower visiting record: *Aster* L. [Asteraceae], *Banksia* L.f. [Proteaceae], *Bursaria* Cav. [Pittosporaceae], *Eucalyptus* L'Hérit. [Myrtaceae], *Leptospermum* Forster & G.Forster [Myrtaceae], *Melaleuca* L. [Myrtaceae].
References: Meade-Waldo, G. (1923). Hymenoptera. Fam. Apidae. Subfam. Prosopidinae. *Genera Insectorum* **181**: 1–45 (as *Hylaeus (Koptogaster) violaceus* (Smith, 1853), *Prosopis cognata* Smith, 1879 is synonymised); Rayment, T. (1953). *Bees of the Portland District*. Victoria : Portland Field Naturalist's Club 39 pp. (flower record).

Hylaeus (Euprosopoides) Michener, 1965

Euprosopoides Michener, C.D. (1965). A classification of the bees of the Australian and South Pacific regions. *Bull. Am. Mus. Nat. Hist.* **130**: 1–362 [131] [proposed with subgeneric rank in *Hylaeus* Fabricius, 1793]. Type species: *Prosopis fulvicornis* Smith, 1853 by original designation.

Extralimital distribution: Caroline Ils, see Houston, T.F. (1981). A revision of the Australian hylaeine bees (Hymenoptera : Colletidae). II. *Aust. J. Zool. Suppl. Ser.* **80**: 1–128 [33].

Hylaeus (Euprosopoides) amatus (Cockerell, 1909)

Prosopis amata Cockerell, T.D.A. (1909). Descriptions and records of bees. XXIII. *Ann. Mag. Nat. Hist. (8)***4**: 393–404 [394].
Type data: holotype, BMNH Hym.17.a.63 ♀.
Type locality: Kuranda, QLD.

Prosopis cyaniventris Friese, H. (1924). Ueber die Bienen Australiens. *Konowia* **3**: 216–249 [226].
Type data: holotype (probable), AMNH 26876 ♀*.
Type locality: Mackay, QLD.

Taxonomic decision for synonymy: Houston, T.F. (1981). A revision of the Australian hylaeine bees (Hymenoptera : Colletidae). II. *Aust. J. Zool. Suppl. Ser.* **80**: 1–128 [33].

Distribution: NE coastal, QLD; only published localities Kuranda, Mackay, Cape York and Cairns district.
Ecology: adult—volant; melliferous, solitary, flower visiting record: *Xanthorrhoea* Sm. [Xanthorrhoeaceae].
Reference: Meade-Waldo, G. (1923). Hymenoptera. Fam. Apidae. Subfam. Prosopidinae. *Genera Insectorum* **181**: 1–45 (as *Hylaeus (Koptogaster) amatus* (Cockerell, 1909)).

Hylaeus (Euprosopoides) cyanurus (W. Kirby, 1802)

Melitta cyanura Kirby, W. (1802). *Monographia Apum Angliae;* or, an attempt to divide into their natural genera and families, such species of the Linnean genus *Apis* as have been discovered in England : with descriptions and observations. To which are prefixed some introductory remarks upon the class Hymenoptera, and a synoptical table of the nomenclature of the external parts of these insects. Ipswich : J. Raw Vol. 1 xxi 258 pp. [212].
Type data: holotype, BMNH (Banks coll.) ♀.
Type locality: NSW (at the time of collection, this referred to the whole eastern coast of Australia), see Houston, T.F. (1981). A revision of the Australian hylaeine bees (Hymenoptera : Colletidae). II. *Aust. J. Zool. Suppl. Ser.* **80**: 1–128 [36].

Prosopis pachygnatha Cockerell, T.D.A. (1910). Descriptions and records of bees. XXX. *Ann. Mag. Nat. Hist. (8)***6**: 17–31 [29].
Type data: holotype, BMNH Hym.17.a.61 ♀.
Type locality: Cooktown, QLD.

Taxonomic decision for synonymy: Houston, T.F. (1981). A revision of the Australian hylaeine bees (Hymenoptera : Colletidae). II. *Aust. J. Zool. Suppl. Ser.* **80**: 1–128 [36].

Distribution: NE coastal, N coastal, QLD, NT; only published localities Cooktown, Jardine River, Mackay and Nourlangie Creek.
Ecology: adult—volant; melliferous, solitary, flower visiting record: (males only) *Dysophylla* Blume [Lamiaceae], *Tristania* R.Br. [Myrtaceae].
References: Illiger, K. (1806). "William Kirby's

Familien der bienenartigen Insekten mit Zusätzen Nachweisungen und Bemerkungen". *Mag. Insektenkd.* **5**: 28–175 (as *Prosopis cyanura* (Kirby, 1802)); Meade-Waldo, G. (1923). Hymenoptera. Fam. Apidae. Subfam. Prosopidinae. *Genera Insectorum* **181**: 1–45 (as *Hylaeus (Koptogaster) cyanurus* (Kirby, 1802)) and *Hylaeus (Koptogaster) pachygnathus* (Cockerell, 1910)).

Hylaeus (Euprosopoides) lubbocki (Cockerell, 1905)

Prosopis lubbocki Cockerell, T.D.A. (1905). Descriptions and records of bees. IV. *Ann. Mag. Nat. Hist. (7)***16**: 392–403 [403] [name proposed for specimen described as male of *Prosopis metallica* Smith, 1862].
Type data: holotype, BMNH ♂* (not found by J.C.C. in 1988).
Type locality: Australia.

Distribution: Australia, exact locality unknown.
Ecology: adult—volant; melliferous, solitary.
References: Meade-Waldo, G. (1923). Hymenoptera. Fam. Apidae. Subfam. Prosopidinae. *Genera Insectorum* **181**: 1–45 (as *Hylaeus (Koptogaster) lubbocki* Cockerell, 1905); Rayment, T. (1935). *A Cluster of Bees.* Sixty essays on the life-histories of Australian bees, with specific descriptions of over 100 new species, and an introduction by Professor E.F. Phillips, D.Ph., Cornell University, U.S.A. Sydney : Endeavour Press 752 pp. (doubtful record, cocoon); Houston, T.F. (1981). A revision of the Australian hylaeine bees (Hymenoptera : Colletidae). II. *Aust. J. Zool. Suppl. Ser.* **80**: 1–128 (taxonomic position doubtful).

Hylaeus (Euprosopoides) musgravei Cockerell, 1929

Hylaeus musgravei Cockerell, T.D.A. (1929). Bees in the Australian Museum collection. *Rec. Aust. Mus.* **17**: 199–243 [220].
Type data: holotype, AM K37253 ♂.
Type locality: King George Sound, WA.

Distribution: SW coastal, WA; only published localities King George Sound, Bunbury and Perth.
Ecology: adult—volant; melliferous, solitary.
References: Michener, C.D. (1965). A classification of the bees of the Australian and South Pacific regions. *Bull. Am. Mus. Nat. Hist.* **130**: 1–362 (as *Hylaeus (Euprosopis) musgravei* Cockerell, 1929); Houston, T.F. (1981). A revision of the Australian hylaeine bees (Hymenoptera : Colletidae). II. *Aust. J. Zool. Suppl. Ser.* **80**: 1–128 (generic placement, redescription).

Hylaeus (Euprosopoides) obtusatus (Smith, 1879)

Prosopis obtusata Smith, F. (1879). *Descriptions of New Species of Hymenoptera in the Collection of the British Museum.* London : British Museum xxi 240 pp. [17].
Type data: holotype, BMNH Hym.17.a.82 ♀.
Type locality: Swan River, WA.

Hylaeus amatiformis Cockerell, T.D.A. (1929). Bees in the Australian Museum collection. *Rec. Aust. Mus.* **17**: 199–243 [222].
Type data: holotype, AM K37234 ♀.
Type locality: King George Sound, WA.

Hylaeus (Euprosopoides) perconvergens Michener, C.D. (1965). A classification of the bees of the Australian and South Pacific regions. *Bull. Am. Mus. Nat. Hist.* **130**: 1–362 [295].
Type data: holotype, NMV ♂.
Type locality: Bunbury, WA.

Taxonomic decision for synonymy: Houston, T.F. (1981). A revision of the Australian hylaeine bees (Hymenoptera : Colletidae). II. *Aust. J. Zool. Suppl. Ser.* **80**: 1–128 [39].

Distribution: SW coastal, WA.
Ecology: adult—volant; melliferous, solitary.
References: Meade-Waldo, G. (1923). Hymenoptera. Fam. Apidae. Subfam. Prosopidinae. *Genera Insectorum* **181**: 1–45 (as *Hylaeus (Koptogaster) obtusatus* (Smith, 1879)); Michener, C.D. (1965). A classification of the bees of the Australian and South Pacific regions. *Bull. Am. Mus. Nat. Hist.* **130**: 1–362 (QLD localities and flower records, p. 237, are excluded by Houston, 1981).

Hylaeus (Euprosopoides) perplexus (Smith, 1854)

Prosopis confusa Smith, F. (1853). *Catalogue of Hymenopterous Insects in the Collection of the British Museum. Part I. Andrenidae and Apidae.* London : British Museum 197 pp. [30] [junior primary homonym of *Prosopis confusa* Nylander, 1852].
Type data: holotype, BMNH Hym.17.a.59 ♀.
Type locality: Australia (as New Holland).

Prosopis perplexa Smith, F. (1854). *Catalogue of Hymenopterous Insects in the Collection of the British Museum. Part II. Apidae.* London : British Museum pp. 199–465 [421] [*nom. nov.* for *Prosopis confusa* Smith, 1853].

Prosopis metallicus Smith, F. (1862). Descriptions of new species of Australian Hymenoptera, and of a species of *Formica* from New Zealand. *Trans. Entomol. Soc. Lond.* (3)**1**: 53–62 [59].
Type data: lectotype, BMNH Hym.17.a.57 ♂ (described as ♀).
Subsequent designation: Cockerell, T.D.A. (1905). Descriptions and records of bees. IV. *Ann. Mag. Nat. Hist.* (7)**16**: 392–403 [403]; Cardale, J.C., this work, interprets Cockerell's incorrect inference of holotype as a lectotype designation (Art. 74, ICZN 1985).
Type locality: Australia.

Prosopis vicina Sichel, J. (1868). Hymenoptera Fossoria et Mellifera. Supplement. pp. 139–156 *in, Reise der österreichischen Fregatte Novara um die Erde in den Jahren 1857, 1858, 1859 unter den Befehlen des Commodore B. von Wüllerstorf-Urbair.* Zoologischer Theil. Wien : K-K Hof- und Staatsdrückerei Vol. 2(1a) [143].
Type data: lectotype, NHMW ♀*.
Subsequent designation: Michener, C.D. (1965). A classification of the bees of the Australian and South Pacific regions. *Bull. Am. Mus. Nat. Hist.* **130**: 1–362 [132].

Type locality: Sydney, NSW (in description as Aukland and Tasmania).

Prosopis major Friese, H. (1924). Ueber die Bienen Australiens. *Konowia* **3**: 216–249 [228].
Type data: holotype, AMNH ♀*.
Type locality: Sydney, NSW.

Taxonomic decision for synonymy: Houston, T.F. (1981). A revision of the Australian hylaeine bees (Hymenoptera : Colletidae). II. *Aust. J. Zool. Suppl. Ser.* **80**: 1–128 [41].

Distribution: NE coastal, SE coastal, QLD, NSW, TAS.
Ecology: adult—volant; melliferous, solitary, flower visiting record: (males only) *Leptospermum* Forster & G.Forster [Myrtaceae].
Reference: Cockerell, T.D.A. (1905). Descriptions and records of bees. IV. *Ann. Mag. Nat. Hist.* (7)**16**: 392–404 (taxonomy); Meade-Waldo, G. (1923) Hymenoptera. Fam. Apidae. Subfam. Prosopidinae. *Genera Insectorum* **181**: 1–45 (as *Hylaeus (Koptogaster) perplexus* (Smith, 1854), *Hylaeus (Koptogaster) metallicus* (Smith, 1862) and *Hylaeus (Koptogaster) vicinus* (Sichel, 1868)).

Hylaeus (Euprosopoides) rotundiceps (Smith, 1879)

Prosopis rotundiceps Smith, F. (1879). *Descriptions of New Species of Hymenoptera in the Collection of the British Museum.* London : British Museum xxi 240 pp. [19].
Type data: holotype, BMNH Hym.17.a.90 ♀.
Type locality: Melbourne, VIC.

Prosopis aposuara Cockerell, T.D.A. (1910). Descriptions and records of bees. XXXI. *Ann. Mag. Nat. Hist.* (8)**6**: 160–168 [164].
Type data: holotype, BMNH Hym.17.a.89 ♂.
Type locality: Mackay, QLD.

Taxonomic decision for synonymy: Houston, T.F. (1981). A revision of the Australian hylaeine bees (Hymenoptera : Colletidae). II. *Aust. J. Zool. Suppl. Ser.* **80**: 1–128 [44].

Distribution: NE coastal, SE coastal, Murray-Darling basin, QLD, NSW, ACT, VIC, TAS.
Ecology: adult—volant; melliferous, solitary, flower visiting record: *Angophora* Cav. [Myrtaceae], *Banksia* L.f. [Proteaceae], *Callistemon* R.Br. [Myrtaceae], *Eucalyptus* L'Hérit. [Myrtaceae], *Eugenia* L. [Myrtaceae], *Jacksonia* Smith [Fabaceae], *Leptospermum* Forster & G.Forster [Myrtaceae], *Pultenaea* Sm. [Fabaceae], *Tristania* R.Br. [Myrtaceae], *Xanthorrhoea* Sm. [Xanthorrhoeaceae].
Reference: Meade-Waldo, G. (1923). Hymenoptera. Fam. Apidae. Subfam. Prosopidinae. *Genera Insectorum* **181**: 1–45 (as *Hylaeus (Koptogaster) rotundiceps* (Smith, 1879) and *Hylaeus (Koptogaster) aposuara* (Cockerell, 1910)).

Hylaeus (Euprosopoides) ruficeps (Smith, 1853)

Taxonomic decision for subspecific arrangement: Houston, T.F. (1981). A revision of the Australian hylaeine bees (Hymenoptera : Colletidae). II. *Aust. J. Zool. Suppl. Ser.* **80**: 1–128 [46, 49].

Hylaeus (Euprosopoides) ruficeps ruficeps (Smith, 1853)

Prosopis ruficeps Smith, F. (1853). *Catalogue of Hymenopterous Insects in the Collection of the British Museum.* Part I. Andrenidae and Apidae. London : British Museum 197 pp. [29].
Type data: holotype, BMNH Hym.17.a.60 ♀.
Type locality: Adelaide, SA.

Prosopis fulvicornis Smith, F. (1853). *Catalogue of Hymenopterous Insects in the Collection of the British Museum.* Part I. Andrenidae and Apidae. London : British Museum 197 pp. [27].
Type data: holotype, BMNH ♂* (described as ♀).
Type locality: Adelaide, SA.

Prosopis purpurata Smith, F. (1879). *Descriptions of New Species of Hymenoptera in the Collection of the British Museum.* London : British Museum xxi 240 pp. [17].
Type data: holotype, BMNH Hym.17.a.53 ♂.
Type locality: Adelaide, SA.

Prosopis cassiae Cockerell, T.D.A. (1910). Descriptions and records of bees. XXX. *Ann. Mag. Nat. Hist. (8)***6**: 17–31 [29].
Type data: syntypes, BMNH ♀ (number of specimens unknown, a specimen is labelled 'type' and has registration number Hym.17.a.44).
Type locality: Mackay, QLD.

Distribution: NE coastal, Murray-Darling basin, N Gulf, S Gulfs, NW coastal, N coastal, QLD, NSW, VIC, SA, WA, NT.
Ecology: adult—volant; melliferous, solitary, flower visiting record: *Angophora* Cav. [Myrtaceae], *Atalaya* Blume [Sapindaceae], *Brachychiton* Schott & Endl. [Sterculiaceae], *?Callistemon* R.Br. [Myrtaceae], *Cassia* L. *s.lat.* [Caesalpiniaceae], *Eucalyptus* L'Hérit. [Myrtaceae], *Eugenia* L. [Myrtaceae], *Grevillea* R.Br. ex J. Knight [Proteaceae], *Melaleuca* L. [Myrtaceae], *Schinus* L. [Anacardiaceae], *Tristania* R.Br. [Myrtaceae], *Xanthorrhoea* Sm. [Xanthorrhoeaceae].
References: Meade-Waldo, G. (1923). Hymenoptera. Fam. Apidae. Subfam. Prosopidinae. *Genera Insectorum* **181**: 1–45 (as *Hylaeus (Koptogaster) ruficeps* (Smith, 1853), *Hylaeus (Koptogaster) fulvicornis* (Smith, 1853), *Hylaeus (Koptogaster) pupurata* (Smith, 1879) and *Hylaeus (Koptogaster) cassiae* (Cockerell, 1910)); Michener, C.D. (1965). A classification of the bees of the Australian and South Pacific regions. *Bull. Am. Mus. Nat. Hist.* **130**: 1 362 (flower record).

Hylaeus (Euprosopoides) ruficeps kalamundae (Cockerell, 1915)

Prosopis kalamundae Cockerell, T.D.A. (1915). Descriptions and records of bees. LXVI. *Ann. Mag. Nat. Hist. (8)***15**: 341–350 [346].
Type data: holotype, BMNH Hym.17.a.84 ♀.
Type locality: Kalamunda, WA.

Prosopis kalamundae jugata Cockerell, T.D.A. (1915). Descriptions and records of bees. LXVI. *Ann. Mag. Nat. Hist. (8)***15**: 341–350 [347].
Type data: holotype, BMNH Hym.17.a.85 ♀.
Type locality: Kalamunda, WA.

Distribution: SW coastal, WA.
Ecology: adult—volant; melliferous, solitary.
Reference: Meade-Waldo, G. (1923). Hymenoptera. Fam. Apidae. Subfam. Prosopidinae. *Genera Insectorum* **181**: 1–45 (as *Hylaeus (Koptogaster) kalamundae* (Cockerell, 1915)).

Hylaeus (Gnathoprosopis) Perkins, 1912

Gnathoprosopis Perkins, R.C.L. (1912). Notes, with descriptions of new species, on aculeate Hymenoptera of the Australian Region. *Ann. Mag. Nat. Hist. (8)***9**: 96–121 [104]. Type species: *Prosopis xanthopoda* Cockerell, 1910 (=*Prosopis euxantha* Cockerell, 1910) by original designation.

Species now known not to occur in Australia: *Prosopis volatilis* Smith, 1879, treated as an Australian species and placed in *Hylaeus (Gnathoprosopis)* by Michener, C.D. (1965). A classification of the bees of the Australian and South Pacific regions. *Bull. Am. Mus. Nat. Hist.* **130**: 1–362 [129], comes from the Sandwich Ils (Hawaii) and does not belong in this subgenus, see Houston, T.F. (1981). A revision of the Australian hylaeine bees (Hymenoptera : Colletidae). II. *Aust. J. Zool. Suppl. Ser.* **80**: 1–128 [50].

Hylaeus (Gnathoprosopis) albonitens (Cockerell, 1905)

Prosopis albonitens Cockerell, T.D.A. (1905). Descriptions and records of bees. IV. *Ann. Mag. Nat. Hist. (7)***16**: 392–403 [399].
Type data: holotype, BMNH Hym.17.a.73 ♂.
Type locality: Mackay, QLD.

Prosopis albipes Friese, H. (1924). Ueber die Bienen Australiens. *Konowia* **3**: 216–249 [224] [junior primary homonym of *Prosopis albipes* Panzer, 1809].
Type data: lectotype, AMNH ♂*.
Subsequent designation: Houston, T.F. (1981). A revision of the Australian hylaeine bees (Hymenoptera : Colletidae). II. *Aust. J. Zool. Suppl. Ser.* **80**: 1–128 [52]; Cardale, J.C., this work, interprets Houston's incorrect inference of holotype as a lectotype designation (Art. 74, ICZN 1985).
Type locality: Mackay, QLD.

Taxonomic decision for synonymy: Houston, T.F. (1981). A revision of the Australian hylaeine bees (Hymenoptera : Colletidae). II. *Aust. J. Zool. Suppl. Ser.* **80**: 1–128 [52].

Distribution: NE coastal, N Gulf, N coastal, NW coastal, QLD, NT, WA.
Ecology: adult—volant; melliferous, solitary, flower visiting record: *Callistemon* R.Br. [Myrtaceae], *Eucalyptus* L'Hérit. [Myrtaceae], *Eugenia* L. [Myrtaceae], *Leptospermum* Forster & G.Forster [Myrtaceae], *Melaleuca* L. [Myrtaceae], *Owenia* F. Muell. [Meliaceae], *Tristania* R.Br. [Myrtaceae],

Xanthorrhoea Sm. [Xanthorrhoeaceae]·
References: Meade-Waldo, G. (1923). Hymenoptera.
Fam. Apidae. Subfam. Prosopidinae. *Genera Insectorum* **181**: 1–45 (as *Hylaeus (Koptogaster) albonitens* (Cockerell, 1905)); Rayment, T. (1939).
Bees from the high lands of New South Wales and
Victoria. *Aust. Zool.* **9**: 263–294 (doubtful record;
White Swamp, NSW, as *Pachyprosopis albonitens*
Cockerell, 1905); Evans, H.E. & Matthews, R.W.
(1973). Systematics and nesting behavior of Australian *Bembix* sand wasps (Hymenoptera, Sphecidae).
Mem. Am. Entomol. Inst. **20**: 1–387 (as prey).

Hylaeus (Gnathoprosopis) amiculiformis (Cockerell, 1909)

Prosopis amiculiformis Cockerell, T.D.A. (1909).
Descriptions and records of bees. XXIII. *Ann. Mag. Nat. Hist. (8)***4**: 393–404 [394].
Type data: holotype, BMNH Hym.17.a.2828 ♀.
Type locality: near Mackay, QLD.

Gnathoprosopis hackeri Cockerell, T.D.A. (1912).
Descriptions and records of bees. XLVII. *Ann. Mag. Nat. Hist. (8)***10**: 484–494 [489].
Type data: holotype, QM Hy/4145 ♂.
Type locality: Sunnybank, Brisbane, QLD.

Gnathoprosopis simpliciventris Cockerell, T.D.A. (1922).
Australian bees in the Queensland Museum. *Mem. Qd Mus.*
7: 257–279 [265].
Type data: holotype, QM Hy/2438 ♂.
Type locality: Brisbane, QLD.

Taxonomic decision for synonymy: Houston, T.F. (1981).
A revision of the Australian hylaeine bees (Hymenoptera :
Colletidae). II. *Aust. J. Zool. Suppl. Ser.* **80**: 1–128 [55].

Distribution: NE coastal, QLD.
Ecology: adult—volant; melliferous, solitary, flower
visiting record: *Callistemon* R.Br. [Myrtaceae], *Eucalyptus* L'Hérit. [Myrtaceae], *Eugenia* L.
[Myrtaceae], *Leptospermum* Forster & G.Forster
[Myrtaceae], *Melaleuca* L. [Myrtaceae], *Tristania*
R.Br. [Myrtaceae], *Xanthorrhoea* Sm.
[Xanthorrhoeaceae].
References: Cockerell, T.D.A. (1910). Descriptions
and records of bees. XXX. *Ann. Mag. Nat. Hist. (8)***6**:
17–31 (description of male); Cockerell, T.D.A.
(1922). Australian bees in the Queensland Museum.
Mem. Qd Mus. **7**: 257–279 (as *Gnathoprosopis
amiculiformis* (Cockerell, 1909)); Meade-Waldo, G.
(1923). Hymenoptera. Fam. Apidae. Subfam. Prosopidinae. *Genera Insectorum* **181**: 1–45 (as *Hylaeus
(Koptogaster) amiculiformis* (Cockerell, 1909);
Michener, C.D. (1965). A classification of the bees
of the Australian and South Pacific regions. *Bull. Am.
Mus. Nat. Hist.* **130**: 1–362 (flower record, as
Hylaeus (Gnathoprosopis) hackeri (Cockerell,
1912)).

Hylaeus (Gnathoprosopis) amiculinus (Cockerell, 1922)

Gnathoprosopis amiculina Cockerell, T.D.A. (1922).
Australian bees in the Queensland Museum. *Mem. Qd Mus.*
7: 257–279 [265] [in error, Cockerell (1916) described what
he thought was a male of *Prosopis amicula* Smith, 1879; in
1922 he realised the male of the species he described
as *Gnathoprosopis amiculinus* with the female as holotype].
Type data: holotype, QM Hy/2437 ♀.
Type locality: Brisbane, QLD.

Distribution: NE coastal, SE coastal, Murray-Darling
basin, S Gulfs, QLD, NSW, ACT, VIC, SA.
Ecology: adult—volant; melliferous, solitary, flower
visiting record: *Angophora* Cav. [Myrtaceae], *Bursaria* Cav. [Pittosporaceae], *Callistemon* R.Br.
[Myrtaceae], *Eucalyptus* L'Hérit. [Myrtaceae], *Jacksonia* Smith [Fabaceae], *Leptospermum* Forster &
G.Forster [Myrtaceae], *Melaleuca* L. [Myrtaceae],
Xanthorrhoea Sm. [Xanthorrhoeaceae].
References: Cockerell, T.D.A. (1916). A collection
of bees from Queensland. *Mem. Qd Mus.* **5**: 197–204
(description of male, as *Gnathoprosopis amicula*
(Smith, 1879)); Michener, C.D. (1965). A classification of the bees of the Australian and South Pacific
regions. *Bull. Am. Mus. Nat. Hist.* **130**: 1–362 (flower
record); Houston, T.F. (1981). A revision of the Australian hylaeine bees (Hymenoptera : Colletidae). II.
Aust. J. Zool. Suppl. Ser. **80**: 1–128 (redescription);
Michener, C.D. (1992). Sexual dimorphism in the
glossa of Colletidae (Hymenoptera, Apoidea). *J.
Kansas Entomol. Soc.* **65**: 1–9 (glossa).

Hylaeus (Gnathoprosopis) amiculus (Smith, 1879)

Prosopis amicula Smith, F. (1879). *Descriptions of New
Species of Hymenoptera in the Collection of the British
Museum.* London : British Museum xxi 240 pp. [19].
Type data: holotype, BMNH Hym.17.a.93 ♀.
Type locality: Geraldton, (as Champion Bay) WA.

Prosopis asinella Cockerell, T.D.A. (1913). Some
Australian bees. *Proc. Acad. Nat. Sci. Philad.* **65**: 28–44
[37].
Type data: holotype, USNM ♂* (not found by J.C.C. in
1988).
Type locality: Purnong, SA.

Gnathoprosopis rowlandi Cockerell, T.D.A. (1914).
Descriptions and records of bees. LXII. *Ann. Mag. Nat.
Hist. (8)***14**: 49–57 [55].
Type data: holotype, BMNH Hym.17.a.117 ♂.
Type locality: Yallingup, WA.

Gnathoprosopis xanthocollaris Rayment, T. (1935). *A
Cluster of Bees.* Sixty essays on the life-histories of
Australian bees, with specific descriptions of over 100 new
species, and an introduction by Professor E.F. Phillips,
D.Ph., Cornell University, U.S.A. Sydney : Endeavour
Press 752 pp. [645].
Type data: holotype, ANIC ♂.
Type locality: Kiata, VIC.

Taxonomic decision for synonymy: Houston, T.F. (1981). A revision of the Australian hylaeine bees (Hymenoptera : Colletidae). II. *Aust. J. Zool. Suppl. Ser.* **80**: 1–128 [59].

Distribution: Murray-Darling basin, S Gulfs, W plateau, SW coastal, NW coastal, NSW, VIC, SA, WA.
Ecology: larva—sedentary : adult—volant; melliferous, solitary, flower visiting record: *Calytrix* Lab. [Myrtaceae], *Eremophila* R.Br. [Myoporaceae], *Eucalyptus* L'Hérit. [Myrtaceae], *Melaleuca* L. [Myrtaceae].
References: Meade-Waldo, G. (1923). Hymenoptera. Fam. Apidae. Subfam. Prosopidinae. *Genera Insectorum* **181**: 1–45 (as *Hylaeus (Koptogaster) amiculus* (Smith, 1879)); Alcock, J. & Houston, T.F. (1987). Resource defense and alternative mating tactics in the banksia bee, *Hylaeus alcyoneus* (Erichson). *Ethology* **76**: 177–188 (biology).

Hylaeus (Gnathoprosopis) chromaticus (Cockerell, 1912)

Prosopis albonitens chromatica Cockerell, T.D.A. (1912). Descriptions and records of bees. XLI. *Ann. Mag. Nat. Hist. (8)***9**: 139–149 [149].
Type data: holotype, BMNH Hym.17.a.179 ♀.
Type locality: Mackay, QLD.

Distribution: NE coastal, SE coastal, Murray-Darling basin, QLD, NSW.
Ecology: adult—volant; melliferous, solitary, flower visiting record: mistletoe, *Alphitonia* Reisseck ex Endl. [Rhamnaceae], *Angophora* Cav. [Myrtaceae], *Boronia* Sm. [Rutaceae], *Bursaria* Cav. [Pittosporaceae], *Callistemon* R.Br. [Myrtaceae], *Eucalyptus* L'Hérit. [Myrtaceae], *Jacksonia* Smith [Fabaceae], *Leptospermum* Forster & G.Forster [Myrtaceae], *Melaleuca* L. [Myrtaceae], *Tristania* R.Br. [Myrtaceae].
References: Cockerell, T.D.A. (1912). Descriptions and records of bees. XLIII. *Ann. Mag. Nat. Hist. (8)***9**: 377–387 (description of male); Meade-Waldo, G. (1923). Hymenoptera. Fam. Apidae. Subfam. Prosopidinae. *Genera Insectorum* **181**: 1–45 (as *Hylaeus (Koptogaster) chromaticus* (Cockerell, 1912)); Michener, C.D. (1965). A classification of the bees of the Australian and South Pacific regions. *Bull. Am. Mus. Nat. Hist.* **130**: 1–362 (flower record); Houston, T.F. (1981). A revision of the Australian hylaeine bees (Hymenoptera : Colletidae). II. *Aust. J. Zool. Suppl. Ser.* **80**: 1–128 (redescription).

Hylaeus (Gnathoprosopis) euxanthus (Cockerell, 1910)

Prosopis xanthopoda Cockerell, T.D.A. (1910). Descriptions and records of bees. XXX. *Ann. Mag. Nat. Hist. (8)***6**: 17–31 [28] [junior primary homonym of *Prosopis xanthopoda* Vachal, 1895].
Type data: syntypes, BMNH ♂♀ (a female specimen is labelled 'type' and has registration number Hym.17.a.114).
Type locality: VIC.

Prosopis euxantha Cockerell, T.D.A. (1910). Descriptions and records of bees. XXXI. *Ann. Mag. Nat. Hist. (8)***6**: 160–168 [166] [*nom. nov.* for *Prosopis xanthopoda* Cockerell, 1910].

Distribution: NE coastal, SE coastal, Murray-Darling basin, S Gulfs, Lake Eyre basin, W plateau, SW coastal, NW coastal, N coastal, QLD, NSW, ACT, VIC, SA, WA, NT.
Ecology: larva—sedentary : adult—volant; melliferous, solitary, flower visiting record: *Althaea* L. [Malvaceae], *Angophora* Cav. [Myrtaceae], *Atalaya* Blume [Sapindaceae], *Callistemon* R.Br. [Myrtaceae], *Eriostemon* Sm. [Rutaceae], *Eucalyptus* L'Hérit. [Myrtaceae], *Eugenia* L. [Myrtaceae], *Grevillea* R.Br. ex J. Knight [Proteaceae], *Leptospermum* Forster & G.Forster [Myrtaceae], *Melaleuca* L. [Myrtaceae], *Schinus* L. [Anacardiaceae].
References: Meade-Waldo, G. (1923). Hymenoptera. Fam. Apidae. Subfam. Prosopidinae. *Genera Insectorum* **181**: 1–45 (illustration, as *Gnathoprosopis xanthopoda* (Cockerell, 1910) and *Gnathoprosopis euxantha* (Cockerell, 1910)); Rayment, T. (1935). *A Cluster of Bees*. Sixty essays on the life-histories of Australian bees, with specific descriptions of over 100 new species, and an introduction by Professor E.F. Phillips, D.Ph., Cornell University, U.S.A. Sydney : Endeavour Press 752 pp. (illustration); Michener, C.D. (1965). A classification of the bees of the Australian and South Pacific regions. *Bull. Am. Mus. Nat. Hist.* **130**: 1–362 (flower record); Houston, T.F. (1981). A revision of the Australian hylaeine bees (Hymenoptera : Colletidae). II. *Aust. J. Zool. Suppl. Ser.* **80**: 1–128 (redescription); Alcock, J. & Houston, T.F. (1987). Resource defense and alternative mating tactics in the banksia bee, *Hylaeus alcyoneus* (Erichson). *Ethology* **76**: 177–188 (biology).

Hylaeus (Gnathoprosopis) theodorei (Perkins, 1912)

Gnathoprosopis theodorei Perkins, R.C.L. (1912). Notes, with descriptions of new species, on aculeate Hymenoptera of the Australian Region. *Ann. Mag. Nat. Hist. (8)***9**: 96–121 [105].
Type data: holotype, BMNH ♂*.
Type locality: Townsville, QLD.

Distribution: NE coastal, QLD.
Ecology: adult—volant; melliferous, solitary, flower visiting record: *Eucalyptus* L'Hérit. [Myrtaceae], *Melaleuca* L. [Myrtaceae].
References: Rayment, T. (1935). *A Cluster of Bees*. Sixty essays on the life-histories of Australian bees, with specific descriptions of over 100 new species, and an introduction by Professor E.F. Phillips, D.Ph., Cornell University, U.S.A. Sydney : Endeavour Press 752 pp. (as *Gnathoprosopis theodori*, incorrect subsequent spelling); Michener, C.D. (1965). A classification of the bees of the Australian and South Pacific regions. *Bull. Am. Mus. Nat. Hist.* **130**: 1–362 (flower

record); Houston, T.F. (1981). A revision of the Australian hylaeine bees (Hymenoptera : Colletidae). II. *Aust. J. Zool. Suppl. Ser.* **80**: 1–128 (redescription).

Hylaeus (Gnathoprosopoides) Michener, 1965

Gnathoprosopoides Michener, C.D. (1965). A classification of the bees of the Australian and South Pacific regions. *Bull. Am. Mus. Nat. Hist.* **130**: 1–362 [127] [proposed with subgeneric rank in *Hylaeus* Fabricius, 1793]. Type species: *Prosopis eburniella* Cockerell, 1912 (=*Prosopis philoleuca* Cockerell, 1910) by original designation.

Hylaeus (Gnathoprosopoides) bituberculatus (Smith, 1879)

Prosopis bituberculata Smith, F. (1879). *Descriptions of New Species of Hymenoptera in the Collection of the British Museum*. London : British Museum xxi 240 pp. [18].
Type data: holotype, BMNH Hym.17.a.115 ♂.
Type locality: Bakewell, Melbourne, VIC.
Hylaeus bituberculatus tasmanicus Cockerell, T.D.A. (1926). Descriptions and records of bees. CXI. *Ann. Mag. Nat. Hist.* (9)**17**: 657–665 [664].
Type data: holotype, BMNH Hym.17.a.116 ♂.
Type locality: Launceston, TAS.
Gnathoprosopis aureopicta Cockerell, T.D.A. (1929). Bees in the Queensland Museum. *Mem. Qd Mus.* **9**: 298–323 [315].
Type data: holotype, QM Hy/3725 ♀.
Type locality: Blackheath, presumably NSW, see Houston, T.F. (1981). A revision of the Australian hylaeine bees (Hymenoptera : Colletidae). II. *Aust. J. Zool. Suppl. Ser.* **80**: 1–128 [68].
Gnathoprosopis nigritarsus Rayment, T. (1929). Bees from East Gippsland. *Vict. Nat.* **46**: 124–129 [124].
Type data: holotype, NMV T3849 ♀.
Type locality: Cann River, Gippsland, VIC.
Gnathoprosopis nigritarsus maculata Rayment, T. (1929). Bees from East Gippsland. *Vict. Nat.* **46**: 124–129 [125].
Type data: holotype, ANIC ♀.
Type locality: Sandringham, VIC.
Gnathoprosopis borchii Rayment, T. (1935). *A Cluster of Bees*. Sixty essays on the life-histories of Australian bees, with specific descriptions of over 100 new species, and an introduction by Professor E.F. Phillips, D.Ph., Cornell University, U.S.A. Sydney : Endeavour Press 752 pp. [644].
Type data: holotype, ANIC ♂.
Type locality: Kiata, VIC.
Gnathoprosopis millariella Rayment, T. (1953). *Bees of the Portland District*. Victoria : Portland Field Naturalist's Club 39 pp. [7].
Type data: holotype, ANIC ♀.
Type locality: Gorae West, VIC.

Taxonomic decision for synonymy: Houston, T.F. (1981). A revision of the Australian hylaeine bees (Hymenoptera : Colletidae). II. *Aust. J. Zool. Suppl. Ser.* **80**: 1–128 [67].

Distribution: NE coastal, SE coastal, Murray-Darling basin, S Gulfs, QLD, NSW, ACT, VIC, SA, TAS.

Ecology: adult—volant; melliferous, solitary, flower visiting record: blackberry, *Angophora* Cav. [Myrtaceae], *Boronia* Sm. [Rutaceae], *Eucalyptus* L'Hérit. [Myrtaceae], *Hypochaeris* L. [Asteraceae], *Leptospermum* Forster & G.Forster [Myrtaceae].
References: Hacker, H. (1921). Catalogue of Australian bees. *Mem. Qd Mus.* **7**: 99–163 (as *Gnathoprosopis bituberculata* (Smith, 1879)); Rayment, T. (1935). *A Cluster of Bees*. Sixty essays on the life-histories of Australian bees, with specific descriptions of over 100 new species, and an introduction by Professor E.F. Phillips, D.Ph., Cornell University, U.S.A. Sydney : Endeavour Press 752 pp. (flower record, as *Gnathoprosopis nigritarsis* Rayment, 1929); Michener, C.D. (1965). A classification of the bees of the Australian and South Pacific regions. *Bull. Am. Mus. Nat. Hist.* **130**: 1–362 [236] (flower record, as *Hylaeus aureopictus* (Cockerell 1929)).

Hylaeus (Gnathoprosopoides) philoleucus (Cockerell, 1910)

Prosopis philoleuca Cockerell, T.D.A. (1910). Descriptions and records of bees. XXXI. *Ann. Mag. Nat. Hist.* (8)**6**: 160–168 [163].
Type data: holotype, BMNH Hym.17.a.79 ♀.
Type locality: Mackay, QLD.
Prosopis eburniella Cockerell, T.D.A. (1912). Descriptions and records of bees. XLI. *Ann. Mag. Nat. Hist.* (8)**9**: 139–149 [148].
Type data: holotype, USNM ♂*.
Type locality: Sydney, NSW.

Taxonomic decision for synonymy: Houston, T.F. (1981). A revision of the Australian hylaeine bees (Hymenoptera : Colletidae). II. *Aust. J. Zool. Suppl. Ser.* **80**: 1–128 [71].

Distribution: NE coastal, SE coastal, Murray-Darling basin, QLD, NSW, VIC.

Ecology: adult—volant; melliferous, solitary, flower visiting record: *Angophora* Cav. [Myrtaceae], *Eucalyptus* L'Hérit. [Myrtaceae], *Leptospermum* Forster & G.Forster [Myrtaceae], *Tristania* R.Br. [Myrtaceae].
References: Meade-Waldo, G. (1923). Hymenoptera. Fam. Apidae. Subfam. Prosopidinae. *Genera Insectorum* **181**: 1–45 (as *Hylaeus (Koptogaster) philoleucus* (Cockerell, 1910)) and *Hylaeus (Koptogaster) eburniellus* (Cockerell)); Michener, C.D. (1965). A classification of the bees of the Australian and South Pacific regions. *Bull. Am. Mus. Nat. Hist.* **130**: 1–362 [237] (flower record, as *Hylaeus (Gnathoprosopoides) eburniellus* (Cockerell, 1912)).

Hylaeus (Hylaeorhiza) Michener, 1965

Hylaeorhiza Michener, C.D. (1965). A classification of the bees of the Australian and South Pacific regions. *Bull. Am. Mus. Nat. Hist.* **130**: 1–362 [141]. Type species: *Prosopis nubilosa* Smith, 1853 by original designation.

Extralimital distribution: New Guinea, see Houston, T.F. (1981). A revision of the Australian hylaeine bees (Hymenoptera : Colletidae). II. *Aust. J. Zool. Suppl. Ser.* **80**: 1–128 [76].

Hylaeus (Hylaeorhiza) nubilosus (Smith, 1853)

Prosopis nubilosa Smith, F. (1853). *Catalogue of Hymenopterous Insects in the Collection of the British Museum.* Part I. Andrenidae and Apidae. London : British Museum 197 pp. [31].
Type data: holotype, BMNH Hym.17.a.201 ♀.
Type locality: Melbourne (as Port Philip), VIC.

Prosopis aureomaculata Cockerell, T.D.A. (1909). Descriptions and records of bees. XXIII. *Ann. Mag. Nat. Hist. (8)***4**: 393–404 [395].
Type data: holotype, BMNH ♂*.
Type locality: Kuranda, QLD.

Prosopis nubilosa subnubilosa Cockerell, T.D.A. (1910). Descriptions and records of bees. XXX. *Ann. Mag. Nat. Hist. (8)***6**: 17–31 [25].
Type data: holotype, BMNH Hym.17.a.202 ♀.
Type locality: Mackay, QLD.

Hylaeus spryi Cockerell, T.D.A. (1926). Descriptions and records of bees. CXI. *Ann. Mag. Nat. Hist. (9)***17**: 657–665 [663].
Type data: holotype, NMV T3848 ♂.
Type locality: Belgrave, VIC.

Hylaeus simillimus tasmani Cockerell, T.D.A. (1929). Bees in the Queensland Museum. *Mem. Qd Mus.* **9**: 298–323 [313].
Type data: holotype, QM Hy/4032 ♀.
Type locality: TAS.

Taxonomic decision for synonymy: Houston, T.F. (1981). A revision of the Australian hylaeine bees (Hymenoptera : Colletidae). II. *Aust. J. Zool. Suppl. Ser.* **80**: 1–128 [73].

Distribution: NE coastal, SE coastal, Murray-Darling basin, S Gulfs, QLD, NSW, ACT, VIC, SA, TAS; also recorded from Lae, New Guinea.
Ecology: larva—sedentary : adult—volant; melliferous, solitary, nest in mudwasp nest, flower visiting record: christmas bush, red bottle brush, privet, *Acacia* Miller [Mimosaceae], *Angophora* Cav. [Myrtaceae], *Boronia* Sm. [Rutaceae], *Bursaria* Cav. [Pittosporaceae], *Callistemon* R.Br. [Myrtaceae], *Eucalyptus* L'Hérit. [Myrtaceae], *Eugenia* L. [Myrtaceae], *Jacksonia* Smith [Fabaceae], *Leptospermum* Forster & G.Forster [Myrtaceae], *Melaleuca* L. [Myrtaceae], *Teucrium* L. [Lamiaceae], *Tristania* R.Br. [Myrtaceae], *Xanthorrhoea* Sm. [Xanthorrhoeaceae].
References: Meade-Waldo, G. (1923). Hymenoptera. Fam. Apidae. Subfam. Prosopidinae. *Genera Insectorum* **181**: 1–45 (as *Palaeorhiza nubilosa* (Smith, 1853)); Raff, J.W. (1929). Note on *Hylaeus nubilosus. Vict. Nat.* **45**: 297 (nest); Rayment, T. (1935). *A Cluster of Bees.* Sixty essays on the life-histories of Australian bees, with specific descriptions of over 100 new species, and an introduction by Professor E.F. Phillips, D.Ph., Cornell University,

U.S.A. Sydney : Endeavour Press 752 pp. (biology); Cane, J.H. (1979). The hind tibiotarsal and tibial spur articulations in bees (Hymenoptera : Apoidea). *J. Kansas Entomol. Soc.* **52**: 123–137 (hind spur); Michener, C.D. (1992). Sexual dimorphism in the glossa of Colletidae (Hymenoptera, Apoidea). *J. Kansas Entomol. Soc.* **65**: 1–9 (glossa).

Hylaeus (Hylaeteron) Michener, 1965

Hylaeteron Michener, C.D. (1965). A classification of the bees of the Australian and South Pacific regions. *Bull. Am. Mus. Nat. Hist.* **130**: 1–362 [126] [proposed with subgeneric rank in *Hylaeus* Fabricius, 1793]. Type species: *Prosopis pulchricrus* Cockerell, 1915 (=*Euryglossa semirufa* Cockerell, 1914) by original designation.

Hylaeus (Hylaeteron) douglasi Michener, 1965

Hylaeus (Prosopisteron) douglasi Michener, C.D. (1965). A classification of the bees of the Australian and South Pacific regions. *Bull. Am. Mus. Nat. Hist.* **130**: 1–362 [290].
Type data: holotype, WAM 50–4447 ♂.
Type locality: Morowa, WA.

Distribution: SW coastal, NW coastal, WA.
Ecology: adult—volant; melliferous, solitary, flower visiting record: *Grevillea* R.Br. ex J. Knight [Proteaceae].
Reference: Houston, T.F. (1981). A revision of the Australian hylaeine bees (Hymenoptera : Colletidae). II. *Aust. J. Zool. Suppl. Ser.* **80**: 1–128 (redescription).

Hylaeus (Hylaeteron) hemirhodus Michener, 1965

Hylaeus (Hylaeteron) hemirhodus Michener, C.D. (1965). A classification of the bees of the Australian and South Pacific regions. *Bull. Am. Mus. Nat. Hist.* **130**: 1–362 [294].
Type data: holotype, WAM 65–731 ♀.
Type locality: Wotjulum, WA.

Distribution: N coastal, WA, NT; only published localities Wotjulum, Birraduk Creek and near Oenpelli.
Ecology: adult—volant; melliferous, solitary, flower visiting record: *Grevillea* R.Br. ex J. Knight [Proteaceae].
Reference: Houston, T.F. (1981). A revision of the Australian hylaeine bees (Hymenoptera : Colletidae). II. *Aust. J. Zool. Suppl. Ser.* **80**: 1–128 (redescription).

Hylaeus (Hylaeteron) murrumbidgeanus Houston, 1981

Hylaeus (Hylaeteron) murrumbidgeanus Houston, T.F. (1981). A revision of the Australian hylaeine bees (Hymenoptera : Colletidae). II. *Aust. J. Zool. Suppl. Ser.* **80**: 1–128 [82].
Type data: holotype, ANIC ♂.
Type locality: Pine Is., Murrumbidgee River, ACT (as F.C.T.).

Distribution: Murray-Darling basin, ACT; known only from type locality.

Ecology: adult—volant; melliferous, solitary, flower visiting record: *Grevillea* R.Br. ex J. Knight [Proteaceae].

Hylaeus (Hylaeteron) riekianus Houston, 1981

Hylaeus (Hylaeteron) riekianus Houston, T.F. (1981). A revision of the Australian hylaeine bees (Hymenoptera : Colletidae). II. *Aust. J. Zool. Suppl. Ser.* **80**: 1–128 [84].
Type data: holotype, ANIC ♂.
Type locality: 30 miles W Coolgardie, WA.

Distribution: SW coastal, W plateau, WA; only published localities near Coolgardie, near McDermid Rock and near Yellowdine.
Ecology: adult—volant; melliferous, solitary, flower visiting record: *Grevillea* R.Br. ex J. Knight [Proteaceae].

Hylaeus (Hylaeteron) semirufus (Cockerell, 1914)

Euryglossa semirufa Cockerell, T.D.A. (1914). Descriptions and records of bees. LXIV. *Ann. Mag. Nat. Hist.* (8)**14**: 464–472 [469].
Type data: holotype, BMNH Hym.17.a.237 ♀.
Type locality: Yarrawin (Brewarrina), NSW.
Prosopis pulchricrus Cockerell, T.D.A. (1915). Descriptions and records of bees. LXV. *Ann. Mag. Nat. Hist.* (8)**15**: 261–269 [266].
Type data: holotype, BMNH Hym.17.a.48 ♂.
Type locality: Yarrawin, NSW.

Taxonomic decision for synonymy: Houston, T.F. (1981). A revision of the Australian hylaeine bees (Hymenoptera : Colletidae). II. *Aust. J. Zool. Suppl. Ser.* **80**: 1–128 [85].

Distribution: Murray-Darling basin, Lake Eyre basin, W plateau, QLD, NSW, SA, NT.
Ecology: adult—volant; melliferous, solitary, flower visiting record: *Cassia* L. *s.lat.* [Caesalpiniaceae], *Grevillea* R.Br. ex J. Knight [Proteaceae], *Hakea* Schrader [Proteaceae].

Hylaeus (Laccohylaeus) Houston, 1981

Laccohylaeus Houston, T.F. (1981). A revision of the Australian hylaeine bees (Hymenoptera : Colletidae). II. *Aust. J. Zool. Suppl. Ser.* **80**: 1–128 [88] [proposed with subgeneric rank in *Hylaeus* Fabricius, 1793]. Type species: *Prosopis cyanophila* Cockerell, 1910 by original designation.

Hylaeus (Laccohylaeus) cyanophilus (Cockerell, 1910)

Prosopis cyanophila Cockerell, T.D.A. (1910). Descriptions and records of bees. XXX. *Ann. Mag. Nat. Hist.* (8)**6**: 17–31 [28].
Type data: holotype, BMNH Hym.17.a.77 ♂.
Type locality: Mackay, QLD.
Prosopis nigropersonata Cockerell, T.D.A. (1910). Descriptions and records of bees. XXX. *Ann. Mag. Nat. Hist.* (8)**6**: 17–31 [27].
Type data: lectotype, BMNH Hym.17.a.69 ♀.
Subsequent designation: Houston, T.F. (1981). A revision of the Australian hylaeine bees (Hymenoptera : Colletidae).

II. *Aust. J. Zool. Suppl. Ser.* **80**: 1–128 [89]; Cardale, J.C., this work, interprets Houston's incorrect inference of holotype as a lectotype designation (Art. 74, ICZN 1985).
Type locality: Mackay, QLD.

Taxonomic decision for synonymy: Houston, T.F. (1981). A revision of the Australian hylaeine bees (Hymenoptera : Colletidae). II. *Aust. J. Zool. Suppl. Ser.* **80**: 1–128 [89].

Distribution: NE coastal, QLD; only published localities Mackay, Redlynch and Goodna.
Ecology: adult—volant; melliferous, solitary.
Reference: Michener, C.D. (1965). A classification of the bees of the Australian and South Pacific regions. *Bull. Am. Mus. Nat. Hist.* **130**: 1–362 [123, 132] (as *Hylaeus (Prosopisteron) cyanophilus* (Cockerell, 1910), *Hylaeus (Euprosopoides) nigropersonatus* (Cockerell, 1910)).

Hylaeus (Macrohylaeus) Michener, 1965

Macrohylaeus Michener, C.D. (1965). A classification of the bees of the Australian and South Pacific regions. *Bull. Am. Mus. Nat. Hist.* **130**: 1–362 [133] [proposed with subgeneric rank in *Hylaeus* Fabricius, 1793]. Type species: *Prosopis vidua* Smith, 1853 (=*Prosopis alcyonea* Erichson, 1842) by original designation.

Hylaeus (Macrohylaeus) alcyoneus (Erichson, 1842)

Prosopis alcyonea Erichson, W.F. (1842). Beitrag zur Fauna von Vandiemensland mit besonderer Rücksicht auf die geographische Verbreitung der Insekten. *Arch. Naturg.* **8**: 83–287 [267].
Type data: holotype (probable), whereabouts unknown ♀*.
Type locality: TAS (as Van Diemens Land).
Prosopis vidua Smith, F. (1853). *Catalogue of Hymenopterous Insects in the Collection of the British Museum.* Part I. Andrenidae and Apidae. London : British Museum 197 pp. [29].
Type data: holotype, BMNH Hym.17.a.64 ♂.
Type locality: Australia (as New Holland).
Hylaeus alcyoneus robustus Cockerell, T.D.A. (1926). Descriptions and records of bees. CXI. *Ann. Mag. Nat. Hist.* (9)**17**: 657–665 [663].
Type data: holotype, BMNH ♂.
Type locality: [Royal] National Park, Australia, see Houston, T.F. (1981). A revision of the Australian hylaeine bees (Hymenoptera : Colletidae). II. *Aust. J. Zool. Suppl. Ser.* **80**: 1–128 [92].

Taxonomic decision for synonymy: Michener, C.D. (1965). A classification of the bees of the Australian and South Pacific regions. *Bull. Am. Mus. Nat. Hist.* **130**: 1–362 [133].

Distribution: NE coastal, SE coastal, Murray-Darling basin, S Gulfs, SW coastal, QLD, NSW, VIC, SA, WA, TAS.
Ecology: larva—sedentary : adult—volant; melliferous, solitary, nest in cavities in wood, including twig of dead *Acacia* Miller [Mimosaceae], flower visiting record: *Banksia* L.f. [Proteaceae] (incorrectly recorded from *Callistemon* R.Br. [Myrtaceae], *Lambertia* Sm. [Proteaceae], *Leptospermum* Forster & G.Forster [Myrtaceae]).

References: Meade-Waldo, G. (1923). Hymenoptera. Fam. Apidae. Subfam. Prosopidinae. *Genera Insectorum* **181**: 1–45 (as *Hylaeus (Koptogaster) alcyoneus* (Erichson, 1842)); Rayment, T. (1935). *A Cluster of Bees*. Sixty essays on the life-histories of Australian bees, with specific descriptions of over 100 new species, and an introduction by Professor E.F. Phillips, D.Ph., Cornell University, U.S.A. Sydney : Endeavour Press 752 pp. (illustration, as *Hylaeus alcyoneus robustus* Cockerell, 1926); Rayment, T. (1954). Incidence of acarid mites on the biology of bees. *Aust. Zool.* **12**: 26–38 (as host, nest and flower records, as *Palaeorhiza alcyonea* (Erichson, 1842); Houston, T.F. (1981). A revision of the Australian hylaeine bees (Hymenoptera : Colletidae). II. *Aust. J. Zool. Suppl. Ser.* **80**: 1–128 (redescription); McGinley, R.J. (1981). Systematics of the Colletidae based on mature larvae with phenetic analysis of apoid larvae (Insecta, Hymenoptera, Apoidea). *Univ. Calif. Publ. Entomol.* **91**: 1–309 (larva); Alcock, J. & Houston, T.F. (1987). Resource defense and alternative mating tactics in the banksia bee, *Hylaeus alcyoneus* (Erichson). *Ethology* **76**: 177–188 (biology); Michener, C.D. (1992). Sexual dimorphism in the glossa of Colletidae (Hymenoptera, Apoidea). *J. Kansas Entomol. Soc.* **65**: 1–9 (glossa).

Hylaeus (Meghylaeus) Cockerell, 1929

Meghylaeus Cockerell, T.D.A. (1929). Bees in the Queensland Museum. *Mem. Qd Mus.* **9**: 298–323 [314] [proposed with subgeneric rank in *Hylaeus* Fabricius, 1793]. Type species: *Palaeorhiza gigantea* Cockerell, 1926 by original designation.

Hylaeus (Meghylaeus) fijiensis (Cockerell, 1909)

Prosopis fijiensis Cockerell, T.D.A. (1909). Descriptions and records of bees. XXIII. *Ann. Mag. Nat. Hist. (8)***4**: 393–404 [393].
Type data: holotype, BMNH Hym.17.a.181 ♀.
Type locality: Australia (wrongly labelled as "Fiji Islands"; this species is known only from Australia), see Houston, T.F. (1981). A revision of the Australian hylaeine bees (Hymenoptera : Colletidae). II. *Aust. J. Zool. Suppl. Ser.* **80**: 1–128 [95].
Prosopis chalybaea Friese, H. (1924). Ueber die Bienen Australiens. *Konowia* **3**: 216–249 [222].
Type data: lectotype, AMNH ♀*.
Subsequent designation: Cockerell, T.D.A. (1926). Descriptions and records of bees. CXI. *Ann. Mag. Nat. Hist. (9)***17**: 657–665 [663]; Cardale, J.C., this work, interprets Cockerell's incorrect inference of holotype as a lectotype designation (Art.74, ICZN 1985).
Type locality: Australia (as "N. Seeld. Riedtm.", this label has led to the species being recorded as from New Zealand, but this species is known only from Australia), see Houston, T.F. (1981). A revision of the Australian hylaeine bees (Hymenoptera : Colletidae). II. *Aust. J. Zool. Suppl. Ser.* **80**: 1–128.

Palaeorhiza gigantea Cockerell, T.D.A. (1926). Descriptions and records of bees. CX. *Ann. Mag. Nat. Hist. (9)***17**: 510–519 [511].
Type data: holotype, NMV T3846 ♀.
Type locality: Raymond Is., VIC.

Taxonomic decision for synonymy: Michener, C.D. (1965). A classification of the bees of the Australian and South Pacific regions. *Bull. Am. Mus. Nat. Hist.* **130**: 1–362 [134].

Distribution: SE coastal, VIC, TAS; only published localities Raymond Is., Rye and Tasmania.
Ecology: adult—volant; melliferous, solitary.
References: Meade-Waldo, G. (1923). Hymenoptera. Fam. Apidae. Subfam. Prosopidinae. *Genera Insectorum* **181**: 1–45 (as *Hylaeus (Koptogaster) fijiensis* (Cockerell, 1909)); Houston, T.F. (1981). A revision of the Australian hylaeine bees (Hymenoptera : Colletidae). II. *Aust. J. Zool. Suppl. Ser.* **80**: 1–128 (redescription).

Hylaeus (Planihylaeus) Houston, 1981

Planihylaeus Houston, T.F. (1981). A revision of the Australian hylaeine bees (Hymenoptera : Colletidae). II. *Aust. J. Zool. Suppl. Ser.* **80**: 1–128 [96] [proposed with subgeneric rank in *Hylaeus* Fabricius, 1793]. Type species: *Prosopis trilobata* Cockerell, 1910 by original designation.

Hylaeus (Planihylaeus) daviesiae Houston, 1981

Hylaeus (Planihylaeus) daviesiae Houston, T.F. (1981). A revision of the Australian hylaeine bees (Hymenoptera : Colletidae). II. *Aust. J. Zool. Suppl. Ser.* **80**: 1–128 [98].
Type data: holotype, QM T6860 ♂.
Type locality: Black Mtn, ACT.

Distribution: NE coastal, SE coastal, Murray-Darling basin, QLD, NSW, ACT.
Ecology: adult—volant; melliferous, solitary, flower visiting record: *Daviesia* Sm. [Fabaceae].

Hylaeus (Planihylaeus) jacksoniae Houston, 1981

Hylaeus (Planihylaeus) jacksoniae Houston, T.F. (1981). A revision of the Australian hylaeine bees (Hymenoptera : Colletidae). II. *Aust. J. Zool. Suppl. Ser.* **80**: 1–128 [101].
Type data: holotype, QM T6864 ♂.
Type locality: Mt Coot-tha, Brisbane, QLD.

Distribution: NE coastal, Murray-Darling basin, QLD, NSW; only published localities Mt Coot-tha and near Woodenbong.
Ecology: adult—volant; melliferous, solitary, flower visiting record: *Jacksonia* Smith [Fabaceae].

Hylaeus (Planihylaeus) probligenatus Houston, 1981

Hylaeus (Planihylaeus) probligenatus Houston, T.F. (1981). A revision of the Australian hylaeine bees (Hymenoptera : Colletidae). II. *Aust. J. Zool. Suppl. Ser.* **80**: 1–128 [102].
Type data: holotype, ANIC ♂.
Type locality: Black Mtn, ACT (as F.C.T.).

Distribution: Murray-Darling basin, ACT; only published localities Canberra and vicinity.
Ecology: adult—volant; melliferous, solitary, flower visiting record: *Daviesia* Sm. [Fabaceae].

Hylaeus (Planihylaeus) quadriceps (Smith, 1879)

Prosopis quadriceps Smith, F. (1879). *Descriptions of New Species of Hymenoptera in the Collection of the British Museum.* London : British Museum xxi 240 pp. [17].
Type data: holotype, BMNH Hym.17.a.87 ♀.
Type locality: Australia.
Prosopis hobartiana Cockerell, T.D.A. (1905). Descriptions and records of bees. V. *Ann. Mag. Nat. Hist. (7)*16: 465–477 [470].
Type data: holotype, BMNH Hym.17.a.86 ♂.
Type locality: Hobart, TAS.
Gnathoprosopis marianella Rayment, T. (1931). Studies in Australian bees. A dweller among the reeds : *Gnathoprosopis marianella* Rayment. *Vict. Nat.* 47: 135–141 [135] [the spelling *marianella* is used here, rather than *marionellus* as used by Michener, C.D. (1965). A classification of the bees of the Australian and South Pacific regions. *Bull. Am. Mus. Nat. Hist.* 130: 1–362 (123); Rayment used *marianella* five times, before stating that the species was dedicated to Miss Marion Bonham and he used *marianella* twice more in 1935, without re-stating Miss Bonham's name; no other mention of "Marion" has been found, so it has not been possible to check which spelling is correct].
Type data: holotype, ANIC ♀.
Type locality: Ferntree Gully (Dandenong), VIC.
Gnathoprosopis striata Rayment, T. (1935). *A Cluster of Bees.* Sixty essays on the life-histories of Australian bees, with specific descriptions of over 100 new species, and an introduction by Professor E.F. Phillips, D.Ph., Cornell University, U.S.A. Sydney : Endeavour Press 752 pp. [647].
Type data: holotype, ANIC ♀.
Type locality: Denmark, WA.

Taxonomic decision for synonymy: Houston, T.F. (1981). A revision of the Australian hylaeine bees (Hymenoptera : Colletidae). II. *Aust. J. Zool. Suppl. Ser.* 80: 1–128 [106].

Distribution: Murray-Darling basin, SE coastal, SW coastal, NSW, VIC, WA, TAS.
Ecology: larva—sedentary : adult—volant; melliferous, solitary, nest in reeds (*Juncus communis*), flower visiting record: *Arctotheca* Wendl. [Asteraceae], *Hypochaeris* L. [Asteraceae], *Pratia* Gaudich. [Campanulaceae].
References: Meade-Waldo, G. (1923). Hymenoptera. Fam. Apidae. Subfam. Prosopidinae. *Genera Insectorum* 181: 1–45 (as *Hylaeus (Koptogaster) quadriceps* (Smith, 1879) and *Hylaeus (Koptogaster) hobartiana* (Cockerell, 1905)); Rayment, T. (1935). *A Cluster of Bees.* Sixty essays on the life-histories of Australian bees, with specific descriptions of over 100 new species, and an introduction by Professor E.F. Phillips, D.Ph., Cornell University, U.S.A. Sydney : Endeavour Press 752 pp. (biology, as *Gnathoprosopis marianella* Rayment, 1931); Miche-

ner, C.D. (1965). A classification of the bees of the Australian and South Pacific regions. *Bull. Am. Mus. Nat. Hist.* 130: 1–362 (as *Hylaeus (Prosopisteron)* spp.).

Hylaeus (Planihylaeus) trilobatus (Cockerell, 1910)

Prosopis trilobata Cockerell, T.D.A. (1910). Some Australian bees in the Berlin Museum. *J. N.Y. Entomol. Soc.* 18: 98–114 [104].
Type data: holotype, ZMB ♂*.
Type locality: Mallee, VIC.
Prosopis melanops Cockerell, T.D.A. (1916). A collection of bees from Queensland. *Mem. Qd Mus.* 5: 197–204 [198].
Type data: holotype, USNM ♀*.
Type locality: Caloundra, QLD.
Prosopis centralis Friese, H. (1924). Ueber die Bienen Australiens. *Konowia* 3: 216–249 [226].
Type data: holotype (probable), AMNH ♂*.
Type locality: Dandenong Ranges, VIC.
Hylaeus (Prosopisteron) melanops crassior Cockerell, T.D.A. (1926). Descriptions and records of bees. CX. *Ann. Mag. Nat. Hist. (9)*17: 510–519 [514].
Type data: holotype, NMV T3676 ♀.
Type locality: Bayswater, VIC.

Taxonomic decision for synonymy: Houston, T.F. (1981). A revision of the Australian hylaeine bees (Hymenoptera : Colletidae). II. *Aust. J. Zool. Suppl. Ser.* 80: 1–128 [108].

Distribution: NE coastal, SE coastal, Murray-Darling basin, QLD, NSW, VIC.
Ecology: adult—volant; melliferous, solitary, flower visiting record: *Daviesia* Sm. [Fabaceae], *Jacksonia* Smith [Fabaceae], *Melaleuca* L. [Myrtaceae], *Pultenaea* Sm. [Fabaceae], *Rubus* L. [Rosaceae].
References: Meade-Waldo, G. (1923). Hymenoptera. Fam. Apidae. Subfam. Prosopidinae. *Genera Insectorum* 181: 1–45 (as *Hylaeus (Koptogaster) trilobatus* (Cockerell, 1910) and *Hylaeus (Koptogaster) melanops* (Cockerell, 1916)); Michener, C.D. (1965). A classification of the bees of the Australian and South Pacific regions. *Bull. Am. Mus. Nat. Hist.* 130: 1–362 [236] (flower record, as *Hylaeus (Prosopisteron) melanops* (Cockerell, 1916)).

Hylaeus (Prosopisteron) Cockerell, 1906

Prosopisteron Cockerell, T.D.A. (1906). Four interesting Australian bees, in the collection of the British Museum. *Entomologist* 39: 15–18 [17]. Type species: *Prosopisteron serotinellum* Cockerell, 1906 by monotypy.

Extralimital distribution: New Zealand, Chatham Ils, New Guinea and Tuamotu Ils, see Michener, C.D. (1965). A classification of the bees of the Australian and South Pacific regions. *Bull. Am. Mus. Nat. Hist.* 130: 1–362 [122].

Hylaeus (Prosopisteron) accipitris (Cockerell, 1914)

Prosopis accipitris Cockerell, T.D.A. (1914). Descriptions and records of bees. LXII. *Ann. Mag. Nat. Hist. (8)*14: 49–57 [53].

Type data: holotype, BMNH Hym.17.a.177 ♂.
Type locality: Eaglehawk Neck, TAS.

Distribution: TAS; known only from type locality.
Ecology: adult—volant; melliferous, solitary.
Reference: Meade-Waldo, G. (1923). Hymenoptera.
Fam. Apidae. Subfam. Prosopidinae. *Genera Insectorum* **181**: 1–45 (as *Hylaeus (Koptogaster) accipitris* (Cockerell, 1914)).

Hylaeus (Prosopisteron) albozebratus Michener, 1965

Hylaeus (Prosopisteron) albozebratus Michener, C.D. (1965). A classification of the bees of the Australian and South Pacific regions. *Bull. Am. Mus. Nat. Hist.* **130**: 1–362 [289].
Type data: holotype, WAM 65–729 ♂.
Type locality: Carnarvon, WA.

Distribution: NW coastal, WA; known only from type locality.
Ecology: adult—volant; melliferous, solitary.

Hylaeus (Prosopisteron) amatulus (Cockerell, 1922)

Prosopis amatula Cockerell, T.D.A. (1922). Australian bees in the Queensland Museum. *Mem. Qd Mus.* **7**: 257–279 [267].
Type data: holotype, QM T2433 ♂.
Type locality: Caloundra, QLD.

Distribution: NE coastal, QLD; known only from type locality.
Ecology: adult—volant; melliferous, solitary.
Reference: Meade-Waldo, G. (1923). Hymenoptera.
Fam. Apidae. Subfam. Prosopidinae. *Genera Insectorum* **181**: 1–45 (as *Hylaeus (Koptogaster) amatula* (Cockerell, 1922)).

Hylaeus (Prosopisteron) aralis (Cockerell, 1916)

Prosopis aralis Cockerell, T.D.A. (1916). Some bees from Australia, Tasmania, and the New Hebrides. *Proc. Acad. Nat. Sci. Philad.* **68**: 360–375 [364].
Type data: syntypes, BMNH 2♀ (a specimen is labelled 'type' and has registration number Hym.17.a.175).
Type locality: Mt Yule, Healesville, VIC.

Distribution: SE coastal, Murray-Darling basin, NSW, VIC; only published localities Gosford—Wyong area, Mt Yule (Healesville), Gunbower and Portland.
Ecology: adult—volant; melliferous, solitary, nest in galleries in dead eucalypt, (?nest in hole in mud-brick wall), flower visiting record: *Eucalyptus* L'Hérit. [Myrtaceae], *Leptospermum* Forster & G.Forster [Myrtaceae], *Schinus* L. [Anacardiaceae].
References: Meade-Waldo, G. (1923). Hymenoptera.
Fam. Apidae. Subfam. Prosopidinae. *Genera Insectorum* **181**: 1–45 (as *Hylaeus (Koptogaster) aralis* (Cockerell, 1916)); Rayment, T. (1935). *A Cluster of Bees.* Sixty essays on the life-histories of Australian bees, with specific descriptions of over 100 new spe-

cies, and an introduction by Professor E.F. Phillips, D.Ph., Cornell University, U.S.A. Sydney : Endeavour Press 752 pp. (?nest, flower record); Rayment, T. (1953). *Bees of the Portland District.* Victoria : Portland Field Naturalist's Club 39 pp. (distribution); Moore, K.M. (1959). Observations on some Australian forest insects. 4. *Xyleborus truncatus* Erichson 1842 (Coleoptera : Scolytidae) associated with dying *Eucalyptus saligna* Smith (Sydney blue-gum). *Proc. Linn. Soc. N.S.W.* **84**: 186–193 (nest).

Hylaeus (Prosopisteron) asperithorax (Rayment, 1927)

Euryglossa asperithorax Rayment, T. (1927). A new Australian cliff-bee. *Euryglossa asperithorax*, sp.n. *Vict. Nat.* **44**: 75.
Type data: holotype, USNM ♀*.
Type locality: Sandringham, VIC.

Distribution: SE coastal, NSW, VIC; only published localities Woy Woy and Sandringham.
Ecology: adult—volant; melliferous, solitary, flower visiting record: *Goodenia* Sm. [Goodeniaceae], *Olearia* Moench [Asteraceae].
References: Cockerell, T.D.A. (1929). Bees from the Australian region. *Am. Mus. Novit.* **346**: 1–18 (taxonomy); Rayment, T. (1935). *A Cluster of Bees.* Sixty essays on the life-histories of Australian bees, with specific descriptions of over 100 new species, and an introduction by Professor E.F. Phillips, D.Ph., Cornell University, U.S.A. Sydney : Endeavour Press 752 pp. (illustration); Rayment, T. (1939). Bees from the high lands of New South Wales and Victoria. *Aust. Zool.* **9**: 263–294 (distribution).

Hylaeus (Prosopisteron) auriferus (Cockerell, 1918)

Prosopis aurifera Cockerell, T.D.A. (1918). Some bees collected in Queensland. *Mem. Qd Mus.* **6**: 112–120 [113].
Type data: holotype, QM Hy/4146 ♀.
Type locality: Stradbroke Is., QLD.

Distribution: NE coastal, QLD; known only from type locality.
Ecology: adult—volant; melliferous, solitary.
Reference: Meade-Waldo, G. (1923). Hymenoptera.
Fam. Apidae. Subfam. Prosopidinae. *Genera Insectorum* **181**: 1–45 (as *Hylaeus (Koptogaster) auriferus* (Cockerell, 1918)).

Hylaeus (Prosopisteron) basilautus (Rayment, 1953)

Meroglossa basilauta Rayment, T. (1953). *Bees of the Portland District.* Victoria : Portland Field Naturalist's Club 39 pp. [11].
Type data: holotype (probable), ANIC ♀.
Type locality: Jamberoo (as Jamboroo), NSW.

Distribution: SE coastal, NSW, VIC; only published localities Jamberoo and Gorae West.
Ecology: adult—volant; melliferous, solitary, nest in galleries in sound, hard wood, flower visiting record:

Eucalyptus L'Hérit. [Myrtaceae], *Leptospermum* Forster & G.Forster [Myrtaceae], *Loranthus* Jacq. [Loranthaceae].
References: Rayment, T. (1954). Incidence of acarid mites on the biology of bees. *Aust. Zool.* **12**: 26–38 (as host); Rayment, T. (1954). Remarkable bees from a rain forest. *Aust. Zool.* **12**: 46–56 (description of female, as new species).

Hylaeus (Prosopisteron) baudinensis (Cockerell, 1905)

Prosopis baudinensis Cockerell, T.D.A. (1905). Descriptions and records of bees. V. *Ann. Mag. Nat. Hist. (7)***16**: 465–477 [471].
Type data: syntypes, BMNH ♀ (number of specimens unknown, a specimen is labelled 'type' and has registration number Hym.17.a.222).
Type locality: Baudin Is., WA.

Distribution: NW coastal, N coastal, WA, NT; only published localities Baudin Is. and Darwin.
Ecology: adult—volant; melliferous, solitary.
References: Cockerell, T.D.A. (1910). Descriptions and records of bees. XXX. *Ann. Mag. Nat. Hist. (8)***6**: 17–31 (distribution, as *Meroglossa baudinensis* (Cockerell, 1905)); Perkins, R.C.L. (1912). Notes, with descriptions of new species, on aculeate Hymenoptera of the Australian Region. *Ann. Mag. Nat. Hist. (8)***9**: 96–121 (taxonomy); Meade-Waldo, G. (1923). Hymenoptera. Fam. Apidae. Subfam. Prosopidinae. *Genera Insectorum* **181**: 1–45 (as *Hylaeus (Koptogaster) baudinensis* (Cockerell, 1905)).

Hylaeus (Prosopisteron) bicoloratus (Smith, 1853)

Prosopis bicolorata Smith, F. (1853). *Catalogue of Hymenopterous Insects in the Collection of the British Museum.* Part I. Andrenidae and Apidae. London : British Museum 197 pp. [27].
Type data: holotype, BMNH Hym.17.a.58 ♀.
Type locality: Adelaide, SA.

Distribution: S Gulfs, SA; known only from type locality.
Ecology: adult—volant; melliferous, solitary.
Reference: Meade-Waldo, G. (1923). Hymenoptera. Fam. Apidae. Subfam. Prosopidinae. *Genera Insectorum* **181**: 1–45 (as *Hylaeus (Koptogaster) bicolorata* (Smith, 1853)).

Hylaeus (Prosopisteron) bicuneatus (Cockerell, 1910)

Prosopis bicuneata Cockerell, T.D.A. (1910). Descriptions and records of bees. XXXI. *Ann. Mag. Nat. Hist. (8)***6**: 160–168 [161].
Type data: holotype, BMNH Hym.17.a.75 ♀.
Type locality: Mackay, QLD.

Distribution: NE coastal, QLD; known only from type locality.
Ecology: adult—volant; melliferous, solitary, flower visiting record: *Cassia* L. *s.lat.* [Caesalpiniaceae].

References: Cockerell, T.D.A. (1911). Descriptions and records of bees. XL. *Ann. Mag. Nat. Hist. (8)***8**: 763–770 (taxonomy); Meade-Waldo, G. (1923). Hymenoptera. Fam. Apidae. Subfam. Prosopidinae. *Genera Insectorum* **181**: 1–45 (as *Hylaeus (Koptogaster) xanthaspis bicuneatus* (Cockerell, 1910)).

Hylaeus (Prosopisteron) bidentatus (Smith, 1853)

Prosopis bidentata Smith, F. (1853). *Catalogue of Hymenopterous Insects in the Collection of the British Museum.* Part I. Andrenidae and Apidae. London : British Museum 197 pp. [28].
Type data: holotype, BMNH ♂*.
Type locality: Australia (as New Holland).

Distribution: NE coastal, QLD; only published localities Stradbroke Is. and near Noosa.
Ecology: larva—sedentary : adult volant; melliferous, solitary, flower visiting record: *Banksia* L.f. [Proteaceae].
References: Cockerell, T.D.A. (1918). Some bees collected in Queensland. *Mem. Qd Mus.* **6**: 112–120 (redescription); Meade-Waldo, G. (1923). Hymenoptera. Fam. Apidae. Subfam. Prosopidinae. *Genera Insectorum* **181**: 1–45 (as *Hylaeus (Koptogaster) bidentata* (Smith, 1853)); Alcock, J. & Houston, T.F. (1987). Resource defense and alternative mating tactics in the banksia bee, *Hylaeus alcyoneus* (Erichson). *Ethology* **76**: 177–188 (biology).

Hylaeus (Prosopisteron) blanchae Rayment, 1953

Hylaeus blanchae Rayment, T. (1953). New bees and wasps, Part XX. *Vict. Nat.* **70**: 68–71 [69].
Type data: holotype, ANIC ♀.
Type locality: Great Lake, TAS.

Distribution: TAS; known only from type locality.
Ecology: adult—volant; melliferous, solitary, flower visiting record: *Helichrysum* Miller *s.lat.* [Asteraceae].

Hylaeus (Prosopisteron) brevior (Cockerell, 1918)

Prosopis perhumilis Cockerell, T.D.A. (1916). A collection of bees from Queensland. *Mem. Qd Mus.* **5**: 197–204 [197] [junior primary homonym of *Prosopis perhumilis* Cockerell, 1914].
Type data: holotype (probable), USNM ♂*.
Type locality: Oxley, Brisbane, QLD.

Prosopis brevior Cockerell, T.D.A. (1918). Descriptions and records of bees. LXXIX. *Ann. Mag. Nat. Hist. (9)***1**: 158–167 [164] [*nom. nov.* for *Prosopis perhumilis* Cockerell, 1916].

Distribution: NE coastal, SE coastal, QLD, NSW; only published localities Brisbane, Caloundra and Sydney.
Ecology: adult—volant; melliferous, solitary.
References: Cockerell, T.D.A. (1922). Australian bees in the Queensland Museum. *Mem. Qd Mus.* **7**: 257–279 (distribution); Meade-Waldo, G. (1923).

Hymenoptera. Fam. Apidae. Subfam. Prosopidinae. *Genera Insectorum* **181**: 1–45 (as *Hylaeus (Koptogaster) brevior* (Cockerell, 1918)); Cockerell, T.D.A. (1930). Australian bees in the Museum of Comparative Zoology. *Psyche (Camb.)* **37**: 141–154 (distribution).

Hylaeus (Prosopisteron) burnsi (Michener, 1965)

Hylaeorhiza burnsi Michener, C.D. (1965). A classification of the bees of the Australian and South Pacific regions. *Bull. Am. Mus. Nat. Hist.* **130**: 1–362 [300].
Type data: holotype, NMV ♀.
Type locality: Bellbird, VIC.

Distribution: SE coastal, VIC; known only from type locality.
Ecology: adult—volant; melliferous, solitary.
Reference: Houston, T.F. (1981). A revision of the Australian hylaeine bees (Hymenoptera : Colletidae). II. *Aust. J. Zool. Suppl. Ser.* **80**: 1–128 (generic placement).

Hylaeus (Prosopisteron) chlorosomus (Cockerell, 1913)

Prosopis chlorosoma Cockerell, T.D.A. (1913). Some Australian bees. *Proc. Acad. Nat. Sci. Philad.* **65**: 28–44 [40].
Type data: syntypes, USNM 7♀*.
Type locality: Croydon, VIC.

Distribution: Murray-Darling basin, SE coastal, SW coastal, QLD, VIC, WA, TAS; only published localities Stanthorpe, Croydon, Launceston and S WA.
Ecology: adult—volant; melliferous, solitary, flower visiting record: *Calothamnus* Lab. [Myrtaceae].
References: Cockerell, T.D.A. (1918). Descriptions and records of bees. LXXIX. *Ann. Mag. Nat. Hist. (9)***1**: 158–167 (distribution); Meade-Waldo, G. (1923). Hymenoptera. Fam. Apidae. Subfam. Prosopidinae. *Genera Insectorum* **181**: 1–45 (as *Hylaeus (Koptogaster) chlorosoma* (Cockerell, 1913)); Cockerell, T.D.A. (1930). New Australian bees. *Mem. Qd Mus.* **10**: 37–50 (distribution); Houston, T.F. (1983). An extraordinary new bee and adaptation of palpi for nectar-feeding in some Australian Colletidae and Pergidae (Hymenoptera). *J. Aust. Entomol. Soc.* **22**: 263–270 (flower record).

Hylaeus (Prosopisteron) cliffordiellus Rayment, 1953

Hylaeus cliffordiellus Rayment, T. (1953). *Bees of the Portland District.* Victoria : Portland Field Naturalist's Club 39 pp. [8].
Type data: holotype, ANIC ♂.
Type locality: Gorae West, VIC.

Distribution: SE coastal, VIC; known only from type locality.
Ecology: adult—volant; melliferous, solitary, nest in cavities in dry stems of sedge (*Lepidosperma*).

Reference: Rayment, T. (1954). Incidence of acarid mites on the biology of bees. *Aust. Zool.* **12**: 26–38 (as host).

Hylaeus (Prosopisteron) crassifemoratus (Cockerell, 1922)

Prosopis crassifemorata Cockerell, T.D.A. (1922). Australian bees in the Queensland Museum. *Mem. Qd Mus.* **7**: 257–279 [266].
Type data: holotype, QM T2427 ♂.
Type locality: Sunnybank, Brisbane, QLD.

Distribution: NE coastal, QLD; known only from type locality.
Ecology: adult—volant; melliferous, solitary.
Reference: Meade-Waldo, G. (1923). Hymenoptera. Fam. Apidae. Subfam. Prosopidinae. *Genera Insectorum* **181**: 1–45 (as *Hylaeus (Koptogaster) crassifemorata* (Cockerell, 1922)).

Hylaeus (Prosopisteron) cyaneomicans (Cockerell, 1910)

Prosopis cyaneomicans Cockerell, T.D.A. (1910). Descriptions and records of bees. XXXI. *Ann. Mag. Nat. Hist. (8)***6**: 160–168 [165].
Type data: syntypes, BMNH 3♀ (a specimen is labelled 'type' and has registration number Hym.17.a.78).
Type locality: Mackay, QLD.

Distribution: NE coastal, QLD; only published localities Mackay, Babinda, Cairns and Halifax.
Ecology: adult—volant; melliferous, solitary, flower visiting record: *Cassia* L. *s.lat.* [Caesalpiniaceae].
References: Meade-Waldo, G. (1923). Hymenoptera. Fam. Apidae. Subfam. Prosopidinae. *Genera Insectorum* **181**: 1–45 (as *Hylaeus (Koptogaster) cyaneomicans* (Cockerell, 1910)); Cockerell, T.D.A. (1930). Australian bees in the Museum of Comparative Zoology. *Psyche (Camb.)* **37**: 141–154 (distribution).

Hylaeus (Prosopisteron) distractus (Cockerell, 1914)

Prosopis distractus Cockerell, T.D.A. (1914). Descriptions and records of bees. LXII. *Ann. Mag. Nat. Hist. (8)***14**: 49–57 [56].
Type data: holotype, BMNH Hym.17.a.178 ♂.
Type locality: Yallingup, WA.

Distribution: SW coastal, WA; known only from type locality.
Ecology: adult—volant; melliferous, solitary.
Reference: Meade-Waldo, G. (1923). Hymenoptera. Fam. Apidae. Subfam. Prosopidinae. *Genera Insectorum* **181**: 1–45 (as *Hylaeus (Koptogaster) distractus* (Cockerell, 1914)).

Hylaeus (Prosopisteron) elongatus (Smith, 1879)

Prosopis elongata Smith, F. (1879). *Descriptions of New Species of Hymenoptera in the Collection of the British*

Museum. London : British Museum xxi 240 pp. [18].
Type data: holotype, BMNH Hym.17.a.81 ♂.
Type locality: Adelaide, SA.

Distribution: SE coastal, S Gulfs, SW coastal, VIC, SA, WA, TAS.
Ecology: adult—volant; melliferous, solitary, flower visiting record: *Leptospermum* Forster & G.Forster [Myrtaceae].
References: Cockerell, T.D.A. (1916). Descriptions and records of bees. LXXII. *Ann. Mag. Nat. Hist. (8)*17: 428–435 (distribution); Cockerell, T.D.A. (1921). Australian bees in the Queensland Museum. *Mem. Qd Mus.* 7: 81–98 (taxonomy); Meade-Waldo, G. (1923). Hymenoptera. Fam. Apidae. Subfam. Prosopidinae. *Genera Insectorum* 181: 1–45 (as *Hylaeus (Koptogaster) elongata* (Smith, 1879)); Cockerell, T.D.A. (1929). Bees in the Queensland Museum. *Mem. Qd Mus.* 9: 298–323 (distribution); Rayment, T. (1953). *Bees of the Portland District*. Victoria : Portland Field Naturalist's Club 39 pp. (flower record); Rayment, T. (1954). Incidence of acarid mites on the biology of bees. *Aust. Zool.* 12: 26–38 (as host).

Hylaeus (Prosopisteron) eugeniellus (Cockerell, 1910)

Prosopis eugeniella Cockerell, T.D.A. (1910). Descriptions and records of bees. XXX. *Ann. Mag. Nat. Hist. (8)*6: 17–31 [25].
Type data: syntypes, BMNH 5♀ (a specimen is labelled 'type' and has registration number Hym.17.a.72).
Type locality: Mackay, QLD.
Prosopis nana Friese, H. (1924). Ueber die Bienen Australiens. *Konowia* 3: 216–249 [224].
Type data: syntypes (probable), AMNH ♀* (number of specimens unknown).
Type locality: Mackay, QLD.

Taxonomic decision for synonymy: Cockerell, T.D.A. (1929). Bees, chiefly Australian species, described or determined by Dr. H. Friese. *Am. Mus. Novit.* 343: 1–20 [19].

Distribution: NE coastal, SE coastal, Murray-Darling basin, QLD, NSW, VIC.
Ecology: adult—volant; melliferous, solitary, flower visiting record: *Angophora* Cav. [Myrtaceae], *Brachyscome* Cass. [Asteraceae], *Callistemon* R.Br. [Myrtaceae], *Eucalyptus* L'Hérit. [Myrtaceae], *Eugenia* L. [Myrtaceae], *Leptospermum* Forster & G.Forster [Myrtaceae].
References: Cockerell, T.D.A. (1918). Some bees collected in Queensland. *Mem. Qd Mus.* 6: 112–120 (distribution); Meade-Waldo, G. (1923). Hymenoptera. Fam. Apidae. Subfam. Prosopidinae. *Genera Insectorum* 181: 1–45 (as *Hylaeus (Koptogaster) eugeniellus* (Cockerell, 1910)); Rayment, T. (1947). New bees and wasps—Part VI. An undescribed *Paracolletes* from the Victorian Alps. *Vict. Nat.* 64: 102–103 (distribution); Rayment, T. (1953). *Bees of the Portland District*. Victoria : Portland Field

Naturalist's Club 39 pp. (flower record); Michener, C.D. (1965). A classification of the bees of the Australian and South Pacific regions. *Bull. Am. Mus. Nat. Hist.* 130: 1–362 (flower record, distribution).

Hylaeus (Prosopisteron) flavojugatus (Cockerell, 1912)

Prosopis flavojugata Cockerell, T.D.A. (1912). Descriptions and records of bees. XLI. *Ann. Mag. Nat. Hist. (8)*9: 139–149 [146].
Type data: syntypes, ANIC 2♀.
Type locality: Como, NSW.

Distribution: SE coastal, NSW; known only from type locality.
Ecology: adult—volant; melliferous, solitary.
Reference: Meade-Waldo, G. (1923). Hymenoptera. Fam. Apidae. Subfam. Prosopidinae. *Genera Insectorum* 181: 1–45 (as *Hylaeus (Koptogaster) flavojugata* (Cockerell, 1912)).

Hylaeus (Prosopisteron) frederici (Cockerell, 1905)

Prosopis similis Smith, F. (1853). *Catalogue of Hymenopterous Insects in the Collection of the British Museum*. Part I. Andrenidae and Apidae. London : British Museum 197 pp. [26] [junior secondary homonym of *Hylaeus similis* Fabricius, 1793].
Type data: holotype, BMNH Hym.17.a.83 ♀.
Type locality: Australia (as New Holland).
Prosopis frederici Cockerell, T.D.A. (1905). Descriptions and records of bees. IV. *Ann. Mag. Nat. Hist. (7)*16: 392–403 [403] [*nom. nov.* for *Prosopis similis* Smith, 1853].

Distribution: NE coastal, Murray-Darling basin, SE coastal, SW coastal, QLD, NSW, WA; only published localities Brisbane, Wallangarra, Deepwater, Sutherland and King George Sound.
Ecology: adult—volant; melliferous, solitary, flower visiting record: *Eucalyptus* L'Hérit. [Myrtaceae], *Jacksonia* Smith [Fabaceae], *Leptospermum* Forster & G.Forster [Myrtaceae].
References: Cockerell, T.D.A. (1910). Descriptions and records of bees. XXV. *Ann. Mag. Nat. Hist. (8)*5: 133–140 (taxonomy); Cockerell, T.D.A. (1916). A collection of bees from Queensland. *Mem. Qd Mus.* 5: 197–204 (distribution); Meade-Waldo, G. (1923). Hymenoptera. Fam. Apidae. Subfam. Prosopidinae. *Genera Insectorum* 181: 1–45 (as *Hylaeus (Koptogaster) frederici* (Cockerell, 1905)); Cockerell, T.D.A. (1929). Bees in the Australian Museum collection. *Rec. Aust. Mus.* 17: 199–243 (distribution); Cockerell, T.D.A. (1930). Australian bees in the Museum of Comparative Zoology. *Psyche (Camb.)* 37: 141–154 (distribution); Michener, C.D. (1965). A classification of the bees of the Australian and South Pacific regions. *Bull. Am. Mus. Nat. Hist.* 130: 1–362 (incorrect subsequent spelling as *Hylaeus fredrici* (Cockerell, 1905), flower records).

Hylaeus (Prosopisteron) greavesi (Rayment, 1935)

Gnathoprosopis greavesi Rayment, T. (1935). *A Cluster of Bees*. Sixty essays on the life-histories of Australian bees, with specific descriptions of over 100 new species, and an introduction by Professor E.F. Phillips, D.Ph., Cornell University, U.S.A. Sydney : Endeavour Press 752 pp. [645].
Type data: holotype, ANIC ♂.
Type locality: Denmark, WA.

Distribution: SW coastal, WA; known only from type locality.
Ecology: adult—volant; melliferous, solitary.

Hylaeus (Prosopisteron) hobartiellus Cockerell, 1929

Hylaeus hobartiellus Cockerell, T.D.A. (1929). Bees in the Queensland Museum. *Mem. Qd Mus.* 9: 298–323 [312].
Type data: holotype, QM Hy/4040 ♂.
Type locality: Hobart, TAS.

Distribution: TAS; known only from type locality.
Ecology: adult—volant; melliferous, solitary.

Hylaeus (Prosopisteron) infans (Cockerell, 1910)

Prosopis infans Cockerell, T.D.A. (1910). Descriptions and records of bees. XXX. *Ann. Mag. Nat. Hist. (8)*6: 17–31 [27].
Type data: holotype, BMNH Hym.17.a.76 ♀.
Type locality: Mackay, QLD.

Distribution: NE coastal, QLD; known only from type locality.
Ecology: adult—volant; melliferous, solitary.
Reference: Meade-Waldo, G. (1923). Hymenoptera. Fam. Apidae. Subfam. Prosopidinae. *Genera Insectorum* 181: 1–45 (as *Hylaeus (Koptogaster) infans* (Cockerell, 1910)).

Hylaeus (Prosopisteron) leai (Cockerell, 1912)

Prosopis leai Cockerell, T.D.A. (1912). Descriptions and records of bees. XLVII. *Ann. Mag. Nat. Hist. (8)*10: 484–494 [490].
Type data: holotype, USNM ♂*.
Type locality: [Royal] National Park, NSW.

Distribution: SE coastal, NSW; known only from type locality.
Ecology: adult—volant; melliferous, solitary.
Reference: Meade-Waldo, G. (1923). Hymenoptera. Fam. Apidae. Subfam. Prosopidinae. *Genera Insectorum* 181: 1–45 (as *Hylaeus (Koptogaster) leai* (Cockerell, 1912)).

Hylaeus (Prosopisteron) littleri (Cockerell, 1918)

Prosopis littleri Cockerell, T.D.A. (1918). Descriptions and records of bees. LXXIX. *Ann. Mag. Nat. Hist. (9)*1: 158–167 [163].
Type data: holotype, BMNH Hym.17.a.100 ♂.
Type locality: George Town, TAS.

Distribution: Murray-Darling basin, SA, TAS; only published localities George Town and Mt Magnificent.
Ecology: larva—sedentary : adult—volant; melliferous, solitary.
References: Meade-Waldo, G. (1923). Hymenoptera. Fam. Apidae. Subfam. Prosopidinae. *Genera Insectorum* 181: 1–45 (as *Hylaeus (Koptogaster) littleri* (Cockerell, 1918)); Alcock, J. & Houston, T.F. (1987). Resource defense and alternative mating tactics in the banksia bee, *Hylaeus alcyoneus* (Erichson). *Ethology* 76: 177–188 (biology).

Hylaeus (Prosopisteron) mediovirens (Cockerell, 1913)

Prosopis mediovirens Cockerell, T.D.A. (1913). Some Australian bees. *Proc. Acad. Nat. Sci. Philad.* 65: 28–44 [39].
Type data: holotype, USNM ♀*.
Type locality: Purnong, SA.

Distribution: Murray-Darling basin, SA, TAS; only published localities Purnong and Launceston.
Ecology: adult—volant; melliferous, solitary.
References: Cockerell, T.D.A. (1918). Descriptions and records of bees. LXXIX. *Ann. Mag. Nat. Hist. (9)*1: 158–167 (distribution); Meade-Waldo, G. (1923). Hymenoptera. Fam. Apidae. Subfam. Prosopidinae. *Genera Insectorum* 181: 1–45 (as *Hylaeus (Koptogaster) mediovirens* (Cockerell, 1913)).

Hylaeus (Prosopisteron) microphenax (Cockerell, 1910)

Prosopis microphenax Cockerell, T.D.A. (1910). Descriptions and records of bees. XXX. *Ann. Mag. Nat. Hist. (8)*6: 17–31 [26].
Type data: holotype, BMNH Hym.17.a.70 ♂.
Type locality: Mackay, QLD.

Distribution: NE coastal, QLD; known only from type locality.
Ecology: adult—volant; melliferous, solitary.
References: Cockerell, T.D.A. (1910). Descriptions and records of bees. XXX. *Ann. Mag. Nat. Hist. (8)*6: 17–31 (variety); Meade-Waldo, G. (1923). Hymenoptera. Fam. Apidae. Subfam. Prosopidinae. *Genera Insectorum* 181: 1–45 (as *Hylaeus (Koptogaster) microphenax* (Cockerell, 1910)).

Hylaeus (Prosopisteron) minusculus (Cockerell, 1913)

Prosopis minuscula Cockerell, T.D.A. (1913). Some Australian bees. *Proc. Acad. Nat. Sci. Philad.* 65: 28–44 [38].
Type data: holotype, BMNH Hym.17.a.97 ♂.
Type locality: Croydon, VIC.

Distribution: NE coastal, SE coastal, QLD, VIC; only published localities Caloundra and Croydon.
Ecology: adult—volant; melliferous, solitary.

References: Meade-Waldo, G. (1923). Hymenoptera. Fam. Apidae. Subfam. Prosopidinae. *Genera Insectorum* **181**: 1–45 (as *Hylaeus (Koptogaster) minuscula* (Cockerell, 1913)); Cockerell, T.D.A. (1929). Bees in the Queensland Museum. *Mem. Qd Mus.* **9**: 298–323 (variety); Michener, C.D. (1965). A classification of the bees of the Australian and South Pacific regions. *Bull. Am. Mus. Nat. Hist.* **130**: 1–362 (as *Hylaeus (Edriohylaeus) minusculus* (Cockerell, 1913)); Houston, T.F. (1981). A revision of the Australian hylaeine bees (Hymenoptera : Colletidae). II. *Aust. J. Zool. Suppl. Ser.* **80**: 1–128 (generic placement).

Hylaeus (Prosopisteron) murrayensis Rayment, 1935

Hylaeus aralis murrayensis Rayment, T. (1935). *A Cluster of Bees*. Sixty essays on the life-histories of Australian bees, with specific descriptions of over 100 new species, and an introduction by Professor E.F. Phillips, D.Ph., Cornell University, U.S.A. Sydney : Endeavour Press 752 pp. [661].
Type data: holotype, ANIC ♀.
Type locality: Gunbower, VIC.

Distribution: Murray-Darling basin, VIC; known only from type locality.
Ecology: adult—volant; melliferous, solitary, flower visiting record: Scotch thistles.

Hylaeus (Prosopisteron) nigrescens (Cockerell, 1918)

Prosopis cyaneomicans nigrescens Cockerell, T.D.A. (1918). Some bees collected in Queensland. *Mem. Qd Mus.* **6**: 112–120 [113].
Type data: holotype (probable), QM Hy/4148 ♀.
Type locality: Bribie Is., QLD.

Distribution: NE coastal, QLD; known only from type locality.
Ecology: adult—volant; melliferous, solitary.
Reference: Meade-Waldo, G. (1923). Hymenoptera. Fam. Apidae. Subfam. Prosopidinae. *Genera Insectorum* **181**: 1–45 (as *Hylaeus (Koptogaster) nigrescens* (Cockerell, 1918)).

Hylaeus (Prosopisteron) perhumilis (Cockerell, 1914)

Prosopis perhumilis Cockerell, T.D.A. (1914). Descriptions and records of bees. LXII. *Ann. Mag. Nat. Hist. (8)***14**: 49–53 [53].
Type data: holotype, BMNH Hym.17.a.176 ♂.
Type locality: Yallingup, WA.

Distribution: NE coastal, SE coastal, SW coastal, QLD, VIC, WA, TAS.
Ecology: larva—sedentary : adult—volant; melliferous, solitary, flower visiting record: *Angophora* Cav. [Myrtaceae], *Aster* L. [Asteraceae], *Callistemon* R.Br. [Myrtaceae], *Eucalyptus* L'Hérit. [Myrtaceae].

References: Cockerell, T.D.A. (1914). Some Tasmanian bees. *Entomologist* **47**: 305–308 (distribution); Cockerell, T.D.A. (1918). Descriptions and records of bees. LXXIX. *Ann. Mag. Nat. Hist. (9)***1**: 158–167 (distribution); Meade-Waldo, G. (1923). Hymenoptera. Fam. Apidae. Subfam. Prosopidinae. *Genera Insectorum* **181**: 1–45 (as *Hylaeus (Koptogaster) perhumilis* (Cockerell, 1914)); Cockerell, T.D.A. (1929). Bees from the Australian region. *Am. Mus. Novit.* **346**: 1–18 (distribution); Rayment, T. (1953). *Bees of the Portland District*. Victoria : Portland Field Naturalist's Club 39 pp. (flower record); Michener, C.D. (1965). A classification of the bees of the Australian and South Pacific regions. *Bull. Am. Mus. Nat. Hist.* **130**: 1–362 (flower record); McGinley, R.J. (1981). Systematics of the Colletidae based on mature larvae with phenetic analysis of apoid larvae (Insecta, Hymenoptera, Apoidea). *Univ. Calif. Publ. Entomol.* **91**: 1–309 (larva).

Hylaeus (Prosopisteron) perpictus Rayment, 1935

Hylaeus perpictus Rayment, T. (1935). *A Cluster of Bees*. Sixty essays on the life-histories of Australian bees, with specific descriptions of over 100 new species, and an introduction by Professor E.F. Phillips, D.Ph., Cornell University, U.S.A. Sydney : Endeavour Press 752 pp. [660].
Type data: holotype, ANIC ♂.
Type locality: Kiata, VIC.

Distribution: Murray-Darling basin, VIC; known only from type locality.
Ecology: adult—volant; melliferous, solitary.

Hylaeus (Prosopisteron) pictulus Michener, 1965

Hylaeus pictus Rayment, T. (1935). *A Cluster of Bees*. Sixty essays on the life-histories of Australian bees, with specific descriptions of over 100 new species, and an introduction by Professor E.F. Phillips, D.Ph., Cornell University, U.S.A. Sydney : Endeavour Press 752 pp. [655] [junior secondary homonym of *Prosopis picta* Smith, 1853].
Type data: holotype, ANIC ♂.
Type locality: Kiata, VIC.

Hylaeus (Prosopisteron) pictulus Michener, C.D. (1965). A classification of the bees of the Australian and South Pacific regions. *Bull. Am. Mus. Nat. Hist.* **130**: 1–362 [123] [*nom. nov.* for *Hylaeus pictus* Rayment, 1935].

Distribution: Murray-Darling basin, VIC; known only from type locality.
Ecology: adult—volant; melliferous, solitary.

Hylaeus (Prosopisteron) primulipictus (Cockerell, 1905)

Prosopis primulipicta Cockerell, T.D.A. (1905). Descriptions and records of bees. V. *Ann. Mag. Nat. Hist. (7)***16**: 465–477 [471].
Type data: holotype, BMNH Hym.17.a.92 ♂.
Type locality: Mackay, QLD.

Distribution: NE coastal, QLD; known only from type locality.
Ecology: adult—volant; melliferous, solitary.
Reference: Meade-Waldo, G. (1923). Hymenoptera. Fam. Apidae. Subfam. Prosopidinae. *Genera Insectorum* **181**: 1–45 (as *Hylaeus (Koptogaster) primulipicta* (Cockerell, 1905)).

Hylaeus (Prosopisteron) procurvus (Rayment, 1939)

Sphaerhylaeus procurvus Rayment, T. (1939). Bees from the high lands of New South Wales and Victoria. *Aust. Zool.* **9**: 263–294 [264].
Type data: holotype, ANIC ♂.
Type locality: Bogong High Plain, 6,000 ft, VIC.

Distribution: Murray-Darling basin, VIC; known only from type locality.
Ecology: adult—volant; melliferous, solitary.
References: Michener, C.D. (1965). A classification of the bees of the Australian and South Pacific regions. *Bull. Am. Mus. Nat. Hist.* **130**: 1–362 [137] (as *Hylaeus (Xenohylaeus) procurvus* (Rayment, 1939)); Houston, T.F. (1981). A revision of the Australian hylaeine bees (Hymenoptera : Colletidae). II. *Aust. J. Zool. Suppl. Ser.* **80**: 1–128 (generic placement).

Hylaeus (Prosopisteron) quadratus (Smith, 1853)

Prosopis quadrata Smith, F. (1853). *Catalogue of Hymenopterous Insects in the Collection of the British Museum*. Part I. Andrenidae and Apidae. London : British Museum 197 pp. [28].
Type data: holotype, BMNH ♂*.
Type locality: Australia (as New Holland).

Distribution: NE coastal, Murray-Darling basin, QLD; only published localities Oxley (Brisbane), Lamington National Park and Wallangarra.
Ecology: adult—volant; melliferous, solitary, flower visiting record: *Leptospermum* Forster & G.Forster [Myrtaceae], *Lomatia* R.Br. [Proteaceae].
References: Cockerell, T.D.A. (1921). Australian bees in the Queensland Museum. *Mem. Qd Mus.* **7**: 81–98 (distribution); Meade-Waldo, G. (1923). Hymenoptera. Fam. Apidae. Subfam. Prosopidinae. *Genera Insectorum* **181**: 1–45 (as *Hylaeus (Koptogaster) quadrata* (Smith, 1853)); Michener, C.D. (1965). A classification of the bees of the Australian and South Pacific regions. *Bull. Am. Mus. Nat. Hist.* **130**: 1–362 (flower record).

Hylaeus (Prosopisteron) sanguinipictus (Cockerell, 1914)

Prosopis sanguinipicta Cockerell, T.D.A. (1914). Descriptions and records of bees. LXII. *Ann. Mag. Nat. Hist.* (8)**14**: 49–57 [54].
Type data: holotype, BMNH Hym.17.a.67 ♂.
Type locality: Yallingup, WA.

Distribution: SW coastal, WA; only published localities Yallingup, Stirling Range and Fitzgerald River.

Ecology: larva—sedentary : adult—volant; melliferous, solitary, flower visiting record: *Banksia* L.f. [Proteaceae], *Dryandra* R.Br. [Proteaceae].
References: Meade-Waldo, G. (1923). Hymenoptera. Fam. Apidae. Subfam. Prosopidinae. *Genera Insectorum* **181**: 1–45 (as *Hylaeus (Koptogaster) sanguinipicta* (Cockerell, 1914)); Alcock, J. & Houston, T.F. (1987). Resource defense and alternative mating tactics in the banksia bee, *Hylaeus alcyoneus* (Erichson). *Ethology* **76**: 177–188 (biology).

Hylaeus (Prosopisteron) scintillans (Cockerell, 1922)

Prosopis scintillans Cockerell, T.D.A. (1922). Australian bees in the Queensland Museum. *Mem. Qd Mus.* **7**: 257–279 [268].
Type data: holotype, QM T2431 ♂.
Type locality: Brisbane, QLD.

Distribution: NE coastal, QLD; known only from type locality.
Ecology: adult—volant; melliferous, solitary.
Reference: Meade-Waldo, G. (1923). Hymenoptera. Fam. Apidae. Subfam. Prosopidinae. *Genera Insectorum* **181**: 1–45 (as *Hylaeus (Koptogaster) scintillans* (Cockerell, 1922)).

Hylaeus (Prosopisteron) scintilliformis (Cockerell, 1913)

Prosopis scintilliformis Cockerell, T.D.A. (1913). Some Australian bees. *Proc. Acad. Nat. Sci. Philad.* **65**: 28–44 [41].
Type data: holotype, USNM ♀*.
Type locality: Croydon, VIC.

Distribution: SE coastal, VIC; only published localities Croydon and Mt Yule (Healesville).
Ecology: adult—volant; melliferous, solitary, flower visiting record: *Eucalyptus* L'Hérit. [Myrtaceae].
Reference: Cockerell, T.D.A. (1916). Some bees from Australia, Tasmania, and the New Hebrides. *Proc. Acad. Nat. Sci. Philad.* **68**: 360–375 (description of male).

Hylaeus (Prosopisteron) scintillus (Cockerell, 1912)

Prosopis scintilla Cockerell, T.D.A. (1912). Descriptions and records of bees. XLI. *Ann. Mag. Nat. Hist.* (8)**9**: 139–149 [147].
Type data: holotype, BMNH Hym.17.a.80 ♀.
Type locality: Mackay, QLD.

Distribution: NE coastal, QLD; only published localities Mackay and Brisbane.
Ecology: adult—volant; melliferous, solitary, flower visiting record: *Leptospermum* Forster & G.Forster [Myrtaceae].
References: Cockerell, T.D.A. (1914). Descriptions and records of bees. LXII. *Ann. Mag. Nat. Hist.* (8)**14**: 49–57 (description of male); Cockerell,

T.D.A. (1929). Bees in the Queensland Museum. *Mem. Qd Mus.* **9**: 298–323 (distribution).

Hylaeus (Prosopisteron) semipersonatus Cockerell, 1929

Hylaeus semipersonatus Cockerell, T.D.A. (1929). Bees in the Queensland Museum. *Mem. Qd Mus.* **9**: 298–323 [314].
Type data: holotype, QM Hy/5003 ♂.
Type locality: Cradle Mtn, TAS.

Distribution: TAS; known only from type locality.
Ecology: adult—volant; melliferous, solitary.
Reference: Houston, T.F. (1981). A revision of the Australian hylaeine bees (Hymenoptera : Colletidae). II. *Aust. J. Zool. Suppl. Ser.* **80**: 1–128 (taxonomy).

Hylaeus (Prosopisteron) serotinellus (Cockerell, 1906)

Prosopisteron serotinellum Cockerell, T.D.A. (1906). Four interesting Australian bees, in the collection of the British Museum. *Entomologist* **39**: 15–18 [17].
Type data: holotype, BMNH Hym.17.a.174 ♀.
Type locality: Mackay, QLD.
Prosopis maculipennis Friese, H. (1924). Ueber die Bienen Australiens. *Konowia* **3**: 216–249 [224] [junior primary homonym of *Prosopis maculipennis* Smith, 1879].
Type data: syntypes (probable), AMNH ♀* (number of specimens unknown).
Type locality: Mackay and Kuranda, QLD.
Prosopis vittipennis Friese, H. (1924). Ueber die Bienen Australiens. *Konowia* **3**: 216–249 [224] [*nom. nov.* for *Prosopis maculipennis* Friese, 1924].

Taxonomic decision for synonymy: Cockerell, T.D.A. (1926). Descriptions and records of bees. CX. *Ann. Mag. Nat. Hist.* (9)**17**: 510–519 [514].

Distribution: NE coastal, Murray-Darling basin, QLD; only published localities Mackay, Brisbane, Wallangarra and near Stanthorpe.
Ecology: adult—volant; melliferous, solitary, flower visiting record: *Cassia* L. *s.lat.* [Caesalpiniaceae], *Eucalyptus* L'Hérit. [Myrtaceae], *Eugenia* L. [Myrtaceae], *Jacksonia* Smith [Fabaceae], *Leptospermum* Forster & G.Forster [Myrtaceae].
References: Cockerell, T.D.A. (1910). Descriptions and records of bees. XXX. *Ann. Mag. Nat. Hist.* (8)**6**: 17–31 (taxonomy); Cockerell, T.D.A. (1918). Some bees collected in Queensland. *Mem. Qd Mus.* **6**: 112–120 (description of male); Meade-Waldo, G. (1923). Hymenoptera. Fam. Apidae. Subfam. Prosopidinae. *Genera Insectorum* **181**: 1–45 (as *Hylaeus (Koptogaster) serotinellus* (Cockerell, 1906)); Michener, C.D. (1965). A classification of the bees of the Australian and South Pacific regions. *Bull. Am. Mus. Nat. Hist.* **130**: 1–362 (flower record).

Hylaeus (Prosopisteron) simplex Houston, T.F. 1993

Hylaeus (Prosopisteron) simplex Michener, C.D. (1965). A classification of the bees of the Australian and South Pacific regions. *Bull. Am. Mus. Nat. Hist.* **130**: 1–362 [291]

[junior secondary homonym of *Nesoprosopis simplex* Perkins, 1899 and *Prosopis simplex* Bingham, 1912].
Type data: holotype, WAM 65–730 ♀.
Type locality: Merredin, WA.

Hylaeus (Prosopisteron) simplus Houston, T.F., this work [*nom. nov.* for *Hylaeus (Prosopisteron) simplex* Michener, 1965].

Distribution: SW coastal, WA; known only from type locality.
Ecology: adult—volant; melliferous, solitary.

Hylaeus (Prosopisteron) subcoronatus Rayment, 1935

Hylaeus subcoronatus Rayment, T. (1935). *A Cluster of Bees.* Sixty essays on the life-histories of Australian bees, with specific descriptions of over 100 new species, and an introduction by Professor F.F Phillips, D.Ph., Cornell University, U.S.A. Sydney : Endeavour Press 752 pp. [658].
Type data: holotype, ANIC ♂.
Type locality: Healesville, VIC.

Distribution: SE coastal, VIC; only published localities Healesville and Beaumaris.
Ecology: adult—volant; melliferous, solitary, flower visiting record: *Dianella* Lam. [Liliaceae], *Eucalyptus* L'Hérit. [Myrtaceae].

Hylaeus (Prosopisteron) trimerops (Cockerell, 1916)

Prosopis trimerops Cockerell, T.D.A. (1916). Some bees from Australia, Tasmania, and the New Hebrides. *Proc. Acad. Nat. Sci. Philad.* **68**: 360–375 [365].
Type data: syntypes, BMNH 2♀ (a specimen is labelled 'type' and has registration number Hym.17.a.187).
Type locality: Yallingup, WA.

Distribution: SW coastal, WA; known only from type locality.
Ecology: adult—volant; melliferous, solitary.
Reference: Meade-Waldo, G. (1923). Hymenoptera. Fam. Apidae. Subfam. Prosopidinae. *Genera Insectorum* **181**: 1–45 (as *Hylaeus (Koptogaster) trimerops* (Cockerell, 1916)).

Hylaeus (Prosopisteron) turgicollaris Michener, 1965

Meroglossa xanthocollaris Rayment, T. (1954). Remarkable bees from a rain forest. *Aust. Zool.* **12**: 46–56 [52] [junior secondary homonym of *Gnathoprosopis xanthocollaris* Rayment, 1935].
Type data: holotype, ANIC ♀.
Type locality: Jamberoo, NSW.

Hylaeus (Prosopisteron) turgicollaris Michener, C.D. (1965). A classification of the bees of the Australian and South Pacific regions. *Bull. Am. Mus. Nat. Hist.* **130**: 1–362 [123] [*nom. nov.* for *Meroglossa xanthocollaris* Rayment, 1954].

Distribution: SE coastal, NSW; known only from type locality.
Ecology: adult—volant; melliferous, solitary, flower visiting record: *Leptospermum* Forster & G.Forster [Myrtaceae].

Hylaeus (Prosopisteron) vittatifrons (Cockerell, 1913)

Prosopis vittatifrons Cockerell, T.D.A. (1913). Some Australian bees. *Proc. Acad. Nat. Sci. Philad.* **65**: 28–44 [39].
Type data: holotype, USNM ♀*.
Type locality: Purnong, SA.

Distribution: Murray-Darling basin, SW coastal, SA, WA; only published localities Purnong and Perth.
Ecology: adult—volant; melliferous, solitary, flower visiting record: *Calothamnus* Lab. [Myrtaceae].
References: Cockerell, T.D.A. (1916). Some bees from Australia, Tasmania, and the New Hebrides. *Proc. Acad. Nat. Sci. Philad.* **68**: 360–375 (distribution); Meade-Waldo, G. (1923). Hymenoptera. Fam. Apidae. Subfam. Prosopidinae. *Genera Insectorum* **181**: 1–45 (as *Hylaeus (Koptogaster) vittatifrons* (Cockerell, 1913)); Houston, T.F. (1983). An extraordinary new bee and adaptation of palpi for nectar-feeding in some Australian Colletidae and Pergidae (Hymenoptera). *J. Aust. Entomol. Soc.* **22**: 263–270 (flower record).

Hylaeus (Prosopisteron) wilsoni (Rayment, 1928)

Euryglossa wilsoni Rayment, T. (1928). A new prosopoid bee. *Vict. Nat.* **45**: 97–98 [98].
Type data: holotype, NMV T1405 ♂.
Type locality: Melbourne, VIC.

Distribution: SE coastal, VIC; known only from type locality.
Ecology: adult—volant; melliferous, solitary, flower visiting record: shirley poppy, *Eucalyptus* L'Hérit. [Myrtaceae].
Reference: Rayment, T. (1935). *A Cluster of Bees.* Sixty essays on the life-histories of Australian bees, with specific descriptions of over 100 new species, and an introduction by Professor E.F. Phillips, D.Ph., Cornell University, U.S.A. Sydney : Endeavour Press 752 pp. (description of female).

Hylaeus (Prosopisteron) woyensis Rayment, 1939

Hylaeus woyensis Rayment, T. (1939). Bees from the high lands of New South Wales and Victoria. *Aust. Zool.* **9**: 263–294 [267].
Type data: holotype, ANIC ♂.
Type locality: Woy Woy, NSW.

Distribution: SE coastal, NSW; known only from type locality.
Ecology: adult—volant; melliferous, solitary.

Hylaeus (Prosopisteron) wynyardensis Cockerell, 1929

Hylaeus wynyardensis Cockerell, T.D.A. (1929). Bees in the Queensland Museum. *Mem. Qd Mus.* **9**: 298–323 [312].
Type data: holotype, QM Hy/5004 ♀.
Type locality: Wynyard, TAS.

Distribution: TAS; known only from type locality.
Ecology: adult—volant; melliferous, solitary.

Hylaeus (Prosopisteron) xanthaspis (Cockerell, 1910)

Prosopis xanthaspis Cockerell, T.D.A. (1910). Descriptions and records of bees. XXXI. *Ann. Mag. Nat. Hist. (8)*6: 160–168 [160].
Type data: syntypes, BMNH 8♀ (a specimen is labelled 'type' and has registration number Hym.17.a.74).
Type locality: Mackay, QLD.
Prosopis mackayensis Friese, H. (1924). Ueber die Bienen Australiens. *Konowia* **3**: 216–249 [225].
Type data: syntypes (probable), AMNH 2♀*.
Type locality: Mackay, QLD.
Prosopis turneri Friese, H. (1924). Ueber die Bienen Australiens. *Konowia* **3**: 216–249 [225].
Type data: holotype (probable), AMNH ♀*.
Type locality: Mackay, QLD.

Taxonomic decision for synonymy: Cockerell, T.D.A. (1929). Bees, chiefly Australian species, described or determined by Dr. H. Friese. *Am. Mus. Novit.* 343: 1–20 [18].

Distribution: NE coastal, QLD; known only from type locality.
Ecology: adult—volant; melliferous, solitary, flower visiting record: *Cassia* L. *s.lat.* [Caesalpiniaceae], *Eucalyptus* L'Hérit. [Myrtaceae].
References: Cockerell, T.D.A. (1911). Descriptions and records of bees. XL. *Ann. Mag. Nat. Hist. (8)*8: 763–770 (taxonomy); Cockerell, T.D.A. (1912). Descriptions and records of bees. XLI. *Ann. Mag. Nat. Hist. (8)*9: 139–149 (description of male); Meade-Waldo, G. (1923). Hymenoptera. Fam. Apidae. Subfam. Prosopidinae. *Genera Insectorum* **181**: 1–45 (as *Hylaeus (Koptogaster) xanthaspis* (Cockerell, 1910)).

Hylaeus (Prosopisteron) xanthognathus Rayment, 1935

Hylaeus xanthognathus Rayment, T. (1935). *A Cluster of Bees.* Sixty essays on the life-histories of Australian bees, with specific descriptions of over 100 new species, and an introduction by Professor E.F. Phillips, D.Ph., Cornell University, U.S.A. Sydney : Endeavour Press 752 pp. [657].
Type data: holotype, ANIC ♂.
Type locality: Malvern, VIC (Melbourne on label).

Distribution: SE coastal, VIC; known only from type locality.
Ecology: adult—volant; melliferous, solitary.

Hylaeus (Prosopisteron) xanthopsyche (Cockerell, 1922)

Prosopis xanthopsyche Cockerell, T.D.A. (1922). Australian bees in the Queensland Museum. *Mem. Qd Mus.* **7**: 257–279 [267].
Type data: holotype, QM T2429 ♂.
Type locality: Brisbane, QLD.

Distribution: NE coastal, QLD; known only from type locality.
Ecology: adult—volant; melliferous, solitary.
Reference: Meade-Waldo, G. (1923). Hymenoptera. Fam. Apidae. Subfam. Prosopidinae. *Genera Insectorum* **181**: 1–45 (as *Hylaeus (Koptogaster) xanthopsyche* (Cockerell, 1922)).

Hylaeus (Pseudhylaeus) Cockerell, 1929

Pseudhylaeus Cockerell, T.D.A. (1929). Bees in the Queensland Museum. *Mem. Qd Mus.* **9**: 298–323 [299].
Type species: *Euryglossa albocuneata* Cockerell, 1913 by original designation.

Hylaeus (Pseudhylaeus) albocuneatus (Cockerell, 1913)

Euryglossa albocuneata Cockerell, T.D.A. (1913). Descriptions and records of bees. LV. *Ann. Mag. Nat. Hist.* (8)**12**: 505–514 [510].
Type data: holotype, USNM ♀*.
Type locality: Windsor, VIC.

Distribution: NE coastal, Murray-Darling basin, SE coastal, QLD, NSW, VIC.
Ecology: adult—volant; melliferous, solitary, flower visiting record: *Wahlenbergia* Roth [Campanulaceae].
References: Cockerell, T.D.A. (1929). Bees in the Queensland Museum. *Mem. Qd Mus.* **9**: 298–323 (description of male, as *Pseudhylaeus albocuneata* (Cockerell, 1913)); Michener, C.D. (1965). A classification of the bees of the Australian and South Pacific regions. *Bull. Am. Mus. Nat. Hist.* **130**: 1–362 (flower record).

Hylaeus (Pseudhylaeus) albomaculatus (Smith, 1879)

Prosopis albomaculata Smith, F. (1879). *Descriptions of New Species of Hymenoptera in the Collection of the British Museum.* London : British Museum xxi 240 pp. [24].
Type data: holotype, BMNH Hym.17.a.68 ♀.
Type locality: Swan River, WA.

Distribution: SW coastal, WA; known only from type locality.
Ecology: adult—volant; melliferous, solitary.
Reference: Meade-Waldo, G. (1923). Hymenoptera. Fam. Apidae. Subfam. Prosopidinae. *Genera Insectorum* **181**: 1–45 (as *Hylaeus (Koptogaster) albomaculatus* (Smith, 1879)).

Hylaeus (Pseudhylaeus) hypoleucus (Cockerell, 1918)

Euryglossa hypoleuca Cockerell, T.D.A. (1918). Some bees collected in Queensland. *Mem. Qd Mus.* **6**: 112–120 [115].
Type data: holotype, QM Hy/4134 ♂.
Type locality: Brisbane, QLD.

Distribution: NE coastal, QLD; only published localities Brisbane and Caloundra.
Ecology: adult—volant; melliferous, solitary.
References: Cockerell, T.D.A. (1922). Australian bees in the Queensland Museum. *Mem. Qd Mus.* **7**: 257–279 (description of female); Cockerell, T.D.A. (1929). Bees in the Queensland Museum. *Mem. Qd Mus.* **9**: 298–323 (as *Pseudhylaeus hypoleucus* (Cockerell, 1918)).

Hylaeus (Pseudhylaeus) mirandus (Rayment, 1930)

Meroglossa miranda Rayment, T. (1930). New and remarkable bees. *Proc. R. Soc. Vict.* **43**: 42–61 [45].
Type data: holotype, WAM 22–284 ♂.
Type locality: Milly Milly Station, WA.

Distribution: NW coastal, WA; known only from type locality.
Ecology: adult—volant; melliferous, solitary, flower visiting record: *Eremophila* R.Br. [Myoporaceae].
References: Rayment, T. (1935). *A Cluster of Bees. Sixty essays on the life-histories of Australian bees, with specific descriptions of over 100 new species, and an introduction by Professor E.F. Phillips, D.Ph., Cornell University, U.S.A.* Sydney : Endeavour Press 752 pp. (illustration); Houston, T.F. (1983). An extraordinary new bee and adaptation of palpi for nectar-feeding in some Australian Colletidae and Pergidae (Hymenoptera). *J. Aust. Entomol. Soc.* **22**: 263–270 (palps).

Hylaeus (Pseudhylaeus) multigibbosus Michener, 1965

Hylaeus (Pseudhylaeus) multigibbosus Michener, C.D. (1965). A classification of the bees of the Australian and South Pacific regions. *Bull. Am. Mus. Nat. Hist.* **130**: 1–362 [296].
Type data: holotype, ANIC ♂.
Type locality: Canberra, ACT.

Distribution: Murray-Darling basin, QLD, ACT; only published localities Jondaryan and Canberra.
Ecology: adult—volant; melliferous, solitary, flower visiting record: *Wahlenbergia* Roth [Campanulaceae].

Hylaeus (Rhodohylaeus) Michener, 1965

Rhodohylaeus Michener, C.D. (1965). A classification of the bees of the Australian and South Pacific regions. *Bull. Am. Mus. Nat. Hist.* **130**: 1–362 [124] [proposed with subgeneric rank in *Hylaeus* Fabricius, 1793]. Type species: *Prosopis cenibera* Cockerell, 1910 by original designation.

Hylaeus (Rhodohylaeus) ancoratus (Cockerell, 1912)

Prosopis ancorata Cockerell, T.D.A. (1912). Descriptions and records of bees. XLI. *Ann. Mag. Nat. Hist. (8)9*: 139–149 [148].
Type data: holotype, BMNH Hym.17.a.96 ♂.
Type locality: Sydney, NSW.

Distribution: SE coastal, NSW; known only from type locality.
Ecology: adult—volant; melliferous, solitary.
Reference: Meade-Waldo, G. (1923). Hymenoptera. Fam. Apidae. Subfam. Prosopidinae. *Genera Insectorum* **181**: 1–45 (as *Hylaeus (Koptogaster) anconatus*, incorrect subsequent spelling).

Hylaeus (Rhodohylaeus) ceniberus (Cockerell, 1910)

Prosopis cenibera Cockerell, T.D.A. (1910). Descriptions and records of bees. XXXI. *Ann. Mag. Nat. Hist. (8)6*: 160–168 [165].
Type data: syntypes, BMNH 2♀ (a specimen is labelled 'type' and has registration number Hym.17.a.45).
Type locality: Mackay, QLD.

Distribution: NE coastal, Murray-Darling basin, QLD.
Ecology: adult—volant; melliferous, solitary, flower visiting record: *Angophora* Cav. [Myrtaceae], *Callistemon* R.Br. [Myrtaceae], *Eucalyptus* L'Hérit. [Myrtaceae], *Leptospermum* Forster & G.Forster [Myrtaceae], *Melaleuca* L. [Myrtaceae], *Xanthorrhoea* Sm. [Xanthorrhoeaceae].
References: Cockerell, T.D.A. (1914). Australian bees of the family Prosopididae. *Insecutor Inscit. Menstr.* **2**: 97–101 (distribution); Meade-Waldo, G. (1923). Hymenoptera. Fam. Apidae. Subfam. Prosopidinae. *Genera Insectorum* **181**: 1–45 (as *Hylaeus (Koptogaster) ceniberus* (Cockerell, 1910)); Michener, C.D. (1965). A classification of the bees of the Australian and South Pacific regions. *Bull. Am. Mus. Nat. Hist.* **130**: 1–362 (flower record).

Hylaeus (Rhodohylaeus) colei Rayment, 1935

Hylaeus lateralis colei Rayment, T. (1935). *A Cluster of Bees.* Sixty essays on the life-histories of Australian bees, with specific descriptions of over 100 new species, and an introduction by Professor E.F. Phillips, D.Ph., Cornell University, U.S.A. Sydney : Endeavour Press 752 pp. [662].
Type data: syntypes, ANIC 1♀, ZMB 1♀.
Type locality: Melbourne, VIC.

Distribution: SE coastal, VIC; known only from type locality.
Ecology: adult—volant; melliferous, solitary.
Reference: Michener, C.D. (1965). A classification of the bees of the Australian and South Pacific regions. *Bull. Am. Mus. Nat. Hist.* **130**: 1–362 [126] (taxonomy).

Hylaeus (Rhodohylaeus) constrictiformis (Cockerell, 1910)

Prosopis constrictiformis Cockerell, T.D.A. (1910). Descriptions and records of bees. XXX. *Ann. Mag. Nat. Hist. (8)6*: 17–31 [27].
Type data: holotype, BMNH Hym.17.a.52 ♂.
Type locality: Cooktown, QLD.

Distribution: NE coastal, QLD; known only from type locality.
Ecology: adult—volant; melliferous, solitary.
Reference: Meade-Waldo, G. (1923). Hymenoptera. Fam. Apidae. Subfam. Prosopidinae. *Genera Insectorum* **181**: 1–45 (as *Hylaeus (Koptogaster) constrictiformis* (Cockerell, 1910)).

Hylaeus (Rhodohylaeus) constrictus (Cockerell, 1905)

Prosopis constricta Cockerell, T.D.A. (1905). Descriptions and records of bees. V. *Ann. Mag. Nat. Hist. (7)16*: 465–477 [468].
Type data: holotype, BMNH Hym.17.a.56 ♂.
Type locality: Mackay, QLD.

Distribution: NE coastal, Murray-Darling basin, QLD.
Ecology: adult—volant; melliferous, solitary, flower visiting record: *Alphitonia* Reisseck ex Endl. [Rhamnaceae], *Angophora* Cav. [Myrtaceae], *Callistemon* R.Br. [Myrtaceae], *Eucalyptus* L'Hérit. [Myrtaceae], *Leptospermum* Forster & G.Forster [Myrtaceae], *Melaleuca* L. [Myrtaceae].
References: Cockerell, T.D.A. (1910). Descriptions and records of bees. XXX. *Ann. Mag. Nat. Hist. (8)6*: 17–31 (distribution); Cockerell, T.D.A. (1918). Some bees collected in Queensland. *Mem. Qd Mus.* **6**: 112–120 (distribution); Meade-Waldo, G. (1923). Hymenoptera. Fam. Apidae. Subfam. Prosopidinae. *Genera Insectorum* **181**: 1–45 (as *Hylaeus (Koptogaster) constrictus* (Cockerell, 1905)).

Hylaeus (Rhodohylaeus) coronatulus (Cockerell, 1914)

Prosopis coronatula Cockerell, T.D.A. (1914). Descriptions and records of bees. LXIV. *Ann. Mag. Nat. Hist. (8)14*: 464–472 [471].
Type data: syntypes, BMNH 2♂ (a specimen is labelled 'type' and has registration number Hym.17.a.95).
Type locality: Brewarrina, NSW.

Distribution: Murray-Darling basin, NSW; known only from type locality.
Ecology: adult—volant; melliferous, solitary.
Reference: Meade-Waldo, G. (1923). Hymenoptera. Fam. Apidae. Subfam. Prosopidinae. *Genera Insectorum* **181**: 1–45 (as *Hylaeus (Koptogaster) coronatula* (Cockerell, 1914)).

Hylaeus (Rhodohylaeus) coronatus (Cockerell, 1905)

Prosopis coronata Cockerell, T.D.A. (1905). Descriptions and records of bees. V. *Ann. Mag. Nat. Hist. (7)***16**: 465–477 [469].
Type data: holotype, BMNH Hym.17.a.51 ♂.
Type locality: Mackay, QLD.

Distribution: NE coastal, Murray-Darling basin, QLD; only published localities Mackay, Brisbane, Wallangarra and Stanthorpe.
Ecology: adult—volant; melliferous, solitary, flower visiting record: *Jacksonia* Smith [Fabaceae], *Leptospermum* Forster & G.Forster [Myrtaceae].
References: Cockerell, T.D.A. (1910). Descriptions and records of bees. XXXI. *Ann. Mag. Nat. Hist. (8)***6**: 160–168 (description of female); Cockerell, T.D.A. (1922). Australian bees in the Queensland Museum. *Mem. Qd Mus.* **7**: 257–279 (variety); Meade-Waldo, G. (1923). Hymenoptera. Fam. Apidae. Subfam. Prosopidinae. *Genera Insectorum* **181**: 1–45 (as *Hylaeus (Koptogaster) coronata* (Cockerell, 1905)); Michener, C.D. (1965). A classification of the bees of the Australian and South Pacific regions. *Bull. Am. Mus. Nat. Hist.* **130**: 1–362 (flower record).

Hylaeus (Rhodohylaeus) haematopodus (Cockerell, 1913)

Prosopis haematopoda Cockerell, T.D.A. (1913). Some Australian bees. *Proc. Acad. Nat. Sci. Philad.* **65**: 28–44 [42].
Type data: holotype, BMNH Hym.17.a.99 ♀.
Type locality: SA.

Distribution: SA; known only from type locality, exact locality unknown.
Ecology: adult—volant; melliferous, solitary.
Reference: Meade-Waldo, G. (1923). Hymenoptera. Fam. Apidae. Subfam. Prosopidinae. *Genera Insectorum* **181**: 1–45 (as *Hylaeus (Koptogaster) haematopodus* (Cockerell, 1913)).

Hylaeus (Rhodohylaeus) indecisus Cockerell, 1929

Hylaeus indecisus Cockerell, T.D.A. (1929). Bees in the Australian Museum collection. *Rec. Aust. Mus.* **17**: 199–243 [224].
Type data: holotype, AM 49022 ♀.
Type locality: Sydney, NSW.

Distribution: SE coastal, NSW; known only from type locality.
Ecology: adult—volant; melliferous, solitary.

Hylaeus (Rhodohylaeus) lateralis (Smith, 1879)

Prosopis lateralis Smith, F. (1879). *Descriptions of New Species of Hymenoptera in the Collection of the British Museum.* London : British Museum xxi 240 pp. [23].
Type data: holotype, BMNH Hym.17.a.49 ♀.
Type locality: Champion Bay (Geraldton), WA.

Hylaeus lateralis simillimus Rayment, T. (1935). *A Cluster of Bees.* Sixty essays on the life-histories of Australian bees, with specific descriptions of over 100 new species, and an introduction by Professor E.F. Phillips, D.Ph., Cornell University, U.S.A. Sydney : Endeavour Press 752 pp. [662].
Type data: holotype, ANIC ♀.
Type locality: Kiata, VIC.

Taxonomic decision for synonymy: Michener, C.D. (1965). A classification of the bees of the Australian and South Pacific regions. *Bull. Am. Mus. Nat. Hist.* **130**: 1–362 [126].

Distribution: NE coastal, Murray-Darling basin, S Gulfs, NW coastal, QLD, VIC, SA, WA; only published localities Mackay, Kiata, Adelaide and Champion Bay.
Ecology: adult—volant; melliferous, solitary, nest in hollow twigs of *Loranthus* Jacq. [Loranthaceae].
References: Cockerell, T.D.A. (1905). Descriptions and records of bees. V. *Ann. Mag. Nat. Hist. (7)***16**: 465–477 (taxonomy); Cockerell, T.D.A. (1910). Some Australian bees in the Berlin Museum. *J. N.Y. Entomol. Soc.* **18**: 98–114 (distribution); Meade-Waldo, G. (1923). Hymenoptera. Fam. Apidae. Subfam. Prosopidinae. *Genera Insectorum* **181**: 1–45 (as *Hylaeus (Koptogaster) lateralis* (Smith, 1879)); Rayment, T. (1935). *A Cluster of Bees.* Sixty essays on the life-histories of Australian bees, with specific descriptions of over 100 new species, and an introduction by Professor E.F. Phillips, D.Ph., Cornell University, U.S.A. Sydney : Endeavour Press 752 pp. (nest); Evans, H.E. & Matthews, R.W. (1973). Systematics and nesting behavior of Australian *Bembix* sand wasps (Hymenoptera, Sphecidae). *Mem. Am. Entomol. Inst.* **20**: 1–387 (as prey); Michener, C.D. (1992). Sexual dimorphism in the glossa of Colletidae (Hymenoptera, Apoidea). *J. Kansas Entomol. Soc.* **65**: 1–9 (glossa).

Hylaeus (Rhodohylaeus) maiellus Rayment, 1935

Hylaeus maiellus Rayment, T. (1935). *A Cluster of Bees.* Sixty essays on the life-histories of Australian bees, with specific descriptions of over 100 new species, and an introduction by Professor E.F. Phillips, D.Ph., Cornell University, U.S.A. Sydney : Endeavour Press 752 pp. [655].
Type data: holotype, ANIC ♂.
Type locality: Borroloola, NT.

Distribution: NE coastal, Murray-Darling basin, N Gulf, QLD, VIC, NT; only published localities Edungalba, Glenmorgan, Gunbower and Borroloola.
Ecology: adult—volant; melliferous, solitary, flower visiting record: *Callistemon* R.Br. [Myrtaceae], *Melaleuca* L. [Myrtaceae].
Reference: Rayment, T. (1954). Incidence of acarid mites on the biology of bees. *Aust. Zool.* **12**: 26–38 (distribution).

Hylaeus (Rhodohylaeus) melanocephalus (Cockerell, 1922)

Prosopis melanocephala Cockerell, T.D.A. (1922). Australian bees in the Queensland Museum. *Mem. Qd Mus.* 7: 257–279 [268].
Type data: holotype, QM T2428 ♀.
Type locality: Darra, QLD.

Distribution: NE coastal, QLD; only published localities Darra and Brisbane.
Ecology: adult—volant; melliferous, solitary.
Reference: Meade-Waldo, G. (1923). Hymenoptera. Fam. Apidae. Subfam. Prosopidinae. *Genera Insectorum* **181**: 1–45 (as *Hylaeus (Koptogaster) melanocephalus* (Cockerell, 1922)).

Hylaeus (Rhodohylaeus) meriti Rayment, 1935

Hylaeus constrictus meriti Rayment, T. (1935). *A Cluster of Bees.* Sixty essays on the life-histories of Australian bees, with specific descriptions of over 100 new species, and an introduction by Professor E.F. Phillips, D.Ph., Cornell University, U.S.A. Sydney : Endeavour Press 752 pp. [656].
Type data: holotype, ANIC ♂.
Type locality: Kiata, VIC.

Distribution: Murray-Darling basin, VIC; known only from type locality.
Ecology: adult—volant; melliferous, solitary.
Reference: Michener, C.D. (1965). A classification of the bees of the Australian and South Pacific regions. *Bull. Am. Mus. Nat. Hist.* **130**: 1–362 [126] (taxonomy).

Hylaeus (Rhodohylaeus) perrufus Cockerell, 1929

Hylaeus perrufus Cockerell, T.D.A. (1929). Bees in the Queensland Museum. *Mem. Qd Mus.* **9**: 298–323 [314].
Type data: holotype, QM Hy/4030 ♀.
Type locality: Bunya Mtns, QLD.

Distribution: Murray-Darling basin, QLD; known only from type locality.
Ecology: adult—volant; melliferous, solitary.

Hylaeus (Rhodohylaeus) proximus (Smith, 1879)

Prosopis proxima Smith, F. (1879). *Descriptions of New Species of Hymenoptera in the Collection of the British Museum.* London : British Museum xxi 240 pp. [24].
Type data: holotype, BMNH Hym.17.a.42 ♀.
Type locality: Geraldton (as Champion Bay), WA.

Distribution: Murray-Darling basin, NW coastal, SA, WA; only published localities Purnong and Champion Bay.
Ecology: adult—volant; melliferous, solitary.
References: Cockerell, T.D.A. (1913). Some Australian bees. *Proc. Acad. Nat. Sci. Philad.* **65**: 28–44 (variety); Meade-Waldo, G. (1923). Hymenoptera. Fam. Apidae. Subfam. Prosopidinae. *Genera Insectorum* **181**: 1–45 (as *Hylaeus (Koptogaster) proximus* (Smith, 1879)); Rayment, T. (1935). *A Cluster*

of Bees. Sixty essays on the life-histories of Australian bees, with specific descriptions of over 100 new species, and an introduction by Professor E.F. Phillips, D.Ph., Cornell University, U.S.A. Sydney : Endeavour Press 752 pp. (variety).

Hylaeus (Rhodohylaeus) rufipes (Smith, 1853)

Prosopis rufipes Smith, F. (1853). *Catalogue of Hymenopterous Insects in the Collection of the British Museum.* Part I. Andrenidae and Apidae. London : British Museum 197 pp. [27].
Type data: holotype, BMNH Hym.17.a.66 ♀.
Type locality: Australia (as New Holland).

Distribution: Australia, exact locality unknown.
Ecology: adult—volant; melliferous, solitary.
References: Cockerell, T.D.A. (1910). Some Australian bees in the Berlin Museum. *J. N.Y. Entomol. Soc.* **18**: 98–114 (description of male); Meade-Waldo, G. (1923). Hymenoptera. Fam. Apidae. Subfam. Prosopidinae. *Genera Insectorum* **181**: 1–45 (as *Hylaeus (Koptogaster) rufipes* (Smith, 1853)).

Hylaeus (Rhodohylaeus) semicastaneus (Cockerell, 1918)

Euryglossa semicastanea Cockerell, T.D.A. (1918). Some bees collected in Queensland. *Mem. Qd Mus.* **6**: 112–120 [115].
Type data: holotype, QM Hy/4136 ♀.
Type locality: Brisbane, QLD.

Distribution: NE coastal, QLD; known only from type locality.
Ecology: adult—volant; melliferous, solitary.
Reference: Cockerell, T.D.A. (1929). Bees in the Australian Museum collection. *Rec. Aust. Mus.* **17**: 199–243 (taxonomy).

Hylaeus (Rhodohylaeus) subconstrictus (Cockerell, 1922)

Prosopis ancorata subconstricta Cockerell, T.D.A. (1922). Australian bees in the Queensland Museum. *Mem. Qd Mus.* 7: 257–279 [268].
Type data: holotype, QM T2432 ♂.
Type locality: Brisbane, QLD.

Distribution: NE coastal, QLD; known only from type locality.
Ecology: adult—volant; melliferous, solitary, flower visiting record: *Melaleuca* L. [Myrtaceae].
References: Meade-Waldo, G. (1923). Hymenoptera. Fam. Apidae. Subfam. Prosopidinae. *Genera Insectorum* **181**: 1–45 (as *Hylaeus (Koptogaster) anconatus subconstrictus* (Cockerell, 1922)); Michener, C.D. (1965). A classification of the bees of the Australian and South Pacific regions. *Bull. Am. Mus. Nat. Hist.* **130**: 1–362 [126] (taxonomy).

Hylaeus (Rhodohylaeus) sublateralis (Cockerell, 1914)

Prosopis sublateralis Cockerell, T.D.A. (1914). Descriptions and records of bees. LXIV. *Ann. Mag. Nat. Hist. (8)*14: 464–472 [471].
Type data: holotype, BMNH Hym.17.a.47 ♂.
Type locality: Yarrawin (Brewarrina), NSW.

Distribution: Murray-Darling basin, NSW; known only from type locality.
Ecology: adult—volant; melliferous, solitary.
Reference: Meade-Waldo, G. (1923). Hymenoptera. Fam. Apidae. Subfam. Prosopidinae. *Genera Insectorum* 181: 1–45 (as *Hylaeus (Koptogaster) sublateralis* (Cockerell, 1914)).

Hylaeus (Rhodohylaeus) subplebeius (Cockerell, 1905)

Prosopis subplebeia Cockerell, T.D.A. (1905). Descriptions and records of bees. V. *Ann. Mag. Nat. Hist. (7)*16: 465–477 [469].
Type data: holotype, BMNH Hym.17.a.50 ♂.
Type locality: Mackay, QLD.

Distribution: NE coastal, QLD; known only from type locality.
Ecology: adult—volant; melliferous, solitary.
Reference: Meade-Waldo, G. (1923). Hymenoptera. Fam. Apidae. Subfam. Prosopidinae. *Genera Insectorum* 181: 1–45 (as *Hylaeus (Koptogaster) subplebeius* (Cockerell, 1905)).

Hylaeus (Sphaerhylaeus) Cockerell, 1929

Sphaerhylaeus Cockerell, T.D.A. (1929). Bees in the Australian Museum collection. *Rec. Aust. Mus.* 17: 199–243 [217] [proposed with subgeneric rank in *Gnathoprosopis* Perkins, 1912]. Type species: *Gnathoprosopis (Sphaerhylaeus) globulifera* Cockerell, 1929 by monotypy.

Hylaeus (Sphaerhylaeus) bicolorellus Michener, 1965

Sphaerhylaeus bicoloratus Rayment, T. (1948). Notes on remarkable wasps and bees. With specific descriptions. *Aust. Zool.* 11: 238–254 [250] [junior secondary homonym of *Prosopis bicolorata* Smith, 1853].
Type data: holotype, ANIC ♂.
Type locality: Narrow Neck, Blue Mtns, NSW.
Hylaeus (Sphaerhylaeus) bicolorellus Michener, C.D. (1965). A classification of the bees of the Australian and South Pacific regions. *Bull. Am. Mus. Nat. Hist.* 130: 1–362 [129] [*nom. nov.* for *Sphaerhylaeus bicoloratus* Rayment, 1948].

Distribution: SE coastal, NSW; only published localities Blue Mts and Fraser Park.
Ecology: adult—volant; melliferous, solitary, flower visiting record: *Telopea* R.Br. [Proteaceae].
Reference: Houston, T.F. (1981). A revision of the Australian hylaeine bees (Hymenoptera : Colletidae).
II. *Aust. J. Zool. Suppl. Ser.* 80: 1–128 (redescription).

Hylaeus (Sphaerhylaeus) globuliferus (Cockerell, 1929)

Gnathoprosopis (Sphaerhylaeus) globulifera Cockerell, T.D.A. (1929). Bees in the Australian Museum collection. *Rec. Aust. Mus.* 17: 199–243 [218].
Type data: holotype, AM K48307 ♂.
Type locality: King George Sound, WA.

Distribution: SW coastal, WA.
Ecology: adult—volant; melliferous, solitary, flower visiting record: *Grevillea* R.Br. ex J. Knight [Proteaceae].
Reference: Houston, T.F. (1981). A revision of the Australian hylaeine bees (Hymenoptera : Colletidae).
II. *Aust. J. Zool. Suppl. Ser.* 80: 1–128 (redescription).

Hylaeus (Xenohylaeus) Michener, 1965

Xenohylaeus Michener, C.D. (1965). A classification of the bees of the Australian and South Pacific regions. *Bull. Am. Mus. Nat. Hist.* 130: 1–362 [136] [proposed with subgeneric rank in *Hylaeus* Fabricius, 1793]. Type species: *Hylaeus (Xenohylaeus) rieki* Michener, 1965 by original designation.

Hylaeus (Xenohylaeus) desertoris Houston, 1981

Hylaeus (Xenohylaeus) desertoris Houston, T.F. (1981). A revision of the Australian hylaeine bees (Hymenoptera : Colletidae). II. *Aust. J. Zool. Suppl. Ser.* 80: 1–128 [116].
Type data: holotype, QM T6868 ♀.
Type locality: Glen Helen, NT.

Distribution: S Gulfs, Lake Eyre basin, SW coastal, W plateau, SA, WA.
Ecology: adult—volant; melliferous, solitary, flower visiting record: *Eremophila* R.Br. [Myoporaceae].

Hylaeus (Xenohylaeus) kelvini (Cockerell, 1912)

Prosopis kelvini Cockerell, T.D.A. (1912). Descriptions and records of bees. XLVII. *Ann. Mag. Nat. Hist. (8)*10: 484–494 [489].
Type data: holotype, QM Hy/4149 ♀.
Type locality: Kelvin Grove, Brisbane, QLD.
Hylaeus gibbonsi Cockerell, T.D.A. (1929). Bees in the Australian Museum collection. *Rec. Aust. Mus.* 17: 199–243 [223].
Type data: holotype, AM K49012 ♀.
Type locality: Sydney, NSW.

Taxonomic decision for synonymy: Houston, T.F. (1981). A revision of the Australian hylaeine bees (Hymenoptera : Colletidae). II. *Aust. J. Zool. Suppl. Ser.* 80: 1–128 [119].

Distribution: NE coastal, SE coastal, QLD, NSW.
Ecology: adult—volant; melliferous, solitary, flower visiting record: *Daviesia* Sm. [Fabaceae], *Jacksonia* Smith [Fabaceae], *Pultenaea* Sm. [Fabaceae].
References: Meade-Waldo, G. (1923). Hymenoptera. Fam. Apidae. Subfam. Prosopidinae. *Genera In-*

sectorum **181**: 1–45 (as *Hylaeus (Koptogaster) kelvini* (Cockerell, 1912)); Cockerell, T.D.A. (1929). Bees in the Australian Museum collection. *Rec. Aust. Mus.* **17**: 199–243 (as *Meroglossa kelvini* (Cockerell, 1912)); Rayment, T. (1948). Notes on remarkable wasps and bees. With specific descriptions. *Aust. Zool.* **11**: 238–254 (description of male, as *Sphaerhylaeus gibbonsi* (Cockerell, 1929)); Michener, C.D. (1965). A classification of the bees of the Australian and South Pacific regions. *Bull. Am. Mus. Nat. Hist.* **130**: 1–362 (flower record); Michener, C.D. (1992). Sexual dimorphism in the glossa of Colletidae (Hymenoptera, Apoidea). *J. Kansas Entomol. Soc.* **65**: 1–9 (glossa).

Hylaeus (Xenohylaeus) leptospermi (Cockerell, 1922)

Prosopis leptospermi Cockerell, T.D.A. (1922). Australian bees in the Queensland Museum. *Mem. Qd Mus.* **7**: 257–279 [266].
Type data: holotype, QM Hy/2430 ♀.
Type locality: Sunnybank, Brisbane, QLD.

Hylaeus (Xenohylaeus) rieki Michener, C.D. (1965). A classification of the bees of the Australian and South Pacific regions. *Bull. Am. Mus. Nat. Hist.* **130**: 1–362 [298].
Type data: holotype, ANIC ♂.
Type locality: Canberra, ACT.

Taxonomic decision for synonymy: Houston, T.F. (1981). A revision of the Australian hylaeine bees (Hymenoptera : Colletidae). II. *Aust. J. Zool. Suppl. Ser.* **80**: 1–128 [122].

Distribution: NE coastal, Murray-Darling basin, SE coastal, QLD, NSW, ACT, VIC.
Ecology: adult—volant; melliferous, solitary, flower visiting record: *Daviesia* Sm. [Fabaceae], *Jacksonia* Smith [Fabaceae], *Leptospermum* Forster & G.Forster [Myrtaceae].
References: Meade-Waldo, G. (1923). Hymenoptera. Fam. Apidae. Subfam. Prosopidinae. *Genera Insectorum* **181**: 1–45 (as *Hylaeus (Koptogaster) leptospermi* (Cockerell, 1922)); Michener, C.D. (1965). A classification of the bees of the Australian and South Pacific regions. *Bull. Am. Mus. Nat. Hist.* **130**: 1–362 (as *Hylaeus (Euprosopis) leptospermi* (Cockerell, 1922)); Michener, C.D. (1992). Sexual dimorphism in the glossa of Colletidae (Hymenoptera, Apoidea). *J. Kansas Entomol. Soc.* **65**: 1–9 (glossa, as *Hylaeus (Xenohylaeus) rieki*).

Hylaeus (Xenohylaeus) scutaticornis Michener, 1965

Hylaeus (Xenohylaeus) scutaticornis Michener, C.D. (1965). A classification of the bees of the Australian and South Pacific regions. *Bull. Am. Mus. Nat. Hist.* **130**: 1–362 [299] [*Xenohylaeus* misspelled as *Zenohylaeus* at head of description].
Type data: holotype, ANIC ♂.
Type locality: Cottonvale, QLD.

Distribution: Murray-Darling basin, SE coastal, S Gulfs, SW coastal, QLD, NSW, VIC, SA, WA.
Ecology: adult—volant; melliferous, solitary, flower visiting record: *Daviesia* Sm. [Fabaceae], *Jacksonia* Smith [Fabaceae], *Pultenaea* Sm. [Fabaceae].
Reference: Houston, T.F. (1981). A revision of the Australian hylaeine bees (Hymenoptera : Colletidae). II. *Aust. J. Zool. Suppl. Ser.* **80**: 1–128 (redescription).

Hylaeus (Unplaced)

Hylaeus anmelanocephalus Rayment, 1954

Hylaeus anmelanocephalus Rayment, T. (1954). Incidence of acarid mites on the biology of bees. *Aust. Zool.* **12**: 26–38 [28].
Type data: holotype (probable), ANIC ♀.
Type locality: Cheltenham, NSW.

Distribution: SE coastal, NSW; only published localities Lane Cove and Cheltenham.
Ecology: adult—volant; melliferous, solitary, nest in galleries in wood.

Hylaeus borchii Rayment, 1935

Hylaeus borchii Rayment, T. (1935). *A Cluster of Bees*. Sixty essays on the life-histories of Australian bees, with specific descriptions of over 100 new species, and an introduction by Professor E.F. Phillips, D.Ph., Cornell University, U.S.A. Sydney : Endeavour Press 752 pp. [661] [junior secondary homonym of *Gnathoprosopis borchii* Rayment, 1935: 644].
Type data: holotype, ANIC ♀ (described as ♂).
Type locality: Kiata, VIC.

Distribution: SE coastal, VIC; known only from type locality.
Ecology: adult—volant; melliferous, solitary.

Hylaeus callosus (Cockerell, 1910)

Prosopis callosa Cockerell, T.D.A. (1910). Some Australian bees in the Berlin Museum. *J. N.Y. Entomol. Soc.* **18**: 98–114 [104].
Type data: holotype, ZMB ♂*.
Type locality: Port Phillip (as Port Philip), VIC.

Distribution: SE coastal, VIC; known only from type locality.
Ecology: adult—volant; melliferous, solitary.
Reference: Meade-Waldo, G. (1923). Hymenoptera. Fam. Apidae. Subfam. Prosopidinae. *Genera Insectorum* **181**: 1–45 (as *Hylaeus (Koptogaster) callosa* (Cockerell, 1910)).

Hylaeus liogonius (Vachal, 1899)

Prosopis liogonia Vachal, J. (1899). Contributions Hyménoptèriques. *Ann. Soc. Entomol. Fr.* **68**: 534–539 [537].
Type data: holotype (probable), MNHP (Sichel coll.) ♀*.
Type locality: Australia.

Distribution: Australia, exact locality unknown.

Ecology: adult—volant; melliferous, solitary.

References: Meade-Waldo, G. (1923). Hymenoptera. Fam. Apidae. Subfam. Prosopidinae. *Genera Insectorum* **181**: 1–45 (as *Hylaeus (Koptogaster) liogonia* (Vachal, 1899)); Houston, T.F. (1975). A revision of the Australian hylaeine bees (Hymenoptera : Colletidae). I. *Aust. J. Zool. Suppl. Ser.* **36**: 1–135 [132].

Hylaeus melaleucae Rayment, 1953

Hylaeus melaleucae Rayment, T. (1953). *Bees of the Portland District.* Victoria : Portland Field Naturalist's Club 39 pp. [9].

Type data: holotype, whereabouts unknown (T. Rayment pers. coll., not found in ANIC) ♀*.

Type locality: Gorae West, VIC.

Distribution: SE coastal, VIC; known only from type locality.

Ecology: adult—volant; melliferous, solitary, flower visiting record: *Melaleuca* L. [Myrtaceae].

Hyleoides Smith, 1853

Hyleoides Smith, F. (1853). *Catalogue of Hymenopterous Insects in the Collection of the British Museum.* Part I. Andrenidae and Apidae. London : British Museum 197 pp. [32]. Type species: *Vespa concinna* Fabricius, 1775 by subsequent designation, see Taschenberg, E.L. (1883). Die Gattungen der Bienen (Anthophila). *Berl. Entomol. Z.* **27**: 37–100 [45].

Hylaeoides Dalla Torre, K.W. (1896). *Catalogus Hymenopterorum Hucusque Descriptorum Systematicus et Synonymicus.* Apidae (Anthophila). Lipsiae : G. Engelmann Vol. x 643 pp. [51] [unjustified emendation of *Hyleoides* Smith, 1853]. Type species: *Vespa concinna* Fabricius, 1775 by subsequent designation, see Taschenberg, E.L. (1883). Die Gattungen der Bienen (Anthophila). *Berl. Entomol. Z.* **27**: 37–100 [45].

Extralimital distribution: New Zealand (accidental introduction), see Donovan, B.J. (1983). Occurrence of the Australian bee *Hyleoides concinna* (Hymenoptera : Colletidae) in New Zealand. *N.Z. J. Zool.* **10**: 345–348 [345].

Hyleoides abnormis Houston, 1975

Hyleoides abnormis Houston, T.F. (1975). A revision of the Australian hylaeine bees (Hymenoptera : Colletidae). I. *Aust. J. Zool. Suppl. Ser.* **36**: 1–135 [48].

Type data: holotype, ANIC ♂.

Type locality: Barringun, NSW.

Distribution: Murray-Darling basin, Lake Eyre basin, QLD, NSW, SA.

Ecology: adult—volant; melliferous, solitary, flower visiting record: *Eremophila* R.Br. [Myoporaceae].

Hyleoides bivulnerata Cockerell, 1921

Hyleoides bivulnerata Cockerell, T.D.A. (1921). Australian bees in the Queensland Museum. *Mem. Qd Mus.* **7**: 81–98 [81].

Type data: holotype, BMNH Hym.17.a.321 ♀.

Type locality: Darra, Brisbane, QLD.

Distribution: NE coastal, Murray-Darling basin, SE coastal, QLD, NSW, VIC.

Ecology: adult—volant; melliferous, solitary, flower visiting record: *Callistemon* R.Br. [Myrtaceae], *Melaleuca* L. [Myrtaceae].

References: Michener, C.D. (1965). A classification of the bees of the Australian and South Pacific regions. *Bull. Am. Mus. Nat. Hist.* **130**: 1–362 (flower record); Houston, T.F. (1975). A revision of the Australian hylaeine bees (Hymenoptera : Colletidae). I. *Aust. J. Zool. Suppl. Ser.* **36**: 1–135 (redescription); Michener, C.D. (1992). Sexual dimorphism in the glossa of Colletidae (Hymenoptera, Apoidea). *J. Kansas Entomol. Soc.* **65**: 1–9 (glossa).

Hyleoides concinna (Fabricius, 1775)

Vespa concinna Fabricius, J.C. (1775). *Systema Entomologiae, sistens insectorum classes, ordines, genera, species, adiectis synonymis, locis, descriptionibus, observationibus.* Korte : Flensburgi et Lipsiae xxvii 832 pp. [367].

Type data: holotype, BMNH (Banks coll.) ♀.

Type locality: Australia (as New Holland).

Hylaeoides concinnus collaris Friese, H. (1924). Ueber die Bienen Australiens. *Konowia* **3**: 216–249 [222].

Type data: holotype, AMNH ♂♀* (number of specimens unknown).

Type locality: Glenbrook, NSW.

Hylaeoides ruficollaris Rayment, T. (1935). *A Cluster of Bees.* Sixty essays on the life-histories of Australian bees, with specific descriptions of over 100 new species, and an introduction by Professor E.F. Phillips, D.Ph., Cornell University, U.S.A. Sydney : Endeavour Press 752 pp. [89] [incorrect subsequent spelling for *collaris* Friese, 1924; name not available].

Taxonomic decision for synonymy: Houston, T.F. (1975). A revision of the Australian hylaeine bees (Hymenoptera : Colletidae). I. *Aust. J. Zool. Suppl. Ser.* **36**: 1–135 [52].

Distribution: NE coastal, Murray-Darling basin, SE coastal, S Gulfs, QLD, NSW, ACT, VIC, SA, TAS; accidentally introduced into New Zealand.

Ecology: larva—sedentary : adult—volant; melliferous, solitary, nest in pre-existing tunnel in stump, or in bamboo stems, flower visiting record: boxthorn, fennel, *Angophora* Cav. [Myrtaceae], *Banksia* L.f. [Proteaceae], *Callistemon* R.Br. [Myrtaceae], *Daviesia* Sm. [Fabaceae], *Eucalyptus* L'Hérit. [Myrtaceae], *Jacksonia* Smith [Fabaceae], *Melaleuca* L. [Myrtaceae], *Pultenaea* Sm. [Fabaceae], *Tristania* R.Br. [Myrtaceae].

References: Smith, F. (1853). *Catalogue of Hymenopterous Insects in the Collection of the British*

Museum. Part I. Andrenidae and Apidae. London : British Museum 197 pp. (generic placement); Dalla Torre, K.W. (1896). *Catalogus Hymenopterorum Hucusque Descriptorum Systematicus et Synonymicus.* Apidae (Anthophila). Lipsiae : G. Engelmann Vol. x 643 pp. (as *Hylaeoides concinnus*); Meade-Waldo, G. (1923). Hymenoptera. Fam. Apidae. Subfam. Prosopidinae. *Genera Insectorum* **181**: 1–45 (illustration); Rayment, T. (1935). *A Cluster of Bees.* Sixty essays on the life-histories of Australian bees, with specific descriptions of over 100 new species, and an introduction by Professor E.F. Phillips, D.Ph., Cornell University, U.S.A. Sydney : Endeavour Press 752 pp. (illustration); Rayment, T. (1961). The maker of the iris. *Proc. R. Zool. Soc. N.S.W.* **1958–59**: 102–107 (biology); Michener, C.D. (1965). A classification of the bees of the Australian and South Pacific regions. *Bull. Am. Mus. Nat. Hist.* **130**: 1–362 (flower record); Houston, T.F. (1967). A bee with a difference. *Wldlf. Aust.* **4**: 68–70 (biology); Cane, J.H. (1979). The hind tibiotarsal and tibial spur articulations in bees (Hymenoptera : Apoidea). *J. Kansas Entomol. Soc.* **52**: 123–137 (hind spur); McGinley, R.J. (1980). Glossal morphology of the Colletidae and recognition of the Stenotritidae at the family level (Hymenoptera : Apoidea). *J. Kansas Entomol. Soc.* **53**: 539–552 (glossa); McGinley, R.J. (1981). Systematics of the Colletidae based on mature larvae with phenetic analysis of apoid larvae (Insecta, Hymenoptera, Apoidea). *Univ. Calif. Publ. Entomol.* **91**: 1–309 (larva); Donovan, B.J. (1983). Occurrence of the Australian bee *Hyleoides concinna* (Hymenoptera : Colletidae) in New Zealand. *N.Z. J. Zool.* **10**: 345–348 (established in N.Z.); Fordham, R.A. (1989). Further New Zealand records of the new immigrant Australian bee *Hyleoides concinna* (Hymenoptera: Colletidae; Hylaeinae). *N.Z. Entomol.* **12**: 65–67 (biology); Michener, C.D. (1992). Sexual dimorphism in the glossa of Colletidae (Hymenoptera, Apoidea). *J. Kansas Entomol. Soc.* **65**: 1–9 (glossa).

Hyleoides concinnula Cockerell, 1909

Hyleoides concinnula Cockerell, T.D.A. (1909). Descriptions and records of bees. XXII. *Ann. Mag. Nat. Hist. (8)***4**: 309–317 [310].
Type data: holotype, BMNH Hym.17.a.326 ♀.
Type locality: WA.

Distribution: SW coastal, NW coastal, WA; only published localities Swan River and N of Carnarvon.
Ecology: adult—volant; melliferous, solitary.
References: Cockerell, T.D.A. (1910). Some Australian bees in the Berlin Museum. *J. N.Y. Entomol. Soc.* **18**: 98–114 (doubtful record; Adelaide, SA); Houston, T.F. (1975). A revision of the Australian hylaeine bees (Hymenoptera : Colletidae). I. *Aust. J. Zool. Suppl. Ser.* **36**: 1–135 (redescription).

Hyleoides planifrons Houston, 1975

Hyleoides planifrons Houston, T.F. (1975). A revision of the Australian hylaeine bees (Hymenoptera : Colletidae). I. *Aust. J. Zool. Suppl. Ser.* **36**: 1–135 [60].
Type data: holotype, ANIC ♀.
Type locality: Blackall, QLD.

Distribution: Murray-Darling basin, Lake Eyre basin, QLD, NSW; only published localities Blackall, Longreach, NE of Boulia and Mt Irvine (this record is doubtful).
Ecology: adult—volant; melliferous, solitary, flower visiting record: *Atalaya* Blume [Sapindaceae].

Hyleoides striatula Cockerell, 1921

Hyleoides striatula Cockerell, T.D.A. (1921). Australian bees in the Queensland Museum. *Mem. Qd Mus.* **7**: 81–98 [81].
Type data: holotype, QM T2415 ♀.
Type locality: Kuranda, QLD.

Distribution: NE coastal, Murray-Darling basin, QLD.
Ecology: adult—volant; melliferous, solitary, flower visiting record: *Angophora* Cav. [Myrtaceae], *Eucalyptus* L'Hérit. [Myrtaceae].
Reference: Houston, T.F. (1975). A revision of the Australian hylaeine bees (Hymenoptera : Colletidae). I. *Aust. J. Zool. Suppl. Ser.* **36**: 1–135 (redescription).

Hyleoides waterhousei Cockerell, 1913

Hyleoides waterhousei Cockerell, T.D.A. (1913). Descriptions and records of bees. LI. *Ann. Mag. Nat. Hist. (8)***11**: 387–394 [387].
Type data: holotype, BMNH Hym.17.a.322 ♀.
Type locality: SA.

Distribution: SE coastal, Murray-Darling basin, S Gulfs, W plateau, SW coastal, VIC, SA, WA.
Ecology: adult—volant; melliferous, solitary, flower visiting record: *Eucalyptus* L'Hérit. [Myrtaceae].
References: Cockerell, T.D.A. (1909). Descriptions and records of bees. XXII. *Ann. Mag. Nat. Hist. (8)***4**: 309–317 (description of male, as *Hyleoides zonalis rufocincta*); Michener, C.D. (1965). A classification of the bees of the Australian and South Pacific regions. *Bull. Am. Mus. Nat. Hist.* **130**: 1–362 (illustration); Houston, T.F. (1975). A revision of the Australian hylaeine bees (Hymenoptera : Colletidae). I. *Aust. J. Zool. Suppl. Ser.* **36**: 1–135 (redescription).

Hyleoides zonalis Smith, 1853

Hyleoides zonalis Smith, F. (1853). *Catalogue of Hymenopterous Insects in the Collection of the British Museum.* Part I. Andrenidae and Apidae. London : British Museum 197 pp. [32].
Type data: holotype, BMNH Hym.17.a.323 ♀.
Type locality: Hunter River, NSW.

Hyleoides zonalis albocincta Cockerell, T.D.A. (1909). Descriptions and records of bees. XXII. *Ann. Mag. Nat. Hist. (8)***4**: 309–317 [309].

Type data: lectotype, BMNH Hym.17.a.324 ♀.
Subsequent designation: Houston, T.F. (1975). A revision of the Australian hylaeine bees (Hymenoptera : Colletidae). I. *Aust. J. Zool. Suppl. Ser.* **36**: 1–135 [66]; Cardale, J.C., this work, interprets Houston's incorrect inference of holotype as a lectotype designation (Art. 74, ICZN 1985).
Type locality: WA.

Hyleoides zonalis rufocincta Cockerell, T.D.A. (1909). Descriptions and records of bees. XXII. *Ann. Mag. Nat. Hist.* (8)**4**: 309–317 [310].
Type data: holotype, BMNH Hym.17.a.325 ♀.
Type locality: Swan River, WA.

Taxonomic decision for synonymy: Houston, T.F. (1975). A revision of the Australian hylaeine bees (Hymenoptera : Colletidae). I. *Aust. J. Zool. Suppl. Ser.* **36**: 1–135 [66].

Distribution: NE coastal, SE coastal (Lord Howe Is.), SW coastal, NW coastal, QLD, NSW, WA.
Ecology: adult—volant; melliferous, solitary, flower visiting record: *Banksia* L.f. [Proteaceae], *Eucalyptus* L'Hérit. [Myrtaceae], *Xylomelum* Sm. [Proteaceae].
References: Rayment, T. (1935). *A Cluster of Bees.* Sixty essays on the life-histories of Australian bees, with specific descriptions of over 100 new species, and an introduction by Professor E.F. Phillips, D.Ph., Cornell University, U.S.A. Sydney : Endeavour Press 752 pp. (doubtful record; Port Lincoln, SA, as *Hylaeoides zonalis rufocincta*).

Meroglossa Smith, 1853

Meroglossa Smith, F. (1853). *Catalogue of Hymenopterous Insects in the Collection of the British Museum.* Part I. Andrenidae and Apidae. London : British Museum 197 pp. [33]. Type species: *Meroglossa canaliculata* Smith, 1853 by monotypy.

Meroglossula Perkins, R.C.L. (1912). Notes, with descriptions of new species, on aculeate Hymenoptera of the Australian Region. *Ann. Mag. Nat. Hist.* (8)**9**: 96–121 [99] [proposed with subgeneric rank in *Meroglossa* Smith, 1853]. Type species: *Meroglossa eucalypti* Cockerell, 1910 by monotypy.

Taxonomic decision for synonymy: Michener, C.D. (1965). A classification of the bees of the Australian and South Pacific regions. *Bull. Am. Mus. Nat. Hist.* **130**: 1–362 [149].

Generic reference: Houston, T.F. (1975). A revision of the Australian hylaeine bees (Hymenoptera : Colletidae). I. *Aust. J. Zool. Suppl. Ser.* **36**: 1–135.

Meroglossa borchi Rayment, 1939

Meroglossa desponsa borchi Rayment, T. (1939). Bees from the high lands of New South Wales and Victoria. *Aust. Zool.* **9**: 263–294 [272].
Type data: status and whereabouts unknown (not located in T. Rayment coll. transferred to ANIC).
Type locality: Grampian hills, VIC.

Distribution: SE coastal, VIC.
Ecology: adult—volant; melliferous; solitary.

Meroglossa canaliculata Smith, 1853

Meroglossa canaliculata Smith, F. (1853). *Catalogue of Hymenopterous Insects in the Collection of the British Museum.* Part I. Andrenidae and Apidae. London : British Museum 197 pp. [33].
Type data: holotype, BMNH Hym.17.a.214 ♂.
Type locality: Port Essington, NT.

Distribution: NE coastal, N coastal, QLD, NT; only published localities Port Essington, Darwin, East Alligator River and Cairns district.
Ecology: adult—volant; melliferous, solitary.
References: Cockerell, T.D.A. (1905). Notes on some bees in the British Museum. *Trans. Am. Entomol. Soc.* **31**: 309–364 (redescription); Rayment, T. (1935). *A Cluster of Bees.* Sixty essays on the life-histories of Australian bees, with specific descriptions of over 100 new species, and an introduction by Professor E.F. Phillips, D.Ph., Cornell University, U.S.A. Sydney : Endeavour Press 752 pp. (illustration); Michener, C.D. (1965). A classification of the bees of the Australian and South Pacific regions. *Bull. Am. Mus. Nat. Hist.* **130**: 1–362 (illustration); Houston, T.F. (1975). A revision of the Australian hylaeine bees (Hymenoptera : Colletidae). I. *Aust. J. Zool. Suppl. Ser.* **36**: 1–135 (redescription); McGinley, R.J. (1980). Glossal morphology of the Colletidae and recognition of the Stenotritidae at the family level (Hymenoptera : Apoidea). *J. Kansas Entomol. Soc.* **53**: 539–552 (glossa); Michener, C.D. (1992). Sexual dimorphism in the glossa of Colletidae (Hymenoptera, Apoidea). *J. Kansas Entomol. Soc.* **65**: 1–9 (glossa).

Meroglossa diversipuncta (Cockerell, 1909)

Prosopis diversipuncta Cockerell, T.D.A. (1909). Descriptions and records of bees. XXIII. *Ann. Mag. Nat. Hist.* (8)**4**: 393–404 [395].
Type data: syntypes, BMNH 2♀* (not found by J.C.C. in 1988).
Type locality: Kuranda, QLD.

Distribution: NE coastal, QLD; only published localities Kuranda, Cairns and Herberton.
Ecology: adult—volant; melliferous, solitary.
References: Perkins, R.C.L. (1912). Notes, with descriptions of new species, on aculeate Hymenoptera of the Australian Region. *Ann. Mag. Nat. Hist.* (8)**9**: 96–121 (generic placement); Meade-Waldo, G. (1923). Hymenoptera. Fam. Apidae. Subfam. Prosopidinae. *Genera Insectorum* **181**: 1–45 (as *Hylaeus (Koptogaster) diversipunctus* (Cockerell, 1909)); Houston, T.F. (1975). A revision of the Australian hylaeine bees (Hymenoptera : Colletidae). I. *Aust. J. Zool. Suppl. Ser.* **36**: 1–135 (redescription).

Meroglossa eucalypti Cockerell, 1910

Meroglossa eucalypti Cockerell, T.D.A. (1910). Descriptions and records of bees. XXX. *Ann. Mag. Nat. Hist.* (8)**6**: 17–31 [18].

Type data: syntypes, BMNH ♂♀ (a male specimen is labelled 'type' and has registration number Hym.17.a.220).
Type locality: Mackay, QLD.

Meroglossa deceptor Perkins, R.C.L. (1912). Notes, with descriptions of new species, on aculeate Hymenoptera of the Australian Region. *Ann. Mag. Nat. Hist. (8)***9**: 96–121 [101].
Type data: lectotype, BMNH Hym.17.a.2624 ♂.
Subsequent designation: Houston, T.F. (1975). A revision of the Australian hylaeine bees (Hymenoptera : Colletidae). I. *Aust. J. Zool. Suppl. Ser.* **36**: 1–135 [116]; Cardale, J.C., this work, interprets Houston's incorrect inference of holotype as a lectotoype designation (Art. 74, ICZN 1985).
Type locality: as Cairns, Herberton, QLD.

Prosopis disjuncta Friese, H. (1924). Ueber die Bienen Australiens. *Konowia* **3**: 216–249 [226] [junior primary homonym of *Prosopis disjuncta* Cockerell, 1905].
Type data: syntypes (probable), whereabouts unknown ♀* (number of specimens unknown).
Type locality: Mackay, QLD.

Taxonomic decision for synonymy: Houston, T.F. (1975). A revision of the Australian hylaeine bees (Hymenoptera : Colletidae). I. *Aust. J. Zool. Suppl. Ser.* **36**: 1–135 [116].

Distribution: NE coastal, N Gulf, N coastal, QLD, NT.
Ecology: adult—volant; melliferous, solitary, flower visiting record: *Barringtonia* Forster & G. Forster [Lecythidaceae], *Borreria* G. Meyer [Rubiaceae], *Cassia* L. *s.lat.* [Caesalpiniaceae], *Eucalyptus* L'Hérit. [Myrtaceae], *Rosa* L. [Rosaceae], *Tristania* R.Br. [Myrtaceae].
References: Perkins, R.C.L. (1912). Notes, with descriptions of new species, on aculeate Hymenoptera of the Australian Region. *Ann. Mag. Nat. Hist. (8)***9**: 96–121 (taxonomy); Cockerell, T.D.A. (1929). Bees, chiefly Australian species, described or determined by Dr. H. Friese. *Am. Mus. Novit.* **343**: 1–20 (taxonomy).

Meroglossa ferruginea Houston, 1975

Meroglossa ferruginea Houston, T.F. (1975). A revision of the Australian hylaeine bees (Hymenoptera : Colletidae). I. *Aust. J. Zool. Suppl. Ser.* **36**: 1–135 [118].
Type data: holotype, SAMA ♀*.
Type locality: Bowen, QLD.

Distribution: NE coastal, QLD; known only from type locality.
Ecology: adult—volant; melliferous, solitary.

Meroglossa gemmata Houston, 1975

Meroglossa gemmata Houston, T.F. (1975). A revision of the Australian hylaeine bees (Hymenoptera : Colletidae). I. *Aust. J. Zool. Suppl. Ser.* **36**: 1–135 [112].
Type data: holotype, QM T6888 ♀.
Type locality: Horn Islet, Sir Edward Pellew Group, NT.

Distribution: N Gulf, N coastal, QLD, NT.
Ecology: adult—volant; melliferous, solitary.

Meroglossa impressifrons (Smith, 1853)

Taxonomic decision for subspecific arrangement: Houston, T.F. (1975). A revision of the Australian hylaeine bees (Hymenoptera : Colletidae). I. *Aust. J. Zool. Suppl. Ser.* **36**: 1–135 [102].

Meroglossa impressifrons impressifrons (Smith, 1853)

Prosopis impressifrons Smith, F. (1853). *Catalogue of Hymenopterous Insects in the Collection of the British Museum.* Part I. Andrenidae and Apidae. London : British Museum 197 pp. [31].
Type data: holotype, BMNH Hym.17.a.225 ♂.
Type locality: Australia (as New Holland).

Prosopis desponsa Smith, F. (1853). *Catalogue of Hymenopterous Insects in the Collection of the British Museum.* Part I. Andrenidae and Apidae. London : British Museum 197 pp. [31].
Type data: holotype, BMNH Hym.17.a.226 ♀.
Type locality: Australia (as New Holland).

Prosopis percrassa Cockerell, T.D.A. (1905). Descriptions and records of bees. V. *Ann. Mag. Nat. Hist. (7)***16**: 465–477 [469].
Type data: holotype, BMNH Hym.17.a.213 ♀.
Type locality: QLD.

Meroglossa desponsa kershawi Cockerell, T.D.A. (1913). Some Australian bees. *Proc. Acad. Nat. Sci. Philad.* **65**: 28–44 [32].
Type data: syntypes, BMNH 2♀*.
Type locality: VIC.

Meroglossa desponsa sydneyana Rayment, T. (1935). *A Cluster of Bees.* Sixty essays on the life-histories of Australian bees, with specific descriptions of over 100 new species, and an introduction by Professor E.F. Phillips, D.Ph., Cornell University, U.S.A. Sydney : Endeavour Press 752 pp. [652].
Type data: holotype, ANIC ♀.
Type locality: Sydney, NSW.

Meroglossa impressifrons tuberculata Rayment, T. (1939). Bees from the high lands of New South Wales and Victoria. *Aust. Zool.* **9**: 263–294 [272].
Type data: holotype, ANIC ♂.
Type locality: Clifton Gardens, Sydney, NSW.

Meroglossa triangulata Rayment, T. (1939). Bees from the high lands of New South Wales and Victoria. *Aust. Zool.* **9**: 263–294 [272].
Type data: holotype, ANIC ♂.
Type locality: Inverell, NSW.

Taxonomic decision for synonymy: Houston, T.F. (1975). A revision of the Australian hylaeine bees (Hymenoptera : Colletidae). I. *Aust. J. Zool. Suppl. Ser.* **36**: 1–135 [102].

Distribution: NE coastal, Murray-Darling basin, SE coastal, QLD, NSW.
Ecology: adult—volant; melliferous, solitary, flower visiting record: *Banksia* L.f. [Proteaceae], *Boronia* Sm. [Rutaceae], *Callistemon* R.Br. [Myrtaceae], *Eucalyptus* L'Hérit. [Myrtaceae], *Jacksonia* Smith [Fabaceae], *Leptospermum* Forster & G.Forster [Myrtaceae], *Loranthus* Jacq. [Loranthaceae],

Rosa L. [Rosaceae], *Xanthorrhoea* Sm. [Xanthorrhoeaceae].
References: Perkins, R.C.L. (1912). Notes, with descriptions of new species, on aculeate Hymenoptera of the Australian Region. *Ann. Mag. Nat. Hist. (8)*9: 96–121 (generic placement); Rayment, T. (1935). *A Cluster of Bees.* Sixty essays on the life-histories of Australian bees, with specific descriptions of over 100 new species, and an introduction by Professor E.F. Phillips, D.Ph., Cornell University, U.S.A. Sydney : Endeavour Press 752 pp. (illustration); Michener, C.D. (1965). A classification of the bees of the Australian and South Pacific regions. *Bull. Am. Mus. Nat. Hist.* **130**: 1–362 (flower record).

Meroglossa impressifrons penetrata (Smith, 1879)

Prosopis penetrata Smith, F. (1879). *Descriptions of New Species of Hymenoptera in the Collection of the British Museum.* London : British Museum xxi 240 pp. [25].
Type data: holotype, BMNH Hym.17.a.212 ♀.
Type locality: Australia.

Distribution: NE coastal, Murray-Darling basin, QLD, NSW; a record from Ororoo, SA, is probably a labelling error.
Ecology: adult—volant; melliferous, solitary, flower visiting record: *Callistemon* R.Br. [Myrtaceae], *Eucalyptus* L'Hérit. [Myrtaceae], *Jacksonia* Smith [Fabaceae], *Leptospermum* Forster & G.Forster [Myrtaceae], *Melaleuca* L. [Myrtaceae].
References: Perkins, R.C.L. (1912). Notes, with descriptions of new species, on aculeate Hymenoptera of the Australian Region. *Ann. Mag. Nat. Hist. (8)*9: 96–121 (generic placement); Meade-Waldo, G. (1923). Hymenoptera. Fam. Apidae. Subfam. Prosopidinae. *Genera Insectorum* **181**: 1–45 (illustration); Rayment, T. (1935). *A Cluster of Bees.* Sixty essays on the life-histories of Australian bees, with specific descriptions of over 100 new species, and an introduction by Professor E.F. Phillips, D.Ph., Cornell University, U.S.A. Sydney : Endeavour Press 752 pp. (illustration); Michener, C.D. (1965). A classification of the bees of the Australian and South Pacific regions. *Bull. Am. Mus. Nat. Hist.* **130**: 1–362 (flower record).

Meroglossa itamuca (Cockerell, 1910)

Prosopis itamuca Cockerell, T.D.A. (1910). Descriptions and records of bees. XXXI. *Ann. Mag. Nat. Hist. (8)*6: 160–168 [163].
Type data: holotype, BMNH Hym.17.a.62 ♀.
Type locality: "NW Australia" (presumably wrongly labelled, all other records are from eastern Australia), see Houston, T.F. (1975). A revision of the Australian hylaeine bees (Hymenoptera : Colletidae). I. *Aust. J. Zool. Suppl. Ser.* **36**: 1–135 [128].
Meroglossa sulcifrons persulcata Cockerell, T.D.A. (1912). Descriptions and records of bees. XLI. *Ann. Mag. Nat. Hist. (8)*9: 139–149 [144].

Type data: holotype, ANIC ♂.
Type locality: S QLD.

Meroglossa (Meroglossula) trigonoides Rayment, T. (1935). *A Cluster of Bees.* Sixty essays on the life-histories of Australian bees, with specific descriptions of over 100 new species, and an introduction by Professor E.F. Phillips, D.Ph., Cornell University, U.S.A. Sydney : Endeavour Press 752 pp. [651].
Type data: holotype, ANIC ♀.
Type locality: Cairns, QLD.

Taxonomic decision for synonymy: Houston, T.F. (1975). A revision of the Australian hylaeine bees (Hymenoptera : Colletidae). I. *Aust. J. Zool. Suppl. Ser.* **36**: 1–135 [127].

Distribution: NE coastal, Murray-Darling basin, SE coastal, QLD, NSW, ACT, VIC.
Ecology: adult—volant; melliferous, solitary, flower visiting record: *Hibbertia* Andrews [Dilleniaceae], *Loranthus* Jacq. [Loranthaceae], *Solanum* L. [Solanaceae].
Reference: Meade-Waldo, G. (1923). Hymenoptera. Fam. Apidae. Subfam. Prosopidinae. *Genera Insectorum* **181**: 1–45 (as *Hylaeus (Koptogaster) itamuca* (Cockerell, 1910)).

Meroglossa modesta Houston, 1975

Meroglossa modesta Houston, T.F. (1975). A revision of the Australian hylaeine bees (Hymenoptera : Colletidae). I. *Aust. J. Zool. Suppl. Ser.* **36**: 1–135 [91].
Type data: holotype, QM T6894 ♂.
Type locality: Charleville, QLD.

Distribution: NE coastal, Murray-Darling basin, QLD, NSW, VIC.
Ecology: adult—volant; melliferous, solitary, flower visiting record: *Atalaya* Blume [Sapindaceae], *Callistemon* R.Br. [Myrtaceae], *Eucalyptus* L'Hérit. [Myrtaceae], *Loranthus* Jacq. [Loranthaceae].

Meroglossa ocellata Michener, 1965

Meroglossa ocellata Michener, C.D. (1965). A classification of the bees of the Australian and South Pacific regions. *Bull. Am. Mus. Nat. Hist.* **130**: 1–362 [304].
Type data: holotype, ANIC ♀.
Type locality: Kings River, NT.

Distribution: N coastal, NT; only published localities Kings River, Koongarra and near Mt Cahill.
Ecology: adult—volant; melliferous, solitary.
Reference: Houston, T.F. (1975). A revision of the Australian hylaeine bees (Hymenoptera : Colletidae). I. *Aust. J. Zool. Suppl. Ser.* **36**: 1–135 (redescription).

Meroglossa plumifera Houston, 1975

Meroglossa plumifera Houston, T.F. (1975). A revision of the Australian hylaeine bees (Hymenoptera : Colletidae). I. *Aust. J. Zool. Suppl. Ser.* **36**: 1–135 [92].
Type data: holotype, ANIC ♂.
Type locality: Yaamba (near Rockhampton), QLD.

Distribution: NE coastal, Murray-Darling basin, QLD.

Ecology: adult—volant; melliferous, solitary.

Meroglossa punctata Rayment, 1935

Meroglossa desponsa punctata Rayment, T. (1935). *A Cluster of Bees.* Sixty essays on the life-histories of Australian bees, with specific descriptions of over 100 new species, and an introduction by Professor E.F. Phillips, D.Ph., Cornell University, U.S.A. Sydney : Endeavour Press 752 pp. [652].
Type data: holotype, ANIC ♀.
Type locality: Brisbane, QLD.

Distribution: NE coastal, Murray-Darling basin, QLD; only published localities Brisbane, Beerwah, Birkdale and The Summit.

Ecology: adult—volant; melliferous, solitary, flower visiting record: *Leptospermum* Forster & G.Forster [Myrtaceae], *Lomatia* R.Br. [Proteaceae].

References: Michener, C.D. (1965). A classification of the bees of the Australian and South Pacific regions. *Bull. Am. Mus. Nat. Hist.* **130**: 1–362 (flower record, taxonomy); Houston, T.F. (1975). A revision of the Australian hylaeine bees (Hymenoptera : Colletidae). I. *Aust. J. Zool. Suppl. Ser.* **36**: 1–135 (redescription).

Meroglossa rubricata (Smith, 1879)

Prosopis rubricata Smith, F. (1879). *Descriptions of New Species of Hymenoptera in the Collection of the British Museum.* London : British Museum xxi 240 pp. [25].
Type data: holotype, BMNH Hym.17.a.224 ♀.
Type locality: Swan River, WA.

Distribution: Lake Eyre basin, W plateau, SW coastal, NW coastal, SA, WA, NT.

Ecology: adult—volant; melliferous, solitary, flower visiting record: *Capparis* L. [Capparaceae], *Hibbertia* Andrews [Dilleniaceae].

References: Perkins, R.C.L. (1912). Notes, with descriptions of new species, on aculeate Hymenoptera of the Australian Region. *Ann. Mag. Nat. Hist. (8)9*: 96–121 (generic placement); Houston, T.F. (1975). A revision of the Australian hylaeine bees (Hymenoptera : Colletidae). I. *Aust. J. Zool. Suppl. Ser.* **36**: 1–135 (redescription).

Meroglossa rugosa Houston, 1975

Meroglossa rugosa Houston, T.F. (1975). A revision of the Australian hylaeine bees (Hymenoptera : Colletidae). I. *Aust. J. Zool. Suppl. Ser.* **36**: 1–135 [129].
Type data: holotype, BMNH Hym.17.a.2862 ♀.
Type locality: Herberton, QLD.

Distribution: NE coastal, QLD; known only from type locality.

Ecology: adult—volant; melliferous, solitary.

Meroglossa sculptissima Cockerell, 1910

Meroglossa sculptissima Cockerell, T.D.A. (1910). Descriptions and records of bees. XXX. *Ann. Mag. Nat. Hist. (8)6*: 17–31 [19].
Type data: lectotype, BMNH Hym.17.a.221 ♂.
Subsequent designation: Houston, T.F. (1975). A revision of the Australian hylaeine bees (Hymenoptera : Colletidae). I. *Aust. J. Zool. Suppl. Ser.* **36**: 1–135 [120]; Cardale, J.C., this work, interprets Houston's incorrect inference of holotype as a lectotype designation (Art. 74, ICZN 1985).
Type locality: Mackay, QLD.

Meroglossa decipiens Perkins, R.C.L. (1912). Notes, with descriptions of new species, on aculeate Hymenoptera of the Australian Region. *Ann. Mag. Nat. Hist. (8)9*: 96–121 [101].
Type data: lectotype, BMNH Hym.17.a.2626 ♂.
Subsequent designation: Houston, T.F. (1975). A revision of the Australian hylaeine bees (Hymenoptera : Colletidae). I. *Aust. J. Zool. Suppl. Ser.* **36**: 1–135 [120]; Cardale, J.C., this work, interprets Houston's incorrect inference of holotype as a lectotype designation (Art. 74, ICZN 1985).
Type locality: Herberton district, QLD.

Meroglossa eucalypti hilli Cockerell, T.D.A. (1929). Bees from the Australian region. *Am. Mus. Novit.* 346: 1–18 [1].
Type data: holotype, AMNH ♀* (described as ♂).
Type locality: Darwin, NT.

Taxonomic decision for synonymy: Houston, T.F. (1975). A revision of the Australian hylaeine bees (Hymenoptera : Colletidae). I. *Aust. J. Zool. Suppl. Ser.* **36**: 1–135 [119].

Distribution: NE coastal, N coastal, QLD, NT.

Ecology: adult—volant; melliferous, solitary, flower visiting record: *Barringtonia* Forster & G. Forster [Lecythidaceae], *Eucalyptus* L'Hérit. [Myrtaceae], *Eugenia* L. [Myrtaceae].

Reference: Cockerell, T.D.A. (1929). Bees, chiefly Australian species, described or determined by Dr. H. Friese. *Am. Mus. Novit.* 343: 1–20 (taxonomy).

Meroglossa setifera Houston, 1975

Meroglossa setifera Houston, T.F. (1975). A revision of the Australian hylaeine bees (Hymenoptera : Colletidae). I. *Aust. J. Zool. Suppl. Ser.* **36**: 1–135 [97].
Type data: holotype, ANIC ♂.
Type locality: 70 miles N Bourke, NSW.

Distribution: Murray-Darling basin, S Gulfs, Lake Eyre basin, NSW, SA.

Ecology: adult—volant; melliferous, solitary, flower visiting record: *Eremophila* R.Br. [Myoporaceae], *Eucalyptus* L'Hérit. [Myrtaceae].

Meroglossa soror Perkins, 1912

Meroglossa soror Perkins, R.C.L. (1912). Notes, with descriptions of new species, on aculeate Hymenoptera of the Australian Region. *Ann. Mag. Nat. Hist. (8)9*: 96–121 [100].
Type data: holotype, BMNH Hym.17.a.2625 ♀.
Type locality: Herberton district, QLD.

Distribution: NE coastal, N coastal, QLD, NT; only published localities Herberton, Darwin and Bathurst Is.

Ecology: adult—volant; melliferous, solitary.

Reference: Houston, T.F. (1975). A revision of the Australian hylaeine bees (Hymenoptera : Colletidae). I. *Aust. J. Zool. Suppl. Ser.* **36**: 1–135 (redescription).

Meroglossa striaticeps (Friese, 1924)

Prosopis striaticeps Friese, H. (1924). Ueber die Bienen Australiens. *Konowia* **3**: 216–249 [229].
Type data: holotype, AMNH ♀*.
Type locality: Mackay, QLD.

Meroglossa chiropterina Cockerell, T.D.A. (1930). Australian bees in the Museum of Comparative Zoology. *Psyche (Camb.)* **37**: 141–154 [148].
Type data: lectotype, MCZ 16342 ♂* (described as ♀).
Subsequent designation: Houston, T.F. (1975). A revision of the Australian hylaeine bees (Hymenoptera : Colletidae). I. *Aust. J. Zool. Suppl. Ser.* **36**: 1–135 [122]; Cardale, J.C., this work, interprets Houston's incorrect inference of holotype as a lectotype designation (Art. 74, ICZN 1985).
Type locality: Halifax, QLD.

Taxonomic decision for synonymy: Houston, T.F. (1975). A revision of the Australian hylaeine bees (Hymenoptera : Colletidae). I. *Aust. J. Zool. Suppl. Ser.* **36**: 1–135 [122].

Distribution: NE coastal, N coastal, QLD, NT.

Ecology: adult—volant; melliferous, solitary, flower visiting record: *Barringtonia* Forster & G. Forster [Lecythidaceae], *Cassia* L. *s.lat.* [Caesalpiniaceae], *Melaleuca* L. [Myrtaceae], *Rosa* L. [Rosaceae], *Xanthorrhoea* Sm. [Xanthorrhoeaceae].

Reference: Cockerell, T.D.A. (1929). Bees, chiefly Australian species, described or determined by Dr. H. Friese. *Am. Mus. Novit.* **343**: 1–20 (as synonym of *Meroglossa (Meroglossula) sculptissima* Cockerell, 1910).

Meroglossa sulcifrons (Smith, 1853)

Prosopis sulcifrons Smith, F. (1853). *Catalogue of Hymenopterous Insects in the Collection of the British Museum.* Part I. Andrenidae and Apidae. London : British Museum 197 pp. [27].
Type data: holotype, BMNH Hym.17.a.216 ♂.
Type locality: Australia (as New Holland).

Prosopis nigrifrons Smith, F. (1853). *Catalogue of Hymenopterous Insects in the Collection of the British Museum.* Part I. Andrenidae and Apidae. London : British Museum 197 pp. [30].
Type data: holotype, BMNH Hym.17.a.215 ♀.
Type locality: Australia (as New Holland).

Prosopis grandis Friese, H. (1924). Ueber die Bienen Australiens. *Konowia* **3**: 216–249 [228].
Type data: holotype (probable), ZMB ♀*.
Type locality: Mackay, QLD.

Taxonomic decision for synonymy: Houston, T.F. (1975). A revision of the Australian hylaeine bees (Hymenoptera : Colletidae). I. *Aust. J. Zool. Suppl. Ser.* **36**: 1–135 [130].

Distribution: NE coastal, Murray-Darling basin, SE coastal, QLD, NSW, ACT, VIC.

Ecology: adult—volant; melliferous, solitary, adults found sheltering in a gallery in an *Acacia* Miller [Mimosaceae] tree, flower visiting record: blackberry, sweet clover, *Boronia* Sm. [Rutaceae], *Daviesia* Sm. [Fabaceae], *Eucalyptus* L'Hérit. [Myrtaceae], *Leptospermum* Forster & G.Forster [Myrtaceae], *Xanthorrhoea* Sm. [Xanthorrhoeaceae].

References: Perkins, R.C.L. (1912). Notes, with descriptions of new species, on aculeate Hymenoptera of the Australian Region. *Ann. Mag. Nat. Hist. (8)***9**: 96–121 (generic placement); Rayment, T. (1935). *A Cluster of Bees.* Sixty essays on the life-histories of Australian bees, with specific descriptions of over 100 new species, and an introduction by Professor E.F. Phillips, D.Ph., Cornell University, U.S.A. Sydney : Endeavour Press 752 pp. (flower record, as *Meroglossa nigrifrons* (Smith, 1853)); Rayment, T. (1954). Remarkable bees from a rain forest. *Aust. Zool.* **12**: 46–56 (biology, as *Meroglossa nigrifrons* (Smith, 1853)); Michener, C.D. (1965). A classification of the bees of the Australian and South Pacific regions. *Bull. Am. Mus. Nat. Hist.* **130**: 1–362 [238] (flower record, as *Meroglossa nigrifrons* (Smith, 1853)).

Meroglossa torrida (Smith, 1879)

Prosopis torrida Smith, F. (1879). *Descriptions of New Species of Hymenoptera in the Collection of the British Museum.* London : British Museum xxi 240 pp. [25].
Type data: holotype, BMNH Hym.17.a.223 ♀.
Type locality: QLD.

Distribution: NE coastal, Lake Eyre basin, N coastal, N Gulf, QLD, WA, NT.

Ecology: adult—volant; melliferous, solitary, though prereproductive adults of both sexes may be found in a nest, nest in twigs of *Cassia* L. *s.lat.* [Caesalpiniaceae], flower visiting record: *Acacia* Miller [Mimosaceae], *Angophora* Cav. [Myrtaceae], *Callistemon* R.Br. [Myrtaceae], *Calytrix* Lab. [Myrtaceae], *Melaleuca* L. [Myrtaceae].

References: Perkins, R.C.L. (1912). Notes, with descriptions of new species, on aculeate Hymenoptera of the Australian Region. *Ann. Mag. Nat. Hist. (8)***9**: 96–121 (generic placement); Michener, C.D. (1960). Notes on the behavior of Australian colletid bees. *J. Kansas Entomol. Soc.* **33**: 22–31 (biology); Michener, C.D. (1965). A classification of the bees of the Australian and South Pacific regions. *Bull. Am. Mus. Nat. Hist.* **130**: 1–362 (illustration, flower record); Houston, T.F. (1975). A revision of the Australian hylaeine bees (Hymenoptera : Colletidae). I. *Aust. J. Zool. Suppl. Ser.* **36**: 1–135 (redescription); McGinley, R.J. (1980). Glossal morphology of the Colletidae and recognition of the Stenotritidae at the family level (Hymenoptera : Apoidea). *J. Kansas Entomol. Soc.* **53**: 539–552 (glossa); Michener, C.D. &

Brooks, R.W. (1984). A comparative study of the glossae of bees (Apoidea). *Contrib. Am. Entomol. Inst.* **22**: 1–73 (glossa); Michener, C.D. (1992). Sexual dimorphism in the glossa of Colletidae (Hymenoptera, Apoidea). *J. Kansas Entomol. Soc.* **65**: 1–9 (glossa).

Palaeorhiza Perkins, 1908

Taxonomic decision for subgeneric arrangement: Hirashima, Y. & Lieftinck, M.A. (1982). Systematic studies on the genus *Palaeorhiza* of New Guinea collected by the third Archbold Expedition (I) (Hymenoptera, Colletidae). *Esakia* **19**: 1–50 [3].

Generic reference: Michener, C.D. (1965). A classification of the bees of the Australian and South Pacific regions. *Bull. Am. Mus. Nat. Hist.* **130**: 1–362.

Palaeorhiza (Palaeorhiza) Perkins, 1908

Palaeorhiza Perkins, R.C.L. (1908). Some remarkable Australian Hymenoptera. *Proc. Hawaii. Entomol. Soc.* **2**: 27–35 [29]. Type species: *Prosopis perviridis* Cockerell, 1905 by original designation.

Extralimital distribution: New Guinea, New Britain, Solomon Ils, Kai, Amboina and Timor, see Hirashima, Y. (1978). A synopsis of the bee genus *Palaeorhiza* Perkins (Hymenoptera, Colletidae) of New Guinea. Part I. Subgenus *Palaeorhiza* s. str. *Esakia* **11**: 89–119 [92].

Palaeorhiza (Palaeorhiza) basilura Cockerell, 1910

Palaeorhiza basilura Cockerell, T.D.A. (1910). Descriptions and records of bees. XXIX. *Ann. Mag. Nat. Hist. (8)***5**: 496–506 [500].
Type data: holotype, BMNH Hym.17.a.199 ♀.
Type locality: Kuranda (as Cairns Kuranda), QLD.

Distribution: NE coastal, QLD; known only from type locality.
Ecology: adult—volant; melliferous, solitary.
References: Cockerell, T.D.A. (1911). The bees of the Solomon Islands. *Proc. Linn. Soc. N.S.W.* **36**: 160–178 (as *Meroglossa basilura* (Cockerell, 1910)); Perkins, R.C.L. (1912). Notes, with descriptions of new species, on aculeate Hymenoptera of the Australian Region. *Ann. Mag. Nat. Hist. (8)***9**: 96–121 (as *Palaeorhiza basilura* Cockerell, 1910).

Palaeorhiza (Palaeorhiza) caerulescens (Friese, 1924)

Prosopis caerulescens Friese, H. (1924). Ueber die Bienen Australiens. *Konowia* **3**: 216–249 [223].
Type data: holotype (probable), AMNH ♀*.
Type locality: Mackay, QLD.

Distribution: NE coastal, QLD; known only from type locality.
Ecology: adult—volant; melliferous, solitary, flower visiting record: *Cassia* L. *s.lat.* [Caesalpiniaceae].
References: Cockerell, T.D.A. (1929). Bees, chiefly

Australian species, described or determined by Dr. H. Friese. *Am. Mus. Novit.* **343**: 1–20 (as synonym of *Palaeorhiza reginarum* (Cockerell, 1905)); Hirashima, Y. (1978). A synopsis of the bee genus *Palaeorhiza* Perkins (Hymenoptera, Colletidae) of New Guinea. Part I. Subgenus *Palaeorhiza* s. str. *Esakia* **11**: 89–119 (taxonomy).

Palaeorhiza (Palaeorhiza) cassiaefloris (Cockerell, 1910)

Meroglossa perviridis cassiaefloris Cockerell, T.D.A. (1910). Descriptions and records of bees. XXX. *Ann. Mag. Nat. Hist. (8)***6**: 17–31 [22].
Type data: syntypes, BMNH 3♀ (a specimen is labelled 'type' and has registration number Hym.17.a.208).
Type locality: Mackay, QLD.

Distribution: NE coastal, QLD; only published localities Mackay and Brisbane.
Ecology: adult—volant; melliferous, solitary, flower visiting record: *Cassia* L. *s.lat.* [Caesalpiniaceae].
References: Hacker, H. (1921). Catalogue of Australian bees. *Mem. Qd Mus.* **7**: 99–163 (as *Palaeorhiza perviridis cassiaefloris* (Cockerell, 1910)); Hirashima, Y. (1978). A synopsis of the bee genus *Palaeorhiza* Perkins (Hymenoptera, Colletidae) of New Guinea. Part I. Subgenus *Palaeorhiza* s. str. *Esakia* **11**: 89–119 (taxonomy).

Palaeorhiza (Palaeorhiza) flavomellea Cockerell, 1910

Palaeorhiza flavomellea Cockerell, T.D.A. (1910). Descriptions and records of bees. XXIX. *Ann. Mag. Nat. Hist. (8)***5**: 496–506 [500].
Type data: syntypes, BMNH 2♂4♀ (a female specimen is labelled 'type' and has registration number Hym.17.a.198).
Type locality: Kuranda (as Cairns Kuranda), QLD.

Distribution: NE coastal, QLD; only published localities Kuranda and Dunk Is.
Ecology: adult—volant; melliferous, solitary.
References: Cockerell, T.D.A. (1911). The bees of the Solomon Islands. *Proc. Linn. Soc. N.S.W.* **36**: 160–178 (as *Meroglossa flavomellea* (Cockerell, 1910)); Cockerell, T.D.A. (1930). New Australian bees. *Mem. Qd Mus.* **10**: 37–50 (distribution).

Palaeorhiza (Palaeorhiza) kurandensis (Cockerell, 1909)

Prosopis turneriana kurandensis Cockerell, T.D.A. (1909). Descriptions and records of bees. XXIII. *Ann. Mag. Nat. Hist. (8)***4**: 393–404 [394].
Type data: holotype, BMNH Hym.17.a.205 ♂.
Type locality: Kuranda, QLD.
Prosopis purpurascens Friese, H. (1924). Ueber die Bienen Australiens. *Konowia* **3**: 216–249 [223].
Type data: syntypes, AMNH ♀* (number of specimens unknown).
Type locality: Kuranda, QLD.

Taxonomic decision for synonymy: Cockerell, T.D.A. (1929). Bees, chiefly Australian species, described or determined by Dr. H. Friese. *Am. Mus. Novit.* **343**: 1–20 [16].

Distribution: NE coastal, QLD; only published localities Kuranda, Cooktown and Mackay.
Ecology: adult—volant; melliferous, solitary, flower visiting record: *Eucalyptus* L'Hérit. [Myrtaceae], *Hibiscus* L. [Malvaceae].
References: Cockerell, T.D.A. (1910). Descriptions and records of bees. XXX. *Ann. Mag. Nat. Hist. (8)***6**: 17–31 (as *Meroglossa turneriana kurandensis* (Cockerell, 1909)); Hacker, H. (1921). Catalogue of Australian bees. *Mem. Qd Mus.* **7**: 99–163 (as *Palaeorhiza turneriana kurandensis* (Cockerell, 1909)).

Palaeorhiza (Palaeorhiza) luxuriosa (Cockerell, 1910)

Meroglossa luxuriosa Cockerell, T.D.A. (1910). Descriptions and records of bees. XXX. *Ann. Mag. Nat. Hist. (8)***6**: 17–31 [22].
Type data: syntypes, BMNH ♂♀ (number of specimens unknown, a female specimen is labelled 'type' and has registration number Hym.17.a.200).
Type locality: Kuranda (as Cairns Kuranda), QLD.

Distribution: NE coastal, QLD; known only from type locality.
Ecology: adult—volant; melliferous, solitary.
Reference: Perkins, R.C.L. (1912). Notes, with descriptions of new species, on aculeate Hymenoptera of the Australian Region. *Ann. Mag. Nat. Hist. (8)***9**: 96–121 (generic placement).

Palaeorhiza (Palaeorhiza) perkinsi Cockerell, 1910

Palaeorhiza perkinsi Cockerell, T.D.A. (1910). Some Australian bees in the Berlin Museum. *J. N.Y. Entomol. Soc.* **18**: 98–114 [June 1910] [98].
Type data: holotype, ZMB ♀*.
Type locality: N QLD.

Distribution: NE coastal, QLD; only published locality Cooktown.
Ecology: adult—volant; melliferous, solitary.
References: Cockerell, T.D.A. (1910). Descriptions and records of bees. XXX. *Ann. Mag. Nat. Hist. (8)***6**: 17–31 [July 1910] (as *Meroglossa perkinsi* (Cockerell, 1910), described again as new); Perkins, R.C.L. (1912). Notes, with descriptions of new species, on aculeate Hymenoptera of the Australian Region. *Ann. Mag. Nat. Hist. (8)***9**: 96–121 (taxonomy).

Palaeorhiza (Palaeorhiza) permiranda (Cockerell, 1909)

Prosopis permiranda Cockerell, T.D.A. (1909). Descriptions and records of bees. XXIII. *Ann. Mag. Nat. Hist. (8)***4**: 393–404 [396].
Type data: holotype, BMNH ♀.
Type locality: Kuranda, QLD.

Distribution: NE coastal, QLD; known only from type locality.
Ecology: adult—volant; melliferous, solitary.
Reference: Meade-Waldo, G. (1923). Hymenoptera. Fam. Apidae. Subfam. Prosopidinae. *Genera Insectorum* **181**: 1–45 (as *Hylaeus (Koptogaster) permirandus* (Cockerell, 1909)).

Palaeorhiza (Palaeorhiza) perviridis (Cockerell, 1905)

Prosopis perviridis Cockerell, T.D.A. (1905). Descriptions and records of bees. IV. *Ann. Mag. Nat. Hist. (7)***16**: 392–403 [401].
Type data: holotype, BMNH Hym.17.a.207 ♀.
Type locality: Adelaide River, NT.

Distribution: NE coastal, N coastal, QLD, NT.
Ecology: adult—volant; melliferous, solitary.
References: Perkins, R.C.L. (1912). Notes, with descriptions of new species, on aculeate Hymenoptera of the Australian Region. *Ann. Mag. Nat. Hist. (8)***9**: 96–121 (generic placement); Cockerell, T.D.A. (1912). Descriptions and records of bees. XLVII. *Ann. Mag. Nat. Hist. (8)***10**: 484–494 (distribution); Hirashima, Y. (1978). A synopsis of the bee genus *Palaeorhiza* Perkins (Hymenoptera, Colletidae) of New Guinea. Part I. Subgenus *Palaeorhiza* s. str. *Esakia* **11**: 89–119 (redescription).

Palaeorhiza (Palaeorhiza) purpureocincta Cockerell, 1926

Palaeorhiza purpureocincta Cockerell, T.D.A. (1926). Descriptions and records of bees. CXI. *Ann. Mag. Nat. Hist. (9)***17**: 657–665 [664].
Type data: holotype, NMV ♂.
Type locality: Endeavour River, QLD.

Distribution: NE coastal, QLD; known only from type locality.
Ecology: adult—volant; melliferous, solitary.

Palaeorhiza (Palaeorhiza) reginarum (Cockerell, 1905)

Prosopis reginarum Cockerell, T.D.A. (1905). Descriptions and records of bees. IV. *Ann. Mag. Nat. Hist. (7)***16**: 392–403 [402].
Type data: holotype, BMNH Hym.17.a.206 ♂ (described as ♀).
Type locality: Mackay, QLD.

Distribution: NE coastal, QLD; only published localities Mackay, Brisbane and Stradbroke Is.
Ecology: adult—volant; melliferous, solitary, flower visiting record: *Cassia* L. *s.lat.* [Caesalpiniaceae].
References: Cockerell, T.D.A. (1910). Descriptions and records of bees. XXX. *Ann. Mag. Nat. Hist. (8)***6**: 17–31 (as *Meroglossa reginarum* (Cockerell, 1905)); Perkins, R.C.L. (1912). Notes, with descriptions of new species, on aculeate Hymenoptera of the Australian Region. *Ann. Mag. Nat. Hist. (8)***9**: 96–121 (ge-

neric placement); Cockerell, T.D.A. (1929). Bees, chiefly Australian species, described or determined by Dr. H. Friese. *Am. Mus. Novit.* **343**: 1–20 (taxonomy); Hirashima, Y. (1978). A synopsis of the bee genus *Palaeorhiza* Perkins (Hymenoptera, Colletidae) of New Guinea. Part I. Subgenus *Palaeorhiza* s. str. *Esakia* **11**: 89–119 (redescription).

Palaeorhiza (Palaeorhiza) varicolor (Smith, 1879)

Prosopis varicolor Smith, F. (1879). *Descriptions of New Species of Hymenoptera in the Collection of the British Museum.* London : British Museum xxi 240 pp. [24].
Type data: holotype, BMNH Hym.17.a.196 ♀.
Type locality: Port Bowen, QLD.

Distribution: NE coastal, QLD; only published localities Bowen, Townsville and Mackay.
Ecology: adult—volant; melliferous, solitary.
References: Dalla Torre, K.W. (1896). *Catalogus Hymenopterorum Hucusque Descriptorum Systematicus et Synonymicus.* Apidae (Anthophila). Lipsiae : G. Engelmann Vol. x 643 pp. (as *Prosopis variicolor*, incorrect subsequent spelling); Cockerell, T.D.A. (1905). Descriptions and records of bees. IV. *Ann. Mag. Nat. Hist. (7)***16**: 392–403 (description of male); Cockerell, T.D.A. (1910). Descriptions and records of bees. XXV. *Ann. Mag. Nat. Hist. (8)***5**: 133–140 (taxonomy); Cockerell, T.D.A. (1910). Descriptions and records of bees. XXX. *Ann. Mag. Nat. Hist. (8)***6**: 17–31 (distribution, as *Meroglossa varicolor* (Smith, 1879)); Perkins, R.C.L. (1912). Notes, with descriptions of new species, on aculeate Hymenoptera of the Australian Region. *Ann. Mag. Nat. Hist. (8)***9**: 96–121 (generic placement).

Palaeorhiza (Anchirhiza) Michener, 1965

Anchirhiza Michener, C.D. (1965). A classification of the bees of the Australian and South Pacific regions. *Bull. Am. Mus. Nat. Hist.* **130**: 1–362 [147] [proposed with subgeneric rank in *Palaeorhiza* Perkins, 1908]. Type species: *Palaeorhiza (Anchirhiza) mandibularis* Michener, 1965 by original designation.

Extralimital distribution: New Guinea, see Hirashima, Y. (1978). A synopsis of the bee genus *Palaeorhiza* Perkins (Hymenoptera, Colletidae) of New Guinea. Part II. Subgenera *Gressittapis, Noonadania, Sphecogaster, Anchirhiza, Ceratorhiza. Esakia* **12**: 63–87 [79].

Palaeorhiza (Anchirhiza) mandibularis Michener, 1965

Palaeorhiza (Anchirhiza) mandibularis Michener, C.D. (1965). A classification of the bees of the Australian and South Pacific regions. *Bull. Am. Mus. Nat. Hist.* **130**: 1–362 [303].
Type data: holotype, QM T6222 ♀.
Type locality: Beaudesert, QLD.

Distribution: NE coastal, QLD; known only from type locality in Australia, also recorded from Mt

Kaindi, near Wau, Papua New Guinea.
Ecology: adult—volant; melliferous, solitary, New Guinea, male was found at tree juice of *Euodia* Forster & G.Forster [Rutaceae].
References: Hirashima, Y. (1978). A synopsis of the bee genus *Palaeorhiza* Perkins (Hymenoptera, Colletidae) of New Guinea. Part II. Subgenera *Gressittapis, Noonadania, Sphecogaster, Anchirhiza, Ceratorhiza. Esakia* **12**: 63–87 (description of male, New Guinea); Hirashima, Y. & Lieftinck, M.A. (1982). Systematic studies on the genus *Palaeorhiza* of New Guinea collected by the third Archbold Expedition (I) (Hymenoptera, Colletidae). *Esakia* **19**: 1–50 (taxonomy).

Palaeorhiza (Callorhiza) Hirashima, 1989

Callorhiza Hirashima, Y. (1989). A synopsis of the bee genus *Palaeorhiza* Perkins (Hymenoptera, Colletidae) of New Guinea. Part VIII. Subgenus *Callorhiza. Esakia* **28**: 1–9 [2] [proposed with subgeneric rank in *Palaeorhiza* Perkins, 1908]. Type species: *Prosopis apicatus* Smith, 1863 by original designation.

Extralimital distribution: Misool, New Guinea and Solomon Ils, see Hirashima, Y. (1989). A synopsis of the bee genus *Palaeorhiza* Perkins (Hymenoptera, Colletidae) of New Guinea. Part VIII. Subgenus *Callorhiza. Esakia* **28**: 1–9 [2].

Palaeorhiza (Callorhiza) disrupta Cockerell, 1914

Palaeorhiza parallela disrupta Cockerell, T.D.A. (1914). Australian bees of the family Prosopidae. *Insecutor Inscit. Menstr.* **2**: 97–101 [98].
Type data: holotype, BMNH Hym.17.a.194 ♀.
Type locality: Kuranda, QLD.

Distribution: NE coastal, QLD; widespread in Papua New Guinea.
Ecology: adult—volant; melliferous, solitary, flower visiting record: *Melastoma* L. [Melastomataceae].
References: Cockerell, T.D.A. (1929). Bees, chiefly Australian species, described or determined by Dr. H. Friese. *Am. Mus. Novit.* **343**: 1–20 [16] (subspecies to species); Cockerell, T.D.A. (1930). Australian bees in the Museum of Comparative Zoology. *Psyche (Camb.)* **37**: 141–154 (distribution); Rayment, T. (1935). *A Cluster of Bees.* Sixty essays on the life-histories of Australian bees, with specific descriptions of over 100 new species, and an introduction by Professor E.F. Phillips, D.Ph., Cornell University, U.S.A. Sydney : Endeavour Press 752 pp. (illustration); Exley, E.M. (1987). Bees at the Jardine, Aug.-Sept. 1985. *Qd Nat.* **28**: 33–34 (flower record); Hirashima, Y. (1989). A synopsis of the bee genus *Palaeorhiza* Perkins (Hymenoptera, Colletidae) of New Guinea. Part VIII. Subgenus *Callorhiza. Esakia* **28**: 1–9 (subgeneric placement).

Palaeorhiza (Callorhiza) eboracina (Cockerell, 1910)

Meroglossa varicolor eboracina Cockerell, T.D.A. (1910). Descriptions and records of bees. XXX. *Ann. Mag. Nat. Hist. (8)*6: 17–31 [23].
Type data: holotype, BMNH Hym.17.a.195 ♂.
Type locality: Cape York, QLD.

Distribution: NE coastal, QLD; only published localities Cape York, Cairns and Kuranda.
Ecology: adult—volant; melliferous, solitary.
References: Perkins, R.C.L. (1912). Notes, with descriptions of new species, on aculeate Hymenoptera of the Australian Region. *Ann. Mag. Nat. Hist. (8)*9: 96–121 (generic placement); Hirashima, Y. (1989). A synopsis of the bee genus *Palaeorhiza* Perkins (Hymenoptera, Colletidae) of New Guinea. Part VIII. Subgenus *Callorhiza*. *Esakia* 28: 1–9 (subgeneric placement).

Palaeorhiza (Callorhiza) turneriana (Cockerell, 1905)

Prosopis turneriana Cockerell, T.D.A. (1905). Descriptions and records of bees. IV. *Ann. Mag. Nat. Hist. (7)*16: 392–403 [402].
Type data: syntypes, BMNH 2♂2♀ (a female specimen is labelled 'type' and has registration number Hym.17.a.203).
Type locality: Mackay, QLD.

Distribution: NE coastal, QLD; only published localities Mackay, Kuranda and Cairns.
Ecology: adult—volant; melliferous, solitary.
References: Cockerell, T.D.A. (1910). Descriptions and records of bees. XXX. *Ann. Mag. Nat. Hist. (8)*6: 17–31 (as *Meroglossa turneriana* (Cockerell, 1905)); Perkins, R.C.L. (1912). Notes, with descriptions of new species, on aculeate Hymenoptera of the Australian Region. *Ann. Mag. Nat. Hist. (8)*9: 96–121 (generic placement); Hirashima, Y. (1978). A synopsis of the bee genus *Palaeorhiza* Perkins (Hymenoptera, Colletidae) of New Guinea. Part I. Subgenus *Palaeorhiza* s. str. *Esakia* 11: 89–119 (note on subgeneric placement); Hirashima, Y. (1989). A synopsis of the bee genus *Palaeorhiza* Perkins (Hymenoptera, Colletidae) of New Guinea. Part VIII. Subgenus *Callorhiza*. *Esakia* 28: 1–9 (subgeneric placement).

Palaeorhiza (Callorhiza) viridimutans (Cockerell, 1910)

Meroglossa turneriana viridimutans Cockerell, T.D.A. (1910). Descriptions and records of bees. XXX. *Ann. Mag. Nat. Hist. (8)*6: 17–31 [21].
Type data: holotype (probable), BMNH Hym.17.a.204 ♀.
Type locality: Darwin, NT.

Distribution: N coastal, NT; known only from type locality.
Ecology: adult—volant; melliferous, solitary.
References: Hacker, H. (1921). Catalogue of Australian bees. *Mem. Qd Mus.* 7: 99–163 (as *Palaeorhiza*

turneriana viridimutans (Cockerell, 1910)); Michener, C.D. (1965). A classification of the bees of the Australian and South Pacific regions. *Bull. Am. Mus. Nat. Hist.* 130: 1–362 [146] (taxonomy); Hirashima, Y. (1989). A synopsis of the bee genus *Palaeorhiza* Perkins (Hymenoptera, Colletidae) of New Guinea. Part VIII. Subgenus *Callorhiza*. *Esakia* 28: 1–9 (subgeneric placement).

Palaeorhiza (Cnemidorhiza) Hirashima, 1981

Cnemidorhiza Hirashima, Y. (1981). A synopsis of the bee genus *Palaeorhiza* Perkins (Hymenoptera, Colletidae) of New Guinea. Part V. Subgenus *Cnemidorhiza*. *Esakia* 17: 1–48 [1] [proposed with subgeneric rank in *Palaeorhiza* Perkins, 1908]. Type species: *Prosopis elegans* Smith, 1864 (=*Palaeorhiza elegantissima* Dalla Torre, 1896) by original designation.

Extralimital distribution: Misool, New Guinea and New Britain, see Hirashima, Y. & Lieftinck, M.A. (1982). Systematic studies on the genus *Palaeorhiza* of New Guinea collected by the third Archbold Expedition (I) (Hymenoptera, Colletidae). *Esakia* 19: 1–50 [37].

Palaeorhiza (Cnemidorhiza) parallela (Cockerell, 1905)

Prosopis parallela Cockerell, T.D.A. (1905). Descriptions and records of bees. IV. *Ann. Mag. Nat. Hist. (7)*16: 392–403 [400].
Type data: syntypes, BMNH 2♀ (a specimen is labelled 'type' and has registration number Hym.17.a.192).
Type locality: Mackay, QLD.

Prosopis regina Friese, H. (1912). Zur Bienenfauna von Neu-Guinea und Oceania. *Mitt. Zool. Mus. Berl.* 6: 93–96 [nom. nud., name and locality only].

Prosopis regina Friese, H. (1924). Ueber die Bienen Australiens. *Konowia* 3: 216–249 [223].
Type data: syntypes, AMNH 2♀*.
Type locality: Mackay, QLD.

Prosopis regina humeralis Friese, H. (1924). Ueber die Bienen Australiens. *Konowia* 3: 216–249 [223].
Type data: syntypes (probable), AMNH ♀* (number of specimens unknown).
Type locality: Mackay, QLD.

Prosopis regalis Friese, H. (1924). Ueber die Bienen Australiens. *Konowia* 3: 216–249 [223].
Type data: syntypes, AMNH ♂* (number of specimens unknown).
Type locality: Mackay, QLD.

Palaeorhiza parallela optima Cockerell, T.D.A. (1929). Bees, chiefly Australian species, described or determined by Dr. H. Friese. *Am. Mus. Novit.* 343: 1–20 [17].
Type data: holotype, AMNH ♀*.
Type locality: Mackay, QLD.

Taxonomic decision for synonymy: Hirashima, Y. (1981). A synopsis of the bee genus *Palaeorhiza* Perkins (Hymenoptera, Colletidae) of New Guinea. Part V. Subgenus *Cnemidorhiza*. *Esakia* 17: 1–48 [27].

Distribution: NE coastal, QLD; also a doubtful record from Ralum, Bismarck Archipelago.

Ecology: adult—volant; melliferous, solitary, flower visiting record: *Cassia* L. *s.lat.* [Caesalpiniaceae], *Eucalyptus* L'Hérit. [Myrtaceae], *Eugenia* L. [Myrtaceae], *Rosa* L. [Rosaceae], *Xanthorrhoea* Sm. [Xanthorrhoeaceae].

References: Cockerell, T.D.A. (1910). Descriptions and records of bees. XXX. *Ann. Mag. Nat. Hist. (8)***6**: 17–31 (as *Meroglossa parallela* (Cockerell, 1905)); Perkins, R.C.L. (1912). Notes, with descriptions of new species, on aculeate Hymenoptera of the Australian Region. *Ann. Mag. Nat. Hist. (8)***9**: 96–121 (as *Palaeorhiza parallela* (Cockerell, 1905)); Meade-Waldo, G. (1923). Hymenoptera. Fam. Apidae. Subfam. Prosopidinae. *Genera Insectorum* **181**: 1–45 (illustration); Rayment, T. (1935). *A Cluster of Bees.* Sixty essays on the life-histories of Australian bees, with specific descriptions of over 100 new species, and an introduction by Professor E.F. Phillips, D.Ph., Cornell University, U.S.A. Sydney : Endeavour Press 752 pp. (illustration); McGinley, R.J. (1980). Glossal morphology of the Colletidae and recognition of the Stenotritidae at the family level (Hymenoptera : Apoidea). *J. Kansas Entomol. Soc.* **53**: 539–552 (glossa); Michener, C.D. & Brooks, R.W. (1984). A comparative study of the glossae of bees (Apoidea). *Contrib. Am. Entomol. Inst.* **22**: 1–73 (glossa); Michener, C.D. (1992). Sexual dimorphism in the glossa of Colletidae (Hymenoptera, Apoidea). *J. Kansas Entomol. Soc.* **65**: 1–9 (glossa).

Palaeorhiza (Cnemidorhiza) recessiva (Cockerell, 1912)

Meroglossa parallela recessiva Cockerell, T.D.A. (1912). Descriptions and records of bees. XLI. *Ann. Mag. Nat. Hist. (8)***9**: 139–149 [149].
Type data: holotype, BMNH Hym.17.a.193 ♂.
Type locality: Mackay, QLD.

Distribution: NE coastal, QLD; only published localities Mackay and Palm Is.
Ecology: adult—volant; melliferous, solitary.
References: Cockerell, T.D.A. (1930). New Australian bees. *Mem. Qd Mus.* **10**: 37–50 (distribution); Michener, C.D. (1965). A classification of the bees of the Australian and South Pacific regions. *Bull. Am. Mus. Nat. Hist.* **130**: 1–362 [146] (taxonomy); Hirashima, Y. (1981). A synopsis of the bee genus *Palaeorhiza* Perkins (Hymenoptera, Colletidae) of New Guinea. Part V. Subgenus *Cnemidorhiza. Esakia* **17**: 1–48 (subgeneric placement, redescription).

Palaeorhiza (Cnemidorhiza) rejecta Cockerell, 1929

Palaeorhiza disrupta rejecta Cockerell, T.D.A. (1929). Bees, chiefly Australian species, described or determined by Dr. H. Friese. *Am. Mus. Novit.* **343**: 1–20 [17].
Type data: holotype, AMNH ♀*.
Type locality: Cairns, QLD.

Distribution: NE coastal, QLD; known only from type locality.
Ecology: adult—volant; melliferous, solitary.
References: Michener, C.D. (1965). A classification of the bees of the Australian and South Pacific regions. *Bull. Am. Mus. Nat. Hist.* **130**: 1–362 [146] (taxonomy); Hirashima, Y. (1981). A synopsis of the bee genus *Palaeorhiza* Perkins (Hymenoptera, Colletidae) of New Guinea. Part V. Subgenus *Cnemidorhiza. Esakia* **17**: 1–48 (subgeneric placement, redescription).

Palaeorhiza (Cnemidorhiza) viridifrons Cockerell, 1921

Palaeorhiza viridifrons Cockerell, T.D.A. (1921). Australian bees in the Queensland Museum. *Mem. Qd Mus.* **7**: 81–98 [86].
Type data: holotype, QM T2412 ♀.
Type locality: Brisbane, QLD.

Distribution: NE coastal, QLD; only published localities Brisbane and Dayboro.
Ecology: adult—volant; melliferous, solitary.
References: Cockerell, T.D.A. (1929). Bees in the Queensland Museum. *Mem. Qd Mus.* **9**: 298–323 (distribution); Hirashima, Y. (1981). A synopsis of the bee genus *Palaeorhiza* Perkins (Hymenoptera, Colletidae) of New Guinea. Part V. Subgenus *Cnemidorhiza. Esakia* **17**: 1–48 (subgeneric placement, redescription).

Palaeorhiza (Heterorhiza) Cockerell, 1929

Heterorhiza Cockerell, T.D.A. (1929). Bees in the Queensland Museum. *Mem. Qd Mus.* **9**: 298–323 [316] [proposed with subgeneric rank in *Palaeorhiza* Perkins, 1908]. Type species: *Palaeorhiza melanura* Cockerell, 1910 by original designation.

Extralimital distribution: Moluccas, Misool and New Guinea, see Hirashima, Y. & Lieftinck, M.A. (1982). Systematic studies on the genus *Palaeorhiza* of New Guinea collected by the third Archbold Expedition (I) (Hymenoptera, Colletidae). *Esakia* **19**: 1–50 [10].

Palaeorhiza (Heterorhiza) denticauda (Cockerell, 1910)

Meroglossa denticauda Cockerell, T.D.A. (1910). Descriptions and records of bees. XXX. *Ann. Mag. Nat. Hist. (8)***6**: 17–31 [24].
Type data: holotype, BMNH Hym.17.a.209 ♂.
Type locality: Mackay, QLD.

Distribution: NE coastal, QLD; known only from type locality.
Ecology: adult—volant; melliferous, solitary.
References: Perkins, R.C.L. (1912). Notes, with descriptions of new species, on aculeate Hymenoptera of the Australian Region. *Ann. Mag. Nat. Hist. (8)***9**: 96–121 (generic placement); Cockerell, T.D.A.

(1929). Bees in the Queensland Museum. *Mem. Qd Mus.* **9**: 298–323 (subgeneric placement).

Palaeorhiza (Heterorhiza) hedleyi Cockerell, 1929

Palaeorhiza (Heterorhiza) hedleyi Cockerell, T.D.A. (1929). Bees in the Australian Museum collection. *Rec. Aust. Mus.* **17**: 199–243 [219].
Type data: syntypes, AM 3♂ (a specimen is labelled 'type' and has registration number K28377).
Type locality: Murray Is., Torres Strait, QLD.

Distribution: NE coastal, QLD; known only from type locality.
Ecology: adult—volant; melliferous, solitary.

Palaeorhiza (Heterorhiza) longiceps (Friese, 1924)

Prosopis longiceps Friese, H. (1924). Ueber die Bienen Australiens. *Konowia* **3**: 216–249 [228].
Type data: holotype (probable), whereabouts unknown ♀*.
Type locality: Mackay, QLD.

Distribution: NE coastal, QLD; known only from type locality.
Ecology: adult—volant; melliferous, solitary, flower visiting record: *Xanthorrhoea* Sm. [Xanthorrhoeaceae].
Reference: Cockerell, T.D.A. (1929). Bees in the Australian Museum collection. *Rec. Aust. Mus.* **17**: 199–243 (generic placement).

Palaeorhiza (Heterorhiza) melanura Cockerell, 1910

Palaeorhiza melanura Cockerell, T.D.A. (1910). Descriptions and records of bees. XXIX. *Ann. Mag. Nat. Hist. (8)***5**: 496–506 [499].
Type data: syntypes, USNM ♂♀*.
Type locality: Cairns, QLD.

Distribution: NE coastal, QLD; only published localities Cairns and Kuranda.
Ecology: adult—volant; melliferous, solitary.
References: Cockerell, T.D.A. (1910). Descriptions and records of bees. XXX. *Ann. Mag. Nat. Hist. (8)***6**: 17–31 (as *Meroglossa melanura* ((Cockerell, 1910)); Perkins, R.C.L. (1912). Notes, with descriptions of new species, on aculeate Hymenoptera of the Austra-

lian Region. *Ann. Mag. Nat. Hist. (8)***9**: 96–121 (taxonomy); Cockerell, T.D.A. (1929). Bees in the Australian Museum collection. *Rec. Aust. Mus.* **17**: 199–243 (generic placement); Michener, C.D. (1965). A classification of the bees of the Australian and South Pacific regions. *Bull. Am. Mus. Nat. Hist.* **130**: 1–362 (illustration); Hirashima, Y. & Lieftinck, M.A. (1982). Systematic studies on the genus *Palaeorhiza* of New Guinea collected by the third Archbold Expedition (I) (Hymenoptera, Colletidae). *Esakia* **19**: 1–50 (taxonomy).

Pharohylaeus Michener, 1965

Pharohylaeus Michener, C.D. (1965). A classification of the bees of the Australian and South Pacific regions. *Bull. Am. Mus. Nat. Hist.* **130**: 1–362 [141]. Type species: *Meroglossa lactifera* Cockerell, 1910 by original designation.

Extralimital distribution: New Guinea, see Hirashima, Y. & Roberts, H. (1986). Discovery of the bee genus *Pharohylaeus* Michener from Papua New Guinea, with description of a new species (Hymenoptera, Colletidae). *Esakia* **24**: 63–66 [63].

Pharohylaeus lactiferus (Cockerell, 1910)

Meroglossa lactifera Cockerell, T.D.A. (1910). Descriptions and records of bees. XXX. *Ann. Mag. Nat. Hist. (8)***6**: 17–31 [19].
Type data: holotype, BMNH Hym.17.a.197 ♂.
Type locality: Mackay, QLD.

Distribution: NE coastal, QLD; only published localities Mackay, Kuranda and Tableland (Atherton).
Ecology: adult—volant; melliferous, solitary.
References: Perkins, R.C.L. (1912). Notes, with descriptions of new species, on aculeate Hymenoptera of the Australian Region. *Ann. Mag. Nat. Hist. (8)***9**: 96–121 (taxonomy); Meade-Waldo, G. (1923). Hymenoptera. Fam. Apidae. Subfam. Prosopidinae. *Genera Insectorum* **181**: 1–45 (as *Palaeorhiza lactifera* (Cockerell, 1910)); Houston, T.F. (1975). A revision of the Australian hylaeine bees (Hymenoptera : Colletidae). I. *Aust. J. Zool. Suppl. Ser.* **36**: 1–135 (redescription).

STENOTRITIDAE

Ctenocolletes smaragdinus   [by A. Hastings]

INTRODUCTION

The Stenotritidae are endemic with two genera of large (12–18 mm), robust, hairy, short-tongued bees. They occur throughout mainland Australia but the family is best represented in Western Australia. Only one genus, *Stenotritus*, occurs in eastern Australia (Houston 1983a, 1983b, 1985). The family is not known from Tasmania.

Stenotritidae have a short, broad, glossa, which is rounded-acute apically; the ocelli are positioned low on the frons, the first antennal flagellar segment is longer than the scape, and the forewing has three submarginal cells. The females have a vestigial sting and carry pollen externally in scopae on the hind legs.

All species are solitary and nest in the ground. Some nests are over three metres deep. The nests may be quite close to each other but no obvious aggregations are formed (Houston 1975, 1984, 1987a; Houston & Thorp 1984). Fossil brood cells were described by Houston (1987b).

References

Houston, T.F. (1975). Nests, behaviour and larvae of the bee *Stenotritus pubescens* (Smith) and behaviour of some related species (Hymenoptera : Apoidea : Stenotritinae). *J. Aust. Entomol. Soc.* **14**: 145–154

Houston, T.F. (1983a). A revision of the bee genus *Ctenocolletes* (Hymenoptera : Stenotritidae). *Rec. West. Aust. Mus.* **10**: 269–306

Houston, T.F. (1983b). A new species of *Ctenocolletes* (Hymenoptera : Stenotritidae). *Rec. West. Aust. Mus.* **10**: 307–313

Houston, T.F. (1984). Biological observations in the genus *Ctenocolletes* (Hymenoptera : Stenotritidae). *Rec. West. Aust. Mus.* **11**: 153–172

Houston, T.F. (1985). Supplement to a revision of the bee genus *Ctenocolletes* (Hymenoptera : Stenotritidae). *Rec. West. Aust. Mus.* **12**: 293–305

Houston, T.F. (1987a). A second contribution to the biology of *Ctenocolletes* bees (Hymenoptera : Apoidea : Stenotritidae). *Rec. West. Aust. Mus.* **13**: 189–201

Houston, T.F. (1987b). Fossil brood cells of stenotritid bees (Hymenoptera : Apoidea) from the Pleistocene of South Australia. *Trans. R. Soc. S. Aust.* **111**: 93–97

Houston, T.F. & Thorp, R.W. (1984). Bionomics of the bee *Stenotritus greavesi* and ethological characteristics of Stenotritidae (Hymenoptera). *Rec. West. Aust. Mus.* **11**: 375–385

McGinley, R.J. (1980). Glossal morphology of the Colletidae and recognition of the Stenotritidae at the family level (Hymenoptera : Apoidea). *J. Kansas Entomol. Soc.* **53**: 539–552

Michener, C.D. (1965). A classification of the bees of the Australian and South Pacific regions. *Bull. Am. Mus. Nat. Hist.* **130**: 1–362

Ctenocolletes Cockerell, 1929

Ctenocolletes Cockerell, T.D.A. (1929). Descriptions and records of bees. CXV. *Ann. Mag. Nat. Hist. (10)***3**: 354–360 [358] [proposed with subgeneric rank in *Stenotritus* Smith, 1853]. Type species: *Stenotritus (Ctenocolletes) nicholsoni* Cockerell, 1929 by monotypy.

Ctenocolletes albomarginatus Michener, 1965

Ctenocolletes albomarginatus Michener, C.D. (1965). A classification of the bees of the Australian and South Pacific regions. *Bull. Am. Mus. Nat. Hist.* **130**: 1–362 [266]. Type data: holotype, ANIC ♀. Type locality: 6 miles N Watheroo, WA.

Distribution: SW coastal, NW coastal, W plateau, WA.
Ecology: larva—sedentary : adult—volant; melliferous, solitary, nest in soil, flower visiting record: *Baeckea* L. [Myrtaceae], *Eucalyptus* L'Hérit. [Myrtaceae], *Hakea* Schrader [Proteaceae], *Melaleuca* L. [Myrtaceae], *Scholtzia* Schauer, *Thryptomene* Endl. [Myrtaceae], *Wehlia* F.Muell. [Myrtaceae], *Westringia* Sm. [Lamiaceae].
References: Houston, T.F. (1983). A revision of the bee genus *Ctenocolletes* (Hymenoptera : Stenotritidae). *Rec. West. Aust. Mus.* **10**: 269–306 (redescription); Fain, A. (1984). A new genus of mite (Acari : Acaridae) phoretic on bees (*Ctenocolletes*) in Australia. *Rec. West. Aust. Mus.* **11**: 77–86 (as host); Houston, T.F. (1984). Biological observations in the genus *Ctenocolletes* (Hymenoptera : Stenotritidae). *Rec. West. Aust. Mus.* **11**: 153–172 (biology); Houston, T.F. (1985). Supplement to a revision of the bee genus *Ctenocolletes* (Hymenoptera : Stenotritidae). *Rec. West. Aust. Mus.* **12**: 293–305 (taxonomy, distribution); Fain, A. & Houston, T.F. (1986). Life cycle stages of mites of the genus *Ctenocolletacarus* Fain (Acari : Acaridae) associated with *Ctenocolletes* bees in Australia. *Rec. West. Aust. Mus.* **13**: 67–77 (as host); Houston, T.F. (1987). A second contribution to the biology of *Ctenocolletes* bees (Hymenoptera : Apoidea : Stenotritidae). *Rec. West. Aust. Mus.* **13**: 189–201 (biology); Houston, T.F. (1988). The symbiosis of acarid mites, genus *Ctenocolletacarus* (Acarina : Acariformes), and stenotritid bees, genus *Ctenocolletes* (Insecta : Hymenoptera). *Aust. J. Zool.* **35**(1987): 459–468 (biology).

Ctenocolletes centralis Houston, 1983

Ctenocolletes centralis Houston, T.F. (1983). A revision of the bee genus *Ctenocolletes* (Hymenoptera : Stenotritidae). *Rec. West. Aust. Mus.* **10**: 269–306 [283]. Type data: holotype, ANIC 7577 ♂. Type locality: 3 miles S Neale Junction, WA.

Distribution: W plateau, WA.
Ecology: larva—sedentary : adult—volant; melliferous, solitary, flower visiting record: *Acacia* Miller [Mimosaceae], *Baeckea* L. [Myrtaceae], *Dicrastylis* J.L. Drumm. ex Harvey [Verbenaceae], *Thryptomene* Endl. [Myrtaceae].
References: Fain, A. (1984). A new genus of mite (Acari : Acaridae) phoretic on bees (*Ctenocolletes*) in Australia. *Rec. West. Aust. Mus.* **11**: 77–86 (as host); Houston, T.F. (1984). Biological observations in the genus *Ctenocolletes* (Hymenoptera : Stenotritidae). *Rec. West. Aust. Mus.* **11**: 153–172 (biology); Houston, T.F. (1985). Supplement to a revision of the bee genus *Ctenocolletes* (Hymenoptera : Stenotritidae). *Rec. West. Aust. Mus.* **12**: 293–305 (distribution); Fain, A. & Houston, T.F. (1986). Life cycle stages of mites of the genus *Ctenocolletacarus* Fain (Acari : Acaridae) associated with *Ctenocolletes* bees in Australia. *Rec. West. Aust. Mus.* **13**: 67–77 (as host); Houston, T.F. (1987). A second contribution to the biology of *Ctenocolletes* bees (Hymenoptera : Apoidea : Stenotritidae). *Rec. West. Aust. Mus.* **13**: 189–201 (biology); Houston, T.F. (1988). The symbiosis of acarid mites, genus *Ctenocolletacarus* (Acarina : Acariformes), and stenotritid bees, genus *Ctenocolletes* (Insecta : Hymenoptera). *Aust. J. Zool.* **35**(1987): 459–468 (biology).

Ctenocolletes fulvescens Houston, 1983

Ctenocolletes fulvescens Houston, T.F. (1983). A revision of the bee genus *Ctenocolletes* (Hymenoptera : Stenotritidae). *Rec. West. Aust. Mus.* **10**: 269–306 [285]. Type data: holotype, WAM 82/818 ♀*. Type locality: 20 miles NE Eucla (WA), SA.

161

Distribution: W plateau, SA, WA; only published localities near Eucla, near Eyre Homestead and near Toolinna Rockhole.

Ecology: larva—sedentary : adult—volant; melliferous, solitary, flower visiting record: *Eucalyptus* L'Hérit. [Myrtaceae].

References: Houston, T.F. (1984). Biological observations in the genus *Ctenocolletes* (Hymenoptera : Stenotritidae). *Rec. West. Aust. Mus.* **11**: 153–172 (biology); Houston, T.F. (1985). Supplement to a revision of the bee genus *Ctenocolletes* (Hymenoptera : Stenotritidae). *Rec. West. Aust. Mus.* **12**: 293–305 (description of male, distribution); Houston, T.F. (1987). A second contribution to the biology of *Ctenocolletes* bees (Hymenoptera : Apoidea : Stenotritidae). *Rec. West. Aust. Mus.* **13**: 189–201 (flower record).

Ctenocolletes nicholsoni (Cockerell, 1929)

Stenotritus (Ctenocolletes) nicholsoni Cockerell, T.D.A. (1929). Descriptions and records of bees. CXV. *Ann. Mag. Nat. Hist. (10)3*: 354–360 [358].
Type data: holotype, AM ♀.
Type locality: Kojarena, WA.

Ctenocolletes notabilis Michener, C.D. (1965). A classification of the bees of the Australian and South Pacific regions. *Bull. Am. Mus. Nat. Hist.* **130**: 1–362 [266].
Type data: holotype, ANIC ♂.
Type locality: Geraldton, WA.

Taxonomic decision for synonymy: Houston, T.F. (1983). A revision of the bee genus *Ctenocolletes* (Hymenoptera : Stenotritidae). *Rec. West. Aust. Mus.* **10**: 269–306 [287].

Distribution: NW coastal, W plateau, WA.

Ecology: larva—sedentary : adult—volant; melliferous, solitary, nest in soil, flower visiting record: *Acacia* Miller [Mimosaceae], *Baeckea* L. [Myrtaceae], *Calytrix* Lab. [Myrtaceae], *Grevillea* R.Br. ex J. Knight [Proteaceae], *Hakea* Schrader [Proteaceae], *Ptilotus* R.Br. [Amaranthaceae], *Scaevola* L. [Goodeniaceae], *Scholtzia* Schauer, *Thryptomene* Endl. [Myrtaceae], *Wehlia* F. Muell. [Myrtaceae].
References: Fain, A. (1984). A new genus of mite (Acari : Acaridae) phoretic on bees (*Ctenocolletes*) in Australia. *Rec. West. Aust. Mus.* **11**: 77–86 (as host); Houston, T.F. (1984). Biological observations in the genus *Ctenocolletes* (Hymenoptera : Stenotritidae). *Rec. West. Aust. Mus.* **11**: 153–172 (biology); Fain, A. & Houston, T.F. (1986). Life cycle stages of mites of the genus *Ctenocolletacarus* Fain (Acari : Acaridae) associated with *Ctenocolletes* bees in Australia. *Rec. West. Aust. Mus.* **13**: 67–77 (as host); Houston, T.F. (1987). A second contribution to the biology of *Ctenocolletes* bees (Hymenoptera : Apoidea : Stenotritidae). *Rec. West. Aust. Mus.* **13**: 189–201 (biology); Houston, T.F. (1988). The symbiosis of acarid mites, genus *Ctenocolletacarus* (Acarina : Acariformes), and stenotritid bees, genus

Ctenocolletes (Insecta : Hymenoptera). *Aust. J. Zool.* **35**(1987): 459–468 (biology).

Ctenocolletes nigricans Houston, 1985

Ctenocolletes nigricans Houston, T.F. (1985). Supplement to a revision of the bee genus *Ctenocolletes* (Hymenoptera : Stenotritidae). *Rec. West. Aust. Mus.* **12**: 293–305 [302].
Type data: holotype, WAM 84/1062 ♂*.
Type locality: 13 km S Wannoo, WA.

Distribution: NW coastal, WA; only published localities near Wannoo and near Mullewa.

Ecology: larva—sedentary : adult—volant; melliferous, solitary, nest in soil, flower visiting record: *Melaleuca* L. [Myrtaceae], *Thryptomene* Endl. [Myrtaceae].
References: Fain, A. & Houston, T.F. (1986). Life cycle stages of mites of the genus *Ctenocolletacarus* Fain (Acari : Acaridae) associated with *Ctenocolletes* bees in Australia. *Rec. West. Aust. Mus.* **13**: 67–77 (as host); Houston, T.F. (1987). A second contribution to the biology of *Ctenocolletes* bees (Hymenoptera : Apoidea : Stenotritidae). *Rec. West. Aust. Mus.* **13**: 189–201 (biology); Houston, T.F. (1988). The symbiosis of acarid mites, genus *Ctenocolletacarus* (Acarina : Acariformes), and stenotritid bees, genus *Ctenocolletes* (Insecta : Hymenoptera). *Aust. J. Zool.* **35**(1987): 459–468 (biology).

Ctenocolletes ordensis Michener, 1965

Ctenocolletes ordensis Michener, C.D. (1965). A classification of the bees of the Australian and South Pacific regions. *Bull. Am. Mus. Nat. Hist.* **130**: 1–362 [267].
Type data: holotype, WAM 65/728 ♂.
Type locality: Wotjulum, WA (locality considered doubtful), see Houston, T.F. (1983). A revision of the bee genus *Ctenocolletes* (Hymenoptera : Stenotritidae). *Rec. West. Aust. Mus.* **10**: 269–306 [291].

Distribution: SW coastal, NW coastal, W plateau, (N coastal), WA.

Ecology: larva—sedentary : adult—volant; melliferous, solitary, nest in soil, flower visiting record: *Acacia* Miller [Mimosaceae], *Cassia* L. s.lat. [Caesalpiniaceae], *Scaevola* L. [Goodeniaceae].
References: Houston, T.F. (1983). A revision of the bee genus *Ctenocolletes* (Hymenoptera : Stenotritidae). *Rec. West. Aust. Mus.* **10**: 269–306 (redescription, distribution); Houston, T.F. (1984). Biological observations in the genus *Ctenocolletes* (Hymenoptera : Stenotritidae). *Rec. West. Aust. Mus.* **11**: 153–172 (biology); Houston, T.F. (1985). Supplement to a revision of the bee genus *Ctenocolletes* (Hymenoptera : Stenotritidae). *Rec. West. Aust. Mus.* **12**: 293–305 (distribution).

Ctenocolletes rufescens Houston, 1983

Ctenocolletes rufescens Houston, T.F. (1983). A revision of the bee genus *Ctenocolletes* (Hymenoptera :

Stenotritidae). *Rec. West. Aust. Mus.* **10**: 269–306 [292].
Type data: holotype, WAM 81/691 ♂*.
Type locality: Balline Station, WA.

Distribution: SW coastal, NW coastal, W plateau, WA.

Ecology: larva—sedentary : adult—volant; melliferous, solitary, flower visiting record: *Eucalyptus* L'Hérit. [Myrtaceae], *Grevillea* R.Br. ex J. Knight [Proteaceae], *Hakea* Schrader [Proteaceae], *Melaleuca* L. [Myrtaceae], *Scholtzia* Schauer, *Wehlia* F. Muell. [Myrtaceae].

Reference: Houston, T.F. (1984). Biological observations in the genus *Ctenocolletes* (Hymenoptera : Stenotritidae). *Rec. West. Aust. Mus.* **11**: 153–172 (biology).

Ctenocolletes smaragdinus (Smith, 1868)

Stenotritus smaragdinus Smith, F. (1868). Descriptions of aculeate Hymenoptera from Australia. *Trans. Entomol. Soc. Lond.* **1868**: 231–258 [254].
Type data: holotype, BMNH Hym.17.a.2745 ♀.
Type locality: Champion Bay (Geraldton), WA.
Melitribus glauerti Rayment, T. (1930). Studies in Australian bees. *Vict. Nat.* **47**: 9–17 [16].
Type data: holotype, WAM 19/224 ♀.
Type locality: Yorkrakine, WA.
Stenotritus speciosus Rayment, T. (1935). *A Cluster of Bees*. Sixty essays on the life-histories of Australian bees, with specific descriptions of over 100 new species, and an introduction by Professor E.F. Phillips, D.Ph., Cornell University, U.S.A. Sydney : Endeavour Press 752 pp. [683].
Type data: holotype, ANIC ♂.
Type locality: Dowerin, WA.

Taxonomic decision for synonymy: Houston, T.F. (1983). A revision of the bee genus *Ctenocolletes* (Hymenoptera : Stenotritidae). *Rec. West. Aust. Mus.* **10**: 269–306 [296].

Distribution: SW coastal, W plateau, WA.

Ecology: larva—sedentary : adult—volant; melliferous, solitary, nest in soil, flower visiting record: *Baeckea* L. [Myrtaceae], *Beaufortia* R.Br. [Myrtaceae], *Leptospermum* Forster & G.Forster. [Myrtaceae], *Melaleuca* L. [Myrtaceae], *Grevillea* R.Br. ex J. Knight [Proteaceae], *Verticordia* DC. [Myrtaceae].

References: Smith, F. (1873). Natural history notices. Insects, Hymenoptera Aculeata. pp. 456–463 pls xliii–xlv *in* Brenchley, J.B. *Jottings During the Cruise of* H.M.S. Curaçoa *among the South Sea Islands in 1865*. London : Longmans, Green & Co. (illustration); Michener, C.D. & Fraser, A. (1978). A comparative anatomical study of mandibular structure in bees. *Univ. Kansas Sci. Bull.* **51**: 463–482 (mandible); Cane, J.H. (1979). The hind tibiotarsal and tibial spur articulations in bees (Hymenoptera : Apoidea). *J. Kansas Entomol. Soc.* **52**: 123–137 (hind spur); Houston, T.F. (1984). Biological observations in the genus *Ctenocolletes* (Hymenoptera :

Stenotritidae). *Rec. West. Aust. Mus.* **11**: 153–172 (biology); Michener, C.D. & Brooks, R.W. (1984). A comparative study of the glossae of bees (Apoidea). *Contrib. Am. Entomol. Inst.* **22**: 1–73 (glossa); Houston, T.F. (1987). A second contribution to the biology of *Ctenocolletes* bees (Hymenoptera : Apoidea : Stenotritidae). *Rec. West. Aust. Mus.* **13**: 189–201 (biology); Michener, C.D. & Houston, T.F. (1991). Apoidea. pp. 993–1000 *in* CSIRO (sponsor) *The Insects of Australia. A textbook for students and research workers.* Melbourne : Melbourne University Press Vol. II 2nd Edn (illustration).

Ctenocolletes tigris Houston, 1983

Ctenocolletes tigris Houston, T.F. (1983). A new species of *Ctenocolletes* (Hymenoptera : Stenotritidae). *Rec. West. Aust. Mus.* **10**: 307–313 [307].
Type data: holotype, WAM 82/1877 ♂*.
Type locality: 36 km NNE Neale Junction, WA.

Distribution: NW coastal, W plateau, WA.

Ecology: larva—sedentary : adult—volant; melliferous, solitary, nest in soil, flower visiting record: *Acacia* Miller [Mimosaceae], *Baeckea* L. [Myrtaceae], *Dicrastylis* J.L.Drumm. ex Harvey [Verbenaceae], *Grevillea* R.Br. ex J. Knight [Proteaceae], *Newcastelia* F. Muell. [Verbenaceae], *Ptilotus* R.Br. [Amaranthaceae], *Solanum* L. [Solanaceae], *Teucrium* L. [Lamiaceae], *Thryptomene* Endl. [Myrtaceae], *Wehlia* F. Muell. [Myrtaceae].

References: Houston, T.F. (1984). Biological observations in the genus *Ctenocolletes* (Hymenoptera : Stenotritidae). *Rec. West. Aust. Mus.* **11**: 153–172 (biology); Houston, T.F. (1985). Supplement to a revision of the bee genus *Ctenocolletes* (Hymenoptera : Stenotritidae). *Rec. West. Aust. Mus.* **12**: 293–305 (distribution); Houston, T.F. (1987). A second contribution to the biology of *Ctenocolletes* bees (Hymenoptera : Apoidea : Stenotritidae). *Rec. West. Aust. Mus.* **13**: 189–201 (biology).

Ctenocolletes tricolor Houston, 1983

Ctenocolletes tricolor Houston, T.F. (1983). A revision of the bee genus *Ctenocolletes* (Hymenoptera : Stenotritidae). *Rec. West. Aust. Mus.* **10**: 269–306 [299].
Type data: holotype, WAM 82/128 ♂*.
Type locality: 8 km S Yellowdine, WA.

Distribution: SW coastal, W plateau, WA.

Ecology: larva—sedentary : adult—volant; melliferous, solitary, flower visiting record: *Grevillea* R.Br. ex J. Knight [Proteaceae], *Melaleuca* L. [Myrtaceae], *Wehlia* F. Muell. [Myrtaceae].

Reference: Houston, T.F. (1984). Biological observations in the genus *Ctenocolletes* (Hymenoptera : Stenotritidae). *Rec. West. Aust. Mus.* **11**: 153–172 (biology).

Stenotritus Smith, 1853

Stenotritus Smith, F. (1853). *Catalogue of Hymenopterous Insects in the Collection of the British Museum.* Part I. Andrenidae and Apidae. London : British Museum 197 pp. [119]. Type species: *Stenotritus elegans* Smith, 1853 by monotypy.

Oestropsis Smith, F. (1868). Descriptions of aculeate Hymenoptera from Australia. *Trans. Entomol. Soc. Lond.* **1868**: 231–258 [253] [junior homonym of *Oestropsis* Brauer, 1868 (Trichoptera)]. Type species: *Oestropsis pubescens* Smith, 1868 by monotypy.

Gastropsis Smith, F. (1868). [A new name for *Oestropsis*]. *Proc. Entomol. Soc. Lond.* **1868**: xxxix [xxxix] [*nom. nov.* for *Oestropsis* Smith, 1868].

Melitribus Rayment, T. (1930). *Microglossa* and *Melitribus*, new genera of Australian bees. *Proc. R. Soc. Vict.* **42**: 211–220 [217]. Type species: *Melitribus greavesi* Rayment, 1930 by monotypy.

Taxonomic decision for synonymy: Michener, C.D. (1965). A classification of the bees of the Australian and South Pacific regions. *Bull. Am. Mus. Nat. Hist.* **130**: 1–362 [82].

Stenotritus elegans Smith, 1853

Stenotritus elegans Smith, F. (1853). *Catalogue of Hymenopterous Insects in the Collection of the British Museum.* Part I. Andrenidae and Apidae. London : British Museum 197 pp. [119].
Type data: holotype, BMNH Hym.17.a.2744 ♀.
Type locality: Sydney, NSW.

Distribution: SE coastal, W plateau, NSW, NT; only published localities Sydney, Tennants Creek.
Ecology: adult—volant; melliferous, solitary.
References: Cockerell, T.D.A. (1905). Notes on some bees in the British Museum. *Trans. Am. Entomol. Soc.* **31**: 309–364 (taxonomy); Cockerell, T.D.A. (1914). Descriptions and records of bees. LVI. *Ann. Mag. Nat. Hist.* (8)**13**: 136–146 (variety A); Michener, C.D. & Brooks, R.W. (1984). A comparative study of the glossae of bees (Apoidea). *Contrib. Am. Entomol. Inst.* **22**: 1–73 (glossa).

Stenotritus elegantior Cockerell, 1921

Stenotritus elegantior Cockerell, T.D.A. (1921). Australian bees in the Queensland Museum. *Mem. Qd Mus.* **7**: 81–98 [91].
Type data: holotype, QM T2487 ♀.
Type locality: QLD (probably Mackay region).

Distribution: (NE coastal), QLD; known only from type locality.
Ecology: adult—volant; melliferous, solitary.

Stenotritus ferricornis (Cockerell, 1916)

Paracolletes ferricornis Cockerell, T.D.A. (1916). Descriptions and records of bees. LXXIII. *Ann. Mag. Nat. Hist.* (8)**18**: 44–53 [52].
Type data: holotype, BMNH Hym.17.a.466 ♂.
Type locality: Hermannsburg, NT.

Distribution: Lake Eyre basin, NT; known only from type locality.
Ecology: adult—volant; melliferous, solitary.
Reference: Michener, C.D. (1965). A classification of the bees of the Australian and South Pacific regions. *Bull. Am. Mus. Nat. Hist.* **130**: 1–362 (generic placement).

Stenotritus greavesi (Rayment, 1930)

Melitribus greavesi Rayment, T. (1930). *Microglossa* and *Melitribus*, new genera of Australian bees. *Proc. R. Soc. Vict.* **42**: 211–220 [218].
Type data: holotype, ANIC ♂.
Type locality: Bungulla (as Bungalla on label), WA.

Distribution: SW coastal, WA; known only from type locality.
Ecology: larva—sedentary : adult—volant; melliferous, solitary, nest in soil, flower visiting record: *Baeckea* L. [Myrtaceae], *Callistemon* R.Br. [Myrtaceae], *Cheiranthera* Brongn. [Pittosporaceae], *Hakea* Schrader [Proteaceae], *Leptospermum* Forster & G.Forster. [Myrtaceae], *Melaleuca* L. [Myrtaceae], *Verticordia* DC. [Myrtaceae].
References: Rayment, T. (1930). Studies in Australian bees. *Vict. Nat.* **47**: 9–17 (illustration); Cockerell, T.D.A. (1934). The bees of Australia. *Aust. Zool.* **8**: 2–38 (generic placement); Rayment, T. (1935). *A Cluster of Bees.* Sixty essays on the life-histories of Australian bees, with specific descriptions of over 100 new species, and an introduction by Professor E.F. Phillips, D.Ph., Cornell University, U.S.A. Sydney : Endeavour Press 752 pp. (taxonomy); Houston, T.F. (1983). A revision of the bee genus *Ctenocolletes* (Hymenoptera : Stenotritidae). *Rec. West. Aust. Mus.* **10**: 269–306 (taxonomy); Houston, T.F. & Thorp, R.W. (1984). Bionomics of the bee *Stenotritus greavesi* and ethological characteristics of Stenotritidae (Hymenoptera). *Rec. West. Aust. Mus.* **11**: 375–385 (biology).

Stenotritus murrayensis (Rayment, 1935)

Ctenocolletes murrayensis Rayment, T. (1935). *A Cluster of Bees.* Sixty essays on the life-histories of Australian bees, with specific descriptions of over 100 new species, and an introduction by Professor E.F. Phillips, D.Ph., Cornell University, U.S.A. Sydney : Endeavour Press 752 pp. [683].
Type data: holotype, ANIC ♀.
Type locality: Wentworth ("Murray R. Redcliffs" on label), NSW.

Distribution: Murray-Darling basin, NSW; known only from type locality.
Ecology: adult—volant; melliferous, solitary.
Reference: Houston, T.F. (1983). A revision of the bee genus *Ctenocolletes* (Hymenoptera : Stenotritidae). *Rec. West. Aust. Mus.* **10**: 269–306 (generic placement).

Stenotritus nigrescens (Friese, 1924)

Gastropsis pubescens nigrescens Friese, H. (1924). Ueber die Bienen Australiens. *Konowia* **3**: 216–249 [249].
Type data: syntypes, whereabouts unknown ♂* (number of specimens unknown).
Type locality: Central Australia.

Distribution: (Lake Eyre basin), NT; known only from type locality.
Ecology: adult—volant; melliferous, solitary.
References: Cockerell, T.D.A. (1929). Descriptions and records of bees. CXV. *Ann. Mag. Nat. Hist. (10)*3: 354–360 (generic placement, subspecies to species); Rayment, T. (1930). New and remarkable bees. *Proc. R. Soc. Vict.* **43**: 42–61 (taxonomy, as *Melitribus pubescens nigrescens* (Friese, 1924)).

Stenotritus nitidus (Smith, 1879)

Paracolletes nitidus Smith, F. (1879). *Descriptions of New Species of Hymenoptera in the Collection of the British Museum*. London : British Museum xxi 240 pp. [3].
Type data: holotype, BMNH Hym.17.a.413 ♀.
Type locality: NW coast Australia.

Distribution: (NW coastal), WA; known only from type locality.
Ecology: adult—volant; melliferous, solitary.
Reference: Cockerell, T.D.A. (1905). Notes on some bees in the British Museum. *Trans. Am. Entomol. Soc.* **31**: 309–364 (taxonomy).

Stenotritus pubescens (Smith, 1868)

Oestropsis pubescens Smith, F. (1868). Descriptions of aculeate Hymenoptera from Australia. *Trans. Entomol. Soc. Lond.* **1868**: 231–258 [253] [the type locality has not been resolved; holotype labelled as WA].
Type data: syntypes, BMNH 2♂ (a male specimen is labelled 'type' and has registration number Hym.17.a.2746).
Type locality: Geraldton (as Champion Bay), WA, SA.

Distribution: NE coastal, Lake Eyre basin, NW coastal, QLD, VIC, SA, WA; only published localities Brisbane, Finniss Springs Station (51 km W Marree) and Champion Bay.
Ecology: larva—sedentary : adult—volant; melliferous, solitary, nest in aggregations in soil, flower visiting record: *Eucalyptus* L'Hérit. [Myrtaceae].
References: Cockerell, T.D.A. (1904). Notes on some bees in the British Museum. *Can. Entomol.* **36**: 301–304 (redescription); Cockerell, T.D.A. (1910). New and little-known bees. *Trans. Am. Entomol. Soc.* **36**: 199–249 (distribution); Cockerell, T.D.A. (1912). Descriptions and records of bees. XLVII. *Ann. Mag. Nat. Hist. (8)*10: 484–494 (distribution); Cockerell, T.D.A. (1929). Descriptions and records of bees. CXV. *Ann. Mag. Nat. Hist. (10)*3: 354–360 (generic placement); Michener, C.D. (1965). A classification of the bees of the Australian and South Pacific regions. *Bull. Am. Mus. Nat. Hist.* **130**: 1–362 (taxon-

omy); Houston, T.F. (1975). Nests, behaviour and larvae of the bee *Stenotritus pubescens* (Smith) and behaviour of some related species (Hymenoptera : Apoidea : Stenotritinae). *J. Aust. Entomol. Soc.* **14**: 145–154 (biology); McGinley, R.J. (1980). Glossal morphology of the Colletidae and recognition of the Stenotritidae at the family level (Hymenoptera : Apoidea). *J. Kansas Entomol. Soc.* **53**: 539–552 (illustration); McGinley, R.J. (1981). Systematics of the Colletidae based on mature larvae with phenetic analysis of apoid larvae (Insecta, Hymenoptera, Apoidea). *Univ. Calif. Publ. Entomol.* **91**: 1–309 (larva); Houston, T.F. (1983). A revision of the bee genus *Ctenocolletes* (Hymenoptera : Stenotritidae). *Rec. West. Aust. Mus.* **10**: 269–306 (illustration); Houston, T.F. & Thorp, R.W. (1984). Bionomics of the bee *Stenotritus greavesi* and ethological characteristics of Stenotritidae (Hymenoptera). *Rec. West. Aust. Mus.* **11**: 375–385 (biology).

Stenotritus rufocollaris (Cockerell, 1921)

Gastropsis victoriae rufocollaris Cockerell, T.D.A. (1921). Australian bees in the Queensland Museum. *Mem. Qd Mus.* **7**: 81–98 [91].
Type data: syntypes, BMNH 2♂ (a male specimen is labelled 'type' and has registration number Hym.17.a.2743).
Type locality: Mallee, VIC.

Distribution: Murray-Darling basin, VIC; known only from type locality.
Ecology: adult—volant; melliferous, solitary.
References: Cockerell, T.D.A. (1929). Descriptions and records of bees. CXV. *Ann. Mag. Nat. Hist. (10)*3: 354–360 (generic placement); Michener, C.D. (1965). A classification of the bees of the Australian and South Pacific regions. *Bull. Am. Mus. Nat. Hist.* **130**: 1–362 [83] (taxonomy).

Stenotritus splendidus (Rayment, 1930)

Melitribus pubescens splendida Rayment, T. (1930). Studies in Australian bees. *Vict. Nat.* **47**: 9–17 [14].
Type data: holotype, ANIC ♂.
Type locality: Geraldton (as Geralton), WA.

Distribution: NW coastal, WA; known only from type locality.
Ecology: adult—volant; melliferous, solitary, flower visiting record: *Eucalyptus* L'Hérit. [Myrtaceae], *Verticordia* DC. [Myrtaceae].
References: Rayment, T. (1930). New and remarkable bees. *Proc. R. Soc. Vict.* **43**: 42–61 (generic placement); Rayment, T. (1935). *A Cluster of Bees. Sixty essays on the life-histories of Australian bees, with specific descriptions of over 100 new species, and an introduction by Professor E.F. Phillips, D.Ph., Cornell University, U.S.A.* Sydney : Endeavour Press 752 pp. (illustration); Michener, C.D. (1965). A classification of the bees of the Australian and South

165

Pacific regions. *Bull. Am. Mus. Nat. Hist.* **130**: 1–362 [83] (taxonomy).

Stenotritus victoriae (Cockerell, 1906)

Gastropsis victoriae Cockerell, T.D.A. (1906). Four interesting Australian bees, in the collection of the British Museum. *Entomologist* **39**: 15–18 [15].
Type data: holotype, BMNH Hym.17.a.2742 ♂.
Type locality: SA.

Distribution: SW coastal, VIC, SA, WA; only published locality Swan River.
Ecology: adult—volant; melliferous, solitary.
References: Cockerell, T.D.A. (1912). Descriptions and records of bees. XLIII. *Ann. Mag. Nat. Hist.* *(8)***9**: 377–387 (variety); Rayment, T. (1930). Studies in Australian bees. *Vict. Nat.* **47**: 9–17 (variety); Cockerell, T.D.A. (1934). The bees of Australia. *Aust. Zool.* **8**: 2–38 (generic placement).

HALICTIDAE

INTRODUCTION

The Halictidae are short-tongued bees, characterized by a short, broad, apically pointed glossa with an elongate prepalpal part of the galeae. The forewing has three submarginal cells. The family is cosmopolitan in distribution.

Three subfamilies are recognised: Halictinae, Nomiinae and Dufoureinae (Michener 1965). The Dufoureinae are not known to occur in Australia (Michener 1979). Flower visiting records are given in Michener (1965), Armstrong (1979), Bernhardt & Walker (1984, 1985) and Bernhardt (1987).

The Halictinae are minute to medium in size (3–12 mm) and moderately hairy bees. The subfamily has a cosmopolitan distribution and is represented in Australia by five genera, two of which occur in Tasmania. Pollen is carried externally in scopae on the hind legs, except in *Homalictus* where the scopa is on the metasomal sterna.

Nomia australica   [by M. Quick]

The subfamily is divided into three tribes: Halictini, with most of the Australian species placed in endemic subgenera of *Lasioglossum* (Michener 1979); Nomioidini, with only one species in Australia; and Augochlorini, which does not occur in Australia. One cleptoparasitic genus of the Halictini, *Sphecodes*, is found in Queensland.

Halictinae usually nest in the soil, occasionally in rotting wood. Australian species may be solitary or communal, with two to many females sharing a nest, each female provisioning and laying eggs in her own cells (Michener 1960; Knerer & Schwarz 1976, 1978; Walker 1986). Polymorphic males have been found in some communal species but no social species (*i.e.* forming colonies with workers and one or a few queens) has been found in Australia (Houston 1970; Knerer 1980; Kukuk & Schwarz 1987, 1988). Trophallaxis has been observed in one communal species (Kukuk & Crozier 1990).

The only major taxonomic revision of Australian species of Halictinae since Michener (1965) is Walker's (1986) treatment of *Homalictus*. Michener (1978a, 1978b) revised mainly non-Australian genera and Pauly (1980a, 1980b, 1980c, 1986) worked on species of several of the genera in this catalogue.

Nomiinae are medium sized (7–12 mm), robust, moderately hairy bees which carry pollen externally in scopae on the hind legs. They have an almost cosmopolitan distribution but are not known from South America. In Australia, they are represented by one genus. They are not known from Tasmania. The adults nest in soil and sometimes form large aggregations (Rayment 1956). No parasitic or social species are known. Pauly (1984) revised the Afrotropical genera.

References

Armstrong, J.A. (1979). Biotic pollination mechanisms in the Australian flora—a review. *N.Z. J. Bot.* **17**: 467–508

Bernhardt, P. (1987). A comparison of the diversity, density, and foraging behavior of bees and wasps on Australian *Acacia. Ann. M. Bot. Gard.* **74**: 42–50

Bernhardt, P. & Walker, K. (1984). Bee foraging on three sympatric species of Australian *Acacia. Int. J. Entomol.* **26**: 322–330

Bernhardt, P. & Walker, K. (1985). Insect foraging on *Acacia retinodes* var. *retinodes* in Victoria, Australia. *Int. J. Entomol.* **27**: 97–101

Houston, T.F. (1970). Discovery of an apparent male soldier caste in a nest of a halictine bee (Hymenoptera : Halictidae), with notes on the nest. *Aust. J. Zool.* **18**: 345–351

Knerer, G. (1980). Evolution of halictine castes. *Naturwissensch.* **67**: 133–135

Knerer, G. & Schwarz, M. (1976). Halictine social evolution : the Australian enigma. *Science* **194**: 445–448

Knerer, G. & Schwarz, M. (1978). Beobachtungen an australischen Furchenbienen (Hymenopteren; Halictinae). *Zool. Anz.* **200**: 321–333

Kukuk, P.F. & Schwarz, M. (1987). Intranest behavior of the communal sweat bee *Lasioglossum (Chilalictus) erythrurum* (Hymenoptera : Halictidae). *J. Kansas Entomol. Soc.* **60**: 58–64

Kukuk, P.F. & Schwarz, M. (1988). Macrocephalic male bees as functional reproductives and probable guards. *Pan-Pac. Entomol.* **64**: 131–137

Kukuk, P.F. & Crozier, R.H. (1990). Trophallaxis in a communal halictine bee *Lasioglossum (Chilalictus) erythrurum. Proc. Natl Acad. Sci. U.S.A.* **87**: 5402–5404

Michener, C.D. (1960). Notes on the biology and supposed parthenogenesis of halictine bees from the Australian region. *J. Kansas Entomol. Soc.* **33**: 85–96

Michener, C.D. (1965). A classification of the bees of the Australian and South Pacific regions. *Bull. Am. Mus. Nat. Hist.* **130**: 1–362

Michener, C.D. (1978a). The parasitic groups of Halictidae (Hymenoptera, Apoidea). *Univ. Kansas Sci. Bull.* **51**: 291–339

Michener, C.D. (1978b). The classification of halictine bees : tribes and Old World nonparasitic genera with strong venation. *Univ. Kansas Sci. Bull.* **51**: 501–538

Michener, C.D. (1979). Biogeography of the bees. *Ann. Mo. Bot. Gdn* **66**: 277–347

Pauly, A. (1980a). Les espèces métalliques afrotropicales du sous-genre *Ctenonomia* du genre *Lasioglossum* (Hymenoptera, Apoidea, Halictidae). *Rev. Zool. Afr.* **94**: 1–10

Pauly, A. (1980b). Descriptions préliminaires de quelques sous-genres afrotropicaux nouveaux de la famille des Halictidae (Hymenoptera, Apoidea). *Rev. Zool. Afr.* **94**: 119–125

Pauly, A. (1980c). Les espèces indonesiennes du genre *Homalictus* Cockerell (Hymenoptera, Apoidea, Halictidae). *Zool. Meded.* **55**: 11–28

Pauly, A. (1984). Contribution à l'étude des genres afrotropicaux de Nomiinae (Hymenoptera Apoidea Halictidae). *Rev. Zool. Afr.* **98**: 693–702

Pauly, A. (1986). Les abeilles de la sous-famille des Halictinae en Nouvelle-Guinée et dans l'Archipel Bismarck (Hymenoptera : Apoidea : Halictidae). *Zool. Verh.* **227**: 1–58

Rayment, T. (1956). The *Nomia australica* Sm. complex. Its taxonomy, morphology and biology with the description of a new mutillid wasp. *Aust. Zool.* **12**: 176–200

Walker, K.L. (1986). Revision of the Australian species of the genus *Homalictus* Cockerell (Hymenoptera : Halictidae). *Mem. Mus. Vict.* **47**: 105–200

HALICTINAE

Homalictus Cockerell, 1919

Taxonomic decision for subgeneric arrangement: Walker, K.L. (1986). Revision of the Australian species of the genus *Homalictus* Cockerell (Hymenoptera : Halictidae). *Mem. Mus. Vict.* **47**: 105–200 [115].

Generic reference: Michener, C.D. (1965). A classification of the bees of the Australian and South Pacific regions. *Bull. Am. Mus. Nat. Hist.* **130**: 1–362.

Homalictus (Homalictus) Cockerell, 1919

Homalictus Cockerell, T.D.A. (1919). The metallic-coloured Halictine bees of the Philippine Islands. *Philipp. J. Sci.* **15**: 9–13 [13] [proposed with subgeneric rank in *Halictus* Latreille, 1804]. Type species: *Halictus taclobanensis* Cockerell, 1915 by original designation.

Indohalictus Blüthgen, P. (1931). Beiträge zur Kenntnis der indomalayanischen *Halictus*- und *Thrincostoma*-Arten (Hym. Apidae. Halictini). *Zool. Jb. Abt. Syst.* **61**: 285–346 [291] [proposed with subgeneric rank in *Halictus* Latreille, 1804]. Type species: *Halictus buccinus* Vachal, 1894 by original designation.

Taxonomic decision for synonymy: Michener, C.D. (1965). A classification of the bees of the Australian and South Pacific regions. *Bull. Am. Mus. Nat. Hist.* **130**: 1–362 [178].

Extralimital distribution: Oriental Region, extending E across Pacific Ocean to Samoa, see Michener, C.D. (1965). A classification of the bees of the Australian and South Pacific regions. *Bull. Am. Mus. Nat. Hist.* **130**: 1–362 [179].

Homalictus (Homalictus) atrus Walker, 1986

Homalictus (Homalictus) atrus Walker, K.L. (1986). Revision of the Australian species of the genus *Homalictus* Cockerell (Hymenoptera : Halictidae). *Mem. Mus. Vict.* **47**: 105–200 [122].
Type data: holotype, ANIC ♀.
Type locality: Moses Creek, 4 km NE Mt Finnigan, QLD.

Distribution: NE coastal, QLD; only published localities Moses Ck and Lockerbie.
Ecology: adult—volant; melliferous, solitary.

Homalictus (Homalictus) behri (Cockerell, 1910)

Halictus behri Cockerell, T.D.A. (1910). New and little-known bees. *Trans. Am. Entomol. Soc.* **36**: 199–249 [228].
Type data: holotype, BMNH Hym.17.a.936 ♀*.
Type locality: Port Darwin, NT.

Distribution: NE coastal, N Gulf, N coastal, QLD, WA, NT.
Ecology: adult—volant; melliferous, flower visiting record: *Borreria* G. Meyer [Rubiaceae], *Dysophylla* Blume [Lamiaceae], *Eucalyptus* L'Hérit. [Myrtaceae], *Parinari* Aublet [Chrysobalanaceae], *Thryptomene* Endl. [Myrtaceae], *Tristaniopsis* Brongn. & Gris [Myrtaceae].
References: Cockerell, T.D.A. (1905). New Australian bees, in the collection of the British Museum. *Entomologist* **38**: 270–273, 302–304 (as variety of *Halictus flindersi* Cockerell, 1905); Cockerell, T.D.A. (1910). New and little-known bees. *Trans. Am. Entomol. Soc.* **36**: 199–249 (as variety of *Halictus flindersi* Cockerell, 1905); Cockerell, T.D.A. (1929). Bees from the Australian region. *Am. Mus. Novit.* **346**: 1–18 (taxonomy); Walker, K.L. (1986). Revision of the Australian species of the genus *Homalictus* Cockerell (Hymenoptera : Halictidae). *Mem. Mus. Vict.* **47**: 105–200 (redescription).

Homalictus (Homalictus) blackburni (Cockerell, 1910)

Halictus blackburni Cockerell, T.D.A. (1910). New and little-known bees. *Trans. Am. Entomol. Soc.* **36**: 199–249 [232].
Type data: holotype, BMNH Hym.17.a.925 ♀*.
Type locality: Mackay, QLD.
Halictus crinitus Friese, H. (1924). Ueber die Bienen Australiens. *Konowia* **3**: 216–249 [243].
Type data: lectotype, AMNH ♂*.
Subsequent designation: Pauly, A. (1986). Les abeilles de la sous-famille des Halictinae en Nouvelle-Guinée et dans l'Archipel Bismarck (Hymenoptera : Apoidea : Halictidae). *Zool. Verh.* **227**: 1–58 [44].
Type locality: Mackay, QLD.

Taxonomic decision for synonymy: Cockerell, T.D.A. (1929). Bees, chiefly Australian species, described or determined by Dr. H. Friese. *Am. Mus. Novit.* **343**: 1–20 [12].

Distribution: NE coastal, N Gulf, N coastal, QLD, NT; also New Guinea and Moluccas Ils.
Ecology: adult—volant; melliferous, flower visiting record: *Cassia* L. *s.lat.* [Caesalpiniaceae], *Eucalyptus* L'Hérit. [Myrtaceae], *Eugenia* L. [Myrtaceae], *Leptospermum* Forster & G.Forster [Myrtaceae], *Melaleuca* L. [Myrtaceae], *Thryptomene* Endl. [Myrtaceae], *Tristaniopsis* Brongn. & Gris [Myrtaceae], *Xanthorrhoea* Sm. [Xanthorrhoeaceae].
References: Pauly, A. (1986). Les abeilles de la sous-famille des Halictinae en Nouvelle-Guinée et dans l'Archipel Bismarck (Hymenoptera : Apoidea : Halictidae). *Zool. Verh.* **227**: 1–58 (distribution); Walker, K.L. (1986). Revision of the Australian species of the genus *Homalictus* Cockerell (Hymenoptera : Halictidae). *Mem. Mus. Vict.* **47**: 105–200 (redescription).

Homalictus (Homalictus) bremerensis (Rayment, 1931)

Halictus (Chloralictus) formosus Rayment, T. (1930). Notes on a collection of bees from Western Australia. *J. Proc. R. Soc. West. Aust.* **16**: 45–56 [52] [junior primary homonym of *Halictus formosus* Dours, 1872].
Type data: holotype, ANIC ♀.
Type locality: Albany, WA.
Halictus bremerensis Rayment, T. (1931). Bees in the collections of the Western Australian Museum and the Agricultural Department, Perth. *J. Proc. R. Soc. West. Aust.* **17**: 157–190 [171].
Type data: holotype, WAM 16–63 ♀.
Type locality: Bremer Bay, WA.
Homalictus formosulus Michener, C.D. (1965). A classification of the bees of the Australian and South Pacific regions. *Bull. Am. Mus. Nat. Hist.* **130**: 1–362 [180] [*nom. nov.* for *Halictus formosus* Rayment, 1930].

Taxonomic decision for synonymy: Walker, K.L. (1986). Revision of the Australian species of the genus *Homalictus* Cockerell (Hymenoptera : Halictidae). *Mem. Mus. Vict.* **47**: 105–200 [125].

Distribution: SW coastal, WA.
Ecology: adult—volant; melliferous, flower visiting record: *Callistemon* R.Br. [Myrtaceae], *Eucalyptus* L'Hérit. [Myrtaceae].
References: Rayment, T. (1935). *A Cluster of Bees*. Sixty essays on the life-histories of Australian bees, with specific descriptions of over 100 new species, and an introduction by Professor E.F. Phillips, D.Ph., Cornell University, U.S.A. Sydney : Endeavour Press 752 pp. (illustration); Rayment, T. (1954). Incidence of acarid mites on the biology of bees. *Aust. Zool.* **12**: 26–38 (as host).

Homalictus (Homalictus) brisbanensis (Cockerell, 1918)

Halictus brisbanensis Cockerell, T.D.A. (1918). Some bees collected in Queensland. *Mem. Qd Mus.* **6**: 112–120 [117].
Type data: holotype, USNM ♀*.
Type locality: Brisbane, QLD.
Halictus botanicus Rayment, T. (1935). *A Cluster of Bees*. Sixty essays on the life-histories of Australian bees, with specific descriptions of over 100 new species, and an introduction by Professor E.F. Phillips, D.Ph., Cornell University, U.S.A. Sydney : Endeavour Press 752 pp. [696].
Type data: holotype, ANIC ♀ (described as ♂).
Type locality: Botanic Gardens, Melbourne, VIC.
Halictus portlandicus Rayment, T. (1953). *Bees of the Portland District*. Victoria : Portland Field Naturalist's Club 39 pp. [18].
Type data: holotype, ANIC ♀.
Type locality: Portland, VIC.

Taxonomic decision for synonymy: Walker, K.L. (1986). Revision of the Australian species of the genus *Homalictus* Cockerell (Hymenoptera : Halictidae). *Mem. Mus. Vict.* **47**: 105–200 [126].

Distribution: NE coastal, Murray-Darling basin, SE coastal, QLD, NSW, VIC.
Ecology: adult—volant; melliferous, flower visiting record: *Acacia* Miller [Mimosaceae], *Amyema* Tieghem [Loranthaceae], *Arctotheca* Wendl. [Asteraceae], *Callistemon* R.Br. [Myrtaceae], *Dendrobium* Sw. [Orchidaceae], *Eucalyptus* L'Hérit. [Myrtaceae], *Hypochaeris* L. [Asteraceae], *Leptospermum* Forster & G.Forster [Myrtaceae], *Lycium* L. [Solanaceae], *Oenothera* L. [Onagraceae], *Salpichroa* Miers [Solanaceae], *Syncarpia* Ten. [Myrtaceae], *Tristaniopsis* Brongn. & Gris [Myrtaceae].
References: Bernhardt, P., Kenrick, J. & Knox, R.B. (1984). Pollination biology and the breeding system of *Acacia retinodes* (Leguminosae: Mimosoideae). *Ann. M. Bot. Gard.* **71**: 17–29 (flower records); Slater, A.T. & Calder, D.M. (1988). The pollination biology of *Dendrobium speciosum* Smith: a case of false advertising? *Aust. J. Bot.* **36**: 145–158 (pollination record); Bernhardt, P. (1987). A comparison of the diversity, density, and foraging behavior of bees and wasps on Australian *Acacia. Ann. M. Bot. Gard.* **74**: 42–50 (flower record).

Homalictus (Homalictus) callaspis (Cockerell, 1915)

Halictus callaspis Cockerell, T.D.A. (1915). Descriptions and records of bees. LXVIII. *Ann. Mag. Nat. Hist. (8)***16**: 1–9 [6].
Type data: holotype, QM Hy4117 ♀.
Type locality: Bribie Is., QLD.

Distribution: NE coastal, SE coastal, QLD, NSW.
Ecology: adult—volant; melliferous, flower visiting record: *Mesembryanthemum* L. [Aizoaceae].

Reference: Walker, K.L. (1986). Revision of the Australian species of the genus *Homalictus* Cockerell (Hymenoptera : Halictidae). *Mem. Mus. Vict.* **47**: 105–200 (redescription).

Homalictus (Homalictus) caloundrensis (Cockerell, 1914)

Halictus caloundrensis Cockerell, T.D.A. (1914). Descriptions and records of bees. LIX. *Ann. Mag. Nat. Hist. (8)*13: 504–522 [505].
Type data: holotype, QM Hy4116 ♀.
Type locality: Caloundra, QLD.

Halictus flindersi leucurus Cockerell, T.D.A. (1914). Descriptions and records of bees. LXIII. *Ann. Mag. Nat. Hist. (8)*14: 361–369 [366].
Type data: holotype, QM Hy4121 ♀.
Type locality: Bribie Is., QLD.

Halictus rufoaeneus Friese, H (1924). Ueber die Bienen Australiens. *Konowia* 3: 216–249 [237].
Type data: holotype, AMNH ♀*.
Type locality: Botanic Gardens, Sydney, NSW.

Halictus viridinitens Friese, H. (1924). Ueber die Bienen Australiens. *Konowia* 3: 216–249 [237].
Type data: lectotype, AMNH ♀*.
Subsequent designation: Walker, K.L. (1986). Revision of the Australian species of the genus *Homalictus* Cockerell (Hymenoptera : Halictidae). *Mem. Mus. Vict.* **47**: 105–200 [128].
Type locality: Botanic Gardens, Sydney, NSW.

Taxonomic decision for synonymy: Walker, K.L. (1986). Revision of the Australian species of the genus *Homalictus* Cockerell (Hymenoptera : Halictidae). *Mem. Mus. Vict.* **47**: 105–200 [128].

Distribution: NE coastal, Murray-Darling basin, SE coastal, QLD, NSW, VIC.
Ecology: adult—volant; melliferous, flower visiting record: *Atalaya* Blume [Sapindaceae], *Eucalyptus* L'Hérit. [Myrtaceae], *Melaleuca* L. [Myrtaceae], *Schinus* L. [Anacardiaceae].

Homalictus (Homalictus) cassiaefloris (Cockerell, 1914)

Halictus cassiaefloris Cockerell, T.D.A. (1914). Descriptions and records of bees. LIX. *Ann. Mag. Nat. Hist. (8)*13: 504–522 [514].
Type data: lectotype, BMNH Hym.17.a.955 ♀*.
Subsequent designation: Walker, K.L. (1986). Revision of the Australian species of the genus *Homalictus* Cockerell (Hymenoptera : Halictidae). *Mem. Mus. Vict.* **47**: 105–200 [129].
Type locality: Mackay, QLD.

Halictus tenuis Friese, H. (1924). Ueber die Bienen Australiens. *Konowia* 3: 216–249 [240] [junior primary homonym of *Halictus tenuis* Ellis, 1913].
Type data: lectotype, AMNH ♀*.
Subsequent designation: Walker, K.L. (1986). Revision of the Australian species of the genus *Homalictus* Cockerell (Hymenoptera : Halictidae). *Mem. Mus. Vict.* **47**: 105–200 [129].
Type locality: Mackay, QLD.

Taxonomic decision for synonymy: Cockerell, T.D.A. (1929). Bees, chiefly Australian species, described or determined by Dr. H. Friese. *Am. Mus. Novit.* 343: 1–20 [12].

Distribution: NE coastal, N Gulf, N coastal, QLD, WA, NT; also New Guinea and the Bismarck Archipelago.
Ecology: adult—volant; melliferous, flower visiting record: *Cassia* L. *s.lat.* [Caesalpiniaceae], *Eucalyptus* L'Hérit. [Myrtaceae], *Securinega* A.L.Juss. [Euphorbiaceae], *Terminalia* L. [Combretaceae], *Tristaniopsis* Brongn. & Gris [Myrtaceae], *Xanthorrhoea* Sm. [Xanthorrhoeaceae].
References: Pauly, A. (1986). Les abeilles de la sous-famille des Halictinae en Nouvelle-Guinée et dans l'Archipel Bismarck (Hymenoptera : Apoidea : Halictidae). *Zool. Verh.* **227**: 1–58 (distribution); Walker, K.L. (1986). Revision of the Australian species of the genus *Homalictus* Cockerell (Hymenoptera : Halictidae). *Mem. Mus. Vict.* **47**: 105–200 (redescription).

Homalictus (Homalictus) ctenander Michener, 1965

Homalictus ctenander Michener, C.D. (1965). A classification of the bees of the Australian and South Pacific regions. *Bull. Am. Mus. Nat. Hist.* **130**: 1–362 [318].
Type data: holotype, NMV ♀.
Type locality: Kerang, VIC.

Distribution: Murray-Darling basin, Lake Eyre basin, S Gulfs, W plateau, NSW, VIC, SA, WA, NT.
Ecology: adult—volant; melliferous, flower visiting record: *Amyema* Tieghem [Loranthaceae], *Atalaya* Blume [Sapindaceae], *Brachychiton* Schott & Endl. [Sterculiaceae], *Eremophila* R.Br. [Myoporaceae], *Eucalyptus* L'Hérit. [Myrtaceae], *Malus* Miller [Rosaceae], *Melaleuca* L. [Myrtaceae], *Pittosporum* Gaertner [Pittosporaceae], *Strelitzia* Banks ex Dryander [Strelitziaceae].
References: Michener, C.D. (1978). The parasitic groups of Halictidae (Hymenoptera, Apoidea). *Univ. Kansas Sci. Bull.* **51**: 291–339 (taxonomy); Walker, K.L. (1986). Revision of the Australian species of the genus *Homalictus* Cockerell (Hymenoptera : Halictidae). *Mem. Mus. Vict.* **47**: 105–200 (redescription).

Homalictus (Homalictus) dampieri (Cockerell, 1905)

Halictus dampieri Cockerell, T.D.A. (1905). New Australian bees, in the collection of the British Museum. *Entomologist* 38: 270–273, 302–304 [270].
Type data: holotype, BMNH Hym.17.a.943 ♀*.
Type locality: Mackay, QLD.

Halictus indigoteus Friese, H. (1924). Ueber die Bienen Australiens. *Konowia* 3: 216–249 [243].
Type data: lectotype, AMNH ♀*.
Subsequent designation: Walker, K.L. (1986). Revision of the Australian species of the genus *Homalictus* Cockerell

(Hymenoptera : Halictidae). *Mem. Mus. Vict.* **47**: 105–200 [131].

Type locality: Mackay, QLD.

Halictus strangulatus Friese, H. (1924). Ueber die Bienen Australiens. *Konowia* **3**: 216–249 [244].

Type data: lectotype, AMNH ♀*.

Subsequent designation: Pauly, A. (1986). Les abeilles de la sous-famille des Halictinae en Nouvelle-Guinée et dans l'Archipel Bismarck (Hymenoptera : Apoidea : Halictidae). *Zool. Verh.* **227**: 1–58 [24].

Type locality: Mackay, QLD.

Taxonomic decision for synonymy: Cockerell, T.D.A. (1929). Bees, chiefly Australian species, described or determined by Dr. H. Friese. *Am. Mus. Novit.* **343**: 1–20 [13].

Distribution: NE coastal, Murray-Darling basin, N Gulf, N coastal, QLD, NSW, NT, WA; also on Solomon Ils, New Guinea and Bismarck Archipelago.

Ecology: adult—volant; melliferous, males found clustering, flower visiting record: yellow composite, *Acacia* Miller [Mimosaceae], *Alphitonia* Reisseck ex Endl. [Rhamnaceae], *Amyema* Tieghem [Loranthaceae], *Angophora* Cav. [Myrtaceae], *Bursaria* Cav. [Pittosporaceae], *Callistemon* R.Br. [Myrtaceae], *Cassia* L. *s.lat.* [Caesalpiniaceae], *Eucalyptus* L'Hérit. [Myrtaceae], *Eugenia* L. [Myrtaceae], *Jacksonia* Smith [Fabaceae], *Leptospermum* Forster & G.Forster [Myrtaceae], *Melaleuca* L. [Myrtaceae], *Terminalia* L. [Combretaceae], *Tristaniopsis* Brongn. & Gris [Myrtaceae], *Xanthorrhoea* Sm. [Xanthorrhoeaceae].

References: Cockerell, T.D.A. (1910). New and little-known bees. *Trans. Am. Entomol. Soc.* **36**: 199–249 (description of male); Cockerell, T.D.A. (1936). Bees from the Solomon Islands. *Proc. R. Entomol. Soc. Lond. (B)***5**: 225–226 (distribution); Cockerell, T.D.A. (1939). Studies of the Pacific bees in the collection of Bishop Museum (Hymenoptera, Apoidea). *Occ. Pap. Bernice P. Bishop Mus.* **15**: 133–140 (taxonomy); Krombein, K.V. (1951). Additional notes on the bees of the Solomon Islands (Hymenoptera : Apoidea). *Proc. Hawaii. Entomol. Soc.* **14**: 277–295 (illustration); Michener, C.D. (1960). Notes on the biology and supposed parthenogenesis of halictine bees from the Australian region. *J. Kansas Entomol. Soc.* **33**: 85–96 (biology); Evans, H.E. & Matthews, R.W. (1973). Systematics and nesting behavior of Australian *Bembix* sand wasps (Hymenoptera, Sphecidae). *Mem. Am. Entomol. Inst.* **20**: 1–387 (as prey); Pauly, A. (1986). Les abeilles de la sous-famille des Halictinae en Nouvelle-Guinée et dans l'Archipel Bismarck (Hymenoptera : Apoidea : Halictidae). *Zool. Verh.* **227**: 1–58 (distribution); Walker, K.L. (1986). Revision of the Australian species of the genus *Homalictus* Cockerell (Hymenoptera : Halictidae). *Mem. Mus. Vict.* **47**: 105–200 (redescription).

Homalictus (Homalictus) dotatus (Cockerell, 1912)

Halictus dotatus Cockerell, T.D.A. (1912). Descriptions and records of bees. XLIII. *Ann. Mag. Nat. Hist. (8)***9**: 377–387 [384].

Type data: holotype, USNM ♀*.

Type locality: Sydney, NSW.

Halictus (Chloralictus) occidentalis Rayment, T. (1930). Notes on a collection of bees from Western Australia. *J. Proc. R. Soc. West. Aust.* **16**: 45–56 [51] [junior primary homonym of *Halictus occidentalis* Cresson, 1872].

Type data: holotype, ANIC ♀.

Type locality: Perth, WA.

Halictus codenticalis Rayment, T. (1935). *A Cluster of Bees*. Sixty essays on the life-histories of Australian bees, with specific descriptions of over 100 new species, and an introduction by Professor E.F. Phillips, D.Ph., Cornell University, U.S.A. Sydney : Endeavour Press 752 pp. [634] [*nom. nov.* for *Halictus occidentalis* Rayment, 1930].

Taxonomic decision for synonymy: Walker, K.L. (1986). Revision of the Australian species of the genus *Homalictus* Cockerell (Hymenoptera : Halictidae). *Mem. Mus. Vict.* **47**: 105–200 [132].

Distribution: NE coastal, N Gulf, Murray-Darling basin, SE coastal, S Gulfs, Lake Eyre basin, W plateau, SW coastal, NW coastal, N coastal, QLD, NSW, VIC, SA, WA, NT.

Ecology: larva—sedentary : adult—volant; melliferous, nest communally in soil, flower visiting record: *Acacia* Miller [Mimosaceae], *Amyema* Tieghem [Loranthaceae], *Angophora* Cav. [Myrtaceae], *Atalaya* Blume [Sapindaceae], *Callistemon* R.Br. [Myrtaceae], *Codonocarpus* Cunn. ex Endl. [Gyrostemonaceae], *Eucalyptus* L'Hérit. [Myrtaceae], *Grevillea* R.Br. ex J. Knight [Proteaceae], *Hakea* Schrader [Proteaceae], *Keraudrenia* Gay [Sterculiaceae], *Leptospermum* Forster & G.Forster [Myrtaceae], *Melaleuca* L. [Myrtaceae], *Ptilotus* R.Br. [Amaranthaceae], *Schinus* L. [Anacardiaceae], *Terminalia* L. [Combretaceae], *Tristaniopsis* Brongn. & Gris [Myrtaceae], *Wahlenbergia* Roth [Campanulaceae].

References: Michener, C.D. (1960). Notes on the biology and supposed parthenogenesis of halictine bees from the Australian region. *J. Kansas Entomol. Soc.* **33**: 85–96 (biology); Michener, C.D. (1965). A classification of the bees of the Australian and South Pacific regions. *Bull. Am. Mus. Nat. Hist.* **130**: 1–362 (flower record); Evans, H.E. & Matthews, R.W. (1973). Systematics and nesting behavior of Australian *Bembix* sand wasps (Hymenoptera, Sphecidae). *Mem. Am. Entomol. Inst.* **20**: 1–387 (as prey); Morris, B., Southcott, R.V. & Gale, A.E. (1988). Effects of stings of Australian native bees. *Med. J. Aust.* **149**: 707–709 (allergic reaction to sting).

Homalictus (Homalictus) eurhodopus (Cockerell, 1914)

Halictus eurhodopus Cockerell, T.D.A. (1914). Descriptions and records of bees. LIX. *Ann. Mag. Nat. Hist.* *(8)*13: 504–522 [514].
Type data: holotype, BMNH Hym.17.a.945 ♀*.
Type locality: Kuranda (as Cairns Kuranda), QLD.

Distribution: NE coastal, QLD; also New Guinea.
Ecology: adult—volant; melliferous, flower visiting record: *Dillwynia* Sm. [Fabaceae], *Eucalyptus* L'Hérit. [Myrtaceae], *Tristaniopsis* Brongn. & Gris [Myrtaceae].
References: Pauly, A.`(1986). Les abeilles de la sous-famille des Halictinae en Nouvelle-Guinée et dans l'Archipel Bismarck (Hymenoptera : Apoidea : Halictidae). *Zool. Verh.* **227**: 1–58 (distribution); Walker, K.L. (1986). Revision of the Australian species of the genus *Homalictus* Cockerell (Hymenoptera : Halictidae). *Mem. Mus. Vict.* **47**: 105–200 (redescription).

Homalictus (Homalictus) exleyae Walker, 1986

Homalictus (Homalictus) exleyae Walker, K.L. (1986). Revision of the Australian species of the genus *Homalictus* Cockerell (Hymenoptera : Halictidae). *Mem. Mus. Vict.* **47**: 105–200 [135].
Type data: holotype, QM ♀*.
Type locality: 6 km S Broome, WA.

Distribution: NE coastal, N coastal, QLD, WA, NT.
Ecology: adult—volant; melliferous, flower visiting record: *Eucalyptus* L'Hérit. [Myrtaceae], *Melaleuca* L. [Myrtaceae].

Homalictus (Homalictus) exophthalmus Walker, 1986

Homalictus (Homalictus) exophthalmus Walker, K.L. (1986). Revision of the Australian species of the genus *Homalictus* Cockercll (Hymenoptera : Halictidae). *Mem. Mus. Vict.* **47**: 105–200 [137].
Type data: holotype, SAMA ♀*.
Type locality: Nyngan, NSW.

Distribution: Murray-Darling basin, NSW; known only from type locality.
Ecology: adult—volant; melliferous, flower visiting record: *Wahlenbergia* Roth [Campanulaceae].

Homalictus (Homalictus) flindersi (Cockerell, 1905)

Halictus flindersi Cockerell, T.D.A. (1905). New Australian bees, in the collection of the British Museum. *Entomologist* **38**: 270–273, 302–304 [271].
Type data: lectotype, BMNH Hym.17.a.942 ♀*.
Subsequent designation: Walker, K.L. (1986). Revision of the Australian species of the genus *Homalictus* Cockerell (Hymenoptera : Halictidae). *Mem. Mus. Vict.* **47**: 105–200 [138]; Cardale, J.C., this work, interprets Walker's incorrect inference of holotype as a lectotype designation (Art. 74, ICZN 1985).
Type locality: Seaforth, Mackay, QLD.

Halictus hilli Cockerell, T.D.A. (1929). Bees from the Australian region. *Am. Mus. Novit.* **346**: 1–18 [2].
Type data: holotype, AMNH ♂*.
Type locality: Darwin, NT.

Taxonomic decision for synonymy: Walker, K.L. (1986). Revision of the Australian species of the genus *Homalictus* Cockerell (Hymenoptera : Halictidae). *Mem. Mus. Vict.* **47**: 105–200 [138].

Distribution: NE coastal, N Gulf, N coastal, QLD, WA, NT; also New Guinea.
Ecology: adult—volant; melliferous, flower visiting record: *Acacia* Miller [Mimosaceae], *Dysophylla* Blume [Lamiaceae], *Eucalyptus* L'Hérit. [Myrtaceae], *Hibiscus* L. [Malvaceae], *Melaleuca* L. [Myrtaceae], *Parinari* Aublet [Chrysobalanaceae], *Pongamia* Vent. [Fabaceae], *Tournefortia* L. [Boraginaceae].
Reference: Pauly, A. (1986). Les abeilles de la sous-famille des Halictinae en Nouvelle-Guinée et dans l'Archipel Bismarck (Hymenoptera : Apoidea : Halictidae). *Zool. Verh.* **227**: 1–58 (distribution).

Homalictus (Homalictus) forrestae Walker, 1986

Homalictus (Homalictus) forrestae Walker, K.L. (1986). Revision of the Australian species of the genus *Homalictus* Cockerell (Hymenoptera : Halictidae). *Mem. Mus. Vict.* **47**: 105–200 [139].
Type data: holotype, SAMA ♂*.
Type locality: 11.3 km N Barkley Hwy, on Burketown Rd, QLD.

Distribution: N Gulf, QLD; known only from type locality.
Ecology: adult—volant; melliferous, solitary.

Homalictus (Homalictus) grossopedalus Walker, 1986

Homalictus (Homalictus) grossopedalus Walker, K.L. (1986). Revision of the Australian species of the genus *Homalictus* Cockerell (Hymenoptera : Halictidae). *Mem. Mus. Vict.* **47**: 105–200 [140].
Type data: holotype, BMNH ♂*.
Type locality: Kuranda, QLD.

Distribution: NE coastal, QLD; known only from type locality.
Ecology: adult—volant; melliferous, solitary.

Homalictus (Homalictus) holochlorus (Cockerell, 1914)

Halictus holochlorus Cockerell, T.D.A. (1914). Descriptions and records of bees. LIX. *Ann. Mag. Nat. Hist.* *(8)*13: 504–522 [507].
Type data: holotype, ANIC ♀.
Type locality: Cheltenham, VIC.

Distribution: NE coastal, SE coastal, QLD, NSW, VIC.
Ecology: adult—volant; melliferous, flower visiting record: *Acacia* Miller [Mimosaceae].

References: Walker, K.L. (1986). Revision of the Australian species of the genus *Homalictus* Cockerell (Hymenoptera : Halictidae). *Mem. Mus. Vict.* **47**: 105–200 (redescription); Bernhardt, P. (1987). A comparison of the diversity, density, and foraging behavior of bees and wasps on Australian *Acacia*. *Ann. M. Bot. Gard.* **74**: 42–50 (flower record).

Homalictus (Homalictus) houstoni Walker, 1986

Homalictus (Homalictus) houstoni Walker, K.L. (1986). Revision of the Australian species of the genus *Homalictus* Cockerell (Hymenoptera : Halictidae). *Mem. Mus. Vict.* **47**: 105–200 [141].
Type data: holotype, SAMA ♀*.
Type locality: 64 km E Norseman, WA.

Distribution: W plateau, WA; known only from type locality.
Ecology: adult—volant; melliferous, flower visiting record: *Eucarya* T. Mitch. [Santalaceae].

Homalictus (Homalictus) imitatus Walker, 1986

Homalictus (Homalictus) imitatus Walker, K.L. (1986). Revision of the Australian species of the genus *Homalictus* Cockerell (Hymenoptera : Halictidae). *Mem. Mus. Vict.* **47**: 105–200 [142].
Type data: holotype, QM ♂*.
Type locality: Prairie Homestead turnoff, 86 km NNE Thargomindah, QLD.

Distribution: Murray-Darling basin, Lake Eyre basin, QLD.
Ecology: adult—volant; melliferous, flower visiting record: *Amyema* Tieghem [Loranthaceae], *Eucalyptus* L'Hérit. [Myrtaceae].

Homalictus (Homalictus) latitarsis (Friese, 1909)

Halictus latitarsis Friese, H. (1909). Die Bienenfauna von Neu-Guinea. *Ann. Hist.-Nat. Mus. Natl. Hung.* **7**: 179–288 [188].
Type data: lectotype, HNHM ♂*.
Subsequent designation: Pauly, A. (1986). Les abeilles de la sous-famille des Halictinae en Nouvelle-Guinée et dans l'Archipel Bismarck (Hymenoptera : Apoidea : Halictidae). *Zool. Verh.* **227**: 1–58 [36].
Type locality: von Friedrich-Wilhemshafen, New Guinea.

Halictus caroli Cockerell, T.D.A. (1919). The black halictine bees of the Philippine islands. *Philipp. J. Sci.* **15**: 269–281 [277].
Type data: holotype, USNM ♀*.
Type locality: Puerto Princesa, Palawan, Philippines.

Halictus mcgregori Cockerell, T.D.A. (1919). The black halictine bees of the Philippine islands. *Philipp. J. Sci.* **15**: 269–281 [277].
Type data: holotype, USNM ♀*.
Type locality: Antique Province, Culasi, Panay, Philippines.

Taxonomic decision for synonymy: Pauly, A. (1986). Les abeilles de la sous-famille des Halictinae en Nouvelle-Guinée et dans l'Archipel Bismarck (Hymenoptera : Apoidea : Halictidae). *Zool. Verh.* **227**: 1–58 [36].

Distribution: NE coastal, QLD; only published locality Peaches Crossing via Coen, also found in New Guinea, Bismarck Archipelago, Philippines and Indonesia.
Ecology: adult—volant; melliferous, flower visiting record: *Tristaniopsis* Brongn. & Gris [Myrtaceae].
Reference: Walker, K.L. (1986). Revision of the Australian species of the genus *Homalictus* Cockerell (Hymenoptera : Halictidae). *Mem. Mus. Vict.* **47**: 105–200 (redescription).

Homalictus (Homalictus) luteoaeneus (Friese, 1924)

Halictus luteoaeneus Friese, H. (1924). Ueber die Bienen Australiens. *Konowia* **3**: 216–249 [236].
Type data: lectotype, AMNH ♀*.
Subsequent designation: Walker, K.L. (1986). Revision of the Australian species of the genus *Homalictus* Cockerell (Hymenoptera : Halictidae). *Mem. Mus. Vict.* **47**: 105–200 [144].
Type locality: VIC.

Distribution: VIC; known only from type locality, exact locality unknown.
Ecology: adult—volant; melliferous, solitary.
References: Cockerell, T.D.A. (1929). Bees, chiefly Australian species, described or determined by Dr. H. Friese. *Am. Mus. Novit.* **343**: 1–20 (redescription); Walker, K.L. (1986). Revision of the Australian species of the genus *Homalictus* Cockerell (Hymenoptera : Halictidae). *Mem. Mus. Vict.* **47**: 105–200 (redescription).

Homalictus (Homalictus) maitlandi (Cockerell, 1910)

Halictus maitlandi Cockerell, T.D.A. (1910). New and little-known bees. *Trans. Am. Entomol. Soc.* **36**: 199–249 [233].
Type data: holotype, BMNH ♀*.
Type locality: Kuranda (as Cairns Kuranda), QLD.

Distribution: NE coastal, QLD; known only from type locality.
Ecology: adult—volant; melliferous, solitary.
References: Cockerell, T.D.A. (1933). The bees of Australia. *Aust. Zool.* **7**: 291–324 (taxonomy, as *Halictus (Pachyhalictus) maitlandi* Cockerell, 1910); Walker, K.L. (1986). Revision of the Australian species of the genus *Homalictus* Cockerell (Hymenoptera : Halictidae). *Mem. Mus. Vict.* **47**: 105–200 (redescription).

Homalictus (Homalictus) megastigmus (Cockerell, 1926)

Halictus megastigmus Cockerell, T.D.A. (1926). Descriptions and records of bees. CXII. *Ann. Mag. Nat. Hist. (9)***18**: 216–227 [219].
Type data: holotype, NMV ♀.
Type locality: Hobart, TAS.

Halictus dixoni Rayment, T. (1935). *A Cluster of Bees. Sixty essays on the life-histories of Australian bees, with*

specific descriptions of over 100 new species, and an introduction by Professor E.F. Phillips, D.Ph., Cornell University, U.S.A. Sydney : Endeavour Press 752 pp. [703].
Type data: holotype, ANIC ♀ (described as ♂).
Type locality: Ferntree Gully, VIC.

Halictus tarltoni hentyi Rayment, T. (1953). *Bees of the Portland District*. Victoria : Portland Field Naturalist's Club 39 pp. [27].
Type data: holotype (probable), ANIC ♀.
Type locality: Gorae West, VIC.

Halictus sevillensis Rayment, T. (1953). *Bees of the Portland District*. Victoria : Portland Field Naturalist's Club 39 pp. [27].
Type data: holotype, ANIC ♀.
Type locality: Seville, VIC.

Taxonomic decision for synonymy: Walker, K.L. (1986). Revision of the Australian species of the genus *Homalictus* Cockerell (Hymenoptera : Halictidae). *Mem. Mus. Vict.* **47**: 105–200 [146].

Distribution: NE coastal, Murray-Darling basin, SE coastal, S Gulfs, SW coastal, QLD, NSW, VIC, SA, WA, TAS.
Ecology: adult—volant; melliferous, flower visiting record: *Acacia* Miller [Mimosaceae], *Arctotheca* Wendl. [Asteraceae], *Bursaria* Cav. [Pittosporaceae], *Calytrix* Lab. [Myrtaceae], *Eremophila* R.Br. [Myoporaceae], *Eucalyptus* L'Hérit. [Myrtaceae], *Lasiopetalum* Sm. [Sterculiaceae], *Leptospermum* Forster & G.Forster [Myrtaceae], *Leucopogon* R.Br. [Epacridaceae], *Tetratheca* Sm. [Tremandraceae].
References: Bernhardt, P. & Walker, K. (1984). Bee foraging on three sympatric species of Australian *Acacia*. *Int. J. Entomol.* **26**: 322–330 (flower record); Bernhardt, P. & Walker, K. (1985). Insect foraging on *Acacia retinodes* var. *retinodes* in Victoria, Australia. *Int. J. Entomol.* **27**: 97–101 (flower record); Ireland, J.C. & Griffin, A.R. (1984). Observations on the pollination ecology of *Eucalyptus muellerana* Howitt in East Gippsland. *Vict. Nat.* **101**: 207–211 (flower record, as *Homalictus dixoni* (Rayment, 1935)); Bernhardt, P. (1987). A comparison of the diversity, density, and foraging behavior of bees and wasps on Australian *Acacia*. *Ann. M. Bot. Gard.* **74**: 42–50 (flower record).

Homalictus (Homalictus) multicavus Walker, 1986

Homalictus (Homalictus) multicavus Walker, K.L. (1986). Revision of the Australian species of the genus *Homalictus* Cockerell (Hymenoptera : Halictidae). *Mem. Mus. Vict.* **47**: 105–200 [147].
Type data: holotype, QM ♀*.
Type locality: McIvor River crossing, 40 km N Cooktown, QLD.

Distribution: NE coastal, QLD; only published localities McIvor River crossing, Finch Bay, Cooktown, Port Douglas and Mt Webb.
Ecology: adult—volant; melliferous, flower visiting

record: *Eucalyptus* L'Hérit. [Myrtaceae], *Thryptomene* Endl. [Myrtaceae].

Homalictus (Homalictus) murrayi (Cockerell, 1905)

Halictus murrayi Cockerell, T.D.A. (1905). New Australian bees, in the collection of the British Museum. *Entomologist* **38**: 270–273, 302–304 [272].
Type data: holotype, BMNH ♀*.
Type locality: Adelaide River, NT.

Distribution: NE coastal, N Gulf, N coastal, (S Gulfs), QLD, NT, WA, (SA).
Ecology: adult—volant; melliferous, flower visiting record: *Anigozanthos* Lab. [Haemodoraceae], *Atalaya* Blume [Sapindaceae], *Borreria* G. Meyer [Rubiaceae], *Bursaria* Cav. [Pittosporaceae], *Eremophila* R.Br. [Myoporaceae], *Eucalyptus* L'Hérit. [Myrtaceae], *Terminalia* L. [Combretaceae], *Tristaniopsis* Brongn. & Gris [Myrtaceae], *Xanthorrhoea* Sm. [Xanthorrhoeaceae].
References: Cockerell, T.D.A. (1930). Australian bees in the Museum of Comparative Zoology. *Psyche (Camb.)* **37**: 141–154 (redescription); Walker, K.L. (1986). Revision of the Australian species of the genus *Homalictus* Cockerell (Hymenoptera : Halictidae). *Mem. Mus. Vict.* **47**: 105–200 (redescription).

Homalictus (Homalictus) niveifrons (Cockerell, 1914)

Halictus niveifrons Cockerell, T.D.A. (1914). Descriptions and records of bees. LIX. *Ann. Mag. Nat. Hist. (8)***13**: 504–522 [520].
Type data: lectotype, BMNH ♂*.
Subsequent designation: Walker, K.L. (1986). Revision of the Australian species of the genus *Homalictus* Cockerell (Hymenoptera : Halictidae). *Mem. Mus. Vict.* **47**: 105–200 [150].
Type locality: TAS.

Halictus oxoniellus Cockerell, T.D.A. (1914). Descriptions and records of bees. LXIII. *Ann. Mag. Nat. Hist. (8)***14**: 361–369 [369].
Type data: holotype, QM Hy2472 ♀*.
Type locality: Bribie Is., QLD.

Halictus mesocyaneus Cockerell, T.D.A. (1922). Australian bees in the Queensland Museum. *Mem. Qd Mus.* **7**: 257–279 [264].
Type data: holotype, QM T2684 ♀.
Type locality: Bribie Is., QLD.

Halictus raymenti Cockerell, T.D.A. (1926). New halictine bees from Australia. *Entomologist* **59**: 246–247 [247].
Type data: holotype, USNM ♀*.
Type locality: Sandringham, VIC.

Halictus tarltoni Cockerell, T.D.A. (1927). Some Australian bees. *Entomologist* **60**: 101–102 [101].
Type data: holotype, USNM ♀*.
Type locality: Brighton, VIC.

Halictus aureoazureus Rayment, T. (1935). *A Cluster of Bees*. Sixty essays on the life-histories of Australian bees, with specific descriptions of over 100 new species, and an introduction by Professor E.F. Phillips, D.Ph., Cornell

University, U.S.A. Sydney : Endeavour Press 752 pp. [697].
Type data: holotype, ANIC ♀.
Type locality: Sandringham, VIC.

Halictus littoralis Rayment, T. (1935). *A Cluster of Bees.* Sixty essays on the life-histories of Australian bees, with specific descriptions of over 100 new species, and an introduction by Professor E.F. Phillips, D.Ph., Cornell University, U.S.A. Sydney : Endeavour Press 752 pp. [700] [junior primary homonym of *Halictus littoralis* Blüthgen, 1923].
Type data: holotype, ANIC ♀.
Type locality: Sandringham, VIC.

Taxonomic decision for synonymy: Walker, K.L. (1986). Revision of the Australian species of the genus *Homalictus* Cockerell (Hymenoptera : Halictidae). *Mem. Mus. Vict.* **47**: 105–200 [150].

Distribution: NE coastal, Murray-Darling basin, SE coastal, S Gulfs, QLD, NSW, VIC, SA, TAS.
Ecology: larva—sedentary : adult—volant; melliferous, nest gregariously in soil, flower visiting record: *Acacia* Miller [Mimosaceae], *Arctotheca* Wendl. [Asteraceae], *Boronia* Sm. [Rutaceae], *Carpobrotus* N.E. Br. [Aizoaceae], *Goodenia* Sm. [Goodeniaceae], *Hibbertia* Andrews [Dilleniaceae], *Hypochaeris* L. [Asteraceae], *Lobelia* L. [Campanulaceae], *Melaleuca* L. [Myrtaceae], *Mesembryanthemum* L. [Aizoaceae], *Olearia* Moench [Asteraceae], *Osteospermum* L. [Chenopodiaceae], *Salpichroa* Miers [Solanaceae], *Tetragonia* L. [Aizoaceae], *Veronica* L. [Scrophulariaceae].
References: Rayment, T. (1931). The furrow-bees and a fly. *Vict. Nat.* **47**: 184–191 (biology, as *Halictus raymenti* Cockerell, 1926); Rayment, T. (1935). *A Cluster of Bees.* Sixty essays on the life-histories of Australian bees, with specific descriptions of over 100 new species, and an introduction by Professor E.F. Phillips, D.Ph., Cornell University, U.S.A. Sydney : Endeavour Press 752 pp. (biology, illustration, as *Halictus raymenti* Cockerell, 1926, *Halictus tarltoni* Cockerell, 1927); Rayment, T. (1953). *Bees of the Portland District.* Victoria : Portland Field Naturalist's Club 39 pp. (taxonomy); Michener, C.D. (1965). A classification of the bees of the Australian and South Pacific regions. *Bull. Am. Mus. Nat. Hist.* **130**: 1–362 [241] (flower record, as *Homalictus oxoniellus* (Cockerell, 1914)); Bernhardt, P., Kenrick, J. & Knox, R.B. (1984). Pollination biology and the breeding system of *Acacia retinodes* (Leguminosae: Mimosoideae). *Ann. M. Bot. Gard.* **71**: 17–29 (flower records, as *Homalictus oxoniellus* (Cockerell, 1914)); Bernhardt, P. (1987). A comparison of the diversity, density, and foraging behavior of bees and wasps on Australian *Acacia. Ann. M. Bot. Gard.* **74**: 42–50 (flower record, as *Homalictus oxoniellus* (Cockerell, 1914)).

Homalictus (Homalictus) pectinalus Walker, 1986

Homalictus (Homalictus) pectinalus Walker, K.L. (1986). Revision of the Australian species of the genus *Homalictus* Cockerell (Hymenoptera : Halictidae). *Mem. Mus. Vict.* **47**: 105–200 [152].
Type data: holotype, ANIC ♀.
Type locality: Millstream Falls National Park, QLD.

Distribution: NE coastal, QLD.
Ecology: adult—volant; melliferous, flower visiting record: *Acacia* Miller [Mimosaceae], *Eucalyptus* L'Hérit. [Myrtaceae].

Homalictus (Homalictus) punctatus (Smith, 1879)

Halictus punctatus Smith, F. (1879). *Descriptions of New Species of Hymenoptera in the Collection of the British Museum.* London : British Museum xxi 240 pp. [36].
Type data: holotype, BMNH ♀*.
Type locality: Champion Bay (Geraldton), WA.
Halictus punctatus exlautus Cockerell, T.D.A. (1905). Descriptions and records of bees. II. *Ann. Mag. Nat. Hist. (7)***16**: 292–301 [300].
Type data: holotype, BMNH Hym.17.a.975 ♀*.
Type locality: Australia.
Halictus hedleyi Cockerell, T.D.A. (1910). New and little-known bees. *Trans. Am. Entomol. Soc.* **36**: 199–249 [231].
Type data: holotype, ZMB 2248 ♂*.
Type locality: Port Phillip (as Port Philip), VIC.
Halictus pallidifrons Rayment, T. (1935). *A Cluster of Bees.* Sixty essays on the life-histories of Australian bees, with specific descriptions of over 100 new species, and an introduction by Professor E.F. Phillips, D.Ph., Cornell University, U.S.A. Sydney : Endeavour Press 752 pp. [692].
Type data: holotype, ANIC ♂.
Type locality: Ringwood, VIC.
Halictus subpallidifrons Rayment, T. (1935). *A Cluster of Bees.* Sixty essays on the life-histories of Australian bees, with specific descriptions of over 100 new species, and an introduction by Professor E.F. Phillips, D.Ph., Cornell University, U.S.A. Sydney : Endeavour Press 752 pp. [693].
Type data: holotype, ANIC ♂.
Type locality: 6 miles E Melbourne, VIC.
Halictus phillipensis Rayment, T. (1935). *A Cluster of Bees.* Sixty essays on the life-histories of Australian bees, with specific descriptions of over 100 new species, and an introduction by Professor E.F. Phillips, D.Ph., Cornell University, U.S.A. Sydney : Endeavour Press 752 pp. [700] [the locality data and the characters of the specimen in the ANIC labelled "type" do not match those given in the original description, see Walker, K.L. (1986). Revision of the Australian species of the genus *Homalictus* Cockerell (Hymenoptera : Halictidae). *Mem. Mus. Vict.* **47**: 105–200 (153)].
Type data: status and whereabouts unknown.
Type locality: Sandringham, VIC.

Taxonomic decision for synonymy: Walker, K.L. (1986). Revision of the Australian species of the genus *Homalictus* Cockerell (Hymenoptera : Halictidae). *Mem. Mus. Vict.* **47**: 105–200 [152].

Distribution: NE coastal, Murray-Darling basin, SE coastal, NW coastal, QLD, NSW, ACT, VIC, WA.

Ecology: adult—volant; melliferous, males cluster at night, flower visiting record: marguerites, *Acacia* Miller [Mimosaceae], *Angophora* Cav. [Myrtaceae], *Arctotheca* Wendl. [Asteraceae], *Boronia* Sm. [Rutaceae], *Bursaria* Cav. [Pittosporaceae], *Coreopsis* L. [Asteraceae], *Eucalyptus* L'Hérit. [Myrtaceae], *Hypochaeris* L. [Asteraceae], *Leucopogon* R.Br. [Epacridaceae], *Mesembryanthemum* L. [Aizoaceae], *Myoporum* Banks & Sol. ex G.Forster [Myoporaceae], *Olearia* Moench [Asteraceae], *Syzygium* Gaertner [Myrtaceae], *Veronica* L. [Scrophulariaceae].

References: Cockerell, T.D.A. (1912). Descriptions and records of bees. XLIII. *Ann. Mag. Nat. Hist.* (8)**9**: 377–387 (taxonomy); Rayment, T. (1931). Bees in the collections of the Western Australian Museum and the Agricultural Department, Perth. *J. Proc. R. Soc. West. Aust.* **17**: 157–190 (illustration); Cockerell, T.D.A. (1933). The bees of Australia. *Aust. Zool.* **7**: 291–324 (taxonomy); Michener, C.D. (1960). Notes on the biology and supposed parthenogenesis of halictine bees from the Australian region. *J. Kansas Entomol. Soc.* **33**: 85–96 (biology, as *Halictus punctulatus*, incorrect subsequent); Michener, C.D. (1965). A classification of the bees of the Australian and South Pacific regions. *Bull. Am. Mus. Nat. Hist.* **130**: 1–362 (flower record); Bernhardt, P. & Walker, K. (1984). Bee foraging on three sympatric species of Australian *Acacia. Int. J. Entomol.* **26**: 322–330 (flower record); Bernhardt, P. & Walker, K. (1985). Insect foraging on *Acacia retinodes* var. *retinodes* in Victoria, Australia. *Int. J. Entomol.* **27**: 97–101 (flower record); Bernhardt, P. (1987). A comparison of the diversity, density, and foraging behavior of bees and wasps on Australian *Acacia. Ann. M. Bot. Gard.* **74**: 42–50 (flower record).

Homalictus (Homalictus) rowlandi (Cockerell, 1910)

Halictus rowlandi Cockerell, T.D.A. (1910). New and little-known bees. *Trans. Am. Entomol. Soc.* **36**: 199–249 [226].
Type data: lectotype, BMNH ♀*.
Subsequent designation: Walker, K.L. (1986). Revision of the Australian species of the genus *Homalictus* Cockerell (Hymenoptera : Halictidae). *Mem. Mus. Vict.* **47**: 105–200 [154].
Type locality: Kuranda (as Cairns Kuranda), QLD.

Distribution: NE coastal, QLD; known only from type locality.
Ecology: adult—volant; melliferous, solitary.
Reference: Walker, K.L. (1986). Revision of the Australian species of the genus *Homalictus* Cockerell (Hymenoptera : Halictidae). *Mem. Mus. Vict.* **47**: 105–200 (redescription).

Homalictus (Homalictus) scrupulosus (Cockerell, 1930)

Halictus limatiformis scrupulosus Cockerell, T.D.A. (1930). New Australian bees. *Mem. Qd Mus.* **10**: 37–50 [45].
Type data: holotype, QM Hy3752 ♀.
Type locality: Nanango district, QLD.

Distribution: NE coastal, Murray-Darling basin, SE coastal, QLD, NSW.
Ecology: larva—sedentary : adult—volant; melliferous, flower visiting record: *Claoxylon* A. Juss. [Euphorbiaceae], *Lomatia* R.Br. [Proteaceae], *Ranunculus* L. [Ranunculaceae].
References: Michener, C.D. (1960). Notes on the biology and supposed parthenogenesis of halictine bees from the Australian region. *J. Kansas Entomol. Soc.* **33**: 85–96 (biology, as *Halictus scrupulosus* Cockerell, 1930); Michener, C.D. (1965). A classification of the bees of the Australian and South Pacific regions. *Bull. Am. Mus. Nat. Hist.* **130**: 1–362 (flower record); Walker, K.L. (1986). Revision of the Australian species of the genus *Homalictus* Cockerell (Hymenoptera : Halictidae). *Mem. Mus. Vict.* **47**: 105–200 (redescription).

Homalictus (Homalictus) sphecodoides (Smith, 1853)

Halictus sphecodoides Smith, F. (1853). *Catalogue of Hymenopterous Insects in the Collection of the British Museum.* Part I. Andrenidae and Apidae. London : British Museum 197 pp. [58].
Type data: holotype, BMNH ♀*.
Type locality: TAS (as Van Diemens Land on label, as New Holland in description).
Halictus limatus Smith, F. (1853). *Catalogue of Hymenopterous Insects in the Collection of the British Museum.* Part I. Andrenidae and Apidae. London : British Museum 197 pp. [59].
Type data: holotype, BMNH ♀*.
Type locality: TAS (as Van Diemens Land).
Halictus humilis Smith, F. (1879). *Descriptions of New Species of Hymenoptera in the Collection of the British Museum.* London : British Museum xxi 240 pp. [36].
Type data: holotype, BMNH ♀*.
Type locality: Champion Bay (Geraldton), WA.
Halictus burkei Cockerell, T.D.A. (1906). New Australian bees in the collection of the British Museum. II. *Entomologist* **39**: 56–60 [58].
Type data: holotype, BMNH Hym.17.a.950 ♀*.
Type locality: Hobart, TAS.
Halictus demissus Cockerell, T.D.A. (1916). Some bees from Australia, Tasmania, and the New Hebrides. *Proc. Acad. Nat. Sci. Philad.* **68**: 360–375 [371].
Type data: syntypes, USNM 2♀*.
Type locality: Launceston, TAS.
Halictus limatiformis Cockerell, T.D.A. (1922). Australian bees in the Queensland Museum. *Mem. Qd Mus.* **7**: 257–279 [263].
Type data: holotype, QM Hy2683 ♀.
Type locality: [Lamington] National Park, QLD.

Halictus humiliformis Cockerell, T.D.A. (1922). Australian bees in the Queensland Museum. *Mem. Qd Mus.* 7: 257–279 [263].
Type data: holotype, QM T2686 ♀.
Type locality: Ebor, NSW.

Taxonomic decision for synonymy: Walker, K.L. (1986). Revision of the Australian species of the genus *Homalictus* Cockerell (Hymenoptera : Halictidae). *Mem. Mus. Vict.* 47: 105–200 [156].

Distribution: NE coastal, Murray-Darling basin, SE coastal, S Gulfs, SW coastal, QLD, NSW, ACT, VIC, SA, TAS.
Ecology: larva—sedentary : adult—volant; melliferous, nest communally and gregariously in soil, flower visiting record: aster, daisy, *Acacia* Miller [Mimosaceae], *Arctotheca* Wendl. [Asteraceae], *Banksia* L.f. [Proteaceae], *Brachyscome* Cass. [Asteraceae], *Brassica* L. [Brassicaceae], *Bursaria* Cav. [Pittosporaceae], *Cotoneaster* Medikus [Rosaceae], *Eucalyptus* L'Hérit. [Myrtaceae], *Gastrolobium* R.Br. [Fabaceae], *Goodenia* Sm. [Goodeniaceae], *Helichrysum* Miller *s.lat.* [Asteraceae], *Helipterum* DC. *s.lat.* [Asteraceae], *Hypochaeris* L. [Asteraceae], *Ixodia* R.Br. [Asteraceae], *Jacksonia* Smith [Fabaceae], *Lagunaria* (DC) Reichb. [Malvaceae], *Leptospermum* Forster & G.Forster [Myrtaceae], *Melaleuca* L. [Myrtaceae], *Schinus* L. [Anacardiaceae], *Taraxacum* G.Weber [Asteraceae], *Veronica* L. [Scrophulariaceae], *Wahlenbergia* Roth [Campanulaceae].
References: Rayment, T. (1935). *A Cluster of Bees.* Sixty essays on the life-histories of Australian bees, with specific descriptions of over 100 new species, and an introduction by Professor E.F. Phillips, D.Ph., Cornell University, U.S.A. Sydney : Endeavour Press 752 pp. (biology, as *Halictus demissus* Cockerell, 1916); Rayment, T. (1953). *Bees of the Portland District.* Victoria : Portland Field Naturalist's Club 39 pp. (biology, as *Halictus demissus* Cockerell, 1916); Michener, C.D. (1960). Notes on the biology and supposed parthenogenesis of halictine bees from the Australian region. *J. Kansas Entomol. Soc.* 33: 85–96 (biology, as *Halictus demissus* Cockerell, 1916, *Halictus limatiformis* Cockerell, 1922); Michener, C.D. (1965). A classification of the bees of the Australian and South Pacific regions. *Bull. Am. Mus. Nat. Hist.* 130: 1–362 (flower record, as *Homalictus limatiformis* (Cockerell, 1922)); Knerer, G. & Schwarz, M. (1976). Halictine social evolution : the Australian enigma. *Science* 194: 445–448 (biology, as *Homalictus demissus* (Cockerell, 1916)); Knerer, G. & Schwarz, M. (1978). Beobachtungen an australischen Furchenbienen (Hymenopteren; Halictinae). *Zool. Anz.* 200: 321–333 (biology, as *Homalictus demissus* (Cockerell, 1916)); Bernhardt, P. & Walker, K. (1985). Insect foraging on *Acacia retinodes* var. *retinodes* in Victoria, Australia. *Int. J. Entomol.* 27: 97–101 (as *Homalictus demissus* (Cock-

erell, 1916)); Bernhardt, P. (1987). A comparison of the diversity, density, and foraging behavior of bees and wasps on Australian *Acacia. Ann. M. Bot. Gard.* 74: 42–50 (flower record, as *Homalictus demissus* (Cockerell, 1916)).

Homalictus (Homalictus) sphecodopsis (Cockerell, 1905)

Halictus sphecodopsis Cockerell, T.D.A. (1905). Descriptions and records of bees. II. *Ann. Mag. Nat. Hist.* (7)16: 292–301 [300].
Type data: holotype (probable), BMNH ♂*.
Type locality: Mackay, QLD.
Halictus eyrei Cockerell, T.D.A. (1910). New and little-known bees. *Trans. Am. Entomol. Soc.* 36: 199–249 [226].
Type data: holotype, BMNH Hym.17.a.976 ♀.
Type locality: Mackay, QLD.
Halictus claripes Friese, H. (1924). Ueber die Bienen Australiens. *Konowia* 3: 216–249 [235].
Type data: lectotype, AMNH ♀*.
Subsequent designation: Pauly, A. (1986). Les abeilles de la sous-famille des Halictinae en Nouvelle-Guinée et dans l'Archipel Bismarck (Hymenoptera : Apoidea : Halictidae). *Zool. Verh.* 227: 1–58 [21].
Type locality: Mackay, QLD.
Halictus eyrei darwiniensis Cockerell, T.D.A. (1929). Bees from the Australian region. *Am. Mus. Novit.* 346: 1–18 [2].
Type data: syntypes, AMNH 5♀*.
Type locality: Darwin, NT.

Taxonomic decision for synonymy: Pauly, A. (1986). Les abeilles de la sous-famille des Halictinae en Nouvelle-Guinée et dans l'Archipel Bismarck (Hymenoptera : Apoidea : Halictidae). *Zool. Verh.* 227: 1–58 [21].

Distribution: NE coastal, Murray-Darling basin, N Gulf, N coastal, QLD, NT; also New Guinea.
Ecology: larva—sedentary : adult—volant; melliferous, flower visiting record: *Angophora* Cav. [Myrtaceae], *Callistemon* R.Br. [Myrtaceae], *Eucalyptus* L'Hérit. [Myrtaceae], *Eugenia* L. [Myrtaceae], *Helipterum* DC. *s.lat.* [Asteraceae], *Hypochaeris* L. [Asteraceae], *Jacksonia* Smith [Fabaceae], *Leptospermum* Forster & G.Forster [Myrtaceae], *Melaleuca* L. [Myrtaceae], *Syncarpia* Ten. [Myrtaceae], *Tristaniopsis* Brongn. & Gris [Myrtaceae], *Xanthorrhoea* Sm. [Xanthorrhoeaceae].
References: Cockerell, T.D.A. (1929). Bees, chiefly Australian species, described or determined by Dr. H. Friese. *Am. Mus. Novit.* 343: 1–20 (taxonomy, as *Halictus eyrei* Cockerell, 1910); Michener, C.D. (1960). Notes on the biology and supposed parthenogenesis of halictine bees from the Australian region. *J. Kansas Entomol. Soc.* 33: 85–96 (biology, as *Halictus eyrei* Cockerell, 1910); Michener, C.D. (1965). A classification of the bees of the Australian and South Pacific regions. *Bull. Am. Mus. Nat. Hist.* 130: 1–362 (flower record, as *Homalictus eyrei* (Cockerell, 1910)); Walker, K.L. (1986). Revision of the Australian species of the genus *Homalictus* Cock-

erell (Hymenoptera : Halictidae). *Mem. Mus. Vict.* **47**: 105–200 (redescription).

Homalictus (Homalictus) stradbrokensis (Cockerell, 1916)

Halictus urbanus stradbrokensis Cockerell, T.D.A. (1916). Some bees from Australia, Tasmania, and the New Hebrides. *Proc. Acad. Nat. Sci. Philad.* **68**: 360–375 [366].
Type data: holotype, USNM ♀*.
Type locality: Stradbroke Is., QLD.

Distribution: NE coastal, QLD.
Ecology: adult—volant; melliferous, flower visiting record: *Angophora* Cav. [Myrtaceae], *Eucalyptus* L'Hérit. [Myrtaceae], *Leptospermum* Forster & G.Forster [Myrtaceae], *Xanthorrhoea* Sm. [Xanthorrhoeaceae].
References: Cockerell, T.D.A. (1930). Australian bees in the Museum of Comparative Zoology. *Psyche (Camb.)* **37**: 141–154 (taxonomy); Michener, C.D. (1965). A classification of the bees of the Australian and South Pacific regions. *Bull. Am. Mus. Nat. Hist.* **130**: 1–362 [181] (taxonomy); Walker, K.L. (1986). Revision of the Australian species of the genus *Homalictus* Cockerell (Hymenoptera : Halictidae). *Mem. Mus. Vict.* **47**: 105–200 (redescription).

Homalictus (Homalictus) tatei (Cockerell, 1910)

Halictus (Chloralictus) tatei Cockerell, T.D.A. (1910). New and little-known bees. *Trans. Am. Entomol. Soc.* **36**: 199–249 [227].
Type data: holotype, BMNH ♀*.
Type locality: Mackay, QLD.
Halictus saycei Cockerell, T.D.A. (1912). Descriptions and records of bees. XLIII. *Ann. Mag. Nat. Hist. (8)***9**: 377–387 [386].
Type data: lectotype, BMNH ♀*.
Subsequent designation: Walker, K.L. (1986). Revision of the Australian species of the genus *Homalictus* Cockerell (Hymenoptera : Halictidae). *Mem. Mus. Vict.* **47**: 105–200 [160].
Type locality: Mackay, QLD.

Taxonomic decision for synonymy: Walker, K.L. (1986). Revision of the Australian species of the genus *Homalictus* Cockerell (Hymenoptera : Halictidae). *Mem. Mus. Vict.* **47**: 105–200 [160].

Distribution: NE coastal, QLD; only published localities Mackay and 40 Mile Scrub via Mt Garnet.
Ecology: adult—volant; melliferous, flower visiting record: *Eucalyptus* L'Hérit. [Myrtaceae].

Homalictus (Homalictus) thor (Cockerell, 1929)

Halictus flindersi thor Cockerell, T.D.A. (1929). Bees from the Australian region. *Am. Mus. Novit.* **346**: 1–18 [12].
Type data: holotype, USNM ♀*.
Type locality: Thursday Is., QLD.

Distribution: NE coastal, N Gulf, QLD; only published localities Thursday Is., Bamaga, Coen, McIlwraith Range and Iron Range.

Ecology: adult—volant; melliferous, flower visiting record: *Calandrinia* Kunth [Portulacaceae], *Dalbergia* L.f. [Fabaceae], *Parinari* Aublet [Chrysobalanaceae].
References: Michener, C.D. (1965). A classification of the bees of the Australian and South Pacific regions. *Bull. Am. Mus. Nat. Hist.* **130**: 1–362 [181] (taxonomy); Walker, K.L. (1986). Revision of the Australian species of the genus *Homalictus* Cockerell (Hymenoptera : Halictidae). *Mem. Mus. Vict.* **47**: 105–200 (redescription).

Homalictus (Homalictus) urbanus (Smith, 1879)

Halictus urbanus Smith, F. (1879). *Descriptions of New Species of Hymenoptera in the Collection of the British Museum.* London : British Museum xxi 240 pp. [35].
Type data: lectotype, BMNH ♀*.
Subsequent designation: Pauly, A. (1986). Les abeilles de la sous-famille des Halictinae en Nouvelle-Guinée et dans l'Archipel Bismarck (Hymenoptera : Apoidea : Halictidae). *Zool. Verh.* **227**: 1–58 [17].
Type locality: Champion Bay (Geraldton), WA.
Halictus urbanus baudinensis Cockerell, T.D.A. (1905). Descriptions and records of bees. III. *Ann. Mag. Nat. Hist. (7)***16**: 301–308 [307].
Type data: holotype, BMNH Hym.17.a.906 ♀*.
Type locality: Baudin Is., WA.
Halictus cretinicola Friese, H. (1909). Die Bienenfauna von Neu-Guinea. *Ann. Hist.-Nat. Mus. Natl. Hung.* **7**: 179–288 [190].
Type data: lectotype, NHMW ♀*.
Subsequent designation: Pauly, A. (1986). Les abeilles de la sous-famille des Halictinae en Nouvelle-Guinée et dans l'Archipel Bismarck (Hymenoptera : Apoidea : Halictidae). *Zool. Verh.* **227**: 1–58 [17].
Type locality: Stephansort, Astrolabe Bay, Papua New Guinea.
Halictus kesteveni Cockerell, T.D.A. (1912). Descriptions and records of bees. XLIII. *Ann. Mag. Nat. Hist. (8)***9**: 377–387 [386].
Type data: holotype (probable), BMNH ♂*.
Type locality: Kuranda (as Cairns Kuranda), QLD.
Halictus hackeriellus Cockerell, T.D.A. (1914). Descriptions and records of bees. LIX. *Ann. Mag. Nat. Hist. (8)***13**: 504–522 [507].
Type data: holotype, QM Hy4118 ♂.
Type locality: Brisbane, QLD.
Halictus pavonellus Cockerell, T.D.A. (1915). Descriptions and records of bees. LXVIII. *Ann. Mag. Nat. Hist. (8)***16**: 1–9 [5].
Type data: holotype, USNM ♀*.
Type locality: Bribie Is., QLD.
Halictus olivinus Cockerell, T.D.A. (1922). Australian bees in the Queensland Museum. *Mem. Qd Mus.* **7**: 257–279 [262].
Type data: holotype, QM T2685 ♂.
Type locality: Brisbane, QLD.
Halictus urbanus lomatiae Cockerell, T.D.A. (1922). Australian bees in the Queensland Museum. *Mem. Qd Mus.* **7**: 257–279 [263].

Type data: holotype, QM T2742 ♀.
Type locality: Sunnybank, Brisbane, QLD.

Halictus microchalceus Cockerell, T.D.A. (1929). Bees from the Australian region. *Am. Mus. Novit.* **346**: 1–18 [13].
Type data: holotype, ANIC ♂.
Type locality: Thirroul, NSW.

Halictus subcarus Cockerell, T.D.A. (1930). Australian bees in the Museum of Comparative Zoology. *Psyche (Camb.)* **37**: 141–154 [152].
Type data: holotype, MCZ ♀*.
Type locality: Halifax, QLD.

Halictus williamsi Cockerell, T.D.A. (1930). Australian bees in the Museum of Comparative Zoology. *Psyche (Camb.)* **37**: 141–154 [153].
Type data: lectotype, MCZ ♀*.
Subsequent designation: Walker, K.L. (1986). Revision of the Australian species of the genus *Homalictus* Cockerell (Hymenoptera : Halictidae). *Mem. Mus. Vict.* **47**: 105–200 [162]; Cardale, J.C., this work, interprets Walker's incorrect inference of holotype as a lectotype designation (Art. 74, ICZN 1985).
Type locality: Halifax, QLD.

Halictus suburbanus Cockerell, T.D.A. (1930). New Australian bees. *Mem. Qd Mus.* **10**: 37–50 [45].
Type data: holotype, QM Hy4099 ♂.
Type locality: [Lamington] National Park, QLD.

Halictus aponi Cheesman, L.E. & Perkins, R.C.L. (1939). Halictine bees from the New Hebrides and Banks Islands (Hymen.). *Trans. R. Entomol. Soc. Lond.* **88**: 161–171 [170].
Type data: holotype, BMNH ♀*.
Type locality: Ounua, Malekula Is., New Hebrides.

Halictus aponi erromangana Cheesman, L.E. & Perkins, R.C.L. (1939). Halictine bees from the New Hebrides and Banks Islands (Hymen.). *Trans. R. Entomol. Soc. Lond.* **88**: 161–171 [170].
Type data: holotype, BMNH ♀*.
Type locality: Erromanga Is., New Hebrides.

Taxonomic decision for synonymy: Pauly, A. (1986). Les abeilles de la sous-famille des Halictinae en Nouvelle-Guinée et dans l'Archipel Bismarck (Hymenoptera : Apoidea : Halictidae). *Zool. Verh.* **227**: 1–58 [17]; Walker, K.L. (1986). Revision of the Australian species of the genus *Homalictus* Cockerell (Hymenoptera : Halictidae). *Mem. Mus. Vict.* **47**: 105–200 [162].

Distribution: NE coastal, Murray-Darling basin, N Gulf, SE coastal, S Gulfs, Lake Eyre basin, W plateau, SW coastal, NW coastal, N coastal, QLD, NSW, ACT, VIC, SA, WA, NT; also Lord Howe Is., New Guinea, Tenimbar, Bismarck Archipelago, New Caledonia, Loyalty Ils and New Hebrides.
Ecology: larva—sedentary : adult—volant; melliferous, nest gregariously and communally in soil, flower visiting record: *Acacia* Miller [Mimosaceae], *Alphitonia* Reisseck ex Endl. [Rhamnaceae], *Amyema* Tieghem [Loranthaceae], *Angophora* Cav. [Myrtaceae], *Arctotheca* Wendl. [Asteraceae], *Atalaya* Blume [Sapindaceae], *Boronia* Sm. [Rutaceae], *Brachychiton* Schott & Endl. [Sterculiaceae], *Bursaria* Cav. [Pittosporaceae], *Calandrinia* Kunth [Portulacaceae], *Callistemon*

R.Br. [Myrtaceae], *Calothamnus* Lab. [Myrtaceae], *Cassia* L. *s.lat.* [Caesalpiniaceae], *Daviesia* Sm. [Fabaceae], *Eucalyptus* L'Hérit. [Myrtaceae], *Frankenia* L. [Frankeniaceae], *Goodenia* Sm. [Goodeniaceae], *Hakea* Schrader [Proteaceae], *Helipterum* DC. *s.lat.* [Asteraceae], *Heterodendrum* Desf. [Sapindaceae], *Hibbertia* Andrews [Dilleniaceae], *Hypochaeris* L. [Asteraceae], *Jacksonia* Sm. [Fabaceae], *Leptospermum* Forster & G.Forster [Myrtaceae], *Lomatia* R.Br. [Proteaceae], *Melaleuca* L. [Myrtaceae], *Morgania* R.Br. [Scrophulariaceae], *Pimelea* Gaertner [Thymelaeaceae], *Pittosporum* Gaertner [Pittosporaceae], *Scaevola* L. [Goodeniaceae], *Swainsona* Salisb. [Fabaceae], *Terminalia* L. [Combretaceae], *Trachymene* Rudge [Apiaceae], *Veronica* L. [Scrophulariaceae], *Wahlenbergia* Roth [Campanulaceae].
References: Rayment, T. (1935). *A Cluster of Bees.* Sixty essays on the life-histories of Australian bees, with specific descriptions of over 100 new species, and an introduction by Professor E.F. Phillips, D.Ph., Cornell University, U.S.A. Sydney : Endeavour Press 752 pp. (flower record); Michener, C.D. (1960). Notes on the biology and supposed parthenogenesis of halictine bees from the Australian region. *J. Kansas Entomol. Soc.* **33**: 85–96 (biology); Michener, C.D. (1965). A classification of the bees of the Australian and South Pacific regions. *Bull. Am. Mus. Nat. Hist.* **130**: 1–362 (flower records, as *Homalictus urbanus* (Smith, 1879), *Homalictus suburbanus* (Cockerell, 1930)); Keighery, G.J. (1975). Parallel evolution of floral structures in *Darwinia* (Myrtaceae) and *Pimelea* (Thymeleaceae). *West. Aust. Nat.* **13**: 46–50 (flower record); Walker, K.L. (1986). Revision of the Australian species of the genus *Homalictus* Cockerell (Hymenoptera : Halictidae). *Mem. Mus. Vict.* **47**: 105–200 (redescription).

Homalictus (Homalictus) woodsi (Cockerell, 1910)

Halictus woodsi Cockerell, T.D.A. (1910). New and little-known bees. *Trans. Am. Entomol. Soc.* **36**: 199–249 [229].
Type data: holotype, BMNH ♀*.
Type locality: Cooktown, QLD.

Halictus behri transvolans Cockerell, T.D.A. (1912). Descriptions and records of bees. XLIII. *Ann. Mag. Nat. Hist. (8)***9**: 377–387 [385].
Type data: holotype, BMNH ♀*.
Type locality: Mackay, QLD.

Taxonomic decision for synonymy: Walker, K.L. (1986). Revision of the Australian species of the genus *Homalictus* Cockerell (Hymenoptera : Halictidae). *Mem. Mus. Vict.* **47**: 105–200 [164].

Distribution: NE coastal, N Gulf, N coastal, QLD, WA, NT.
Ecology: adult—volant; melliferous, flower visiting

record: *Borreria* G. Meyer [Rubiaceae], *Eucalyptus* L'Hérit. [Myrtaceae], *Eugenia* L. [Myrtaceae], *Melaleuca* L. [Myrtaceae].

References: Cockerell, T.D.A. (1929). Bees from the Australian region. *Am. Mus. Novit.* **346**: 1–18 (taxonomy); Walker, K.L. (1986). Revision of the Australian species of the genus *Homalictus* Cockerell (Hymenoptera : Halictidae). *Mem. Mus. Vict.* **47**: 105–200 (redescription).

Homalictus (Quasilictus) Walker, 1986

Quasilictus Walker, K.L. (1986). Revision of the Australian species of the genus *Homalictus* Cockerell (Hymenoptera : Halictidae). *Mem. Mus. Vict.* **47**: 105–200 [166] [proposed with subgeneric rank in *Homalictus* Cockerell, 1919]. Type species: *Homalictus (Quasilictus) brevicornutus* Walker, 1986 by original designation.

Homalictus (Quasilictus) brevicornutus Walker, 1986

Homalictus (Quasilictus) brevicornutus Walker, K.L. (1986). Revision of the Australian species of the genus *Homalictus* Cockerell (Hymenoptera : Halictidae). *Mem. Mus. Vict.* **47**: 105–200 [166].
Type data: holotype, ANIC ♀.
Type locality: Batten Point, 30 km NE by E Borroloola, NT.

Distribution: N Gulf, N coastal, NT, WA; only published localities Batten Point and West Kimberley.
Ecology: adult—volant; melliferous, solitary.

Lasioglossum Curtis, 1833

Lasioglossum Curtis, J. (1833). *British Entomology; being illustrations and descriptions of the genera of insects found in Great Britain and Ireland : containing coloured figures from nature of the most rare and beautiful species, and in many instances of the plants upon which they are found.* London : John [pl. 448]. Type species: *Lasioglossum tricingulum* Curtis, 1833 (=*Melitta xanthopus* W. Kirby, 1802) by original designation. Compiled from secondary source: Sandhouse, G.A. (1943). The type species of the genera and subgenera of bees. *Proc. U.S. Natl Mus.* **92**(3156): 519–619.

Taxonomic decision for subgeneric arrangement: Michener, C.D. (1965). A classification of the bees of the Australian and South Pacific regions. *Bull. Am. Mus. Nat. Hist.* **130**: 1–362.

Extralimital distribution: Palaearctic, Oriental, Afrotropical, Neotropical and Nearctic Regions, see Ebmer, P.A.W. (1987). Die europäischen Arten der Gattungen *Halictus* Latreille 1804 und *Lasioglossum* Curtis 1833 mit illustrierten Bestimmungstabellen (Insecta: Hymenoptera: Apoidea: Halictidae: Halictinae). 1. Allgemeiner Teil, Tabelle der Gattungen. *Senckenberg. Biol.* **68**: 59–148 [80].

Generic reference: Michener, C.D. (1986). A *Lasioglossum* from Borneo with possible Australian affinities (Hymenoptera : Halictidae). *J. Kansas Entomol. Soc.* **59**: 666–671 [666].

Lasioglossum (Australictus) Michener, 1965

Australictus Michener, C.D. (1965). A classification of the bees of the Australian and South Pacific regions. *Bull. Am. Mus. Nat. Hist.* **130**: 1–362 [165] [proposed with subgeneric rank in *Lasioglossum* Curtis, 1833]. Type species: *Halictus peraustralis* Cockerell, 1904 by original designation.

Lasioglossum (Australictus) davide (Cockerell, 1910)

Halictus davidis Cockerell, T.D.A. (1910). New and little-known bees. *Trans. Am. Entomol. Soc.* **36**: 199–249 [234].
Type data: holotype, BMNH Hym.17.a.914 ♀.
Type locality: Kuranda (as Cairns Kuranda), QLD.
Halictus nigroscopaceus Friese, H. (1917). Results of Dr. E. Mjöberg's Swedish Scientific Expeditions to Australia, 1910–1913. 13. Apidae. *Ark. Zool.* **11**(2): 1–9 [4].
Type data: syntypes, AMNH ♂♀*, NHMW ♂♀*.
Type locality: Cairns and Malanda, QLD.

Taxonomic decision for synonymy: Cockerell, T.D.A. (1929). Bees, chiefly Australian species, described or determined by Dr. H. Friese. *Am. Mus. Novit.* **343**: 1–20 [12].

Distribution: NE coastal, QLD; only published localities Cairns, Kuranda and Malanda.
Ecology: adult—volant; melliferous, solitary.

Lasioglossum (Australictus) franki (Friese, 1924)

Halictus franki Friese, H. (1924). Ueber die Bienen Australiens. *Konowia* **3**: 216–249 [241].
Type data: syntypes, AMNH ♀* (number of specimens unknown).
Type locality: Fremantle (as Freemantle), WA.

Distribution: SW coastal, WA; known only from type locality.
Ecology: adult—volant; melliferous, solitary.
Reference: Cockerell, T.D.A. (1929). Bees, chiefly Australian species, described or determined by Dr. H. Friese. *Am. Mus. Novit.* **343**: 1–20 (redescription, doubtful record, from Sydney).

Lasioglossum (Australictus) fulvofasciae Michener, 1965

Lasioglossum (Australictus) fulvofasciae Michener, C.D. (1965). A classification of the bees of the Australian and South Pacific regions. *Bull. Am. Mus. Nat. Hist.* **130**: 1–362 [310].
Type data: holotype, QM T6910 ♂.
Type locality: 3 miles W Cunninghams Gap, QLD.

Distribution: Murray-Darling basin, QLD; known only from type locality.
Ecology: adult—volant; melliferous, flower visiting record: *Bursaria* Cav. [Pittosporaceae].

Lasioglossum (Australictus) insculptum (Cockerell, 1918)

Parasphecodes insculptus Cockerell, T.D.A. (1918). Some bees collected in Queensland. *Mem. Qd Mus.* **6**: 112–120 [118].
Type data: holotype, QM Hy4142 ♀.
Type locality: Mt Tamborine, QLD.

Distribution: NE coastal, Murray-Darling basin, QLD; only published localities Mt Tamborine and W of Cunninghams Gap.
Ecology: adult—volant; melliferous, flower visiting record: *Bursaria* Cav. [Pittosporaceae].
Reference: Michener, C.D. (1965). A classification of the bees of the Australian and South Pacific regions. *Bull. Am. Mus. Nat. Hist.* **130**: 1–362 (flower record).

Lasioglossum (Australictus) kurandense (Cockerell, 1914)

Halictus kurandensis Cockerell, T.D.A. (1914). Descriptions and records of bees. LIX. *Ann. Mag. Nat. Hist. (8)***13**: 504–522 [515].
Type data: holotype, BMNH Hym.17.a.956 ♂.
Type locality: Kuranda (as Cairns Kuranda), QLD.

Distribution: NE coastal, QLD; known only from type locality.
Ecology: adult—volant; melliferous, solitary.

Lasioglossum (Australictus) odyneroides (Rayment, 1939)

Halictus odyneroides Rayment, T. (1939). Bees from the high lands of New South Wales and Victoria. *Aust. Zool.* **9**: 263–294 [279].
Type data: holotype, whereabouts unknown (T. Rayment, pers. coll., not found in ANIC) ♀*.
Type locality: White Swamp, NSW.

Distribution: SE coastal, NSW; known only from type locality.
Ecology: adult—volant; melliferous, flower visiting record: *Lomatia* R.Br. [Proteaceae].

Lasioglossum (Australictus) peraustrale (Cockerell, 1904)

Halictus peraustralis Cockerell, T.D.A. (1904). The halictine bees of the Australian region. *Ann. Mag. Nat. Hist. (7)***14**: 208–213 [211].
Type data: holotype, BMNH Hym.17.a.963 ♀.
Type locality: SA.

Distribution: NE coastal, Murray-Darling basin, SE coastal, QLD, NSW, SA; exact locality in SA unknown.
Ecology: larva—sedentary : adult—volant; melliferous, nest gregariously in rotten wood in trunk of tree (*Eucalyptus* L'Hérit. [Myrtaceae]), flower visiting record: *Angophora* Cav. [Myrtaceae], *Bursaria* Cav. [Pittosporaceae], *Eucalyptus* L'Hérit. [Myrtaceae], *Leptospermum* Forster & G.Forster [Myrtaceae], *Tristania* R.Br. [Myrtaceae].

References: Cockerell, T.D.A. (1914). Descriptions and records of bees. LIX. *Ann. Mag. Nat. Hist. (8)***13**: 504–522 (distribution); Rayment, T. (1954). Fungi and bees. *Vict. Nat.* **70**: 230–231 (as host); Rayment, T. (1954). Incidence of acarid mites on the biology of bees. *Aust. Zool.* **12**: 26–38 (biology); Rayment, T. (1957). First steps from the cave. *Proc. R. Zool. Soc. N.S.W.* **1955–56**: 83–86 (biology); Michener, C.D. (1965). A classification of the bees of the Australian and South Pacific regions. *Bull. Am. Mus. Nat. Hist.* **130**: 1–362 (illustration, flower record).

Lasioglossum (Australictus) plorator (Cockerell, 1910)

Parasphecodes plorator Cockerell, T.D.A. (1910). Descriptions and records of bees. XXXII. *Ann. Mag. Nat. Hist. (8)***6**: 272–284 [274].
Type data: holotype, BMNH Hym.17.a.633 ♀.
Type locality: Melbourne, VIC.

Distribution: SE coastal, NSW, VIC, TAS.
Ecology: larva—sedentary : adult—volant; melliferous, nest in rotten wood, flower visiting record: aster, *Helichrysum* Miller s.lat. [Asteraceae], *Leptospermum* Forster & G.Forster [Myrtaceae].
References: Meyer, R. (1920). Apidae—Halictinae. I. Gatt. *Parasphecodes* Sm. *Arch. Naturg.* **85**(A)11: 112–137 (taxonomy); Cockerell, T.D.A. (1929). Bees from the Australian region. *Am. Mus. Novit.* **346**: 1–18 (flower record); Rayment, T. (1935). *A Cluster of Bees. Sixty essays on the life-histories of Australian bees, with specific descriptions of over 100 new species, and an introduction by Professor E.F. Phillips, D.Ph., Cornell University, U.S.A.* Sydney : Endeavour Press 752 pp. (incorrect subsequent spelling as *Parasphecodes plorata*, illustration); Rayment, T. (1953). *Bees of the Portland District.* Victoria : Portland Field Naturalist's Club 39 pp. (description of male, flower record); Rayment, T. (1957). First steps from the cave. *Proc. R. Zool. Soc. N.S.W.* **1955–56**: 83–86 (biology); Knerer, G. & Schwarz, M. (1978). Beobachtungen an australischen Furchenbienen (Hymenopteren; Halictinae). *Zool. Anz.* **200**: 321–333 (biology).

Lasioglossum (Australictus) rufitarsum (Rayment, 1929)

Parasphecodes rufitarsus Rayment, T. (1929). Bees from East Gippsland. *Vict. Nat.* **46**: 124–129 [127].
Type data: holotype, NMV ♀.
Type locality: Cann River, VIC.

Distribution: SE coastal, VIC; known only from type locality.
Ecology: adult—volant; melliferous, flower visiting record: *Leptospermum* Forster & G.Forster [Myrtaceae].

Lasioglossum (Australictus) tertium (Dalla Torre, 1896)

Halictus rufipes Smith, F. (1853). *Catalogue of Hymenopterous Insects in the Collection of the British Museum.* Part I. Andrenidae and Apidae. London : British Museum 197 pp. [56] [junior primary homonym of *Halictus rufipes* Fabricius, 1793].
Type data: holotype, BMNH Hym.17.a.2837 ♀.
Type locality: Melbourne, VIC.

Halictus tertius Dalla Torre, K.W. (1896). *Catalogus Hymenopterorum Hucusque Descriptorum Systematicus et Synonymicus.* Apidae (Anthophila). Lipsiae : G. Engelmann Vol. x 643 pp. [86] [*nom. nov.* for *Halictus rufipes* Smith, 1853].

Distribution: SE coastal, Murray-Darling basin, NSW, VIC; only published localities White Swamp, Melbourne, Croydon and Lake Hattah.
Ecology: adult—volant; melliferous, solitary.
References: Cockerell, T.D.A. (1904). The halictine bees of the Australian region. *Ann. Mag. Nat. Hist. (7)***14**: 208–213 (as synonym of *Halictus bicingulatus* Smith, 1853); Cockerell, T.D.A. (1914). Descriptions and records of bees. LIX. *Ann. Mag. Nat. Hist. (8)***13**: 504–522 (valid species); Cockerell, T.D.A. (1926). Descriptions and records of bees. CXII. *Ann. Mag. Nat. Hist. (9)***18**: 216–227 (distribution); Rayment, T. (1939). Bees from the high lands of New South Wales and Victoria. *Aust. Zool.* **9**: 263–294 (distribution).

Lasioglossum (Austrevylaeus) Michener, 1965

Austrevylaeus Michener, C.D. (1965). A classification of the bees of the Australian and South Pacific regions. *Bull. Am. Mus. Nat. Hist.* **130**: 1–362 [170] [proposed with subgeneric rank in *Lasioglossum* Curtis, 1833]. Type species: *Halictus sordidus* Smith, 1853 by original designation.

Extralimital distribution: New Zealand, see Michener, C.D. (1965). A classification of the bees of the Australian and South Pacific regions. *Bull. Am. Mus. Nat. Hist.* **130**: 1–362 [171].

Lasioglossum (Austrevylaeus) ewarti (Cockerell, 1910)

Halictus ewarti Cockerell, T.D.A. (1910). New and little-known bees. *Trans. Am. Entomol. Soc.* **36**: 199–249 [230].
Type data: holotype, BMNH Hym.17.a.982 ♀.
Type locality: Kuranda (as Cairns Kuranda), QLD.

Distribution: NE coastal, QLD; known only from type locality.
Ecology: adult—volant; melliferous, solitary.
Reference: Cockerell, T.D.A. (1923). Descriptions and records of bees. XCVIII. *Ann. Mag. Nat. Hist. (9)***12**: 238–247 (taxonomy).

Lasioglossum (Austrevylaeus) exoneuroides (Rayment, 1953)

Halictus exoneuroides Rayment, T. (1953). *Bees of the Portland District.* Victoria : Portland Field Naturalist's Club 39 pp. [17].
Type data: holotype, ANIC ♀.
Type locality: Gorae West, VIC.

Distribution: SE coastal, VIC; known only from type locality.
Ecology: adult—volant; melliferous, solitary.

Lasioglossum (Austrevylaeus) melanurum (Cockerell, 1919)

Halictus melanurus Cockerell, T.D.A. (1919). Descriptions and records of bees. LXXXIII. *Ann. Mag. Nat. Hist. (9)***3**: 118–125 [125].
Type data: holotype, USNM ♀*.
Type locality: York, WA.

Distribution: SW coastal, WA; known only from type locality.
Ecology: adult—volant; melliferous, solitary.

Lasioglossum (Austrevylaeus) pertasmaniae (Rayment, 1953)

Halictus pertasmaniae Rayment, T. (1953). *Bees of the Portland District.* Victoria : Portland Field Naturalist's Club 39 pp. [22].
Type data: holotype, ANIC ♀.
Type locality: Gorae West, VIC.

Distribution: SE coastal, VIC; known only from type locality.
Ecology: larva—sedentary : adult—volant; melliferous, solitary.

Lasioglossum (Austrevylaeus) pertribuarium (Rayment, 1935)

Halictus pertribuarius Rayment, T. (1935). *A Cluster of Bees.* Sixty essays on the life-histories of Australian bees, with specific descriptions of over 100 new species, and an introduction by Professor E.F. Phillips, D.Ph., Cornell University, U.S.A. Sydney : Endeavour Press 752 pp. [705].
Type data: holotype, ANIC ♀.
Type locality: Grampians, VIC.

Distribution: Murray-Darling basin, VIC; known only from type locality.
Ecology: adult—volant; melliferous, solitary.

Lasioglossum (Austrevylaeus) rufibase (Cockerell, 1923)

Halictus rufibasis Cockerell, T.D.A. (1923). Descriptions and records of bees. XCVIII. *Ann. Mag. Nat. Hist. (9)***12**: 238–247 [238].
Type data: holotype, QM Hy2741 ♀.
Type locality: [Lamington] National Park, QLD.

Distribution: NE coastal, QLD; known only from type locality.
Ecology: adult—volant; melliferous, solitary.

Lasioglossum (Callalictus) Michener, 1965

Callalictus Michener, C.D. (1965). A classification of the bees of the Australian and South Pacific regions. *Bull. Am. Mus. Nat. Hist.* **130**: 1–362 [170] [proposed with subgeneric rank in *Lasioglossum* Curtis, 1833]. Type species: *Parasphecodes tooloomensis* Cockerell, 1929 by original designation.

Lasioglossum (Callalictus) anomalum (Rayment, 1935)

Callomelitta anomala Rayment, T. (1935). *A Cluster of Bees.* Sixty essays on the life-histories of Australian bees, with specific descriptions of over 100 new species, and an introduction by Professor E.F. Phillips, D.Ph., Cornell University, U.S.A. Sydney : Endeavour Press 752 pp. [654] [junior secondary homonym of *Halictus anomalus* Robertson, 1892].
Type data: holotype, ANIC ♀.
Type locality: Bilpin, Kurrajong Heights, NSW.

Distribution: SE coastal, Murray-Darling basin, NSW, VIC; only published localities Bilpin and Grampians.
Ecology: larva—sedentary : adult—volant; melliferous, nest in soil.
Reference: Rayment, T. (1957). First steps from the cave. *Proc. R. Zool. Soc. N.S.W.* **1955–56**: 83–86 (biology).

Lasioglossum (Callalictus) aurantiacum (Cockerell, 1916)

Parasphecodes aurantiacus Cockerell, T.D.A. (1916). A collection of bees from Queensland. *Mem. Qd Mus.* **5**: 197–204 [200].
Type data: holotype, QM Hy4143 ♀.
Type locality: Brisbane, QLD.

Distribution: NE coastal, QLD; known only from type locality.
Ecology: adult—volant; melliferous, solitary.

Lasioglossum (Callalictus) callomelittinum (Cockerell, 1910)

Parasphecodes callomelittinus Cockerell, T.D.A. (1910). New and little-known bees. *Trans. Am. Entomol. Soc.* **36**: 199–249 [237].
Type data: holotype, BMNH Hym.17.a.624 ♀.
Type locality: Melbourne, VIC.

Distribution: NE coastal, SE coastal, QLD, NSW; only published localities Bribie Is. and Melbourne.
Ecology: adult—volant; melliferous, solitary.
References: Meyer, R. (1920). Apidae—Halictinae. I. Gatt. *Parasphecodes* Sm. *Arch. Natur.* **85**(A)11: 112–137 (taxonomy); Cockerell, T.D.A. (1921). Australian bees in the Queensland Museum. *Mem. Qd Mus.* **7**: 81–98 (distribution).

Lasioglossum (Callalictus) contaminatum (Cockerell, 1910)

Parasphecodes contaminatus Cockerell, T.D.A. (1910). New and little-known bees. *Trans. Am. Entomol. Soc.* **36**: 199–249 [238].
Type data: holotype, BMNH Hym.17.a.625 ♂.
Type locality: Kuranda (as Cairns Kuranda), QLD.

Distribution: NE coastal, QLD; known only from type locality.
Ecology: adult—volant; melliferous, solitary.
Reference: Meyer, R. (1920). Apidae—Halictinae. I. Gatt. *Parasphecodes* Sm. *Arch. Natur.* **85**(A)11: 112–137 (taxonomy).

Lasioglossum (Callalictus) musgravei (Cockerell, 1929)

Parasphecodes tooloomensis musgravei Cockerell, T.D.A. (1929). Bees in the Australian Museum collection. *Rec. Aust. Mus.* **17**: 199–243 [230].
Type data: holotype, AM K57736 ♀.
Type locality: [Lamington] National Park, Macpherson Range, QLD.

Distribution: NE coastal, QLD; known only from type locality.
Ecology: adult—volant; melliferous, solitary.

Lasioglossum (Callalictus) ruficolle (Friese, 1924)

Halictus ruficollis Friese, H. (1924). Ueber die Bienen Australiens. *Konowia* **3**: 216–249 [237].
Type data: holotype (probable), whereabouts unknown ♂*.
Type locality: Adelaide, SA.

Distribution: S Gulfs, SA; known only from type locality.
Ecology: adult—volant; melliferous, solitary.

Lasioglossum (Callalictus) rufocollare (Cockerell, 1930)

Parasphecodes rufocollaris Cockerell, T.D.A. (1930). New Australian bees. *Mem. Qd Mus.* **10**: 37–50 [37].
Type data: holotype, QM Hy4096 ♀.
Type locality: [Lamington] National Park, QLD.

Distribution: NE coastal, QLD; known only from type locality.
Ecology: adult—volant; melliferous, solitary.

Lasioglossum (Callalictus) tooloomense (Cockerell, 1929)

Parasphecodes tooloomensis Cockerell, T.D.A. (1929). Bees in the Queensland Museum. *Mem. Qd Mus.* **9**: 298–323 [317].
Type data: syntypes, QM ♀ (a specimen has the type registration number Hy3748).
Type locality: Tooloom, NSW.

Distribution: SE coastal, NSW; known only from type locality.
Ecology: adult—volant; melliferous, solitary.

Lasioglossum (Chilalictus) Michener, 1965

Chilalictus Michener, C.D. (1965). A classification of the bees of the Australian and South Pacific regions. *Bull. Am. Mus. Nat. Hist.* **130**: 1–362 [174] [proposed with subgeneric rank in *Lasioglossum* Curtis, 1833]. Type species: *Halictus subinclinans* Cockerell, 1915 by original designation.

Extralimital distribution: New Caledonia, see Michener, C.D. (1965). A classification of the bees of the Australian and South Pacific regions. *Bull. Am. Mus. Nat. Hist.* **130**: 1–362 [175].

Lasioglossum (Chilalictus) alboguttatum (Friese, 1924)

Halictus alboguttatus Friese, H. (1924). Ueber die Bienen Australiens. *Konowia* **3**: 216–249 [240].
Type data: holotype (K. Walker pers. comm.), AMNH ♀*.
Type locality: Central Australia.

Distribution: Central Australia; known only from type locality, exact locality unknown.
Ecology: adult—volant; melliferous, solitary.
Reference: Cockerell, T.D.A. (1933). The bees of Australia. *Aust. Zool.* **7**: 291–324 (taxonomy).

Lasioglossum (Chilalictus) anexoneuroides (Rayment, 1953)

Halictus anexoneuroides Rayment, T. (1953). *Bees of the Portland District.* Victoria : Portland Field Naturalist's Club 39 pp. [11].
Type data: holotype, ANIC ♀.
Type locality: Gorae West, VIC.

Distribution: SE coastal, VIC; known only from type locality.
Ecology: adult—volant; melliferous, solitary.

Lasioglossum (Chilalictus) appositum (Rayment, 1939)

Halictus erythrurus appositus Rayment, T. (1939). Bees from the high lands of New South Wales and Victoria. *Aust. Zool.* **9**: 263–294 [281].
Type data: holotype, ANIC ♀.
Type locality: White Swamp, NSW.

Distribution: SE coastal, NSW; known only from type locality.
Ecology: adult—volant; melliferous, solitary.
References: Michener, C.D. (1965). A classification of the bees of the Australian and South Pacific regions. *Bull. Am. Mus. Nat. Hist.* **130**: 1–362 (as *Homalictus appositus* (Rayment, 1939), taxonomy); Walker, K.L. (1986). Revision of the Australian species of the genus *Homalictus* Cockerell (Hymenoptera : Halictidae). *Mem. Mus. Vict.* **47**: 105–200 [167] (generic placement).

Lasioglossum (Chilalictus) aptum (Rayment, 1935)

Halictus seductus aptus Rayment, T. (1935). *A Cluster of Bees.* Sixty essays on the life-histories of Australian bees, with specific descriptions of over 100 new species, and an introduction by Professor E.F. Phillips, D.Ph., Cornell University, U.S.A. Sydney : Endeavour Press 752 pp. [706].
Type data: holotype, ANIC ♀.
Type locality: Hurstbridge (as Hurst's Bridge), VIC.

Distribution: SE coastal, VIC; known only from type locality.
Ecology: adult—volant; melliferous, flower visiting record: *Bursaria* Cav. [Pittosporaceae].
Reference: Michener, C.D. (1965). A classification of the bees of the Australian and South Pacific regions. *Bull. Am. Mus. Nat. Hist.* **130**: 1–362 [175] (taxonomy).

Lasioglossum (Chilalictus) asperithorax (Cockerell, 1910)

Halictus asperithorax Cockerell, T.D.A. (1910). Descriptions and records of bees. XXXII. *Ann. Mag. Nat. Hist. (8)***6**: 272–284 [274].
Type data: holotype, BMNH Hym.17.a.917 ♀.
Type locality: Melbourne, VIC.

Distribution: SE coastal, Murray-Darling basin, VIC; only published localities Melbourne, Sandringham and Mt Buffalo.
Ecology: larva—sedentary : adult—volant; melliferous, nest communally in soil, flower visiting record: *Coreopsis* L. [Asteraceae], *Gazania* Gaertner [Asteraceae], *Hypochaeris* L. [Asteraceae], *Stylidium* Willd. [Stylidiaceae], *Veronica* L. [Scrophulariaceae].
References: Cockerell, T.D.A. (1926). Descriptions and records of bees. CXII. *Ann. Mag. Nat. Hist. (9)***18**: 216–227 (flower record); Rayment, T. (1935). *A Cluster of Bees.* Sixty essays on the life-histories of Australian bees, with specific descriptions of over 100 new species, and an introduction by Professor E.F. Phillips, D.Ph., Cornell University, U.S.A. Sydney : Endeavour Press 752 pp. (biology); Rayment, T. (1947). Bees from the Victorian Alps. *Vict. Nat.* **64**: 103–107 (distribution); Rayment, T. (1948). Some bees from the Victorian Alps. *Vict. Nat.* **65**: 201–202 (flower record); Michener, C.D. (1960). Notes on the biology and supposed parthenogenesis of halictine bees from the Australian region. *J. Kansas Entomol. Soc.* **33**: 85–96 (biology).

Lasioglossum (Chilalictus) atrocyaneum (Cockerell, 1918)

Halictus erythrurus atrocyaneus Cockerell, T.D.A. (1918). Some bees collected in Queensland. *Mem. Qd Mus.* **6**: 112–120 [117].
Type data: holotype, USNM ♀*.
Type locality: Brisbane, QLD.

Distribution: NE coastal, Murray-Darling basin, QLD, NSW; only published localities Brisbane, Armidale and Glen Innes.
Ecology: adult—volant; melliferous, flower visiting

185

record: *Hibbertia* Andrews [Dilleniaceae], *Wahlenbergia* Roth [Campanulaceae].
Reference: Michener, C.D. (1965). A classification of the bees of the Australian and South Pacific regions. *Bull. Am. Mus. Nat. Hist.* **130**: 1–362 (flower record, taxonomy).

Lasioglossum (Chilalictus) basilucens (Cockerell, 1923)

Halictus basilucens Cockerell, T.D.A. (1923). Descriptions and records of bees. XCVIII. *Ann. Mag. Nat. Hist.* *(9)***12**: 238–247 [239].
Type data: syntypes, QM 2♀ (a female has the type registration number Hy2744).
Type locality: Bribie Is., QLD.

Distribution: NE coastal, QLD; known only from type locality.
Ecology: adult—volant; melliferous, solitary.

Lasioglossum (Chilalictus) bassi (Cockerell, 1915)

Halictus bassi Cockerell, T.D.A. (1915). Descriptions and records of bees. LXIX. *Ann. Mag. Nat. Hist.* *(8)***16**: 96–104 [102].
Type data: holotype, BMNH Hym.17.a.927 ♂.
Type locality: Mt Wellington, TAS.

Distribution: SE coastal, VIC, TAS; only published localities Portland, Mt Wellington and Great Lake.
Ecology: adult—volant; melliferous, flower visiting record: *Helichrysum* Miller *s.lat.* [Asteraceae], *Pultenaea* Sm. [Fabaceae].
References: Rayment, T. (1953). New bees and wasps, Part XX. *Vict. Nat.* **70**: 68–71 (distribution); Rayment, T. (1953). *Bees of the Portland District.* Victoria : Portland Field Naturalist's Club 39 pp. (flower record).

Lasioglossum (Chilalictus) baudini (Cockerell, 1915)

Halictus baudini Cockerell, T.D.A. (1915). Descriptions and records of bees. LXIX. *Ann. Mag. Nat. Hist.* *(8)***16**: 96–104 [102].
Type data: syntypes, BMNH 3♂ (a female is labelled 'type' and has registration number Hym.17.a.926).
Type locality: Mt Wellington, TAS.

Distribution: TAS; only published localities Mt Wellington and Great Lake.
Ecology: adult—volant; melliferous, solitary.
Reference: Rayment, T. (1953). New bees and wasps, Part XX. *Vict. Nat.* **70**: 68–71 (distribution, also illustration, as *Halictus bourdini,* incorrect subsequent spelling).

Lasioglossum (Chilalictus) bicingulatum (Smith, 1853)

Halictus bicingulatus Smith, F. (1853). *Catalogue of Hymenopterous Insects in the Collection of the British Museum.* Part I. Andrenidae and Apidae. London : British Museum 197 pp. [57].
Type data: holotype (probable) Walcott coll. ♀*, presumed lost (K. Walker pers. comm.).
Type locality: Melbourne, VIC.

Distribution: NE coastal, SE coastal, QLD, NSW, VIC.
Ecology: adult—volant; melliferous, nest in soil, flower visiting record: *Leptospermum* Forster & G.Forster [Myrtaceae].
References: Cockerell, T.D.A. (1904). The halictine bees of the Australian region. *Ann. Mag. Nat. Hist.* *(7)***14**: 208–213 (taxonomy); Cockerell, T.D.A. (1905). New Australian bees, in the collection of the British Museum. *Entomologist* **38**: 270–273, 302–304 (taxonomy); Cockerell, T.D.A. (1910). New and little-known bees. *Trans. Am. Entomol. Soc.* **36**: 199–249 (variety); Cockerell, T.D.A. (1914). Descriptions and records of bees. LIX. *Ann. Mag. Nat. Hist.* *(8)***13**: 504–522 (distribution); Cockerell, T.D.A. (1922). Australian bees in the Queensland Museum. *Mem. Qd Mus.* **7**: 257–279 (flower record).

Lasioglossum (Chilalictus) blighi (Cockerell, 1915)

Halictus blighi Cockerell, T.D.A. (1915). Descriptions and records of bees. LXIX. *Ann. Mag. Nat. Hist.* *(8)***16**: 96–104 [102].
Type data: holotype, BMNH Hym.17.a.928 ♂.
Type locality: Mt Wellington, TAS.

Distribution: TAS; known only from type locality.
Ecology: adult—volant; melliferous, solitary.

Lasioglossum (Chilalictus) boweni (Cockerell, 1915)

Halictus boweni Cockerell, T.D.A. (1915). Descriptions and records of bees. LXIX. *Ann. Mag. Nat. Hist.* *(8)***16**: 96–104 [103].
Type data: holotype, BMNH Hym.17.a.931 ♂.
Type locality: Eaglehawk Neck, TAS.

Distribution: TAS; only published localities Eaglehawk Neck and Great Lake.
Ecology: adult—volant; melliferous, flower visiting record: *Helichrysum* Miller *s.lat.* [Asteraceae].
References: Cockerell, T.D.A. (1933). The bees of Australia. *Aust. Zool.* **7**: 291–324 (taxonomy); Rayment, T. (1953). New bees and wasps, Part XX. *Vict. Nat.* **70**: 68–71 (distribution).

Lasioglossum (Chilalictus) brazieri (Cockerell, 1916)

Halictus brazieri Cockerell, T.D.A. (1916). Some bees from Australia, Tasmania, and the New Hebrides. *Proc. Acad. Nat. Sci. Philad.* **68**: 360–375 [367].
Type data: holotype, BMNH Hym.17.a.915 ♀ (described as ♂).
Type locality: Yallingup, WA.

Distribution: SW coastal, WA; only published localities Yallingup, Kalamunda and Denmark.

Ecology: adult—volant; melliferous, solitary.

Reference: Rayment, T. (1931). Bees in the collections of the Western Australian Museum and the Agricultural Department, Perth. *J. Proc. R. Soc. West. Aust.* **17**: 157–190 (distribution).

Lasioglossum (Chilalictus) bursariae (Cockerell, 1916)

Halictus bursariae Cockerell, T.D.A. (1916). A collection of bees from Queensland. *Mem. Qd Mus.* **5**: 197–204 [203].
Type data: holotype, ANIC ♂.
Type locality: Kelvin Grove, Brisbane, QLD.

Distribution: NE coastal, QLD; only published localities Brisbane, Caloundra, Mt Tamborine and [Lamington] National Park.
Ecology: adult—volant; melliferous, flower visiting record: *Bursaria* Cav. [Pittosporaceae].
Reference: Cockerell, T.D.A. (1929). Bees in the Australian Museum collection. *Rec. Aust. Mus.* **17**: 199–243 (distribution).

Lasioglossum (Chilalictus) calophyllae (Rayment, 1935)

Halictus calophyllae Rayment, T. (1935). *A Cluster of Bees*. Sixty essays on the life-histories of Australian bees, with specific descriptions of over 100 new species, and an introduction by Professor E.F. Phillips, D.Ph., Cornell University, U.S.A. Sydney : Endeavour Press 752 pp. [709].
Type data: holotype, ANIC ♀.
Type locality: Sandringham, VIC.

Distribution: SE coastal, QLD; known only from type locality.
Ecology: adult—volant; melliferous, solitary.

Lasioglossum (Chilalictus) cambagei (Cockerell, 1910)

Halictus cambagei Cockerell, T.D.A. (1910). New and little-known bees. *Trans. Am. Entomol. Soc.* **36**: 199–249 [236].
Type data: syntypes, ZMB 4♂*, USNM ♂*.
Type locality: Adelaide, SA.

Distribution: Murray-Darling basin, S Gulfs, VIC, SA; only published localities Albury and Adelaide.
Ecology: adult—volant; melliferous, solitary.
Reference: Rayment, T. (1939). Bees from the high lands of New South Wales and Victoria. *Aust. Zool.* **9**: 263–294 (distribution).

Lasioglossum (Chilalictus) cephalochilum Michener, 1965

Lasioglossum (Chilalictus) cephalochilum Michener, C.D. (1965). A classification of the bees of the Australian and South Pacific regions. *Bull. Am. Mus. Nat. Hist.* **130**: 1–362 [314].
Type data: holotype, ANIC ♀.
Type locality: Glen Innes, NSW.

Distribution: Murray-Darling basin, NSW; known only from type locality.
Ecology: adult—volant; melliferous, flower visiting record: *Leptorhynchos* Less. [Asteraceae].

Lasioglossum (Chilalictus) chapmani (Cockerell, 1910)

Halictus chapmani Cockerell, T.D.A. (1910). Descriptions and records of bees. XXXII. *Ann. Mag. Nat. Hist.* *(8)***6**: 272–284 [273].
Type data: holotype, ZMB 2564 ♀*.
Type locality: WA.

Distribution: SW coastal, WA; only published locality Denmark.
Ecology: adult—volant; melliferous, solitary.
Reference: Rayment, T. (1931). Bees in the collections of the Western Australian Museum and the Agricultural Department, Perth. *J. Proc. R. Soc. West. Aust.* **17**: 157–190 (distribution, illustration).

Lasioglossum (Chilalictus) circumdatum (Cockerell, 1914)

Halictus circumdatus Cockerell, T.D.A. (1914). Descriptions and records of bees. LIX. *Ann. Mag. Nat. Hist.* *(8)***13**: 504–522 [512].
Type data: holotype, BMNH Hym.17.a.959 ♀.
Type locality: Rutherglen, VIC.

Distribution: SE coastal, Murray-Darling basin, VIC; only published localities Portland and Rutherglen.
Ecology: adult—volant; melliferous, flower visiting record: *Eucalyptus* L'Hérit. [Myrtaceae], *Hibbertia* Andrews [Dilleniaceae].
Reference: Rayment, T. (1953). *Bees of the Portland District*. Victoria : Portland Field Naturalist's Club 39 pp. (distribution, flower record).

Lasioglossum (Chilalictus) clariventre (Friese, 1924)

Halictus clariventris Friese, H. (1924). Ueber die Bienen Australiens. *Konowia* **3**: 216–249 [241].
Type data: holotype (probable), AMNH ♀*.
Type locality: Adelaide, SA.

Distribution: S Gulfs, SA; known only from type locality.
Ecology: adult—volant; melliferous, solitary.
Reference: Cockerell, T.D.A. (1929). Bees, chiefly Australian species, described or determined by Dr. H. Friese. *Am. Mus. Novit.* **343**: 1–20 (redescription).

Lasioglossum (Chilalictus) clelandi (Cockerell, 1910)

Halictus clelandi Cockerell, T.D.A. (1910). Descriptions and records of bees. XXXII. *Ann. Mag. Nat. Hist.* *(8)***6**: 272–284 [272].
Type data: holotype, ZMB ♂*.
Type locality: Adelaide, SA.

Distribution: S Gulfs, SA; known only from type locality.
Ecology: adult—volant; melliferous, solitary.

Lasioglossum (Chilalictus) cognatum (Smith, 1853)

Halictus cognatus Smith, F. (1853). *Catalogue of Hymenopterous Insects in the Collection of the British Museum.* Part I. Andrenidae and Apidae. London : British Museum 197 pp. [59].
Type data: holotype (probable), BMNH Hym.17.a.900 ♂.
Type locality: TAS (as Van Diemens Land).

Distribution: TAS; only published locality Launceston.
Ecology: adult—volant; melliferous, solitary.
Reference: Cockerell, T.D.A. (1914). Some Tasmanian bees. *Entomologist* **47**: 305–308 (distribution).

Lasioglossum (Chilalictus) colonicum (Rayment, 1953)

Halictus colonicus Rayment, T. (1953). *Bees of the Portland District.* Victoria : Portland Field Naturalist's Club 39 pp. [12].
Type data: holotype, ANIC ♀.
Type locality: Glenelg River, VIC.

Distribution: SE coastal, VIC; known only from type locality.
Ecology: adult—volant; melliferous, solitary.

Lasioglossum (Chilalictus) confusellum (Cockerell, 1916)

Halictus confusellus Cockerell, T.D.A. (1916). Some bees from Australia, Tasmania, and the New Hebrides. *Proc. Acad. Nat. Sci. Philad.* **68**: 360–375 [374].
Type data: holotype, BMNH Hym.17.a.987 ♀.
Type locality: Launceston, TAS.

Distribution: TAS; only published localities Launceston and Great Lake.
Ecology: adult—volant; melliferous, flower visiting record: *Bursaria* Cav. [Pittosporaceae].
Reference: Rayment, T. (1953). New bees and wasps, Part XX. *Vict. Nat.* **70**: 68–71 (distribution).

Lasioglossum (Chilalictus) conspicuum (Smith, 1879)

Halictus conspicuus Smith, F. (1879). *Descriptions of New Species of Hymenoptera in the Collection of the British Museum.* London : British Museum xxi 240 pp. [34].
Type data: holotype, BMNH Hym.17.a.970 ♀.
Type locality: Australia.

Distribution: Australia, known only from type locality, exact locality unknown.
Ecology: adult—volant; melliferous, solitary.
References: Cockerell, T.D.A. (1914). Descriptions and records of bees. LX. *Ann. Mag. Nat. Hist.* (8)**14**: 1–13 (taxonomy); Cockerell, T.D.A. (1933). The bees of Australia. *Aust. Zool.* **7**: 291–324 (taxonomy).

Lasioglossum (Chilalictus) convexum (Smith, 1879)

Halictus convexus Smith, F. (1879). *Descriptions of New Species of Hymenoptera in the Collection of the British Museum.* London : British Museum xxi 240 pp. [35].
Type data: holotype, BMNH Hym.17.a.902 ♀.
Type locality: VIC.

Distribution: Murray-Darling basin, VIC; only published locality Gunbower.
Ecology: adult—volant; melliferous, flower visiting record: *Schinus* L. [Anacardiaceae].
References: Cockerell, T.D.A. (1904). The halictine bees of the Australian region. *Ann. Mag. Nat. Hist.* (7)**14**: 208–213 (taxonomy); Rayment, T. (1935). *A Cluster of Bees.* Sixty essays on the life-histories of Australian bees, with specific descriptions of over 100 new species, and an introduction by Professor E.F. Phillips, D.Ph., Cornell University, U.S.A. Sydney : Endeavour Press 752 pp. (flower record).

Lasioglossum (Chilalictus) cyclognathum (Cockerell, 1914)

Halictus cyclognathus Cockerell, T.D.A. (1914). Descriptions and records of bees. LIX. *Ann. Mag. Nat. Hist.* (8)**13**: 504–522 [511].
Type data: holotype, ANIC ♂.
Type locality: Croydon, VIC.

Distribution: SE coastal, VIC, TAS; only published localities Croydon and Eaglehawk Neck.
Ecology: adult—volant; melliferous, solitary.
Reference: Cockerell, T.D.A. (1915). Descriptions and records of bees. LXIX. *Ann. Mag. Nat. Hist.* (8)**16**: 96–104 (taxonomy).

Lasioglossum (Chilalictus) darwiniellum (Cockerell, 1932)

Halictus (Evylaeus) darwiniellus Cockerell, T.D.A. (1932). Bees collected by Charles Darwin on the voyage of the "Beagle". *J. N.Y. Entomol. Soc.* **40**: 519–522 [519].
Type data: holotype, OUM ♀* (not found by J.C.C. in 1988).
Type locality: Sydney, NSW.

Distribution: SE coastal, NSW; known only from type locality.
Ecology: adult—volant; melliferous, solitary.

Lasioglossum (Chilalictus) dimorphum (Rayment, 1954)

Halictus erythrurus dimorphus Rayment, T. (1954). Incidence of acarid mites on the biology of bees. *Aust. Zool.* **12**: 26–38 [31].
Type data: syntypes, ANIC ♀ (number of specimens unknown).
Type locality: Dandenong, VIC.

Distribution: SE coastal, VIC; only published localities Dandenong and Mt Macedon.
Ecology: larva—sedentary : adult—volant; melliferous, nest communally in soil.

References: Rayment, T. (1955). Dimorphism and parthenogenesis in halictine bees. *Aust. Zool.* **12**: 142–153 (biology); Rayment, T. (1957). First steps from the cave. *Proc. R. Zool. Soc. N.S.W.* **1955–56**: 83–86 (illustration); Michener, C.D. (1960). Notes on the biology and supposed parthenogenesis of halictine bees from the Australian region. *J. Kansas Entomol. Soc.* **33**: 85–96 (lists as *nom. nud.*); Michener, C.D. (1965). A classification of the bees of the Australian and South Pacific regions. *Bull. Am. Mus. Nat. Hist.* **130**: 1–362 (lists as *nom. nud.*, taxonomy); Knerer, G. & Schwarz, M. (1978). Beobachtungen an australischen Furchenbienen (Hymenopteren; Halictinae). *Zool. Anz.* **200**: 321–333 (biology).

Lasioglossum (Chilalictus) disclusum (Cockerell, 1914)

Halictus disclusus Cockerell, T.D.A. (1914). Australian halictine bees. *Entomologist* **47**: 242–244 [243].
Type data: holotype, BMNH Hym.17.a.979 ♂.
Type locality: Eaglehawk Neck, TAS.

Distribution: TAS; only published localities Eaglehawk Neck and Great Lake.
Ecology: adult—volant; melliferous, flower visiting record: *Helichrysum* Miller *s.lat.* [Asteraceae].
Reference: Rayment, T. (1953). New bees and wasps, Part XX. *Vict. Nat.* **70**: 68–71 (flower record).

Lasioglossum (Chilalictus) dolichocerum (Cockerell, 1916)

Halictus dolichocerus Cockerell, T.D.A. (1916). Some bees from Australia, Tasmania, and the New Hebrides. *Proc. Acad. Nat. Sci. Philad.* **68**: 360–375 [370].
Type data: holotype, USNM ♂*.
Type locality: Yarrawin, NSW.

Distribution: Murray-Darling basin, NSW; only published localities Yarrawin and Brewarrina.
Ecology: adult—volant; melliferous, solitary.

Lasioglossum (Chilalictus) dorsicyaneum (Cockerell, 1930)

Halictus dorsicyaneus Cockerell, T.D.A. (1930). New Australian bees. *Mem. Qd Mus.* **10**: 37–50 [46].
Type data: holotype, USNM ♀*.
Type locality: Launceston, TAS.

Distribution: TAS; known only from type locality.
Ecology: adult—volant; melliferous, solitary.

Lasioglossum (Chilalictus) doweri (Rayment, 1935)

Halictus doweri Rayment, T. (1935). *A Cluster of Bees.* Sixty essays on the life-histories of Australian bees, with specific descriptions of over 100 new species, and an introduction by Professor E.F. Phillips, D.Ph., Cornell University, U.S.A. Sydney : Endeavour Press 752 pp. [694].
Type data: holotype, ANIC ♀.
Type locality: Cheltenham, Port Phillip, VIC.

Distribution: SE coastal, VIC; only published localities Cheltenham and Malvern.
Ecology: adult—volant; melliferous, flower visiting record: *Eucalyptus* L'Hérit. [Myrtaceae].

Lasioglossum (Chilalictus) eboracense (Cockerell, 1918)

Halictus eboracensis Cockerell, T.D.A. (1918). Some bees collected in Queensland. *Mem. Qd Mus.* **6**: 112–120 [117].
Type data: holotype, BMNH Hym.17.a.957 ♀.
Type locality: Ebor, NSW.

Distribution: SE coastal, Murray-Darling basin, NSW, VIC; only published localities Ebor, Barrington Tops, Sandringham and Gunbower.
Ecology: larva—sedentary : adult—volant; melliferous, flower visiting record: *Callistemon* R.Br. [Myrtaceae], *Leucopogon* R.Br. [Epacridaceae].
References: Cockerell, T.D.A. (1929). Bees in the Australian Museum collection. *Rec. Aust. Mus.* **17**: 199–243 (distribution); Rayment, T. (1939). Bees from the high lands of New South Wales and Victoria. *Aust. Zool.* **9**: 263–294 (description of male); Rayment, T. (1955). Dimorphism and parthenogenesis in halictine bees. *Aust. Zool.* **12**: 142–153 (biology).

Lasioglossum (Chilalictus) elliottii (Rayment, 1929)

Halictus elliottii Rayment, T. (1929). Bees from East Gippsland. *Vict. Nat.* **46**: 124–129 [125] [incorrect original spelling as *Halictus elliotii*, species name dedicated to Senator R.D. Elliott; emendation Cardale, J.C., this work].
Type data: holotype, NMV ♀.
Type locality: Cann River, East Gippsland, VIC.

Distribution: SE coastal, VIC; known only from type locality.
Ecology: adult—volant; melliferous, flower visiting record: *Leptospermum* Forster & G.Forster [Myrtaceae].

Lasioglossum (Chilalictus) emeraldense (Rayment, 1936)

Halictus emeraldensis Rayment, T. (1936). Biology of a new halictine bee and specific descriptions of its parasites. *Arb. Physiol. Ang. Entomol. Berl.* **3**: 289–294 [289].
Type data: syntypes, ANIC ♂♀.
Type locality: Emerald, VIC.

Distribution: SE coastal, VIC; only published localities Emerald and the Dandenongs.
Ecology: larva—sedentary : adult—volant; melliferous, nest communally in soil, flower visiting record: aster, *Acacia* Miller [Mimosaceae], *Arctotheca* Wendl. [Asteraceae], *Epacris* Cav. [Epacridaceae], *Goodenia* Sm. [Goodeniaceae], *Leptospermum* Forster & G.Forster [Myrtaceae], *Pimelea* Gaertner [Thymelaeaceae], *Platylobium* Sm. [Fabaceae], *Prostanthera* Labill. [Lamiaceae].
References: Rayment, T. (1937). Biology of a new

halictine bee and specific descriptions of its parasites. *Arb. Physiol. Ang. Entomol. Berl.* **4**: 30–60 (biology, described as new); Rayment, T. (1954). Incidence of acarid mites on the biology of bees. *Aust. Zool.* **12**: 26–38 (as host); Michener, C.D. (1960). Notes on the biology and supposed parthenogenesis of halictine bees from the Australian region. *J. Kansas Entomol. Soc.* **33**: 85–96 (biology).

Lasioglossum (Chilalictus) erythrurum (Cockerell, 1914)

Halictus erythrurus Cockerell, T.D.A. (1914). Descriptions and records of bees. LIX. *Ann. Mag. Nat. Hist. (8)***13**: 504–522 [504].
Type data: syntypes, USNM ♀*, NMV ♀*.
Type locality: Croydon, VIC.

Distribution: NE coastal, Murray-Darling basin, SE coastal, SW coastal, QLD, NSW, VIC, WA, TAS.
Ecology: larva—sedentary : adult—volant; melliferous, nest communally in soil, "soldier" males found in nest, flower visiting record: *Aotus* Smith [Fabaceae], *Boronia* Sm. [Rutaceae], *Dillwynia* Sm. [Fabaceae], *Hibbertia* Andrews [Dilleniaceae], *Jacksonia* Smith [Fabaceae], *Leptospermum* Forster & G.Forster [Myrtaceae], *Senecio* L. [Asteraceae], *Wahlenbergia* Roth [Campanulaceae].
References: Cockerell, T.D.A. (1919). Descriptions and records of bees. LXXXIII. *Ann. Mag. Nat. Hist. (9)***3**: 118–125 (taxonomy); Cockerell, T.D.A. (1929). Bees, chiefly Australian species, described or determined by Dr. H. Friese. *Am. Mus. Novit.* **343**: 1–20 (taxonomy); Rayment, T. (1931). Bees in the collections of the Western Australian Museum and the Agricultural Department, Perth. *J. Proc. R. Soc. West. Aust.* **17**: 157–190 (distribution); Rayment, T. (1953). *Bees of the Portland District*. Victoria : Portland Field Naturalist's Club 39 pp. (flower record); Rayment, T. (1955). Dimorphism and parthenogenesis in halictine bees. *Aust. Zool.* **12**: 142–153 (biology); Michener, C.D. (1960). Notes on the biology and supposed parthenogenesis of halictine bees from the Australian region. *J. Kansas Entomol. Soc.* **33**: 85–96 (biology); Michener, C.D. (1965). A classification of the bees of the Australian and South Pacific regions. *Bull. Am. Mus. Nat. Hist.* **130**: 1–362 (flower record); Houston, T.F. (1970). Discovery of an apparent male soldier caste in a nest of a halictine bee (Hymenoptera : Halictidae), with notes on the nest. *Aust. J. Zool.* **18**: 345–351 (biology); Knerer, G. & Schwarz, M. (1976). Halictine social evolution : the Australian enigma. *Science* **194**: 445–448 (biology); Knerer, G. & Schwarz, M. (1978). Beobachtungen an australischen Furchenbienen (Hymenopteren; Halictinae). *Zool. Anz.* **200**: 321–333 (biology); Knerer, G. (1980). Evolution of halictine castes. *Naturwissensch.* **67**: 133–135 (biology); Walker, K.L. (1986). Revision of the Australian species of the genus *Homalictus* Cockerell (Hymenoptera :

Halictidae). *Mem. Mus. Vict.* **47**: 105–200 (biology); Kukuk, P.F. & Schwarz, M. (1987). Intranest behavior of the communal sweat bee *Lasioglossum (Chilalictus) erythrurum* (Hymenoptera : Halictidae). *J. Kansas Entomol. Soc.* **60**: 58–64 (biology); Kukuk, P.F. & Schwarz, M. (1988). Macrocephalic male bees as functional reproductives and probable guards. *Pan-Pac. Entomol.* **64**: 131–137 (biology); Kukuk, P.F. & Crozier, R.H. (1990). Trophallaxis in a communal halictine bee *Lasioglossum (Chilalictus) erythrurum*. *Proc. Natl Acad. Sci. U.S.A.* **87**: 5402–5404 (biology).

Lasioglossum (Chilalictus) euryurum (Cockerell, 1930)

Halictus euryurus Cockerell, T.D.A. (1930). New Australian bees. *Mem. Qd Mus.* **10**: 37–50 [44].
Type data: holotype, QM Hy5002 ♂.
Type locality: Adaminaby, NSW.

Distribution: Murray-Darling basin, NSW; known only from type locality.
Ecology: adult—volant; melliferous, solitary.

Lasioglossum (Chilalictus) evasum (Cockerell, 1930)

Halictus evasus Cockerell, T.D.A. (1930). New Australian bees. *Mem. Qd Mus.* **10**: 37–50 [45].
Type data: holotype, QM Hy5000 ♀.
Type locality: Coolangatta, QLD.

Distribution: NE coastal, SE coastal, QLD, VIC; only published localities Coolangatta and Portland.
Ecology: adult—volant; melliferous, flower visiting record: *Pultenaea* Sm. [Fabaceae].
Reference: Rayment, T. (1953). *Bees of the Portland District*. Victoria : Portland Field Naturalist's Club 39 pp. (distribution).

Lasioglossum (Chilalictus) exceptum (Cockerell, 1930)

Halictus exceptus Cockerell, T.D.A. (1930). New Australian bees. *Mem. Qd Mus.* **10**: 37–50 [43].
Type data: syntypes, QM 2♀* (a female has registration number QM Hy3750).
Type locality: Tooloom, NSW.

Distribution: NE coastal, SE coastal, QLD, NSW, VIC; only published localities Mt Glorious, Lamington National Park, Tooloom and Portland.
Ecology: adult—volant; melliferous, flower visiting record: *Claoxylon* A. Juss. [Euphorbiaceae], *Rubus* L. [Rosaceae].
References: Rayment, T. (1953). *Bees of the Portland District*. Victoria : Portland Field Naturalist's Club 39 pp. (distribution); Michener, C.D. (1965). A classification of the bees of the Australian and South Pacific regions. *Bull. Am. Mus. Nat. Hist.* **130**: 1–362 (flower record).

Lasioglossum (Chilalictus) excusum (Cockerell, 1930)

Halictus excusus Cockerell, T.D.A. (1930). New Australian bees. *Mem. Qd Mus.* **10**: 37–50 [42].
Type data: holotype, BMNH Hym.17.a.984 ♂.
Type locality: Pyengana, TAS.

Distribution: TAS; known only from type locality.
Ecology: adult—volant; melliferous, solitary.

Lasioglossum (Chilalictus) expansifrons (Cockerell, 1914)

Halictus expansifrons Cockerell, T.D.A. (1914). Descriptions and records of bees. LIX. *Ann. Mag. Nat. Hist.* (8)**13**: 504–522 [521].
Type data: syntypes, BMNH 2♂ (a specimen is labelled 'type' and has registration number Hym.17.a.946).
Type locality: NSW.

Distribution: NSW; known only from type locality, exact locality unknown.
Ecology: adult—volant; melliferous, solitary.

Lasioglossum (Chilalictus) familiare (Erichson, 1842)

Hylaeus familiaris Erichson, W.F. (1842). Beitrag zur Fauna von Vandiemensland mit besonderer Rücksicht auf die geographische Verbreitung der Insekten. *Arch. Naturg.* **8**: 83–287 [268].
Type data: holotype (probable), whereabouts unknown ♀*.
Type locality: TAS (as Van Diemens Land).

Distribution: TAS; known only from type locality.
Ecology: adult—volant; melliferous, solitary.
Reference: Cockerell, T.D.A. (1905). New Australian bees, in the collection of the British Museum. *Entomologist* **38**: 270–273, 302–304 (taxonomy, as *Halictus familiaris* (Erichson, 1842)).

Lasioglossum (Chilalictus) festivum (Rayment, 1935)

Halictus festivus Rayment, T. (1935). *A Cluster of Bees.* Sixty essays on the life-histories of Australian bees, with specific descriptions of over 100 new species, and an introduction by Professor E.F. Phillips, D.Ph., Cornell University, U.S.A. Sydney : Endeavour Press 752 pp. [707].
Type data: holotype, ANIC ♀.
Type locality: West Warburton, VIC.

Distribution: SE coastal, VIC; known only from type locality.
Ecology: adult—volant; melliferous, solitary.

Lasioglossum (Chilalictus) florale (Smith, 1853)

Halictus floralis Smith, F. (1853). *Catalogue of Hymenopterous Insects in the Collection of the British Museum.* Part I. Andrenidae and Apidae. London : British Museum 197 pp. [57].
Type data: holotype, BMNH Hym.17.a.897 ♀.
Type locality: Australia (as New Holland).

Distribution: Australia, known only from type locality, exact locality unknown.
Ecology: adult—volant; melliferous, solitary.
References: Cockerell, T.D.A. (1904). The halictine bees of the Australian region. *Ann. Mag. Nat. Hist.* (7)**14**: 208–213 (taxonomy); Cockerell, T.D.A. (1933). The bees of Australia. *Aust. Zool.* **7**: 291–324 (taxonomy).

Lasioglossum (Chilalictus) forticorne (Cockerell, 1916)

Halictus forticornis Cockerell, T.D.A. (1916). Some bees from Australia, Tasmania and the New Hebrides. *Proc. Acad. Nat. Sci. Philad.* **68**: 360–375 [372].
Type data: holotype, BMNH Hym.17.a.940 ♂.
Type locality: Kalamunda, WA.

Distribution: SW coastal, WA; known only from type locality.
Ecology: adult—volant; melliferous, solitary.

Lasioglossum (Chilalictus) furneauxi (Cockerell, 1915)

Halictus furneauxi Cockerell, T.D.A. (1915). Descriptions and records of bees. LXIX. *Ann. Mag. Nat. Hist.* (8)**16**: 96–104 [101].
Type data: holotype, BMNH Hym.17.a.930 ♀.
Type locality: Eaglehawk Neck, TAS.

Distribution: SE coastal, VIC, TAS; only published localities Portland and Eaglehawk Neck.
Ecology: adult—volant; melliferous, flower visiting record: *Pultenaea* Sm. [Fabaceae].
Reference: Rayment, T. (1953). *Bees of the Portland District.* Victoria : Portland Field Naturalist's Club 39 pp. (distribution).

Lasioglossum (Chilalictus) gilesi (Cockerell, 1905)

Halictus gilesi Cockerell, T.D.A. (1905). New Australian bees, in the collection of the British Museum. *Entomologist* **38**: 270–273, 302–304 [304].
Type data: holotype, BMNH Hym.17.a.916 ♀.
Type locality: VIC.

Distribution: SE coastal, Murray-Darling basin, VIC; only published localities Gorae West and Mt Buffalo.
Ecology: larva—sedentary : adult—volant; melliferous, nest gregariously in soil, flower visiting record: *Brachyscome* Cass. [Asteraceae], *Eucalyptus* L'Hérit. [Myrtaceae].
References: Rayment, T. (1947). Bees from the Victorian Alps. *Vict. Nat.* **64**: 103–107 (distribution); Rayment, T. (1948). Some bees from the Victorian Alps. *Vict. Nat.* **65**: 201–202 (flower record); Rayment, T. (1953). *Bees of the Portland District.* Victoria : Portland Field Naturalist's Club 39 pp. (flower record); Rayment, T. (1954). Incidence of acarid mites on the biology of bees. *Aust. Zool.* **12**: 26–38 (biology).

Lasioglossum (Chilalictus) gippsii (Rayment, 1935)

Halictus seductus gippsii Rayment, T. (1935). *A Cluster of Bees*. Sixty essays on the life-histories of Australian bees, with specific descriptions of over 100 new species, and an introduction by Professor E.F. Phillips, D.Ph., Cornell University, U.S.A. Sydney : Endeavour Press 752 pp. [707].
Type data: holotype, ANIC ♀.
Type locality: Leongatha, Gippsland, VIC.

Distribution: SE coastal, VIC; known only from type locality.
Ecology: adult—volant; melliferous, solitary.
Reference: Michener, C.D. (1965). A classification of the bees of the Australian and South Pacific regions. *Bull. Am. Mus. Nat. Hist.* **130**: 1–362 [176] (taxonomy).

Lasioglossum (Chilalictus) glauerti (Rayment, 1931)

Halictus glauerti Rayment, T. (1931). Bees in the collections of the Western Australian Museum and the Agricultural Department, Perth. *J. Proc. R. Soc. West. Aust.* **17**: 157–190 [170].
Type data: holotype, ANIC ♀.
Type locality: Perth, WA.

Distribution: SW coastal, WA; known only from type locality.
Ecology: adult—volant; melliferous, solitary.

Lasioglossum (Chilalictus) globosum (Smith, 1853)

Halictus globosus Smith, F. (1853). *Catalogue of Hymenopterous Insects in the Collection of the British Museum*. Part I. Andrenidae and Apidae. London : British Museum 197 pp. [59].
Type data: holotype, BMNH Hym.17.a.899 ♀.
Type locality: TAS (as Van Diemens Land).

Distribution: TAS; known only from type locality.
Ecology: adult—volant; melliferous, solitary.
Reference: Cockerell, T.D.A. (1904). The halictine bees of the Australian region. *Ann. Mag. Nat. Hist.* *(7)***14**: 208–213 (taxonomy).

Lasioglossum (Chilalictus) goraeense (Rayment, 1953)

Halictus goraeensis Rayment, T. (1953). *Bees of the Portland District*. Victoria : Portland Field Naturalist's Club 39 pp. [18].
Type data: holotype, ANIC ♀.
Type locality: Gorae West, VIC.

Distribution: SE coastal, VIC; known only from type locality.
Ecology: larva—sedentary : adult—volant; melliferous, flower visiting record: aster, *Arctotheca* Wendl. [Asteraceae], *Eucalyptus* L'Hérit. [Myrtaceae], *Leucopogon* R.Br. [Epacridaceae].
Reference: Michener, C.D. (1960). Notes on the biology and supposed parthenogenesis of halictine bees from the Australian region. *J. Kansas Entomol. Soc.* **33**: 85–96 (biology).

Lasioglossum (Chilalictus) granulithorax (Cockerell, 1914)

Halictus granulithorax Cockerell, T.D.A. (1914). Descriptions and records of bees. LIX. *Ann. Mag. Nat. Hist.* *(8)***13**: 504–522 [519].
Type data: holotype, BMNH Hym.17.a.919 ♀.
Type locality: VIC.

Distribution: SE coastal, VIC, TAS; only published localities Melbourne, Point Lonsdale and New Norfolk.
Ecology: adult—volant; melliferous, flower visiting record: everlasting daisies.
References: Cockerell, T.D.A. (1929). Bees from the Australian region. *Am. Mus. Novit.* **346**: 1–18 (distribution); Cockerell, T.D.A. (1933). The bees of Australia. *Aust. Zool.* **7**: 291–324 (distribution); Rayment, T. (1953). New bees and wasps, Part XX. *Vict. Nat.* **70**: 68–71 (distribution).

Lasioglossum (Chilalictus) greavesi (Rayment, 1930)

Halictus (Chloralictus) greavesi Rayment, T. (1930). Notes on a collection of bees from Western Australia. *J. Proc. R. Soc. West. Aust.* **16**: 45–56 [53] [incorrect original spelling as *greavessi*; name dedicated to Mr Tom Greaves; emendation Rayment, T. (1931). Bees in the collections of the Western Australian Museum and the Agricultural Department, Perth. *J. Proc. R. Soc. West. Aust.* **17**: 157–190].
Type data: holotype, ANIC ♀.
Type locality: Bungulla, WA.

Distribution: SW coastal, WA; only published localities Bungulla and Perth.
Ecology: adult—volant; melliferous, solitary.
References: Rayment, T. (1931). Bees in the collections of the Western Australian Museum and the Agricultural Department, Perth. *J. Proc. R. Soc. West. Aust.* **17**: 157–190 (distribution); Cockerell, T.D.A. (1933). The bees of Australia. *Aust. Zool.* **7**: 291–324 (spelling of name corrected).

Lasioglossum (Chilalictus) griseovittatum (Cockerell, 1914)

Halictus griseovittatus Cockerell, T.D.A. (1914). Descriptions and records of bees. LIX. *Ann. Mag. Nat. Hist.* *(8)***13**: 504–522 [509].
Type data: holotype, USNM ♀*.
Type locality: Kelvin Grove, QLD.
Halictus mjobergi Friese, H. (1917). Results of Dr. E. Mjöberg's Swedish Scientific Expeditions to Australia, 1910–1913. 13. Apidae. *Ark. Zool.* **11**(2): 1–9 [5].
Type data: holotype (probable), AMNH ♀*.
Type locality: Adelaide, SA (label believed to be incorrect, species probably from QLD), see Cockerell, T.D.A. (1929). Bees, chiefly Australian species, described or determined by Dr. H. Friese. *Am. Mus. Novit.* **343**: 1–20 [13].

Taxonomic decision for synonymy: Cockerell, T.D.A. (1929). Bees, chiefly Australian species, described or determined by Dr. H. Friese. *Am. Mus. Novit.* 343: 1–20 [13].

Distribution: NE coastal, QLD.

Ecology: larva—sedentary : adult—volant; melliferous, flower visiting record: *Aotus* Smith [Fabaceae], *Jacksonia* Smith [Fabaceae], *Leptospermum* Forster & G.Forster [Myrtaceae], *Melaleuca* L. [Myrtaceae], *Pultenaea* Sm. [Fabaceae].

References: Cockerell, T.D.A. (1933). The bees of Australia. *Aust. Zool.* 7: 291–324 (taxonomy); Michener, C.D. (1960). Notes on the biology and supposed parthenogenesis of halictine bees from the Australian region. *J. Kansas Entomol. Soc.* 33: 85–96 (biology); Michener, C.D. (1965). A classification of the bees of the Australian and South Pacific regions. *Bull. Am. Mus. Nat. Hist.* 130: 1–362 (flower record).

Lasioglossum (Chilalictus) gunbowerense (Rayment, 1939)

Halictus gunbowerensis Rayment, T. (1939). Bees from the high lands of New South Wales and Victoria. *Aust. Zool.* 9: 263–294 [280].
Type data: holotype, ANIC ♀.
Type locality: Gunbower Is., VIC.

Distribution: Murray-Darling basin, VIC; known only from type locality.

Ecology: adult—volant; melliferous, solitary.

Lasioglossum (Chilalictus) gynochilum Michener, 1965

Lasioglossum (Chilalictus) gynochilum Michener, C.D. (1965). A classification of the bees of the Australian and South Pacific regions. *Bull. Am. Mus. Nat. Hist.* 130: 1–362 [314].
Type data: holotype, ANIC ♀.
Type locality: Helidon, QLD.

Distribution: NE coastal, Murray-Darling basin, QLD; only published localities Helidon and Clifton.

Ecology: adult—volant; melliferous, flower visiting record: *Wahlenbergia* Roth [Campanulaceae].

Lasioglossum (Chilalictus) haematopum (Cockerell, 1914)

Halictus haematopus Cockerell, T.D.A. (1914). Some Tasmanian bees. *Entomologist* 47: 305–308 [307].
Type data: holotype, BMNH Hym.17.a.989 ♂.
Type locality: Launceston, TAS.

Distribution: NE coastal, QLD, TAS; only published localities Brisbane and Launceston.

Ecology: adult—volant; melliferous, flower visiting record: *Eucalyptus* L'Hérit. [Myrtaceae], *Eugenia* L. [Myrtaceae].

References: Cockerell, T.D.A. (1915). Descriptions and records of bees. LXIX. *Ann. Mag. Nat. Hist.* (8)16: 96–104 (taxonomy); Michener, C.D. (1965). A classification of the bees of the Australian and South Pacific regions. *Bull. Am. Mus. Nat. Hist.* 130: 1–362 (flower record).

Lasioglossum (Chilalictus) haematostoma (Cockerell, 1914)

Halictus haematostoma Cockerell, T.D.A. (1914). Descriptions and records of bees. LIX. *Ann. Mag. Nat. Hist.* (8)13: 504–522 [506].
Type data: holotype, USNM ♂*.
Type locality: Windsor, VIC.

Distribution: SE coastal, VIC; known only from type locality.

Ecology: adult—volant; melliferous, solitary.

Lasioglossum (Chilalictus) helichrysi (Cockerell, 1914)

Halictus helichrysi Cockerell, T.D.A. (1914). Descriptions and records of bees. LIX. *Ann. Mag. Nat. Hist.* (8)13: 504–522 [515].
Type data: holotype (probable), QM Hy4123 ♀.
Type locality: Mt Tamborine, QLD.

Distribution: NE coastal, QLD; only published localities Mt Tamborine and Brisbane.

Ecology: adult—volant; melliferous, flower visiting record: *Helichrysum* Miller *s.lat.* [Asteraceae].

Reference: Cockerell, T.D.A. (1933). The bees of Australia. *Aust. Zool.* 7: 291–324 (taxonomy).

Lasioglossum (Chilalictus) hemichalceum (Cockerell, 1923)

Halictus hemichalceus Cockerell, T.D.A. (1923). Descriptions and records of bees. XCVIII. *Ann. Mag. Nat. Hist.* (9)12: 238–247 [239].
Type data: holotype, QM Hy2743 ♀.
Type locality: Brisbane, QLD.

Distribution: NE coastal, QLD; known only from type locality.

Ecology: larva—sedentary : adult—volant; melliferous, solitary.

References: Cockerell, T.D.A. (1933). The bees of Australia. *Aust. Zool.* 7: 291–324 (taxonomy, 1932 reference given in this paper was not found); Kukuk, P.F. & Crozier, R.H. (1990). Trophallaxis in a communal halictine bee *Lasioglossum (Chilalictus) erythrurum. Proc. Natl. Acad. Sci. U.S.A.* 87: 5402–5404 (biology).

Lasioglossum (Chilalictus) humei (Cockerell, 1905)

Halictus humei Cockerell, T.D.A. (1905). New Australian bees, in the collection of the British Museum. *Entomologist* 38: 270–273, 302–304 [303].
Type data: holotype, BMNH Hym.17.a.961 ♀.
Type locality: Australia.

Distribution: Australia, known only from type locality, exact locality unknown.

Ecology: adult—volant; melliferous, solitary.

Reference: Cockerell, T.D.A. (1933). The bees of Australia. *Aust. Zool.* **7**: 291–324 (taxonomy).

Lasioglossum (Chilalictus) idoneum (Cockerell, 1914)

Halictus idoneus Cockerell, T.D.A. (1914). Descriptions and records of bees. LIX. *Ann. Mag. Nat. Hist.* *(8)***13**: 504–522 [517].
Type data: holotype, Qm Hy4119 ♂.
Type locality: Brisbane, QLD.

Distribution: NE coastal, Murray-Darling basin, QLD, NSW; only published localities Brisbane, The Summit, Stanthorpe, Legume and Armidale.
Ecology: adult—volant; melliferous, flower visiting record: *Jacksonia* Smith [Fabaceae], *Pultenaea* Sm. [Fabaceae].
Reference: Michener, C.D. (1965). A classification of the bees of the Australian and South Pacific regions. *Bull. Am. Mus. Nat. Hist.* **130**: 1–362 (flower records).

Lasioglossum (Chilalictus) imitans (Cockerell, 1914)

Halictus imitans Cockerell, T.D.A. (1914). Descriptions and records of bees. LIX. *Ann. Mag. Nat. Hist.* *(8)***13**: 504–522 [516].
Type data: syntypes, BMNH 2♀ (a specimens is labelled 'type' and has registration number Hym.17.a.921).
Type locality: VIC.

Distribution: SE coastal, Murray-Darling basin, VIC, TAS; only published localities Gorae West, Mt Buffalo and George Town (as Georgetown).
Ecology: adult—volant; melliferous, flower visiting record: *Brachyscome* Cass. [Asteraceae], *Eucalyptus* L'Hérit. [Myrtaceae].
References: Cockerell, T.D.A. (1933). The bees of Australia. *Aust. Zool.* **7**: 291–324 (distribution); Rayment, T. (1936). Biology of a new halictine bee and specific descriptions of its parasites. *Arb. Physiol. Ang. Entomol. Berl.* **3**: 289–294 (illustration); Rayment, T. (1947). Bees from the Victorian Alps. *Vict. Nat.* **64**: 103–107 (distribution); Rayment, T. (1953). *Bees of the Portland District*. Victoria : Portland Field Naturalist's Club 39 pp. (flower record).

Lasioglossum (Chilalictus) inclinans (Smith, 1879)

Halictus inclinans Smith, F. (1879). *Descriptions of New Species of Hymenoptera in the Collection of the British Museum.* London : British Museum xxi 240 pp. [36].
Type data: holotype, BMNH Hym.17.a.908 ♀.
Type locality: Champion Bay (Geraldton), WA.

Distribution: Murray-Darling basin, SE coastal, NW coastal, ACT, VIC, WA, TAS.
Ecology: larva—sedentary : adult—volant; melliferous, nest communally in soil, flower visiting record: *Helichrysum* Miller *s.lat.* [Asteraceae].
References: Cockerell, T.D.A. (1912). Descriptions

and records of bees. XLIII. *Ann. Mag. Nat. Hist.* *(8)***9**: 377–387 (distribution); Rayment, T. (1953). New bees and wasps, Part XX. *Vict. Nat.* **70**: 68–71 (distribution); Knerer, G. & Schwarz, M. (1976). Halictine social evolution : the Australian enigma. *Science* **194**: 445–448 (biology); Knerer, G. & Schwarz, M. (1978). Beobachtungen an australischen Furchenbienen (Hymenopteren; Halictinae). *Zool. Anz.* **200**: 321–333 (biology).

Lasioglossum (Chilalictus) infimum (Erichson, 1842)

Andrena infima Erichson, W.F. (1842). Beitrag zur Fauna von Vandiemensland mit besonderer Rücksicht auf die geographische Verbreitung der Insekten. *Arch. Naturg.* **8**: 83–287 [268].
Type data: holotype (probable), whereabouts unknown ♂*.
Type locality: TAS (as Van Diemens Land).

Distribution: TAS; known only from type locality.
Ecology: adult—volant; melliferous, solitary.
References: Alfken, J.D. (1907). Apidae. pp. 259–261 *in* Michaelsen, W. & Hartmeyer, R. (eds) *Die Fauna Südwest-Australiens.* Jena : G. Fischer Bd 1 Lfg 6 (misidentification, suggests synonymy with *Leioproctus advena* (Smith, 1862)); Cockerell, T.D.A. (1933). The bees of Australia. *Aust. Zool.* **7**: 291–324 (taxonomy, suggests *Halictus lanarius* Smith, 1853 may be a synonym).

Lasioglossum (Chilalictus) infrahirtum (Cockerell, 1920)

Parasphecodes infrahirtus Cockerell, T.D.A. (1920). Descriptions and records of bees. LXXXVIII. *Ann. Mag. Nat. Hist. (9)* **5**: 113–119 [118].
Type data: holotype, USNM ♂*.
Type locality: Launceston, TAS.

Halictus obscuripes Friese, H. (1924). Ueber die Bienen Australiens. *Konowia* **3**: 216–249 [242] [junior primary homonym of *Halictus obscuripes* Friese, 1916].
Type data: syntypes (probable), AMNH ♂* (number of specimens unknown).
Type locality: Adelaide, SA.

Taxonomic decision for synonymy: Cockerell, T.D.A. (1929). Bees, chiefly Australian species, described or determined by Dr. H. Friese. *Am. Mus. Novit.* **343**: 1–20 [14].

Distribution: S Gulfs, SA, TAS; only published localities Adelaide and Launceston.
Ecology: adult—volant; melliferous, solitary.

Lasioglossum (Chilalictus) instabilis (Cockerell, 1914)

Halictus instabilis Cockerell, T.D.A. (1914). Descriptions and records of bees. LIX. *Ann. Mag. Nat. Hist.* *(8)***13**: 504–522 [510].
Type data: holotype, USNM ♀*.
Type locality: Croydon, VIC.

Distribution: SE coastal, VIC; only published localities Croydon, Gorae West and Windsor.
Ecology: adult—volant; melliferous, solitary.
Reference: Rayment, T. (1953). *Bees of the Portland District.* Victoria : Portland Field Naturalist's Club 39 pp. (distribution).

Lasioglossum (Chilalictus) isthmale (Cockerell, 1914)

Halictus isthmalis Cockerell, T.D.A. (1914). Descriptions and records of bees. LXIII. *Ann. Mag. Nat. Hist. (8)*14: 361–369 [367].
Type data: holotype, BMNH Hym.17.a.929 ♂.
Type locality: Eaglehawk Neck, TAS.

Distribution: TAS; only published localities Eaglehawk Neck and Mt Wellington.
Ecology: adult—volant; melliferous, solitary.
References: Cockerell, T.D.A. (1915). Descriptions and records of bees. LXIX. *Ann. Mag. Nat. Hist. (8)*16: 96–104 (description of female); Cockerell, T.D.A. (1916). A collection of bees from Queensland. *Mem. Qd Mus.* 5: 197–204 (taxonomy).

Lasioglossum (Chilalictus) lanariellum (Cockerell, 1916)

Halictus lanariellus Cockerell, T.D.A. (1916). Some bees from Australia, Tasmania, and the New Hebrides. *Proc. Acad. Nat. Sci. Philad.* 68: 360–375 [373].
Type data: holotype, BMNH Hym.17.a.958 ♀.
Type locality: Yarrawin, NSW.

Distribution: SE coastal, Murray-Darling basin, NSW, VIC; only published localities Middle Harbour, Yarrawin, Gippsland, Portland and Kewell.
Ecology: adult—volant; melliferous, flower visiting record: *Eucalyptus* L'Hérit. [Myrtaceae], *Hypochaeris* L. [Asteraceae].
References: Cockerell, T.D.A. (1926). Descriptions and records of bees. CXII. *Ann. Mag. Nat. Hist. (9)*18: 216–227 (distribution); Cockerell, T.D.A. (1929). Bees in the Australian Museum collection. *Rec. Aust. Mus.* 17: 199–243 (description of male); Rayment, T. (1930). The pioneers. *Vict. Nat.* 46: 221–223 (flower record); Rayment, T. (1953). *Bees of the Portland District.* Victoria : Portland Field Naturalist's Club 39 pp. (distribution).

Lasioglossum (Chilalictus) lanarium (Smith, 1853)

Halictus lanarius Smith, F. (1853). *Catalogue of Hymenopterous Insects in the Collection of the British Museum.* Part I. Andrenidae and Apidae. London : British Museum 197 pp. [57].
Type data: holotype, BMNH Hym.17.a.894 ♀.
Type locality: Hunter River, NSW.
Halictus lanuginosus Smith, F. (1879). *Descriptions of New Species of Hymenoptera in the Collection of the British Museum.* London : British Museum xxi 240 pp. [34].
Type data: syntypes, BMNH ♂♀ (a male specimen is labelled 'type' and has registration number Hym.17.a.901).
Type locality: Australia.

Taxonomic decision for synonymy: Cockerell, T.D.A. (1913). A small collection of bees from Tasmania. *Proc. Linn. Soc. N.S.W.* 37: 596–599 [597].

Distribution: NE coastal, SE coastal, Murray-Darling basin, S Gulfs, QLD, NSW, ACT, VIC, SA, (WA), TAS.
Ecology: larva—sedentary : adult—volant; melliferous, nest communally in soil, sometimes in aggregations, flower visiting record: *Coreopsis* L. [Asteraceae], *Dahlia* Cav. [Asteraceae], *Diuris* Sm. [Orchidaceae], *Eucalyptus* L'Hérit. [Myrtaceae], *Hibbertia* Andrews [Dilleniaceae], *Hypochaeris* L. [Asteraceae], *Jacksonia* Smith [Fabaceae], *Leptospermum* Forster & G.Forster [Myrtaceae], *Pultenaea* Sm. [Fabaceae], *Senecio* L. [Asteraceae], *Taraxacum* G.Weber [Asteraceae], *Veronica* L. [Scrophulariaceae], *Wahlenbergia* Roth [Campanulaceae].
References: Cockerell, T.D.A. (1910). New and little-known bees. *Trans. Am. Entomol. Soc.* 36: 199–249 (taxonomy); Coleman, E. (1932). Pollination of *Diuris pedunculata* R. Br. *Vict. Nat.* 49: 179–186 (flower record, as *Halictus languinosus*, incorrect subsequent spelling); Coleman, E. (1933). Further notes on the pollination of *Diuris pedunculata* R. Br. *Vict. Nat.* 49: 243–245 (flower record, as *Halictus languinosus*, incorrect subsequent spelling); Rayment, T. (1935). *A Cluster of Bees.* Sixty essays on the life-histories of Australian bees, with specific descriptions of over 100 new species, and an introduction by Professor E.F. Phillips, D.Ph., Cornell University, U.S.A. Sydney : Endeavour Press 752 pp. (biology); Rayment, T. (1953). *Bees of the Portland District.* Victoria : Portland Field Naturalist's Club 39 pp. (flower record); Michener, C.D. (1960). Notes on the biology and supposed parthenogenesis of halictine bees from the Australian region. *J. Kansas Entomol. Soc.* 33: 85–96 (biology); Michener, C.D. (1965). A classification of the bees of the Australian and South Pacific regions. *Bull. Am. Mus. Nat. Hist.* 130: 1–362 (flower record, as *Lasioglossum languinosum*, incorrect subsequent spelling); Knerer, G. & Schwarz, M. (1976). Halictine social evolution : the Australian enigma. *Science* 194: 445–448 (biology); Knerer, G. & Schwarz, M. (1978). Beobachtungen an australischen Furchenbienen (Hymenopteren; Halictinae). *Zool. Anz.* 200: 321–333 (biology); Walker, K.L. (1986). Revision of the Australian species of the genus *Homalictus* Cockerell (Hymenoptera : Halictidae). *Mem. Mus. Vict.* 47: 105–200 (biology); Morris, B., Southcott, R.V. & Gale, A.E. (1988). Effects of stings of Australian native bees. *Med. J. Aust.* 149: 707–709 (possibly responsible for allergic response and death, of man).

Lasioglossum (Chilalictus) leai (Cockerell, 1910)

Halictus leai Cockerell, T.D.A. (1910). New and little-known bees. *Trans. Am. Entomol. Soc.* **36**: 199–249 [237].
Type data: holotype, BMNH Hym.17.a.968 ♀.
Type locality: VIC.

Distribution: NE coastal, SE coastal, QLD, VIC.
Ecology: larva—sedentary : adult—volant; melliferous, nest gregariously in soil, some nests with more than one female, flower visiting record: easter daisy, *Eucalyptus* L'Hérit. [Myrtaceae], *Leptospermum* Forster & G.Forster [Myrtaceae], *Melaleuca* L. [Myrtaceae].
References: Cockerell, T.D.A. (1913). Some Australian bees. *Proc. Acad. Nat. Sci. Philad.* **65**: 28–44 (taxonomy); Cockerell, T.D.A. (1914). Descriptions and records of bees. LIX. *Ann. Mag. Nat. Hist.* (8)**13**: 504–522 (as variety of *Halictus bicingulatus* Smith, 1853); Rayment, T. (1953). *Bees of the Portland District*. Victoria : Portland Field Naturalist's Club 39 pp. (flower record); Rayment, T. (1954). Fungi and bees. *Vict. Nat.* **70**: 230–231 (as host); Rayment, T. (1954). Incidence of acarid mites on the biology of bees. *Aust. Zool.* **12**: 26–38 (biology); Rayment, T. (1955). Dimorphism and parthenogenesis in halictine bees. *Aust. Zool.* **12**: 142–153 (biology); Michener, C.D. (1965). A classification of the bees of the Australian and South Pacific regions. *Bull. Am. Mus. Nat. Hist.* **130**: 1–362 (flower record); Cardale, J.C. & Turner, J.W. (1966). Nest structure and biology of *Halictus leai* Cockerell (Hymenoptera : Halictidae). *Proc. R. Soc. Qd* **77**: 93–97 (biology).

Lasioglossum (Chilalictus) littleri (Cockerell, 1914)

Halictus littleri Cockerell, T.D.A. (1914). Some Tasmanian bees. *Entomologist* **47**: 305–308 [307].
Type data: holotype, USNM ♀*.
Type locality: Launceston, TAS.

Distribution: SE coastal, VIC, TAS; only published localities Gorae West, Mt Clay and Launceston.
Ecology: larva—sedentary : adult—volant; melliferous, nest communally in soil, flower visiting record: aster, *Eucalyptus* L'Hérit. [Myrtaceae], *Leptospermum* Forster & G.Forster [Myrtaceae].
References: Rayment, T. (1953). *Bees of the Portland District*. Victoria : Portland Field Naturalist's Club 39 pp. (description of male, flower record); Rayment, T. (1954). Incidence of acarid mites on the biology of bees. *Aust. Zool.* **12**: 26–38 (biology).

Lasioglossum (Chilalictus) luctificum (Cockerell, 1930)

Halictus luctificus Cockerell, T.D.A. (1930). New Australian bees. *Mem. Qd Mus.* **10**: 37–50 [46].
Type data: holotype, ANIC ♀.
Type locality: Launceston, TAS.

Distribution: TAS; known only from type locality.
Ecology: adult—volant; melliferous, solitary.

Lasioglossum (Chilalictus) macrops (Cockerell, 1916)

Halictus macrops Cockerell, T.D.A. (1916). Some bees from Australia, Tasmania, and the New Hebrides. *Proc. Acad. Nat. Sci. Philad.* **68**: 360–375 [373].
Type data: holotype, BMNH Hym.17.a.947 ♂.
Type locality: Launceston, TAS.

Distribution: TAS; known only from type locality.
Ecology: adult—volant; melliferous, solitary.
Reference: Cockerell, T.D.A. (1929). Bees from the Australian region. *Am. Mus. Novit.* **346**: 1–18 (taxonomy).

Lasioglossum (Chilalictus) maiusculum (Rayment, 1930)

Halictus erythrurus maiusculus Rayment, T. (1930). Notes on a collection of bees from Western Australia. *J. Proc. R. Soc. West. Aust.* **16**: 45–56 [53].
Type data: holotype, ANIC ♀.
Type locality: Perth, WA.

Distribution: SW coastal, WA; known only from type locality.
Ecology: adult—volant; melliferous, solitary.
Reference: Rayment, T. (1935). *A Cluster of Bees*. Sixty essays on the life-histories of Australian bees, with specific descriptions of over 100 new species, and an introduction by Professor E.F. Phillips, D.Ph., Cornell University, U.S.A. Sydney : Endeavour Press 752 pp. (taxonomy).

Lasioglossum (Chilalictus) mediopolitum (Cockerell, 1914)

Halictus mediopolitus Cockerell, T.D.A. (1914). Descriptions and records of bees. LIX. *Ann. Mag. Nat. Hist.* (8)**13**: 504–522 [518].
Type data: syntypes (probable), USNM 3♀*.
Type locality: Purnong, SA.

Distribution: Murray-Darling basin, SA; known only from type locality.
Ecology: adult—volant; melliferous, solitary.

Lasioglossum (Chilalictus) melanopterum (Cockerell, 1914)

Halictus melanopterus Cockèrell, T.D.A. (1914). Australian halictine bees. *Entomologist* **47**: 242–244 [243].
Type data: holotype, BMNH Hym.17.a.909 ♀.
Type locality: Yallingup, WA.

Distribution: SW coastal, WA; known only from type locality.
Ecology: adult—volant; melliferous, solitary.
Reference: Rayment, T. (1935). *A Cluster of Bees*. Sixty essays on the life-histories of Australian bees, with specific descriptions of over 100 new species, and an introduction by Professor E.F. Phillips, D.Ph.,

Cornell University, U.S.A. Sydney : Endeavour Press 752 pp. (illustration).

Lasioglossum (Chilalictus) mesembryanthemi (Cockerell, 1926)

Halictus mesembryanthemi Cockerell, T.D.A. (1926). New halictine bees from Australia. *Entomologist* **59**: 246–247 [246].
Type data: holotype, USNM ♀*.
Type locality: Port Phillip, VIC.

Distribution: NE coastal, SE coastal, QLD, VIC.
Ecology: larva—sedentary : adult—volant; melliferous, nest communally in soil, males cluster, flower visiting record: *Arctotheca* Wendl. [Asteraceae], *Carpobrotus* N.E. Br. [Aizoaceae], *Mesembryanthemum* L. [Aizoaceae], *Veronica* L. [Scrophulariaccac].
References: Cockerell, T.D.A. (1929). Bees in the Queensland Museum. *Mem. Qd Mus.* **9**: 298–323 (distribution); Cockerell, T.D.A. (1929). Bees from the Australian region. *Am. Mus. Novit.* **346**: 1–18 (distribution); Cockerell, T.D.A. (1930). Australian bees in the Museum of Comparative Zoology. *Psyche (Camb.)* **37**: 141–154 (distribution); Rayment, T. (1935). *A Cluster of Bees.* Sixty essays on the life-histories of Australian bees, with specific descriptions of over 100 new species, and an introduction by Professor E.F. Phillips, D.Ph., Cornell University, U.S.A. Sydney : Endeavour Press 752 pp. (biology); Rayment, T. (1953). *Bees of the Portland District.* Victoria : Portland Field Naturalist's Club 39 pp. (flower record).

Lasioglossum (Chilalictus) mesembryanthemiellum (Rayment, 1935)

Halictus mesembryanthemiellus Rayment, T. (1935). *A Cluster of Bees.* Sixty essays on the life-histories of Australian bees, with specific descriptions of over 100 new species, and an introduction by Professor E.F. Phillips, D.Ph., Cornell University, U.S.A. Sydney : Endeavour Press 752 pp. [699].
Type data: holotype, ANIC ♀.
Type locality: Sandringham, VIC.

Distribution: SE coastal, VIC; only published localities Sandringham, Studley Park, Emerald and Portland.
Ecology: larva—sedentary : adult—volant; melliferous, nest gregariously and communally in soil, flower visiting record: chrysanthemum, marguerites, *Goodenia* Sm. [Goodeniaceae], *Hypochaeris* L. [Asteraceae], *Lobelia* L. [Campanulaceae], *Mesembryanthemum* L. [Aizoaceae], *Veronica* L. [Scrophulariaceae].
References: Rayment, T. (1953). *Bees of the Portland District.* Victoria : Portland Field Naturalist's Club 39 pp. (distribution); Knerer, G. & Schwarz, M. (1978). Beobachtungen an australischen Furchenbienen (Hymenopteren; Halictinae). *Zool. Anz.* **200**: 321–333 (biology); Knerer, G. (1980).

Evolution of halictine castes. *Naturwissensch.* **67**: 133–135 (biology).

Lasioglossum (Chilalictus) micridoneum (Cockerell, 1930)

Halictus micridoneus Cockerell, T.D.A. (1930). New Australian bees. *Mem. Qd Mus.* **10**: 37–50 [43].
Type data: holotype, QM Hy4039 ♂.
Type locality: Brisbane, QLD.

Distribution: NE coastal, QLD; known only from type locality.
Ecology: adult—volant; melliferous, solitary.

Lasioglossum (Chilalictus) milleri (Rayment, 1935)

Halictus milleri Rayment, T. (1935). *A Cluster of Bees.* Sixty essays on the life-histories of Australian bees, with specific descriptions of over 100 new species, and an introduction by Professor E.F. Phillips, D.Ph., Cornell University, U.S.A. Sydney : Endeavour Press 752 pp. [709].
Type data: holotype, ANIC ♀.
Type locality: Bayswater, VIC.

Distribution: SE coastal, VIC; known only from type locality.
Ecology: adult—volant; melliferous, solitary.

Lasioglossum (Chilalictus) mirandum (Cockerell, 1914)

Halictus mirandus Cockerell, T.D.A. (1914). Descriptions and records of bees. LX. *Ann. Mag. Nat. Hist. (8)***14**: 1–13 [8].
Type data: syntypes, BMNH 4♀ (a specimen is labelled 'type' and has registration number Hym.17.a.971).
Type locality: Yallingup, WA.

Distribution: SW coastal, WA; known only from type locality.
Ecology: adult—volant; melliferous, solitary.

Lasioglossum (Chilalictus) mitchelli (Cockerell, 1906)

Halictus mitchelli Cockerell, T.D.A. (1906). New Australian bees in the collection of the British Museum. II. *Entomologist* **39**: 56–60 [58].
Type data: holotype, BMNH Hym.17.a.933 ♀.
Type locality: Hobart, TAS.

Distribution: TAS; known only from type locality.
Ecology: adult—volant; melliferous, solitary.

Lasioglossum (Chilalictus) moreense (Cockerell, 1930)

Halictus moreensis Cockerell, T.D.A. (1930). New Australian bees. *Mem. Qd Mus.* **10**: 37–50 [40].
Type data: holotype, QM Hy5001 ♀.
Type locality: Moree, NSW.

Distribution: Murray-Darling basin, NSW; known only from type locality.
Ecology: adult—volant; melliferous, solitary.

Lasioglossum (Chilalictus) mundulum (Cockerell, 1916)

Halictus mundulus Cockerell, T.D.A. (1916). Some bees from Australia, Tasmania and the New Hebrides. *Proc. Acad. Nat. Sci. Philad.* **68**: 360–375 [366].
Type data: holotype, BMNH Hym.17.a.939 ♀.
Type locality: Kalamunda, WA.

Distribution: SW coastal, WA; known only from type locality.
Ecology: adult—volant; melliferous, solitary.

Lasioglossum (Chilalictus) nigropolitum (Cockerell, 1929)

Halictus nigropolitus Cockerell, T.D.A. (1929). Bees from the Australian region. *Am. Mus. Novit.* **346**: 1–18 [3].
Type data: holotype, BMNH Hym.17.a.990 ♀.
Type locality: Darwin, NT.

Distribution: N coastal, NT; known only from type locality.
Ecology: adult—volant; melliferous, solitary.

Lasioglossum (Chilalictus) nigropurpureum (Rayment, 1935)

Halictus nigropurpureus Rayment, T. (1935). *A Cluster of Bees.* Sixty essays on the life-histories of Australian bees, with specific descriptions of over 100 new species, and an introduction by Professor E.F. Phillips, D.Ph., Cornell University, U.S.A. Sydney : Endeavour Press 752 pp. [701].
Type data: holotype, ANIC ♀.
Type locality: Sandringham, VIC.

Distribution: SE coastal, VIC; known only from type locality.
Ecology: adult—volant; melliferous, solitary.

Lasioglossum (Chilalictus) nudum (Rayment, 1935)

Halictus seductus nudus Rayment, T. (1935). *A Cluster of Bees.* Sixty essays on the life-histories of Australian bees, with specific descriptions of over 100 new species, and an introduction by Professor E.F. Phillips, D.Ph., Cornell University, U.S.A. Sydney : Endeavour Press 752 pp. [706].
Type data: holotype, ANIC ♀.
Type locality: Sorrento, Port Phillip, VIC.

Distribution: SE coastal, VIC; known only from type locality.
Ecology: adult—volant; melliferous, solitary.
Reference: Michener, C.D. (1965). A classification of the bees of the Australian and South Pacific regions. *Bull. Am. Mus. Nat. Hist.* **130**: 1–362 [177] (taxonomy).

Lasioglossum (Chilalictus) oblitum (Smith, 1879)

Halictus oblitus Smith, F. (1879). *Descriptions of New Species of Hymenoptera in the Collection of the British Museum.* London : British Museum xxi 240 pp. [35].

Type data: holotype, BMNH Hym.17.a.903 ♀.
Type locality: Swan River, WA.

Distribution: SW coastal, WA; only published localities Swan River and Serpentine.
Ecology: adult—volant; melliferous, solitary.
References: Cockerell, T.D.A. (1904). The halictine bees of the Australian region. *Ann. Mag. Nat. Hist. (7)***14**: 208–213 (taxonomy); Alfken, J.D. (1907). Apidae. pp. 259–261 *in* Michaelsen, W. & Hartmeyer, R. (eds) *Die Fauna Südwest-Australiens.* Jena : G. Fischer Bd 1 Lfg 6 (distribution).

Lasioglossum (Chilalictus) obscurissimum Michener, 1965

Lasioglossum (Chilalictus) obscurissimum Michener, C.D. (1965). A classification of the bees of the Australian and South Pacific regions. *Bull. Am. Mus. Nat. Hist.* **130**: 1–362 [315].
Type data: holotype, ANIC ♀.
Type locality: Helidon, QLD.

Distribution: NE coastal, Murray-Darling basin, QLD; only published localities Helidon, Warwick and near Stanthorpe.
Ecology: adult—volant; melliferous, flower visiting record: *Wahlenbergia* Roth [Campanulaceae].

Lasioglossum (Chilalictus) omnivagum (Rayment, 1935)

Halictus omnivagus Rayment, T. (1935). *A Cluster of Bees.* Sixty essays on the life-histories of Australian bees, with specific descriptions of over 100 new species, and an introduction by Professor E.F. Phillips, D.Ph., Cornell University, U.S.A. Sydney : Endeavour Press 752 pp. [705].
Type data: syntypes, ANIC ♀, NMV 2♀.
Type locality: Kiata, Grampians and Carrum, VIC.

Distribution: Murray-Darling basin, VIC; only published localities Kiata, Grampians and Carrum.
Ecology: adult—volant; melliferous, solitary.

Lasioglossum (Chilalictus) opacicolle (Cockerell, 1914)

Halictus opacicollis Cockerell, T.D.A. (1914). Descriptions and records of bees. LIX. *Ann. Mag. Nat. Hist. (8)***13**: 504–522 [519].
Type data: holotype, BMNH Hym.17.a.918 ♀.
Type locality: VIC.

Distribution: SE coastal, VIC, TAS; only published localities Portland and Hobart.
Ecology: adult—volant; melliferous, flower visiting record: aster, *Lythrum* L. [Lythraceae].
References: Cockerell, T.D.A. (1932). Bees collected by Charles Darwin on the voyage of the "Beagle". *J. N.Y. Entomol. Soc.* **40**: 519–522 (distribution); Rayment, T. (1953). *Bees of the Portland District.* Victoria : Portland Field Naturalist's Club 39 pp. (distribution).

Lasioglossum (Chilalictus) orbatum (Smith, 1853)

Halictus orbatus Smith, F. (1853). *Catalogue of Hymenopterous Insects in the Collection of the British Museum.* Part I. Andrenidae and Apidae. London : British Museum 197 pp. [58].
Type data: holotype (probable), whereabouts unknown (Baly coll.) ♀*.
Type locality: TAS (as Van Diemens Land).

Distribution: NE coastal, SE coastal, Murray-Darling basin, QLD, NSW, VIC, TAS.
Ecology: larva—sedentary : adult—volant; melliferous, flower visiting record: fruit blossom, *Daviesia* Sm. [Fabaceae], *Hypòchaeris* L. [Asteraceae], *Jacksonia* Smith [Fabaceae], *Pultenaea* Sm. [Fabaceae], *Swainsona* Salisb. [Fabaceae].
References: Cockerell, T.D.A. (1914). Descriptions and records of bees. LIX. *Ann. Mag. Nat. Hist. (8)***13**: 504–522 (distribution); Rayment, T. (1934). Contributions to the fauna of Rottnest Island. VIII. Apoidea. With description of new species. *J. Proc. R. Soc. West. Aust.* **20**: 201–212 (doubtful record, from Rottnest Is.); Rayment, T. (1935). *A Cluster of Bees.* Sixty essays on the life-histories of Australian bees, with specific descriptions of over 100 new species, and an introduction by Professor E.F. Phillips, D.Ph., Cornell University, U.S.A. Sydney : Endeavour Press 752 pp. (description of male); Michener, C.D. (1960). Notes on the biology and supposed parthenogenesis of halictine bees from the Australian region. *J. Kansas Entomol. Soc.* **33**: 85–96 (biology).

Lasioglossum (Chilalictus) ornatum (Rayment, 1935)

Halictus ornatus Rayment, T. (1935). *A Cluster of Bees.* Sixty essays on the life-histories of Australian bees, with specific descriptions of over 100 new species, and an introduction by Professor E.F. Phillips, D.Ph., Cornell University, U.S.A. Sydney : Endeavour Press 752 pp. [691].
Type data: holotype, ANIC ♂.
Type locality: Sandringham, VIC.

Distribution: SE coastal, VIC; known only from type locality.
Ecology: adult—volant; melliferous, flower visiting record: *Eucalyptus* L'Hérit. [Myrtaceae].

Lasioglossum (Chilalictus) pachycephalum (Cockerell, 1916)

Halictus pachycephalus Cockerell, T.D.A. (1916). Some bees from Australia, Tasmania, and the New Hebrides. *Proc. Acad. Nat. Sci. Philad.* **68**: 360–375 [369].
Type data: holotype, BMNH Hym.17.a.986 ♂.
Type locality: Yarrawin, NSW.

Distribution: Murray-Darling basin, NSW; known only from type locality.
Ecology: adult—volant; melliferous, solitary.

Lasioglossum (Chilalictus) percingulatum (Rayment, 1935)

Halictus percingulatus Rayment, T. (1935). *A Cluster of Bees.* Sixty essays on the life-histories of Australian bees, with specific descriptions of over 100 new species, and an introduction by Professor E.F. Phillips, D.Ph., Cornell University, U.S.A. Sydney : Endeavour Press 752 pp. [708].
Type data: holotype, whereabouts unknown (T. Rayment, pers. coll., not found in ANIC) ♀*.
Type locality: Sandringham, VIC.

Distribution: SE coastal, VIC; only published localities Sandringham and Ferntree Gully.
Ecology: adult—volant; melliferous, solitary.

Lasioglossum (Chilalictus) platycephalum (Rayment, 1927)

Halictus platycephalus Rayment, T. (1927). A new Halictine bee. *Halictus platycephalus*, sp.n. *Vict. Nat.* **44**: 101–102 [101].
Type data: holotype (probable), ANIC ♀.
Type locality: Sandringham, Port Phillip, VIC.

Distribution: SE coastal, VIC; known only from type locality.
Ecology: adult—volant; melliferous, flower visiting record: *Goodenia* Sm. [Goodeniaceae], *Olearia* Moench [Asteraceae].
References: Cockerell, T.D.A. (1933). The bees of Australia. *Aust. Zool.* **7**: 291–324 (taxonomy); Rayment, T. (1935). *A Cluster of Bees.* Sixty essays on the life-histories of Australian bees, with specific descriptions of over 100 new species, and an introduction by Professor E.F. Phillips, D.Ph., Cornell University, U.S.A. Sydney : Endeavour Press 752 pp. (illustration).

Lasioglossum (Chilalictus) plebeium (Cockerell, 1914)

Halictus plebeius Cockerell, T.D.A. (1914). Descriptions and records of bees. LIX. *Ann. Mag. Nat. Hist. (8)***13**: 504–522 [517].
Type data: holotype, BMNH Hym.17.a.962 ♀.
Type locality: Purnong, SA.

Distribution: SE coastal, Murray-Darling basin, VIC, SA; only published localities Portland and Purnong.
Ecology: adult—volant; melliferous, flower visiting record: *Pultenaea* Sm. [Fabaceae].
Reference: Rayment, T. (1953). *Bees of the Portland District.* Victoria : Portland Field Naturalist's Club 39 pp. (distribution).

Lasioglossum (Chilalictus) pulvitectum (Cockerell, 1915)

Halictus pulvitectus Cockerell, T.D.A. (1915). Descriptions and records of bees. LXIX. *Ann. Mag. Nat. Hist. (8)***16**: 96–104 [98].

Type data: holotype, BMNH Hym.17.a.922 ♀.
Type locality: Eaglehawk Neck, TAS.

Distribution: NE coastal, SE coastal, QLD, NSW, VIC, TAS.
Ecology: adult—volant; melliferous, nest in soil, flower visiting record: *Aotus* Smith [Fabaceae], *Dillwynia* Sm. [Fabaceae].
References: Cockerell, T.D.A. (1933). The bees of Australia. *Aust. Zool.* **7**: 291–324 (taxonomy, record from Sandringham is not this species); Rayment, T. (1934). Contributions to the fauna of Rottnest Island. VIII. Apoidea. With description of new species. *J. Proc. R. Soc. West. Aust.* **20**: 201–212 (doubtful record, from Rottnest Is.); Rayment, T. (1953). *Bees of the Portland District*. Victoria : Portland Field Naturalist's Club 39 pp. (distribution); Michener, C.D. (1965). A classification of the bees of the Australian and South Pacific regions. *Bull. Am. Mus. Nat. Hist.* **130**: 1–362 (flower record).

Lasioglossum (Chilalictus) purnongense (Cockerell, 1913)

Halictus (Chloralictus) purnongensis Cockerell, T.D.A. (1913). Descriptions and records of bees. LI. *Ann. Mag. Nat. Hist. (8)***11**: 387–394 [393].
Type data: holotype, USNM ♂*.
Type locality: Purnong, SA.

Distribution: NE coastal, SE coastal, Murray-Darling basin, QLD, VIC, SA; only published localities Brisbane, Rainbow and Purnong.
Ecology: adult—volant; melliferous, solitary.
References: Cockerell, T.D.A. (1922). Australian bees in the Queensland Museum. *Mem. Qd Mus.* **7**: 257–279 (distribution); Evans, H.E. & Matthews, R.W. (1973). Systematics and nesting behavior of Australian *Bembix* sand wasps (Hymenoptera, Sphecidae). *Mem. Am. Entomol. Inst.* **20**: 1–387 (as prey).

Lasioglossum (Chilalictus) purpureum (Rayment, 1935)

Halictus doweri purpureus Rayment, T. (1935). *A Cluster of Bees*. Sixty essays on the life-histories of Australian bees, with specific descriptions of over 100 new species, and an introduction by Professor E.F. Phillips, D.Ph., Cornell University, U.S.A. Sydney : Endeavour Press 752 pp. [695] [a specimen in ANIC is labelled syntype].
Type data: syntypes, ANIC ♀ (number of specimens unknown).
Type locality: Malvern, E of Melbourne, VIC.

Distribution: SE coastal, VIC; known only from type locality.
Ecology: adult—volant; melliferous, solitary.
References: Michener, C.D. (1965). A classification of the bees of the Australian and South Pacific regions. *Bull. Am. Mus. Nat. Hist.* **130**: 1–362 (as *Homalictus purpureus* (Rayment, 1935), taxonomy); Walker, K.L. (1986). Revision of the Australian spe-

cies of the genus *Homalictus* Cockerell (Hymenoptera : Halictidae). *Mem. Mus. Vict.* **47**: 105–200 [168] (generic placement).

Lasioglossum (Chilalictus) repertum (Cockerell, 1914)

Halictus repertus Cockerell, T.D.A. (1914). Descriptions and records of bees. LIX. *Ann. Mag. Nat. Hist. (8)***13**: 504–522 [521].
Type data: holotype, BMNH Hym.17.a.952 ♂.
Type locality: near Melbourne, VIC.

Distribution: SE coastal, VIC, TAS; only published localities near Melbourne, Portland and Hobart.
Ecology: adult—volant; melliferous, flower visiting record: *Pultenaea* Sm. [Fabaceae].
References: Cockerell, T.D.A. (1932). Bees collected by Charles Darwin on the voyage of the "Beagle". *J. N.Y. Entomol. Soc.* **40**: 519–522 (distribution); Rayment, T. (1953). *Bees of the Portland District*. Victoria : Portland Field Naturalist's Club 39 pp. (distribution).

Lasioglossum (Chilalictus) repraesentans (Smith, 1853)

Halictus repraesentans Smith, F. (1853). *Catalogue of Hymenopterous Insects in the Collection of the British Museum. Part I. Andrenidae and Apidae*. London : British Museum 197 pp. [60].
Type data: syntypes, BMNH ♂♀ (a female specimen is labelled 'type' and has registration number Hym.17.a.895).
Type locality: Australia (as New Holland).

Distribution: SE coastal, VIC, TAS; only published localities Bacchus Marsh, Emerald, Portland and Hobart.
Ecology: adult—volant; melliferous, flower visiting record: *Arctotheca* Wendl. [Asteraceae].
References: Cockerell, T.D.A. (1904). The halictine bees of the Australian region. *Ann. Mag. Nat. Hist. (7)***14**: 208–213 (taxonomy); Cockerell, T.D.A. (1905). New Australian bees, in the collection of the British Museum. *Entomologist* **38**: 270–273, 302–304 (taxonomy); Cockerell, T.D.A. (1914). Descriptions and records of bees. LIX. *Ann. Mag. Nat. Hist. (8)***13**: 504–522 (distribution); Rayment, T. (1953). *Bees of the Portland District*. Victoria : Portland Field Naturalist's Club 39 pp. (flower record).

Lasioglossum (Chilalictus) rufotinctum (Cockerell, 1915)

Halictus rufotinctus Cockerell, T.D.A. (1915). Descriptions and records of bees. LXVIII. *Ann. Mag. Nat. Hist. (8)***16**: 1–9 [7].
Type data: holotype, QM Hy4120 ♀.
Type locality: Brisbane, QLD.

Distribution: NE coastal, S Gulfs, QLD, SA; only published localities Brisbane and Kadina.
Ecology: adult—volant; melliferous, solitary.

Reference: Morris, B., Southcott, R.V. & Gale, A.E. (1988). Effects of stings of Australian native bees. *Med. J. Aust.* **149**: 707–709 (possibly responsible for allergic response and death, of man).

Lasioglossum (Chilalictus) sanguinipes (Cockerell, 1914)

Halictus sanguinipes Cockerell, T.D.A. (1914). Descriptions and records of bees. LIX. *Ann. Mag. Nat. Hist. (8)***13**: 504–522 [513].
Type data: holotype, USNM ♂*.
Type locality: Windsor, VIC.

Distribution: SE coastal, NSW, VIC; only published localities White Swamp, Windsor, Emerald and Melbourne.
Ecology: adult—volant; melliferous, solitary.
Reference: Rayment, T. (1939). Bees from the high lands of New South Wales and Victoria. *Aust. Zool.* **9**: 263–294 (distribution).

Lasioglossum (Chilalictus) sculpturatum (Cockerell, 1930)

Halictus sculpturatus Cockerell, T.D.A. (1930). New Australian bees. *Mem. Qd Mus.* **10**: 37–50 [44].
Type data: holotype, QM Hy4037 ♂.
Type locality: Stradbroke Is., QLD.

Distribution: NE coastal, QLD; known only from type locality.
Ecology: adult—volant; melliferous, solitary.

Lasioglossum (Chilalictus) seductum (Cockerell, 1914)

Halictus seductus Cockerell, T.D.A. (1914). Descriptions and records of bees. LIX. *Ann. Mag. Nat. Hist. (8)***13**: 504–522 [512].
Type data: holotype, BMNH Hym.17.a.972 ♀.
Type locality: Windsor, VIC.

Distribution: SE coastal, VIC, TAS; only published localities Windsor, Sandringham, Launceston and Bridport.
Ecology: larva—sedentary : adult—volant; melliferous, nest in soil, flower visiting record: marguerites, rosemary, tree lucerne, *Acacia* Miller [Mimosaceae], *Arctotheca* Wendl. [Asteraceae], *Leucopogon* R.Br. [Epacridaceae], *Myoporum* Banks & Sol. ex G.Forster [Myoporaceae], *Veronica* L. [Scrophulariaceae].
References: Cockerell, T.D.A. (1929). Bees in the Australian Museum collection. *Rec. Aust. Mus.* **17**: 199–243 (distribution); Cockerell, T.D.A. (1933). The bees of Australia. *Aust. Zool.* **7**: 291–324 (distribution); Rayment, T. (1935). *A Cluster of Bees*. Sixty essays on the life-histories of Australian bees, with specific descriptions of over 100 new species, and an introduction by Professor E.F. Phillips, D.Ph., Cornell University, U.S.A. Sydney : Endeavour Press 752 pp. (biology); Michener, C.D. (1960). Notes on the biology and supposed parthenogenesis of halict-ine bees from the Australian region. *J. Kansas Entomol. Soc.* **33**: 85–96 (biology).

Lasioglossum (Chilalictus) seminitens (Cockerell, 1929)

Halictus seminitens Cockerell, T.D.A. (1929). Bees in the Australian Museum collection. *Rec. Aust. Mus.* **17**: 199–243 [230].
Type data: syntypes, AM 2♀.
Type locality: Wyalkatchem (as Wyalcatchem), WA.

Distribution: SW coastal, WA; known only from type locality.
Ecology: adult—volant; melliferous, solitary.

Lasioglossum (Chilalictus) spenceri (Cockerell, 1916)

Halictus spenceri Cockerell, T.D.A. (1916). Some bees from Australia, Tasmania, and the New Hebrides. *Proc. Acad. Nat. Sci. Philad.* **68**: 360–375 [368].
Type data: holotype, BMNH Hym.17.a.935 ♂.
Type locality: Yallingup, WA.

Distribution: SW coastal, WA; known only from type locality.
Ecology: adult—volant; melliferous, solitary.

Lasioglossum (Chilalictus) suberythrurum (Rayment, 1935)

Halictus suberythrurus Rayment, T. (1935). *A Cluster of Bees*. Sixty essays on the life-histories of Australian bees, with specific descriptions of over 100 new species, and an introduction by Professor E.F. Phillips, D.Ph., Cornell University, U.S.A. Sydney : Endeavour Press 752 pp. [691].
Type data: holotype, ANIC ♀.
Type locality: Balmoral, VIC.

Distribution: SE coastal, VIC; only published localities Balmoral and Portland.
Ecology: adult—volant; melliferous, flower visiting record: aster.
Reference: Rayment, T. (1953). *Bees of the Portland District*. Victoria : Portland Field Naturalist's Club 39 pp. (distribution).

Lasioglossum (Chilalictus) subetheridgei (Rayment, 1953)

Halictus subetheridgei Rayment, T. (1953). *Bees of the Portland District*. Victoria : Portland Field Naturalist's Club 39 pp. [23].
Type data: holotype, ANIC ♂.
Type locality: Gorae West, VIC.

Distribution: SE coastal, VIC; only published localities Gorae West and Emerald.
Ecology: adult—volant; melliferous, flower visiting record: *Eucalyptus* L'Hérit. [Myrtaceae], *Leptospermum* Forster & G.Forster [Myrtaceae].

Lasioglossum (Chilalictus) subinclinans (Cockerell, 1915)

Halictus subinclinans Cockerell, T.D.A. (1915). Descriptions and records of bees. LXVIII. *Ann. Mag. Nat. Hist. (8)***16**: 1–9 [8].
Type data: holotype, USNM ♀*.
Type locality: Launceston, TAS.

Distribution: Murray-Darling basin, SE coastal, S Gulfs, QLD, NSW, VIC, SA, TAS.
Ecology: larva—sedentary : adult—volant; melliferous, flower visiting record: aster, *Arctotheca* Wendl. [Asteraceae], *Caladenia* R.Br. [Orchidaceae], *Citrus* L. [Rutaceae], *Hypochaeris* L. [Asteraceae], *Jacksonia* Smith [Fabaceae], *Mesembryanthemum* L. [Aizoaceae], *Veronica* L. [Scrophulariaceae].
References: Cockerell, T.D.A. (1926). Descriptions and records of bees. CXII. *Ann. Mag. Nat. Hist. (9)***18**: 216–227 (taxonomy); Rogers, R.S. (1931). Pollination of *Caladenia deformis* R.Br. *Trans. Proc. R. Soc. S. Aust.* **55**: 143–146 (flower record); Rayment, T. (1935). *A Cluster of Bees.* Sixty essays on the life-histories of Australian bees, with specific descriptions of over 100 new species, and an introduction by Professor E.F. Phillips, D.Ph., Cornell University, U.S.A. Sydney : Endeavour Press 752 pp. (description of male); Erickson, R. (1951). *Orchids of the West.* Perth : Paterson Brokensha 109 pp. (flower record); Rayment, T. (1953). *Bees of the Portland District.* Victoria : Portland Field Naturalist's Club 39 pp. (distribution); Michener, C.D. (1960). Notes on the biology and supposed parthenogenesis of halictine bees from the Australian region. *J. Kansas Entomol. Soc.* **33**: 85–96 (biology); Michener, C.D. (1965). A classification of the bees of the Australian and South Pacific regions. *Bull. Am. Mus. Nat. Hist.* **130**: 1–362 (flower record).

Lasioglossum (Chilalictus) subplebeium (Cockerell, 1930)

Halictus subplebeius Cockerell, T.D.A. (1930). New Australian bees. *Mem. Qd Mus.* **10**: 37–50 [42].
Type data: syntypes, QM 2♂ (a specimen has the type registration number Hy3751).
Type locality: [Lamington] National Park, QLD.

Distribution: NE coastal, Murray-Darling basin, QLD, VIC; only published localities [Lamington] National Park and Mt Buffalo.
Ecology: adult—volant; melliferous, solitary.
Reference: Rayment, T. (1946). Native bees on Mount Buffalo. With description of a new subspecies. *Vict. Nat.* **63**: 23–24 (distribution).

Lasioglossum (Chilalictus) supralucens (Cockerell, 1916)

Halictus supralucens Cockerell, T.D.A. (1916). Some bees from Australia, Tasmania, and the New Hebrides. *Proc. Acad. Nat. Sci. Philad.* **68**: 360–375 [371].

Type data: syntypes (probable), BMNH ♀ (number of specimens unknown, a female specimen is labelled 'type' and has registration number Hym.17.a.934).
Type locality: Kalamunda, WA.

Distribution: SW coastal, WA; known only from type locality.
Ecology: adult—volant; melliferous, solitary.

Lasioglossum (Chilalictus) tamburinei (Friese, 1917)

Halictus tamburinei Friese, H. (1917). Results of Dr. E. Mjöberg's Swedish Scientific Expeditions to Australia, 1910–1913. 13. Apidae. *Ark. Zool.* **11**(2): 1–9 [6].
Type data: syntypes, AMNH ♂♀*.
Type locality: Mt Tamborine, QLD.

Distribution: NE coastal, QLD; known only from type locality.
Ecology: adult—volant; melliferous, solitary.
Reference: Cockerell, T.D.A. (1929). Bees, chiefly Australian species, described or determined by Dr. H. Friese. *Am. Mus. Novit.* **343**: 1–20 (taxonomy, as *Parasphecodes tamburinei* (Friese, 1917)).

Lasioglossum (Chilalictus) tasmaniae (Cockerell, 1905)

Sphecodes tasmaniae Cockerell, T.D.A. (1905). Descriptions and records of bees. II. *Ann. Mag. Nat. Hist. (7)***16**: 292–301 [299].
Type data: holotype, BMNH Hym.17.a.594 ♂.
Type locality: Hobart, TAS.

Distribution: SE coastal, NSW, TAS; only published localities Sydney, Hobart and St Helens.
Ecology: adult—volant; melliferous, solitary.
References: Cockerell, T.D.A. (1910). New and little-known bees. *Trans. Am. Entomol. Soc.* **36**: 199–249 (as *Halictus tasmaniae* (Cockerell, 1905)); Cockerell, T.D.A. (1918). Descriptions and records of bees. LXXIX. *Ann. Mag. Nat. Hist. (9)***1**: 158–167 (distribution); Rayment, T. (1939). Bees from the high lands of New South Wales and Victoria. *Aust. Zool.* **9**: 263–294 (distribution).

Lasioglossum (Chilalictus) veronicae (Cockerell, 1926)

Halictus (Chloralictus) veronicae Cockerell, T.D.A. (1926). Descriptions and records of bees. CXII. *Ann. Mag. Nat. Hist. (9)***18**: 216–227 [220].
Type data: holotype, USNM ♀*.
Type locality: Sandringham, VIC.

Distribution: SE coastal, VIC; known only from type locality.
Ecology: adult—volant; melliferous, flower visiting record: *Veronica* L. [Scrophulariaceae].
Reference: Rayment, T. (1935). *A Cluster of Bees.* Sixty essays on the life-histories of Australian bees, with specific descriptions of over 100 new species, and an introduction by Professor E.F. Phillips, D.Ph.,

Cornell University, U.S.A. Sydney : Endeavour Press 752 pp. (illustration).

Lasioglossum (Chilalictus) victoriae (Cockerell, 1926)

Halictus victoriae Cockerell, T.D.A. (1926). New halictine bees from Australia. *Entomologist* 59: 246–247 [247].
Type data: holotype, ANIC ♀.
Type locality: Sandringham, Port Phillip, VIC.

Distribution: SE coastal, VIC; only published localities Sandringham and Beaumaris.
Ecology: larva—sedentary : adult—volant; melliferous, nest in soil, flower visiting record: marigolds, *Achillea* L. [Asteraceae], *Goodenia* Sm. [Goodeniaceae], *Hypochaeris* L. [Asteraceae], *Mesembryanthemum* L. [Aizoaceae], *Myoporum* Banks & Sol. ex G.Forster [Myoporaceae], *Veronica* L. [Scrophulariaceae].
References: Cockerell, T.D.A. (1929). Bees from the Australian region. *Am. Mus. Novit.* 346: 1–18 (flower record); Rayment, T. (1934). Contributions to the fauna of Rottnest Island. VIII. Apoidea. With description of new species. *J. Proc. R. Soc. West. Aust.* 20: 201–212 (description of male, doubtful record, from Rottnest Is.); Rayment, T. (1935). *A Cluster of Bees.* Sixty essays on the life-histories of Australian bees, with specific descriptions of over 100 new species, and an introduction by Professor E.F. Phillips, D.Ph., Cornell University, U.S.A. Sydney : Endeavour Press 752 pp. (biology).

Lasioglossum (Chilalictus) victoriellum (Cockerell, 1914)

Halictus victoriellus Cockerell, T.D.A. (1914). Descriptions and records of bees. LIX. *Ann. Mag. Nat. Hist.* (8)13: 504–522 [517].
Type data: syntypes, BMNH 2♀ (a specimen is labelled 'type' and has registration number Hym.17.a.920).
Type locality: VIC.

Distribution: SE coastal, VIC, TAS; only published localities Sandringham and Forthside.
Ecology: larva—sedentary : adult—volant; melliferous, nest gregariously in loose sand, flower visiting record: *Arctotheca* Wendl. [Asteraceae], *Veronica* L. [Scrophulariaceae].
References: Cockerell, T.D.A. (1926). Descriptions and records of bees. CX. *Ann. Mag. Nat. Hist.* (9)17: 510–519 (description of male); Cockerell, T.D.A. (1926). Descriptions and records of bees. CXII. *Ann. Mag. Nat. Hist.* (9)18: 216–227 (taxonomy); Rayment, T. (1927). The sand-hopper bees. *Vict. Nat.* 44: 103–109 (biology); Rayment, T. (1935). *A Cluster of Bees.* Sixty essays on the life-histories of Australian bees, with specific descriptions of over 100 new species, and an introduction by Professor E.F. Phillips, D.Ph., Cornell University, U.S.A. Sydney : Endeavour Press 752 pp. (biology); Michener, C.D. (1960). Notes on the biology and supposed parthenogenesis

of halictine bees from the Australian region. *J. Kansas Entomol. Soc.* 33: 85–96 (biology); Anon. (1972). Insect pest occurrences in Tasmania '70/71. *Insect Pest Survey, Tas. Dept Agric.* 4: 1–39 (distribution).

Lasioglossum (Chilalictus) viridarii (Cockerell, 1930)

Halictus viridarii Cockerell, T.D.A. (1930). New Australian bees. *Mem. Qd Mus.* 10: 37–50 [42].
Type data: holotype, QM Hy4038 ♂.
Type locality: [Lamington] National Park, QLD.

Distribution: NE coastal, QLD; known only from type locality.
Ecology: adult—volant; melliferous, solitary.

Lasioglossum (Chilalictus) vitripenne (Smith, 1879)

Halictus vitripennis Smith, F. (1879). *Descriptions of New Species of Hymenoptera in the Collection of the British Museum.* London : British Museum xxi 240 pp. [34].
Type data: holotype, BMNH Hym.17.a.973 ♀.
Type locality: Champion Bay (Geraldton), WA.
Halictus sphecodoides mackayensis Friese, H. (1924). Ueber die Bienen Australiens. *Konowia* 3: 216–249 [236].
Type data: syntypes (probable), ?AMNH ♀* (number of specimens unknown).
Type locality: Mackay, QLD.

Taxonomic decision for synonymy: Cockerell, T.D.A. (1929). Bees, chiefly Australian species, described or determined by Dr. H. Friese. *Am. Mus. Novit.* 343: 1–20 [13].

Distribution: NE coastal, Murray-Darling basin, SW coastal, NW coastal, QLD, SA, WA.
Ecology: larva—sedentary : adult—volant; melliferous, flower visiting record: *Alphitonia* Reisseck ex Endl. [Rhamnaceae], *Angophora* Cav. [Myrtaceae], *Baeckea* L. [Myrtaceae], *Boronia* Sm. [Rutaceae], *Callistemon* R.Br. [Myrtaceae], *Cassia* L. *s.lat.* [Caesalpiniaceae], *Eucalyptus* L'Hérit. [Myrtaceae], *Jacksonia* Smith [Fabaceae], *Melaleuca* L. [Myrtaceae], *Taraxacum* G.Weber [Asteraceae].
References: Cockerell, T.D.A. (1904). The halictine bees of the Australian region. *Ann. Mag. Nat. Hist.* (7)14: 208–213 (taxonomy); Cockerell, T.D.A. (1905). Descriptions and records of bees. II. *Ann. Mag. Nat. Hist.* (7)16: 292–301 (distribution); Cockerell, T.D.A. (1914). Descriptions and records of bees. LIX. *Ann. Mag. Nat. Hist.* (8)13: 504–522 (variety); Rayment, T. (1931). Bees in the collections of the Western Australian Museum and the Agricultural Department, Perth. *J. Proc. R. Soc. West. Aust.* 17: 157–190 (description of male); Michener, C.D. (1960). Notes on the biology and supposed parthenogenesis of halictine bees from the Australian region. *J. Kansas Entomol. Soc.* 33: 85–96 (biology); Michener, C.D. (1965). A classification of the bees of the Australian and South Pacific regions. *Bull. Am. Mus. Nat. Hist.* 130: 1–362 (flower record).

Lasioglossum (Chilalictus) vividum (Smith, 1879)

Halictus vividus Smith, F. (1879). *Descriptions of New Species of Hymenoptera in the Collection of the British Museum.* London : British Museum xxi 240 pp. [35].
Type data: syntypes, BMNH ♂♀ (a female specimen is labelled 'type' and has registration number Hym.17.a.904).
Type locality: Swan River, WA.

Distribution: SW coastal, W plateau, WA; only published localities Swan River and Kalgoorlie.
Ecology: adult—volant; melliferous, solitary.
References: Cockerell, T.D.A. (1904). The halictine bees of the Australian region. *Ann. Mag. Nat. Hist.* (7)**14**: 208–213 (as synonym of *Halictus floralis* Smith, 1853); Rayment, T. (1931). Bees in the collections of the Western Australian Museum and the Agricultural Department, Perth. *J. Proc. R. Soc. West. Aust.* **17**: 157–190 (redescription); Cockerell, T.D.A. (1933). The bees of Australia. *Aust. Zool.* **7**: 291–324 (taxonomy).

Lasioglossum (Chilalictus) wahlenbergiae Michener, 1965

Lasioglossum (Chilalictus) wahlenbergiae Michener, C.D. (1965). A classification of the bees of the Australian and South Pacific regions. *Bull. Am. Mus. Nat. Hist.* **130**: 1–362 [317].
Type data: holotype, ANIC ♀.
Type locality: 8 miles W Armidale, NSW.

Distribution: NE coastal, Murray-Darling basin, QLD, NSW.
Ecology: adult—volant; melliferous, flower visiting record: *Wahlenbergia* Roth [Campanulaceae].

Lasioglossum (Chilalictus) whiteleyi (Rayment, 1939)

Halictus whiteleyi Rayment, T. (1939). Bees from the high lands of New South Wales and Victoria. *Aust. Zool.* **9**: 263–294 [281].
Type data: holotype, ANIC ♀.
Type locality: Mt Canobolas, NSW.

Distribution: Murray-Darling basin, NSW; known only from type locality.
Ecology: adult—volant; melliferous, solitary.

Lasioglossum (Chilalictus) willsi (Cockerell, 1906)

Halictus willsi Cockerell, T.D.A. (1906). New Australian bees in the collection of the British Museum. II. *Entomologist* **39**: 56–60 [59].
Type data: holotype, BMNH Hym.17.a.954 ♀.
Type locality: Australia (as New Holland).

Distribution: SE coastal, VIC; only published locality Portland.
Ecology: adult—volant; melliferous, flower visiting record: *Arctotheca* Wendl. [Asteraceae].
Reference: Rayment, T. (1953). *Bees of the Portland District.* Victoria : Portland Field Naturalist's Club 39 pp. (distribution).

Lasioglossum (Ctenonomia) Cameron, 1903

Ctenonomia Cameron, P. (1903). Descriptions of new genera and species of Hymenoptera taken by Mr. Robert Shelford at Sarawak, Borneo. *J. Straits Br. R. Asiatic Soc.* **39**: 89–181 [178]. Type species: *Ctenonomia carinata* Cameron, 1903 by monotypy.

Extralimital distribution: Afrotropical and Oriental Regions, extending E to New Guinea, see Pauly, A. (1986). Les abeilles de la sous-famille des Halictinae en Nouvelle-Guinée et dans l'Archipel Bismarck (Hymenoptera : Apoidea : Halictidae). *Zool. Verh.* **227**: 1–58 [10].

Generic reference: Sakagami, S.F. (1989). Taxonomic notes on a Malesian bee *Lasioglossum carinatum*, the type species of the subgenus *Ctenonomia*, and its allies (Hymenoptera: Halictidae). *J. Kansas Entomol. Soc.* **62**: 496–510.

Lasioglossum (Ctenonomia) barretti (Cockerell, 1929)

Halictus barretti Cockerell, T.D.A. (1929). Bees from the Australian region. *Am. Mus. Novit.* **346**: 1–18 [14].
Type data: holotype, AMNH ♀*.
Type locality: Seaforth, VIC.

Distribution: SE coastal, VIC; known only from type locality.
Ecology: adult—volant; melliferous, solitary.
Reference: Cockerell, T.D.A. (1933). The bees of Australia. *Aust. Zool.* **7**: 291–324 (taxonomy).

Lasioglossum (Ctenonomia) blandulum (Cockerell, 1929)

Halictus blandulus Cockerell, T.D.A. (1929). Bees in the Australian Museum collection. *Rec. Aust. Mus.* **17**: 199–243 [228].
Type data: holotype, AM K48342 ♀.
Type locality: King George Sound, WA.

Distribution: SW coastal, WA; known only from type locality.
Ecology: larva—sedentary : adult—volant; melliferous, solitary.
Reference: Cockerell, T.D.A. (1933). The bees of Australia. *Aust. Zool.* **7**: 291–324 (taxonomy).

Lasioglossum (Ctenonomia) cyclurum (Cockerell, 1915)

Halictus cyclurus Cockerell, T.D.A. (1915). Descriptions and records of bees. LXIX. *Ann. Mag. Nat. Hist.* (8)**16**: 96–104 [99].
Type data: holotype, QM Hy4122 ♀.
Type locality: Mt Tamborine, QLD.

Distribution: NE coastal, SE coastal, QLD, VIC; only published localities Mt Tamborine and Portland.
Ecology: larva—sedentary : adult—volant; melliferous, nest communally in soil, flower visiting record: aster, *Cryptostemma* R.Br. [Asteraceae], *Helichrysum*

Miller *s.lat.* [Asteraceae].
References: Cockerell, T.D.A. (1923). Descriptions and records of bees. XCVIII. *Ann. Mag. Nat. Hist. (9)***12**: 238–247 (flower record); Rayment, T. (1953). *Bees of the Portland District.* Victoria : Portland Field Naturalist's Club 39 pp. (distribution, flower records); Rayment, T. (1955). Dimorphism and parthenogenesis in halictine bees. *Aust. Zool.* **12**: 142–153 (biology); Michener, C.D. (1960). Notes on the biology and supposed parthenogenesis of halictine bees from the Australian region. *J. Kansas Entomol. Soc.* **33**: 85–96 (biology); Knerer, G. & Schwarz, M. (1976). Halictine social evolution : the Australian enigma. *Science* **194**: 445–448 (biology); Knerer, G. & Schwarz, M. (1978). Beobachtungen an australischen · Furchenbienen (Hymenopteren; Halictinae). *Zool. Anz.* **200**: 321–333 (biology, as *Lasioglossum cyclurum* complex).

Lasioglossum (Ctenonomia) expulsum (Cockerell, 1916)

Halictus semipolitus expulsus Cockerell, T.D.A. (1916). Some bees from Australia, Tasmania, and the New Hebrides. *Proc. Acad. Nat. Sci. Philad.* **68**: 360–375 [372]·
Type data: holotype (probable), USNM ♀*.
Type locality: George Town (as Georgetown), TAS.

Distribution: SE coastal, VIC, TAS; only published localities Portland and George Town.
Ecology: adult—volant; melliferous, flower visiting record: *Samolus* L. [Primulaceae].
Reference: Rayment, T. (1953). *Bees of the Portland District.* Victoria : Portland Field Naturalist's Club 39 pp. (distribution, flower record).

Lasioglossum (Ctenonomia) picticorne (Cockerell, 1930)

Halictus picticornis Cockerell, T.D.A. (1930). New Australian bees. *Mem. Qd Mus.* **10**: 37–50 [41].
Type data: holotype, QM Hy5008 ♂.
Type locality: Caloundra, QLD.

Distribution: NE coastal, QLD; known only from type locality.
Ecology: adult—volant; melliferous, solitary.

Lasioglossum (Ctenonomia) repertulum (Cockerell, 1916)

Halictus repertulus Cockerell, T.D.A. (1916). A collection of bees from Queensland. *Mem. Qd Mus.* **5**: 197–204 [203].
Type data: holotype, USNM ♂*.
Type locality: Brisbane, QLD.

Distribution: NE coastal, QLD; known only from type locality.
Ecology: adult—volant; melliferous, solitary.

Lasioglossum (Ctenonomia) semipolitum (Cockerell, 1916)

Halictus semipolitus Cockerell, T.D.A. (1916). A collection of bees from Queensland. *Mem. Qd Mus.* **5**: 197–204 [202].
Type data: holotype, USNM ♀*.
Type locality: Bribie Is., QLD.

Distribution: NE coastal, QLD; only published localities Bribie Is., Brisbane and Mt Tamborine.
Ecology: adult—volant; melliferous, flower visiting record: *Helichrysum* Miller *s.lat.* [Asteraceae].
References: Cockerell, T.D.A. (1918). Some bees collected in Queensland. *Mem. Qd Mus.* **6**: 112–120 (distribution); Cockerell, T.D.A. (1929). Bees in the Queensland Museum. *Mem. Qd Mus.* **9**: 298–323 (distribution, flower record).

Lasioglossum (Ctenonomia) speculellum (Cockerell, 1918)

Halictus speculellus Cockerell, T.D.A. (1918). Some bees collected in Queensland. *Mem. Qd Mus.* **6**: 112–120 [117].
Type data: holotype, QM Hy4124 ♀.
Type locality: Brisbane, QLD.

Distribution: NE coastal, QLD; known only from type locality.
Ecology: adult—volant; melliferous.

Lasioglossum (Ctenonomia) sturti (Cockerell, 1906)

Halictus sturti Cockerell, T.D.A. (1906). New Australian bees in the collection of the British Museum. II. *Entomologist* **39**: 56–60 [59].
Type data: holotype, BMNH Hym.17.a.923 ♀.
Type locality: Mackay, QLD.

Halictus globularis Friese, H. (1924). Ueber die Bienen Australiens. *Konowia* **3**: 216–249 [244].
Type data: syntypes, AMNH ♂♀*.
Type locality: Mackay, QLD.

Taxonomic decision for synonymy: Cockerell, T.D.A. (1929). Bees, chiefly Australian species, described or determined by Dr. H. Friese. *Am. Mus. Novit.* **343**: 1–20 [12].

Distribution: NE coastal, QLD; only published localities Mackay and Halifax.
Ecology: adult—volant; melliferous, flower visiting record: *Cassia* L. *s.lat.* [Caesalpiniaceae], *Eucalyptus* L'Hérit. [Myrtaceae], *Eugenia* L. [Myrtaceae].
References: Cockerell, T.D.A. (1912). Descriptions and records of bees. XLIII. *Ann. Mag. Nat. Hist. (8)***9**: 377–387 (flower record); Cockerell, T.D.A. (1930). Australian bees in the Museum of Comparative Zoology. *Psyche (Camb.)* **37**: 141–154 (distribution).

Lasioglossum (Glossalictus) Michener, 1965

Glossalictus Michener, C.D. (1965). A classification of the bees of the Australian and South Pacific regions. *Bull. Am. Mus. Nat. Hist.* **130**: 1–362 [173] [proposed with subgeneric rank in *Lasioglossum* Curtis, 1833]. Type species: *Halictus etheridgei* Cockerell, 1916 by original designation.

Lasioglossum (Glossalictus) etheridgei (Cockerell, 1916)

Halictus etheridgei Cockerell, T.D.A. (1916). Descriptions and records of bees. LXXII. *Ann. Mag. Nat. Hist.* (8)**17**: 428–435 [433].
Type data: holotype, BMNH Hym.17.a.932 ♀.
Type locality: Yallingup, WA.

Distribution: SW coastal, WA; known only from type locality.
Ecology: adult—volant; melliferous, solitary.

Lasioglossum (Parasphecodes) Smith, 1853

Parasphecodes Smith, F. (1853). *Catalogue of Hymenopterous Insects in the Collection of the British Museum.* Part I. Andrenidae and Apidae. London : British Museum 197 pp. [39]. Type species: *Parasphecodes hilactus* Smith, 1853 by subsequent designation, see Sandhouse, G.A.(1943). The type species of the genera and subgenera of bees. *Proc. U.S. Natl Mus.* **92**(3156): 519–619 [585].

Aphalictus Cockerell, T.D.A. (1930). New Australian bees. *Mem. Qd Mus.* **10**: 37–50 [40] [proposed with subgeneric rank in *Parasphecodes* Smith, 1853]. Type species: *Parasphecodes bribiensis* Cockerell, 1916 by original designation.

Taxonomic decision for synonymy: Michener, C.D. (1965). A classification of the bees of the Australian and South Pacific regions. *Bull. Am. Mus. Nat. Hist.* **130**: 1–362 [165].

Extralimital distribution: New Guinea, see Michener, C.D. (1965). A classification of the bees of the Australian and South Pacific regions. *Bull. Am. Mus. Nat. Hist.* **130**: 1–362 [167].

Lasioglossum (Parasphecodes) adelaidae (Cockerell, 1905)

Parasphecodes adelaidae Cockerell, T.D.A. (1905). Descriptions and records of bees. II. *Ann. Mag. Nat. Hist.* (7)**16**: 292–301 [297].
Type data: holotype, BMNH Hym.17.a.628 ♀.
Type locality: Adelaide, SA.

Distribution: S Gulfs, SA; known only from type locality.
Ecology: adult—volant; melliferous, solitary.
References: Meyer, R. (1920). Apidae—Halictinae. I. Gatt. *Parasphecodes* Sm. *Arch. Naturg.* **85**(A)11: 112–137 (taxonomy); Cockerell, T.D.A. (1932). The bees of Australia. *Aust. Zool.* **7**: 206–218 (taxonomy).

Lasioglossum (Parasphecodes) altichum (Smith, 1853)

Parasphecodes altichus Smith, F. (1853). *Catalogue of Hymenopterous Insects in the Collection of the British Museum.* Part I. Andrenidae and Apidae. London : British Museum 197 pp. [42].

Type data: holotype, BMNH Hym.17.a.620 ♂.
Type locality: TAS (as Van Diemens Land).

Distribution: SE coastal, NSW, VIC, TAS; only published localities Jamberoo and Portland.
Ecology: adult—volant; melliferous, flower visiting record: aster, *Leptospermum* Forster & G.Forster [Myrtaceae].
References: Meyer, R. (1920). Apidae—Halictinae. I. Gatt. *Parasphecodes* Sm. *Arch. Naturg.* **85**(A)11: 112–137 (taxonomy); Rayment, T. (1953). *Bees of the Portland District.* Victoria : Portland Field Naturalist's Club 39 pp. (distribution); Rayment, T. (1954). Remarkable bees from a rain forest. *Aust. Zool.* **12**: 46–56 (distribution); Michener, C.D. (1970). Superfamily Apoidea. pp. 943–951 *in* CSIRO (sponsor) *The Insects of Australia.* A textbook for students and research workers. Melbourne : Melbourne Univ. Press (illustration).

Lasioglossum (Parasphecodes) anhybodinum (Cockerell, 1930)

Parasphecodes anhybodinus Cockerell, T.D.A. (1930). New Australian bees. *Mem. Qd Mus.* **10**: 37–50 [38].
Type data: holotype, QM Hy4094 ♂.
Type locality: Cheltenham, VIC.

Distribution: SE coastal, VIC; only published localities Cheltenham, Sandringham, Brighton and Portland.
Ecology: adult—volant; melliferous, flower visiting record: *Eucalyptus* L'Hérit. [Myrtaceae], *Leptospermum* Forster & G.Forster [Myrtaceae].
References: Rayment, T. (1935) *A Cluster of Bees.* Sixty essays on the life-histories of Australian bees, with specific descriptions of over 100 new species, and an introduction by Professor E.F. Phillips, D.Ph., Cornell University, U.S.A. Sydney : Endeavour Press 752 pp. (flower record); Rayment, T. (1947). Biology and taxonomy of the solitary bee, *Parasphecodes fulviventris* (Friese). *Aust. Zool.* **11**: 76–95 (redescription); Rayment, T. (1953). *Bees of the Portland District.* Victoria : Portland Field Naturalist's Club 39 pp. (flower record).

Lasioglossum (Parasphecodes) annexum (Cockerell, 1922)

Parasphecodes annexus Cockerell, T.D.A. (1922). Australian bees in the Queensland Museum. *Mem. Qd Mus.* **7**: 257–279 [261].
Type data: holotype, QM T2678 ♀.
Type locality: Adaminaby, NSW.

Distribution: Murray-Darling basin, NSW; known only from type locality.
Ecology: adult—volant; melliferous, solitary.

Lasioglossum *(Parasphecodes)* *arciferum*
(Cockerell, 1914)

Parasphecodes arciferus Cockerell, T.D.A. (1914).
Descriptions and records of bees. LVI. *Ann. Mag. Nat. Hist.*
*(8)***13**: 136–146 [142].
Type data: holotype, ANIC ♀.
Type locality: Mordialloc, VIC.

Distribution: SE coastal, VIC; only published locali-
ties Mordialloc, Melbourne, Brighton, Sandringham
and Gorae West.
Ecology: adult—volant; melliferous, flower visiting
record: *Dillwynia* Sm. [Fabaceae], *Eucalyptus*
L'Hérit. [Myrtaceae], *Hibbertia* Andrews
[Dilleniaceae], *Leucopogon* R.Br. [Epacridaceae].
References: Meyer, R. (1920). Apidae—Halictinae. I.
Gatt. *Parasphecodes* Sm. *Arch. Naturg.* **85**(A)11:
112–137 (taxonomy); Cockerell, T.D.A. (1930). Australian bees in the Museum of Comparative Zoology.
Psyche (Camb.) **37**: 141–154 (description of male);
Rayment, T. (1935). *A Cluster of Bees.* Sixty essays
on the life-histories of Australian bees, with specific
descriptions of over 100 new species, and an introduction by Professor E.F. Phillips, D.Ph., Cornell
University, U.S.A. Sydney : Endeavour Press 752 pp.
(flower record); Rayment, T. (1947). Biology and
taxonomy of the solitary bee, *Parasphecodes
fulviventris* (Friese). *Aust. Zool.* **11**: 76–95 (taxonomy); Rayment, T. (1953). *Bees of the Portland District.* Victoria : Portland Field Naturalist's Club 39
pp. (distribution).

Lasioglossum *(Parasphecodes)* *atronitens*
(Cockerell, 1914)

Parasphecodes atronitens Cockerell, T.D.A. (1914).
Australian halictine bees. *Entomologist* **47**: 242–244 [242].
Type data: holotype, QM Hy4138 ♀.
Type locality: Caloundra (as Calsundra), QLD.

Distribution: NE coastal, SE coastal, QLD, NSW;
only published localities Caloundra, Nanango district
and Jamberoo.
Ecology: adult—volant; melliferous, flower visiting
record: *Prostanthera* Labill. [Lamiaceae].
References: Cockerell, T.D.A. (1929). Bees in the
Queensland Museum. *Mem. Qd Mus.* **9**: 298–323
(distribution); Rayment, T. (1954). Remarkable bees
from a rain forest. *Aust. Zool.* **12**: 46–56 (flower record).

Lasioglossum *(Parasphecodes)* *atrorufescens*
(Cockerell, 1914)

Parasphecodes atrorufescens Cockerell, T.D.A. (1914).
Descriptions and records of bees. LVI. *Ann. Mag. Nat. Hist.*
*(8)***13**: 136–146 [145].
Type data: holotype, ANIC ♀.
Type locality: Purnong, SA.

Distribution: Murray-Darling basin, SA; known only
from type locality.

Ecology: adult—volant; melliferous, solitary.
Reference: Meyer, R. (1920). Apidae—Halictinae. I.
Gatt. *Parasphecodes* Sm. *Arch. Naturg.* **85**(A)11:
112–137 (taxonomy).

Lasioglossum *(Parasphecodes)* *basilautum*
(Cockerell, 1910)

Parasphecodes basilautus Cockerell, T.D.A. (1910). New
and little-known bees. *Trans. Am. Entomol. Soc.* **36**:
199–249 [242].
Type data: holotype, BMNH Hym.17.a.626 ♀.
Type locality: Kuranda (as Cairns Kuranda), QLD.
Halictus pilicollis Friese, H. (1924). Ueber die Bienen
Australiens. *Konowia* **3**: 216–249 [238].
Type data: holotype (probable), AMNH ♀*.
Type locality: Cairns, QLD.

Taxonomic decision for synonymy: Cockerell, T.D.A.
(1929). Bees, chiefly Australian species, described or determined by Dr. H. Friese. *Am. Mus. Novit.* **343**: 1–20 [14].

Distribution: NE coastal, SE coastal, QLD, VIC; only
published localities Cairns, Kuranda and Portland.
Ecology: adult—volant; melliferous, flower visiting
record: aster, *Acacia* Miller [Mimosaceae].
References: Meyer, R. (1920). Apidae—Halictinae. I.
Gatt. *Parasphecodes* Sm. *Arch. Naturg.* **85**(A)11:
112–137 (taxonomy); Rayment, T. (1953). *Bees of
the Portland District.* Victoria : Portland Field
Naturalist's Club 39 pp. (distribution).

Lasioglossum (Parasphecodes) bribiense (Cockerell,
1916)

Parasphecodes bribiensis Cockerell, T.D.A. (1916). A
collection of bees from Queensland. *Mem. Qd Mus.* **5**:
197–204 [201].
Type data: holotype, QM Hy4139 ♀.
Type locality: Bribie Is., QLD.

Distribution: NE coastal, QLD; only published localities Bribie and Stradbroke Ils.
Ecology: adult—volant; melliferous, solitary.
References: Cockerell, T.D.A. (1918). Some bees
collected in Queensland. *Mem. Qd Mus.* **6**: 112–120
(distribution); Cockerell, T.D.A. (1930). New Australian bees. *Mem. Qd Mus.* **10**: 37–50 (as
Parasphecodes (Aphalictus) bribiensis Cockerell,
1916).

Lasioglossum *(Parasphecodes)* *bribiensiforme*
(Cockerell, 1930)

Parasphecodes (Aphalictus) bribiensiformis Cockerell,
T.D.A. (1930). New Australian bees. *Mem. Qd Mus.* **10**:
37–50 [40].
Type data: holotype, QM Hy4047 ♀.
Type locality: Bribie Is., QLD.

Distribution: NE coastal, QLD; known only from
type locality.
Ecology: adult—volant; melliferous, solitary.

Lasioglossum   (Parasphecodes)   bryotrichum
(Cockerell, 1912)

Parasphecodes bryotrichus Cockerell, T.D.A. (1912).
Descriptions and records of bees. XLII. *Ann. Mag. Nat.
Hist. (8)*9: 220–229 [225].
Type data: holotype, ANIC ♀.
Type locality: Cheltenham, VIC.

Distribution: SE coastal, VIC; only published locali-
ties Cheltenham and Port Phillip.
Ecology: adult—volant; melliferous, solitary.
Reference: Meyer, R. (1920). Apidae—Halictinae. I.
Gatt. *Parasphecodes* Sm. *Arch. Naturg.* **85**(A)11:
112–137 (taxonomy).

Lasioglossum (Parasphecodes) butleri (Rayment,
1935)

Halictus butleri Rayment, T. (1935). *A Cluster of Bees.*
Sixty essays on the life-histories of Australian bees, with
specific descriptions of over 100 new species, and an
introduction by Professor E.F. Phillips, D.Ph., Cornell
University, U.S.A. Sydney : Endeavour Press 752 pp.
[694].
Type data: holotype, ANIC ♀.
Type locality: Lakes Entrance, VIC.

Distribution: SE coastal, VIC; known only from type
locality.
Ecology: adult—volant; melliferous, solitary.

Lasioglossum (Parasphecodes) carbonarium (Smith,
1853)

Halictus carbonarius Smith, F. (1853). *Catalogue of
Hymenopterous Insects in the Collection of the British
Museum.* Part I. Andrenidae and Apidae. London : British
Museum 197 pp. [58].
Type data: holotype, BMNH Hym.17.a.896 ♀.
Type locality: Sydney, NSW.

Distribution: SE coastal, NSW; known only from
type locality.
Ecology: adult—volant; melliferous, solitary.
References: Cockerell, T.D.A. (1914). Descriptions
and records of bees. LVI. *Ann. Mag. Nat. Hist. (8)*13:
136–146 (taxonomy); Meyer, R. (1920). Apidae—
Halictinae. I. Gatt. *Parasphecodes* Sm. *Arch. Naturg.*
85(A)11: 112–137 (taxonomy).

Lasioglossum (Parasphecodes) cervicale (Cockerell,
1915)

Parasphecodes cervicalis Cockerell, T.D.A. (1915).
Descriptions and records of bees. LXIX. *Ann. Mag. Nat.
Hist. (8)*16: 96–104 [96].
Type data: holotype (probable), BMNH Hym.17.a.640 ♀.
Type locality: Eaglehawk Neck, TAS.

Distribution: NE coastal, Murray-Darling basin,
QLD, TAS; only published localities [Lamington]
National Park (QLD), The Summit and Eaglehawk
Neck.
Ecology: adult—volant; melliferous, flower visiting

record: *Boronia* Sm. [Rutaceae].
References: Cockerell, T.D.A. (1922). Australian
bees in the Queensland Museum. *Mem. Qd Mus.* **7**:
257–279 (description of male); Michener, C.D.
(1965). A classification of the bees of the Australian
and South Pacific regions. *Bull. Am. Mus. Nat. Hist.*
130: 1–362 (flower record).

Lasioglossum   (Parasphecodes)   cirriferum
(Cockerell, 1910)

Parasphecodes cirriferus Cockerell, T.D.A. (1910). New
and little-known bees. *Trans. Am. Entomol. Soc.* **36**:
199–249 [241].
Type data: holotype, BMNH Hym.17.a.622 ♀.
Type locality: VIC.

Distribution: Murray-Darling basin, SE coastal,
NSW, VIC; only published localities White Swamp,
Gorae West and Mt Buffalo.
Ecology: adult—volant; melliferous, flower visiting
record: arum lily, aster, *Arctotheca* Wendl. [As-
teraceae], *Eucalyptus* L'Hérit. [Myrtaceae],
Microseris D. Don [Asteraceae].
References: Meyer, R. (1920). Apidae—Halictinae. I.
Gatt. *Parasphecodes* Sm. *Arch. Naturg.* **85**(A)11:
112–137 (taxonomy); Rayment, T. (1939). Bees from
the high lands of New South Wales and Victoria.
Aust. Zool. **9**: 263–294 (distribution); Rayment, T.
(1947). Bees from the Victorian Alps. *Vict. Nat.* **64**:
103–107 (distribution); Rayment, T. (1953). *Bees of
the Portland District.* Victoria : Portland Field
Naturalist's Club 39 pp. (description of male, flower
record); Rayment, T. (1954). Incidence of acarid
mites on the biology of bees. *Aust. Zool.* **12**: 26–38
(as host).

Lasioglossum   (Parasphecodes)   clarigaster
(Cockerell, 1918)

Halictus clarigaster Cockerell, T.D.A. (1918). Some bees
collected in Queensland. *Mem. Qd Mus.* **6**: 112–120 [117].
Type data: holotype, BMNH Hym.17.a.988 ♀.
Type locality: Caloundra, QLD.

Distribution: NE coastal, QLD; only published localities Caloundra and Dunwich.
Ecology: adult—volant; melliferous, flower visiting
record: *Hibbertia* Andrews [Dilleniaceae].
References: Cockerell, T.D.A. (1923). Descriptions
and records of bees. XCVIII.·*Ann. Mag. Nat. Hist.
(9)*12: 238–247 (taxonomy); Michener, C.D. (1965).
A classification of the bees of the Australian and
South Pacific regions. *Bull. Am. Mus. Nat. Hist.* **130**:
1–362 (flower record, illustration).

Lasioglossum   (Parasphecodes)   dissimulator
(Cockerell, 1914)

Parasphecodes dissimulator Cockerell, T.D.A. (1914).
Descriptions and records of bees. LVI. *Ann. Mag. Nat. Hist.
(8)*13: 136–146 [145].

Type data: holotype, ANIC ♀.
Type locality: Carrum (as Carrom), VIC.

Distribution: SE coastal, VIC; known only from type locality.
Ecology: adult—volant; melliferous, solitary.
Reference: Meyer, R. (1920). Apidae—Halictinae. I. Gatt. *Parasphecodes* Sm. *Arch. Naturg.* **85**(A)11: 112–137 (taxonomy).

Lasioglossum (Parasphecodes) doddi (Cockerell, 1914)

Halictus doddi Cockerell, T.D.A. (1914). Descriptions and records of bees. LXIII. *Ann. Mag. Nat. Hist.* (8)**14**: 361–369 [368].
Type data: holotype, BMNH Hym.17.a.949 ♀.
Type locality: Kuranda, QLD.

Distribution: NE coastal, QLD; known only from type locality.
Ecology: adult—volant; melliferous, solitary.
Reference: Cockerell, T.D.A. (1916). A collection of bees from Queensland. *Mem. Qd Mus.* **5**: 197–204 (taxonomy).

Lasioglossum (Parasphecodes) excultum (Cockerell, 1913)

Parasphecodes excultus Cockerell, T.D.A. (1913). Australian bees. i. A new *Crocisa*, with a list of the Australian species of the genus. *Proc. Linn. Soc. N.S.W.* **37**: 594–595 [596].
Type data: holotype, ANIC ♀.
Type locality: Magnet, TAS.

Distribution: TAS; only published localities Magnet and Mt Wellington.
Ecology: adult—volant; melliferous, solitary.
References: Cockerell, T.D.A. (1913). Descriptions and records of bees. LIV. *Ann. Mag. Nat. Hist.* (8)**12**: 368–376 (taxonomy); Cockerell, T.D.A. (1914). Descriptions and records of bees. LXI. *Ann. Mag. Nat. Hist.* (8)**14**: 39–42 (taxonomy); Meyer, R. (1920). Apidae—Halictinae. I. Gatt. *Parasphecodes* Sm. *Arch. Naturg.* **85**(A)11: 112–137 (taxonomy).

Lasioglossum (Parasphecodes) flavopunctatum (Friese, 1924)

Nomia flavopunctata Friese, H. (1924). Ueber die Bienen Australiens. *Konowia* **3**: 216–249 [246].
Type data: holotype (probable), whereabouts unknown ♀*.
Type locality: Mackay, QLD.

Distribution: NE coastal, SE coastal, QLD, NSW; only published localities Mackay and Jamberoo.
Ecology: adult—volant; melliferous, flower visiting record: *Parsonsia* R.Br. [Apocyanaceae], *Xanthorrhoea* Sm. [Xanthorrhoeaceae].
References: Cockerell, T.D.A. (1931). The bees of Australia. *Aust. Zool.* **7**: 34–54 (as ?*Paracolletes flavopunctatus* (Friese, 1924)); Rayment, T. (1954). Remarkable bees from a rain forest. *Aust. Zool.* **12**:

46–56 (description of male, as *Halictus flavopunctatus* (Friese, 1924)).

Lasioglossum (Parasphecodes) forresti (Cockerell, 1906)

Halictus forresti Cockerell, T.D.A. (1906). New Australian bees in the collection of the British Museum. II. *Entomologist* **39**: 56–60 [60].
Type data: holotype, BMNH Hym.17.a.913 ♂.
Type locality: QLD.
[*Halictus scutellatus* (part)] Friese, H. (1924). Ueber die Bienen Australiens. *Konowia* **3**: 216–249 [242] [♂ syntype is conspecific with *Halictus forresti* Cockerell, 1906; ♀ syntype is conspecific with *Halictus leichardti* Cockerell, 1906].
Type data: syntypes, AMNH ♂*.
Type locality: Mackay, QLD.

Taxonomic decision for synonymy: Cockerell, T.D.A. (1929). Bees, chiefly Australian species, described or determined by Dr. H. Friese. *Am. Mus. Novit.* **343**: 1–20 [14].

Distribution: NE coastal, QLD; only published locality Mackay.
Ecology: adult—volant; melliferous, solitary.
Reference: Cockerell, T.D.A. (1910). New and little-known bees. *Trans. Am. Entomol. Soc.* **36**: 199–249 (taxonomy).

Lasioglossum (Parasphecodes) frenchellum Michener, 1965

Halictus frenchi Rayment, T. (1935). *A Cluster of Bees. Sixty essays on the life-histories of Australian bees, with specific descriptions of over 100 new species, and an introduction by Professor E.F. Phillips, D.Ph., Cornell University, U.S.A.* Sydney : Endeavour Press 752 pp. [701] [junior secondary homonym of *Halictus frenchi* (Cockerell, 1904)].
Type data: holotype, ANIC ♀.
Type locality: VIC.
Lasioglossum (Parasphecodes) frenchellum Michener, C.D. (1965). A classification of the bees of the Australian and South Pacific regions. *Bull. Am. Mus. Nat. Hist.* **130**: 1–362 [167] [*nom. nov.* for *Halictus frenchi* Rayment, 1935].

Distribution: VIC; known only from type locality, exact locality unknown.
Ecology: adult—volant; melliferous, solitary.

Lasioglossum (Parasphecodes) frenchi (Cockerell, 1904)

Parasphecodes frenchi Cockerell, T.D.A. (1904). The halictine bees of the Australian region. *Ann. Mag. Nat. Hist.* (7)**14**: 208–213 [210].
Type data: holotype, BMNH Hym.17.a.631 ♀.
Type locality: Melbourne, VIC.

Distribution: SE coastal, VIC; known only from type locality.
Ecology: adult—volant; melliferous, solitary.
Reference: Meyer, R. (1920). Apidae—Halictinae. I.

Gatt. *Parasphecodes* Sm. *Arch. Naturg.* **85**(A)11: 112–137 (taxonomy).

Lasioglossum (Parasphecodes) froggatti (Cockerell, 1905)

Parasphecodes froggatti Cockerell, T.D.A. (1905). Descriptions and records of bees. II. *Ann. Mag. Nat. Hist.* (7)**16**: 292–301 [296].
Type data: holotype, BMNH Hym.17.a.627 ♂.
Type locality: Bathurst, NSW.

Distribution: SE coastal, Murray-Darling basin, NSW, VIC; only published localities Bathurst, Gosford and Port Phillip.
Ecology: adult—volant; melliferous, solitary.
References: Cockerell, T.D.A. (1907). On a collection of Australian and Asiatic bees. *Bull. Am. Mus. Nat. Hist.* **23**: 221–236 (taxonomy); Cockerell, T.D.A. (1910). New and little-known bees. *Trans. Am. Entomol. Soc.* **36**: 199–249 (distribution); Meyer, R. (1920). Apidae—Halictinae. I. Gatt. *Parasphecodes* Sm. *Arch. Naturg.* **85**(A)11: 112–137 (taxonomy); Rayment, T. (1939). Bees from the high lands of New South Wales and Victoria. *Aust. Zool.* **9**: 263–294 (distribution).

Lasioglossum (Parasphecodes) fultoni (Cockerell, 1914)

Parasphecodes fultoni Cockerell, T.D.A. (1914). Descriptions and records of bees. LVI. *Ann. Mag. Nat. Hist.* (8)**13**: 136–146 [143].
Type data: holotype, USNM ♀*.
Type locality: Croydon, VIC.
Parasphecodes punctatissimus Meyer, R. (1920). Apidae—Halictinae. I. Gatt. *Parasphecodes* Sm. *Arch. Naturg.* **85**(A)11: 112–137 [131].
Type data: holotype, ZMB 1947 ♀*.
Type locality: TAS (as Van Diemens Land).
Halictus rubriventris Friese, H. (1924). Ueber die Bienen Australiens. *Konowia* **3**: 216–249 [239].
Type data: holotype (probable), AMNH ♀*.
Type locality: Ararat, VIC.

Taxonomic decision for synonymy: Cockerell, T.D.A. (1929). Bees, chiefly Australian species, described or determined by Dr. H. Friese. *Am. Mus. Novit.* **343**: 1–20 [15].

Distribution: SE coastal, Murray-Darling basin, NSW, VIC, TAS.
Ecology: larva—sedentary : adult—volant; melliferous, nest in ground, flower visiting record: aster, *Acacia* Miller [Mimosaceae], *Arctotheca* Wendl. [Asteraceae], *Bursaria* Cav. [Pittosporaceae], *Choisya* Kunth [Rutaceae], *Dillwynia* Sm. [Fabaceae], *Eucalyptus* L'Hérit. [Myrtaceae], *Genista* L. [Fabaceae], *Hardenbergia* Benth. [Fabaceae], *Hibbertia* Andrews [Dilleniaceae], *Hypochaeris* L. [Asteraceae], *Leptospermum* Forster & G.Forster [Myrtaceae], *Myoporum* Banks & Sol. ex G.Forster [Myoporaceae].
References: Meyer, R. (1920). Apidae—Halictinae. I.

Gatt. *Parasphecodes* Sm. *Arch. Naturg.* **85**(A)11: 112–137 (taxonomy); Rayment, T. (1953). *Bees of the Portland District.* Victoria : Portland Field Naturalist's Club 39 pp. (flower record); Rayment, T. (1954). Incidence of acarid mites on the biology of bees. *Aust. Zool.* **12**: 26–38 (biology); Rayment, T. (1954). Remarkable bees from a rain forest. *Aust. Zool.* **12**: 46–56 (distribution).

Lasioglossum (Parasphecodes) fulviventre (Friese, 1924)

Halictus fulviventris Friese, H. (1924). Ueber die Bienen Australiens. *Konowia* **3**: 216–249 [240].
Type data: holotype (probable), AMNH ♀*.
Type locality: Melbourne, VIC.

Distribution: SE coastal, VIC; only published localities Melbourne and Sandringham.
Ecology: larva—sedentary : adult—volant; melliferous, nest gregariously in soil, males cluster in evening.
References: Cockerell, T.D.A. (1929). Bees, chiefly Australian species, described or determined by Dr. H. Friese. *Am. Mus. Novit.* **343**: 1–20 (redescription); Rayment, T. (1947). Biology and taxonomy of the solitary bee, *Parasphecodes fulviventris* (Friese). *Aust. Zool.* **11**: 76–95 (biology); Rayment, T. (1954). Incidence of acarid mites on the biology of bees. *Aust. Zool.* **12**: 26–38 (biology); Rayment, T. (1957). Closer than a brother. *Proc. R. Zool. Soc. N.S.W.* **1955–56**: 87–90 (as host).

Lasioglossum (Parasphecodes) fumidicaudum (Cockerell, 1914)

Parasphecodes fumidicaudus Cockerell, T.D.A. (1914). Descriptions and records of bees. LVI. *Ann. Mag. Nat. Hist.* (8)**13**: 136–146 [144].
Type data: holotype, QM Hy4140 ♀.
Type locality: Stradbroke Is., QLD.

Distribution: NE coastal, QLD; only published localities Stradbroke Is., Brisbane and Bribie Is.
Ecology: adult—volant; melliferous, solitary.
References: Meyer, R. (1920). Apidae—Halictinae. I. Gatt. *Parasphecodes* Sm. *Arch. Naturg.* **85**(A)11: 112–137 (taxonomy); Hacker, H. (1921). Catalogue of Australian bees. *Mem. Qd Mus.* **7**: 99–163 (distribution).

Lasioglossum (Parasphecodes) gentianae (Rayment, 1951)

Parasphecodes gentianae Rayment, T. (1951). New bees and wasps—Part XV. Bees from two mountains, with description of a new species and notes on the biology of another. *Vict. Nat.* **68**: 10–13 [10].
Type data: holotype, ANIC ♂.
Type locality: Mt Buffalo, VIC.

Distribution: Murray-Darling basin, VIC; known only from type locality.

Ecology: adult—volant; melliferous, flower visiting record: *Gentiana* L. [Gentianaceae].

Lasioglossum (Parasphecodes) gibbosum (Friese, 1924)

Halictus gibbosus Friese, H. (1924). Ueber die Bienen Australiens. *Konowia* 3: 216–249 [238].
Type data: lectotype, AMNH ♀*.
Subsequent designation: Cockerell, T.D.A. (1929). Bees, chiefly Australian species, described or determined by Dr. H. Friese. *Am. Mus. Novit.* 343: 1–20 [15].
Type locality: Sydney, NSW.

Distribution: SE coastal, NSW; known only from type locality.
Ecology: adult—volant; melliferous, solitary.
Reference: Cockerell, T.D.A. (1929). Bees, chiefly Australian species, described or determined by Dr. H. Friese. *Am. Mus. Novit.* 343: 1–20 (redescription).

Lasioglossum (Parasphecodes) grande (Meyer, 1920)

Parasphecodes grandis Meyer, R. (1920). Apidae—Halictinae. I. Gatt. *Parasphecodes* Sm. *Arch. Naturg.* 85(A)11: 112–137 [135].
Type data: holotype, ZMB 1950 ♂*.
Type locality: TAS (as Van Diemens Land).

Distribution: TAS; known only from type locality.
Ecology: adult—volant; melliferous, solitary.

Lasioglossum (Parasphecodes) griseipenne (Cockerell, 1929)

Parasphecodes wellingtoni griseipennis Cockerell, T.D.A. (1929). Bees from the Australian region. *Am. Mus. Novit.* 346: 1–18 [11].
Type data: holotype, ANIC ♀.
Type locality: Jenolan, NSW.

Distribution: SE coastal, NSW; only published localities Jenolan and Blue Mts.
Ecology: adult—volant; melliferous, flower visiting record: *Helichrysum* Miller *s.lat.* [Asteraceae].
References: Rayment, T. (1947). Bees from the Victorian Alps. *Vict. Nat.* 64: 103–107 (flower record); Michener, C.D. (1965). A classification of the bees of the Australian and South Pacific regions. *Bull. Am. Mus. Nat. Hist.* 130: 1–362 [168] (taxonomy).

Lasioglossum (Parasphecodes) hilactum (Smith, 1853)

Parasphecodes hilactus Smith, F. (1853). *Catalogue of Hymenopterous Insects in the Collection of the British Museum.* Part I. Andrenidae and Apidae. London : British Museum 197 pp. [39].
Type data: syntypes, BMNH 2♂ (a specimen is labelled 'type' and has registration number Hym.17.a.610).
Type locality: Adelaide, SA; Swan River, WA.

Distribution: S Gulfs, SW coastal, SA, WA; only published localities Adelaide and Swan River.
Ecology: adult—volant; melliferous, solitary.
References: Cockerell, T.D.A. (1904). The halictine bees of the Australian region. *Ann. Mag. Nat. Hist.* (7)14: 208–213 (taxonomy); Meyer, R. (1920). Apidae—Halictinae. I. Gatt. *Parasphecodes* Sm. *Arch. Naturg.* 85(A)11: 112–137 (taxonomy).

Lasioglossum (Parasphecodes) hiltacum (Smith, 1853)

Parasphecodes hiltacus Smith, F. (1853). *Catalogue of Hymenopterous Insects in the Collection of the British Museum.* Part I. Andrenidae and Apidae, London : British Museum 197 pp. [39].
Type data: holotype, BMNH Hym.17.a.611 ♀.
Type locality: Australia (as New Holland).

Distribution: TAS; only published localities Australia (as New Holland) and TAS (as Van Diemens Land).
Ecology: adult—volant; melliferous, solitary.
References: Cockerell, T.D.A. (1904). The halictine bees of the Australian region. *Ann. Mag. Nat. Hist.* (7)14: 208–213 (taxonomy); Meyer, R. (1920). Apidae—Halictinae. I. Gatt. *Parasphecodes* Sm. *Arch. Naturg.* 85(A)11: 112–137 (taxonomy).

Lasioglossum (Parasphecodes) hirtiventre (Cockerell, 1922)

Parasphecodes hirtiventris Cockerell, T.D.A. (1922). Australian bees in the Queensland Museum. *Mem. Qd Mus.* 7: 257–279 [260].
Type data: holotype, QM T2676 ♀.
Type locality: Ebor, NSW.

Distribution: Murray-Darling basin, SE coastal, QLD, NSW, VIC.
Ecology: adult—volant; melliferous, flower visiting record: *Boronia* Sm. [Rutaceae], *Daviesia* Sm. [Fabaceae], *Eucalyptus* L'Hérit. [Myrtaceae], *Hibbertia* Andrews [Dilleniaceae], *?Microseris* D. Don [Asteraceae], *Stylidium* Willd. [Stylidiaceae].
References: Rayment, T. (1929). Bees from East Gippsland. *Vict. Nat.* 46: 124–129 (distribution); Rayment, T. (1956). She trips the trigger. *Proc. R. Zool. Soc. N.S.W.* 1954–1955: 55–59 (flower record); Erickson, R. (1958). *Triggerplants.* Perth : Paterson Brokensha 229 pp. (flower record); Michener, C.D. (1965). A classification of the bees of the Australian and South Pacific regions. *Bull. Am. Mus. Nat. Hist.* 130: 1–362 (flower record); Carlquist, S. (1969). Studies in Stylidiaceae : new taxa, field observations, evolutionary tendencies. *Aliso* 7: 13–64 (flower record, as *Parasphecodes hirsiventris*, incorrect subsequent spelling).

Lasioglossum (Parasphecodes) hybodinum (Cockerell, 1912)

Parasphecodes hybodinus Cockerell, T.D.A. (1912). Descriptions and records of bees. XLII. *Ann. Mag. Nat. Hist. (8)9*: 220–229 [227].
Type data: holotype, ANIC ♂.
Type locality: Windsor, VIC.

Distribution: SE coastal, VIC; only published localities Windsor, Cranbourne, Sandringham and Brighton.
Ecology: adult—volant; melliferous, flower visiting record: *Eucalyptus* L'Hérit. [Myrtaceae].
References: Meyer, R. (1920). Apidae—Halictinae. I. Gatt. *Parasphecodes* Sm. *Arch. Naturg.* **85**(A)11: 112–137 (taxonomy); Rayment, T. (1935). *A Cluster of Bees.* Sixty essays on the life-histories of Australian bees, with specific descriptions of over 100 new species, and an introduction by Professor E.F. Phillips, D.Ph., Cornell University, U.S.A. Sydney : Endeavour Press 752 pp. (flower record); Rayment, T. (1947). Biology and taxonomy of the solitary bee, *Parasphecodes fulviventris* (Friese). *Aust. Zool.* **11**: 76–95 (taxonomy).

Lasioglossum (Parasphecodes) insigne (Meyer, 1920)

Parasphecodes insignis Meyer, R. (1920). Apidae—Halictinae. I. Gatt. *Parasphecodes* Sm. *Arch. Naturg.* **85**(A)11: 112–137 [123].
Type data: holotype, ZMB 1844 ♀*.
Type locality: TAS (as Van Diemens Land).

Distribution: TAS; known only from type locality.
Ecology: adult—volant; melliferous, solitary.

Lasioglossum (Parasphecodes) lacthium (Smith, 1853)

Parasphecodes lacthius Smith, F. (1853). *Catalogue of Hymenopterous Insects in the Collection of the British Museum.* Part I. Andrenidae and Apidae. London : British Museum 197 pp. [40].
Type data: holotype, BMNH Hym.17.a.615 ♀.
Type locality: Australia (as New Holland).

Distribution: Australia, known only from type locality, exact locality unknown.
Ecology: adult—volant; melliferous, solitary.
References: Cockerell, T.D.A. (1904). The halictine bees of the Australian region. *Ann. Mag. Nat. Hist. (7)14*: 208–213 (taxonomy); Meyer, R. (1920). Apidae—Halictinae. I. Gatt. *Parasphecodes* Sm. *Arch. Naturg.* **85**(A)11: 112–137 (taxonomy).

Lasioglossum (Parasphecodes) latissimum (Cockerell, 1915)

Parasphecodes latissimus Cockerell, T.D.A. (1915). Descriptions and records of bees. LXIX. *Ann. Mag. Nat. Hist. (8)16*: 96–104 [96].

Type data: holotype, ANIC ♀.
Type locality: Bridport, TAS.

Distribution: TAS; known only from type locality.
Ecology: adult—volant; melliferous, solitary.

Lasioglossum (Parasphecodes) leichardti (Cockerell, 1906)

Halictus leichardti Cockerell, T.D.A. (1906). New Australian bees in the collection of the British Museum. II. *Entomologist* **39**: 56–60 [59].
Type data: holotype, BMNH Hym.17.a.965 ♀.
Type locality: Mackay, QLD.

Halictus paracolletinus Cockerell, T.D.A. (1910). New and little-known bees. *Trans. Am. Entomol. Soc.* **36**: 199–249 [201].
Type data: syntypes, BMNH 3♀ (a specimen is labelled 'type' and has registration number Hym.17.a.966).
Type locality: Mackay, QLD.

[*Halictus scutellatus* (part)] Friese, H. (1924). Ueber die Bienen Australiens. *Konowia* **3**: 216–249 [242] [♀ syntype is conspecific with *Halictus leichardti* Cockerell, 1906; ♂ syntype is conspecific with *Halictus forresti* Cockerell, 1906].
Type data: syntypes, AMNH ♀*.
Type locality: Mackay, QLD.

Taxonomic decision for synonymy: Cockerell, T.D.A. (1912). Descriptions and records of bees. XLVII. *Ann. Mag. Nat. Hist. (8)10*: 484–494 [486]; Cockerell, T.D.A. (1929). Bees, chiefly Australian species, described or determined by Dr. H. Friese. *Am. Mus. Novit.* **343**: 1–20 [12].

Distribution: NE coastal, SE coastal, QLD, NSW.
Ecology: adult—volant; melliferous, flower visiting record: *Erigeron* L. [Asteraceae], *Leptospermum* Forster & G.Forster [Myrtaceae].
References: Cockerell, T.D.A. (1912). Descriptions and records of bees. XLIII. *Ann. Mag. Nat. Hist. (8)9*: 377–387 (description of male, as *Halictus paracolletinus* Cockerell, 1910); Rayment, T. (1954). Remarkable bees from a rain forest. *Aust. Zool.* **12**: 46–56 (distribution); Michener, C.D. (1965). A classification of the bees of the Australian and South Pacific regions. *Bull. Am. Mus. Nat. Hist.* **130**: 1–362 (flower record).

Lasioglossum (Parasphecodes) leptospermi (Cockerell, 1916)

Parasphecodes leptospermi Cockerell, T.D.A. (1916). A collection of bees from Queensland. *Mem. Qd Mus.* **5**: 197–204 [202].
Type data: holotype, QM Hy4144 ♀.
Type locality: Oxley, Brisbane, QLD.

Distribution: NE coastal, QLD; known only from type locality.
Ecology: adult—volant; melliferous, solitary.
Reference: Rayment, T. (1947). Biology and taxonomy of the solitary bee, *Parasphecodes fulviventris* (Friese). *Aust. Zool.* **11**: 76–95 (taxonomy).

Lasioglossum (Parasphecodes) leucorhinum
(Cockerell, 1926)

Halictus leucorhinus Cockerell, T.D.A. (1926).
Descriptions and records of bees. CXII. *Ann. Mag. Nat. Hist. (9)***18**: 216–227 [226].
Type data: holotype, ANIC ♂.
Type locality: Sandringham, VIC.

Distribution: SE coastal, VIC; only published localities Sandringham and Hampton.
Ecology: larva—sedentary : adult—volant; melliferous, flower visiting record: *Eucalyptus* L'Hérit. [Myrtaceae], *Veronica* L. [Scrophulariaceae].
References: Rayment, T. (1935). *A Cluster of Bees.* Sixty essays on the life-histories of Australian bees, with specific descriptions of over 100 new species, and an introduction by Professor E.F. Phillips, D.Ph., Cornell University, U.S.A. Sydney : Endeavour Press 752 pp. (biology); Rayment, T. (1955). Dimorphism and parthenogenesis in halictine bees. *Aust. Zool.* **12**: 142–153 (biology).

Lasioglossum (Parasphecodes) lichatinum
(Cockerell, 1922)

Parasphecodes lichatinus Cockerell, T.D.A. (1922). Australian bees in the Queensland Museum. *Mem. Qd Mus.* **7**: 257–279 [260].
Type data: holotype, QM T2745 ♀.
Type locality: Ararat, VIC.

Distribution: SE coastal, VIC; only published localities Ararat and Port Phillip.
Ecology: larva—sedentary : adult—volant; melliferous, solitary.
Reference: Rayment, T. (1935). *A Cluster of Bees.* Sixty essays on the life-histories of Australian bees, with specific descriptions of over 100 new species, and an introduction by Professor E.F. Phillips, D.Ph., Cornell University, U.S.A. Sydney : Endeavour Press 752 pp. (biology).

Lasioglossum (Parasphecodes) lichatum (Smith, 1853)

Parasphecodes lichatus Smith, F. (1853). *Catalogue of Hymenopterous Insects in the Collection of the British Museum.* Part I. Andrenidae and Apidae. London : British Museum 197 pp. [40].
Type data: holotype, BMNH Hym.17.a.614 ♀.
Type locality: WA.

Distribution: NW coastal, SW coastal, WA; only published localities Eradu, Kojarena, Swan River and Perth.
Ecology: adult—volant; melliferous, solitary.
References: Cockerell, T.D.A. (1904). The halictine bees of the Australian region. *Ann. Mag. Nat. Hist. (7)***14**: 208–213 (taxonomy); Meyer, R. (1920). Apidae—Halictinae. I. Gatt. *Parasphecodes* Sm. *Arch. Naturg.* **85**(A)11: 112–137 (taxonomy); Cockerell, T.D.A. (1929). Bees in the Australian Museum

collection. *Rec. Aust. Mus.* **17**: 199–243 (distribution); Rayment, T. (1931). Bees in the collections of the Western Australian Museum and the Agricultural Department, Perth. *J. Proc. R. Soc. West. Aust.* **17**: 157–190 (distribution); Rayment, T. (1935). *A Cluster of Bees.* Sixty essays on the life-histories of Australian bees, with specific descriptions of over 100 new species, and an introduction by Professor E.F. Phillips, D.Ph., Cornell University, U.S.A. Sydney : Endeavour Press 752 pp. (doubtful record, from Port Phillip).

Lasioglossum (Parasphecodes) lithuscum (Smith, 1853)

Parasphecodes lithusca Smith, F. (1853). *Catalogue of Hymenopterous Insects in the Collection of the British Museum.* Part I. Andrenidae and Apidae. London : British Museum 197 pp. [41].
Type data: holotype (probable), BMNH Hym.17.a.618 ♀.
Type locality: TAS (as Van Diemens Land).

Distribution: TAS; only published locality Lenah Valley.
Ecology: larva—sedentary : adult—volant; melliferous, nest in rotting wood.
References: Froggatt, W.W. (1892). Catalogue of the described Hymenoptera of Australia. Part II. *Proc. Linn. Soc. N.S.W. (2)***7**: 205–248 (as *Parasphecodes licthusca*, incorrect subsequent spelling); Cockerell, T.D.A. (1904). The halictine bees of the Australian region. *Ann. Mag. Nat. Hist. (7)***14**: 208–213 (taxonomy); Meyer, R. (1920). Apidae—Halictinae. I. Gatt. *Parasphecodes* Sm. *Arch. Naturg.* **85**(A)11: 112–137 (taxonomy); Rayment, T. (1957). First steps from the cave. *Proc. R. Zool. Soc. N.S.W.* **1955–56**: 83–86 (biology).

Lasioglossum (Parasphecodes) longmani
(Cockerell, 1922)

Parasphecodes longmani Cockerell, T.D.A. (1922). Australian bees in the Queensland Museum. *Mem. Qd Mus.* **7**: 257–279 [259].
Type data: holotype, QM T2746 ♂.
Type locality: Caloundra, QLD.

Distribution: NE coastal, SE coastal, QLD, VIC; only published localities Caloundra and east of Melbourne.
Ecology: adult—volant; melliferous, flower visiting record: *Leptospermum* Forster & G.Forster [Myrtaceae].
Reference: Rayment, T. (1935). *A Cluster of Bees.* Sixty essays on the life-histories of Australian bees, with specific descriptions of over 100 new species, and an introduction by Professor E.F. Phillips, D.Ph., Cornell University, U.S.A. Sydney : Endeavour Press 752 pp. (flower record).

Lasioglossum (Parasphecodes) loweri (Cockerell, 1905)

Parasphecodes loweri Cockerell, T.D.A. (1905). Descriptions and records of bees. II. *Ann. Mag. Nat. Hist. (7)***16**: 292–301 [298].
Type data: holotype, BMNH Hym.17.a.630 ♀.
Type locality: Adelaide, SA.

Distribution: S Gulfs, SA; known only from type locality.
Ecology: adult—volant; melliferous, solitary.
Reference: Meyer, R. (1920). Apidae—Halictinae. I. Gatt. *Parasphecodes* Sm. *Arch. Naturg.* **85**(A)11: 112–137 (taxonomy).

Lasioglossum (Parasphecodes) melbournense (Cockerell, 1904)

Parasphecodes melbournensis Cockerell, T.D.A. (1904). The halictine bees of the Australian region. *Ann. Mag. Nat. Hist. (7)***14**: 208–213 [210].
Type data: holotype, BMNH Hym.17.a.632 ♀.
Type locality: Melbourne, VIC.

Distribution: SE coastal, Murray-Darling basin, VIC; only published localities Melbourne, Emerald, Sandringham and Mt Buffalo.
Ecology: adult—volant; melliferous, solitary.
References: Meyer, R. (1920). Apidae—Halictinae. I. Gatt. *Parasphecodes* Sm. *Arch. Naturg.* **85**(A)11: 112–137 (taxonomy); Rayment, T. (1947). Bees from the Victorian Alps. *Vict. Nat.* **64**: 103–107 (distribution).

Lasioglossum (Parasphecodes) microdontum (Cockerell, 1912)

Parasphecodes microdontus Cockerell, T.D.A. (1912). Descriptions and records of bees. XLII. *Ann. Mag. Nat. Hist. (8)***9**: 220–229 [226].
Type data: holotype, BMNH Hym.17.a.634 ♀.
Type locality: Melbourne, VIC.

Distribution: SE coastal, VIC; known only from type locality.
Ecology: adult—volant; melliferous, solitary.
Reference: Meyer, R. (1920). Apidae—Halictinae. I. Gatt. *Parasphecodes* Sm. *Arch. Naturg.* **85**(A)11: 112–137 (taxonomy).

Lasioglossum (Parasphecodes) musicum (Cockerell, 1913)

Halictus musicus Cockerell, T.D.A. (1913). Descriptions and records of bees. LII. *Ann. Mag. Nat. Hist. (8)***11**: 530–542 [540].
Type data: holotype, BMNH Hym.17.a.960 ♀.
Type locality: Mt Tamborine, QLD.

Halictus trimaculatus Friese, H. (1924). Ueber die Bienen Australiens. *Konowia* **3**: 216–249 [241].
Type data: holotype (probable), AMNH ♀*.
Type locality: Central Australia.

Taxonomic decision for synonymy: Cockerell, T.D.A. (1929). Bees, chiefly Australian species, described or determined by Dr. H. Friese. *Am. Mus. Novit.* **343**: 1–20 [12].

Distribution: NE coastal, Murray-Darling basin, SE coastal, QLD, NSW; only published localities Mt Tamborine, Mt Glorious, Bunya Mts, Tooloom and "Central Australia".
Ecology: adult—volant; melliferous, flower visiting record: *Erigeron* L. [Asteraceae], *Rubus* L. [Rosaceae], *Solanum* L. [Solanaceae].
References: Cockerell, T.D.A. (1929). Bees in the Queensland Museum. *Mem. Qd Mus.* **9**: 298–323 (distribution); Michener, C.D. (1965). A classification of the bees of the Australian and South Pacific regions. *Bull. Am. Mus. Nat. Hist.* **130**: 1–362 (illustration, flower record).

Lasioglossum (Parasphecodes) niveatum (Meyer, 1920)

Parasphecodes punctatissimus niveatus Meyer, R. (1920). Apidae—Halictinae. I. Gatt. *Parasphecodes* Sm. *Arch. Naturg.* **85**(A)11: 112–137 [131].
Type data: holotype (probable), ZMB 1946 ♀*.
Type locality: TAS (as Van Diemens Land).

Distribution: TAS; known only from type locality.
Ecology: adult—volant; melliferous, solitary.
Reference: Michener, C.D. (1965). A classification of the bees of the Australian and South Pacific regions. *Bull. Am. Mus. Nat. Hist.* **130**: 1–362 [168] (taxonomy).

Lasioglossum (Parasphecodes) niveorufum (Friese, 1924)

Halictus niveorufus Friese, H. (1924). Ueber die Bienen Australiens. *Konowia* **3**: 216–249 [239].
Type data: holotype, AMNH ♀*.
Type locality: Ararat, VIC.

Distribution: SE coastal, VIC; known only from type locality.
Ecology: adult—volant; melliferous, solitary.
Reference: Cockerell, T.D.A. (1933). The bees of Australia. *Aust. Zool.* **7**: 291–324 (taxonomy, as ?*Parasphecodes niveorufus* (Friese, 1924)).

Lasioglossum (Parasphecodes) noachinum (Cockerell, 1914)

Parasphecodes noachinus Cockerell, T.D.A. (1914). Descriptions and records of bees. LVI. *Ann. Mag. Nat. Hist. (8)***13**: 136–146 [144].
Type data: syntypes, USNM 2♀*.
Type locality: Ararat, VIC.

Distribution: SE coastal, Murray-Darling basin, NSW, VIC.
Ecology: larva—sedentary : adult—volant; melliferous, nest in soil, flower visiting record: *Leptospermum* Forster & G.Forster [Myrtaceae], *Leucopogon* R.Br. [Epacridaceae].

References: Meyer, R. (1920). Apidae—Halictinae. I. Gatt. *Parasphecodes* Sm. *Arch. Naturg.* **85**(A)11: 112–137 (taxonomy); Rayment, T. (1939). Bees from the high lands of New South Wales and Victoria. *Aust. Zool.* **9**: 263–294 (description of male, distribution); Rayment, T. (1953). *Bees of the Portland District.* Victoria : Portland Field Naturalist's Club 39 pp. (flower record); Rayment, T. (1957). First steps from the cave. *Proc. R. Zool. Soc. N.S.W.* **1955–56**: 83–86 (biology).

Lasioglossum (Parasphecodes) notescens (Cockerell, 1930)

Parasphecodes notescens Cockerell, T.D.A. (1930). New Australian bees. *Mem. Qd Mus.* **10**: 37–50 [38].
Type data: holotype, QM Hy4092 ♂.
Type locality: Beaconsfield, VIC.

Distribution: SE coastal, VIC; only published localities Beaconsfield and Portland.
Ecology: adult—volant; melliferous, solitary.
Reference: Rayment, T. (1953). *Bees of the Portland District.* Victoria : Portland Field Naturalist's Club 39 pp. (distribution).

Lasioglossum (Parasphecodes) olgae (Rayment, 1935)

Halictus olgae Rayment, T. (1935). *A Cluster of Bees.* Sixty essays on the life-histories of Australian bees, with specific descriptions of over 100 new species, and an introduction by Professor E.F. Phillips, D.Ph., Cornell University, U.S.A. Sydney : Endeavour Press 752 pp. [696].
Type data: holotype, ANIC ♀.
Type locality: Monbulk, VIC.

Distribution: SE coastal, VIC; known only from type locality.
Ecology: adult—volant; melliferous, flower visiting record: *Hypochaeris* L. [Asteraceae].
Reference: Michener, C.D. (1965). A classification of the bees of the Australian and South Pacific regions. *Bull. Am. Mus. Nat. Hist.* **130**: 1–362 (illustration).

Lasioglossum ·(Parasphecodes) paramelaenum (Cockerell, 1922)

Parasphecodes paramelaenus Cockerell, T.D.A. (1922). Australian bees in the Queensland Museum. *Mem. Qd Mus.* **7**: 257–279 [260].
Type data: holotype, QM T2677 ♀.
Type locality: [Lamington] National Park, QLD.

Distribution: NE coastal, QLD; known only from type locality.
Ecology: adult—volant; melliferous, solitary.
Reference: Cockerell, T.D.A. (1929). Bees, chiefly Australian species, described or determined by Dr. H. Friese. *Am. Mus. Novit.* **343**: 1–20 (as synonym of *Parasphecodes tamburinei* (Friese, 1917)).

Lasioglossum (Parasphecodes) patongense (Rayment, 1948)

Halictus patongensis Rayment, T. (1948). Notes on remarkable wasps and bees. With specific descriptions. *Aust. Zool.* **11**: 238–254 [252].
Type data: holotype, ANIC ♂.
Type locality: Patonga, NSW.

Distribution: SE coastal, NSW; known only from type locality.
Ecology: adult—volant; melliferous, flower visiting record: *Leptospermum* Forster & G.Forster [Myrtaceae].

Lasioglossum (Parasphecodes) perustum (Cockerell, 1914)

Parasphecodes perustus Cockerell, T.D.A. (1914). Descriptions and records of bees. LXII. *Ann. Mag. Nat. Hist.* (8)**14**: 49–57 [52].
Type data: holotype, BMNH Hym.17.a.639 ♂.
Type locality: Mt Wellington, TAS.

Distribution: TAS; known only from type locality.
Ecology: adult—volant; melliferous, solitary.
Reference: Meyer, R. (1920). Apidae—Halictinae. I. Gatt. *Parasphecodes* Sm. *Arch. Naturg.* **85**(A)11: 112–137 (taxonomy).

Lasioglossum (Parasphecodes) proximum (Rayment, 1947)

Parasphecodes fulviventris proximus Rayment, T. (1947). Biology and taxonomy of the solitary bee, *Parasphecodes fulviventris* (Friese). *Aust. Zool.* **11**: 76–95 [79].
Type data: holotype (probable), whereabouts unknown *.
Type locality: Sandringham, VIC.

Distribution: SE coastal, VIC; known only from type locality.
Ecology: adult—volant; melliferous, solitary.
Reference: Michener, C.D. (1965). A classification of the bees of the Australian and South Pacific regions. *Bull. Am. Mus. Nat. Hist.* **130**: 1–362 [168] (taxonomy).

Lasioglossum (Parasphecodes) recantans (Cockerell, 1912)

Parasphecodes recantans Cockerell, T.D.A. (1912). Descriptions and records of bees. XLII. *Ann. Mag. Nat. Hist.* (8)**9**: 220–229 [227].
Type data: holotype, BMNH Hym.17.a.635 ♂.
Type locality: VIC.

Distribution: VIC; known only from type locality, exact locality unknown.
Ecology: adult—volant; melliferous, solitary.
Reference: Meyer, R. (1920). Apidae—Halictinae. I. Gatt. *Parasphecodes* Sm. *Arch. Naturg.* **85**(A)11: 112–137 (taxonomy).

Lasioglossum (Parasphecodes) recessum (Cockerell, 1914)

Parasphecodes recessus Cockerell, T.D.A. (1914). Descriptions and records of bees. LXII. *Ann. Mag. Nat. Hist. (8)***14**: 49–57 [51].
Type data: holotype, BMNH Hym.17.a.638 ♀.
Type locality: Mt Wellington, TAS.

Distribution: SE coastal, VIC, TAS; only published localities Portland and Mt Wellington.
Ecology: adult—volant; melliferous, flower visiting record: *Arctotheca* Wendl. [Asteraceae].
References: Meyer, R. (1920). Apidae—Halictinae. I. Gatt. *Parasphecodes* Sm. *Arch. Naturg.* **85**(A)11: 112–137 (taxonomy); Rayment, T. (1953). *Bees of the Portland District*. Victoria : Portland Field Naturalist's Club 39 pp. (distribution, flower record).

Lasioglossum (Parasphecodes) rhodopterum (Cockerell, 1914)

Parasphecodes rhodopterus Cockerell, T.D.A. (1914). Some Tasmanian bees. *Entomologist* **47**: 305–308 [306].
Type data: holotype, ANIC ♀.
Type locality: Launceston, TAS.

Distribution: TAS; known only from type locality.
Ecology: adult—volant; melliferous, solitary.

Lasioglossum (Parasphecodes) rufotegulare (Cockerell, 1914)

Parasphecodes rufotegularis Cockerell, T.D.A. (1914). Some Tasmanian bees. *Entomologist* **47**: 305–308 [306].
Type data: holotype, USNM ♂*.
Type locality: Launceston, TAS.

Distribution: SE coastal, VIC, TAS; only published localities Portland and Launceston.
Ecology: adult—volant; melliferous, flower visiting record: *Leptospermum* Forster & G.Forster [Myrtaceae].
Reference: Rayment, T. (1953). *Bees of the Portland District*. Victoria : Portland Field Naturalist's Club 39 pp. (distribution).

Lasioglossum (Parasphecodes) rufulum (Friese, 1924)

Halictus rufulus Friese, H. (1924). Ueber die Bienen Australiens. *Konowia* **3**: 216–249 [239].
Type data: lectotype, AMNH ♂*.
Subsequent designation: Cockerell, T.D.A. (1929). Bees, chiefly Australian species, described or determined by Dr. H. Friese. *Am. Mus. Novit.* **343**: 1–20 [16].
Type locality: VIC.

Distribution: NE coastal, QLD, VIC; exact locality unknown, only published locality Mackay.
Ecology: adult—volant; melliferous, solitary.
Reference: Cockerell, T.D.A. (1929). Bees, chiefly Australian species, described or determined by Dr. H. Friese. *Am. Mus. Novit.* **343**: 1–20 (redescription).

Lasioglossum (Parasphecodes) schomburgki (Cockerell, 1910)

Parasphecodes schomburgki Cockerell, T.D.A. (1910). New and little-known bees. *Trans. Am. Entomol. Soc.* **36**: 199–249 [239].
Type data: holotype, ZMB 22122 ♀*.
Type locality: Adelaide, SA.

Distribution: S Gulfs, SA; known only from type locality.
Ecology: adult—volant; melliferous, solitary.
Reference: Meyer, R. (1920). Apidae—Halictinae. I. Gatt. *Parasphecodes* Sm. *Arch. Naturg.* **85**(A)11: 112–137 (taxonomy).

Lasioglossum (Parasphecodes) sextum (Cockerell, 1910)

Parasphecodes sextus Cockerell, T.D.A. (1910). New and little-known bees. *Trans. Am. Entomol. Soc.* **36**: 199–249 [239].
Type data: holotype, ZMB 22114 ♂*.
Type locality: Adelaide, SA.

Distribution: SE coastal, S Gulfs, NSW, VIC, SA; only published localities White Swamp, Portland, Rocklands and Adelaide.
Ecology: larva—sedentary : adult—volant; melliferous, males found clustering, flower visiting record: aster.
References: Meyer, R. (1920). Apidae—Halictinae. I. Gatt. *Parasphecodes* Sm. *Arch. Naturg.* **85**(A)11: 112–137 (taxonomy); Rayment, T. (1939). Bees from the high lands of New South Wales and Victoria. *Aust. Zool.* **9**: 263–294 (distribution); Rayment, T. (1947). Biology and taxonomy of the solitary bee, *Parasphecodes fulviventris* (Friese). *Aust. Zool.* **11**: 76–95 (biology); Rayment, T. (1953). *Bees of the Portland District*. Victoria : Portland Field Naturalist's Club 39 pp. (distribution); Rayment, T. (1954). Incidence of acarid mites on the biology of bees. *Aust. Zool.* **12**: 26–38 (biology).

Lasioglossum (Parasphecodes) solis (Cockerell, 1922)

Parasphecodes solis Cockerell, T.D.A. (1922). Australian bees in the Queensland Museum. *Mem. Qd Mus.* **7**: 257–279 [258].
Type data: holotype, QM T2679 ♂.
Type locality: Sunnybank, Brisbane, QLD.

Distribution: NE coastal, SE coastal, QLD, VIC; only published localities Brisbane, Port Phillip, Brighton, Mordialloc and Daylesford.
Ecology: adult—volant; melliferous, flower visiting record: *Bursaria* Cav. [Pittosporaceae], *Cytisus* Desf. [Fabaceae], *Eucalyptus* L'Hérit. [Myrtaceae].
Reference: Rayment, T. (1935). *A Cluster of Bees*. Sixty essays on the life-histories of Australian bees, with specific descriptions of over 100 new species, and an introduction by Professor E.F. Phillips, D.Ph.,

Cornell University, U.S.A. Sydney : Endeavour Press 752 pp. (flower record).

Lasioglossum (Parasphecodes) sordidulum (Cockerell, 1914)

Parasphecodes bryotrichus sordidulus Cockerell, T.D.A. (1914). Descriptions and records of bees. LXIII. *Ann. Mag. Nat. Hist. (8)***14**: 361–369 [369].
Type data: holotype, QM Hy4141 ♀.
Type locality: Brisbane, QLD.

Distribution: NE coastal, QLD; known only from type locality.
Ecology: adult—volant; melliferous, solitary.
Reference: Cockerell, T.D.A. (1916). A collection of bees from Queensland. *Mem. Qd Mus.* **5**: 197–204 (taxonomy).

Lasioglossum (Parasphecodes) speculiferum (Cockerell, 1912)

Parasphecodes speculiferus Cockerell, T.D.A. (1912). Descriptions and records of bees. XLII. *Ann. Mag. Nat. Hist. (8)***9**: 220–229 [228].
Type data: holotype, BMNH Hym.17.a.641 ♀.
Type locality: VIC.

Distribution: NE coastal, SE coastal, Murray-Darling basin, QLD, NSW, VIC.
Ecology: larva—sedentary : adult—volant; melliferous, flower visiting record: broom, *Angophora* Cav. [Myrtaceae], *Boronia* Sm. [Rutaceae], *Eucalyptus* L'Hérit. [Myrtaceae], *Leptospermum* Forster & G.Forster [Myrtaceae], *Pultenaea* Sm. [Fabaceae], *Wahlenbergia* Roth [Campanulaceae].
References: Cockerell, T.D.A. (1916). A collection of bees from Queensland. *Mem. Qd Mus.* **5**: 197–204 (redescription); Meyer, R. (1920). Apidae—Halictinae. I. Gatt. *Parasphecodes* Sm. *Arch. Naturg.* **85**(A)11: 112–137 (taxonomy); Rayment, T. (1935). *A Cluster of Bees.* Sixty essays on the life-histories of Australian bees, with specific descriptions of over 100 new species, and an introduction by Professor E.F. Phillips, D.Ph., Cornell University, U.S.A. Sydney : Endeavour Press 752 pp. (illustration); Michener, C.D. (1960). Notes on the biology and supposed parthenogenesis of halictine bees from the Australian region. *J. Kansas Entomol. Soc.* **33**: 85–96 (biology); Michener, C.D. (1965). A classification of the bees of the Australian and South Pacific regions. *Bull. Am. Mus. Nat. Hist.* **130**: 1–362 (flower record).

Lasioglossum (Parasphecodes) stuchilum (Smith, 1853)

Parasphecodes stuchila Smith, F. (1853). *Catalogue of Hymenopterous Insects in the Collection of the British Museum.* Part I. Andrenidae and Apidae. London : British Museum 197 pp. [42].
Type data: holotype, BMNH Hym.17.a.613 ♂.
Type locality: TAS (as Van Diemens Land).

Distribution: SE coastal, VIC, TAS; only published locality Portland.
Ecology: adult—volant; melliferous, flower visiting record: *Leptospermum* Forster & G.Forster [Myrtaceae].
References: Cockerell, T.D.A. (1904). The halictine bees of the Australian region. *Ann. Mag. Nat. Hist. (7)***14**: 208–213 (taxonomy); Meyer, R. (1920). Apidae—Halictinae. I. Gatt. *Parasphecodes* Sm. *Arch. Naturg.* **85**(A)11: 112–137 (taxonomy); Rayment, T. (1953). *Bees of the Portland District.* Victoria : Portland Field Naturalist's Club 39 pp. (distribution).

Lasioglossum (Parasphecodes) subfultoni (Cockerell, 1930)

Parasphecodes subfultoni Cockerell, T.D.A. (1930). New Australian bees. *Mem. Qd Mus.* **10**: 37–50 [39].
Type data: holotype, QM Hy4090 ♀.
Type locality: VIC.

Distribution: SE coastal, VIC; only published localities Portland and Dandenong.
Ecology: larva—sedentary : adult—volant; melliferous, nest in soil, flower visiting record: aster.
References: Rayment, T. (1947). Biology and taxonomy of the solitary bee, *Parasphecodes fulviventris* (Friese). *Aust. Zool.* **11**: 76–95 (biology); Rayment, T. (1953). *Bees of the Portland District.* Victoria : Portland Field Naturalist's Club 39 pp. (taxonomy, distribution).

Lasioglossum (Parasphecodes) submeracum (Cockerell, 1930)

Parasphecodes submeracus Cockerell, T.D.A. (1930). New Australian bees. *Mem. Qd Mus.* **10**: 37–50 [39].
Type data: holotype, QM Hy4091 ♀.
Type locality: Stanthorpe, QLD.

Distribution: Murray-Darling basin, SE coastal, QLD, NSW; only published localities Stanthorpe and Jamberoo.
Ecology: adult—volant; melliferous, flower visiting record: *Leptospermum* Forster & G.Forster [Myrtaceae].
Reference: Rayment, T. (1954). Remarkable bees from a rain forest. *Aust. Zool.* **12**: 46–56 (distribution).

Lasioglossum (Parasphecodes) submoratum (Cockerell, 1930)

Parasphecodes submoratus Cockerell, T.D.A. (1930). New Australian bees. *Mem. Qd Mus.* **10**: 37–50 [39].
Type data: holotype, QM Hy4093 ♀.
Type locality: Russell Falls National Park, TAS.

Distribution: SE coastal, VIC, TAS; only published localities Portland and Russell Falls National Park.
Ecology: adult—volant; melliferous, flower visiting record: aster.

Reference: Rayment, T. (1953). *Bees of the Portland District*. Victoria : Portland Field Naturalist's Club 39 pp. (distribution).

Lasioglossum (Parasphecodes) subrussatum (Cockerell, 1922)

Parasphecodes subrussatus Cockerell, T.D.A. (1922). Australian bees in the Queensland Museum. *Mem. Qd Mus.* 7: 257–279 [259].
Type data: holotype, QM T2747 ♂.
Type locality: Kosciusko, NSW.

Distribution: Murray-Darling basin, NSW; known only from type locality.
Ecology: adult—volant; melliferous, solitary.
Reference: Cockerell, T.D.A. (1929). Bees, chiefly Australian species, described or determined by Dr. H. Friese. *Am. Mus. Novit.* **343**: 1–20 (taxonomy).

Lasioglossum (Parasphecodes) sulthicum (Smith, 1853)

Parasphecodes sulthica Smith, F. (1853). *Catalogue of Hymenopterous Insects in the Collection of the British Museum*. Part I. Andrenidae and Apidae. London : British Museum 197 pp. [40].
Type data: holotype, BMNH Hym.17.a.612 ♂.
Type locality: Australia (as New Holland).

Distribution: Australia, known only from type locality, exact locality unknown.
Ecology: adult—volant; melliferous, solitary.
References: Cockerell, T.D.A. (1904). The halictine bees of the Australian region. *Ann. Mag. Nat. Hist.* (7)**14**: 208–213 (taxonomy); Meyer, R. (1920). Apidae—Halictinae. I. Gatt. *Parasphecodes* Sm. *Arch. Naturg.* **85**(A)11: 112–137 (taxonomy); Rayment, T. (1935). *A Cluster of Bees*. Sixty essays on the life-histories of Australian bees, with specific descriptions of over 100 new species, and an introduction by Professor E.F. Phillips, D.Ph., Cornell University, U.S.A. Sydney : Endeavour Press 752 pp. (illustration).

Lasioglossum (Parasphecodes) talchium (Smith, 1853)

Parasphecodes talchius Smith, F. (1853). *Catalogue of Hymenopterous Insects in the Collection of the British Museum*. Part I. Andrenidae and Apidae. London : British Museum 197 pp. [42].
Type data: holotype (probable), OUM ♂.
Type locality: TAS (as Van Diemens Land).

Distribution: SE coastal, VIC, TAS; only published locality Portland.
Ecology: adult—volant; melliferous, flower visiting record: aster.
References: Cockerell, T.D.A. (1904). The halictine bees of the Australian region. *Ann. Mag. Nat. Hist.* (7)**14**: 208–213 (taxonomy); Cockerell, T.D.A. (1905). Descriptions and records of bees. II. *Ann.*

Mag. Nat. Hist. (7)**16**: 292–301 (taxonomy); Meyer, R. (1920). Apidae—Halictinae. I. Gatt. *Parasphecodes* Sm. *Arch. Naturg.* **85**(A)11: 112–137 (taxonomy); Rayment, T. (1953). *Bees of the Portland District*. Victoria : Portland Field Naturalist's Club 39 pp. (distribution).

Lasioglossum (Parasphecodes) taluche (Smith, 1853)

Parasphecodes taluchis Smith, F. (1853). *Catalogue of Hymenopterous Insects in the Collection of the British Museum*. Part I. Andrenidae and Apidae. London : British Museum 197 pp. [43].
Type data: holotype, BMNH Hym.17.a.619 ♀.
Type locality: TAS (as Van Diemens Land).

Distribution: SE coastal, VIC, TAS; only published locality Portland.
Ecology: adult—volant; melliferous, flower visiting record: *Eucalyptus* L'Hérit. [Myrtaceae].
References: Cockerell, T.D.A. (1904). The halictine bees of the Australian region. *Ann. Mag. Nat. Hist.* (7)**14**: 208–213 (taxonomy); Meyer, R. (1920). Apidae—Halictinae. I. Gatt. *Parasphecodes* Sm. *Arch. Naturg.* **85**(A)11: 112–137 (taxonomy); Rayment, T. (1953). *Bees of the Portland District*. Victoria : Portland Field Naturalist's Club 39 pp. (distribution).

Lasioglossum (Parasphecodes) tepperi (Cockerell, 1905)

Parasphecodes tepperi Cockerell, T.D.A. (1905). Descriptions and records of bees. II. *Ann. Mag. Nat. Hist.* (7)**16**: 292–301 [299].
Type data: syntypes, BMNH 2♀ (a specimen is labelled 'type' and has registration number Hym.17.a.629).
Type locality: Adelaide, SA.

Distribution: S Gulfs, SA; known only from type locality.
Ecology: adult—volant; melliferous, solitary.
Reference: Meyer, R. (1920). Apidae—Halictinae. I. Gatt. *Parasphecodes* Sm. *Arch. Naturg.* **85**(A)11: 112–137 (taxonomy).

Lasioglossum (Parasphecodes) testaciventre (Rayment, 1953)

Parasphecodes testaciventris Rayment, T. (1953). *Bees of the Portland District*. Victoria : Portland Field Naturalist's Club 39 pp. [30].
Type data: holotype, ANIC ♀.
Type locality: Gorae West, VIC.

Distribution: SE coastal, VIC; known only from type locality.
Ecology: adult—volant; melliferous, flower visiting record: *Eucalyptus* L'Hérit. [Myrtaceae].

Lasioglossum (Parasphecodes) tilachiforme (Cockerell, 1907)

Parasphecodes tilachiformis Cockerell, T.D.A. (1907). On a collection of Australian and Asiatic bees. *Bull. Am. Mus. Nat. Hist.* **23**: 221–236 [234].
Type data: holotype, AMNH 322 ♀*.
Type locality: NSW.

Distribution: SE coastal, NSW; only published locality Jamberoo.
Ecology: adult—volant; melliferous, flower visiting record: *Leptospermum* Forster & G.Forster [Myrtaceae].
References: Meyer, R. (1920). Apidae—Halictinae. I. Gatt. *Parasphecodes* Sm. *Arch. Naturg.* **85**(A)11: 112–137 (taxonomy); Rayment, T. (1954). Incidence of acarid mites on the biology of bees. *Aust. Zool.* **12**: 26–38 (as host); Rayment, T. (1954). Remarkable bees from a rain forest. *Aust. Zool.* **12**: 46–56 (distribution).

Lasioglossum (Parasphecodes) tilachum (Smith, 1853)

Parasphecodes tilachus Smith, F. (1853). *Catalogue of Hymenopterous Insects in the Collection of the British Museum.* Part I. Andrenidae and Apidae. London : British Museum 197 pp. [41].
Type data: holotype, BMNH Hym.17.a.617 ♀.
Type locality: TAS (as Van Diemens Land).

Distribution: SE coastal, Murray-Darling basin, NSW, VIC, TAS; only published localities Portland and Mt Buffalo.
Ecology: adult—volant; melliferous, solitary.
References: Cockerell, T.D.A. (1904). The halictine bees of the Australian region. *Ann. Mag. Nat. Hist.* (7)**14**: 208–213 (taxonomy); Cockerell, T.D.A. (1907). On a collection of Australian and Asiatic bees. *Bull. Am. Mus. Nat. Hist.* **23**: 221–236 (distribution); Meyer, R. (1920). Apidae—Halictinae. I. Gatt. *Parasphecodes* Sm. *Arch. Naturg.* **85**(A)11: 112–137 (taxonomy); Rayment, T. (1947). Bees from the Victorian Alps. *Vict. Nat.* **64**: 103–107 (distribution); Rayment, T. (1953). *Bees of the Portland District.* Victoria : Portland Field Naturalist's Club 39 pp. (distribution).

Lasioglossum (Parasphecodes) tribuarium (Rayment, 1935)

Halictus tribuarius Rayment, T. (1935). *A Cluster of Bees.* Sixty essays on the life-histories of Australian bees, with specific descriptions of over 100 new species, and an introduction by Professor E.F. Phillips, D.Ph., Cornell University, U.S.A. Sydney : Endeavour Press 752 pp. [703].
Type data: holotype, ANIC ♀.
Type locality: Grampians, VIC.

Distribution: Murray-Darling basin, VIC; known only from type locality.
Ecology: adult—volant; melliferous, solitary.

Lasioglossum (Parasphecodes) tripunctatum (Cockerell, 1929)

Parasphecodes tripunctatus Cockerell, T.D.A. (1929). Bees from the Australian region. *Am. Mus. Novit.* **346**: 1–18 [12].
Type data: holotype, AMNH ♂*.
Type locality: Ararat, VIC.

Distribution: SE coastal, VIC; known only from type locality.
Ecology: adult—volant; melliferous, solitary.

Lasioglossum (Parasphecodes) tuchilas (Smith, 1853)

Parasphecodes tuchilas Smith, F. (1853). *Catalogue of Hymenopterous Insects in the Collection of the British Museum.* Part I. Andrenidae and Apidae. London : British Museum 197 pp. [41].
Type data: holotype, BMNH Hym.17.a.616 ♀.
Type locality: Australia (as New Holland).

Distribution: Australia, known only from type locality, exact locality unknown.
Ecology: adult—volant; melliferous, solitary.
References: Cockerell, T.D.A. (1904). The halictine bees of the Australian region. *Ann. Mag. Nat. Hist.* (7)**14**: 208–213 (taxonomy); Meyer, R. (1920). Apidae—Halictinae. I. Gatt. *Parasphecodes* Sm. *Arch. Naturg.* **85**(A)11: 112–137 (taxonomy).

Lasioglossum (Parasphecodes) turneri (Cockerell, 1914)

Parasphecodes turneri Cockerell, T.D.A. (1914). Descriptions and records of bees. LXII. *Ann. Mag. Nat. Hist.* (8)**14**: 49–57 [50].
Type data: holotype, BMNH Hym.17.a.637 ♀.
Type locality: Eaglehawk Neck, TAS.

Distribution: TAS; known only from type locality.
Ecology: adult—volant; melliferous, solitary.
Reference: Meyer, R. (1920). Apidae—Halictinae. I. Gatt. *Parasphecodes* Sm. *Arch. Naturg.* **85**(A)11: 112–137 (taxonomy).

Lasioglossum (Parasphecodes) vau (Cockerell, 1910)

Parasphecodes vau Cockerell, T.D.A. (1910). New and little-known bees. *Trans. Am. Entomol. Soc.* **36**: 199–249 [242].
Type data: holotype, BMNH Hym.17.a.621 ♀.
Type locality: NW Australia.

Distribution: NW Australia; known only from type locality, exact locality unknown.
Ecology: larva—sedentary : adult—volant; melliferous.
Reference: Meyer, R. (1920). Apidae—Halictinae. I.

Gatt. *Parasphecodes* Sm. *Arch. Naturg.* **85**(A)11: 112–137 (taxonomy).

Lasioglossum (Parasphecodes) vermiculatum (Cockerell, 1914)

Parasphecodes vermiculatus Cockerell, T.D.A. (1914). Descriptions and records of bees. LVI. *Ann. Mag. Nat. Hist. (8)***13**: 136–146 [141].
Type data: holotype, ANIC ♂.
Type locality: VIC (as 'Australia, presumably VIC' in description).

Distribution: SE coastal, VIC; only published locality Beaumaris.
Ecology: larva—sedentary : adult—volant; melliferous, flower visiting record: *Achillea* L. [Asteraceae].
References: Meyer, R. (1920). Apidae—Halictinae. I. Gatt. *Parasphecodes* Sm. *Arch. Naturg.* **85**(A)11: 112–137 (taxonomy); Cockerell, T.D.A. (1929). Bees from the Australian region. *Am. Mus. Novit.* **346**: 1–18 (distribution, flower record); Rayment, T. (1935). *A Cluster of Bees.* Sixty essays on the life-histories of Australian bees, with specific descriptions of over 100 new species, and an introduction by Professor E.F. Phillips, D.Ph., Cornell University, U.S.A. Sydney : Endeavour Press 752 pp. (biology).

Lasioglossum (Parasphecodes) vulneratum (Cockerell, 1910)

Parasphecodes vulneratus Cockerell, T.D.A. (1910). New and little-known bees. *Trans. Am. Entomol. Soc.* **36**: 199–249 [240].
Type data: holotype, BMNH Hym.17.a.623 ♂.
Type locality: VIC.

Distribution: SE coastal, NSW, VIC; only published localities White Swamp and Portland.
Ecology: adult—volant; melliferous, flower visiting record: aster.
References: Meyer, R. (1920). Apidae—Halictinae. I. Gatt. *Parasphecodes* Sm. *Arch. Naturg.* **85**(A)11: 112–137 (taxonomy); Rayment, T. (1939). Bees from the high lands of New South Wales and Victoria. *Aust. Zool.* **9**: 263–294 (distribution); Rayment, T. (1953). *Bees of the Portland District.* Victoria : Portland Field Naturalist's Club 39 pp. (distribution).

Lasioglossum (Parasphecodes) warburtoni (Cockerell, 1906)

Halictus warburtoni Cockerell, T.D.A. (1906). New Australian bees in the collection of the British Museum. II. *Entomologist* **39**: 56–60 [58].
Type data: holotype, BMNH Hym.17.a.924 ♂.
Type locality: Hobart, TAS.

Distribution: TAS; known only from type locality.
Ecology: adult—volant; melliferous, solitary.

Lasioglossum (Parasphecodes) waterhousei (Cockerell, 1915)

Halictus waterhousei Cockerell, T.D.A. (1915). Descriptions and records of bees. LXVIII. *Ann. Mag. Nat. Hist. (8)***16**: 1–9 [4].
Type data: holotype, BMNH Hym.17.a.964 ♀.
Type locality: Woodford, NSW.

Distribution: SE coastal, NSW; known only from type locality.
Ecology: adult—volant; melliferous, solitary.

Lasioglossum (Parasphecodes) wellingtoni (Cockerell, 1914)

Parasphecodes wellingtoni Cockerell, T.D.A. (1914). Descriptions and records of bees. LXI. *Ann. Mag. Nat. Hist. (8)***14**: 39–49 [45].
Type data: syntypes, BMNH 4♀ (a specimen is labelled 'type' and has registration number Hym.17.a.636).
Type locality: Mt Wellington, TAS.

Distribution: SE coastal, Murray-Darling basin, VIC, TAS; only published localities Gorae West, Portland, Mt Buffalo and Mt Wellington.
Ecology: larva—sedentary : adult—volant; melliferous, nest in decaying wood above ground (dead stump of *Eucalyptus* L'Hérit. [Myrtaceae]), flower visiting record: aster, *Brachyscome* Cass. [Asteraceae], *Leptospermum* Forster & G.Forster [Myrtaceae], *Leucopogon* R.Br. [Epacridaceae].
References: Meyer, R. (1920). Apidae—Halictinae. I. Gatt. *Parasphecodes* Sm. *Arch. Naturg.* **85**(A)11: 112–137 (taxonomy); Rayment, T. (1947). Bees from the Victorian Alps. *Vict. Nat.* **64**: 103–107 (distribution); Rayment, T. (1948). Some bees from the Victorian Alps. *Vict. Nat.* **65**: 201–202 (flower record); Rayment, T. (1951). New bees and wasps—Part XV. Bees from two mountains, with description of a new species and notes on the biology of another. *Vict. Nat.* **68**: 10–13 (biology); Rayment, T. (1953). *Bees of the Portland District.* Victoria : Portland Field Naturalist's Club 39 pp. (biology); Rayment, T. (1957). First steps from the cave. *Proc. R. Zool. Soc. N.S.W.* **1955–56**: 83–86 (biology); Knerer, G. & Schwarz, M. (1978). Beobachtungen an australischen Furchenbienen (Hymenopteren; Halictinae). *Zool. Anz.* **200**: 321–333 (biology).

Lasioglossum (Parasphecodes) wilmattae (Cockerell, 1929)

Parasphecodes wilmattae Cockerell, T.D.A. (1929). Bees from the Australian region. *Am. Mus. Novit.* **346**: 1–18 [11].
Type data: holotype, ANIC ♀.
Type locality: Jenolan, NSW.

Distribution: SE coastal, NSW; known only from type locality.
Ecology: adult—volant; melliferous, flower visiting record: *Helichrysum* Miller *s.lat.* [Asteraceae].

Lasioglossum (Parasphecodes) zamelanum (Cockerell, 1930)

Parasphecodes zamelanus Cockerell, T.D.A. (1930). New Australian bees. *Mem. Qd Mus.* **10**: 37–50 [37].
Type data: syntypes, QM 2♂ (a specimen has type registration number Hy4095).
Type locality: Dunalley, TAS.

Distribution: TAS; known only from type locality.
Ecology: adult—volant; melliferous, solitary.

Lasioglossum (Pseudochilalictus) Michener, 1965

Pseudochilalictus Michener, C.D. (1965). A classification of the bees of the Australian and South Pacific regions. *Bull. Am. Mus. Nat. Hist.* **130**: 1–362 [170] [proposed with subgeneric rank in *Lasioglossum* Curtis, 1833]. Type species: *Lasioglossum (Pseudochilalictus) imitator* Michener, 1965 by original designation.

Lasioglossum (Pseudochilalictus) imitator Michener, 1965

Lasioglossum (Pseudochilalictus) imitator Michener, C.D. (1965). A classification of the bees of the Australian and South Pacific regions. *Bull. Am. Mus. Nat. Hist.* **130**: 1–362 [313].
Type data: holotype, ANIC ♀.
Type locality: 11 miles S Uralla, NSW.

Distribution: Murray-Darling basin, QLD, NSW; only published localities Bunya Mtns, near Uralla, Guyra and Glen Innes.
Ecology: adult—volant; melliferous, flower visiting record: *Daviesia* Sm. [Fabaceae], *Helichrysum* Miller *s.lat.* [Asteraceae], *Helipterum* DC. *s.lat.* [Asteraceae], *Hypochaeris* L. [Asteraceae], *Leptorhynchos* Less. [Asteraceae].

Nomioides Schenck, 1866

Nomioides Schenck, A. (1866). Verzeichniss der nassauischen Hymenoptera aculeata mit Hinzufügung der übrigen deutschen Arten. *Berl. Entomol. Z.* **10**: 317–369 [333] [placed on the Official List of Generic Names in Zoology (Name No. 2261), Opinion 1319]. Type species: *Apis minutissima* Rossi, 1790 by subsequent designation, see International Commission on Zoological Nomenclature (1985). Opinion 1319. *Nomioides* Schenk, 1866 (Insecta, Hymenoptera) : designation of type species. *Bull. Zool. Nomen.* **42**: 173–174.

Taxonomic decision for subgeneric arrangement: Michener, C.D. (1978). The classification of halictine bees : tribes and Old World nonparasitic genera with strong venation. *Univ. Kansas Sci. Bull.* **51**: 501–538 [504].

Extralimital distribution: S Palaearctic, Afrotropical and Oriental Regions, extending E to Indonesia, see Michener, C.D. (1978). The classification of halictine bees : tribes and Old World nonparasitic genera with strong venation. *Univ. Kansas Sci. Bull.* **51**: 501–538 [504].

Generic reference: Pesenko, Yu.A. (1983). [Hymenoptera volume 17, part 1. Halictidae. Subfamily Halictinae, tribe Nomioidini (Palaearctic fauna).] *Fauna SSSR (N.S.)* **129**: 1–199 [In Russian] [120].

Nomioides (Ceylalictus) Strand, 1913

Ceylalictus Strand, E. (1913). Apidae von Ceylon, gesammelt 1899 von Herrn Dr. W. Horn. *Arch. Naturg.* **79**(A)2: 135–150 [137] [proposed with subgeneric rank in *Halictus* Latreille, 1804]. Type species: *Halictus horni* Strand, 1913 by original designation.

Extralimital distribution: Afrotropical and Oriental Regions, see Michener, C.D. (1978). The classification of halictine bees : tribes and Old World nonparasitic genera with strong venation. *Univ. Kansas Sci. Bull.* **51**: 501–538 [504].

Nomioides (Ceylalictus) perditellus Cockerell, 1905

Nomioides perditellus Cockerell, T.D.A. (1905). Descriptions and records of bees. I. *Ann. Mag. Nat. Hist.* (7)**16**: 216–225 [221].
Type data: syntypes, BMNH 3♀ (a specimen is labelled 'type' and has registration number Hym.17.a.1079).
Type locality: QLD.

Halictus (Nomioides) obliquus Friese, H. (1924). Ueber die Bienen Australiens. *Konowia* **3**: 216–249 [236].
Type data: syntypes, ZMB ♀* (number of specimens unknown).
Type locality: Mackay, QLD.

Taxonomic decision for synonymy: Blüthgen, P. (1925). Die Bienengattung *Nomioides* Schenck. *Stettin. Entomol. Ztg.* **86**: 1–100 [2].

Distribution: NE coastal, N Gulf, Murray-Darling basin, Lake Eyre basin, NW coastal, N coastal, QLD, NSW, WA, NT.
Ecology: adult—volant; melliferous, flower visiting record: *Acacia* Miller [Mimosaceae], *Angophora* Cav. [Myrtaceae], *Atalaya* Blume [Sapindaceae], *Brachychiton* Schott & Endl. [Sterculiaceae], *Eucalyptus* L'Hérit. [Myrtaceae], *Grevillea* R.Br. ex J. Knight [Proteaceae], *Lophostemon* Schott [Myrtaceae], *Melaleuca* L. [Myrtaceae], *Parsonsia* R.Br. [Apocyanaceae], *Salsola* L. [Chenopodiaceae], *Schinus* L. [Anacardiaceae], *Syzygium* Gaertner [Myrtaceae], *Wahlenbergia* Roth [Campanulaceae], *Xanthorrhoea* Sm. [Xanthorrhoeaceae].
References: Cockerell, T.D.A. (1910). New and little-known bees. *Trans. Am. Entomol. Soc.* **36**: 199–249 (description of male); Michener, C.D. (1965). A classification of the bees of the Australian and South Pacific regions. *Bull. Am. Mus. Nat. Hist.* **130**: 1–362 [178, 183] (illustration, as *Nomioides perditella* Cockerell, 1905); Yeates, D.K. & Exley, E.M. (1986). The genus *Nomioides* Schenck (Hymenoptera : Halictidae) in Australia. *J. Aust. Entomol. Soc.* **25**: 115–121 (redescription, distribution, flower records).

Pachyhalictus Cockerell, 1929

Taxonomic decision for subgeneric arrangement: Michener, C.D. (1978). The classification of halictine bees : tribes and Old World nonparasitic genera with strong venation. *Univ. Kansas Sci. Bull.* **51**: 501–538 [517].

Generic reference: Pauly, A. (1986). Les abeilles de la sous-famille des Halictinae en Nouvelle-Guinée et dans l'Archipel Bismarck (Hymenoptera : Apoidea : Halictidae). *Zool. Verh.* **227**: 1–58.

Pachyhalictus (Pachyhalictus) Cockerell, 1929

Pachyhalictus Cockerell, T.D.A. (1929). Descriptions and records of bees. CXX. *Ann. Mag. Nat. Hist. (10)*4: 584–594 [589] [proposed with subgeneric rank in *Halictus* Latreille, 1804]. Type species: *Halictus merescens* Cockerell, 1919 by original designation.

Extralimital distribution: Oriental Region, extending E to New Guinea, see Michener, C.D. (1978). The classification of halictine bees : tribes and Old World nonparasitic genera with strong venation. *Univ. Kansas Sci. Bull.* **51**: 501–538 [517].

Pachyhalictus (Pachyhalictus) binghami W.F. Kirby, 1900

Halictus binghami Kirby, W.F. (1900). Hymenoptera. pp. 81–88 *in* Andrews, C.W. *A Monograph of Christmas Island (Indian Ocean): physical features and geology; with descriptions of the fauna and flora by numerous contributors.* London : British Museum 337+20 pp. [86]. Type data: syntypes, BMNH 4♀ (a specimen is labelled 'type' and has registration number Hym.17.a.742).
Type locality: Christmas Is.

Distribution: Christmas Is.; known only from type locality.
Ecology: adult—volant; melliferous, solitary.
References: Cockerell, T.D.A. (1904). The halictine bees of the Australian region. *Ann. Mag. Nat. Hist. (7)*14: 208–213 (redescription); Michener, C.D. (1978). The classification of halictine bees : tribes and Old World nonparasitic genera with strong venation. *Univ. Kansas Sci. Bull.* **51**: 501–538 (generic placement).

Pachyhalictus (Pachyhalictus) stirlingi (Cockerell, 1910)

Halictus stirlingi Cockerell, T.D.A. (1910). New and little-known bees. *Trans. Am. Entomol. Soc.* **36**: 199–249 [232].
Type data: holotype, BMNH Hym.17.a.969 ♀.
Type locality: Mackay, QLD.

Distribution: NE coastal, QLD; only published localities Mackay and Babinda.
Ecology: adult—volant; melliferous, solitary.
References: Cockerell, T.D.A. (1930). Australian bees in the Museum of Comparative Zoology. *Psyche (Camb.)* **37**: 141–154 (distribution); Cockerell, T.D.A. (1933). The bees of Australia. *Aust. Zool.* **7**:

291–324 (as *Halictus (Pachyhalictus) stirlingi* Cockerell, 1910); Michener, C.D. (1978). The classification of halictine bees : tribes and Old World nonparasitic genera with strong venation. *Univ. Kansas Sci. Bull.* **51**: 501–538 (taxonomy).

Sphecodes Latreille, 1804

Taxonomic decision for subgeneric arrangement: Michener, C.D. (1978). The parasitic groups of Halictidae (Hymenoptera, Apoidea). *Univ. Kansas Sci. Bull.* **51**: 291–339 [325].

Sphecodes (Sphecodes) Latreille, 1804

Sphecodes Latreille, P.A. (1804). Tableau méthodique des insectes. pp. 129–200 *in, Nouveau Dictionnaire d'Histoire Naturelle.* Vol. 24. Tableaux méthodiques. Paris : Déterville [182]. Type species: *Sphex gibba* Linnaeus, 1758 (=*Nomada gibba* Fabricius, 1804) by monotypy. Compiled from secondary source: Sandhouse, G.A. (1943). The type species of the genera and subgenera of bees. *Proc. U.S. Natl Mus.* **92**(3156): 519–619.

Extralimital distribution: Nearctic, Palaearctic, Afrotropical and Oriental Regions, New Guinea, see Michener, C.D. (1978). The parasitic groups of Halictidae (Hymenoptera, Apoidea). *Univ. Kansas Sci. Bull.* **51**: 291–339 [326].

Sphecodes (Sphecodes) manskii (Rayment, 1935)

Mellitidia manskii Rayment, T. (1935). *A Cluster of Bees.* Sixty essays on the life-histories of Australian bees, with specific descriptions of over 100 new species, and an introduction by Professor E.F. Phillips, D.Ph., Cornell University, U.S.A. Sydney : Endeavour Press 752 pp. [711].
Type data: holotype, ANIC ♀.
Type locality: Cairns, QLD.

Distribution: NE coastal, QLD; known only from type locality.
Ecology: adult—volant; melliferous, cleptoparasitic, possibly on *Nomia*.
Reference: Michener, C.D. (1978). The parasitic groups of Halictidae (Hymenoptera, Apoidea). *Univ. Kansas Sci. Bull.* **51**: 291–339 (redescription).

Sphecodes (Sphecodes) profugus Cockerell, 1910

Sphecodes profugus Cockerell, T.D.A. (1910). New and little-known bees. *Trans. Am. Entomol. Soc.* **36**: 199–249 [244].
Type data: holotype, BMNH Hym.17.a.593 ♀.
Type locality: Mackay, QLD.

Distribution: NE coastal, QLD; only published localities Mackay, Cairns, Halifax, Birkdale and Brisbane.
Ecology: adult—volant; melliferous, cleptoparasitic, probably on other halictines.
References: Cockerell, T.D.A. (1930). Australian bees in the Museum of Comparative Zoology. *Psyche (Camb.)* **37**: 141–154 (distribution); Rayment, T. (1935). *A Cluster of Bees.* Sixty essays on the life-histories of Australian bees, with specific descrip-

tions of over 100 new species, and an introduction by Professor E.F. Phillips, D.Ph., Cornell University, U.S.A. Sydney : Endeavour Press 752 pp. (illustration); Michener, C.D. (1978). The parasitic groups of Halictidae (Hymenoptera, Apoidea). *Univ. Kansas Sci. Bull.* **51**: 291–339 (taxonomy).

Incertae sedis

Halictus andrewsi Kirby, W.F. (1900). Hymenoptera. pp. 81–88 *in* Andrews, C.W. *A Monograph of Christmas Island (Indian Ocean)*: physical features and geology; with descriptions of the fauna and flora by numerous contributors. London : British Museum 337+20 pp. [86].
Type data: syntypes, BMNH 11♀ (a specimen is labelled 'type' and has registration number Hym.17.a.741).
Type locality: Christmas Is.

Halictus intermedia Rayment, T. (1927). A new Halictine bee *Halictus platycephalus*, sp.n. *Vict. Nat.* **44**: 101–102 [pl. V, fig. 8 on p. 102, caption on p. 101] [name introduced and used only as caption to fig.; junior primary homonym of *Halictus intermedius* Schenk, 1870].
Type data: holotype (probable), whereabouts unknown *.
Type locality: Port Phillip, VIC.

Halictus portlandensis Rayment, T. (1953). *Bees of the Portland District*. Victoria : Portland Field Naturalist's Club 39 pp. [23].
Type data: holotype (probable), whereabouts unknown ♀*.
Type locality: Portland District, VIC.

Parasphecodes minimus Meyer, R. (1920). Apidae—Halictinae. I. Gatt. *Parasphecodes* Sm. *Arch. Naturg.* **85**(A)11: 112–137 [131].
Type data: holotype, ZMB 2632 ♂*.
Type locality: Port Phillip (as Port Philip), VIC.

Parasphecodes nigritus Meyer, R. (1920). Apidae—Halictinae. I. Gatt. *Parasphecodes* Sm. *Arch. Naturg.* **85**(A)11: 112–137 [135].
Type data: holotype, ZMB 1951 ♂*.
Type locality: TAS (as Van Diemens Land).

Parasphecodes percallomelittinus Rayment, T. (1954). Remarkable bees from a rain forest. *Aust. Zool.* **12**: 46–56 [53].
Type data: holotype, ANIC ♂.
Type locality: Jamberoo, NSW.

NOMIINAE

Nomia Latreille, 1804

Nomia Latreille, P.A. (1804). Tableau méthodique des insectes. pp. 129–200 *in*, *Nouveau Dictionnaire d'Histoire Naturelle*. Vol. 24. Tableaux méthodiques. Paris : Déterville [182]. Type species: *Andrena curvipes* Fabricius, 1781 by monotypy. Compiled from secondary source: Sandhouse, G.A (1943). The type species of the genera and subgenera of bees. *Proc. U.S. Natl Mus.* **92**(3156): 519–619.

Taxonomic decision for subgeneric arrangement: Michener, C.D. (1965). A classification of the bees of the Australian and South Pacific regions. *Bull. Am. Mus. Nat. Hist.* **130**: 1–362 [152].

Extralimital distribution: Palaearctic and Afrotropical Regions, see Hurd, P.D. (1979). Superfamily Apoidea. pp. 1741–2209 *in* Krombein, K.V., Hurd, P.D., Smith, D.R. & Burks, B.D. (eds) (1979). *Catalog of Hymenoptera in America North of Mexico* Vol. 2, Washington : Smithsonian Institution [1941].

Nomia (Austronomia) Michener, 1965

Austronomia Michener, C.D. (1965). A classification of the bees of the Australian and South Pacific regions. *Bull. Am. Mus. Nat. Hist.* **130**: 1–362 [156] [proposed with subgeneric rank in *Nomia* Latreille, 1804]. Type species: *Nomia australica* Smith, 1875 by original designation.

Extralimital distribution: Afrotropical and Oriental Regions, extending E to Solomon Ils, see Pauly, A. (1984). Contribution à l'étude des genres afrotropicaux de Nomiinae (Hymenoptera Apoidea Halictidae). *Rev. Zool. Afr.* **98**: 693–702 [697].

Nomia (Austronomia) adelaidella Cockerell, 1910

Nomia flavoviridis adelaidella Cockerell, T.D.A. (1910). Some Australian bees in the Berlin Museum. *J. N.Y. Entomol. Soc.* **18**: 98–114 [106].
Type data: syntypes, ZMB ♂♀*.
Type locality: Adelaide, SA.

Distribution: S Gulfs, SA; known only from type locality.
Ecology: adult—volant; melliferous, solitary.
Reference: Michener, C.D. (1965). A classification of the bees of the Australian and South Pacific regions. *Bull. Am. Mus. Nat. Hist.* **130**: 1–362 [156] (taxonomy).

Nomia (Austronomia) aenea Smith, 1875

Nomia aenea Smith, F. (1875). Descriptions of new species of bees belonging to the genus *Nomia* of Latreille. *Trans. Entomol. Soc. Lond.* **1875**: 53–70 pl. ii [63].
Type data: holotype, BMNH Hym.17.a.1743 ♂.
Type locality: Port Essington, NT.

Distribution: N coastal, NT; known only from type locality.
Ecology: adult—volant; melliferous, solitary.
References: Cockerell, T.D.A. (1929). Bees in the Australian Museum collection. *Rec. Aust. Mus.* **17**: 199–243 (taxonomy); Cockerell, T.D.A. (1931). The bees of Australia. *Aust. Zool.* **7**: 34–54 (taxonomy).

Nomia (Austronomia) aerata Smith, 1875

Nomia aerata Smith, F. (1875). Descriptions of new species of bees belonging to the genus *Nomia* of Latreille. *Trans. Entomol. Soc. Lond.* **1875**: 53–70 pl. ii [63].
Type data: holotype, BMNH Hym.17.a.1759 ♂.
Type locality: Australia.

Distribution: Australia, known only from type locality, exact locality unknown.
Ecology: adult—volant; melliferous, solitary.

Reference: Cockerell, T.D.A. (1931). The bees of Australia. *Aust. Zool.* **7**: 34–54 (taxonomy).

Nomia (Austronomia) alboscopacea Friese, 1917

Nomia alboscopacea Friese, H. (1917). Results of Dr. E. Mjöberg's Swedish Scientific Expeditions to Australia, 1910–1913. 13. Apidae. *Ark. Zool.* **11**(2): 1–9 [6].
Type data: syntypes, NHRM ♂♀* (number of specimens unknown).
Type locality: Mackay (as Makay), Cairns, Atherton and Colosseum, QLD.

Distribution: NE coastal, QLD; only published localities Mackay, Colosseum, Atherton and Cairns.
Ecology: adult—volant; melliferous, flower visiting record: *Eucalyptus* L'Hérit. [Myrtaceae].
Reference: Cockerell, T.D.A. (1931). The bees of Australia. *Aust. Zool.* **7**: 34–54 (taxonomy).

Nomia (Austronomia) analis Friese, 1924

Nomia analis Friese, H. (1924). Ueber die Bienen Australiens. *Konowia* **3**: 216–249 [244].
Type data: syntypes (probable), ?AMNH ♀* (number of specimens unknown).
Type locality: Mackay, QLD.

Distribution: NE coastal, QLD; known only from type locality.
Ecology: adult—volant; melliferous, flower visiting record: *Cassia* L. *s.lat.* [Caesalpiniaceae].
Reference: Cockerell, T.D.A. (1929). Bees, chiefly Australian species, described or determined by Dr. H. Friese. *Am. Mus. Novit.* **343**: 1–20 (taxonomy).

Nomia (Austronomia) argentifrons Smith, 1862

Nomia argentifrons Smith, F. (1862). Descriptions of new species of Australian Hymenoptera, and of a species of *Formica* from New Zealand. *Trans. Entomol. Soc. Lond.* (*3*)**1**: 53–62 [60].
Type data: syntypes (probable), whereabouts unknown (Sir John Lubbock coll.)* (number of specimens unknown).
Type locality: Australia.

Distribution: Australia, known only from type locality, exact locality unknown.
Ecology: adult—volant; melliferous, solitary.
Reference: Cockerell, T.D.A. (1931). The bees of Australia. *Aust. Zool.* **7**: 34–54 (taxonomy).

Nomia (Austronomia) australica Smith, 1875

Nomia australica Smith, F. (1875). Descriptions of new species of bees belonging to the genus *Nomia* of Latreille. *Trans. Entomol. Soc. Lond.* **1875**: 53–70 pl. ii [60].
Type data: syntypes, BMNH ♂♀* (number of specimens unknown, a male specimen is labelled 'type' and has the registration number Hym.17.a.1735).
Type locality: Moreton Bay, QLD; Port Philip, VIC; Adelaide, SA; Swan River, Champion Bay, WA.

Distribution: NE coastal, SE coastal, S Gulfs, SW coastal, QLD, NSW, VIC, SA, WA.
Ecology: larva—sedentary : adult—volant; mellifer-

ous, nest gregariously in soil, males cluster, flower visiting record: lucerne, *Acacia* Miller [Mimosaceae], *Angophora* Cav. [Myrtaceae], *Brunonia* R.Br. [Brunoniaceae], *Callistemon* R.Br. [Myrtaceae], *Carduus* L. [Asteraceae], *Cassia* L. *s.lat.* [Caesalpiniaceae], *Coreopsis* L. [Asteraceae], *Daviesia* Sm. [Fabaceae], *?Epacris* Cav. [Epacridaceae], *Eucalyptus* L'Hérit. [Myrtaceae], *Hibbertia* Andrews [Dilleniaceae], *Hypochaeris* L. [Asteraceae], *Leptospermum* Forster & G.Forster [Myrtaceae], *Leucopogon* R.Br. [Epacridaceae], *Melaleuca* L. [Myrtaceae], *Melastoma* L. [Melastomataceae], *Oxylobium* Andrews [Fabaceae], *Plectronia* L. [Rubiaceae], *Rosa* L. [Rosaceae], *Rubus* L. [Rosaceae].

References: Dalla Torre, K.W. (1896). *Catalogus Hymenopterorum Hucusque Descriptorum Systematicus et Synonymicus.* Apidae (Anthophila). Lipsiae : G. Engelmann Vol. x 643 pp. (unnecessary emendation to *Nomia australiaca*); Cockerell, T.D.A. (1905). Notes on some bees in the British Museum. *Trans. Am. Entomol. Soc.* **31**: 309–364 (taxonomy); Friese, H. (1917). Results of Dr. E. Mjöberg's Swedish Scientific Expeditions to Australia, 1910–1913. 13. Apidae. *Ark. Zool.* **11**(2): 1–9 (as *Nomia australasiaca*, incorrect subsequent spelling); Cockerell, T.D.A. (1931). The bees of Australia. *Aust. Zool.* **7**: 34–54 (taxonomy); Rayment, T. (1931). Bees in the collections of the Western Australian Museum and the Agricultural Department, Perth. *J. Proc. R. Soc. West. Aust.* **17**: 157–190 (taxonomy); Rayment, T. (1935). *A Cluster of Bees.* Sixty essays on the life-histories of Australian bees, with specific descriptions of over 100 new species, and an introduction by Professor E.F. Phillips, D.Ph., Cornell University, U.S.A. Sydney : Endeavour Press 752 pp. (biology); Rayment, T. (1956). The *Nomia australica* Sm. complex. Its taxonomy, morphology and biology with the description of a new mutillid wasp. *Aust. Zool.* **12**: 176–200 (biology); Doull, K.M. (1961). Insect problems of lucerne seed production in South Australia. *J. Aust. Inst. agric. Sci.* **27**: 11–15 (biology); Michener, C.D. (1965). A classification of the bees of the Australian and South Pacific regions. *Bull. Am. Mus. Nat. Hist.* **130**: 1–362 (flower record); Michener, C.D. & Houston, T.F. (1991). Apoidea. pp. 993–1000 *in* CSIRO (sponsor) *The Insects of Australia.* A textbook for students and research workers. Melbourne : Melbourne University Press Vol. II 2nd Edn (illustration).

Nomia (Austronomia) babindensis Cockerell, 1930

Nomia babindensis Cockerell, T.D.A. (1930). Australian bees in the Museum of Comparative Zoology. *Psyche (Camb.)* **37**: 141–154 [147].
Type data: holotype, MCZ ♀*.
Type locality: Babinda, QLD.

Distribution: NE coastal, QLD; known only from type locality.

Ecology: adult—volant; melliferous, solitary.

Nomia (Austronomia) brisbanensis Cockerell, 1913

Nomia brisbanensis Cockerell, T.D.A. (1913). Descriptions and records of bees. LV. *Ann. Mag. Nat. Hist. (8)***12**: 505–514 [508].
Type data: syntypes (probable), BMNH ♀ (number of specimens unknown, a specimen is labelled 'type' and has registration number Hym.17.a.1766).
Type locality: Brisbane, QLD.

Distribution: NE coastal, Murray-Darling basin, SE coastal, QLD, NSW.

Ecology: adult—volant; melliferous, flower visiting record: *Boronia* Sm. [Rutaceae], *Daviesia* Sm. [Fabaceae], *Hibbertia* Andrews [Dilleniaceae], *Pultenaea* Sm. [Fabaceae].

References: Cockerell, T.D.A. (1929). Bees, chiefly Australian species, described or determined by Dr. H. Friese, *Am. Mus. Novit.* **343**: 1–20 (distribution); Cockerell, T.D.A. (1931). The bees of Australia. *Aust. Zool.* **7**: 34–54 (taxonomy); Michener, C.D. (1965). A classification of the bees of the Australian and South Pacific regions. *Bull. Am. Mus. Nat. Hist.* **130**: 1–362 (flower record).

Nomia (Austronomia) cyanella Cockerell, 1913

Nomia flavoviridis cyanella Cockerell, T.D.A. (1913). Descriptions and records of bees. LV. *Ann. Mag. Nat. Hist. (8)***12**: 505–514 [506].
Type data: holotype, BMNH Hym.17.a.1745 ♂.
Type locality: Cooktown, QLD.

Distribution: NE coastal, QLD; known only from type locality.

Ecology: adult—volant; melliferous, solitary.

Reference: Michener, C.D. (1965). A classification of the bees of the Australian and South Pacific regions. *Bull. Am. Mus. Nat. Hist.* **130**: 1–362 [156] (taxonomy).

Nomia (Austronomia) dentiventris Smith, 1875

Nomia dentiventris Smith, F. (1875). Descriptions of new species of bees belonging to the genus *Nomia* of Latreille. *Trans. Entomol. Soc. Lond.* **1875**: 53–70 pl. ii [62].
Type data: holotype, BMNH Hym.17.a.1758 ♂.
Type locality: Sydney, NSW.

Distribution: NE coastal, SE coastal, QLD, NSW; only published localities Mackay, Sydney and Gosford.

Ecology: adult—volant; melliferous, flower visiting record: *Eucalyptus* L'Hérit. [Myrtaceae].

References: Friese, H. (1924). Ueber die Bienen Australiens. *Konowia* **3**: 216–249 (flower record); Cockerell, T.D.A. (1931). The bees of Australia. *Aust. Zool.* **7**: 34–54 (taxonomy); Rayment, T. (1939). Bees from the high lands of New South Wales and Victoria. *Aust. Zool.* **9**: 263–294 (distribution).

Nomia (Austronomia) dimissa Cockerell, 1921

Nomia dimissa Cockerell, T.D.A. (1921). Australian bees in the Queensland Museum. *Mem. Qd Mus.* **7**: 81–98 [83].
Type data: holotype, QM T2460 ♂.
Type locality: Cairns district, QLD.

Distribution: NE coastal, (N coastal), QLD, (WA); only published locality Cairns district.

Ecology: adult—volant; melliferous, flower visiting record: ?*Solanum* L. [Solanaceae].

Reference: Anderson, G.J. & Symon, D. (1988). Insect foragers on *Solanum* flowers in Australia. *Ann. M. Bot. Gard.* **75**: 842–852 (?flower record).

Nomia (Austronomia) doddii Cockerell, 1905

Nomia flavoviridis doddii Cockerell, T.D.A. (1905). New Australian bees of the genus *Nomia*. *Entomologist* **38**: 217–223 [222].
Type data: syntypes, BMNH Hym.17.a.1746 6♂1♀.
Type locality: Townsville, QLD and Parry Harbour, Cape Bougainville, WA.

Distribution: NE coastal, NW coastal, N coastal, QLD, WA; only published localities Townsville, Parry Harbour (Cape Bougainville) and Monte Bello Ils.

Ecology: adult—volant; melliferous, solitary.

References: Cockerell, T.D.A. (1912). Some bees of the genus *Nomia* from Australia. *Entomologist* **45**: 119–122 (taxonomy); Montague, P.D. (1914). A report on the fauna of the Monte Bello islands. *Proc. Zool. Soc. Lond.* **1914**: 625–652 (distribution); Michener, C.D. (1965). A classification of the bees of the Australian and South Pacific regions. *Bull. Am. Mus. Nat. Hist.* **130**: 1–362 (as *Nomia doddi*, incorrect subsequent spelling).

Nomia (Austronomia) excellens Cockerell, 1929

Nomia flavoviridis excellens Cockerell, T.D.A. (1929). Bees in the Australian Museum collection. *Rec. Aust. Mus.* **17**: 199–243 [226].
Type data: holotype, AM K49021 ♂.
Type locality: Sydney, NSW.

Distribution: SE coastal, NSW; known only from type locality.

Ecology: adult—volant; melliferous, solitary.

References: Cockerell, T.D.A. (1931). Descriptions and records of bees. CXXVI. *Ann. Mag. Nat. Hist. (10)***7**: 273–281 (taxonomy); Michener, C.D. (1965). A classification of the bees of the Australian and South Pacific regions. *Bull. Am. Mus. Nat. Hist.* **130**: 1–362 [156] (taxonomy).

Nomia (Austronomia) ferricauda Cockerell, 1913

Nomia ferricauda Cockerell, T.D.A. (1913). Descriptions and records of bees. LV. *Ann. Mag. Nat. Hist. (8)***12**: 505–514 [507].

Type data: syntypes, QM 2♀ (a specimen has the type registration number T4126).
Type locality: Brisbane, QLD.

Distribution: NE coastal, SE coastal, QLD, NSW; only published localities Brisbane, Capalaba, Glenmorgan, White Swamp and Gosford.
Ecology: adult—volant; melliferous, flower visiting record: *Callistemon* R.Br. [Myrtaceae], *Jacksonia* Smith [Fabaceae], *Melaleuca* L. [Myrtaceae].
References: Rayment, T. (1939). Bees from the high lands of New South Wales and Victoria. *Aust. Zool.* **9**: 263–294 (distribution); Michener, C.D. (1965). A classification of the bees of the Australian and South Pacific regions. *Bull. Am. Mus. Nat. Hist.* **130**: 1–362 (flower record).

Nomia (Austronomia) flavoviridis Cockerell, 1905

Nomia flavoviridis Cockerell, T.D.A. (1905). New Australian bees of the genus *Nomia*. *Entomologist* **38**: 217–223 [222].
Type data: syntypes, BMNH 2♂ (a specimen is labelled 'type' and has registration number Hym.17.a.1744).
Type locality: Mackay, QLD.

Nomia aenescens Friese, H. (1912). Zur Bienenfauna von Neu-Guinea und Oceania. *Mitt. Zool. Mus. Berl.* **6**: 93–96 [94].
Type data: holotype, ZMB ♀*.
Type locality: Sialum, Papua New Guinea (as German New Guinea).

Nomia flavoviridis rubra Rayment, T. (1931). Bees in the collections of the Western Australian Museum and the Agricultural Department, Perth. *J. Proc. R. Soc. West. Aust.* **17**: 157–190 [172] [junior primary homonym of *Nomia rubra* Friese, 1904].
Type data: syntypes, WADA 5♀*.
Type locality: Gosnells and Perth, WA.

Taxonomic decision for synonymy: Krombein, K.V. (1951). Additional notes on the bees of the Solomon Islands (Hymenoptera : Apoidea). *Proc. Hawaii. Entomol. Soc.* **14**: 277–295 [284].

Distribution: NE coastal, SE coastal, Murray-Darling basin, S Gulfs, SW coastal, N coastal, QLD, NSW, VIC, SA, WA; also on Solomon Ils and New Guinea.
Ecology: larva—sedentary : adult—volant; melliferous, males cluster, flower visiting record: *Cassia* L. *s.lat.* [Caesalpiniaceae], *Jacksonia* Smith [Fabaceae], *Melastoma* L. [Melastomataceae], *Solanum* L. [Solanaceae], *Wahlenbergia* Roth [Campanulaceae], *Xanthorrhoea* Sm. [Xanthorrhoeaceae].
References: Cockerell, T.D.A. (1910). New and little-known bees. *Trans. Am. Entomol. Soc.* **36**: 199–249 (distribution); Cockerell, T.D.A. (1913). Descriptions and records of bees. LV. *Ann. Mag. Nat. Hist.* (8)**12**: 505–514 (description of female); Friese, H. (1924). Ueber die Bienen Australiens. *Konowia* **3**: 216–249 (redescription, as *Nomia aenescens* Friese, 1912); Cockerell, T.D.A. (1929). Bees, chiefly Australian species, described or determined by Dr. H. Friese. *Am. Mus. Novit.* **343**: 1–20 (taxonomy); Cock-

erell, T.D.A. (1931). The bees of Australia. *Aust. Zool.* **7**: 34–54 (taxonomy); Rayment, T. (1939). Bees from the high lands of New South Wales and Victoria. *Aust. Zool.* **9**: 263–294 (distribution); Rayment, T. (1947). Biology and taxonomy of the solitary bee, *Parasphecodes fulviventris* (Friese). *Aust. Zool.* **11**: 76–95 (biology); Krombein, K.V. (1951). Additional notes on the bees of the Solomon Islands (Hymenoptera : Apoidea). *Proc. Hawaii. Entomol. Soc.* **14**: 277–295 (distribution); Michener, C.D. (1965). A classification of the bees of the Australian and South Pacific regions. *Bull. Am. Mus. Nat. Hist.* **130**: 1–362 (flower record); Anderson, G.J. & Symon, D. (1988). Insect foragers on *Solanum* flowers in Australia. *Ann. M. Bot. Gard.* **75**: 842–852 (flower record).

Nomia (Austronomia) fortior Cockerell, 1929

Nomia kurandina fortior Cockerell, T.D.A. (1929). Bees in the Australian Museum collection. *Rec. Aust. Mus.* **17**: 199–243 [226].
Type data: holotype, AM K55812 ♂.
Type locality: Gundamaian, Port Hacking, NSW.

Distribution: SE coastal, NSW; known only from type locality.
Ecology: adult—volant; melliferous, solitary.
Reference: Michener, C.D. (1965). A classification of the bees of the Australian and South Pacific regions. *Bull. Am. Mus. Nat. Hist.* **130**: 1–362 [156] (taxonomy).

Nomia (Austronomia) frenchi Cockerell, 1912

Nomia frenchi Cockerell, T.D.A. (1912). Some bees of the genus *Nomia* from Australia. *Entomologist* **45**: 119–122 [120].
Type data: holotype, USNM ♂*.
Type locality: Woodend, VIC.

Distribution: SE coastal, VIC, (SA); only published localities Woodend and Melbourne.
Ecology: adult—volant; melliferous, solitary.
Reference: Cockerell, T.D.A. (1930). Australian bees in the Museum of Comparative Zoology. *Psyche (Camb.)* **37**: 141–154 (distribution).

Nomia (Austronomia) generosa Smith, 1875

Nomia generosa Smith, F. (1875). Descriptions of new species of bees belonging to the genus *Nomia* of Latreille. *Trans. Entomol. Soc. Lond.* **1875**: 53–70 pl. ii [61].
Type data: holotype, BMNH Hym.17.a.1754 ♂.
Type locality: Moreton Bay, QLD.

Distribution: NE coastal, SE coastal, QLD, VIC; only published localities Mackay, Moreton Bay and Portland.
Ecology: adult—volant; melliferous, flower visiting record: aster.
References: Cockerell, T.D.A. (1929). Bees, chiefly Australian species, described or determined by Dr. H.

Friese. *Am. Mus. Novit.* **343**: 1–20 (redescription); Rayment, T. (1953). *Bees of the Portland District.* Victoria : Portland Field Naturalist's Club 39 pp. (distribution).

Nomia (Austronomia) geophila Cockerell, 1930

Nomia geophila Cockerell, T.D.A. (1930). New Australian bees. *Mem. Qd Mus.* **10**: 37–50 [49].
Type data: syntypes (probable), QM ♂* (a male has the registration number Hy3747).
Type locality: Moree, NSW.

Distribution: Murray-Darling basin, NSW; known only from type locality.
Ecology: adult—volant; melliferous, solitary.

Nomia (Austronomia) gilberti Cockerell, 1905

Nomia gilberti Cockerell, T.D.A. (1905). Descriptions and records of bees. III. *Ann. Mag. Nat. Hist. (7)***16**· 301–308 [304].
Type data: holotype, BMNH Hym.17.a.1765 ♀.
Type locality: Mackay, QLD.

Distribution: NE coastal, QLD; only published localities Mackay, Halifax and Thursday Is.
Ecology: adult—volant; melliferous, solitary.
References: Cockerell, T.D.A. (1929). Descriptions and records of bees. CXVII. *Ann. Mag. Nat. Hist. (10)***4**: 132–141 (distribution); Cockerell, T.D.A. (1930). Australian bees in the Museum of Comparative Zoology. *Psyche (Camb.)* **37**: 141–154 (distribution).

Nomia (Austronomia) gracilipes Smith, 1875

Nomia gracilipes Smith, F. (1875). Descriptions of new species of bees belonging to the genus *Nomia* of Latreille. *Trans. Entomol. Soc. Lond.* **1875**: 53–70 pl. ii [61] [March 1875].
Type data: syntypes, BMNH ♂♀ Hym.17.a.1753a,b.
Type locality: Adelaide, SA.

Distribution: NE coastal, SE coastal, Murray-Darling basin, S Gulfs, QLD, VIC, SA; only published localities Brisbane, Cann River, Gunbower and Adelaide.
Ecology: adult—volant; melliferous, solitary.
References: Westwood, J.O. (1875). Descriptions of some new species of short-tongued bees belonging to the genus *Nomia* of Latreille. *Trans. Entomol. Soc. Lond.* **1875**: 207–222 [217] (as *Nomia haemorrhoidalis*, manuscript name); Cockerell, T.D.A. (1913). Descriptions and records of bees. LV. *Ann. Mag. Nat. Hist. (8)***12**: 505–514 (taxonomy); Cockerell, T.D.A. (1916). A collection of bees from Queensland. *Mem. Qd Mus.* **5**: 197–204 (taxonomy); Rayment, T. (1929). Bees from East Gippsland. *Vict. Nat.* **46**: 124–129 (distribution).

Nomia (Austronomia) grisella Cockerell, 1913

Nomia grisella Cockerell, T.D.A. (1913). Descriptions and records of bees. LV. *Ann. Mag. Nat. Hist. (8)***12**: 505–514 [508].

Type data: holotype, BMNH Hym.17.a.1767 ♀.
Type locality: Cape York, QLD.

Distribution: NE coastal, QLD; only published localities Cape York and Gordonvale.
Ecology: adult—volant; melliferous, solitary.
Reference: Cockerell, T.D.A. (1930). New Australian bees. *Mem. Qd Mus.* **10**: 37–50 (distribution).

Nomia (Austronomia) hippophila Cockerell, 1910

Nomia hippophila Cockerell, T.D.A. (1910). Some Australian bees in the Berlin Museum. *J. N.Y. Entomol. Soc.* **18**: 98–114 [106].
Type data: holotype, ZMB ♂*.
Type locality: Port Phillip (as Port Philip), VIC.

Distribution: Murray-Darling basin, SE coastal, NSW, VIC; only published localities Yarrawin, Port Philip, Windsor and near Melbourne.
Ecology: adult—volant; melliferous, solitary.
References: Cockerell, T.D.A. (1913). Descriptions and records of bees. LV. *Ann. Mag. Nat. Hist. (8)***12**: 505–514 (distribution); Cockerell, T.D.A. (1916). New and little-known bees. *Entomologist* **49**: 156–160 (description of female).

Nomia (Austronomia) hypodonta Cockerell, 1905

Nomia hypodonta Cockerell, T.D.A. (1905). New Australian bees of the genus *Nomia. Entomologist* **38**: 217–223 [220].
Type data: holotype, BMNH Hym.17.a.1771 ♂.
Type locality: QLD.

Distribution: NE coastal, QLD; known only from type locality.
Ecology: adult—volant; melliferous, solitary.
Reference: Cockerell, T.D.A. (1910). New and little-known bees. *Trans. Am. Entomol. Soc.* **36**: 199–249 (description of male).

Nomia (Austronomia) kurandina Cockerell, 1910

Nomia kurandina Cockerell, T.D.A. (1910). New and little-known bees. *Trans. Am. Entomol. Soc.* **36**: 199–249 [222].
Type data: holotype, BMNH Hym.17.a.1763 ♂.
Type locality: Kuranda (as Cairns Kuranda), QLD.
Nomia macularis Friese, H. (1924). Ueber die Bienen Australiens. *Konowia* **3**: 216–249 [246].
Type data: holotype (probable), whereabouts unknown ♂*.
Type locality: Mackay, QLD.

Taxonomic decision for synonymy: Cockerell, T.D.A. (1929). Bees from the Australian region. *Am. Mus. Novit.* **346**: 1–18 [4].

Distribution: NE coastal, QLD; only published localities Kuranda, Mackay and Brisbane.
Ecology: adult—volant; melliferous, flower visiting record: *Leptospermum* Forster & G.Forster [Myrtaceae].
References: Cockerell, T.D.A. (1912). Some bees of the genus *Nomia* from Australia. *Entomologist* **45**:

119–122 (description of female); Cockerell, T.D.A. (1921). Australian bees in the Queensland Museum. *Mem. Qd Mus.* **7**: 81–98 (distribution).

Nomia (Austronomia) latetibialis Friese, 1924

Nomia latetibialis Friese, H. (1924). Ueber die Bienen Australiens. *Konowia* **3**: 216–249 [248].
Type data: holotype (probable), AMNH ♂*.
Type locality: Adelaide, SA.

Distribution: S Gulfs, SA; known only from type locality.
Ecology: adult—volant; melliferous, solitary.
References: Cockerell, T.D.A. (1929). Bees, chiefly Australian species, described or determined by Dr. H. Friese. *Am. Mus. Novit.* **343**: 1–20 (redescription); Cockerell, T.D.A. (1931). The bees of Australia. *Aust. Zool.* **7**: 34–54 (taxonomy).

Nomia (Austronomia) melanodonta Cockerell, 1926

Nomia melanodonta Cockerell, T.D.A. (1926). Descriptions and records of bees. CXII. *Ann. Mag. Nat. Hist. (9)***18**: 216–227 [221].
Type data: holotype, NMV ♂.
Type locality: Wodonga, VIC.

Distribution: Murray-Darling basin, VIC; known only from type locality.
Ecology: adult—volant; melliferous, solitary.

Nomia (Austronomia) melanoptera Cockerell, 1910

Nomia melanoptera Cockerell, T.D.A. (1910). New and little-known bees. *Trans. Am. Entomol. Soc.* **36**: 199–249 [224].
Type data: holotype, BMNH Hym.17.a.1762 ♀.
Type locality: Kuranda (as Cairns Kuranda), QLD.

Distribution: NE coastal, QLD; known only from type locality.
Ecology: adult—volant; melliferous, solitary.
Reference: Cockerell, T.D.A. (1931). The bees of Australia. *Aust. Zool.* **7**: 34–54 (taxonomy).

Nomia (Austronomia) melvilliana Cockerell, 1929

Nomia melvilliana Cockerell, T.D.A. (1929). Bees from the Australian region. *Am. Mus. Novit.* **346**: 1–18 [4].
Type data: holotype, AMNH ♂*.
Type locality: Melville Is., NT.

Distribution: N coastal, NT; only published localities Melville Is. and Darwin.
Ecology: adult—volant; melliferous, solitary.

Nomia (Austronomia) miranda Rayment, 1954

Nomia miranda Rayment, T. (1954). Remarkable bees from a rain forest. *Aust. Zool.* **12**: 46–56 [55].
Type data: holotype, ANIC ♂.
Type locality: Jamberoo, NSW.

Distribution: SE coastal, NSW; known only from type locality.
Ecology: adult—volant; melliferous, flower visiting

record: *Leptospermum* Forster & G.Forster [Myrtaceae].
Reference: Rayment, T. (1956). The *Nomia australica* Sm. complex. Its taxonomy, morphology and biology with the description of a new mutillid wasp. *Aust. Zool.* **12**: 176–200 (taxonomy).

Nomia (Austronomia) moerens Smith, 1875

Nomia moerens Smith, F. (1875). Descriptions of new species of bees belonging to the genus *Nomia* of Latreille. *Trans. Entomol. Soc. Lond.* **1875**: 53–70 pl. ii [60].
Type data: holotype, BMNH Hym.17.a.1755 ♀.
Type locality: Australia (as New Holland).

Distribution: NE coastal, SE coastal, QLD, VIC, (TAS); only published localities [Lamington] National Park (QLD), North Gippsland, Wandin and Ferntree Gully.
Ecology: adult—volant; melliferous, flower visiting record: *Hypochaeris* L. [Asteraceae].
References: Westwood, J.O. (1875). Descriptions of some new species of short-tongued bees belonging to the genus *Nomia* of Latreille. *Trans. Entomol. Soc. Lond.* **1875**: 207–222 (distribution, from Van Diemens Land); Dalla Torre, K.W. (1896). *Catalogus Hymenopterorum Hucusque Descriptorum Systematicus et Synonymicus.* Apidae (Anthophila). Lipsiae : G. Engelmann Vol. x 643 pp. (as *Nomia maerens*, incorrect subsequent spelling); Cockerell, T.D.A. (1913). Descriptions and records of bees. LV. *Ann. Mag. Nat. Hist. (8)***12**: 505–514 (distribution); Cockerell, T.D.A. (1922). Australian bees in the Queensland Museum. *Mem. Qd Mus.* **7**: 257–279 (distribution); Rayment, T. (1935). *A Cluster of Bees.* Sixty essays on the life-histories of Australian bees, with specific descriptions of over 100 new species, and an introduction by Professor E.F. Phillips, D.Ph., Cornell University, U.S.A. Sydney : Endeavour Press 752 pp. (flower record).

Nomia (Austronomia) muscosa Cockerell, 1910

Nomia muscosa Cockerell, T.D.A. (1910). New and little-known bees. *Trans. Am. Entomol. Soc.* **36**: 199–249 [224].
Type data: holotype, BMNH Hym.17.a.1764 ♀.
Type locality: Mackay, QLD.

Distribution: NE coastal, QLD, NSW; only published localities Mackay, Brisbane and Stradbroke Is., exact locality in NSW unknown.
Ecology: adult—volant; melliferous, solitary.
References: Cockerell, T.D.A. (1913). Descriptions and records of bees. LV. *Ann. Mag. Nat. Hist. (8)***12**: 505–514 (description of male); Cockerell, T.D.A. (1913). Some Australian bees. *Proc. Acad. Nat. Sci. Philad.* **65**: 28–44 (distribution); Hacker, H. (1921). Catalogue of Australian bees. *Mem. Qd Mus.* **7**: 99–163 (distribution).

Nomia (Austronomia) musgravei Cockerell, 1929

Nomia ferricauda musgravei Cockerell, T.D.A. (1929). Bees in the Australian Museum collection. *Rec. Aust. Mus.* **17**: 199–243 [226].
Type data: holotype, AM K49335 ♀.
Type locality: Como, near Sydney, NSW.

Distribution: SE coastal, NSW; known only from type locality.
Ecology: adult—volant; melliferous, solitary.
Reference: Michener, C.D. (1965). A classification of the bees of the Australian and South Pacific regions. *Bull. Am. Mus. Nat. Hist.* **130**: 1–362 [157] (taxonomy).

Nomia (Austronomia) nana Smith, 1875

Nomia nana Smith, F. (1875). Descriptions of new species of bees belonging to the genus *Nomia* of Latreille. *Trans. Entomol. Soc. Lond.* **1875**: 53–70 pl. ii [62].
Type data: holotype, BMNH Hym.17.a.1756 ♀.
Type locality: Adelaide, SA.
Nomia ruficornis Smith, F. (1875). Descriptions of new species of bees belonging to the genus *Nomia* of Latreille. *Trans. Entomol. Soc. Lond.* **1875**: 53–70 pl. ii [62] [junior primary homonym of *Nomia ruficornis* Spinola, 1838].
Type data: holotype, BMNH Hym.17.a.1757 ♂.
Type locality: Sydney, NSW.
Nomia smithella Gribodo, G. (1894). Note imenotterologiche. Nota II, continuazione. *Boll. Soc. Entomol. Ital.* **26**: 76–136, 262–314 [128] [*nom. nov.* for *Nomia ruficornis* Smith, 1875].

Taxonomic decision for synonymy: Cockerell, T.D.A. (1905). Notes on some bees in the British Museum. *Trans. Am. Entomol. Soc.* **31**: 309–364 [322].

Distribution: Murray-Darling basin, SE coastal, S Gulfs, (NW coastal), QLD, NSW, VIC, SA, (WA).
Ecology: adult—volant; melliferous, solitary.
References: Cockerell, T.D.A. (1910). New and little-known bees. *Trans. Am. Entomol. Soc.* **36**: 199–249 (distribution, specimen from NW Australia); Cockerell, T.D.A. (1929). Bees, chiefly Australian species, described or determined by Dr. H. Friese. *Am. Mus. Novit.* **343**: 1–20 (distribution); Cockerell, T.D.A. (1931). The bees of Australia. *Aust. Zool.* **7**: 34–54 (distribution, WA record doubtful); Rayment, T. (1939). Bees from the high lands of New South Wales and Victoria. *Aust. Zool.* **9**: 263–294 (distribution).

Nomia (Austronomia) nuda Rayment, 1939

Nomia australica nuda Rayment, T. (1939). Bees from the high lands of New South Wales and Victoria. *Aust. Zool.* **9**: 263–294 [277].
Type data: syntypes, ANIC ♀ (number of specimens unknown).
Type locality: Inverell, NSW.

Distribution: Murray-Darling basin, NSW; known only from type locality.
Ecology: adult—volant; melliferous, flower visiting record: *Carduus* L. [Asteraceae].
Reference: Michener, C.D. (1965). A classification of the bees of the Australian and South Pacific regions. *Bull. Am. Mus. Nat. Hist.* **130**: 1–362 [157] (taxonomy).

Nomia (Austronomia) pennata Friese, 1924

Nomia pennata Friese, H. (1924). Ueber die Bienen Australiens. *Konowia* **3**: 216–249 [248].
Type data: holotype (probable), whereabouts unknown ♂*.
Type locality: Adelaide, SA.

Distribution: S Gulfs, SA; known only from type locality.
Ecology: adult—volant; melliferous, solitary.

Nomia (Austronomia) phanerura Cockerell, 1913

Nomia flavoviridis phanerura Cockerell, T.D.A. (1913). Descriptions and records of bees. LV. *Ann. Mag. Nat. Hist.* (8)**12**: 505–514 [506].
Type data: holotype, USNM ♀*.
Type locality: Mackay, QLD.

Distribution: NE coastal, QLD; only published localities Mackay, Brisbane, Stradbroke Is. and Sandgate.
Ecology: adult—volant; melliferous, solitary.
References: Hacker, H. (1921). Catalogue of Australian bees. *Mem. Qd Mus.* **7**: 99–163 (distribution); Cockerell, T.D.A. (1931). The bees of Australia. *Aust. Zool.* **7**: 34–54 (taxonomy).

Nomia (Austronomia) purnongensis Cockerell, 1913

Nomia hippophila purnongensis Cockerell, T.D.A. (1913). Descriptions and records of bees. LV. *Ann. Mag. Nat. Hist.* (8)**12**: 505–514 [505].
Type data: syntypes, USNM 2♂*.
Type locality: Purnong, SA.

Distribution: Murray-Darling basin, SA; known only from type locality.
Ecology: adult—volant; melliferous, solitary.
Reference: Michener, C.D. (1965). A classification of the bees of the Australian and South Pacific regions. *Bull. Am. Mus. Nat. Hist.* **130**: 1–362 [157] (taxonomy).

Nomia (Austronomia) reginae Cockerell, 1905

Nomia australica reginae Cockerell, T.D.A. (1905). New Australian bees of the genus *Nomia*. *Entomologist* **38**: 217–223 [221].
Type data: syntypes, BMNH Hym.17.a.1737a,b (♂,♀).
Type locality: Mackay, QLD.

Distribution: NE coastal, SE coastal, Murray-Darling basin, QLD, VIC, SA; only published localities Mackay, Townsville, Portland and Meningie.
Ecology: larva—sedentary : adult—volant; melliferous, nest gregariously in soil, flower visiting record:

Eucalyptus L'Hérit. [Myrtaceae], *Leucopogon* R.Br. [Epacridaceae].
References: Rayment, T. (1953). *Bees of the Portland District.* Victoria : Portland Field Naturalist's Club 39 pp. (flower record); Rayment, T. (1954). Incidence of acarid mites on the biology of bees. *Aust. Zool.* **12**: 26–38 (biology); Rayment, T. (1956). The *Nomia australica* Sm. complex. Its taxonomy, morphology and biology with the description of a new mutillid wasp. *Aust. Zool.* **12**: 176–200 (taxonomy); Michener, C.D. (1965). A classification of the bees of the Australian and South Pacific regions. *Bull. Am. Mus. Nat. Hist.* **130**: 1–362 [157] (taxonomy).

Nomia (Austronomia) regis Cockerell, 1910

Nomia australica regis Cockerell, T.D.A. (1910). New and little-known bees. *Trans. Am. Entomol. Soc.* **36**: 199–249 [221].
Type data: holotype, BMNH Hym.17.a.1736 ♂.
Type locality: NW Australia.

Distribution: NW coastal, N coastal, WA, NT; only published localities NW Australia and Katherine.
Ecology: adult—volant; melliferous, solitary.
References: Rayment, T. (1953). *Bees of the Portland District.* Victoria : Portland Field Naturalist's Club 39 pp. (doubtful record, from Portland, VIC); Rayment, T. (1956). The *Nomia australica* Sm. complex. Its taxonomy, morphology and biology with the description of a new mutillid wasp. *Aust. Zool.* **12**: 176–200 (taxonomy); Michener, C.D. (1965). A classification of the bees of the Australian and South Pacific regions. *Bull. Am. Mus. Nat. Hist.* **130**: 1–362 [157] (taxonomy).

Nomia (Austronomia) rufocognita Cockerell, 1905

Nomia rufocognita Cockerell, T.D.A. (1905). New Australian bees of the genus *Nomia. Entomologist* **38**: 217–223 [219].
Type data: holotype, BMNH Hym.17.a.1742 ♂.
Type locality: Mackay, QLD.

Distribution: NE coastal, QLD; only published localities Mackay and Kuranda.
Ecology: adult—volant; melliferous, solitary.
References: Cockerell, T.D.A. (1912). Some bees of the genus *Nomia* from Australia. *Entomologist* **45**: 119–122 (taxonomy); Cockerell, T.D.A. (1931). The bees of Australia. *Aust. Zool.* **7**: 34–54 (taxonomy).

Nomia (Austronomia) satelles Cockerell, 1912

Nomia satelles Cockerell, T.D.A. (1912). Some bees of the genus *Nomia* from Australia. *Entomologist* **45**: 119–122 [120].
Type data: holotype, USNM ♂*.
Type locality: Rutherglen, VIC.

Distribution: SE coastal, Murray-Darling basin, NSW, VIC; only published localities Mittagong and Rutherglen.
Ecology: adult—volant; melliferous, solitary.

Nomia (Austronomia) semiaurea Cockerell, 1905

Nomia semiaurea Cockerell, T.D.A. (1905). Descriptions and records of bees. III. *Ann. Mag. Nat. Hist. (7)***16**: 301–308 [305].
Type data: syntypes, BMNH 2♀ (a specimen is labelled 'type' and has registration number Hym.17.a.1042).
Type locality: Mackay, QLD.
Nomia latiuscula Friese, H. (1924). Ueber die Bienen Australiens. *Konowia* **3**: 216–249 [245].
Type data: holotype (probable), whereabouts unknown ♀*.
Type locality: Mackay, QLD.

Taxonomic decision for synonymy: Cockerell, T.D.A. (1931). The bees of Australia. *Aust. Zool.* **7**: 34–54 [49].

Distribution: NE coastal, QLD; only published localities Mackay, Kuranda and Thursday Is.
Ecology: adult—volant; melliferous, flower visiting record: *Antigonon* Endl. [Polygonaceae], *Eucalyptus* L'Hérit. [Myrtaceae].
References: Cockerell, T.D.A. (1912). Some bees of the genus *Nomia* from Australia. *Entomologist* **45**: 119–122 (taxonomy); Cockerell, T.D.A. (1929). Descriptions and records of bees. CXVII. *Ann. Mag. Nat. Hist. (10)***4**: 132–141 (description of male, later renamed *Nomia semiaurea thor* Cockerell, 1930); Cockerell, T.D.A. (1929). Bees, chiefly Australian species, described or determined by Dr. H. Friese. *Am. Mus. Novit.* **343**: 1–20 (description of male).

Nomia (Austronomia) semipallida Cockerell, 1905

Nomia semipallida Cockerell, T.D.A. (1905). New Australian bees of the genus *Nomia. Entomologist* **38**: 217–223 [220].
Type data: holotype, BMNH Hym.17.a.1773 ♀.
Type locality: Mackay, QLD.

Distribution: NE coastal, QLD; known only from type locality.
Ecology: adult—volant; melliferous, solitary.

Nomia (Austronomia) stalkeri Cockerell, 1910

Nomia stalkeri Cockerell, T.D.A. (1910). New and little-known bees. *Trans. Am. Entomol. Soc.* **36**: 199–249 [223].
Type data: holotype, BMNH Hym.17.a.1772 ♂.
Type locality: Alexandria, NT.

Distribution: N Gulf, NT; known only from type locality.
Ecology: adult—volant; melliferous, solitary.
Reference: Cockerell, T.D.A. (1931). The bees of Australia. *Aust. Zool.* **7**: 34–54 (taxonomy).

Nomia (Austronomia) subaustralica Cockerell, 1910

Nomia subaustralica Cockerell, T.D.A. (1910). Some Australian bees in the Berlin Museum. *J. N.Y. Entomol. Soc.* **18**: 98–114 [105].
Type data: holotype, ZMB ♀*.
Type locality: Tennants Creek, NT.

Distribution: Lake Eyre basin, NT; only published localities Tennant Creek and Finke River, Hermannsburg.
Ecology: adult—volant; melliferous, solitary.

Nomia (Austronomia) submoerens Cockerell, 1914

Nomia submoerens Cockerell, T.D.A. (1914). Some Tasmanian bees. *Entomologist* **47**: 305–308 [307].
Type data: holotype, BMNH Hym.17.a.1768 ♀.
Type locality: Bridport, TAS.

Distribution: TAS; only published localities Bridport, Eaglehawk Neck and Hobart.
Ecology: adult—volant; melliferous, solitary.
References: Cockerell, T.D.A. (1915). Descriptions and records of bees. LXVII. *Ann. Mag. Nat. Hist. (8)***15**: 529–537 (distribution); Cockerell, T.D.A. (1926). Descriptions and records of bees. CXII. *Ann. Mag. Nat. Hist. (9)***18**: 216–227 (distribution).

Nomia (Austronomia) tenuihirta Cockerell, 1905

Nomia tenuihirta Cockerell, T.D.A. (1905). New Australian bees of the genus *Nomia*. *Entomologist* **38**: 217–223 [219].
Type data: holotype, BMNH Hym.17.a.1769 ♂.
Type locality: Mackay, QLD.
Nomia latitarsis Friese, H. (1924). Ueber die Bienen Australiens. *Konowia* **3**: 216–249 [246].
Type data: holotype (probable), AMNH ♀*.
Type locality: Mackay (as Colosseum), QLD.

Taxonomic decision for synonymy: Cockerell, T.D.A. (1929). Bees, chiefly Australian species, described or determined by Dr. H. Friese. *Am. Mus. Novit.* **343**: 1–20 [10].

Distribution: NE coastal, QLD; known only from type localities.
Ecology: adult—volant; melliferous, flower visiting record: *Cassia* L. *s.lat.* [Caesalpiniaceae].
References: Cockerell, T.D.A. (1905). Descriptions and records of bees. III. *Ann. Mag. Nat. Hist. (7)***16**: 301–308 (description of female); Cockerell, T.D.A. (1931). The bees of Australia. *Aust. Zool.* **7**: 34–54 (taxonomy).

Nomia (Austronomia) testaceipes Friese, 1924

Nomia argentifrons testaceipes Friese, H. (1924). Ueber die Bienen Australiens. *Konowia* **3**: 216–249 [245].
Type data: syntypes (probable), AMNH ♂* (number of specimens unknown).
Type locality: Central Australia.

Distribution: Central Australia; known only from type locality, exact locality unknown.
Ecology: adult—volant; melliferous, solitary.

References: Cockerell, T.D.A. (1929). Bees, chiefly Australian species, described or determined by Dr. H. Friese. *Am. Mus. Novit.* **343**: 1–20 (taxonomy); Michener, C.D. (1965). A classification of the bees of the Australian and South Pacific regions. *Bull. Am. Mus. Nat. Hist.* **130**: 1–362 [157] (taxonomy).

Nomia (Austronomia) thor Cockerell, 1930

Nomia semiaurea thor Cockerell, T.D.A. (1930). Descriptions and records of bees. CXXI. *Ann. Mag. Nat. Hist. (10)***5**: 108–115 [115].
Type data: syntypes (probable), whereabouts unknown ♂♀*.
Type locality: Thursday Is., QLD.

Distribution: NE coastal, QLD; known only from type locality.
Ecology: adult—volant; melliferous, flower visiting record: *Antigonon* Endl. [Polygonaceae].
References: Cockerell, T.D.A. (1929). Descriptions and records of bees. CXVII. *Ann. Mag. Nat. Hist. (10)***4**: 132–141 (male, as *Nomia semiaurea* Cockerell, 1905); Cockerell, T.D.A. (1931). The bees of Australia. *Aust. Zool.* **7**: 34–54 (taxonomy); Michener, C.D. (1965). A classification of the bees of the Australian and South Pacific regions. *Bull. Am. Mus. Nat. Hist.* **130**: 1–362 [157] (taxonomy).

Nomia (Austronomia) turneri Friese, 1924

Nomia turneri Friese, H. (1924). Ueber die Bienen Australiens. *Konowia* **3**: 216–249 [247].
Type data: holotype (probable), whereabouts unknown ♂*.
Type locality: Mackay, QLD.

Distribution: NE coastal, QLD; known only from type locality.
Ecology: adult—volant; melliferous, flower visiting record: *Eucalyptus* L'Hérit. [Myrtaceae].
Reference: Cockerell, T.D.A. (1931). The bees of Australia. *Aust. Zool.* **7**: 34–54 (taxonomy).

Nomia (Austronomia) ulongensis Cockerell, 1929

Nomia moerens ulongensis Cockerell, T.D.A. (1929). Bees in the Australian Museum collection. *Rec. Aust. Mus.* **17**: 199–243 [227].
Type data: syntypes, AM 6♂ (a specimen has the registration number K49706).
Type locality: Ulong, East Dorrigo, NSW.

Distribution: SE coastal, NSW, VIC; only published localities Ulong (East Dorrigo), Dorrigo and Portland.
Ecology: adult—volant; melliferous, flower visiting record: chrysanthemum.
References: Rayment, T. (1939). Bees from the high lands of New South Wales and Victoria. *Aust. Zool.* **9**: 263–294 (distribution); Rayment, T. (1953). *Bees of the Portland District*. Victoria : Portland Field Naturalist's Club 39 pp. (flower record); Michener, C.D. (1965). A classification of the bees of the Aus-

tralian and South Pacific regions. *Bull. Am. Mus. Nat. Hist.* **130**: 1–362 [157] (taxonomy).

Nomia (Austronomia) victoriae Cockerell, 1910

Nomia victoriae Cockerell, T.D.A. (1910). Some Australian bees in the Berlin Museum. *J. N.Y. Entomol. Soc.* **18**: 98–114 [107].
Type data: syntypes (probable), ZMB 2♀*.
Type locality: Ararat, VIC.
Nomia fulvoanalis Friese, H. (1924). Ueber die Bienen Australiens. *Konowia* **3**: 216–249 [245].
Type data: syntypes, ?AMNH ♀* (number of specimens unknown).
Type locality: Ararat, VIC.

Taxonomic decision for synonymy: Cockerell, T.D.A. (1929). Bees, chiefly Australian species, described or determined by Dr. H. Friese. *Am. Mus. Novit.* **343**: 1–20 [9].

Distribution: SE coastal, VIC; known only from type localities.
Ecology: adult—volant; melliferous, solitary.

Nomia (Curvinomia) Michener, 1944

Paranomia Friese, H. (1897). Monographie der Bienengattung *Nomia* (Latr.). (Palaearctische Formen). pp. 45–84 *in*, *Festschrift zur Feier des funfzigjahrigen Bestehens des Vereins für schlesische Insektenkunde in Breslau, 1847–1897.* Breslau : Maruschke & Behrendt [48] [proposed with subgeneric rank in *Nomia* Latreille, 1804; junior homonym of *Paranomia* Conrad, 1860 (Mollusca)]. Type species: *Nomia chalybeata* Smith, 1875 by subsequent designation, see Cockerell, T.D.A. (1910). The North American bees of the genus *Nomia. Proc. U.S. Natl Mus.* **38**: 289–298 [290].
Paranomina Michener, C.D. (1944). Comparative external morphology, phylogeny, and a classification of the bees (Hymenoptera). *Bull. Am. Mus. Nat. Hist.* **82**: 151–326 [251] [*nom. nov.* for *Paranomia* Friese, 1897; junior homonym of *Paranomina* Hendel, 1907 (Diptera)].
Curvinomia Michener, C.D. (1944). Comparative external morphology, phylogeny, and a classification of the bees (Hymenoptera). *Bull. Am. Mus. Nat. Hist.* **82**: 151–326 [251] [proposed with subgeneric rank in *Nomia* Latreille, 1804]. Type species: *Nomia californiensis* Michener, 1937 (=*Nomia tetrazonata* Cockerell, 1910) by original designation.

Extralimital distribution: Nearctic, N Neotropical, E Palaearctic, Afrotropical and Oriental Regions, see Michener, C.D. (1965). A classification of the bees of the Australian and South Pacific regions. *Bull. Am. Mus. Nat. Hist.* **130**: 1–362 [154].

Nomia (Curvinomia) aurantifer Cockerell, 1910

Nomia aurantifer Cockerell, T.D.A. (1910). Descriptions and records of bees. XXIX. *Ann. Mag. Nat. Hist. (8)***5**: 496–506 [501].
Type data: syntypes, BMNH 2♀ (a specimen is labelled 'type' and has registration number Hym.17.a.1741).
Type locality: Kuranda (as Cairns Kuranda), QLD.
Nomia luteofasciata Friese, H. (1917). Results of Dr. E. Mjöberg's Swedish Scientific Expeditions to Australia,

1910–1913. 13. Apidae. *Ark. Zool.* **11**(2): 1–9 [7].
Type data: syntypes, ?NHRM 2♀*.
Type locality: Cairns and Atherton, QLD.

Taxonomic decision for synonymy: Cockerell, T.D.A. (1921). Australian bees in the Queensland Museum. *Mem. Qd Mus.* **7**: 81–98 [83].

Distribution: NE coastal, QLD; only published localities Kuranda, Cairns and Atherton.
Ecology: adult—volant; melliferous, solitary.
References: Cockerell, T.D.A. (1929). Bees in the Australian Museum collection. *Rec. Aust. Mus.* **17**: 199–243 (taxonomy); Rayment, T. (1935). *A Cluster of Bees.* Sixty essays on the life-histories of Australian bees, with specific descriptions of over 100 new species, and an introduction by Professor E.F. Phillips, D.Ph., Cornell University, U.S.A. Sydney : Endeavour Press 752 pp. (illustration); Michener, C.D. (1965). A classification of the bees of the Australian and South Pacific regions. *Bull. Am. Mus. Nat. Hist.* **130**: 1–362 (illustration).

Nomia (Curvinomia) swainsoniae Cockerell, 1921

Nomia aurantifer swainsoniae Cockerell, T.D.A. (1921). Australian bees in the Queensland Museum. *Mem. Qd Mus.* **7**: 81–98 [82].
Type data: holotype, QM T2458 ♀.
Type locality: [Lamington] National Park, QLD.

Distribution: NE coastal, SE coastal, QLD, NSW; only published localities [Lamington] National Park (QLD) and Sydney.
Ecology: adult—volant; melliferous, flower visiting record: *Swainsona* Salisb. [Fabaceae].
References: Cockerell, T.D.A. (1929). Bees in the Australian Museum collection. *Rec. Aust. Mus.* **17**: 199–243 (distribution); Michener, C.D. (1965). A classification of the bees of the Australian and South Pacific regions. *Bull. Am. Mus. Nat. Hist.* **130**: 1–362 [154] (taxonomy).

Nomia (Hoplonomia) Ashmead, 1904

Hoplonomia Ashmead, W.H. (1904). Class I, Hexapoda. Order I, Hymenoptera. A list of the Hymenoptera of the Philippine Islands, with descriptions of new species. *J. N.Y. Entomol. Soc.* **12**: 1–22 [4]. Type species: *Hoplonomia quadrifasciata* Ashmead, 1904 by subsequent designation, see Cockerell, T.D.A. (1910). The North American bees of the genus *Nomia. Proc. U.S. Natl Mus.* **38**: 289–298 [289].

Extralimital distribution: SE Palaearctic, Afrotropical and Oriental Regions, extending E to Solomon Ils, see Michener, C.D. (1965). A classification of the bees of the Australian and South Pacific regions. *Bull. Am. Mus. Nat. Hist.* **130**: 1–362 [154].

Nomia (Hoplonomia) austrovagans Cockerell, 1905

Nomia (Hoplonomia) pulchribalteata austrovagans Cockerell, T.D.A. (1905). New Australian bees of the genus *Nomia. Entomologist* **38**: 217–223 [218].
Type data: holotype, BMNH Hym.17.a.1778 ♂.

Type locality: Adelaide, SA (label may be incorrect), see Cockerell, T.D.A. (1931). The bees of Australia. *Aust. Zool.* **7**: 34–54 [51].

Distribution: (S Gulfs), (SA); known only from type locality.

Ecology: adult—volant; melliferous, solitary.

References: Cockerell, T.D.A. (1931). The bees of Australia. *Aust. Zool.* **7**: 34–54 (distribution); Michener, C.D. (1965). A classification of the bees of the Australian and South Pacific regions. *Bull. Am. Mus. Nat. Hist.* **130**: 1–362 (distribution; taxonomy).

Nomia (Hoplonomia) darwinorum Cockerell, 1910

Nomia darwinorum Cockerell, T.D.A. (1910). Descriptions and records of bees. XXIX. *Ann. Mag. Nat. Hist. (8)***5**: 496–506 [502].
Type data: holotype, BMNH Hym.17.a.1738 ♂.
Type locality: Port Darwin, NT.

Distribution: NE coastal, N coastal, QLD, NT; only published localities Halifax, Babinda and Darwin.

Ecology: adult—volant; melliferous, solitary.

Reference: Cockerell, T.D.A. (1930). Australian bees in the Museum of Comparative Zoology. *Psyche (Camb.)* **37**: 141–154 (distribution).

Nomia (Hoplonomia) lyonsiae Cockerell, 1912

Nomia lyonsiae Cockerell, T.D.A. (1912). Descriptions and records of bees. XLVII. *Ann. Mag. Nat. Hist. (8)***10**: 484–494 [491].
Type data: holotype, QM T4125 ♀.
Type locality: Brisbane, QLD.

Distribution: NE coastal, QLD; only published localities Brisbane and Stradbroke Is.

Ecology: adult—volant; melliferous, flower visiting record: *Lyonsia* R.Br. [Apocynaceae].

References: Cockerell, T.D.A. (1931). The bees of Australia. *Aust. Zool.* **7**: 34–54 (taxonomy); Michener, C.D. (1965). A classification of the bees of the Australian and South Pacific regions. *Bull. Am. Mus. Nat. Hist.* **130**: 1–362 (illustration).

Nomia (Hoplonomia) rubroviridis Cockerell, 1905

Nomia rubroviridis Cockerell, T.D.A. (1905). New Australian bees of the genus *Nomia*. *Entomologist* **38**: 217–223 [223] [type locality not resolved; discrepancy between label data and description data].
Type data: holotype, BMNH Hym.17.a.1739 ♀.
Type locality: as NW Australia (Nicol Bay, Swan River or Champion Bay in description), see Cockerell, T.D.A. (1931). The bees of Australia. *Aust. Zool.* **7**: 34–54 [51].

Distribution: N coastal, WA, NT; only published localities near Broome, Derby, Halls Creek and Victoria River.

Ecology: adult—volant; melliferous, flower visiting record: *Solanum* L. [Solanaceae].

References: Cockerell, T.D.A. (1930). Australian bees in the Museum of Comparative Zoology. *Psyche (Camb.)* **37**: 141–154 (taxonomy); Cockerell, T.D.A.

(1931). The bees of Australia. *Aust. Zool.* **7**: 34–54 (taxonomy); Anderson, G.J. & Symon, D. (1988). Insect foragers on *Solanum* flowers in Australia. *Ann. M. Bot. Gard.* **75**: 842–852 (flower record).

Nomia (Mellitidia) Guérin-Méneville, 1838

Mellitidia Guérin-Méneville, F.E. (1838). Insectes. pp. 57–302 *in* Lesson, M. (ed.) *Voyage Autour du Monde, Exécuté par Ordre du Roi, sur la Corvette de sa Majesté, La Coquille, Pendant les Années 1822, 1823, 1824, et 1825.* Zoologie. Paris : Bertrand Vol. ii Pt 2 Div. 1 ch. xiii [270]. Publication date established from Bequaert, J.C. (1926). The date of publication of the Hymenoptera and Diptera described by Guérin in Duperrey's "Voyage de La Coquille". *Entomol. Mitt.* **15**: 186–195 [192]. Type species: *Andrena australis* Guérin-Méneville, 1831 by monotypy.

Extralimital distribution: New Guinea and nearby islands, see Michener, C.D. (1965). A classification of the bees of the Australian and South Pacific regions. *Bull. Am. Mus. Nat. Hist.* **130**: 1–362 [161].

Nomia (Mellitidia) tomentifera Friese, 1909

Nomia cincta tomentifera Friese, H. (1909). Die Bienenfauna von Neu-Guinea. *Ann. Hist.-Nat. Mus. Natl. Hung.* **7**: 179–288 [194].
Type data: syntypes, NHMW ♂♀*.
Type locality: Huon Gulf and Astrolabe Bay, Papua New Guinea and Cairns, QLD.

Distribution: NE coastal, QLD; only published localities Kuranda, Cooktown, Atherton, Dunk Is., Babinda and also New Guinea.

Ecology: adult—volant; melliferous, solitary.

References: Cockerell, T.D.A. (1910). New and little-known bees. *Trans. Am. Entomol. Soc.* **36**: 199–249 (taxonomy, distribution, subspecies to species); Friese, H. (1917). Results of Dr. E. Mjöberg's Swedish Scientific Expeditions to Australia, 1910–1913. 13. Apidae. *Ark. Zool.* **11**(2): 1–9 (distribution); Cockerell, T.D.A. (1926). Descriptions and records of bees. CX. *Ann. Mag. Nat. Hist. (9)***17**: 510–519 (distribution); Cockerell, T.D.A. (1929). Bees, chiefly Australian species, described or determined by Dr. H. Friese. *Am. Mus. Novit.* **343**: 1–20 (taxonomy); Cockerell, T.D.A. (1930). Australian bees in the Museum of Comparative Zoology. *Psyche (Camb.)* **37**: 141–154 (distribution).

Nomia (Pseudapis) W.F. Kirby, 1900

Pseudapis Kirby, W.F. (1900). The expedition to Sokotra. XII. Descriptions of the new species of Hymenoptera. *Bull. Liverpool Museums* **3**: 13–24 [15]. Type species: *Pseudapis anomala* W.F. Kirby, 1900 by monotypy.

Extralimital distribution: S Palaearctic, Afrotropical and Oriental Regions, see Michener, C.D. (1965). A classification of the bees of the Australian and South Pacific regions. *Bull. Am. Mus. Nat. Hist.* **130**: 1–362 [157].

Nomia (Pseudapis) lepidota Cockerell, 1905

Nomia lepidota Cockerell, T.D.A. (1905). New Australian bees of the genus *Nomia. Entomologist* **38**: 217–223 [218].
Type data: holotype, BMNH ♀.
Type locality: Sydney, NSW (label is believed incorrect, species is probably African), see Michener, C.D. (1961). Comments on some groups of Nomiinae (Hymenoptera, Halictidae). *Acta Hymen.* **1**: 239–240 [240].

Distribution: (SE coastal), (NSW); known only from type locality.
Ecology: adult—volant; melliferous, solitary.

Nomia (Reepenia) Friese, 1909

Reepenia Friese, H. (1909). Die Bienenfauna von Neu-Guinea. *Ann. Hist.-Nat. Mus. Natl. Hung.* **7**: 179–288 [205] [proposed with subgeneric rank in *Nomia* Latreille, 1804; placed on the Official List of Generic Names in Zoology (Name No. 1737), Opinion 788]. Type species: *Nomia variabilis* Friese, 1909 by monotypy, see International Commission on Zoological Nomenclature (1966). Opinion 788. *Megalopta* Smith, 1853 (Insecta, Hymenoptera) : designation of a type-species under the plenary powers. *Bull. Zool. Nomen.* **23**: 211–212.

Megaloptodes Moure, J.S. (1958). On the species of *Megalopta* described by F. Smith (Hymenoptera, Apoidea). *J. N.Y. Entomol. Soc.* **66**: 179–190 [183]. Type species: *Megalopta bituberculata* Smith, 1853 by original designation.

Taxonomic decision for synonymy: Michener, C.D. (1965). A classification of the bees of the Australian and South Pacific regions. *Bull. Am. Mus. Nat. Hist.* **130**: 1–362 [159].

Extralimital distribution: New Guinea and nearby islands, see Michener, C.D. (1965). A classification of the bees of the Australian and South Pacific regions. *Bull. Am. Mus. Nat. Hist.* **130**: 1–362 [160].

Nomia (Reepenia) bituberculata (Smith, 1853)

Megalopta bituberculata Smith, F. (1853). *Catalogue of Hymenopterous Insects in the Collection of the British Museum.* Part I. Andrenidae and Apidae. London : British Museum 197 pp. [84].
Type data: holotype, BMNH Hym.17.a.1275 ♂.
Type locality: Australia (as Brazil; label is incorrect), see Michener, C.D. (1965). A classification of the bees of the Australian and South Pacific regions. *Bull. Am. Mus. Nat. Hist.* **130**: 1–362 [306].

Tetralonia testacea Smith, F. (1854). *Catalogue of Hymenopterous Insects in the Collection of the British Museum.* Part II. Apidae. London : British Museum pp. 199–465 [301].
Type data: lectotype, BMNH ♂.
Subsequent designation: Michener, C.D. (1965). A classification of the bees of the Australian and South Pacific regions. *Bull. Am. Mus. Nat. Hist.* **130**: 1–362 [306].
Type locality: Australia (as Africa, label is incorrect, discrepancy discussed in Michener, 1965).

Nomia (Reepenia) eboracina Cockerell, T.D.A. (1912). Descriptions and records of bees. XLIII. *Ann. Mag. Nat. Hist. (8)***9**: 377–387 [377].

Type data: holotype, USNM ♂*.
Type locality: Cape York, QLD.

Taxonomic decision for synonymy: Michener, C.D. (1965). A classification of the bees of the Australian and South Pacific regions. *Bull. Am. Mus. Nat. Hist.* **130**: 1–362 [306].

Distribution: NE coastal, QLD; only published localities Cape York and Gordonvale.
Ecology: adult—volant; melliferous, flower visiting record: *Lantana* L. [Verbenaceae].
References: Cockerell, T.D.A. (1909). Descriptions and records of bees. XXII. *Ann. Mag. Nat. Hist. (8)***4**: 309–317 (redescription, as *Tetralonia testacea* Smith, 1854); Cockerell, T.D.A. (1921). Australian bees in the Queensland Museum. *Mem. Qd Mus.* **7**: 81–98 (distribution, as *Reepenia eboracina* (Cockerell, 1912)); Cockerell, T.D.A. (1932). Bees collected by Charles Darwin on the voyage of the "Beagle". *J. N.Y. Entomol. Soc.* **40**: 519–522 (taxonomy); Rayment, T. (1935). *A Cluster of Bees.* Sixty essays on the life-histories of Australian bees, with specific descriptions of over 100 new species, and an introduction by Professor E.F. Phillips, D.Ph., Cornell University, U.S.A. Sydney : Endeavour Press 752 pp. (illustration, as *Reepenia eboracina* (Cockerell, 1912)); Moure, J.S. (1958). On the species of *Megalopta* described by F. Smith (Hymenoptera, Apoidea). *J. N.Y. Entomol. Soc.* **66**: 179–190 (redescription, as *Megaloptodes bituberculatus* (Smith, 1853)); Michener, C.D. & Moure, J.S. (1964). *Megalopta*, 1853 (Insecta, Hymenoptera) : proposed designation of a type-species under the plenary powers. Z.N.(S.) 1624. *Bull. Zool. Nomen.* **21**: 148–149 (as *Reepenia bituberculata* (Smith, 1853)).

Nomia (Rhopalomelissa) Alfken, 1926

Rhopalomelissa Alfken, J.D. (1926). Fauna Buruana. Hymenoptera, Fam. Apidae. *Treubia* **7**: 259–275 [267]. Type species: *Rhopalomelissa xanthogaster* Alfken, 1926 by subsequent designation, see Sandhouse, G.A. (1943). The type species of the genera and subgenera of bees. *Proc. U.S. Natl Mus.* **92**(3156): 519–619 [596].

Extralimital distribution: Afrotropical and Oriental Regions, extending E to Solomon Ils, see Michener, C.D. (1965). A classification of the bees of the Australian and South Pacific regions. *Bull. Am. Mus. Nat. Hist.* **130**: 1–362 [159].

Nomia (Rhopalomelissa) halictella Cockerell, 1905

Nomia halictella Cockerell, T.D.A. (1905). Descriptions and records of bees. III. *Ann. Mag. Nat. Hist. (7)***16**: 301–308 [306].
Type data: syntypes, BMNH 4♀ (a specimen is labelled 'type' and has registration number Hym.17.a.1747).
Type locality: Mackay, QLD.

Distribution: NE coastal, Murray-Darling basin, QLD; also Solomon Ils and New Guinea.
Ecology: larva—sedentary : adult—volant; melliferous, nest gregariously in soil, turret above shaft,

flower visiting record: *Eucalyptus* L'Hérit. [Myrtaceae], *Melaleuca* L. [Myrtaceae], *Wahlenbergia* Roth [Campanulaceae].
References: Cockerell, T.D.A. (1912). Some bees of the genus *Nomia* from Australia. *Entomologist* **45**: 119–122 (description of male); Cockerell, T.D.A. (1929). Bees, chiefly Australian species, described or determined by Dr. H. Friese. *Am. Mus. Novit.* **343**: 1–20 (taxonomy); Cockerell, T.D.A. (1930). Australian bees in the Museum of Comparative Zoology. *Psyche (Camb.)* **37**: 141–154 (distribution); Cockerell, T.D.A. (1931). The bees of Australia. *Aust. Zool.* **7**: 34–54 (taxonomy); Krombein, K.V. (1951). Additional notes on the bees of the Solomon Islands (Hymenoptera : Apoidea). *Proc. Hawaii. Entomol. Soc.* **14**: 277–295 (distribution); Rayment, T. (1956). The *Nomia australica* Sm. complex. Its taxonomy, morphology and biology with the description of a new mutillid wasp. *Aust. Zool.* **12**: 176–200 (biology); Michener, C.D. (1961). Comments on some groups of Nomiinae (Hymenoptera, Halictidae). *Acta Hymen.* **1**: 239–240 (generic placement); Michener, C.D. (1965). A classification of the bees of the Australian and South Pacific regions. *Bull. Am. Mus. Nat. Hist.* **130**: 1–362 (flower record, illustration).

Nomia (Rhopalomelissa) triangularis Cockerell, 1905

Nomia halictella triangularis Cockerell, T.D.A. (1905). Descriptions and records of bees. III. *Ann. Mag. Nat. Hist.* *(7)***16**: 301–308 [307].

Type data: holotype, BMNH Hym.17.a.1748 ♀.
Type locality: Mackay, QLD.
Nomia pseudoceratina Cockerell, T.D.A. (1910). New and little-known bees. *Trans. Am. Entomol. Soc.* **36**: 199–249 [222].
Type data: holotype, BMNH Hym.17.a.601 ♂.
Type locality: Mackay, QLD.

Taxonomic decision for synonymy: Cockerell, T.D.A. (1930). Australian bees in the Museum of Comparative Zoology. *Psyche (Camb.)* **37**: 141–154 [146].

Distribution: NE coastal, QLD; only published localities Mackay, Halifax and Babinda.
Ecology: adult—volant; melliferous, solitary.
References: Cockerell, T.D.A. (1931). The bees of Australia. *Aust. Zool.* **7**: 34–54 (taxonomy); Michener, C.D. (1961). Comments on some groups of Nomiinae (Hymenoptera, Halictidae). *Acta Hymen.* **1**: 239–240 (generic placement).

Nomia (Rhopalomelissa) williamsi Cockerell, 1930

Nomia williamsi Cockerell, T.D.A. (1930). Australian bees in the Museum of Comparative Zoology. *Psyche (Camb.)* **37**: 141–154 [147].
Type data: holotype, MCZ ♂*.
Type locality: Halifax, QLD.

Distribution: NE coastal, QLD; known only from type locality.
Ecology: adult—volant; melliferous, solitary.
Reference: Michener, C.D. (1961). Comments on some groups of Nomiinae (Hymenoptera, Halictidae). *Acta Hymen.* **1**: 239–240 (generic placement).

CTENOPLECTRIDAE

INTRODUCTION

This family occurs mainly in the Afrotropical and Indomalayan Regions. One species, known only from one specimen, has been recorded from northern Queensland (Michener & Greenberg 1980).

Adult Ctenoplectridae have a long tongue similar to that found in other long-tongued bees. The glossae and labial palps, however, are short, as found in the Halictidae and Colletidae. There are two submarginal cells in the forewing and the apical part of the marginal cell curves away from the wing margin. The female has a distinctive, large, crescentic inner hind tibial spur (Michener 1965). Nothing is known of the biology of the Australian species. Related, non-Australian species nest in pre-existing cavities in wood and carry in soil to construct cells. They provision the cells with oil from flowers of Cucurbitaceae.

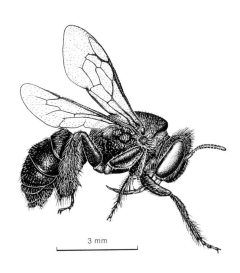

3 mm

Ctenoplectra australica   [by G. Thompson]

References

Michener, C.D. (1965). A classification of the bees of the Australian and South Pacific regions. *Bull. Am. Mus. Nat. Hist.* **130**: 1–362

Michener, C.D. & Greenberg, L. (1980). Ctenoplectridae and the origin of long-tongued bees. *Zool. J. Linn. Soc.* **69**: 183–203

Ctenoplectra W. Kirby, 1826

Ctenoplectra Kirby, W. (1826). *In* Kirby, W. & Spence, W. *An Introduction to Entomology:* or elements of the natural history of insects : with plates. London : Longman *et al.* Vol. 3 i–viii, 720 pp. [681] [proposed as a subgenus related to *Saropoda* Latreille, 1809]. Type species: *Ctenoplectra chalybea* Smith, 1858 by subsequent designation, see Sandhouse, G.A. (1943). The type species of the genera and subgenera of bees. *Proc. U.S. Natl Mus.* **92**(3156): 519–619 [542].

Ctenoplectra Smith, F. (1858). Catalogue of the hymenopterous insects collected at Sarawak, Borneo; Mount Ophir, Malacca; and at Singapore, by A.R. Wallace. *J. Proc. Linn. Soc. Lond. Zool.* **2**: 42–130 [44] [junior homonym and junior objective synonym of *Ctenoplectra* W. Kirby, 1826]. Type species: *Ctenoplectra chalybea* Smith, 1858 by monotypy.

Generic reference: Michener, C.D. (1942). Taxonomic observations on bees with descriptions of new genera and species (Hymenoptera, Apoidea). *J. N.Y. Entomol. Soc.* **50**: 273–282 [277].

Extralimital distribution: E Palaearctic, Afrotropical and Oriental Regions, extending E to New Guinea, see Michener, C.D. & Greenberg, L. (1980). Ctenoplectridae and the origin of long-tongued bees. *Zool. J. Linn. Soc.* **69**: 183–203 [194].

Ctenoplectra australica Cockerell, 1926

Ctenoplectra australica Cockerell, T.D.A. (1926). Descriptions and records of bees. CX. *Ann. Mag. Nat. Hist.* (9)**17**: 510–519 [513].
Type data: holotype, NMV ♀.
Type locality: Claudie River, QLD.

Distribution: NE coastal, QLD; known only from type locality.

Ecology: adult—volant; melliferous, solitary.

References: Cockerell, T.D.A. (1930). The bees of Australia. *Aust. Zool.* **6**: 137–156, 205–236 (taxonomy); Michener, C.D. (1965). A classification of the bees of the Australian and South Pacific regions. *Bull. Am. Mus. Nat. Hist.* **130**: 1–362 (illustration); Michener, C.D. & Greenberg, L. (1980). Ctenoplectridae and the origin of long-tongued bees. *Zool. J. Linn. Soc.* **69**: 183–203 (taxonomy).

MEGACHILIDAE

INTRODUCTION

Megachile chrysopyga   [by M. Quick]

The Megachilidae is a family of long-tongued, small to very large (5–39 mm), robust bees. It is a cosmopolitan family divided into three subfamilies, the cosmopolitan Lithurginae and Megachilinae, and the Fideliinae, found only in the Afrotropical and Neotropical Regions (Michener 1965).

Adults transport pollen externally on a scopa on the metasomal sterna. There are two submarginal cells in the forewing. The basitibial and pygidial plates are absent except in males of the genus *Lithurge*, which have a pygidial plate. All species are solitary and nests are often made in pre-existing burrows. The genus *Coelioxys* is cleptoparasitic. Rozen (1973) and King (1984) described larvae, and flower visiting records are given in Michener (1965) and Armstrong (1979).

In Australia, the subfamily Lithurginae (Michener 1983) is represented by the genus *Lithurge* and is found only in the northern half of the continent. Species of *Lithurge* provision their cells with coarse-grained pollen, mainly from flowers of Malvaceae, and nest in burrows in dead wood (Houston 1971).

The Megachilinae are characterized by a short jugal lobe on the hind wing. In Australia, the subfamily is represented by six genera and includes most of the Australian species of Megachilidae. Three genera are known from Tasmania.

Adults nest usually in pre-existing burrows or holes in wood but nests may also be built in mud nests of other Hymenoptera or, in a few species, fully exposed on rocks or plants. They are constructed of pieces of leaves (*Megachile* species) or resin and/or masticated leaves (*Chalicodoma* species) (Hacker 1915; Rayment 1928; Rayment 1935; Bray 1973). The most recent work on the Australian species is by King & Exley (1985a, 1985b, 1985c).

References

Armstrong, J.A. (1979). Biotic pollination mechanisms in the Australian flora—a review. *N.Z. J. Bot.* **17**: 467–508

Bray, R.A. (1973). Characteristics of some bees of the family Megachilidae in southeast Queensland and their potential as lucerne pollinators. *J. Aust. Entomol. Soc.* **12**: 99–102

Hacker, H. (1915). Notes on the genus *Megachile* and some rare insects collected during 1913–14. *Mem. Qd Mus.* **3**: 137–141

Houston, T.F. (1971). Notes on the biology of a lithurgine bee (Hymenoptera : Megachilidae) in Queensland. *J. Aust. Entomol. Soc.* **10**: 31–36

King, J. (1984). Immature stages of some Megachilidae (Hymenoptera : Apoidea). *J. Aust. Entomol. Soc.* **23**: 51–57

King, J. & Exley, E.M. (1985a). A reinstatement and revision of the genus *Thaumatosoma* Smith (Apoidea : Megachilidae). *J. Aust. Entomol. Soc.* **24**: 87–92

King, J. & Exley, E.M. (1985b). A revision of *Chalicodoma (Chalicodomoides)* Michener (Hymenoptera : Megachilidae). *J. Aust. Entomol. Soc.* **24**: 187–191

King, J. & Exley, E.M. (1985c). A revision of *Chalicodoma (Rhodomegachile)* Michener (Hymenoptera : Megachilidae). *J. Aust. Entomol. Soc.* **24**: 199–204

Michener, C.D. (1965). A classification of the bees of the Australian and South Pacific regions. *Bull. Am. Mus. Nat. Hist.* **130**: 1–362

Michener, C.D. (1983). The classification of the Lithurginae (Hymenoptera : Megachilidae). *Pan-Pac. Entomol.* **59**: 176–187

Rayment, T. (1928). Studies of Australian bees. I. The leaf-cutting bees (*Megachile macularis*, Dalla Torre, and other species). II. The clay-bees. (*Lithurgus atratiformis*, Cockerell). *Vict. Nat.* **45**: 79–86

Rayment, T. (1935). *A Cluster of Bees.* Sixty essays on the life-histories of Australian bees, with specific descriptions of over 100 new species, and an introduction by Professor E.F. Phillips, D.Ph., Cornell University, U.S.A. Sydney : Endeavour Press 752 pp.

Rozen, J.G. (1973). Immature stages of lithurgine bees with descriptions of the Megachilidae and Fideliidae based on mature larvae (Hymenoptera, Apoidea). *Am. Mus. Novit.* **2527**: 1–14

LITHURGINAE

Lithurge Latreille, 1825

Taxonomic decision for subgeneric arrangement: Michener, C.D. (1983). The classification of the Lithurginae (Hymenoptera : Megachilidae). *Pan-Pac. Entomol.* **59**: 176–187 [182].

Generic reference: Michener, C.D. (1965). A classification of the bees of the Australian and South Pacific regions. *Bull. Am. Mus. Nat. Hist.* **130**: 1–362.

Lithurge (Lithurge) Latreille, 1825

Lithurge Latreille, P.A. (1825). *Familles Naturelles du Règne Animal,* exposées succinctement et dans un ordre analytique, avec l'indication de leurs genres. Paris : Baillière 570 pp. [463]. Type species: *Andrena cornuta* Fabricius, 1787 by monotypy.

Lithurgus Berthold, A.A. (1827). *Latreille's natürliche Familien des Thierreichs.* Aus dem Französischen. Mit Anmerkungen und Zusätzen. Weimar : Landes-Industrie-Comptoir 602 pp. [467] [unjustified emendation of *Lithurge* Latreille, 1825]. Type species: *Andrena cornuta* Fabricius, 1787 by monotypy.

Extralimital distribution: Nearctic, Neotropical, Palaearctic, Afrotropical and Oriental Regions, extending E to Tahiti, see Michener, C.D. (1983). The

classification of the Lithurginae (Hymenoptera : Megachilidae). *Pan-Pac. Entomol.* **59**: 176–187 [183].

Lithurge (Lithurge) andrewsi Cockerell, 1909

Lithurgus andrewsi Cockerell, T.D.A. (1909). Descriptions and records of bees. XXII. *Ann. Mag. Nat. Hist.* (8)**4**: 309–317 [312].
Type data: holotype, BMNH Hym.17.a.2068a ♀.
Type locality: near Flying-Fish Cove, Christmas Is.

Distribution: Christmas Is.; known only from type locality.
Ecology: adult—volant; melliferous, solitary.

Lithurge (Lithurge) atratiformis Cockerell, 1905

Lithurgus atratiformis Cockerell, T.D.A. (1905). Descriptions and records of bees. II. *Ann. Mag. Nat. Hist.* (7)**16**: 292–301 [295].
Type data: holotype, BMNH Hym.17.a.2098 ♀.
Type locality: NW coast of Australia.

Distribution: NE coastal, SE coastal, NW coastal, QLD, NSW, (VIC), WA; also in Fiji (probably introduced) and New Guinea.
Ecology: adult—volant; melliferous, solitary, nests in unlined tunnels in rotten branches and stumps of *Banksia* L.f. [Proteaceae] and in dead sticks (doubtful

239

record of mud nests in longicorn burrows), flower visiting record: *Hibiscus* L. [Malvaceae], *Ipomoea* L. [Convolvulaceae].

References: Cockerell, T.D.A. (1905). Descriptions and records of bees. III. *Ann. Mag. Nat. Hist.* *(7)*16: 301–308 (taxonomy); Cockerell, T.D.A. (1906). Descriptions and records of bees. XI. *Ann. Mag. Nat. Hist.* *(7)*17: 527–539 (description of male); Rayment, T. (1928). Studies of Australian bees. I. The leaf-cutting bees (*Megachile macularis*, Dalla Torre, and other species). II. The clay-bees. (*Lithurgus atratiformis*, Cockerell). *Vict. Nat.* **45**: 79–86 (doubtful record of nest, VIC); Cockerell, T.D.A. (1929). Bees in the Australian Museum collection. *Rec. Aust. Mus.* **17**: 199–243 (distribution); Cockerell, T.D.A. (1930). The bees of Australia. *Aust. Zool.* **6**: 137–156, 205–236 (taxonomy); Rayment, T. (1935). *A Cluster of Bees*. Sixty essays on the life-histories of Australian bees, with specific descriptions of over 100 new species, and an introduction by Professor E.F. Phillips, D.Ph., Cornell University, U.S.A. Sydney : Endeavour Press 752 pp. (doubtful record); Michener, C.D. (1965). A classification of the bees of the Australian and South Pacific regions. *Bull. Am. Mus. Nat. Hist.* **130**: 1–362 (distribution); Houston, T.F. (1971). Notes on the biology of a lithurgine bee (Hymenoptera : Megachilidae) in Queensland. *J. Aust. Entomol. Soc.* **10**: 31–36 (biology); Rozen, J.G. (1973). Immature stages of lithurgine bees with descriptions of the Megachilidae and Fideliidae based on mature larvae (Hymenoptera, Apoidea). *Am. Mus. Novit.* 2527: 1–14 (larva); McGinley, R.J. (1981). Systematics of the Colletidae based on mature larvae with phenetic analysis of apoid larvae (Insecta, Hymenoptera, Apoidea). *Univ. Calif. Publ. Entomol.* **91**: 1–309 (larva); Eardley, C.D. (1988). A revision of the genus *Lithurge* Latreille (Hymenoptera: Megachilidae) of sub-saharan Africa. *J. Entomol. Soc. S. Afr.* **51**: 251–263 (wrongly recorded from S Africa).

Lithurge (Lithurge) atratus Smith, 1853

Lithurgus atratus Smith, F. (1853). *Catalogue of Hymenopterous Insects in the Collection of the British Museum. Part I. Andrenidae and Apidae.* London : British Museum 197 pp. [145].
Type data: syntypes, BMNH 4♀ (a specimen is labelled 'type' and has registration number Hym.17.a.2094).
Type locality: India.

Lithurgus dentipes Smith, F. (1853). *Catalogue of Hymenopterous Insects in the Collection of the British Museum. Part I. Andrenidae and Apidae.* London : British Museum 197 pp. [146] [Michener, C.D. (1965). A classification of the bees of the Australian and South Pacific regions. *Bull. Am. Mus. Nat. Hist.* **130**: 1–362 (185) states "false type in B.M."].
Type data: holotype, BMNH ♂* (not found by J.C.C. in 1988).
Type locality: Australia (as New Holland).

Taxonomic decision for synonymy: Lieftinck, M.A. (1939). Uit het leven van *Lithurgus atratus*, een indisch houtbijtje. *Trop. Natuur.* **28**: 193–201 [193].

Distribution: NE coastal, SE coastal, QLD, NSW; only published localities Cairns, Wollongbar and Sydney, also in India, Indonesia, New Guinea and Bismarck Archipelago.
Ecology: adult—volant; melliferous, solitary, nest in dead wood (doubtful record of mud nest in beetle burrow in wood).
References: Cockerell, T.D.A. (1905). Notes on some bees in the British Museum. *Trans. Am. Entomol. Soc.* **31**: 309–364 (taxonomy); Friese, H. (1909). Die Bienenfauna von Neu-Guinea. *Ann. Hist.-Nat. Mus. Natl. Hung.* **7**: 179–288 (distribution); Cockerell, T.D.A. (1930). The bees of Australia. *Aust. Zool.* **6**: 137–156, 205–236 (taxonomy, as *Lithurgus dentipes* Smith, 1853); Michener, C.D. (1965). A classification of the bees of the Australian and South Pacific regions. *Bull. Am. Mus. Nat. Hist.* **130**: 1–362 (distribution); Houston, T.F. (1971). Notes on the biology of a lithurgine bee (Hymenoptera : Megachilidae) in Queensland. *J. Aust. Entomol. Soc.* **10**: 31–36 (nest, as *Lithurge dentipes* Smith, 1853).

Lithurge (Lithurge) cognatus Smith, 1868

Lithurgus cognatus Smith, F. (1868). Descriptions of aculeate Hymenoptera from Australia. *Trans. Entomol. Soc. Lond.* **1868**: 231–258 [255].
Type data: syntypes, BMNH ♂♀ (female specimen is labelled 'type' and has registration number Hym.17.a.2099).
Type locality: Champion Bay (Geraldton), WA.

Distribution: NW coastal, WA; known only from type locality.
Ecology: adult—volant; melliferous, solitary.
References: Friese, H. (1909). Die Bienenfauna von Neu-Guinea. *Ann. Hist.-Nat. Mus. Natl. Hung.* **7**: 179–288 (distribution, doubtful specimens from Sydney and Mackay); Hacker, H. (1921). Catalogue of Australian bees. *Mem. Qd Mus.* **7**: 99–163 (as synonym of *Lithurgus rubricatus* Smith, 1853); Cockerell, T.D.A. (1930). The bees of Australia. *Aust. Zool.* **6**: 137–156, 205–236 (taxonomy); Michener, C.D. (1965). A classification of the bees of the Australian and South Pacific regions. *Bull. Am. Mus. Nat. Hist.* **130**: 1–362 (taxonomy).

Lithurge (Lithurge) rubricatus Smith, 1853

Lithurgus rubricatus Smith, F. (1853). *Catalogue of Hymenopterous Insects in the Collection of the British Museum. Part I. Andrenidae and Apidae.* London : British Museum 197 pp. [146].
Type data: syntypes, BMNH ♂♀ (female specimen is labelled 'type' and has registration number Hym.17.a.2096).
Type locality: Cape Upstart, QLD (as New Holland, labelled as Cape Upstart, N.H.).

Distribution: NE coastal, SE coastal, (SW coastal), NW coastal, N coastal, QLD, NSW, WA, NT.
Ecology: adult—volant; melliferous, solitary, nest (doubtful record, of mud cells), flower visiting record: *Hibiscus* L. [Malvaceae].
References: Cockerell, T.D.A. (1905). Notes on some bees in the British Museum. *Trans. Am. Entomol. Soc.* **31**: 309–364 (taxonomy); Cockerell, T.D.A. (1906). Descriptions and records of bees. XI. *Ann. Mag. Nat. Hist.* *(7)***17**: 527–539 (taxonomy); Friese, H. (1909). Die Bienenfauna von Neu-Guinea. *Ann. Hist.-Nat. Mus. Natl. Hung.* **7**: 179–288 (distribution); Cockerell, T.D.A. (1926). Descriptions and records of bees. CX. `Ann. Mag. Nat. Hist.* *(9)***17**: 510–519 (distribution); Cockerell, T.D.A. (1929). Bees from the Australian region. *Am. Mus. Novit.* **346**: 1–18 (distribution); Rayment, T. (1954). Incidence of acarid mites on the biology of bees. *Aust. Zool.* **12**: 26–38 (doubtful record, mud nest); Michener, C.D. (1965). A classification of the bees of the Australian and South Pacific regions. *Bull. Am. Mus. Nat. Hist.* **130**: 1–362 (flower record); Michener, C.D. (1983). The classification of the Lithurginae (Hymenoptera : Megachilidae). *Pan-Pac. Entomol.* **59**: 176–187 (taxonomy).

MEGACHILINAE

Anthidiellum Cockerell, 1904

Anthidiellum Cockerell, T.D.A. (1904). The bees of southern California. *Bull. South. Calif. Acad. Sci.* **3**: 3–6 [3]. Type species: *Trachusa strigata* Panzer, 1805 by original designation. Compiled from secondary source: Michener, C.D. (1965). A classification of the bees of the Australian and South Pacific regions. *Bull. Am. Mus. Nat. Hist.* **130**: 1–362 [213].

Taxonomic decision for subgeneric arrangement: Michener, C.D. (1965). A classification of the bees of the Australian and South Pacific regions. *Bull. Am. Mus. Nat. Hist.* **130**: 1–362 [213].

Extralimital distribution: Palaearctic, Afrotropical and Oriental Regions, see Pasteels, J.J. (1969). La systematique generique et subgenerique des Anthidiinae (Hymenoptera, Apoidea, Megachilidae) de l'ancien monde. *Mém. Soc. R. Entomol. Belg.* **31**: 1–148 [45].

Anthidiellum (Pycnanthidium) Krombein, 1951

Pycnanthidium Krombein, K.V. (1951). Additional notes on the bees of the Solomon Islands (Hymenoptera : Apoidea). *Proc. Hawaii. Entomol. Soc.* **14**: 277–295 [292]. Type species: *Pycnanthidium solomonis* Krombein, 1951 by original designation.

Extralimital distribution: Indonesia, New Guinea and Solomon Ils, see Pasteels, J.J. (1969). La systematique generique et subgenerique des Anthidiinae

(Hymenoptera, Apoidea, Megachilidae) de l'ancien monde. *Mém. Soc. R. Entomol. Belg.* **31**: 1–148 [47].

Anthidiellum (Pycnanthidium) melanaspis Cockerell, 1929

Anthidiellum melanaspis Cockerell, T.D.A. (1929). Descriptions and records of bees. CXVIII. *Ann. Mag. Nat. Hist.* *(10)***4**: 142–152 [145]. Type data: holotype, BMNH Hym.17.a.1953 ♂. Type locality: Thursday Is.

Distribution: NE coastal, QLD; known only from type locality.
Ecology: adult—volant; melliferous, solitary.
References: Krombein, K.V. (1951). Additional notes on the bees of the Solomon Islands (Hymenoptera : Apoidea). *Proc. Hawaii. Entomol. Soc.* **14**: 277–295 (as *?Pycnanthidium melanaspis* (Cockerell, 1929)); Michener, C.D. (1965). A classification of the bees of the Australian and South Pacific regions. *Bull. Am. Mus. Nat. Hist.* **130**: 1–362 (taxonomy, illustration).

Anthidiellum (Pycnanthidium) turneri (Friese, 1909)

Anthidium turneri Friese, H. (1909). Die Bienenfauna von Neu-Guinea. *Ann. Hist.-Nat. Mus. Natl. Hung.* **7**: 179–288 [257]. Type data: holotype, whereabouts unknown ♀*. Type locality: Mackay, QLD.

Distribution: NE coastal, QLD; known only from type locality.
Ecology: adult—volant; melliferous, solitary.
References: Cockerell, T.D.A. (1929). Descriptions and records of bees. CXVIII. *Ann. Mag. Nat. Hist.* *(10)***4**: 142–152 (taxonomy); Krombein, K.V. (1951). Additional notes on the bees of the Solomon Islands (Hymenoptera : Apoidea). *Proc. Hawaii. Entomol. Soc.* **14**: 277–295 (as *Pycnanthidium turneri* (Friese, 1909)).

Chalicodoma Lepeletier, 1841

Chalicodoma Lepeletier, A. (1841). *Histoire Naturelle des Insectes.* Hyménoptères. Paris : Roret Vol. ii (1841) 680 pp. [309]. Type species: *Apis muraria* Fabricius, 1798 by subsequent designation, see Girard, M. (1879). *Traité élémentaire d'Entomologie.* Tom. ii Fasc. 2 Hyménoptères porte-aiguillon. Paris : Baillière pp. 577–1028 7 pls [778]. Compiled from secondary source: Michener, C.D. (1962). Observations on the classification of the bees commonly placed in the genus *Megachile* (Hymenoptera : Apoidea). *J. N.Y. Entomol. Soc.* **70**: 17–29 [20].

Taxonomic decision for subgeneric arrangement: Michener, C.D. (1965). A classification of the bees of the Australian and South Pacific regions. *Bull. Am. Mus. Nat. Hist.* **130**: 1–362 [187].

Extralimital distribution: Palaearctic, see Michener, C.D. (1979). Biogeography of the bees. *Ann. M. Bot. Gard.* **66**: 277–347.

Chalicodoma (Austrochile) Michener, 1965

Austrochile Michener, C.D. (1965). A classification of the bees of the Australian and South Pacific regions. *Bull. Am. Mus. Nat. Hist.* **130**: 1–362 [202] [proposed with subgeneric rank in *Chalicodoma* Lepeletier, 1841]. Type species: *Megachile resinifera* Meade-Waldo, 1915 by original designation.

Chalicodoma (Austrochile) kirbiella (Rayment, 1953)

Megachile kirbiella Rayment, T. (1953). *Bees of the Portland District.* Victoria : Portland Field Naturalist's Club 39 pp. [35].
Type data: holotype, ANIC ♂.
Type locality: Gorae West, VIC.

Distribution: SE coastal, VIC; known only from type locality.
Ecology: adult—volant; melliferous, solitary, flower visiting record: *Leptospermum* Forster & G.Forster [Myrtaceae].
Reference: Rayment, T. (1954). New bees and wasps—Part XXIII. *Vict. Nat.* **71**: 59–61 (illustration).

Chalicodoma (Austrochile) kirbyana (Cockerell, 1906)

Megachile kirbyana Cockerell, T.D.A. (1906). Descriptions and records of bees. XI. *Ann. Mag. Nat. Hist. (7)***17**: 527–539 [537].
Type data: holotype, BMNH Hym.17.a.2372 ♂.
Type locality: Fremantle, WA.

Distribution: SW coastal, WA; only published localities Fremantle and Yallingup.
Ecology: adult—volant; melliferous, solitary.
Reference: Meade-Waldo, G. (1915). Notes on the Apidae (Hymenoptera) in the collection of the British Museum, with descriptions of new species. VI. *Ann. Mag. Nat. Hist. (8)***15**: 325–335 (distribution).

Chalicodoma (Austrochile) portlandiana (Rayment, 1953)

Megachile portlandiana Rayment, T. (1953). *Bees of the Portland District.* Victoria : Portland Field Naturalist's Club 39 pp. [36].
Type data: holotype, ANIC ♂.
Type locality: Cape Nelson Rd, Portland, VIC.

Distribution: SE coastal, VIC; known only from type locality.
Ecology: adult—volant; melliferous, solitary.
Reference: Rayment, T. (1954). New bees and wasps—Part XXIII. *Vict. Nat.* **71**: 59–61 (illustration).

Chalicodoma (Austrochile) recisa (Cockerell, 1913)

Megachile recisa Cockerell, T.D.A. (1913). Descriptions and records of bees. LII. *Ann. Mag. Nat. Hist. (8)***11**: 530–542 [534].

Type data: syntypes, QM 2♂ (a specimen has registration number Hy/4130).
Type locality: Kewell, VIC.

Distribution: NE coastal, SE coastal, QLD, VIC; only published localities Brisbane and Kewell.
Ecology: adult—volant; melliferous, solitary, flower visiting record: *Daviesia* Sm. [Fabaceae].
Reference: Hacker, H. (1915). Notes on the genus *Megachile* and some rare insects collected during 1913–14. *Mem. Qd Mus.* **3**: 137–141 (flower record).

Chalicodoma (Austrochile) remotula (Cockerell, 1910)

Megachile remotula Cockerell, T.D.A. (1910). Some Australian bees in the Berlin Museum. *J. N.Y. Entomol. Soc.* **18**: 98–114 [111].
Type data: syntypes, ZMB 1003 2♀*.
Type locality: as Eastern Australia (this label may be an error for Western Australia), see Cockerell, T.D.A. (1930). The bees of Australia. *Aust. Zool.* **6**: 137–156, 205–236 [229, note under *Megachile preissi* Cockerell, 1910].

Distribution: SW coastal, WA, (E Australia).
Ecology: adult—volant; melliferous, solitary.
Reference: Meade-Waldo, G. (1915). Notes on the Apidae (Hymenoptera) in the collection of the British Museum, with descriptions of new species. VI. *Ann. Mag. Nat. Hist. (8)***15**: 325–335 (taxonomy); King, J. (1986). The systematics of some Australian Megachilidae (Hymenoptera : Apoidea). Unpubl. PhD Thesis. Brisbane : Univ. of Queensland 439 pp. (distribution).

Chalicodoma (Austrochile) resinifera (Meade-Waldo, 1915)

Megachile resinifera Meade-Waldo, G. (1915). Notes on the Apidae (Hymenoptera) in the collection of the British Museum, with descriptions of new species. VI. *Ann. Mag. Nat. Hist. (8)***15**: 325–335 [329].
Type data: syntypes, BMNH ♂♀ (female specimen labelled 'type' and has registration number Hym.17.a.2341).
Type locality: Yallingup, WA.

Distribution: SW coastal, WA; known only from type locality.
Ecology: adult—volant; melliferous, solitary, nest of resin, probably in aggregation in sandy bank.
Reference: Cockerell, T.D.A. (1930). The bees of Australia. *Aust. Zool.* **6**: 137–156, 205–236 (taxonomy).

Chalicodoma (Austrochile) rottnestensis (Rayment, 1934)

Megachile rottnestensis Rayment, T. (1934). Contributions to the fauna of Rottnest Island. VIII. Apoidea. With description of new species. *J. Proc. R. Soc. West. Aust.* **20**: 201–212 [209].
Type data: holotype, WAM 31–1856 ♂.
Type locality: Rottnest Is., WA.

Distribution: SW coastal, WA; known only from type locality.
Ecology: adult—volant; melliferous, solitary.

Chalicodoma (Austrochile) rufomaculata (Rayment, 1935)

Megachile rufomaculata Rayment, T. (1935). *A Cluster of Bees*. Sixty essays on the life-histories of Australian bees, with specific descriptions of over 100 new species, and an introduction by Professor E.F. Phillips, D.Ph., Cornell University, U.S.A. Sydney : Endeavour Press 752 pp. [717].
Type data: holotype, ANIC ♂.
Type locality: Sydney, NSW.

Distribution: SE coastal, NSW; known only from type locality.
Ecology: adult—volant; melliferous, solitary.

Chalicodoma (Austrochile) sexmaculata (Smith, 1868)

Megachile sexmaculata Smith, F. (1868). Descriptions of aculeate Hymenoptera from Australia. *Trans. Entomol. Soc. Lond.* **1868**: 231–258 [257].
Type data: holotype, BMNH Hym.17.a.2370 ♀.
Type locality: Champion Bay (Geraldton), WA.

Distribution: SW coastal, NW coastal, WA; only published localities Perth, O'Connor, Yallingup and Champion Bay.
Ecology: adult—volant; melliferous, solitary.
References: Meade-Waldo, G. (1915). Notes on the Apidae (Hymenoptera) in the collection of the British Museum, with descriptions of new species. VI. *Ann. Mag. Nat. Hist. (8)***15**: 325–335 (distribution); Rayment, T. (1931). Bees in the collections of the Western Australian Museum and the Agricultural Department, Perth. *J. Proc. R. Soc. West. Aust.* **17**: 157–190 (distribution).

Chalicodoma (Austrochile) subferox (Meade-Waldo, 1915)

Megachile subferox Meade-Waldo, G. (1915). Notes on the Apidae (Hymenoptera) in the collection of the British Museum, with descriptions of new species. VI. *Ann. Mag. Nat. Hist. (8)***15**: 325–335 [333].
Type data: syntypes, BMNH 5♂♀ (female specimen is labelled 'type' and has registration number Hym.17.a.2349).
Type locality: Yallingup, WA.

Distribution: SW coastal, WA; only published localities Yallingup and Busselton.
Ecology: adult—volant; melliferous, solitary.

Chalicodoma (Callomegachile) Michener, 1962

Callomegachile Michener, C.D. (1962). Observations on the classification of the bees commonly placed in the genus *Megachile* (Hymenoptera : Apoidea). *J. N.Y. Entomol. Soc.* **70**: 17–29 [21] [proposed with subgeneric rank in *Chalicodoma* Lepeletier, 1841]. Type species: *Chalicodoma*

(Callomegachile) mystaceana Michener, 1962 by original designation.

Extralimital distribution: E Palaearctic, Afrotropical and Oriental Regions, extending E to Hawaii, see Michener, C.D. (1965). A classification of the bees of the Australian and South Pacific regions. *Bull. Am. Mus. Nat. Hist.* **130**: 1–362 [190].

Chalicodoma (Callomegachile) albobasalis (Smith, 1879)

Megachile albobasalis Smith, F. (1879). *Descriptions of New Species of Hymenoptera in the Collection of the British Museum*. London : British Museum xxi 240 pp. [65].
Type data: holotype, BMNH Hym.17.a.2064 ♀*.
Type locality: Murray Is., Torres Strait.

Distribution: NE coastal, QLD; in Australia known only from type locality, also New Guinea and (doubtfully) Aru.
Ecology: adult—volant; melliferous, solitary.
References: Friese, H. (1909). Die Bienenfauna von Neu-Guinea. *Ann. Hist.-Nat. Mus. Natl. Hung.* **7**: 179–288 (distribution); Meade-Waldo, G. (1912). Notes on the Apidae (Hymenoptera) in the collection of the British Museum, with descriptions of new species. *Ann. Mag. Nat. Hist. (8)***10**: 461–478 (distribution).

Chalicodoma (Callomegachile) biroi (Friese, 1903)

Megachile (Eumegachile) biroi Friese, H. (1903). Neue *Megachile*-Arten des Sunda-Archipel. (Hym.). *Z. Syst. Hymenopterol. Dipterol.* **3**: 241–245 [244].
Type data: holotype, NHMW ♀*.
Type locality: Milne Bay, Papua New Guinea.

Distribution: Australia, exact locality unknown, also New Guinea.
Ecology: adult—volant; melliferous, solitary.
References: Friese, H. (1909). Die Bienenfauna von Neu-Guinea. *Ann. Hist.-Nat. Mus. Natl. Hung.* **7**: 179–288 (redescription); Cockerell, T.D.A. (1929). Bees in the Australian Museum collection. *Rec. Aust. Mus.* **17**: 199–243 (distribution); Michener, C.D. (1962). Observations on the classification of the bees commonly placed in the genus *Megachile* (Hymenoptera : Apoidea). *J. N.Y. Entomol. Soc.* **70**: 17–29 (generic placement); Michener, C.D. (1965). A classification of the bees of the Australian and South Pacific regions. *Bull. Am. Mus. Nat. Hist.* **130**: 1–362 (record from Australia).

Chalicodoma (Callomegachile) cincturata (Cockerell, 1912)

Megachile cincturata Cockerell, T.D.A. (1912). Descriptions and records of bees. XLII. *Ann. Mag. Nat. Hist. (8)***9**: 220–229 [222].
Type data: holotype, USNM ♀*.
Type locality: Cape York, QLD.

Distribution: NE coastal, QLD; only published localities Cape York and Cairns.
Ecology: adult—volant; melliferous, solitary.
Reference: Cockerell, T.D.A. (1930). Australian bees in the Museum of Comparative Zoology. *Psyche (Camb.)* **37**: 141–154 (distribution).

Chalicodoma (Callomegachile) luteiceps (Friese, 1911)

Megachile luteiceps Friese, H. (1911). Auffallende *Megachile*-Arten des Sunda-Archipels. (Apidae) *Dtsch. Entomol. Zeit.* **1911**: 217–220 [219].
Type data: syntypes (probable), whereabouts unknown 2♀*.
Type locality: Finschhafen, New Guinea.

Distribution: Australia, exact locality unknown, also New Guinea.
Ecology: adult—volant; melliferous, solitary.
Reference: Michener, C.D. (1965). A classification of the bees of the Australian and South Pacific regions. *Bull. Am. Mus. Nat. Hist.* **130**: 1–362 (record from Australia).

Chalicodoma (Callomegachile) mystaceana Michener, 1962

Chalicodoma (Callomegachile) mystaceana Michener, C.D. (1962). Observations on the classification of the bees commonly placed in the genus *Megachile* (Hymenoptera : Apoidea). *J. N.Y. Entomol. Soc.* **70**: 17–29 [22].
Type data: holotype, QM T6733 ♀.
Type locality: Brisbane, QLD.

Distribution: NE coastal, QLD.
Ecology: adult—volant; melliferous, solitary, nest (of resin, gum, or mud) in old mud-wasp (*Sceliphron laetum* (Smith) (Sphecidae) nest, in cardboard trap nest, in drilled wooden blocks or in polystyrene bee boards, flower visiting record: lucerne, *Pongamia* Vent. [Fabaceae].
References: Hacker, H. (1915). Notes on the genus *Megachile* and some rare insects collected during 1913–14. *Mem. Qd Mus.* **3**: 137–141 (nest, as *Megachile mystacea* (Fabricius, 1775)); Michener, C.D. (1962). Observations on the classification of the bees commonly placed in the genus *Megachile* (Hymenoptera : Apoidea). *J. N.Y. Entomol. Soc.* **70**: 17–29 (misidentified by many authors as *Megachile mystacea* (Fabricius, 1775) =*Chalicodoma mystaceana* Michener, 1962); Michener, C.D. (1965). A classification of the bees of the Australian and South Pacific regions. *Bull. Am. Mus. Nat. Hist.* **130**: 1–362 (flower record); Bray, R.A. (1973). Characteristics of some bees of the family Megachilidae in southeast Queensland and their potential as lucerne pollinators. *J. Aust. Entomol. Soc.* **12**: 99–102 (biology); King, J. (1984). Immature stages of some Megachilidae (Hymenoptera : Apoidea). *J. Aust. Entomol. Soc.* **23**: 51–57 (immature stages); Skou, J.P. & King, J. (1984). *Ascosphaera osmophila* sp. nov., an Australian spore cyst fungus. *Aust. J. Bot.* **32**: 225–231 (as host).

Chalicodoma (Callomegachile) nitidiscutata (Friese, 1920)

Megachile mystacea nitidiscutata Friese, H. (1920). Neue Arten der Bauchsammler (Hym` *Dtsch. Entomol. Zeit.* **1920**: 49–55 [53].
Type data: holotype, ZMB ♀*.
Type locality: Mackay (as Makay), QLD.

Distribution: NE coastal, QLD; known only from type locality.
Ecology: adult—volant; melliferous, solitary.
Reference: Cockerell, T.D.A. (1930). The bees of Australia. *Aust. Zool.* **6**: 137–156, 205–236 (possibly a synonym of *Megachile ustulata* Smith, 1862).

Chalicodoma (Callomegachile) pretiosa (Friese, 1909)

Megachile (Eumegachile) pretiosa Friese, H. (1909). Die Bienenfauna von Neu-Guinea. *Ann. Hist.-Nat. Mus. Natl. Hung.* **7**: 179–288 [251].
Type data: holotype (probable), whereabouts unknown ♀*.
Type locality: Cairns, QLD.

Distribution: NE coastal, QLD; known only from type locality in Australia, also New Guinea.
Ecology: adult—volant; melliferous, solitary.
References: Friese, H. (1908). Hymenoptera. II. Apidae. Nova Guinea. pp. 353–359 pl. XV *in* Wichmann, A. *Résultats de L'Expedition Scientifique Néerlandaise à la Nouvelle Guinée en 1903*. Leiden : E.J. Brill (illustration, as *Megachile albobasalis* Smith, 1879); Cockerell, T.D.A. (1929). Bees in the Australian Museum collection. *Rec. Aust. Mus.* **17**: 199–243 (distribution); Michener, C.D. (1962). Observations on the classification of the bees commonly placed in the genus *Megachile* (Hymenoptera : Apoidea). *J. N.Y. Entomol. Soc.* **70**: 17–29 (generic placement).

Chalicodoma (Callomegachile) viridinitens (Cockerell, 1930)

Megachile viridinitens Cockerell, T.D.A. (1930). Australian bees in the Museum of Comparative Zoology. *Psyche (Camb.)* **37**: 141–154 [144].
Type data: holotype, MCZ ♀*.
Type locality: Cairns, QLD.

Distribution: NE coastal, QLD; known only from type locality.
Ecology: adult—volant; melliferous, solitary.

Chalicodoma (Chalicodomoides) Michener, 1962

Chalicodomoides Michener, C.D. (1962). Observations on the classification of the bees commonly placed in the genus *Megachile* (Hymenoptera : Apoidea). *J. N.Y. Entomol. Soc.* **70**: 17–29 [24] [proposed with subgeneric rank in *Chalicodoma* Lepeletier, 1841]. Type species: *Megachile aethiops* Smith, 1853 by original designation.

Chalicodoma (Chalicodomoides) aethiops (Smith, 1853)

Megachile aethiops Smith, F. (1853). *Catalogue of Hymenopterous Insects in the Collection of the British Museum*. Part I. Andrenidae and Apidae. London : British Museum 197 pp. [166].
Type data: holotype, BMNH Hym.17.a.2251 ♀.
Type locality: Australia (as Africa but species known only from Australia), see Michener, C.D. (1962). Observations on the classification of the bees commonly placed in the genus *Megachile* (Hymenoptera : Apoidea). *J. N.Y. Entomol. Soc.* **70**: 17–29 [24].

Megachile doddiana clarkei Cockerell, T.D.A. (1914). Descriptions and records of bees. LXIV. *Ann. Mag. Nat. Hist.* (8)**14**: 464–472 [464].
Type data: holotype, USNM 54907 ♂* (described as ♀).
Type locality: Geraldton, WA.

Taxonomic decision for synonymy: Michener, C.D. (1962). Observations on the classification of the bees commonly placed in the genus *Megachile* (Hymenoptera : Apoidea). *J. N.Y. Entomol. Soc.* **70**: 17–29 [24].

Distribution: NE coastal, Lake Eyre basin, SW coastal, NW coastal, N coastal, N Gulf, QLD, WA, NT.

Ecology: adult—volant; melliferous, solitary, nest in abandoned cells of *Sceliphron laetum* (Smith) (Sphecidae), cells lined with mixture of resin and plant fibres, flower visiting record: *Eucalyptus* L'Hérit. [Myrtaceae].
References: Meade-Waldo, G. (1912). Notes on the Apidae (Hymenoptera) in the collection of the British Museum, with descriptions of new species. *Ann. Mag. Nat. Hist.* (8)**10**: 461–478 (taxonomy); Cockerell, T.D.A. (1929). Bees from the Australian region. *Am. Mus. Novit.* **346**: 1–18 (doubtful record, Townsville, as *Megachile clarkei* Cockerell, 1914); Michener, C.D. (1962). Observations on the classification of the bees commonly placed in the genus *Megachile* (Hymenoptera : Apoidea). *J. N.Y. Entomol. Soc.* **70**: 17–29 (as *Megachile (Megachile) clarki*, incorrect subsequent spelling); Michener, C.D. (1965). A classification of the bees of the Australian and South Pacific regions. *Bull. Am. Mus. Nat. Hist.* **130**: 1–362 (illustration); Naumann, I.D. (1983).The biology of mud nesting Hymenoptera (and their associates) and Isoptera in rock shelters of the Kakadu Region, Northern Territory. *Aust. Natl Parks & Wildlf. Serv. Spec. Publ.* **10**: 127–189 (nest); King, J. & Exley, E.M. (1985). A revision of *Chalicodoma (Chalicodomoides)* Michener (Hymenoptera : Megachilidae). *J. Aust. Entomol. Soc.* **24**: 187–191 (redescription).

Chalicodoma (Chalicodomoides) doddiana (Cockerell, 1906)

Megachile doddiana Cockerell, T.D.A. (1906). Descriptions and records of bees. XI. *Ann. Mag. Nat. Hist.* (7)**17**: 527–539 [530].

Type data: holotype, BMNH Hym.17.a.2300 ♀.
Type locality: Townsville, QLD.

Megachile oppidalis Cockerell, T.D.A. (1926). Descriptions and records of bees. CX. *Ann. Mag. Nat. Hist.* (9)**17**: 510–519 [512].
Type data: syntypes, NMV 3♂*.
Type locality: Townsville, QLD.

Taxonomic decision for synonymy: King, J. & Exley, E.M. (1985). A revision of *Chalicodoma (Chalicodomoides)* Michener (Hymenoptera : Megachilidae). *J. Aust. Entomol. Soc.* **24**: 187–191 [190].

Distribution: NE coastal, QLD; known only from type locality.
Ecology: adult—volant; melliferous, solitary.
References: Cockerell, T.D.A. (1929). Descriptions and records of bees. CXV. *Ann. Mag. Nat. Hist.* (10)**3**: 354–360 (description of male); Michener, C.D. (1962). Observations on the classification of the bees commonly placed in the genus *Megachile* (Hymenoptera : Apoidea). *J. N.Y. Entomol. Soc.* **70**: 17–29 (as synonym of *Chalicodoma (Chalicodomoides) aethiops* Smith, 1853).

Chalicodoma (Chelostomoda) Michener, 1962

Chelostomoda Michener, C.D. (1962). Observations on the classification of the bees commonly placed in the genus *Megachile* (Hymenoptera : Apoidea). *J. N.Y. Entomol. Soc.* **70**: 17–29 [24] [proposed with subgeneric rank in *Chalicodoma* Lepeletier, 1841]. Type species: *Megachile spissula parvula* Strand, 1913 by original designation.

Extralimital distribution: SE Palaearctic and Oriental Regions, extending E to New Guinea and Solomon Ils, see Michener, C.D. (1965). A classification of the bees of the Australian and South Pacific regions. *Bull. Am. Mus. Nat. Hist.* **130**: 1–362 [204].

Chalicodoma (Chelostomoda) carteri (Cockerell, 1929)

Megachile carteri Cockerell, T.D.A. (1929). Bees in the Australian Museum collection. *Rec. Aust. Mus.* **17**: 199–243 [238].
Type data: holotype, AM K46514 ♀.
Type locality: Kuranda, QLD.

Distribution: NE coastal, QLD; known only from type locality.
Ecology: adult—volant; melliferous, solitary.
Reference: Michener, C.D. (1962). Observations on the classification of the bees commonly placed in the genus *Megachile* (Hymenoptera : Apoidea). *J. N.Y. Entomol. Soc.* **70**: 17–29 (generic placement).

Chalicodoma (Chelostomoda) inflaticauda (Cockerell, 1939)

Megachile inflaticauda Cockerell, T.D.A. (1939). Studies of the Pacific bees in the collection of Bishop Museum (Hymenoptera, Apoidea). *Occ. Pap. Bernice P. Bishop Mus.* **15**: 133–140 [138].

Type data: holotype, BPBM ♀*.
Type locality: Thursday Is., QLD.

Distribution: NE coastal, QLD; known only from type locality.
Ecology: adult—volant; melliferous, solitary.

Chalicodoma (Hackeriapis) Cockerell, 1922

Hackeriapis Cockerell, T.D.A. (1922). Descriptions and records of bees. XCV. *Ann. Mag. Nat. Hist. (9)*10: 265–269 [267] [proposed with subgeneric rank in *Megachile* Latreille, 1802]. Type species: *Megachile rhodura* Cockerell, 1906 by original designation.

Extralimital distribution: New Guinea, see Michener, C.D. (1965). A classification of the bees of the Australian and South Pacific regions. *Bull. Am. Mus. Nat. Hist.* **130**: 1–362 [197].

Chalicodoma (Hackeriapis) alani (Cockerell, 1929)

Megachile alani Cockerell, T.D.A. (1929). Bees in the Queensland Museum. *Mem. Qd Mus.* **9**: 298–323 [302].
Type data: holotype, QM 2♀ (a specimen has registration number Hy/4025).
Type locality: Moree, NSW.

Distribution: Murray-Darling basin, NSW; known only from type locality.
Ecology: adult—volant; melliferous, solitary.

Chalicodoma (Hackeriapis) alleynae (Rayment, 1935)

Megachile alleynae Rayment, T. (1935). *A Cluster of Bees.* Sixty essays on the life-histories of Australian bees, with specific descriptions of over 100 new species, and an introduction by Professor E.F. Phillips, D.Ph., Cornell University, U.S.A. Sydney : Endeavour Press 752 pp. [722].
Type data: holotype, ANIC ♀.
Type locality: Botanic Gardens, Melbourne, VIC.

Distribution: SE coastal, VIC; known only from type locality.
Ecology: adult—volant; melliferous, solitary, flower visiting record: *Swainsona* Salisb. [Fabaceae].

Chalicodoma (Hackeriapis) apicata (Smith, 1853)

Megachile apicata Smith, F. (1853). *Catalogue of Hymenopterous Insects in the Collection of the British Museum.* Part I. Andrenidae and Apidae. London : British Museum 197 pp. [172].
Type data: holotype, BMNH Hym.17.a.2298 ♀.
Type locality: Adelaide, SA.

Distribution: NE coastal, SE coastal, S Gulfs, SW coastal, QLD, VIC, SA, WA.
Ecology: adult—volant; melliferous, solitary.
References: Cockerell, T.D.A. (1906). Descriptions and records of bees. XI. *Ann. Mag. Nat. Hist. (7)*17: 527–539 (taxonomy, as *Megachile modesta* Smith, 1862); Cockerell, T.D.A. (1907). On a collection of Australian and Asiatic bees. *Bull. Am. Mus. Nat.*

Hist. **23**: 221–236 (taxonomy); Cockerell, T.D.A. (1913). Bees of the genus *Megachile* from Australia. *Entomologist* **46**: 164–168 (distribution); Meade-Waldo, G. (1915). Notes on the Apidae (Hymenoptera) in the collection of the British Museum, with descriptions of new species. VI. *Ann. Mag. Nat. Hist. (8)*15: 325–335 (distribution); Cockerell, T.D.A. (1929). Bees from the Australian region. *Am. Mus. Novit.* **346**: 1–18 (taxonomy).

Chalicodoma (Hackeriapis) apposita (Rayment, 1939)

Megachile apposita Rayment, T. (1939). Bees from the high lands of New South Wales and Victoria. *Aust. Zool.* **9**: 263–294 [285].
Type data: holotype, ANIC ♂.
Type locality: Botanic Gardens, Melbourne, VIC.

Distribution: SE coastal, VIC; known only from type locality.
Ecology: adult—volant; melliferous, solitary, flower visiting record: *Swainsona* Salisb. [Fabaceae].

Chalicodoma (Hackeriapis) argentifer (Cockerell, 1910)

Megachile nasuta argentifer Cockerell, T.D.A. (1910). Some Australian bees in the Berlin Museum. *J. N.Y. Entomol. Soc.* **18**: 98–114 [110].
Type data: holotype, ZMB ♀*.
Type locality: Melbourne, VIC.

Distribution: SE coastal, SW coastal, NW coastal, VIC, WA; only published localities Melbourne, Ararat, Ascot and Eradu.
Ecology: adult—volant; melliferous, solitary.
References: Cockerell, T.D.A. (1929). Descriptions and records of bees. CXV. *Ann. Mag. Nat. Hist. (10)*3: 354–360 (distribution); Cockerell, T.D.A. (1929). Bees, chiefly Australian species, described or determined by Dr. H. Friese. *Am. Mus. Novit.* **343**: 1–20 (distribution); Rayment, T. (1931). Bees in the collections of the Western Australian Museum and the Agricultural Department, Perth. *J. Proc. R. Soc. West. Aust.* **17**: 157–190 (distribution); Michener, C.D. (1965). A classification of the bees of the Australian and South Pacific regions. *Bull. Am. Mus. Nat. Hist.* **130**: 1–362 [197] (taxonomy).

Chalicodoma (Hackeriapis) atrella (Cockerell, 1906)

Megachile atrella Cockerell, T.D.A. (1906). Descriptions and records of bees. XI. *Ann. Mag. Nat. Hist. (7)*17: 527–539 [532].
Type data: holotype, BMNH Hym.17.a.2396 ♀.
Type locality: WA.

Distribution: WA; known only from type locality, exact locality unknown.
Ecology: adult—volant; melliferous, solitary.

Chalicodoma (Hackeriapis) aurifrons (Smith, 1853)

Megachile aurifrons Smith, F. (1853). *Catalogue of Hymenopterous Insects in the Collection of the British Museum*. Part I. Andrenidae and Apidae. London : British Museum 197 pp. [168].
Type data: holotype, BMNH Hym.17.a.2307 ♀.
Type locality: Australia (as New Holland).

Megachile oculipes Cockerell, T.D.A. (1910). Descriptions and records of bees. XXXIII. *Ann. Mag. Nat. Hist. (8)*6: 356–366 [363].
Type data: holotype, BMNH Hym.17.a.2296 ♂.
Type locality: Townsville, QLD.

Taxonomic decision for synonymy: Cockerell, T.D.A. (1913). Bees of the genus *Megachile* from Australia. *Entomologist* 46: 164–168 [168].

Distribution: NE coastal, SE coastal, Murray-Darling basin, Lake Eyre basin, N Gulf, SW coastal, QLD, NSW, VIC, WA.
Ecology: adult—volant; melliferous, solitary, nest in abandoned mud-wasp cells, lined and closed with chewed leaf pulp.
References: Cockerell, T.D.A. (1910). Descriptions and records of bees. XXXII. *Ann. Mag. Nat. Hist. (8)*6: 272–284 (description of female); Cockerell, T.D.A. (1930). The bees of Australia. *Aust. Zool.* 6: 137–156, 205–236 (distribution); Rayment, T. (1956). Some have eyes—others have none. *Proc. R. Zool. Soc. N.S.W.* 1954–1955: 50–54 (biology); Wylie, F.R., Walsh, G.L. & Yule, R.A. (1987). Insect damage to aboriginal relics at burial and rock-art sites near Carnarvon in central Queensland. *J. Aust. Entomol. Soc.* 26: 335–345 (biology).

Chalicodoma (Hackeriapis) axillaris (Meade-Waldo, 1915)

Megachile axillaris Meade-Waldo, G. (1915). Notes on the Apidae (Hymenoptera) in the collection of the British Museum, with descriptions of new species. VI. *Ann. Mag. Nat. Hist. (8)*15: 325–335 [328].
Type data: syntypes, BMNH 18♀ (a specimen is labelled 'type' and has registration number Hym.17.a.2346).
Type locality: Yallingup, WA.

Distribution: SW. coastal, WA; known only from type locality.
Ecology: adult—volant; melliferous, solitary.

Chalicodoma (Hackeriapis) barvonensis (Cockerell, 1914)

Megachile barvonensis Cockerell, T.D.A. (1914). Descriptions and records of bees. LXIV. *Ann. Mag. Nat. Hist. (8)*14: 464–472 [467].
Type data: holotype, USNM 54911 ♂*.
Type locality: Yarrawin, NSW.

Distribution: Murray-Darling basin, N coastal, NSW, NT; only published localities Yarrawin and Darwin.
Ecology: adult—volant; melliferous, solitary.

Reference: Cockerell, T.D.A. (1929). Bees from the Australian region. *Am. Mus. Novit.* 346: 1–18 (distribution).

Chalicodoma (Hackeriapis) beutenmulleri (Cockerell, 1907)

Megachile beutenmulleri Cockerell, T.D.A. (1907). On a collection of Australian and Asiatic bees. *Bull. Am. Mus. Nat. Hist.* 23: 221–236 [222].
Type data: holotype, AMNH 302 ♂*.
Type locality: VIC.

Distribution: VIC; known only from type locality, exact locality unknown.
Ecology: adult—volant; melliferous, solitary.

Chalicodoma (Hackeriapis) calida (Smith, 1879)

Megachile calida Smith, F. (1879). *Descriptions of New Species of Hymenoptera in the Collection of the British Museum*. London : British Museum xxi 240 pp. [64].
Type data: syntypes, BMNH ♂♀* (a specimen is labelled type and has registration number 17.a.2395).
Type locality: QLD (in description), (Australia NW coast on label of syntype female, J. King, pers. comm.).

Distribution: (QLD), (WA); known only from type locality.
Ecology: adult—volant; melliferous, solitary.

Chalicodoma (Hackeriapis) callura (Cockerell, 1914)

Thaumatosoma callurum Cockerell, T.D.A. (1914). Descriptions and records of bees. LXIV. *Ann. Mag. Nat. Hist. (8)*14: 464–472 [467].
Type data: holotype, BMNH Hym.17.a.2579 ♂.
Type locality: Yarrawin, NSW.

Distribution: Murray-Darling basin, NSW; known only from type locality.
Ecology: adult—volant; melliferous, solitary.

Chalicodoma (Hackeriapis) canifrons (Smith, 1853)

Megachile canifrons Smith, F. (1853). *Catalogue of Hymenopterous Insects in the Collection of the British Museum*. Part I. Andrenidae and Apidae. London : British Museum 197 pp. [171].
Type data: holotype, BMNH Hym.17.a.2273 ♂.
Type locality: WA.

Distribution: NE coastal, QLD, WA; only published locality Brisbane, exact locality in WA unknown.
Ecology: adult—volant; melliferous, solitary.
References: Cockerell, T.D.A. (1921). Australian bees in the Queensland Museum. *Mem. Qd Mus.* 7: 81–98 (distribution); King, J. (1984). Immature stages of some Megachilidae (Hymenoptera : Apoidea). *J. Aust. Entomol. Soc.* 23: 51–57 (cocoon).

Chalicodoma (Hackeriapis) cliffordi (Rayment, 1953)

Megachile cliffordi Rayment, T. (1953). *Bees of the Portland District*. Victoria : Portland Field Naturalist's Club 39 pp. [33].
Type data: holotype, ANIC ♂.
Type locality: Gorae West, VIC.

Distribution: SE coastal, VIC; known only from type locality.
Ecology: adult—volant; melliferous, solitary, nest of resin, in beetle tunnel in dry wood (*Eucalyptus* L'Hérit. [Myrtaceae]), flower visiting record: *Leptospermum* Forster & G.Forster [Myrtaceae], *Lotus* L. [Fabaceae].
Reference: Rayment, T. (1954). New bees and wasps—Part XXIII. *Vict. Nat.* **71**: 59–61 (description of female, biology).

Chalicodoma (Hackeriapis) clypeata (Smith, 1853)

Megachile clypeata Smith, F. (1853). *Catalogue of Hymenopterous Insects in the Collection of the British Museum.* Part I. Andrenidae and Apidae. London : British Museum 197 pp. [170].
Type data: holotype, OUM ♀*.
Type locality: WA.

Megachile clypeata grandis Rayment, T. (1934). Contributions to the fauna of Rottnest Island. VIII. Apoidea. With description of new species. *J. Proc. R. Soc. West. Aust.* **20**: 201–212 [209].
Type data: holotype, WAM 32–89 ♀.
Type locality: Rottnest Is., WA.

Taxonomic decision for synonymy: Michener, C.D. (1965). A classification of the bees of the Australian and South Pacifie regions. *Bull. Am. Mus. Nat. Hist.* **130**: 1–362 [197].

Distribution: SW coastal, WA; only published localities Busselton, Yallingup, Rottnest Is. and South Perth.
Ecology: adult—volant; melliferous, solitary.
References: Meade-Waldo, G. (1915). Notes on the Apidae (Hymenoptera) in the collection of the British Museum, with descriptions of new species. VI. *Ann. Mag. Nat. Hist.* (8)**15**: 325–335 (distribution); Rayment, T. (1931). Bees in the collections of the Western Australian Museum and the Agricultural Department, Perth. *J. Proc. R. Soc. West. Aust.* **17**: 157–190 (distribution).

Chalicodoma (Hackeriapis) derelicta (Cockerell, 1913)

Megachile derelicta Cockerell, T.D.A. (1913). Bees of the genus *Megachile* from Australia. *Entomologist* **46**: 164–168 [166].
Type data: holotype, QM Hy/4128 ♀.
Type locality: Windsor, VIC.

Distribution: NE coastal, SE coastal, Murray-Darling basin, QLD, VIC, TAS; only published localities Brisbane, Windsor and Grampians.

Ecology: adult—volant; melliferous, solitary, nest of resin, flower visiting record: *Bursaria* Cav. [Pittosporaceae], *Daviesia* Sm. [Fabaceae], *Dillwynia* Sm. [Fabaceae], *Dipodium* R.Br. [Orchidaceae], *Eucalyptus* L'Hérit. [Myrtaceae], *Jacksonia* Smith [Fabaceae], ?*Stylidium* Willd. [Stylidiaceae], *Wahlenbergia* Roth [Campanulaceae].
References: Hacker, H. (1915). Notes on the genus *Megachile* and some rare insects collected during 1913–14. *Mem. Qd Mus.* **3**: 137–141 (biology); Cockerell, T.D.A. (1930). The bees of Australia. *Aust. Zool.* **6**: 137–156, 205–236 (distribution); Bernhardt, P. & Burns-Balogh P. (1983). Pollination and pollinarium of *Dipodium punctatum* R.Br. *Vict. Nat.* **100**: 197–199 (flower record).

Chalicodoma (Hackeriapis) dinognatha (Cockerell, 1929)

Megachile dinognatha Cockerell, T.D.A. (1929). Bees in the Queensland Museum. *Mem. Qd Mus.* **9**: 298–323 [303].
Type data: holotype, QM Hy/4023 ♀.
Type locality: Hughenden, QLD.

Distribution: NE coastal, N Gulf, QLD, NT; only published localities Hughenden, Carnarvon Range and Roper River.
Ecology: adult—volant; melliferous, solitary, nest of resin in abandoned mud-wasp nest (probably built by *Sceliphron laetum* (Smith) (Sphecidae), modified by an eumenine).
References: Cockerell, T.D.A. (1929). Bees from the Australian region. *Am. Mus. Novit.* **346**: 1–18 (distribution); Cockerell, T.D.A. (1930). The bees of Australia. *Aust. Zool.* **6**: 137–156, 205–236 (taxonomy); Wylie, F.R., Walsh, G.L. & Yule, R.A. (1987). Insect damage to aboriginal relics at burial and rock-art sites near Carnarvon in central Queensland. *J. Aust. Entomol. Soc.* **26**: 335–345 (biology).

Chalicodoma (Hackeriapis) erythropyga (Smith, 1853)

Megachile erythropyga Smith, F. (1853). *Catalogue of Hymenopterous Insects in the Collection of the British Museum.* Part I. Andrenidae and Apidae. London : British Museum 197 pp. [167].
Type data: syntypes, BMNH ♂♀ (a male specimen is labelled 'type' and has registration number Hym.17.a.2267).
Type locality: WA.

Distribution: SE coastal, SW coastal, VIC, WA.
Ecology: adult—volant; melliferous, solitary.
References: Cockerell, T.D.A. (1913). Bees of the genus *Megachile* from Australia. *Entomologist* **46**: 164–168 (redescription); Meade-Waldo, G. (1915). Notes on the Apidae (Hymenoptera) in the collection of the British Museum, with descriptions of new species. VI. *Ann. Mag. Nat. Hist.* (8)**15**: 325–335 (distribution); Rayment, T. (1931). Bees in the collections of the Western Australian Museum and the Agricul-

tural Department, Perth. *J. Proc. R. Soc. West. Aust.* **17**: 157–190 (taxonomy); Rayment, T. (1954). Incidence of acarid mites on the biology of bees. *Aust. Zool.* **12**: 26–38 (as host).

Chalicodoma (Hackeriapis) eucalypti (Cockerell, 1910)

Megachile eucalypti Cockerell, T.D.A. (1910). Descriptions and records of bees. XXXIII. *Ann. Mag. Nat. Hist. (8)***6**: 356–366 [360].
Type data: syntypes, BMNH ♂♀ (a female is labelled 'type' and has registration number Hym.17.a.2340).
Type locality: Mackay, QLD.

Distribution: NE coastal, QLD; known only from type locality.
Ecology: adult—volant; melliferous, solitary, flower visiting record: *Eucalyptus* L'Hérit. [Myrtaceae].
Reference: Cockerell, T.D.A. (1930). The bees of Australia. *Aust. Zool.* **6**: 137–156, 205–236 (taxonomy).

Chalicodoma (Hackeriapis) ferox (Smith, 1879)

Megachile ferox Smith, F. (1879). *Descriptions of New Species of Hymenoptera in the Collection of the British Museum.* London : British Museum xxi 240 pp. [64].
Type data: holotype, BMNH Hym.17.a.2400 ♂.
Type locality: Swan River, WA.

Distribution: NE coastal, SE coastal, SW coastal, QLD, VIC, WA; only published localities Brisbane, Ararat, Swan River and Yallingup.
Ecology: adult—volant; melliferous, solitary, flower visiting record: *Daviesia* Sm. [Fabaceae].
References: Cockerell, T.D.A. (1910). Descriptions and records of bees. XXXII. *Ann. Mag. Nat. Hist. (8)***6**: 272–284 (distribution); Cockerell, T.D.A. (1913). Descriptions and records of bees. LII. *Ann. Mag. Nat. Hist. (8)***11**: 530–542 (description of female); Hacker, H. (1915). Notes on the genus *Megachile* and some rare insects collected during 1913–14. *Mem. Qd Mus.* **3**: 137–141 (flower record); Meade-Waldo, G. (1915). Notes on the Apidae (Hymenoptera) in the collection of the British Museum, with descriptions of new species. VI. *Ann. Mag. Nat. Hist. (8)***15**: 325–335 (description of female); Rayment, T. (1928). Studies of Australian bees. I. The leaf-cutting bees (*Megachile macularis*, Dalla Torre, and other species). II. The clay-bees. (*Lithurgus atratiformis*, Cockerell). *Vict. Nat.* **45**: 79–86 (doubtful record, as leafcutter).

Chalicodoma (Hackeriapis) franki (Friese, 1920)

Thaumatosoma franki Friese, H. (1920). Neue Arten der Bauchsammler (Hym.). *Dtsch. Entomol. Zeit.* **1920**: 49–55 [53].
Type data: holotype, ZMB ♀*.
Type locality: Fremantle (as Freemantle), WA.

Distribution: SW coastal, WA; known only from type locality.
Ecology: adult—volant; melliferous, solitary.

Chalicodoma (Hackeriapis) fultoni (Cockerell, 1913)

Megachile fultoni Cockerell, T.D.A. (1913). Descriptions and records of bees. LII. *Ann. Mag. Nat. Hist. (8)***11**: 530–542 [535].
Type data: holotype, USNM 55471 ♀*.
Type locality: Purnong, SA.

Distribution: Murray-Darling basin, SA, WA; only published localities Purnong and WA.
Ecology: adult—volant; melliferous, solitary.

Chalicodoma (Hackeriapis) fulvomarginata (Cockerell, 1906)

Megachile fulvomarginata Cockerell, T.D.A. (1906). Descriptions and records of bees. XI. *Ann. Mag. Nat. Hist. (7)***17**: 527–539 [531].
Type data: holotype, BMNH Hym.17.a.2272 ♀.
Type locality: Mackay, QLD.

Distribution: NE coastal, QLD; only published localities Mackay and Almaden.
Ecology: adult—volant; melliferous, solitary.
Reference: Cockerell, T.D.A. (1929). Bees in the Australian Museum collection. *Rec. Aust. Mus.* **17**: 199–243 (distribution).

Chalicodoma (Hackeriapis) fumipennis (Smith, 1868)

Megachile fumipennis Smith, F. (1868). Descriptions of aculeate Hymenoptera from Australia. *Trans. Entomol. Soc. Lond.* **1868**: 231–258 [257].
Type data: holotype, BMNH Hym.17.a.2350 ♀.
Type locality: Champion Bay (Geraldton), WA.

Distribution: SW coastal, NW coastal, Lake Eyre basin, WA, NT; only published localities Southern Cross, Champion Bay and Tennant Creek.
Ecology: adult—volant; melliferous, solitary.
References: Cockerell, T.D.A. (1913). Bees of the genus *Megachile* from Australia. *Entomologist* **46**: 164–168 (distribution); Cockerell, T.D.A. (1913). Some Australian bees. *Proc. Acad. Nat. Sci. Philad.* **65**: 28–44 (distribution); King, J. & Exley, E.M. (1985). A revision of *Chalicodoma (Chalicodomoides)* Michener (Hymenoptera : Megachilidae). *J. Aust. Entomol. Soc.* **24**: 187–191 (taxonomy).

Chalicodoma (Hackeriapis) gilbertiella (Cockerell, 1910)

Megachile gilbertiella Cockerell, T.D.A. (1910). Descriptions and records of bees. XXXIII. *Ann. Mag. Nat. Hist. (8)***6**: 356–366 [362].
Type data: holotype, BMNH Hym.17.a.2375 ♀.
Type locality: Cooktown, QLD.

Distribution: NE coastal, SE coastal, Murray-Darling basin, QLD, NSW; only published localities Cooktown, Cairns, Halifax, Woy Woy and Broken Hill, and also New Guinea.

Ecology: adult—volant; melliferous, solitary.

References: Cockerell, T.D.A. (1929). Bees from the Australian region. *Am. Mus. Novit.* **346**: 1–18 (distribution); Cockerell, T.D.A. (1930). Australian bees in the Museum of Comparative Zoology. *Psyche (Camb.)* **37**: 141–154 (distribution); Rayment, T. (1939). Bees from the high lands of New South Wales and Victoria. *Aust. Zool.* **9**: 263–294 (distribution); Rayment, T. (1951). *In* Erickson, R. & Rayment, T. Simple social bees of Western Australia. *West. Aust. Nat.* **3**: 45–59 (distribution); Michener, C.D. (1965). A classification of the bees of the Australian and South Pacific regions. *Bull. Am. Mus. Nat. Hist.* **130**: 1–362 (distribution).

Chalicodoma (Hackeriapis) hackeri (Cockerell, 1913)

Megachile hackeri Cockerell, T.D.A. (1913). Bees of the genus *Megachile* from Australia. *Entomologist* **46**: 164–168 [166].
Type data: holotype, QM Hy/4129 ♀.
Type locality: Kelvin Grove, Brisbane, QLD.

Distribution: NE coastal, SE coastal, QLD, NSW; only published localities suburbs of Brisbane, Stradbroke Is., Bribie Is. and Sydney.

Ecology: adult—volant; melliferous, solitary, nest of resin in old mud-wasp (*Abispa*—Vespidae: Eumeninae) nest.

References: Hacker, H. (1915). Notes on the genus *Megachile* and some rare insects collected during 1913–14. *Mem. Qd Mus.* **3**: 137–141 (nest); Cockerell, T.D.A. (1922). Descriptions and records of bees. XCV. *Ann. Mag. Nat. Hist.* (9)**10**: 265–269 (as *Megachile (Hackeriapis) hackeri* Cockerell, 1913); Cockerell, T.D.A. (1929). Bees in the Australian Museum collection. *Rec. Aust. Mus.* **17**: 199–243 (distribution).

Chalicodoma (Hackeriapis) hardyi (Cockerell, 1929)

Megachile hardyi Cockerell, T.D.A. (1929). Bees in the Queensland Museum. *Mem. Qd Mus.* **9**: 298–323 [305].
Type data: holotype, QM Hy/5007 ♂.
Type locality: Blackheath, NSW.

Distribution: SE coastal, NSW; known only from type locality.

Ecology: adult—volant; melliferous, solitary.

Chalicodoma (Hackeriapis) heliophila (Cockerell, 1913)

Megachile heliophila Cockerell, T.D.A. (1913). Descriptions and records of bees. LIII. *Ann. Mag. Nat. Hist.* (8)**12**: 103–110 [103].

Type data: holotype, USNM 55487 ♀* (described as ♂).
Type locality: Sunnybank, Brisbane, QLD.

Distribution: NE coastal, QLD; only published localities Sunnybank and Kelvin Grove, Brisbane.

Ecology: adult—volant; melliferous, solitary, flower visiting record: *Daviesia* Sm. [Fabaceae].

References: Hacker, H. (1915). Notes on the genus *Megachile* and some rare insects collected during 1913–14. *Mem. Qd Mus.* **3**: 137–141 (flower record); Cockerell, T.D.A. (1929). Bees in the Queensland Museum. *Mem. Qd Mus.* **9**: 298–323 (possible synonym of *Megachile rhodogastra* Cockerell, 1910); Cockerell, T.D.A. (1930). The bees of Australia. *Aust. Zool.* **6**: 137–156, 205–236 (taxonomy).

Chalicodoma (Hackeriapis) henrici (Cockerell, 1907)

Megachile henrici Cockerell, T.D.A. (1907). On a collection of Australian and Asiatic bees. *Bull. Am. Mus. Nat. Hist.* **23**: 221–236 [223].
Type data: holotype, AMNH ♀*.
Type locality: NSW.

Distribution: SE coastal, S Gulfs, NSW, VIC, SA.

Ecology: adult—volant; melliferous, solitary, flower visiting record: *Rubus* L. [Rosaceae].

References: Cockerell, T.D.A. (1929). Bees in the Queensland Museum. *Mem. Qd Mus.* **9**: 298–323 (distribution); Cockerell, T.D.A. (1930). The bees of Australia. *Aust. Zool.* **6**: 137–156, 205–236 (distribution); Rayment, T. (1935). *A Cluster of Bees*. Sixty essays on the life-histories of Australian bees, with specific descriptions of over 100 new species, and an introduction by Professor E.F. Phillips, D.Ph., Cornell University, U.S.A. Sydney : Endeavour Press 752 pp. (description of male).

Chalicodoma (Hackeriapis) heriadiformis (Smith, 1853)

Megachile heriadiformis Smith, F. (1853). *Catalogue of Hymenopterous Insects in the Collection of the British Museum*. Part I. Andrenidae and Apidae. London : British Museum 197 pp. [172].
Type data: holotype, BMNH Hym.17.a.2320 ♀*.
Type locality: Adelaide, SA.

Megachile eriadiformis Meade-Waldo, G. (1912). Notes on the Apidae (Hymenoptera) in the collection of the British Museum, with descriptions of new species. *Ann. Mag. Nat. Hist.* (8)**10**: 461–478 [476] [unjustified emendation of *Megachile heriadiformis* Smith, 1853].

Distribution: S Gulfs, SW coastal, N coastal, SA, WA.

Ecology: adult—volant; melliferous, solitary.

References: Meade-Waldo, G. (1915). Notes on the Apidae (Hymenoptera) in the collection of the British Museum, with descriptions of new species. VI. *Ann. Mag. Nat. Hist.* (8)**15**: 325–335 (distribution, as *Megachile eriadiformis* Meade-Waldo, 1912); Cockerell, T.D.A. (1930). The bees of Australia. *Aust.*

Zool. **6**: 137–156, 205–236 (taxonomy); Rayment, T. (1930). Notes on a collection of bees from Western Australia. *J. Proc. R. Soc. West. Aust.* **16**: 45–56 (taxonomy); Rayment, T. (1931). Bees in the collections of the Western Australian Museum and the Agricultural Department, Perth. *J. Proc. R. Soc. West. Aust.* **17**: 157–190 (distribution).

Chalicodoma (Hackeriapis) holura (Cockerell, 1912)

Megachile holura Cockerell, T.D.A. (1912). Descriptions and records of bees. XLII. *Ann. Mag. Nat. Hist. (8)***9**: 220–229 [221].
Type data: holotype, ANIC ♂.
Type locality: Rutherglen, VIC.

Distribution: Murray-Darling basin, VIC; known only from type locality.
Ecology: adult—volant; melliferous, solitary.

Chalicodoma (Hackeriapis) horatii (Cockerell, 1913)

Megachile horatii Cockerell, T.D.A. (1913). Bees of the genus *Megachile* from Australia. *Entomologist* **46**: 164–168 [165].
Type data: holotype, USNM 55472 ♂*.
Type locality: Southern Cross, WA.

Distribution: SW coastal, WA; known only from type locality.
Ecology: adult—volant; melliferous, solitary.

Chalicodoma (Hackeriapis) ignita (Smith, 1853)

Megachile ignita Smith, F. (1853). *Catalogue of Hymenopterous Insects in the Collection of the British Museum.* Part I. Andrenidae and Apidae. London : British Museum 197 pp. [169].
Type data: holotype, BMNH Hym.17.a.2266 ♂.
Type locality: Australia (as New Holland).

Distribution: Australia, only published locality WA, exact locality unknown.
Ecology: adult—volant; melliferous, solitary.
References: Meade-Waldo, G. (1912). Notes on the Apidae (Hymenoptera) in the collection of the British Museum, with descriptions of new species. *Ann. Mag. Nat. Hist. (8)***10**: 461–478 (taxonomy); Cockerell, T.D.A. (1913). Bees of the genus *Megachile* from Australia. *Entomologist* **46**: 164–168 (taxonomy).

Chalicodoma (Hackeriapis) latericauda (Cockerell, 1921)

Megachile latericauda Cockerell, T.D.A. (1921). Australian bees in the Queensland Museum. *Mem. Qd Mus.* **7**: 81–98 [88].
Type data: holotype, BMNH Hym.17.a.2362 ♂.
Type locality: Swan River, WA.

Distribution: Murray-Darling basin, SW coastal, NSW, WA; only published localities Albury and Swan River.
Ecology: adult—volant; melliferous, solitary.
References: Rayment, T. (1935). *A Cluster of Bees.* Sixty essays on the life-histories of Australian bees, with specific descriptions of over 100 new species, and an introduction by Professor E.F. Phillips, D.Ph., Cornell University, U.S.A. Sydney : Endeavour Press 752 pp. (illustration); Rayment, T. (1939). Bees from the high lands of New South Wales and Victoria. *Aust. Zool.* **9**: 263–294 (distribution).

Chalicodoma (Hackeriapis) leeuwinensis (Meade-Waldo, 1915)

Megachile leeuwinensis Meade-Waldo, G. (1915). Notes on the Apidae (Hymenoptera) in the collection of the British Museum, with descriptions of new species. VI. *Ann. Mag. Nat. Hist. (8)***15**: 325–335 [330].
Type data: syntypes, BMNH 8♂10♀ (a female specimen is labelled 'type' and has registration number Hym.17.a.2314).
Type locality: Yallingup, WA.

Distribution: SW coastal, WA; known only from type locality.
Ecology: adult—volant; melliferous, solitary.

Chalicodoma (Hackeriapis) leucopyga (Smith, 1853)

Megachile leucopyga Smith, F. (1853). *Catalogue of Hymenopterous Insects in the Collection of the British Museum.* Part I. Andrenidae and Apidae. London : British Museum 197 pp. [173].
Type data: holotype (probable), BMNH Hym.17.a.2348 ♀.
Type locality: TAS (as Van Diemens Land).

Distribution: TAS; known only from type locality, exact locality unknown.
Ecology: adult—volant; melliferous, solitary.
Reference: Meade-Waldo, G. (1912). Notes on the Apidae (Hymenoptera) in the collection of the British Museum, with descriptions of new species. *Ann. Mag. Nat. Hist. (8)***10**: 461–478 (taxonomy).

Chalicodoma (Hackeriapis) longiceps (Meade-Waldo, 1915)

Megachile longiceps Meade-Waldo, G. (1915). Notes on the Apidae (Hymenoptera) in the collection of the British Museum, with descriptions of new species. VI. *Ann. Mag. Nat. Hist. (8)***15**: 325–335 [332].
Type data: holotype, BMNH Hym.17.a.2312 ♀.
Type locality: Yallingup, WA.

Distribution: SW coastal, WA; only published localities Yallingup and Busselton.
Ecology: adult—volant; melliferous, solitary.

Chalicodoma (Hackeriapis) lucidiventris (Smith, 1853)

Megachile lucidiventris Smith, F. (1853). *Catalogue of Hymenopterous Insects in the Collection of the British Museum.* Part I. Andrenidae and Apidae. London : British Museum 197 pp. [168].
Type data: holotype, BMNH Hym.17.a.2327 ♀.
Type locality: Australia (as New Holland).
Megachile latipes Smith, F. (1853). *Catalogue of Hymenopterous Insects in the Collection of the British Museum.* Part I. Andrenidae and Apidae. London : British Museum 197 pp. [169].
Type data: holotype, BMNH Hym.17.a.2281 ♂.
Type locality: Australia (as New Holland).
Megachile lucidiventris nuda Rayment, T. (1935). *A Cluster of Bees.* Sixty essays on the life-histories of Australian bees, with specific descriptions of over 100 new species, and an introduction by Professor E.F. Phillips, D.Ph., Cornell University, U.S.A. Sydney : Endeavour Press 752 pp. [723] [junior primary homonym of *Megachile nuda* Mitchell, 1930].
Type data: syntypes, ANIC 2♀.
Type locality: Arcadia, Berowra Creek, NSW.

Taxonomic decision for synonymy: Cockerell, T.D.A. (1929). Bees in the Queensland Museum. *Mem. Qd Mus.* **9**: 298–323 [300]; Michener, C.D. (1965). A classification of the bees of the Australian and South Pacific regions. *Bull. Am. Mus. Nat. Hist.* **130**: 1–362 [198].

Distribution: NE coastal, SE coastal, Murray-Darling basin, S Gulfs, QLD, NSW, VIC, SA.
Ecology: adult—volant; melliferous, solitary, nest of resin or wax in galleries of longicorn beetle in dead *Eucalyptus* L'Hérit. [Myrtaceae], flower visiting record: *Eucalyptus* L'Hérit. [Myrtaceae].
References: Nicholson, A.J. (1927). A new theory of mimicry in insects. *Aust. Zool.* **5**: 10–104 (illustration, as *Megachile suffusipennis* Cockerell, 1906); Cockerell, T.D.A. (1930). The bees of Australia. *Aust. Zool.* **6**: 137–156, 205–236 (taxonomy); Rayment, T. (1953). *Bees of the Portland District.* Victoria : Portland Field Naturalist's Club 39 pp. (nest); Rayment, T. (1956). Some have eyes—others have none. *Proc. R. Zool. Soc. N.S.W.* **1954–1955**: 50–54 (illustration, as *Megachile latipes* Smith, 1853).

Chalicodoma (Hackeriapis) mackayensis (Cockerell, 1910)

Megachile mackayensis Cockerell, T.D.A. (1910). Descriptions and records of bees. XXXII. *Ann. Mag. Nat. Hist. (8)***6**: 272–284 [279].
Type data: holotype, BMNH Hym.17.a.2359 ♀.
Type locality: Mackay, QLD.

Distribution: NE coastal, QLD, NSW, Lord Howe Is. (possibly introduced); exact locality in NSW unknown, only published localities [Lamington] National Park, Mackay and NSW.
Ecology: adult—volant; melliferous, solitary.
References: Cockerell, T.D.A. (1921). Australian bees in the Queensland Museum. *Mem. Qd Mus.* **7**: 81–98 (distribution); Cockerell, T.D.A. (1930). The bees of Australia. *Aust. Zool.* **6**: 137–156, 205–236 (taxonomy).

Chalicodoma (Hackeriapis) macleayi (Cockerell, 1907)

Megachile macleayi Cockerell, T.D.A. (1907). On a collection of Australian and Asiatic bees. *Bull. Am. Mus. Nat. Hist.* **23**: 221–236 [222].
Type data: holotype, AMNH 299 ♀*.
Type locality: NSW.

Distribution: N Gulf, QLD, NSW; exact locality in NSW unknown, only published locality Hughenden.
Ecology: adult—volant; melliferous, solitary.
Reference: Cockerell, T.D.A. (1929). Bees in the Queensland Museum. *Mem. Qd Mus.* **9**: 298–323 (distribution).

Chalicodoma (Hackeriapis) micrerythrura (Cockerell, 1910)

Megachile micrerythrura Cockerell, T.D.A. (1910). Descriptions and records of bees. XXXII. *Ann. Mag. Nat. Hist. (8)***6**: 272–284 [281].
Type data: syntypes, BMNH 2♂♀ (female specimen is labelled 'type' and has registration number Hym.17.a.2309).
Type locality: Darwin, NT.

Distribution: N coastal, NT; known only from type locality.
Ecology: adult—volant; melliferous, solitary.
Reference: King, J. & Exley, E.M. (1985). A revision of *Chalicodoma (Rhodomegachile)* Michener (Hymenoptera : Megachilidae). *J. Aust. Entomol. Soc.* **24**: 199–204 (male designated "allotype" of *Megachile deanii* Rayment, 1935 is this species: this specimen has no type status).

Chalicodoma (Hackeriapis) modesta (Smith, 1862)

Megachile modestus Smith, F. (1862). Descriptions of new species of Australian Hymenoptera, and of a species of *Formica* from New Zealand. *Trans. Entomol. Soc. Lond. (3)***1**: 53–62 [62].
Type data: syntypes, BMNH ♂♀ (female specimen is labelled 'type' and has a registration number Hym.17.a.2285).
Type locality: Australia.

Distribution: NE coastal, SE coastal, QLD, NSW, VIC; record from Mackay is in error.
Ecology: adult—volant; melliferous, solitary.
References: Cockerell, T.D.A. (1907). On a collection of Australian and Asiatic bees. *Bull. Am. Mus. Nat. Hist.* **23**: 221–236 (taxonomy); Cockerell, T.D.A. (1930). The bees of Australia. *Aust. Zool.* **6**: 137–156, 205–236 (taxonomy); King, J. (1986). The systematics of some Australian Megachilidae (Hymenoptera : Apoidea). Unpubl. PhD Thesis. Brisbane : Univ. of Queensland 439 pp. (distribution).

Chalicodoma (Hackeriapis) monkmani (Rayment, 1935)

Megachile monkmani Rayment, T. (1935). *A Cluster of Bees.* Sixty essays on the life-histories of Australian bees, with specific descriptions of over 100 new species, and an introduction by Professor E.F. Phillips, D.Ph., Cornell University, U.S.A. Sydney : Endeavour Press 752 pp. [715].
Type data: holotype, ANIC ♀ (described as ♂).
Type locality: Gunbower, VIC.

Distribution: Murray-Darling basin, VIC; known only from type locality.
Ecology: adult—volant; melliferous, solitary, flower visiting record: *Callistemon* R.Br. [Myrtaceae].

Chalicodoma (Hackeriapis) mundifica (Cockerell, 1921)

Megachile mundifica Cockerell, T.D.A. (1921). Australian bees in the Queensland Museum. *Mem. Qd Mus.* 7: 81–98 [90].
Type data: holotype, QM T2504 ♀.
Type locality: [Lamington] National Park, QLD.

Distribution: NE coastal, QLD; known only from type locality.
Ecology: adult—volant; melliferous, solitary.

Chalicodoma (Hackeriapis) nasuta (Smith, 1868)

Megachile nasuta Smith, F. (1868). Descriptions of aculeate Hymenoptera from Australia. *Trans. Entomol. Soc. Lond.* **1868**: 231–258 [258].
Type data: holotype, BMNH Hym.17.a.2280 ♀.
Type locality: Champion Bay (Geraldton), WA.

Distribution: SW coastal, NW coastal, WA; only published localities Yallingup, Moora, Swan River and Champion Bay.
Ecology: adult—volant; melliferous, solitary, nest of resin, probably in sandy bank.
References: Meade-Waldo, G. (1915). Notes on the Apidae (Hymenoptera) in the collection of the British Museum, with descriptions of new species. VI. *Ann. Mag. Nat. Hist.* (8)**15**: 325–335 (biology); Cockerell, T.D.A. (1930). The bees of Australia. *Aust. Zool.* **6**: 137–156, 205–236 (taxonomy); Rayment, T. (1931). Bees in the collections of the Western Australian Museum and the Agricultural Department, Perth. *J. Proc. R. Soc. West. Aust.* **17**: 157–190 (distribution).

Chalicodoma (Hackeriapis) nigrovittata (Cockerell, 1906)

Megachile nigrovittata Cockerell, T.D.A. (1906). Descriptions and records of bees. XI. *Ann. Mag. Nat. Hist.* (7)**17**: 527–539 [535].
Type data: holotype, BMNH Hym.17.a.2363 ♂.
Type locality: NW coast of Australia.

Distribution: (NW coastal), WA; known only from type locality.
Ecology: adult—volant; melliferous, solitary.

Reference: Cockerell, T.D.A. (1930). The bees of Australia. *Aust. Zool.* **6**: 137–156, 205–236 (taxonomy).

Chalicodoma (Hackeriapis) oblonga (Smith, 1879)

Megachile oblonga Smith, F. (1879). *Descriptions of New Species of Hymenoptera in the Collection of the British Museum.* London : British Museum xxi 240 pp. [65].
Type data: holotype (probable), BMNH Hym.17.a.2286 ♀.
Type locality: WA.

Distribution: WA; known only from type locality, exact locality unknown.
Ecology: adult—volant; melliferous, solitary.
Reference: Meade-Waldo, G. (1912). Notes on the Apidae (Hymenoptera) in the collection of the British Museum, with descriptions of new species. *Ann. Mag. Nat. Hist.* (8)**10**: 461–478 (taxonomy).

Chalicodoma (Hackeriapis) oculiformis (Rayment, 1956)

Megachile oculiformis Rayment, T. (1956). Some have eyes—others have none. *Proc. R. Zool. Soc. N.S.W.* **1954–1955**: 50–54 [51] [holotype labeled "allotype"; description states "Type: female, Allotype: male"].
Type data: holotype, ANIC ♀.
Type locality: Mt Buffalo, VIC.

Distribution: Murray-Darling basin, VIC; only published localities Mt Buffalo and Glen Wills.
Ecology: adult—volant; melliferous, solitary.

Chalicodoma (Hackeriapis) ordinaria (Smith, 1853)

Megachile ordinaria Smith, F. (1853). *Catalogue of Hymenopterous Insects in the Collection of the British Museum.* Part I. Andrenidae and Apidae. London : British Museum 197 pp. [174].
Type data: holotype, BMNH Hym.17.a.2268 ♀.
Type locality: TAS (as Van Diemens Land).

Distribution: TAS; known only from type locality, exact locality unknown.
Ecology: adult—volant; melliferous, solitary.
Reference: Meade-Waldo, G. (1912). Notes on the Apidae (Hymenoptera) in the collection of the British Museum, with descriptions of new species. *Ann. Mag. Nat. Hist.* (8)**10**: 461–478 (taxonomy).

Chalicodoma (Hackeriapis) paracallida (Rayment, 1935)

Megachile paracallida Rayment, T. (1935). *A Cluster of Bees.* Sixty essays on the life-histories of Australian bees, with specific descriptions of over 100 new species, and an introduction by Professor E.F. Phillips, D.Ph., Cornell University, U.S.A. Sydney : Endeavour Press 752 pp. [717].
Type data: holotype, ANIC ♀.
Type locality: Wyndham, WA.

Distribution: NE coastal, N coastal, QLD, WA; only published localities Carnarvon Range and Wyndham.

Ecology: adult—volant; melliferous, solitary, nest of resin in abandoned mud-wasp nest (probably built by *Sceliphron laetum* (Smith) (Sphecidae), modified by an eumenine).
Reference: Wylie, F.R., Walsh, G.L. & Yule, R.A. (1987). Insect damage to aboriginal relics at burial and rock-art sites near Carnarvon in central Queensland. *J. Aust. Entomol. Soc.* **26**: 335–345 (biology).

Chalicodoma (Hackeriapis) pararhodura (Cockerell, 1910)

Megachile pararhodura Cockerell, T.D.A. (1910). Descriptions and records of bees. XXXII. *Ann. Mag. Nat. Hist. (8)***6**: 272–284 [278].
Type data: holotype, BMNH Hym.17.a.2381 ♂.
Type locality: Mackay, QLD.

Distribution: NE coastal, QLD; known only from type locality.
Ecology: adult—volant; melliferous, solitary.

Chalicodoma (Hackeriapis) paratasmanica (Rayment, 1955)

Megachile paratasmanica Rayment, T. (1955). New species of bees and wasps—Part XXIV. *Vict. Nat.* **71**: 145–147 [145].
Type data: holotype (probable), ANIC ♂.
Type locality: Gorae West, VIC.

Distribution: SE coastal, VIC; known only from type locality.
Ecology: adult—volant; melliferous, solitary, nest of "vegetable putty" (masticated leaves) in gallery (probably of longicorn beetle) in dead *Eucalyptus* L'Hérit. [Myrtaceae], flower visiting record: *Lotus* L. [Fabaceae].
Reference: Rayment, T. (1954). New bees and wasps—Part XXIII. *Vict. Nat.* **71**: 59–61 (illustration).

Chalicodoma (Hackeriapis) phillipensis (Rayment, 1935)

Megachile phillipensis Rayment, T. (1935). *A Cluster of Bees*. Sixty essays on the life-histories of Australian bees, with specific descriptions of over 100 new species, and an introduction by Professor E.F. Phillips, D.Ph., Cornell University, U.S.A. Sydney : Endeavour Press 752 pp. [720].
Type data: holotype, ANIC ♀.
Type locality: Sandringham, VIC.

Distribution: SE coastal, VIC; known only from type locality.
Ecology: adult—volant; melliferous, solitary.

Chalicodoma (Hackeriapis) preissi (Cockerell, 1910)

Megachile preissi Cockerell, T.D.A. (1910). Some Australian bees in the Berlin Museum. *J. N.Y. Entomol. Soc.* **18**: 98–114 [110].

Type data: holotype, ZMB 1008 ♀*.
Type locality: Eastern Australia (this label may be an error for Western Australia), see Cockerell, T.D.A. (1930). The bees of Australia. *Aust. Zool.* **6**: 137 156, 205 236 [229].

Distribution: SW coastal, WA.
Ecology: adult—volant; melliferous, solitary.
References: Meade-Waldo, G. (1915). Notes on the Apidae (Hymenoptera) in the collection of the British Museum, with descriptions of new species. VI. *Ann. Mag. Nat. Hist. (8)***15**: 325–335 (taxonomy); Cockerell, T.D.A. (1930). The bees of Australia. *Aust. Zool.* **6**: 137–156, 205–236 (taxonomy); Rayment, T. (1934). Contributions to the fauna of Rottnest Island. VIII. Apoidea. With description of new species. *J. Proc. R. Soc. West. Aust.* **20**: 201–212 (distribution).

Chalicodoma (Hackeriapis) punctata (Smith, 1853)

Megachile punctata Smith, F. (1853). *Catalogue of Hymenopterous Insects in the Collection of the British Museum*. Part I. Andrenidae and Apidae. London : British Museum 197 pp. [168].
Type data: holotype, BMNH Hym.17.a.2321 ♂.
Type locality: Australia (as New Holland).

Distribution: Australia, known only from type locality, exact locality unknown.
Ecology: adult—volant; melliferous, solitary.
Reference: Meade-Waldo, G. (1912). Notes on the Apidae (Hymenoptera) in the collection of the British Museum, with descriptions of new species. *Ann. Mag. Nat. Hist. (8)***10**: 461–478 (taxonomy).

Chalicodoma (Hackeriapis) ramulipes (Cockerell, 1913)

Megachile ramulipes Cockerell, T.D.A. (1913). Descriptions and records of bees. LII. *Ann. Mag. Nat. Hist. (8)***11**: 530–542 [534].
Type data: holotype, BMNH Hym.17.a.2384 ♂.
Type locality: Kewell, VIC.

Distribution: NE coastal, SE coastal, QLD, VIC; only published localities Carnarvon Range and Kewell.
Ecology: adult—volant; melliferous, solitary, nest of resin and mud.
References: King, J. & Exley, E.M. (1985). A revision of *Chalicodoma (Rhodomegachile)* Michener (Hymenoptera : Megachilidae). *J. Aust. Entomol. Soc.* **24**: 199–204 (taxonomy); Wylie, F.R., Walsh, G.L. & Yule, R.A. (1987). Insect damage to aboriginal relics at burial and rock-art sites near Carnarvon in central Queensland. *J. Aust. Entomol. Soc.* **26**: 335–345 (biology).

Chalicodoma (Hackeriapis) relicta (Cockerell, 1913)

Megachile relicta Cockerell, T.D.A. (1913). Descriptions and records of bees. LII. *Ann. Mag. Nat. Hist. (8)***11**: 530–542 [538].

Type data: holotype, BMNH Hym.17.a.2324 ♀.
Type locality: Tennant Creek, NT (as SA).

Distribution: Lake Eyre basin, NT; known only from type locality.
Ecology: adult—volant; melliferous, solitary.

Chalicodoma (Hackeriapis) revicta (Cockerell, 1913)

Megachile revicta Cockerell, T.D.A. (1913). Descriptions and records of bees. LII. *Ann. Mag. Nat. Hist. (8)*11: 530–542 [539].
Type data: holotype, USNM 55490 ♀*.
Type locality: 60 miles N Perth, WA.

Distribution: SW coastal, WA; only published localities 60 miles N of Perth and Sawyers Valley.
Ecology: adult—volant; melliferous, solitary.
References: Rayment, T. (1931). Bees in the collections of the Western Australian Museum and the Agricultural Department, Perth. *J. Proc. R. Soc. West. Aust.* 17: 157–190 (description of male); Rayment, T. (1954). Incidence of acarid mites on the biology of bees. *Aust. Zool.* 12: 26–38 (as host).

Chalicodoma (Hackeriapis) rhodura (Cockerell, 1906)

Megachile rhodura Cockerell, T.D.A. (1906). Descriptions and records of bees. XI. *Ann. Mag. Nat. Hist. (7)*17: 527–539 [539].
Type data: holotype, BMNH Hym.17.a.2371 ♂.
Type locality: Mackay, QLD.

Distribution: NE coastal, QLD; only published localities Mackay, Caloundra and Brisbane.
Ecology: adult—volant; melliferous, solitary, nest of resin, flower visiting record: *Eucalyptus* L'Hérit. [Myrtaceae].
References: Cockerell, T.D.A. (1910). Descriptions and records of bees. XXXII. *Ann. Mag. Nat. Hist. (8)*6: 272–284 (description of female); Hacker, H. (1915). Notes on the genus *Megachile* and some rare insects collected during 1913–14. *Mem. Qd Mus.* 3: 137–141 (biology); Cockerell, T.D.A. (1922). Descriptions and records of bees. XCV. *Ann. Mag. Nat. Hist. (9)*10: 265–269 (as *Megachile (Hackeriapis) rhodura* Cockerell, 1906); Cockerell, T.D.A. (1930). The bees of Australia. *Aust. Zool.* 6: 137–156, 205–236 (distribution).

Chalicodoma (Hackeriapis) rufapicata (Cockerell, 1929)

Megachile rufapicata Cockerell, T.D.A. (1929). Bees in the Australian Museum collection. *Rec. Aust. Mus.* 17: 199–243 [237].
Type data: holotype, AM K58131 ♀.
Type locality: Almaden, QLD.

Distribution: NE coastal, QLD; known only from type locality.
Ecology: adult—volant; melliferous, solitary.

Chalicodoma (Hackeriapis) rufolobata (Cockerell, 1913)

Megachile rufolobata Cockerell, T.D.A. (1913). Descriptions and records of bees. LII. *Ann. Mag. Nat. Hist. (8)*11: 530–542 [536].
Type data: holotype, BMNH Hym.17.a.2279 ♂.
Type locality: 60 miles N Perth, WA.

Distribution: SW coastal, WA; only published localities 60 miles N of Perth, Swan River and Gnangara.
Ecology: adult—volant; melliferous, solitary.
References: Rayment, T. (1931). Bees in the collections of the Western Australian Museum and the Agricultural Department, Perth. *J. Proc. R. Soc. West. Aust.* 17: 157–190 (distribution); Rayment, T. (1935). *A Cluster of Bees*. Sixty essays on the life-histories of Australian bees, with specific descriptions of over 100 new species, and an introduction by Professor E.F. Phillips, D.Ph., Cornell University, U.S.A. Sydney : Endeavour Press 752 pp. (description of female).

Chalicodoma (Hackeriapis) rugosa (Smith, 1879)

Megachile rugosa Smith, F. (1879). *Descriptions of New Species of Hymenoptera in the Collection of the British Museum*. London : British Museum xxi 240 pp. [65].
Type data: holotype, BMNH Hym.17.a.2342 ♂.
Type locality: WA.

Distribution: WA; known only from type locality, exact locality unknown.
Ecology: adult—volant; melliferous, solitary.
Reference: Meade-Waldo, G. (1912). Notes on the Apidae (Hymenoptera) in the collection of the British Museum, with descriptions of new species. *Ann. Mag. Nat. Hist. (8)*10: 461–478 (taxonomy).

Chalicodoma (Hackeriapis) semicandens (Cockerell, 1910)

Megachile semicandens Cockerell, T.D.A. (1910). Some Australian bees in the Berlin Museum. *J. N.Y. Entomol. Soc.* 18: 98–114 [108].
Type data: holotype, ZMB 19407 ♂*.
Type locality: Adelaide, SA.

Distribution: S Gulfs, SA; known only from type locality.
Ecology: adult—volant; melliferous, solitary.

Chalicodoma (Hackeriapis) semiluctuosa (Smith, 1853)

Megachile semiluctuosa Smith, F. (1853). *Catalogue of Hymenopterous Insects in the Collection of the British Museum*. Part I. Andrenidae and Apidae. London : British Museum 197 pp. [172].
Type data: syntypes, BMNH ♂♀ (a female specimen is labelled 'type' and has registration number Hym.17.a.2393).
Type locality: Adelaide, SA.

Megachile blackburnii Froggatt, W.W. (1893). Hymenoptera (of the Elder Expedition). *Trans. R. Soc. S. Aust.* **16**: 69–73 [72].
Type data: lectotype, SAMA ♂*.
Subsequent designation: Michener, C.D. (1965). A classification of the bees of the Australian and South Pacific regions. *Bull. Am. Mus. Nat. Hist.* **130**: 1–362 [323].
Type locality: Mt Squires, NT.

Taxonomic decision for synonymy: Michener, C.D. (1965). A classification of the bees of the Australian and South Pacific regions. *Bull. Am. Mus. Nat. Hist.* **130**: 1–362 [323].

Distribution: Murray-Darling basin, S Gulfs, Lake Eyre basin, SW coastal, NW coastal, VIC, SA, WA, NT.
Ecology: adult—volant; melliferous, solitary, nest of resin cells in *Acacia* Miller [Mimosaceae] wood, flower visiting record: *Eremophila* R.Br. [Myoporaceae], *Swainsona* Salisb. [Fabaceae].
References: Froggatt, W.W. (1907). *Australian Insects.* Sydney : Brooks 449 pp. (illustration, pl. XVI, as *Megachile blackburni* Froggatt, 1893); Meade-Waldo, G. (1912). Notes on the Apidae (Hymenoptera) in the collection of the British Museum, with descriptions of new species. *Ann. Mag. Nat. Hist.* (8)**10**: 461–478 (as *Megachile (Eumegachile) semiluctuosa* Smith, 1853); Cockerell, T.D.A. (1913). Bees of the genus *Megachile* from Australia. *Entomologist* **46**: 164–168 (distribution); Cockerell, T.D.A. (1930). The bees of Australia. *Aust. Zool.* **6**: 137–156, 205–236 (distribution); Rayment, T. (1950). A new and remarkable organ on a resin-bee. *Vict. Nat.* **66**: 163–168 (biology); Rayment, T. (1954). Incidence of acarid mites on the biology of bees. *Aust. Zool.* **12**: 26–38 (biology); Hopper, S.D. (1981). Foraging behaviour of megachilid bees on *Swainsona canescens* (Fabaceae) and its coevolutionary implications. *West. Aust. Nat.* **15**: 8–11 (flower record).

Chalicodoma (Hackeriapis) sericeicauda (Cockerell, 1910)

Megachile sericeicauda Cockerell, T.D.A. (1910). Descriptions and records of bees. XXXIII. *Ann. Mag. Nat. Hist.* (8)**6**: 356–366 [364].
Type data: holotype, BMNH Hym.17.a.2337 ♂.
Type locality: Mackay, QLD.

Distribution: NE coastal, QLD; known only from type locality.
Ecology: adult—volant; melliferous, solitary.
Reference: Cockerell, T.D.A. (1929). Bees, chiefly Australian species, described or determined by Dr. H. Friese. *Am. Mus. Novit.* **343**: 1–20 (taxonomy).

Chalicodoma (Hackeriapis) silvestris (Rayment, 1951)

Megachile gilbertiella silvestris Rayment, T. (1951). *In* Erickson, R. & Rayment, T. Simple social bees of Western Australia. *West. Aust. Nat.* **3**: 45–59 [53].

Type data: holotype, whereabouts unknown ♀*.
Type locality: 40 miles S Perth, WA.

Distribution: SW coastal, WA; known only from type locality.
Ecology: adult—volant; melliferous, solitary, female found inside dead *Xanthorrhoea* flower stalk.

Chalicodoma (Hackeriapis) simpliciformis (Cockerell, 1918)

Megachile simpliciformis Cockerell, T.D.A. (1918). Some bees collected in Queensland. *Mem. Qd Mus.* **6**: 112–120 [119].
Type data: holotype, QM Hy/4127 ♀.
Type locality: Stradbroke Is., QLD.

Distribution: NE coastal, QLD; known only from type locality.
Ecology: adult—volant; melliferous, solitary.

Chalicodoma (Hackeriapis) speluncarum (Meade-Waldo, 1915)

Megachile speluncarum Meade-Waldo, G. (1915). Notes on the Apidae (Hymenoptera) in the collection of the British Museum, with descriptions of new species. VI. *Ann. Mag. Nat. Hist.* (8)**15**: 325–335 [329].
Type data: syntypes, BMNH 12♀ (a female is labelled 'type' and has registration number Hym.17.a.2358).
Type locality: Yallingup, WA.

Distribution: SW coastal, WA; known only from type locality.
Ecology: adult—volant; melliferous, solitary.

Chalicodoma (Hackeriapis) stalkeri (Cockerell, 1910)

Megachile stalkeri Cockerell, T.D.A. (1910). Descriptions and records of bees. XXXII. *Ann. Mag. Nat. Hist.* (8)**6**: 272–284 [282].
Type data: holotype, BMNH Hym.17.a.2269 ♀.
Type locality: Alexandria, NT.

Distribution: N Gulf, NT; known only from type locality.
Ecology: adult—volant; melliferous, solitary.

Chalicodoma (Hackeriapis) subabdominalis (Rayment, 1935)

Megachile subabdominalis Rayment, T. (1935). *A Cluster of Bees.* Sixty essays on the life-histories of Australian bees, with specific descriptions of over 100 new species, and an introduction by Professor E.F. Phillips, D.Ph., Cornell University, U.S.A. Sydney : Endeavour Press 752 pp. [720].
Type data: holotype, ANIC ♂.
Type locality: Gunbower, VIC.

Distribution: Murray-Darling basin, VIC; known only from type locality.
Ecology: adult—volant; melliferous, solitary.

Chalicodoma (Hackeriapis) subremotula (Rayment, 1934)

Megachile subremotula Rayment, T. (1934). Contributions to the fauna of Rottnest Island. VIII. Apoidea. With description of new species. *J. Proc. R. Soc. West. Aust.* 20: 201–212 [210].
Type data: holotype, WAM 31–1846 ♀.
Type locality: Rottnest Is., WA.

Distribution: SW coastal, WA; known only from type locality.
Ecology: adult—volant; melliferous, solitary.

Chalicodoma (Hackeriapis) subserricauda (Rayment, 1935)

Megachile subserricauda Rayment, T. (1935). *A Cluster of Bees*. Sixty essays on the life-histories of Australian bees, with specific descriptions of over 100 new species, and an introduction by Professor E.F. Phillips, D.Ph., Cornell University, U.S.A. Sydney : Endeavour Press 752 pp. [719].
Type data: holotype, ANIC ♂.
Type locality: Eltham, VIC.

Distribution: SE coastal, VIC; known only from type locality.
Ecology: adult—volant; melliferous, solitary.

Chalicodoma (Hackeriapis) suffusipennis (Cockerell, 1906)

Megachile suffusipennis Cockerell, T.D.A. (1906). Descriptions and records of bees. XI. *Ann. Mag. Nat. Hist.* (7)17: 527–539 [531].
Type data: holotype (probable), BMNH Hym.17.a.2336 ♀.
Type locality: Mackay, QLD.

Distribution: NE coastal, Murray-Darling basin, SE coastal, QLD, NSW.
Ecology: adult—volant; melliferous, solitary, flower visiting record: asters, cherry, lilac, roses, *Daviesia* Sm. [Fabaceae], *Eucalyptus* L'Hérit. [Myrtaceae], *Jacksonia* Smith [Fabaceae], *Persoonia* Sm. [Proteaceae], *Robinia* L. [Fabaceae], *Swainsona* Salisb. [Fabaceae].
References: Hacker, H. (1915). Notes on the genus *Megachile* and some rare insects collected during 1913–14. *Mem. Qd Mus.* 3: 137–141 (description of male); Rayment, T. (1928). Studies of Australian bees. I. The leaf-cutting bees (*Megachile macularis*, Dalla Torre, and other species). II. The clay-bees. (*Lithurgus atratiformis*, Cockerell). *Vict. Nat.* 45: 79–86 (illustration); Cockerell, T.D.A. (1930). The bees of Australia. *Aust. Zool.* 6: 137–156, 205–236 (taxonomy); Rayment, T. (1935). *A Cluster of Bees*. Sixty essays on the life-histories of Australian bees, with specific descriptions of over 100 new species, and an introduction by Professor E.F. Phillips, D.Ph., Cornell University, U.S.A. Sydney : Endeavour Press 752 pp. (flower record); Rayment, T. (1939). Bees from the high lands of New South Wales and Victo-

ria. *Aust. Zool.* 9: 263–294 (distribution); Michener, C.D. (1965). A classification of the bees of the Australian and South Pacific regions. *Bull. Am. Mus. Nat. Hist.* 130: 1–362 (flower record).

Chalicodoma (Hackeriapis) tasmanica (Cockerell, 1916)

Megachile tasmanica Cockerell, T.D.A. (1916). Descriptions and records of bees. LXXI. *Ann. Mag. Nat. Hist.* (8)17: 277–287 [277].
Type data: holotype, BMNH Hym.17.a.2347 ♂.
Type locality: George Town, TAS.

Distribution: NE coastal, QLD, TAS; only published localities Brisbane and George Town.
Ecology: adult—volant; melliferous, solitary
References: Cockerell, T.D.A. (1921). Australian bees in the Queensland Museum. *Mem. Qd Mus.* 7: 81–98 (distribution); Rayment, T. (1955). New species of bees and wasps—Part XXIV. *Vict. Nat.* 71: 145–147 (taxonomy).

Chalicodoma (Hackeriapis) tomentella (Cockerell, 1906)

Megachile tomentella Cockerell, T.D.A. (1906). Descriptions and records of bees. XI. *Ann. Mag. Nat. Hist.* (7)17: 527–539 [538].
Type data: holotype, BMNH Hym.17.a.2325 ♂.
Type locality: Swan River, WA.

Distribution: SW coastal, WA, VIC; exact locality unknown, only published locality Swan River.
Ecology: adult—volant; melliferous, solitary.
References: Cockerell, T.D.A. (1910). Descriptions and records of bees. XXXII. *Ann. Mag. Nat. Hist.* (8)6: 272–284 (distribution); Cockerell, T.D.A. (1926). Descriptions and records of bees. CXII. *Ann. Mag. Nat. Hist.* (9)18: 216–227 (taxonomy).

Chalicodoma (Hackeriapis) tosticauda (Cockerell, 1912)

Megachile trichognatha tosticauda Cockerell, T.D.A. (1912). Descriptions and records of bees. XLII. *Ann. Mag. Nat. Hist.* (8)9: 220–229 [221].
Type data: holotype (probable), BMNH Hym.17.a.2385 ♀.
Type locality: Mackay, QLD.

Distribution: NE coastal, Murray-Darling basin, QLD, NSW, VIC; only published localities Mackay, Moama and Gunbower.
Ecology: adult—volant; melliferous, solitary, nest of resin, kino and wax in tunnels bored by longicorn beetles in dry timber.
References: Rayment, T. (1939). Bees from the high lands of New South Wales and Victoria. *Aust. Zool.* 9: 263–294 (taxonomy); Rayment, T. (1954). Incidence of acarid mites on the biology of bees. *Aust. Zool.* 12: 26–38 (nest); Michener, C.D. (1965). A classification of the bees of the Australian and South

Pacific regions. *Bull. Am. Mus. Nat. Hist.* **130**: 1–362 [199] (taxonomy).

Chalicodoma (Hackeriapis) trichognatha (Cockerell, 1910)

Megachile trichognatha Cockerell, T.D.A. (1910). Some Australian bees in the Berlin Museum. *J. N.Y. Entomol. Soc.* **18**: 98–114 [112].
Type data: syntypes, ZMB 19409 3♂4♀*.
Type locality: Adelaide, SA.

Distribution: NE coastal, SE coastal, Murray-Darling basin, S Gulfs, SW coastal, QLD, NSW, VIC, SA, WA.
Ecology: adult—volant; melliferous, solitary, flower visiting record: *Angophora* Cav. [Myrtaceae], *Callistemon* R.Br. [Myrtaceae], *Jacksonia* Smith [Fabaceae], *Leptospermum* Forster & G.Forster [Myrtaceae], *Melaleuca* L. [Myrtaceae].
References: Cockerell, T.D.A. (1930). The bees of Australia. *Aust. Zool.* **6**: 137–156, 205–236 (taxonomy); Rayment, T. (1939). Bees from the high lands of New South Wales and Victoria. *Aust. Zool.* **9**: 263–294 (variety); Michener, C.D. (1965). A classification of the bees of the Australian and South Pacific regions. *Bull. Am. Mus. Nat. Hist.* **130**: 1–362 (flower record).

Chalicodoma (Hackeriapis) trichomarginata (Rayment, 1930)

Megachile trichomarginata Rayment, T. (1930). Notes on a collection of bees from Western Australia. *J. Proc. R. Soc. West. Aust.* **16**: 45–56 [54].
Type data: holotype, ANIC ♀.
Type locality: Perth, WA.

Distribution: SW coastal, WA; known only from type locality.
Ecology: adult—volant; melliferous, solitary.

Chalicodoma (Hackeriapis) turneri (Meade-Waldo, 1913)

Thaumatosoma turneri Meade-Waldo, G. (1913). Four new species of Apidae (Hymenoptera) with notes on other species. *Ann. Mag. Nat. Hist. (8)***12**: 491–497 [491].
Type data: holotype, BMNH Hym.17.a.2583 ♂.
Type locality: Kuranda, QLD.

Distribution: NE coastal, N coastal, QLD, WA, NT; only published localities Kuranda, Mackay, Darwin and Baudin Is.
Ecology: adult—volant; melliferous, solitary.
Reference: Cockerell, T.D.A. (1930). The bees of Australia. *Aust. Zool.* **6**: 137–156, 205–236 (taxonomy).

Chalicodoma (Hackeriapis) ustulata (Smith, 1862)

Megachile ustulata Smith, F. (1862). Descriptions of new species of Australian Hymenoptera, and of a species of

Formica from New Zealand. *Trans. Entomol. Soc. Lond. (3)***1**: 53–62 [61].
Type data: holotype, BMNH Hym.17.a.2308 ♀.
Type locality: Australia.

Distribution: NE coastal, QLD; only published localities Kuranda, Mackay, Brisbane, Pialba and [Lamington] National Park, Macpherson Range, also recorded from New Guinea.
Ecology: adult—volant; melliferous, solitary, nest of resin in crevices and holes in timber.
References: Friese, H. (1911). Auffallende *Megachile*-Arten des Sunda-Archipels. (Apidae) *Dtsch. Entomol. Zeit.* **1911**: 217–220 (description of male, New Guinea); Hacker, H. (1915). Notes on the genus *Megachile* and some rare insects collected during 1913–14. *Mem. Qd Mus.* **3**: 137–141 (biology); Cockerell, T.D.A. (1922). Descriptions and records of bees. XCV. *Ann. Mag. Nat. Hist. (9)***10**: 265–269 (as *Megachile (Hackeriapis) ustulata* Smith, 1862); Cockerell, T.D.A. (1929). Bees in the Australian Museum collection. *Rec. Aust. Mus.* **17**: 199–243 (distribution).

Chalicodoma (Hackeriapis) victoriae (Cockerell, 1913)

Megachile victoriae Cockerell, T.D.A. (1913). Bees of the genus *Megachile* from Australia. *Entomologist* **46**: 164–168 [167].
Type data: holotype, BMNH Hym.17.a.2271 ♂.
Type locality: VIC.

Distribution: SE coastal, Murray-Darling basin, VIC, SA; only published localities Bayswater and Purnong.
Ecology: adult—volant; melliferous, solitary.
References: Cockerell, T.D.A. (1913). Descriptions and records of bees. LII. *Ann. Mag. Nat. Hist. (8)***11**: 530–542 (taxonomy); Cockerell, T.D.A. (1926). Descriptions and records of bees. CXII. *Ann. Mag. Nat. Hist. (9)***18**: 216–227 (taxonomy); Rayment, T. (1928). Studies of Australian bees. I. The leaf-cutting bees (*Megachile macularis*, Dalla Torre, and other species). II. The clay-bees. (*Lithurgus atratiformis*, Cockerell). *Vict. Nat.* **45**: 79–86 (doubtful record of nest, as leafcutter).

Chalicodoma (Hackeriapis) ` wilsoni (Cockerell, 1929)

Megachile wilsoni Cockerell, T.D.A. (1929). Bees in the Queensland Museum. *Mem. Qd Mus.* **9**: 298–323 [304].
Type data: holotype, QM Hy/4026 ♂.
Type locality: Kiata, VIC.

Distribution: Murray-Darling basin, VIC; known only from type locality.
Ecology: adult—volant; melliferous, solitary.

Chalicodoma (Rhodomegachile) Michener, 1965

Rhodomegachile Michener, C.D. (1965). A classification of the bees of the Australian and South Pacific regions. *Bull. Am. Mus. Nat. Hist.* **130**: 1–362 [201] [proposed with subgeneric rank in *Chalicodoma* Lepeletier, 1841]. Type species: *Megachile abdominalis* Smith, 1853 by original designation.

Chalicodoma (Rhodomegachile) abdominalis (Smith, 1853)

Megachile abdominalis Smith, F. (1853). *Catalogue of Hymenopterous Insects in the Collection of the British Museum.* Part I. Andrenidae and Apidae. London : British Museum 197 pp. [169].
Type data: holotype, BMNH Hym.17.a.2295 ♂.
Type locality: Macintyre River, NSW (on label), (as New Holland in description).

Distribution: NE coastal, Murray-Darling basin, SE coastal, QLD, NSW.
Ecology: adult—volant; melliferous, solitary, nest of wax cells in any suitable cavity, generally wood, or nest of mud and resin in abandoned mud-wasp nest, flower visiting record: *Angophora* Cav. [Myrtaceae], *Eucalyptus* L'Hérit. [Myrtaceae], (*Jacksonia* Smith [Fabaceae]), *Leptospermum* Forster & G.Forster [Myrtaceae].
References: Radoschkowsky, O. de B. (1874). Supplément indispensable à l'article publié par M. Gerstaecker, en 1869, sur quelques genres d'hyménoptères. *Bull. Soc. Imp. Nat. Moscou* **48**: 132–164 [=Radoszkowski, O.I.] (illustration); Hacker, H. (1915). Notes on the genus *Megachile* and some rare insects collected during 1913–14. *Mem. Qd Mus.* **3**: 137–141 (flower record, doubtful record); Rayment, T. (1935). *A Cluster of Bees.* Sixty essays on the life-histories of Australian bees, with specific descriptions of over 100 new species, and an introduction by Professor E.F. Phillips, D.Ph., Cornell University, U.S.A. Sydney : Endeavour Press 752 pp. (illustration); Rayment, T. (1954). Incidence of acarid mites on the biology of bees. *Aust. Zool.* **12**: 26–38 (nest); King, J. & Exley, E.M. (1985). A revision of *Chalicodoma (Rhodomegachile)* Michener (Hymenoptera :- Megachilidae). *J. Aust. Entomol. Soc.* **24**: 199–204 (redescription); Wylie, F.R., Walsh, G.L. & Yule, R.A. (1987). Insect damage to aboriginal relics at burial and rock-art sites near Carnarvon in central Queensland. *J. Aust. Entomol. Soc.* **26**: 335–345 (biology).

Chalicodoma (Rhodomegachile) ferruginea King and Exley, 1985

Chalicodoma (Rhodomegachile) ferrugineum King, J. & Exley, E.M. (1985). A revision of *Chalicodoma (Rhodomegachile)* Michener (Hymenoptera : Megachilidae). *J. Aust. Entomol. Soc.* **24**: 199–204 [203].
Type data: holotype, WAM ♀*.
Type locality: Bamboo Creek, WA.

Distribution: NW coastal, W plateau, WA; only published localities Bamboo Creek and near Yuinmery Homestead.
Ecology: adult—volant; melliferous, solitary, flower visiting record: *Eucalyptus* L'Hérit. [Myrtaceae].

Chalicodoma (Schizomegachile) Michener, 1965

Schizomegachile Michener, C.D. (1965). A classification of the bees of the Australian and South Pacific regions. *Bull. Am. Mus. Nat. Hist.* **130**: 1–362 [199] [proposed with subgeneric rank in *Chalicodoma* Lepeletier, 1841]. Type species: *Megachile monstrosa* Smith, 1868 by original designation.

Chalicodoma (Schizomegachile) monstrosa (Smith, 1868)

Megachile monstrosa Smith, F. (1868). Descriptions of aculeate Hymenoptera from Australia. *Trans. Entomol. Soc. Lond.* **1868**: 231–258 [256].
Type data: holotype, BMNH Hym.17.a.2293 ♀.
Type locality: Champion Bay (Geraldton), WA.

Megachile cornifera Radoschkowsky, O. de B. (1874). Supplément indispensable à l'article publié par M. Gerstaecker, en 1869, sur quelques genres d'hyménoptères. *Bull. Soc. Imp. Nat. Moscou* **48**: 132–164 [=Radoszkowski, O.I.] [148].
Type data: holotype (probable), whereabouts unknown ♀*.
Type locality: Sydney, NSW (record from Sydney likely to be in error, subsequently collected from Southern Cross, WA), see Cockerell, T.D.A. (1913). Bees of the genus *Megachile* from Australia. *Entomologist* **46**: 164–168 [164].

Taxonomic decision for synonymy: Cockerell, T.D.A. (1913). Some Australian bees. *Proc. Acad. Nat. Sci. Philad.* **65**: 28–44 [44].

Distribution: NE coastal, SE coastal, Murray-Darling basin, SW coastal, NW coastal, QLD, NSW, VIC, WA.
Ecology: adult—volant; melliferous, solitary.
References: Smith, F. (1873). Natural history notices. Insects, Hymenoptera Aculeata. pp. 456–463 pls XLIII–XLV *in* Brenchley, J.B. *Jottings During the Cruise of* H.M.S. Curaçoa *among the South Sea Islands in 1865.* London : Longmans, Green & Co. (illustration); Cockerell, T.D.A. (1913). Bees of the genus *Megachile* from Australia. *Entomologist* **46**: 164–168 (description of male, as *Megachile cornifera* Radoszkowsky, 1874); Cockerell, T.D.A. (1930). The bees of Australia. *Aust. Zool.* **6**: 137–156, 205–236 (taxonomy); Rayment, T. (1950). A new and remarkable organ on a resin-bee. *Vict. Nat.* **66**: 163–168 (taxonomy); Michener, C.D. (1965). A classification of the bees of the Australian and South Pacific regions. *Bull. Am. Mus. Nat. Hist.* **130**: 1–362 (illustration).

Coelioxys Latreille, 1809

Taxonomic decision for subgeneric arrangement: Mitchell, T.B. (1973). A subgeneric revision of the bees of the genus *Coelioxys* of the Western Hemisphere (Hymenoptera :

Megachilidae). *Contrib. Dep. Entomol. North Carolina State Univ.* 129 pp. [7].

Generic reference: Michener, C.D. (1965). A classification of the bees of the Australian and South Pacific regions. *Bull. Am. Mus. Nat. Hist.* **130**: 1–362.

Coelioxys (Coelioxys) Latreille, 1809

Coelioxys Latreille, P.A. (1809). *Genera Crustaceorum et Insectorum* secundem ordinem naturalem in familias disposita, iconibus exemplisque plurimis explicata. Paris : A. Koenig Vol. 4 397 pp. [166]. Type species: *Apis conica* Linnaeus, 1758 (=*Apis quadridentata* Linnaeus, 1758) by subsequent designation, see Latreille, P.A. (1810). *Considérations Générales sur l'Ordre Naturel des Animaux Composant les Classes des Crustacès, des Arachnides, et des Insectes;* avec un Tableau Méthodique de leurs Genres, Disposés en Familles. Paris : F. Schoell 444 pp. [439]. Compiled from secondary source: Sandhouse, G.A. (1943). The type species of the genera and subgenera of bees. *Proc. U.S. Natl Mus.* **92**(3156): 519–619.

Liothyrapis Cockerell, T.D.A. (1911). Bees in the collection of the United States National Museum. 2. *Proc. U.S. Natl Mus.* **40**: 241–264 [246] [proposed with subgeneric rank in *Coelioxys* Latreille, 1809]. Type species: *Coelioxys apicata* Smith, 1854 (=*Coelioxys decipiens* Spinola, 1836) by monotypy. Compiled from secondary source: Michener, C.D. (1965). A classification of the bees of the Australian and South Pacific regions. *Bull. Am. Mus. Nat. Hist.* **130**: 1–362.

Taxonomic decision for synonymy: Mitchell, T.B. (1973). A subgeneric revision of the bees of the genus *Coelioxys* of the Western Hemisphere (Hymenoptera : Megachilidae). *Contrib. Dep. Entomol. North Carolina State Univ.* 129 pp. [7]; for alternative taxonomic arrangement see Michener, C.D. (1965). A classification of the bees of the Australian and South Pacific regions. *Bull. Am. Mus. Nat. Hist.* **130**: 1–362 [212] (*Liothyrapis* stands as a subgenus of *Coelioxys*; see also *Coelioxys weinlandi* Schulz, 1904).

Extralimital distribution: Nearctic, Neotropical, Palaearctic, Afrotropical and Oriental Regions, extending E to New Guinea and Solomon Ils, see Michener, C.D. (1965). A classification of the bees of the Australian and South Pacific regions. *Bull. Am. Mus. Nat. Hist.* **130**: 1–362 [212].

Coelioxys (Coelioxys) albolineata Cockerell, 1905

Coelioxys albolineata Cockerell, T.D.A. (1905). Descriptions and records of bees. I. *Ann. Mag. Nat. Hist.* (7)**16**: 216–225 [222].
Type data: syntypes, BMNH 2♀ (a specimen is labelled 'type' and has registration number Hym.17.b.30).
Type locality: Mackay, QLD.

Distribution: NE coastal, (Murray-Darling basin), N coastal, QLD, NSW, NT.
Ecology: adult—volant; melliferous, solitary, cleptoparasitic, flower visiting record: (*Spiranthes* Rich. [Orchidaceae]).
References: Cockerell, T.D.A. (1910). Descriptions and records of bees. XXIX. *Ann. Mag. Nat. Hist.*

(8)**5**: 496–506 (description of male); Cockerell, T.D.A. (1911). The bees of the Solomon Islands. *Proc. Linn. Soc. N.S.W.* **36**: 160–178 (taxonomy); Cockerell, T.D.A. (1929). Bees from the Australian region. *Am. Mus. Novit.* **346**: 1–18 (distribution); Rayment, T. (1935). *A Cluster of Bees.* Sixty essays on the life-histories of Australian bees, with specific descriptions of over 100 new species, and an introduction by Professor E.F. Phillips, D.Ph., Cornell University, U.S.A. Sydney : Endeavour Press 752 pp. (flower record, doubtful record, Holbrook NSW); Cockerell, T.D.A. (1939). Studies of the Pacific bees in the collection of Bishop Museum (Hymenoptera, Apoidea). *Occ. Pap. Bernice P. Bishop Mus.* **15**: 133–140 (distribution); Rayment, T. (1954). Incidence of acarid mites on the biology of bees. *Aust. Zool.* **12**: 26–38 (as host).

Coelioxys (Coelioxys) darwiniensis Cockerell, 1929

Coelioxys albolineata darwiniensis Cockerell, T.D.A. (1929). Bees from the Australian region. *Am. Mus. Novit.* **346**: 1–18 [8].
Type data: holotype, AMNH ♂*.
Type locality: Darwin, NT.

Distribution: NE coastal, N coastal, QLD, NT; only published localities Halifax and Darwin.
Ecology: adult—volant; melliferous, solitary, cleptoparasitic.
References: Cockerell, T.D.A. (1930). Australian bees in the Museum of Comparative Zoology. *Psyche (Camb.)* **37**: 141–154 (distribution); Michener, C.D. (1965). A classification of the bees of the Australian and South Pacific regions. *Bull. Am. Mus. Nat. Hist.* **130**: 1–362 (as *Coelioxys (Coelioxys) darwinensis*, incorrect subsequent spelling).

Coelioxys (Coelioxys) froggatti Cockerell, 1911

Coelioxys froggatti Cockerell, T.D.A. (1911). The bees of the Solomon Islands. *Proc. Linn. Soc. N.S.W.* **36**: 160–178 [170].
Type data: syntypes (probable), USNM ♂♀*.
Type locality: VIC.

Distribution: Murray-Darling basin, SW coastal, VIC, WA, TAS; only published localities Gunbower, Eaglehawk Neck, Yallingup and Swan River.
Ecology: adult—volant; melliferous, solitary, cleptoparasitic, flower visiting record: *Callistemon* R.Br. [Myrtaceae].
References: Meade-Waldo, G. (1914). Notes on the Hymenoptera in the collection of the British Museum, with descriptions of new species. V. *Ann. Mag. Nat. Hist.* (8)**14**: 450–464 (distribution); Rayment, T. (1929). The cuckoo-bees, *Coelioxys froggatti* Cockerell. *Vict. Nat.* **46**: 58–61 (biology); Cockerell, T.D.A. (1930). The bees of Australia. *Aust. Zool.* **6**: 137–156, 205–236 (distribution); Rayment, T. (1935). *A Cluster of Bees.* Sixty essays on the life-histories of Australian bees, with specific descrip-

tions of over 100 new species, and an introduction by Professor E.F. Phillips, D.Ph., Cornell University, U.S.A. Sydney : Endeavour Press 752 pp. (biology); Rayment, T. (1954). Incidence of acarid mites on the biology of bees. *Aust. Zool.* **12**: 26–38 (as host).

Coelioxys (Coelioxys) reginae Cockerell, 1905

Coelioxys reginae Cockerell, T.D.A. (1905). Descriptions and records of bees. I. *Ann. Mag. Nat. Hist. (7)***16**: 216–225 [221].
Type data: holotype, BMNH Hym.17.b.29 ♀.
Type locality: Mackay, QLD.

Distribution: NE coastal, N coastal, QLD, NT; only published localities Mackay, Brisbane and Darwin.
Ecology: adult—volant; melliferous, solitary, cleptoparasitic.
References: Cockerell, T.D.A. (1910). Descriptions and records of bees. XXIX. *Ann. Mag. Nat. Hist. (8)***5**: 496–506 (description of male); Cockerell, T.D.A. (1929). Bees in the Queensland Museum. *Mem. Qd Mus.* **9**: 298–323 (distribution); Cockerell, T.D.A. (1930). The bees of Australia. *Aust. Zool.* **6**: 137–156, 205–236 (distribution).

Coelioxys (Coelioxys) victoriae Rayment, 1935

Coelioxys victoriae Rayment, T. (1935). *A Cluster of Bees. Sixty essays on the life-histories of Australian bees, with specific descriptions of over 100 new species, and an introduction by Professor E.F. Phillips, D.Ph., Cornell University, U.S.A.* Sydney : Endeavour Press 752 pp. [723].
Type data: holotype, ANIC ♀.
Type locality: Gunbower, VIC.

Distribution: Murray-Darling basin, VIC; known only from type locality.
Ecology: adult—volant; melliferous, solitary, cleptoparasitic.

Coelioxys (Coelioxys) weinlandi Schulz, 1904

Coelioxys weinlandi Schulz, W.A. (1904). Ein Beitrag zur Kenntnis der papuanischen Hymenopteren-Fauna. *Berl. Entomol. Z.* **49**: 209–239 [234].
Type data: holotype, BMNH Hym.17.b.24 ♀.
Type locality: Finschhafen, Papua New Guinea (as German New Guinea).
Coelioxys albiceps Friese, H. (1909). Die Bienenfauna von Neu-Guinea. *Ann. Hist.-Nat. Mus. Natl. Hung.* **7**: 179–288 [269].
Type data: syntypes (probable), NHMW ♀*(number of specimens unknown).
Type locality: Cairns, QLD and Bogadjim (as Stephansort), Austrolabe Bay, Simbang and Huon Gulf, New Guinea.

Taxonomic decision for synonymy: Cockerell, T.D.A. (1911). The bees of the Solomon Islands. *Proc. Linn. Soc. N.S.W.* **36**: 160–178 [169].

Distribution: NE coastal, QLD; only published localities Cairns, Kuranda and Cape York, also New Guinea and Aru Archipelago.

Ecology: adult—volant; melliferous, solitary, cleptoparasitic.
References: Cockerell, T.D.A. (1910). Descriptions and records of bees. XXIX. *Ann. Mag. Nat. Hist. (8)***5**: 496–506 (description of male, as *Coelioxys albiceps* Friese, 1909); Michener, C.D. (1965). A classification of the bees of the Australian and South Pacific regions. *Bull. Am. Mus. Nat. Hist.* **130**: 1–362 [212] (as *Coelioxys (Liothyrapis) weinlandi*).

Creightonella Cockerell, 1908

Creightonella Cockerell, T.D.A. (1908). A new subgenus of African bees. *Entomologist* **41**: 146–147 [146] [proposed with subgeneric rank in *Megachile* Latreille, 1802]. Type species: *Megachile (Creightonella) mitimia* Cockerell, 1908 by original designation.

Extralimital distribution: E Palaearctic, Afrotropical and Oriental Regions, extending E to Solomon Ils, see Michener, C.D. (1965). A classification of the bees of the Australian and South Pacific regions. *Bull. Am. Mus. Nat. Hist.* **130**: 1–362 [204].

Creightonella frontalis (Fabricius, 1804)

Anthophora frontalis Fabricius, J.C. (1804). *Systema Piezatorum.* Brunsvigae : C. Reichard xiv 439 pp. [375].
Type data: holotype, ZMK ♂*.
Type locality: Amboina.
Megachile lachesis Smith, F. (1861). Catalogue of hymenopterous insects collected by Mr. A.R. Wallace in the islands of Bachian, Kaisaa, Amboyna, Gilolo, and at Dory in New Guinea. *J. Proc. Linn. Soc. Lond. Zool.* **5**: 93–143 [133].
Type data: lectotype, OUM ♀*.
Subsequent designation: Lieftinck, M.A. (1958). The identity of some Fabrician types of bees (Hymenoptera, Apoidea) II. One *Amegilla* Friese and two species of *Megachile* Latr. *Proc. K. Ned. Akad. Wet. (C)***61**: 461–465 [464].
Type locality: Amboina (as Bachian, Amboyna).

Taxonomic decision for synonymy: Lieftinck, M.A. (1958). The identity of some Fabrician types of bees (Hymenoptera, Apoidea) II. One *Amegilla* Friese and two species of *Megachile* Latr. *Proc. K. Ned. Akad. Wet. (C)***61**: 461–465 [463].

Distribution: (NE coastal), (QLD); species recorded from Indonesia, New Guinea, Solomon Ils and the Philippines, Australian record seems doubtful, as species has not been re-collected here.
Ecology: adult—volant; melliferous, solitary.
References: Friese, H. (1909). Die Bienenfauna von Neu-Guinea. *Ann. Hist.-Nat. Mus. Natl. Hung.* **7**: 179–288 (Australian record, as *Megachile lachesis* Smith, 1861); Michener, C.D. & Szent-Ivany, J.J.H. (1960). Observations on the biology of a leaf-cutter bee "*Megachile frontalis*" in New Guinea. *Papua New Guinea Agric. J.* **13**: 22–35 (biology); Baltazar, C.R. (1966). A catalogue of Philippine Hymenoptera (with a bibliography, 1758–1963). *Pac. Insects Monogr.* **8**: 1–488 (Australian record, as *Megachile*

atrata Smith, 1853); Willmer, P.G. & Stone, G.N. (1989). Incidence of entomophilous pollination of lowland coffee (*Coffea canephora*); the role of leaf cutter bees in Papua New Guinea. *Entomol. Exp. Appl.* **50**: 113–124 (biology).

Megachile Latreille, 1802

Megachile Latreille, P.A. (1802). *Histoire Naturelle des Fourmis et Recueil de Mémoires et d'Observations sur les Abeilles, les Areignées, les Faucheurs et autres Insectes.* Paris : Barrois 445 pp. [434] [placed on the Official List of Generic Names in Zoology (Name No. 651), Opinion 219]. Type species: *Apis centuncularis* Linnaeus, 1758 by subsequent designation, see Curtis, J. (1828). *British Entomology;* being illustrations· and descriptions of the genera of insects found in Great Britain and Ireland : containing coloured figures from nature of the most rare and beautiful species, and in many instances of the plants upon which they are found. London : John Curtis Vol. 5 pls 195–241 [pl. 218]. Compiled from secondary source: International Commission on Zoological Nomenclature (1954). Opinion 219. Addition to the *Official List of Generic Names in Zoology* of *Megachile* Latreille, 1802, with *Apis centuncularis* Linnaeus, 1758, as type species (Class Insecta, Order Hymenoptera). *Opin. Decl. Int. Comm. Zool. Nomen.* **4**: 93–102.

Taxonomic decision for subgeneric arrangement: Michener, C.D. (1965). A classification of the bees of the Australian and South Pacific regions. *Bull. Am. Mus. Nat. Hist.* **130**: 1–362 [206].

Extralimital distribution: Palaearctic and Nearctic Regions, see Hurd, P.D. (1979). Superfamily Apoidea. pp. 1741–2209 *in* Krombein, K.V., Hurd, P.D., Smith, D.R. & Burks, B.D. (eds) (1979). *Catalog of Hymenoptera in America North of Mexico.* Washington : Smithsonian Institution Vol. 2.

Megachile (Callochile) Michener, 1962

Callochile Michener, C.D. (1962). Observations on the classification of the bees commonly placed in the genus *Megachile* (Hymenoptera : Apoidea). *J. N.Y. Entomol. Soc.* **70**: 17–29 [27] [proposed with subgeneric rank in *Megachile* Latreille, 1802]. Type species: *Megachile ustulatiformis* Cockerell, 1910 (=*Apis mystacea* Fabricius, 1775) by original designation.

Extralimital distribution: E Palaearctic and Oriental Regions, extending E to Solomon Ils, see Michener, C.D. (1965). A classification of the bees of the Australian and South Pacific regions. *Bull. Am. Mus. Nat. Hist.* **130**: 1–362 [210].

Megachile (Callochile) hilli Cockerell, 1929

Megachile hilli Cockerell, T.D.A. (1929). Bees from the Australian region. *Am. Mus. Novit.* **346**: 1–18 [16]. Type data: holotype, AMNH ♀*. Type locality: Townsville, QLD.

Distribution: NE coastal, QLD; only published localities Townsville and Halifax. Ecology: adult—volant; melliferous, solitary.

Reference: Cockerell, T.D.A. (1930). Australian bees in the Museum of Comparative Zoology. *Psyche (Camb.)* **37**: 141–154 (taxonomy).

Megachile (Callochile) mystacea (Fabricius, 1775)

Apis mystacea Fabricius, J.C. (1775). *Systema Entomologiae,* sistens insectorum classes, ordines, genera, species, adiectis synonymis, locis, descriptionibus, observationibus. Korte : Flensburgi et Lipsiae xxvii 832 pp. [385]. Type data: holotype, BMNH (Banks coll.) ♀. Type locality: Australia (as New Holland). *Megachile ustulatiformis* Cockerell, T.D.A. (1910). Descriptions and records of bees. XXXII. *Ann. Mag. Nat. Hist. (8)6*: 272–284 [280]. Type data: holotype, BMNH Hym.17.a.2294 ♂. Type locality: Kuranda (as Cairns Kuranda), QLD.

Taxonomic decision for synonymy: Michener, C.D. (1962). Observations on the classification of the bees commonly placed in the genus *Megachile* (Hymenoptera : Apoidea). *J. N.Y. Entomol. Soc.* **70**: 17–29 [29].

Distribution: NE coastal, (SE coastal), N coastal, QLD, (NSW), NT, WA; a record from Sydney seems doubtful. Ecology: adult—volant; melliferous, solitary (record of a nest of resin is probably of *Chalicodoma mystaceana* Michener, 1962), flower visiting record: *Pongamia* Vent. [Fabaceae]. References: Fabricius, J.C. (1804). *Systema Piezatorum.* Brunsvigae : C. Reichard xiv 439 pp. (as *Anthophora mystacea* (Fabricius, 1775)); Smith, F. (1853). *Catalogue of Hymenopterous Insects in the Collection of the British Museum.* Part I. Andrenidae and Apidae. London : British Museum 197 pp. (redescription); Cockerell, T.D.A. (1906). Descriptions and records of bees. XI. *Ann. Mag. Nat. Hist. (7)17*: 527–539 (distribution); Hacker, H. (1915). Notes on the genus *Megachile* and some rare insects collected during 1913–14. *Mem. Qd Mus.* **3**: 137–141 (doubtful record, of resin nest, probably misidentification of *Chalicodoma (Callomegachile) mystaceana* Michener, 1962); Cockerell, T.D.A. (1930). Australian bees in the Museum of Comparative Zoology. *Psyche (Camb.)* **37**: 141–154 (distribution); Rayment, T. (1935). *A Cluster of Bees.* Sixty essays on the life-histories of Australian bees, with specific descriptions of over 100 new species, and an introduction by Professor E.F. Phillips, D.Ph., Cornell University, U.S.A. Sydney : Endeavour Press 752 pp. (description of female, as *Megachile ustulatiformis* Cockerell, 1918); Michener, C.D. (1965). A classification of the bees of the Australian and South Pacific regions. *Bull. Am. Mus. Nat. Hist.* **130**: 1–362 (flower record).

Megachile (Eutricharaea) Thomson, 1872

Eutricharaea Thomson, C.G. (1872). *Hymenoptera Scandinaviae.* Lund : Berling Vol. 2 286 pp. [228] [proposed with subgeneric rank in *Megachile* Latreille,

1802]. Type species: *Apis argentata* Fabricius, 1793 by monotypy.

Androgynella Cockerell, T.D.A. (1911). Descriptions and records of bees. XXXV. *Ann. Mag. Nat. Hist. (8)*7: 310–319 [313]. Type species: *Megachile detersa* Cockerell, 1910 by original designation.

Taxonomic decision for synonymy: Michener, C.D. (1965). A classification of the bees of the Australian and South Pacific regions. *Bull. Am. Mus. Nat. Hist.* **130**: 1–362 [206].

Extralimital distribution: Nearctic (introduced), Neotropical (introduced), Palaearctic, Afrotropical and Oriental Regions, extending E to Tahiti, see Michener, C.D. (1965). A classification of the bees of the Australian and South Pacific regions. *Bull. Am. Mus. Nat. Hist.* **130**: 1–362 [209].

Megachile (Eutricharaea) austeni Cockerell, 1906

Megachile austeni Cockerell, T.D.A. (1906). Descriptions and records of bees. XI. *Ann. Mag. Nat. Hist. (7)*17: 527–539 [539].
Type data: holotype, BMNH Hym.17.a.2313 ♂.
Type locality: Australia (probably QLD, from description).

Distribution: NE coastal, QLD; only published localities Cairns, Mackay and Stradbroke Is.
Ecology: adult—volant; melliferous, solitary, flower visiting record: *Ipomoea* L. [Convolvulaceae].
References: Cockerell, T.D.A. (1910). Descriptions and records of bees. XXXII. *Ann. Mag. Nat. Hist. (8)*6: 272–284 (distribution); Hacker, H. (1915). Notes on the genus *Megachile* and some rare insects collected during 1913–14. *Mem. Qd Mus.* **3**: 137–141 (description of female).

Megachile (Eutricharaea) australasiae Dalla Torre, 1896

Megachile imitata Smith, F. (1868). Descriptions of aculeate Hymenoptera from Australia. *Trans. Entomol. Soc. Lond.* **1868**: 231–258 [257] [junior primary homonym of *Megachile imitata* Smith, 1853].
Type data: holotype, BMNH Hym.17.a.2355 ♀.
Type locality: Champion Bay (Geraldton), WA.
Megachile australasiae Dalla Torre, K.W. (1896). *Catalogus Hymenopterorum Hucusque Descriptorum Systematicus et Synonymicus.* Apidae (Anthophila). Lipsiae : G. Engelmann Vol. x 643 pp. [421] [*nom. nov.* for *Megachile imitata* Smith, 1868].

Distribution: NE coastal, NW coastal, QLD, WA; only published localities Cairns, (Mackay), Champion Bay and Roebourne, also New Guinea, New Ireland and New Caledonia.
Ecology: adult—volant; melliferous, solitary.
References: Friese, H. (1909). Die Bienenfauna von Neu-Guinea. *Ann. Hist.-Nat. Mus. Natl. Hung.* **7**: 179–288 (distribution); Friese, H. (1911). Zur Bienenfauna Neuguineas und der benachbarten Gebiete (Hym.) (Nachtrag II). *Dtsch. Entomol. Zeit.* **1911**: 448–453 (incorrect subsequent spelling as *Megachile australiaca* Dalla Torre); Cockerell,

T.D.A. (1929). Bees, chiefly Australian species, described or determined by Dr. H. Friese. *Am. Mus. Novit.* **343**: 1–20 (taxonomy).

Megachile (Eutricharaea) captionis Cockerell, 1914

Megachile captionis Cockerell, T.D.A. (1914). Descriptions and records of bees. LXIV. *Ann. Mag. Nat. Hist. (8)*14: 464–472 [466].
Type data: holotype, BMNH Hym.17.a.2374 ♂.
Type locality: Brewarrina, NSW.

Distribution: NE coastal, Murray-Darling basin, SE coastal, QLD, NSW, VIC; only published localities S QLD, Brewarrina, Yarrawin and Woodend.
Ecology: adult—volant; melliferous, solitary, flower visiting record: *Eremophila* R.Br. [Myoporaceae].
References: Michener, C.D. (1965). A classification of the bees of the Australian and South Pacific regions. *Bull. Am. Mus. Nat. Hist.* **130**: 1–362 (as *Megachile (Eutricharaea) capitonis*, incorrect subsequent spelling); Allsopp, P.G. (1977). Insects associated with *Eremophila gilesii* F. Muell. in southern Queensland. *Qd J. Agric. Anim. Sci.* **34**: 157–161 (flower record).

Megachile (Eutricharaea) cetera Cockerell, 1912

Megachile cetera Cockerell, T.D.A. (1912). Descriptions and records of bees. XLII. *Ann. Mag. Nat. Hist. (8)*9: 220–229 [220].
Type data: holotype, ANIC ♀.
Type locality: Nagambie, VIC.

Distribution: NE coastal, SE coastal, Murray-Darling basin, SW coastal, N coastal, QLD, NSW, VIC, SA, WA, NT.
Ecology: adult—volant; melliferous, solitary, nest of cut leaves, in gallery in wood, flower visiting record: asters, lucerne (in cage).
References: Cockerell, T.D.A. (1913). Descriptions and records of bees. LII. *Ann. Mag. Nat. Hist. (8)*11: 530–542 (variety); Cockerell, T.D.A. (1929). Bees from the Australian region. *Am. Mus. Novit.* **346**: 1–18 (distribution); Cockerell, T.D.A. (1930). The bees of Australia. *Aust. Zool.* **6**: 137–156, 205–236 (taxonomy); Rayment, T. (1931). Bees in the collections of the Western Australian Museum and the Agricultural Department, Perth. *J. Proc. R. Soc. West. Aust.* **17**: 157–190 (distribution); Rayment, T. (1935). *A Cluster of Bees.* Sixty essays on the life-histories of Australian bees, with specific descriptions of over 100 new species, and an introduction by Professor E.F. Phillips, D.Ph., Cornell University, U.S.A. Sydney : Endeavour Press 752 pp. (description of male, biology); Rayment, T. (1939). Bees from the high lands of New South Wales and Victoria. *Aust. Zool.* **9**: 263–294 (distribution); Bray, R.A. (1973). Characteristics of some bees of the family Megachilidae in southeast Queensland and their potential as lucerne pollinators. *J. Aust. Entomol. Soc.* **12**: 99–102 (biology).

Megachile (Eutricharaea) chrysopyga Smith, 1853

Megachile chrysopyga Smith, F. (1853). *Catalogue of Hymenopterous Insects in the Collection of the British Museum.* Part I. Andrenidae and Apidae. London : British Museum 197 pp. [173].
Type data: syntypes, BMNH Hym.17.a.229 ♀ (number of specimens unknown).
Type locality: WA.

Megachile maculariformis Cockerell, T.D.A. (1907). On a collection of Australian and Asiatic bees. *Bull. Am. Mus. Nat. Hist.* **23**: 221–236 [223].
Type data: holotype, AMNH 303 ♀*.
Type locality: NSW.

Taxonomic decision for synonymy: Cockerell, T.D.A. (1910). Descriptions and records of bees. XXIV. *Ann. Mag. Nat. Hist.* (8)**5**: 22–30 [29].

Distribution: NE coastal, SE coastal, Murray-Darling basin, SW coastal, NW coastal, QLD, NSW, VIC, WA, TAS; also recorded from New Guinea.
Ecology: adult—volant; melliferous, solitary, nest of cut leaves—under loose bark on log, under the exposed root of a tree, in soil, or in cracks in a rock, flower visiting record: *Angophora* Cav. [Myrtaceae], *Daviesia* Sm. [Fabaceae], *Eucalyptus* L'Hérit. [Myrtaceae], *Jacksonia* Smith [Fabaceae], *Kunzea* Reichb. [Myrtaceae], *Oxylobium* Andrews [Fabaceae], *Plectronia* L. [Rubiaceae], *Pultenaea* Sm. [Fabaceae].
References: Friese, H. (1912). Zur Bienenfauna von Neu-Guinea und Oceania. *Mitt. Zool. Mus. Berl.* **6**: 93–96 (distribution); Hacker, H. (1915). Notes on the genus *Megachile* and some rare insects collected during 1913–14. *Mem. Qd Mus.* **3**: 137–141 (biology); Cockerell, T.D.A. (1926). Descriptions and records of bees. CXII. *Ann. Mag. Nat. Hist.* (9)**18**: 216–227 (taxonomy); Rayment, T. (1928). Studies of Australian bees. I. The leaf-cutting bees (*Megachile macularis*, Dalla Torre, and other species). II. The clay-bees. (*Lithurgus atratiformis*, Cockerell). *Vict. Nat.* **45**: 79–86 (illustration); Cockerell, T.D.A. (1930). The bees of Australia. *Aust. Zool.* **6**: 137–156, 205–236 (distribution); Rayment, T. (1935). *A Cluster of Bees.* Sixty essays on the life-histories of Australian bees, with specific descriptions of over 100 new species, and an introduction by Professor E.F. Phillips, D.Ph., Cornell University, U.S.A. Sydney : Endeavour Press 752 pp. (biology); Rayment, T. (1939). Bees from the high lands of New South Wales and Victoria. *Aust. Zool.* **9**: 263–294 (biology); Rayment, T. (1947). Bees from the Victorian Alps. *Vict. Nat.* **64**: 103–107 (distribution); Rayment, T. (1953). *Bees of the Portland District.* Victoria : Portland Field Naturalist's Club 39 pp. (biology, flower record); Rayment, T. (1953). Pictorial biology of a leafcutter bee, *Megachile chrysopyga* Smith. *Vict. Nat.* **70**: 50–51 (biology); Rayment, T. (1954). Incidence of acarid mites on the biology of bees. *Aust. Zool.* **12**: 26–38 (as host); Michener, C.D.

(1965). A classification of the bees of the Australian and South Pacific regions. *Bull. Am. Mus. Nat. Hist.* **130**: 1–362 (flower record); Michener, C.D. & Houston, T.F. (1991). Apoidea. pp. 993–1000 *in* CSIRO (sponsor) *The Insects of Australia.* A textbook for students and research workers. Melbourne : Melbourne University Press Vol. II 2nd Edn (illustration).

Megachile (Eutricharaea) chrysopygopsis Cockerell, 1929

Megachile chrysopygopsis Cockerell, T.D.A. (1929). Bees in the Queensland Museum. *Mem. Qd Mus.* **9**: 298–323 [302].
Type data: holotype, QM Hy/4024 ♀.
Type locality: Perth, WA.

Distribution: SW coastal, WA; known only from type locality.
Ecology: adult—volant; melliferous, solitary.

Megachile (Eutricharaea) ciliatipes Cockerell, 1921

Megachile ciliatipes Cockerell, T.D.A. (1921). Australian bees in the Queensland Museum. *Mem. Qd Mus.* **7**: 81–98 [89].
Type data: holotype, BMNH Hym.17.a.2380 ♂.
Type locality: Brisbane, QLD.

Distribution: NE coastal, QLD; only published localities Brisbane, Kuranda, Halifax and Babinda.
Ecology: adult—volant; melliferous, solitary.
References: Cockerell, T.D.A. (1930). The bees of Australia. *Aust. Zool.* **6**: 137–156, 205–236 (taxonomy); Cockerell, T.D.A. (1930). Australian bees in the Museum of Comparative Zoology. *Psyche (Camb.)* **37**: 141–154 (distribution).

Megachile (Eutricharaea) cygnorum Cockerell, 1906

Megachile cygnorum Cockerell, T.D.A. (1906). Descriptions and records of bees. XI. *Ann. Mag. Nat. Hist.* (7)**17**: 527–539 [536].
Type data: holotype, BMNH Hym.17.a.2377 ♂.
Type locality: Swan River, WA.

Distribution: NE coastal, SE coastal, S Gulfs, SW coastal, QLD, NSW, VIC, SA, WA.
Ecology: adult—volant; melliferous, solitary.
References: Cockerell, T.D.A. (1910). Some Australian bees in the Berlin Museum. *J. N.Y. Entomol. Soc.* **18**: 98–114 (taxonomy); Meade-Waldo, G. (1915). Notes on the Apidae (Hymenoptera) in the collection of the British Museum, with descriptions of new species. VI. *Ann. Mag. Nat. Hist.* (8)**15**: 325–335 (distribution); Cockerell, T.D.A. (1930). The bees of Australia. *Aust. Zool.* **6**: 137–156, 205–236 (distribution); Rayment, T. (1931). Bees in the collections of the Western Australian Museum and the Agricultural Department, Perth. *J. Proc. R. Soc. West. Aust.* **17**: 157–190 (description of female).

Megachile (Eutricharaea) darwiniana Cockerell, 1906

Megachile darwiniana Cockerell, T.D.A. (1906). Descriptions and records of bees. XI. *Ann. Mag. Nat. Hist. (7)*17: 527–539 [535].
Type data: holotype, BMNH Hym.17.a.2326 ♂.
Type locality: Darwin, NT.

Distribution: N coastal, NT; known only from type locality.
Ecology: adult—volant; melliferous, solitary.
Reference: Cockerell, T.D.A. (1930). The bees of Australia. *Aust. Zool.* 6: 137–156, 205–236 (taxonomy).

Megachile (Eutricharaea) detersa Cockerell, 1910

Megachile detersa Cockerell, T.D.A. (1910). Descriptions and records of bees. XXXII. *Ann. Mag. Nat. Hist. (8)*6: 272–284 [283].
Type data: holotype, BMNH 17.a.2474 ♂ (described as ♀).
Type locality: Mackay, QLD.

Distribution: NE coastal, QLD; only published localities Mackay and Kuranda.
Ecology: adult—volant; melliferous, solitary.
References: Cockerell, T.D.A. (1911). Descriptions and records of bees. XXXV. *Ann. Mag. Nat. Hist. (8)*7: 310–319 (description of male, as *Androgynella detersa* (Cockerell, 1910)); Cockerell, T.D.A. (1930). The bees of Australia. *Aust. Zool.* 6: 137–156, 205–236 (taxonomy).

Megachile (Eutricharaea) gahani Cockerell, 1906

Megachile gahani Cockerell, T.D.A. (1906). Descriptions and records of bees. XI. *Ann. Mag. Nat. Hist. (7)*17: 527–539 [537].
Type data: holotype, BMNH Hym.17.a.2282 ♂.
Type locality: Australia (as New Holland).

Distribution: Australia, known only from type locality, exact locality unknown.
Ecology: adult—volant; melliferous, solitary.
Reference: Cockerell, T.D.A. (1930). The bees of Australia. *Aust. Zool.* 6: 137–156, 205–236 (taxonomy).

Megachile (Eutricharaea) haematogastra Cockerell, 1921

Megachile haematogastra Cockerell, T.D.A. (1921). Australian bees in the Queensland Museum. *Mem. Qd Mus.* 7: 81–98 [90].
Type data: holotype, QM T2505 ♀.
Type locality: Cairns district, QLD.

Distribution: NE coastal, QLD; known only from type locality.
Ecology: adult—volant; melliferous, solitary.

Megachile (Eutricharaea) hampsoni Cockerell, 1906

Megachile hampsoni Cockerell, T.D.A. (1906). Descriptions and records of bees. XI. *Ann. Mag. Nat. Hist. (7)*17: 527–539 [533].
Type data: holotype, BMNH Hym.17.a.2376 ♀.
Type locality: Fremantle, WA.

Distribution: SW coastal, WA; only published localities Fremantle and Yallingup.
Ecology: adult—volant; melliferous, solitary.
Reference: Meade-Waldo, G. (1915). Notes on the Apidae (Hymenoptera) in the collection of the British Museum, with descriptions of new species. VI. *Ann. Mag. Nat. Hist. (8)*15: 325–335 (distribution).

Megachile (Eutricharaea) ignescens Cockerell, 1929

Megachile ignescens Cockerell, T.D.A. (1929). Bees from the Australian region. *Am. Mus. Novit.* 346: 1–18 [6].
Type data: holotype, AMNH ♀*.
Type locality: Melville Is., NT.

Distribution: NE coastal, N coastal, QLD, NT; only published localities Townsville, Halifax, Melville Is. and Darwin.
Ecology: adult—volant; melliferous, solitary.
Reference: Cockerell, T.D.A. (1930). Australian bees in the Museum of Comparative Zoology. *Psyche (Camb.)* 37: 141–154 (distribution).

Megachile (Eutricharaea) kurandensis Cockerell, 1910

Megachile kurandensis Cockerell, T.D.A. (1910). Descriptions and records of bees. XXXIII. *Ann. Mag. Nat. Hist. (8)*6: 356–366 [359].
Type data: holotype, BMNH Hym.17.a.2382 ♂.
Type locality: Kuranda, QLD.

Distribution: NE coastal, QLD; known only from type locality.
Ecology: adult—volant; melliferous, solitary.

Megachile (Eutricharaea) kuschei Cockerell, 1939

Megachile kuschei Cockerell, T.D.A. (1939). Studies of the Pacific bees in the collection of Bishop Museum (Hymenoptera, Apoidea). *Occ. Pap. Bernice P. Bishop Mus.* 15: 133–140 [134].
Type data: holotype, BPBM ♂*.
Type locality: Prince of Wales Is., QLD.

Distribution: NE coastal, QLD; known only from type locality.
Ecology: adult—volant; melliferous, solitary.

Megachile (Eutricharaea) leucopogon Cockerell, 1929

Megachile leucopogon Cockerell, T.D.A. (1929). Bees from the Australian region. *Am. Mus. Novit.* 346: 1–18 [6].
Type data: holotype, AMNH ♂*.
Type locality: Darwin, NT.

Distribution: NE coastal, N coastal, QLD, NT; only published localities Thursday Is. and Darwin.
Ecology: adult—volant; melliferous, solitary.
Reference: Rayment, T. (1935). *A Cluster of Bees.* Sixty essays on the life-histories of Australian bees, with specific descriptions of over 100 new species, and an introduction by Professor E.F. Phillips, D.Ph., Cornell University, U.S.A. Sydney : Endeavour Press 752 pp. (illustration).

Megachile (Eutricharaea) lineatipes Cockerell, 1910

Megachile lineatipes Cockerell, T.D.A. (1910). Descriptions and records of bees. XXXIII. *Ann. Mag. Nat. Hist. (8)6*: 356–366 [364].
Type data: holotype, BMNH Hym.17.a.2401 ♂.
Type locality: Kuranda (as Cairns Kuranda), QLD.

Distribution: NE coastal, QLD; known only from type locality.
Ecology: adult—volant; melliferous, solitary.
References: Rayment, T. (1935). *A Cluster of Bees.* Sixty essays on the life-histories of Australian bees, with specific descriptions of over 100 new species, and an introduction by Professor E.F. Phillips, D.Ph., Cornell University, U.S.A. Sydney : Endeavour Press 752 pp. (illustration); Rayment, T. (1956). Some have eyes—others have none. *Proc. R. Zool. Soc. N.S.W.* **1954–1955**: 50–54 (illustration).

Megachile (Eutricharaea) macularis Dalla Torre, 1896

Megachile maculata Smith, F. (1853). *Catalogue of Hymenopterous Insects in the Collection of the British Museum.* Part I. Andrenidae and Apidae. London : British Museum 197 pp. [170] [junior primary homonym of *Megachile maculata* Smith, 1853: 160].
Type data: syntypes, BMNH ♂♀ (female specimen is labelled 'type' and has registration number Hym.17.a.2440).
Type locality: WA.
Megachile macularis Dalla Torre, K.W. (1896). *Catalogus Hymenopterorum Hucusque Descriptorum Systematicus et Synonymicus.* Apidae (Anthophila). Lipsiae : G. Engelmann Vol. x 643 pp. [437] [*nom. nov.* for *Megachile maculata* Smith, 1853: 170].

Distribution: NE coastal, Murray-Darling basin, SE coastal, SW coastal, QLD, NSW, VIC, WA.
Ecology: adult—volant; melliferous, solitary, nest of cut leaves (lucerne, *Desmodium* Desv. [Fabaceae])—between stems at plant bases in cages, in crack in tree stump, in holes in soil, flower visiting record: lucerne, *Bursaria* Cav. [Pittosporaceae], *Daviesia* Sm. [Fabaceae], *Jacksonia* Smith [Fabaceae], *Lotononis* (DC) Ecklon & Zeyher [Fabaceae], *Wahlenbergia* Roth [Campanulaceae].
References: Cockerell, T.D.A. (1913). Bees of the genus *Megachile* from Australia. *Entomologist* **46**: 164–168 (distribution); Cockerell, T.D.A. (1914). Descriptions and records of bees. LXIV. *Ann. Mag.*

Nat. Hist. (8)14: 464–472 (taxonomy); Hacker, H. (1915). Notes on the genus *Megachile* and some rare insects collected during 1913–14. *Mem. Qd Mus.* **3**: 137–141 (flower record); Rayment, T. (1928). Studies of Australian bees. I. The leaf-cutting bees (*Megachile macularis*, Dalla Torre, and other species). II. The clay-bees. (*Lithurgus atratiformis*, Cockerell). *Vict. Nat.* **45**: 79–86 (biology); Cockerell, T.D.A. (1930). The bees of Australia. *Aust. Zool.* **6**: 137–156, 205–236 (taxonomy); Rayment, T. (1931). Bees in the collections of the Western Australian Museum and the Agricultural Department, Perth. *J. Proc. R. Soc. West. Aust.* **17**: 157–190 (distribution); Rayment, T. (1935). *A Cluster of Bees.* Sixty essays on the life-histories of Australian bees, with specific descriptions of over 100 new species, and an introduction by Professor E.F. Phillips, D.Ph., Cornell University, U.S.A. Sydney : Endeavour Press 752 pp. (biology); Bray, R.A. (1973). Characteristics of some bees of the family Megachilidae in southeast Queensland and their potential as lucerne pollinators. *J. Aust. Entomol. Soc.* **12**: 99–102 (biology); King, J. (1984). Immature stages of some Megachilidae (Hymenoptera : Apoidea). *J. Aust. Entomol. Soc.* **23**: 51–57 (immature stages).

Megachile (Eutricharaea) obtusa Smith, 1853

Megachile obtusa Smith, F. (1853). *Catalogue of Hymenopterous Insects in the Collection of the British Museum.* Part I. Andrenidae and Apidae. London : British Museum 197 pp. [170].
Type data: holotype (probable), OUM ♂.
Type locality: WA.

Distribution: SW coastal, WA; only published locality Yallingup.
Ecology: adult—volant; melliferous, solitary.
Reference: Meade-Waldo, G. (1915). Notes on the Apidae (Hymenoptera) in the collection of the British Museum, with descriptions of new species. VI. *Ann. Mag. Nat. Hist. (8)15*: 325–335 (distribution).

Megachile (Eutricharaea) phenacopyga Cockerell, 1910

Megachile phenacopyga Cockerell, T.D.A. (1910). Some Australian bees in the Berlin Museum. *J. N.Y. Entomol. Soc.* **18**: 98–114 [109].
Type data: holotype, ZMB 1004 ♂*.
Type locality: Eastern Australia (this label may be an error for Western Australia), see Cockerell, T.D.A. (1930). The bees of Australia. *Aust. Zool.* **6**: 137–156, 205–236 [229, note under *Megachile preissi* Cockerell, 1910].

Distribution: SE coastal, SW coastal, VIC, WA; only published localities Broadmeadows (as Broad Meadows) and Waroona.
Ecology: adult—volant; melliferous, solitary.
References: Cockerell, T.D.A. (1913). Bees of the genus *Megachile* from Australia. *Entomologist* **46**: 164–168 (taxonomy); Cockerell, T.D.A. (1926). De-

scriptions and records of bees. CXII. *Ann. Mag. Nat. Hist. (9)***18**: 216–227 (taxonomy).

Megachile (Eutricharaea) pictiventris Smith, 1879

Megachile senex Smith, F. (1862). Descriptions of new species of Australian Hymenoptera, and of a species of *Formica* from New Zealand. *Trans. Entomol. Soc. Lond. (3)***1**: 53–62 [61] [junior primary homonym of *Megachile senex* Smith, 1853].
Type data: syntypes, OUM 2♀*.
Type locality: Richmond River, NSW.
Megachile pictiventris Smith, F. (1879). *Descriptions of New Species of Hymenoptera in the Collection of the British Museum.* London : British Museum xxi 240 pp. [65].
Type data: holotype, BMNH Hym.17.a.2399 ♀.
Type locality: Richmond River, NSW.
Megachile secunda Dalla Torre, K.W. (1896). *Catalogus Hymenopterorum Hucusque Descriptorum Systematicus et Synonymicus.* Apidae (Anthophila). Lipsiae : G. Engelmann Vol. x 643 pp. [448] [*nom. nov.* for *Megachile senex* Smith, 1862].

Taxonomic decision for synonymy: Cockerell, T.D.A. (1906). Descriptions and records of bees. XI. *Ann. Mag. Nat. Hist. (7)***17**: 527–539 [530].

Distribution: NE coastal, SE coastal, QLD, NSW; also recorded from New Guinea.
Ecology: adult—volant; melliferous, solitary, flower visiting record: lucerne, *Duranta* L. [Verbenaceae].
References: Friese, H. (1909). Die Bienenfauna von Neu-Guinea. *Ann. Hist.-Nat. Mus. Natl. Hung.* **7**: 179–288 (distribution); Hacker, H. (1915). Notes on the genus *Megachile* and some rare insects collected during 1913–14. *Mem. Qd Mus.* **3**: 137–141 (flower record); Cockerell, T.D.A. (1930). Australian bees in the Museum of Comparative Zoology. *Psyche (Camb.)* **37**: 141–154 (distribution); Cockerell, T.D.A. (1930). The bees of Australia. *Aust. Zool.* **6**: 137–156, 205–236 (taxonomy); Bray, R.A. (1973). Characteristics of some bees of the family Megachilidae in southeast Queensland and their potential as lucerne pollinators. *J. Aust. Entomol. Soc.* **12**: 99–102 (flower record).

Megachile (Eutricharaea) quinquelineata Cockerell, 1906

Megachile quinquelineata Cockerell, T.D.A. (1906). Descriptions and records of bees. XI. *Ann. Mag. Nat. Hist. (7)***17**: 527–539 [534].
Type data: holotype, BMNH Hym.17.a.2360 ♀.
Type locality: Mackay, QLD.
Megachile glaberrima Friese, H. (1911). Zur Bienenfauna Neuguineas und der benachbarten Gebiete (Hym.) (Nachtrag II). *Dtsch. Entomol. Zeit.* **1911**: 448–453 [452].
Type data: syntypes (probable), whereabouts unknown ♂♀*.
Type locality: Cairns, Mackay and Kuranda (as Curanda), QLD.

Taxonomic decision for synonymy: Cockerell, T.D.A. (1929). Bees, chiefly Australian species, described or determined by Dr. H. Friese. [7].

Distribution: NE coastal, SE coastal, Murray-Darling basin, SW coastal, QLD, NSW, VIC, SA, WA.
Ecology: adult—volant; melliferous, solitary, nest of cut leaves in ground, using burrows originally formed by spiders, flower visiting record: heliotrope, lucerne, *Daviesia* Sm. [Fabaceae], *Pongamia* Vent. [Fabaceae].
References: Cockerell, T.D.A. (1912). Descriptions and records of bees. XLII. *Ann. Mag. Nat. Hist. (8)***9**: 220–229 (distribution, as *Megachile glaberrima* Friese, 1911); Meade-Waldo, G. (1915). Notes on the Apidae (Hymenoptera) in the collection of the British Museum, with descriptions of new species. VI. *Ann. Mag. Nat. Hist. (8)***15**: 325–335 (distribution); Tillyard, R.J. (1926). *The Insects of Australia and New Zealand.* Sydney : Angus & Robertson 560 pp. (illustration); Cockerell, T.D.A. (1930). The bees of Australia. *Aust. Zool.* **6**: 137–156, 205–236 (distribution); Rayment, T. (1954). Incidence of acarid mites on the biology of bees. *Aust. Zool.* **12**: 26–38 (as host); Doull, K.M. (1961). Insect problems of lucerne seed production in South Australia. *J. Aust. Inst. agric. Sci.* **27**: 11–15 (biology, as *Megachile quinquilineata*, incorrect subsequent spelling); Michener, C.D. (1965). A classification of the bees of the Australian and South Pacific regions. *Bull. Am. Mus. Nat. Hist.* **130**: 1–362 (flower record); Bray, R.A. (1973). Characteristics of some bees of the family Megachilidae in southeast Queensland and their potential as lucerne pollinators. *J. Aust. Entomol. Soc.* **12**: 99–102 (flower record).

Megachile (Eutricharaea) rhodogastra Cockerell, 1910

Megachile rhodogastra Cockerell, T.D.A. (1910). Descriptions and records of bees. XXXII. *Ann. Mag. Nat. Hist. (8)***6**: 272–284 [283].
Type data: holotype, BMNH Hym.17.a.2398 ♂.
Type locality: Mackay, QLD.

Distribution: NE coastal, QLD; only published localities Mackay, Brisbane, Townsville, Halifax and Prince of Wales Is.
Ecology: adult—volant; melliferous, solitary, nest of leaves (of *Bauhinia* L. [Caesalpiniaceae], *Desmodium* Desv. [Fabaceae], *Mallotus* Lour. [Euphorbiaceae], roses), in pre-existing holes (in iron pipe, tree stump, fence post, drilled wooden blocks), flower visiting record: lucerne, *Pongamia* Vent. [Fabaceae].
References: Hacker, H. (1915). Notes on the genus *Megachile* and some rare insects collected during 1913–14. *Mem. Qd Mus.* **3**: 137–141 (nest); Hacker, H. (1918). Entomological contributions. *Mem. Qd Mus.* **6**: 106–111 pls 31–32 (biology); Cockerell, T.D.A. (1922). Descriptions and records of bees. XCV. *Ann. Mag. Nat. Hist. (9)***10**: 265–269 (descrip-

tion of female); Cockerell, T.D.A. (1929). Bees from the Australian region. *Am. Mus. Novit.* **346**: 1–18 (taxonomy); Cockerell, T.D.A. (1929). Bees in the Queensland Museum. *Mem. Qd Mus.* **9**: 298–323 (taxonomy); Cockerell, T.D.A. (1930). Australian bees in the Museum of Comparative Zoology. *Psyche (Camb.)* **37**: 141–154 (distribution); Rayment, T. (1935). *A Cluster of Bees.* Sixty essays on the life-histories of Australian bees, with specific descriptions of over 100 new species, and an introduction by Professor E.F. Phillips, D.Ph., Cornell University, U.S.A. Sydney : Endeavour Press 752 pp. (biology); Cockerell, T.D.A. (1939). Studies of the Pacific bees in the collection of Bishop Museum (Hymenoptera, Apoidea). *Occ. Pap. Bernice P. Bishop Mus.* **15**: 133–140 (distribution); Michener, C.D. (1965). A classification of the bees of the Australian and South Pacific regions. *Bull. Am. Mus. Nat. Hist.* **130**: 1–362 (flower record); Bray, R.A. (1973). Characteristics of some bees of the family Megachilidae in southeast Queensland and their potential as lucerne pollinators. *J. Aust. Entomol. Soc.* **12**: 99–102 (biology).

Megachile (Eutricharaea) rotundata (Fabricius, 1787)

Apis rotundata Fabricius, J.C. (1787). *Mantissa Insectorum* sistens eorum species nuper detectas adiectis characteribus genericus, differentiis specificis, emendationibus, observationibus. Hafniae : C.G. Proft Tom. I. 348 pp. [303] [before 1978, this species was misidentified as *Megachile pacifica* (Panzer, 1798)].
Type data: neotype, ZMK ♀*.
Subsequent designation: International Commission on Zoological Nomenclature (1977). Opinion 1093. Designation under the plenary powers of a neotype for *Apis rotundata* Fabricius, 1787 (Insecta, Hymenoptera). *Bull. Zool. Nomen.* **34**: 143–146 [143].
Type locality: W Hungary, see Roberts, R.B. (1978). *Megachile rotundata* (Fabricius), not *Megachile pacifica* (Panzer), is the name of the alfalfa leafcutting bee (Hymenoptera, Megachilidae). *Bull. Entomol. Soc. Amer.* **24**: 392 [392].

Distribution: S Gulfs, SA; introduced into Australia from New Zealand and released in SA in March 1987, established probably (1993), a native of the Palaearctic Region which has been introduced to all continents except Antarctica.
Ecology: adult– volant; melliferous, solitary, nest of cut leaves in pre-existing cavities (natural or artificial galleries in wood or other materials, *e.g.* trap nests), flower visiting record: lucerne.
References: Fearn, J.T. (1974). A quarantine success story. The problems of importing leafcutter bees. *Anim. Quarantine* **3**(3): 10–15 (first importation to Australia, not released); Fearn, J.T. (1974). Chalk brood in imported leafcutter bees. *Am. Bee J.* **114**: 209 (first importation to Australia, not released); Doull, K.M. (1976). Termination of the leafcutter bee project. *Australas. Beekpr* **77**: 271–272 (second im-

portation to Australia, not released); Briggs, L. (1983). Importation of leafcutter bees from New Zealand. *Australas. Beekpr* **85**: 28–29 (conditions for entry to Australia); Anon. (1987). Leafcutter bees released in S.A. *Australas. Beekpr* **88**: 175 (released in Australia); Altmann, J. (1987). Pollination of lucerne (*Medicago sativa*). *Australas. Beekpr* **88**: 240–247 (bibliography); Whitfield, G.H., Richards, K.W. & Kveder, T.M. (1987). Number of instars of larvae of the alfalfa leafcutter bee, *Megachile rotundata* (F.) (Hymenoptera : Megachilidae). *Can. Entomol.* **119**: 859–865 (larval instars); Winn, B. (1988). Importation and release of leafcutter bees in South Australia. pp. 209–210 *in* Rhodes, J.W. (ed.) *Bee keeping in the year 2000*. Second Australian and International Beekeeping Congress. Surfers Paradise, Gold Coast, Queensland, Australia. July 21–26 (release in SA); Hurd, P.D. (1979). Superfamily Apoidea. pp. 1741–2209 *in* Krombein, K.V., Hurd, P.D., Smith, D.R. & Burks, B.D. (eds) (1979). *Catalog of Hymenoptera in America North of Mexico.* Vol. 2. Washington : Smithsonian Institution (misidentified as *Megachile pacifica* by many authors (Panzer, 1798)); Woodward, D. (1993). Lucerne pollination service. *Australas. Beekpr.* **94**: 336–338, 340–341 (spread in SA).

Megachile (Eutricharaea) rowlandi Cockerell, 1930

Megachile rowlandi Cockerell, T.D.A. (1930). Australian bees in the Museum of Comparative Zoology. *Psyche (Camb.)* **37**: 141–154 [143].
Type data: holotype, USNM ♀*.
Type locality: Mackay, QLD.

Distribution: NE coastal, QLD; known only from type locality.
Ecology: adult—volant; melliferous, solitary.

Megachile (Eutricharaea) rufopilosa Friese, 1911

Megachile rufopilosa Friese, H. (1911). Zur Bienenfauna Neuguineas und der benachbarten Gebiete (Hym.) (Nachtrag II). *Dtsch. Entomol. Zeit.* **1911**: 448–453 [453].
Type data: holotype, whereabouts unknown ♂*.
Type locality: Fremantle, WA.

Distribution: SW coastal, WA; known only from type locality.
Ecology: adult—volant; melliferous, solitary.

Megachile (Eutricharaea) sequior Cockerell, 1910

Megachile sequior Cockerell, T.D.A. (1910). Some Australian bees in the Berlin Museum. *J. N.Y. Entomol. Soc.* **18**: 98–114 [108].
Type data: holotype, ZMB 20640 ♂*.
Type locality: Adelaide, SA (the label is probably in error, the species is believed to come from Darwin), see Cockerell, T.D.A. (1930). The bees of Australia. *Aust. Zool.* **6**: 137–156, 205–236 [232].

Distribution: NE coastal, (S Gulfs), NW coastal, N coastal, QLD, (SA), WA, NT; only published localities Eidsvold, (Adelaide), NW Australia and Darwin.

Ecology: adult—volant; melliferous, solitary.
References: Cockerell, T.D.A. (1910). Descriptions and records of bees. XXXII. *Ann. Mag. Nat. Hist. (8)*6: 272–284 (description of female); Cockerell, T.D.A. (1921). Australian bees in the Queensland Museum. *Mem. Qd Mus.* 7: 81–98 (distribution); Cockerell, T.D.A. (1929). Bees from the Australian region. *Am. Mus. Novit.* 346: 1–18 (distribution).

Megachile (Eutricharaea) serricauda Cockerell, 1910

Megachile serricauda Cockerell, T.D.A. (1910). Descriptions and records of bees. XXXIII. *Ann. Mag. Nat. Hist. (8)*6: 356–366 [361].
Type data: holotype, BMNH Hym.17.a.2322 ♂.
Type locality: Mackay, QLD.

Distribution: NE coastal, Murray-Darling basin, SW coastal, QLD, NSW, VIC, WA; also in the New Hebrides (presumably introduced).
Ecology: adult—volant; melliferous, solitary, nest of cut leaves, flower visiting record: *Mesembryanthemum* L. [Aizoaceae].
References: Cockerell, T.D.A. (1913). Bees of the genus *Megachile* from Australia. *Entomologist* 46: 164–168 (distribution); Cockerell, T.D.A. (1914). Descriptions and records of bees. LXIV. *Ann. Mag. Nat. Hist. (8)*14: 464–472 (New Hebrides); Hacker, H. (1915). Notes on the genus *Megachile* and some rare insects collected during 1913–14. *Mem. Qd Mus.* 3: 137–141 (flower record); Meade-Waldo, G. (1915). Notes on the Apidae (Hymenoptera) in the collection of the British Museum, with descriptions of new species. VI. *Ann. Mag. Nat. Hist. (8)*15: 325–335 (distribution); Rayment, T. (1934). Contributions to the fauna of Rottnest Island. VIII. Apoidea. With description of new species. *J. Proc. R. Soc. West. Aust.* 20: 201–212 (illustration); Rayment, T. (1935). *A Cluster of Bees.* Sixty essays on the life-histories of Australian bees, with specific descriptions of over 100 new species, and an introduction by Professor E.F. Phillips, D.Ph., Cornell University, U.S.A. Sydney : Endeavour Press 752 pp. (misidentification of *Megachile subsericeicauda* Rayment, 1939); Rayment, T. (1939). Bees from the high lands of New South Wales and Victoria. *Aust. Zool.* 9: 263–294 (taxonomy).

Megachile (Eutricharaea) simplex Smith, 1853

Megachile simplex Smith, F. (1853). *Catalogue of Hymenopterous Insects in the Collection of the British Museum. Part I. Andrenidae and Apidae.* London : British Museum 197 pp. [169].
Type data: holotype, BMNH Hym.17.a.2386 ♀.
Type locality: Australia (as New Holland).

Distribution: NE coastal, SE coastal, QLD, VIC; only published localities Brisbane and Ararat.
Ecology: adult—volant; melliferous, solitary, flower visiting record: *Daviesia* Sm. [Fabaceae].

References: Cockerell, T.D.A. (1913). Descriptions and records of bees. LII. *Ann. Mag. Nat. Hist. (8)*11: 530–542 (distribution); Hacker, H. (1915). Notes on the genus *Megachile* and some rare insects collected during 1913–14. *Mem. Qd Mus.* 3: 137–141 (flower record); Cockerell, T.D.A. (1930). The bees of Australia. *Aust. Zool.* 6: 137–156, 205–236 (taxonomy).

Megachile (Eutricharaea) subsericeicauda Rayment, 1939

Megachile subsericeicauda Rayment, T. (1939). Bees from the high lands of New South Wales and Victoria. *Aust. Zool.* 9: 263–294 [287].
Type data: holotype, ANIC ♂.
Type locality: Sydney, NSW.

Distribution: SE coastal, NSW; known only from type locality.
Ecology: adult—volant; melliferous, solitary.
Reference: Rayment, T. (1935). *A Cluster of Bees.* Sixty essays on the life-histories of Australian bees, with specific descriptions of over 100 new species, and an introduction by Professor E.F. Phillips, D.Ph., Cornell University, U.S.A. Sydney : Endeavour Press 752 pp. (description of female, as *Megachile serricauda* Cockerell, 1910).

Megachile (Eutricharaea) tenuicincta Cockerell, 1929

Megachile tenuicincta Cockerell, T.D.A. (1929). Bees from the Australian region. *Am. Mus. Novit.* 346: 1–18 [7].
Type data: holotype, AMNH ♀*.
Type locality: 30 miles E Darwin, NT.

Distribution: N coastal, NT; only published localities Darwin and vicinity.
Ecology: adult—volant; melliferous, solitary.

Megachile (Eutricharaea) waterhousei Cockerell, 1906

Megachile waterhousei Cockerell, T.D.A. (1906). Descriptions and records of bees. XI. *Ann. Mag. Nat. Hist. (7)*17: 527–539 [534].
Type data: holotype, BMNH Hym.17.a.2394 ♀.
Type locality: Mackay, QLD.

Distribution: NE coastal, QLD; known only from type locality.
Ecology: adult—volant; melliferous, solitary.

Megachile (Eutricharaea) wyndhamensis Rayment, 1935

Megachile wyndhamensis Rayment, T. (1935). *A Cluster of Bees.* Sixty essays on the life-histories of Australian bees, with specific descriptions of over 100 new species, and an introduction by Professor E.F. Phillips, D.Ph., Cornell University, U.S.A. Sydney : Endeavour Press 752 pp. [714].
Type data: holotype, ANIC ♀.
Type locality: Wyndham, WA.

Distribution: N coastal, WA; known only from type locality.

Ecology: adult—volant; melliferous, solitary.

Megachile (Mitchellapis) Michener, 1965

Mitchellapis Michener, C.D. (1965). A classification of the bees of the Australian and South Pacific regions. *Bull. Am. Mus. Nat. Hist.* **130**: 1–362 [211] [proposed with subgeneric rank in *Megachile* Latreille, 1802]. Type species: *Megachile fabricator* Smith, 1868 by original designation.

Megachile (Mitchellapis) batchelori Cockerell, 1929

Megachile batchelori Cockerell, T.D.A. (1929). Bees in the Queensland Museum. *Mem. Qd Mus.* **9**: 298–323 [304].
Type data: holotype, QM Hy/4021 ♀.
Type locality: Hughenden, QLD.

Distribution: N Gulf, QLD; known only from type locality.

Ecology: adult—volant; melliferous, solitary.

Megachile (Mitchellapis) conaminis Cockerell, 1926

Megachile (Eumegachile) conaminis Cockerell, T.D.A. (1926). Descriptions and records of bees. CX. *Ann. Mag. Nat. Hist. (9)***17**: 510–519 [512].
Type data: holotype, NMV ♀.
Type locality: Endeavour River, QLD.

Distribution: NE coastal, QLD; known only from type locality.

Ecology: adult—volant; melliferous, solitary.

Megachile (Mitchellapis) fabricator Smith, 1868

Megachile fabricator Smith, F. (1868). Descriptions of aculeate Hymenoptera from Australia. *Trans. Entomol. Soc. Lond.* **1868**: 231–258 [256].
Type data: syntypes, BMNH ♂♀ (a female is labelled 'type' and has registration number Hym.17.a.2315).
Type locality: Geraldton (as Champion Bay), WA.

Distribution: SW coastal, NW coastal, WA; only published localities Kalamunda, Perth and Geraldton (as Champion Bay).

Ecology: adult—volant; melliferous, solitary.

Reference: Meade-Waldo, G. (1915). Notes on the Apidae (Hymenoptera) in the collection of the British Museum, with descriptions of new species. VI. *Ann. Mag. Nat. Hist. (8)***15**: 325–335 (distribution).

Megachile (Mitchellapis) fuscitarsis Cockerell, 1912

Megachile fuscitarsis Cockerell, T.D.A. (1912). Descriptions and records of bees. XLII. *Ann. Mag. Nat. Hist. (8)***9**: 220–229 [223].
Type data: holotype, BMNH Hym.17.a.2387 ♂.
Type locality: QLD.

Distribution: QLD; known only from type locality, exact locality unknown.

Ecology: adult—volant; melliferous, solitary.

Megachile (Mitchellapis) semiclara Cockerell, 1929

Megachile semiclara Cockerell, T.D.A. (1929). Bees in the Queensland Museum. *Mem. Qd Mus.* **9**: 298–323 [303].
Type data: holotype, QM Hy/4022 ♀.
Type locality: Cairns, QLD.

Distribution: NE coastal, QLD; known only from type locality.

Ecology: adult—volant; melliferous, solitary.

Megachile (Mitchellapis) vestitor Cockerell, 1910

Megachile vestitor Cockerell, T.D.A. (1910). Some Australian bees in the Berlin Museum. *J. N.Y. Entomol. Soc.* **18**: 98–114 [109].
Type data: holotype, ZMB 1002 ♂*.
Type locality: Eastern Australia (this label may be an error for Western Australia), see Cockerell, T.D.A. (1930). The bees of Australia. *Aust. Zool.* **6**: 137–156, 205–236 [229, note under *Megachile preissi* Cockerll, 1910].

Distribution: WA; only published localities "E Australia" and WA.

Ecology: adult—volant; melliferous, solitary.

Reference: Cockerell, T.D.A. (1913). Descriptions and records of bees. LII. *Ann. Mag. Nat. Hist. (8)***11**: 530–542 (taxonomy).

Megachile (Unplaced)

Megachile adelaidae Cockerell, 1910

Megachile adelaidae Cockerell, T.D.A. (1910). Some Australian bees in the Berlin Museum. *J. N.Y. Entomol. Soc.* **18**: 98–114 [111].
Type data: syntypes (probable), ZMB 19410 2♀*.
Type locality: Adelaide, SA.

Distribution: S Gulfs, NW coastal, WA; only published localities Adelaide and Mullewa.

Ecology: adult—volant; melliferous, solitary.

References: Rayment, T. (1931). Bees in the collections of the Western Australian Museum and the Agricultural Department, Perth. *J. Proc. R. Soc. West. Aust.* **17**: 157–190 (variety); Michener, C.D. (1965). A classification of the bees of the Australian and South Pacific regions. *Bull. Am. Mus. Nat. Hist.* **130**: 1–362 (taxonomy).

Megachile castaneipes Friese, 1908

Megachile annae castaneipes Friese, H. (1908). Hymenoptera. II. Apidae. Nova Guinea. pp. 353–359 pl. XV *in* Wichmann, A. *Résultats de L'Expedition Scientifique Néerlandaise à la Nouvelle Guinée en 1903*. Leiden : E.J. Brill [357] [illustration, pl. XV fig. 10, on page following 360 is not referred to in description].
Type data: holotype (probable), whereabouts unknown ♀*.
Type locality: Cairns, QLD.

Distribution: NE coastal, QLD; known only from type locality.

Ecology: adult—volant; melliferous, solitary.

Reference: Michener, C.D. (1965). A classification of

the bees of the Australian and South Pacific regions. *Bull. Am. Mus. Nat. Hist.* **130**: 1–362 (taxonomy).

Megachile swarbrecki Rayment, 1946

Megachile macularis swarbrecki Rayment, T. (1946). Native bees on Mount Buffalo. With description of a new subspecies. *Vict. Nat.* **63**: 23–24 [24].
Type data: holotype, whereabouts unknown ♀* (not located in T. Rayment coll. transferred to ANIC).
Type locality: Mt Buffalo, VIC.

Distribution: Murray-Darling basin, VIC; known only from type locality.
Ecology: adult—volant; melliferous, solitary, flower visiting record: *Podolepis* Labill. [Asteraceae].
Reference: Michener, C.D. (1965). A classification of the bees of the Australian and South Pacific regions. *Bull. Am. Mus. Nat. Hist.* **130**: 1–362 (taxonomy).

Thaumatosoma Smith, 1865

Thaumatosoma Smith, F. (1865). Descriptions of some new species of hymenopterous insects belonging to the families Thynnidae, Masaridae, and Apidae. *Trans. Entomol. Soc. Lond.* (3)**2**: 389–399 [394]. Type species: *Thaumatosoma duboulaii* Smith, 1865 by monotypy.

Thaumatosoma duboulaii Smith, 1865

Thaumatosoma duboulaii Smith, F. (1865). Descriptions of some new species of hymenopterous insects belonging to the families Thynnidae, Masaridae, and Apidae. *Trans. Entomol. Soc. Lond.* (3)**2**: 389–399 [395].
Type data: holotype, BMNH Hym.17.a.2580 ♂.
Type locality: Swan River, WA, see Smith, F. (1865). Observations on the genus *Dorylus*, and upon a new genus of Apidae. *Entomol. Mon. Mag.* **2**: 3–5 [3] (as *Thaumatosoma duboulayi*).

Distribution: SW coastal, NW coastal, WA.
Ecology: adult—volant; melliferous, solitary, flower visiting record: *Goodenia* Sm. [Goodeniaceae], *Scaevola* L. [Goodeniaceae].
References: Meade-Waldo, G. (1915). Notes on the Apidae (Hymenoptera) in the collection of the British Museum, with descriptions of new species. VI. *Ann. Mag. Nat. Hist.* (8)**15**: 325–335 (description of female, as *Thaumatosoma duboulayi*); Cockerell, T.D.A. (1930). The bees of Australia. *Aust. Zool.* **6**: 137–156, 205–236 (taxonomy); Michener, C.D. (1965). A classification of the bees of the Australian and South Pacific regions. *Bull. Am. Mus. Nat. Hist.* **130**: 1–362 (as *Chalicodoma (Thaumatosoma) duboulaii* (Smith, 1865)); King, J. & Exley, E.M. (1985). A reinstatement and revision of the genus *Thaumatosoma* Smith (Apoidea : Megachilidae). *J. Aust. Entomol. Soc.* **24**: 87–92 (generic placement, redescription, distribution).

Thaumatosoma remeata (Cockerell, 1913)

Megachile remeata Cockerell, T.D.A. (1913). Descriptions and records of bees. LII. *Ann. Mag. Nat. Hist.* (8)**11**: 530–542 [538].
Type data: holotype, BMNH Hym.17.a.2339 ♀.
Type locality: WA.

Distribution: Murray-Darling basin, S Gulfs, Lake Eyre basin, W plateau, SW coastal, NW coastal, NSW, SA, WA.
Ecology: adult—volant; melliferous, solitary, flower visiting record: (*Diuris* Sm. [Orchidaceae]), *Eremophila* R.Br. [Myoporaceae].
References: Rayment, T. (1950). A new and remarkable organ on a resin-bee. *Vict. Nat.* **66**: 163–168 (description of male, doubtful record); Erickson, R. (1951). *Orchids of the West.* Perth : Paterson Brokensha 109 pp. (flower record); Erickson, R. (1965). *Orchids of the West.* 2nd edn. Perth : Paterson Brokensha 107 pp. (flower record); Michener, C.D. (1965). A classification of the bees of the Australian and South Pacific regions. *Bull. Am. Mus. Nat. Hist.* **130**: 1–362 (as *Chalicodoma (Hackeriapis) remeata* (Cockerell, 1913)); King, J. & Exley, E.M. (1985). A reinstatement and revision of the genus *Thaumatosoma* Smith (Apoidea : Megachilidae). *J. Aust. Entomol. Soc.* **24**: 87–92 (generic placement, redescription, distribution).

Incertae sedis

Megachile nivescens Kirby, W.F. (1900). Hymenoptera. pp. 81–88 *in* Andrews, C.W. *A Monograph of Christmas Island (Indian Ocean)*: physical features and geology; with descriptions of the fauna and flora by numerous contributors. London : British Museum 337+20 pp. [88].
Type data: syntypes, BMNH ♂♀ (12 specimens, numbers of each sex unknown, a female specimen is labelled 'type' and has registration number Hym.17.a.2502).
Type locality: Christmas Is.

Megachile rotundipennis Kirby, W.F. (1900). Hymenoptera. pp. 81–88 *in* Andrews, C.W. *A Monograph of Christmas Island (Indian Ocean)*: physical features and geology; with descriptions of the fauna and flora by numerous contributors. London : British Museum 337+20 pp. [87].
Type data: syntypes, BMNH 5♂1♀ (a male specimen is labelled 'type' and has registration number Hym.17.a.2068b).
Type locality: Christmas Is.

Megachile deanii Rayment, T. (1935). *A Cluster of Bees.* Sixty essays on the life-histories of Australian bees, with specific descriptions of over 100 new species, and an introduction by Professor E.F. Phillips, D.Ph., Cornell University, U.S.A. Sydney : Endeavour Press 752 pp. [716].
Type data: holotype, ANIC ♀.
Type locality: Mt Tamborine, QLD.

Megachile subatrella Rayment, T. (1939). Bees from the high lands of New South Wales and Victoria. *Aust. Zool.* **9**: 263–294 [284].
Type data: holotype, whereabouts unknown (T. Rayment, pers. coll., not found in ANIC) ♀*.
Type locality: Inverell, NSW.

ANTHOPHORIDAE

INTRODUCTION

This family of long-tongued bees is divided into three subfamilies: Anthophorinae, Nomadinae and Xylocopinae. All three subfamilies are represented in Australia but the species diversity is poor compared to that in other parts of the world. Adults have a distinctive wing venation. Except in cleptoparasitic species, the females have scopae on the hind legs. The evolution of cleptoparasitism in the family was studied by Rozen (1991). Flower visiting records are given in Michener (1965a) and Armstrong (1979).

The Anthophorinae are represented in Australia by two tribes, Anthophorini and Melectini, neither of which is found in Tasmania. The Anthophorini (Brooks 1988) are medium to large (8–20 mm), robust, hairy bees with scopae on the hind legs. Adults are solitary but often nest in aggregations, usually in the soil (Michener 1960; Cardale 1968a, 1968b; Houston 1991). The Melectini are moderate to large (8–13 mm), robust bees. They lack scopae on the hind legs and are cleptoparasitic on the Anthophorini (Cardale 1968c; Lieftinck 1958, 1959, 1962). Larvae of Australian species were described by Cardale (1968d).

Amegilla cingulata   [by M. Quick]

The Nomadinae are cosmopolitan in distribution. There are numerous tribes and genera (Alexander 1990, 1991; Roig-Alsina 1991) but, in Australia, the subfamily is represented only by the genus *Nomada*. Australian species are small (*c.* 6 mm) and slender, sparsely haired and lack a scopa. The biology of Australian species is not known but elsewhere members of the genus are parasitic.

The subfamily Xylocopinae has a cosmopolitan distribution and is represented in Australia by three tribes (Sakagami & Michener 1987). The Xylocopini, the carpenter bees (Hurd & Moure 1963), are the largest (12–20 mm), most robust of the native bees in Australia. Adults carry pollen externally in scopae on the hind legs. They excavate burrows in dead wood or in dead flower stems of *Xanthorrhoea* (Gerling *et al.* 1989; Houston 1974, 1992). The Ceratinini are small (3–5 mm), sparsely haired bees represented by one species in Australia, which is found in Queensland and New South Wales. Adults nest in pithy stems (Michener 1962). The Allodapini (Michener 1977) are small (3–8 mm), sparsely haired bees which nest in pithy stems or in pre-existing holes in wood. They are unique among bees in not constructing brood cells. The larvae are reared together and fed progressively. Several females may be found in one nest and at least some species are primitively social, with differential egg-laying and foraging by individual females of one nest (Houston 1977; Schwarz 1986, 1987, 1988a, 1988b; Schwarz & O'Keefe 1991; Schwarz *et al.* 1987). Some species are parasitic on others within the tribe (Michener 1965a, 1965b, 1966, 1983). Eggs were described by Michener (1973), larvae by Syed (1963), Michener & Syed (1962) and Houston (1976) and pupae by Michener & Scheiring (1976).

References

Alexander, B. (1990). A cladistic analysis of the nomadine bees (Hymenoptera: Apoidea). *Syst. Entomol.* **15**: 121–152

Alexander, B. (1991). *Nomada* phylogeny reconsidered (Hymenoptera: Anthophoridae). *J. Nat. Hist.* **25**: 315–330

Armstrong, J.A. (1979). Biotic pollination mechanisms in the Australian flora—a review. *N.Z. J. Bot.* **17**: 467–508

Brooks, R.W. (1988). Systematics and phylogeny of the anthophorine bees (Hymenoptera: Anthophoridae; Anthophorini). *Univ. Kansas Sci. Bull.* **53**: 436–575

Cardale, J. (1968a). Nests and nesting behaviour of *Amegilla (Amegilla) pulchra* (Smith) (Hymenoptera : Apoidea : Anthophorinae). *Aust. J. Zool.* **16**: 689–707

Cardale, J. (1968b). Observations on nests and nesting behaviour of *Amegilla (Asaropoda)* sp. (Hymenoptera : Apoidea : Anthophorinae). *Aust. J. Zool.* **16**: 709–713

Cardale, J. (1968c). Parasites and other organisms associated with nests of *Amegilla* Friese (Hymenoptera : Anthophorinae). *J. Aust. Entomol. Soc.* **7**: 29–34

Cardale, J. (1968d). Immature stages of Australian Anthophorinae (Hymenoptera : Apoidea). *J. Aust. Entomol. Soc.* **7**: 35–41

Gerling, D., Velthuis, H.H.W. & Hefetz, A. (1989). Bionomics of the large carpenter bees of the genus *Xylocopa*. *Ann. Rev. Entomol.* **34**: 163–190

Houston, T.F. (1974). Notes on the behaviour of an Australian carpenter bee, genus *Xylocopa* Latr. (Hymenoptera : Xylocopinae). *Aust. Entomol. Mag.* **2**: 36–38

Houston, T.F. (1976). New Australian allodapine bees (subgenus *Exoneurella* Michener) and their immatures (Hymenoptera : Anthophoridae). *Trans. R. Soc. S. Aust.* **100**: 15–28

Houston, T.F. (1977). Nesting biology of three allodapine bees in the subgenus *Exoneurella* Michener (Hymenoptera : Anthophoridae). *Trans. R. Soc. S. Aust.* **101**: 99–113

Houston, T.F. (1991). Ecology and behaviour of the bee *Amegilla (Asaropoda) dawsoni* (Rayment) with notes on a related species (Hymenoptera: Anthophoridae). *Rec. West. Aust. Mus.* **15**: 535–553

Houston, T.F. (1992). Biological observations of the Australian green carpenter bees, genus *Lestis* (Hymenoptera: Anthophoridae: Xylocopini). *Rec. West. Aust. Mus.* **15**: 785–798

Hurd, P.D., Jr & Moure, J.S. (1963). A classification of the large carpenter bees (Xylocopini) (Hymenoptera : Apoidea). *Univ. Calif. Publ. Entomol.* **29**: 1–365

Lieftinck, M.A. (1958). Revision of the Indo-Australian species of the genus *Thyreus* Panzer (=*Crocisa* Jurine) (Hym., Apoidea, Anthophoridae). Part 1. Introduction and list of species. *Nova Guinea (ns)* **9**: 21–30

Lieftinck, M.A. (1959). Revision of the Indo-Australian species of the genus *Thyreus* Panzer (=*Crocisa* Jurine) (Hym., Apoidea, Anthophoridae). Part 2. *Thyreus nitidulus* (Fabricius). *Nova Guinea (ns)* **10**: 99–130

Lieftinck, M.A. (1962). Revision of the Indo-Australian species of the genus *Thyreus* Panzer (=*Crocisa* Jurine) (Hym., Apoidea, Anthophoridae). Part 3. Oriental and Australian species. *Zool. Verh.* **53**: 1–212

Michener, C.D. (1960). Observations on the behaviour of a burrowing bee (*Amegilla*) near Brisbane, Queensland (Hymenoptera, Anthophorinae). *Qd Nat.* **16**: 63–67

Michener, C.D. (1962). The genus *Ceratina* in Australia, with notes on its nests (Hymenoptera : Apoidea). *J. Kansas Entomol. Soc.* **35**: 414–421

Michener, C.D. (1965a). A classification of the bees of the Australian and South Pacific regions. *Bull. Am. Mus. Nat. Hist.* **130**: 1–362

Michener, C.D. (1965b). The life cycle and social organization of bees of the genus *Exoneura* and their parasite, *Inquilina* (Hymenoptera : Xylocopinae). *Univ. Kansas Sci. Bull.* **46**: 317–358

Michener, C.D. (1966). Parasitism among Indoaustralian bees of the genus *Allodapula* (Hymenoptera : Ceratinini). *J. Kansas Entomol. Soc.* **39**: 705–708

Michener, C.D. (1973). Size and form of eggs of allodapine bees. *J. Entomol. Soc. S. Afr.* **36**: 281–285

Michener, C.D. (1977). Discordant evolution and the classification of allodapine bees. *Syst. Zool.* **26**: 32–56

Michener, C.D. (1983). The parasitic Australian allodapine genus *Inquilina* (Hymenoptera, Anthophoridae). *J. Kansas Entomol. Soc.* **56**: 555–559

Michener, C.D. & Scheiring, J.F. (1976). Pupae of allodapine bees (Hymenoptera : Xylocopinae). *J. Aust. Entomol. Soc.* **15**: 63–70

Michener, C.D. & Syed, I.H. (1962). Specific characters of the larvae and adults of *Allodapula* in the Australian region (Hymenoptera : Ceratinini). *J. Entomol. Soc. Qd* **1**: 30–41

Roig-Alsina, A. (1991). Cladistic analysis of the Nomadinae s.str. with description of a new genus (Hymenoptera: Anthophoridae). *J. Kansas Entomol. Soc.* **64**: 23–27

Rozen, J.G. (1991). Evolution of cleptoparasitism in anthophorid bees as revealed by their mode of parasitism and first instars (Hymenoptera: Apoidea). *Am. Mus. Novit.* **3029**: 1–36

Sakagami, S.F. & Michener, C.D. (1987). Tribes of Xylocopinae and origin of the Apidae (Hymenoptera : Apoidea). *Ann. Entomol. Soc. Am.* **80**: 439–450

Schwarz, M.P. (1986). Persistent multi-female nests in an Australian allodapine bee, *Exoneura bicolor* (Hymenoptera, Anthophoridae). *Insectes Soc.* **33**: 258–277

Schwarz, M.P. (1987). Intra-colony relatedness and sociality in the allodapine bee *Exoneura bicolor. Behav. Ecol. Sociobiol.* **21**: 387–392

Schwarz, M.P. (1988a). Notes on cofounded nests in three species of social bees in the genus *Exoneura* (Hymenoptera; Anthophoridae). *Vict. Nat.* **105**: 212–215

Schwarz, M.P. (1988b). Local resource enhancement and sex ratios in a primitively social bee. *Nature* **331**: 346–348

Schwarz, M.P. & O'Keefe, K.J. (1991). Cooperative nesting and ovarian development in females of the predominantly social bee *Exoneura bicolor* Smith (Hymenoptera: Anthophoridae) after forced solitary eclosion. *J. Aust. Entomol. Soc.* **30**: 251–255

Schwarz, M.P., Scholz, O. & Jensen, G. (1987). Ovarian inhibition among nestmates of *Exoneura bicolor* Smith (Hymenoptera : Xylocopinae). *J. Aust. Entomol. Soc.* **26**: 355–359

Syed, I.H. (1963). Comparative studies of larvae of Australian ceratinine bees (Hymenoptera, Apoidea). *Univ. Kansas Sci. Bull.* **64**: 263–280

ANTHOPHORINAE

Amegilla Friese, 1897

Amegilla Friese, H. (1897). *Die Bienen Europa's (Apidae europaeae) nach ihren Gattungen, Arten und Varietäten auf vergleichend morphologisch-biologischer Grundlage.* Theil III. Solitäre Apiden. Genus *Podalirius.* Berlin : Friedländer & Sohn vi 316 pp. 61 Figs [18] [proposed with subgeneric rank in *Podalirius* Latreille, 1802]. Type species: *Apis quadrifasciata* Villers, 1789 by subsequent designation, see Cockerell, T.D.A. (1931). Descriptions and records of bees. CXXVI. *Ann. Mag. Nat. Hist. (10)*7: 273–281 [277]. Compiled from secondary source: Sandhouse, G.A. (1943). The type species of the genera and subgenera of bees. *Proc. U.S. Natl Mus.* 92(3156): 519–619.

Alfkenella Börner, C. (1919). Stammesgeschichte der Hautflügler. *Biol. Zentralbl.* **39**: 145–186 [168] [junior objective synonym of *Amegilla* Friese (1897)]. Type species: *Apis quadrifasciata* Villers, 1789 by subsequent designation. Compiled from secondary source: Sandhouse, G.A. (1943). The type species of the genera and subgenera of bees. *Proc. U.S. Natl Mus.* 92(3156): 519–619.

Taxonomic decision for subgeneric arrangement: Brooks, R.W. (1988). Systematics and phylogeny of the anthophorine bees (Hymenoptera: Anthophoridae; Anthophorini). *Univ. Kansas Sci. Bull.* **53**: 436–575 [496].

Extralimital distribution: Palaearctic, Afrotropical and Oriental Regions, see Brooks, R.W. (1988). Systematics and phylogeny of the anthophorine bees (Hymenoptera: Anthophoridae; Anthophorini). *Univ. Kansas Sci. Bull.* **53**: 436–575 [496].

Generic reference: Michener, C.D. (1965). A classification of the bees of the Australian and South Pacific regions. *Bull. Am. Mus. Nat. Hist.* **130**: 1–362 [215].

Amegilla (Asaropoda) Cockerell, 1926

Asaropoda Cockerell, T.D.A. (1926). Descriptions and records of bees. CXII. *Ann. Mag. Nat. Hist. (9)*18: 216–227

[216]. Type species: *Saropoda bombiformis* Smith, 1854 by original designation.

Extralimital distribution: New Guinea and Bismarck Archipelago, see Brooks, R.W. (1988). Systematics and phylogeny of the anthophorine bees (Hymenoptera: Anthophoridae; Anthophorini). *Univ. Kansas Sci. Bull.* **53**: 436–575 [513].

Amegilla (Asaropoda) albiceps (Rayment, 1951)

Asaropoda albiceps Rayment, T. (1951). A critical revision of species in the genus *Asaropoda* by new characters. *Mem. Natl Mus. Vict.* **17**: 65–80 [71].
Type data: holotype, NMV ♂.
Type locality: Studley Park, Melbourne, VIC.

Distribution: SE coastal, VIC; known only from type locality.
Ecology: adult—volant; melliferous, solitary.

Amegilla (Asaropoda) albigenella Michener, 1965

Asaropoda albigena Rayment, T. (1931). Bees in the collections of the Western Australian Museum and the Agricultural Department, Perth. *J. Proc. R. Soc. West. Aust.* **17**: 157–190 [182] [junior secondary homonym of *Anthophora albigena* Lepeletier, 1841].
Type data: holotype (probable), whereabouts unknown ♂*.
Type locality: Landor Station, WA.
Amegilla (Asaropoda) albigenella Michener, C.D. (1965). A classification of the bees of the Australian and South Pacific regions. *Bull. Am. Mus. Nat. Hist.* **130**: 1–362 [217] [*nom. nov.* for *Asaropoda albigena* Rayment, 1931].

Distribution: NW coastal, WA; known only from type locality.
Ecology: adult—volant; melliferous, solitary.
References: Rayment, T. (1935). *A Cluster of Bees.* Sixty essays on the life-histories of Australian bees, with specific descriptions of over 100 new species, and an introduction by Professor E.F. Phillips, D.Ph.,

Cornell University, U.S.A. Sydney : Endeavour Press 752 pp. (illustration); Rayment, T. (1951). A critical revision of species in the genus *Asaropoda* by new characters. *Mem. Natl Mus. Vict.* **17**: 65–80 (taxonomy).

Amegilla (Asaropoda) alpha (Cockerell, 1904)

Saropoda alpha Cockerell, T.D.A. (1904). New and little known bees in the collection of the British Museum. *Ann. Mag. Nat. Hist. (7)***14**: 203–208 [204].
Type data: holotype, BMNH ♂*.
Type locality: Australia.

Distribution: NE coastal, Murray-Darling basin, QLD; only published localities Toowoomba and Mackay.
Ecology: adult—volant; melliferous, solitary.
References: Cockerell, T.D.A. (1926). Descriptions and records of bees. CXII. *Ann. Mag. Nat. Hist. (9)***18**: 216–227 (as *Asaropoda alpha* (Cockerell, 1904)); Rayment, T. (1951). A critical revision of species in the genus *Asaropoda* by new characters. *Mem. Natl Mus. Vict.* **17**: 65–80 (distribution).

Amegilla (Asaropoda) anomala (Cockerell, 1929)

Asaropoda anomala Cockerell, T.D.A. (1929). Bees from the Australian region. *Am. Mus. Novit.* **346**: 1–18 [15].
Type data: syntypes, AMNH ♂♀* (number of specimens unknown, male specimen labelled 'type').
Type locality: Brisbane, QLD.

Distribution: NE coastal, SE coastal, QLD, NSW; only published localities Brisbane and Lismore.
Ecology: adult—volant; melliferous, solitary.
Reference: Rayment, T. (1951). A critical revision of species in the genus *Asaropoda* by new characters. *Mem. Natl Mus. Vict.* **17**: 65–80 (redescription, distribution).

Amegilla (Asaropoda) bombiformis (Smith, 1854)

Saropoda bombiformis Smith, F. (1854). *Catalogue of Hymenopterous Insects in the Collection of the British Museum.* Part II. Apidae. London : British Museum pp. 199–465 [318].
Type data: lectotype, BMNH 99–303 ♀*.
Subsequent designation: Brooks, R.W. (1988). Systematics and phylogeny of the anthophorine bees (Hymenoptera: Anthophoridae; Anthophorini). *Univ. Kansas Sci. Bull.* **53**: 436–575 [556].
Type locality: Richmond River, NSW.

Distribution: NE coastal, Murray-Darling basin, SE coastal, QLD, NSW, VIC; also New Guinea.
Ecology: larva—sedentary : adult—volant; melliferous, solitary, nest in soil, males found clustering on plant stems.
References: Sichel, J. (1869). *In* Dours, J.A. Monographie iconographique du genre *Anthophora*, Latr. *Mém. Soc. Linn. N. Fr.* **2**: 5–211 (as *Anthophora bombiformis* (Smith, 1854)); Dalla Torre, K.W. (1896). *Catalogus Hymenopterorum Hucusque*

Descriptorum Systematicus et Synonymicus. Apidae (Anthophila). Lipsiae : G. Engelmann Vol. x 643 pp. (as *Podalirius bombiformis* (Smith, 1854)); Cockerell, T.D.A. (1914). Descriptions and records of bees. LXIV. *Ann. Mag. Nat. Hist. (8)***14**: 464–472 (distribution); Cockerell, T.D.A. (1926). Descriptions and records of bees. CXII. *Ann. Mag. Nat. Hist. (9)***18**: 216–227 (type species of *Asaropoda*); Rayment, T. (1931). Bees in the collections of the Western Australian Museum and the Agricultural Department, Perth. *J. Proc. R. Soc. West. Aust.* **17**: 157–190 (illustration); Rayment, T. (1935). *A Cluster of Bees.* Sixty essays on the life-histories of Australian bees, with specific descriptions of over 100 new species, and an introduction by Professor E.F. Phillips, D.Ph., Cornell University, U.S.A. Sydney : Endeavour Press 752 pp. (illustration); Rayment, T. (1951). A critical revision of species in the genus *Asaropoda* by new characters. *Mem. Natl Mus. Vict.* **17**: 65–80 (distribution); Rayment, T. (1954). Incidence of acarid mites on the biology of bees. *Aust. Zool.* **12**: 26–38 (as host); Michener, C.D. (1965). A classification of the bees of the Australian and South Pacific regions. *Bull. Am. Mus. Nat. Hist.* **130**: 1–362 [215, 216] (illustration); Cardale, J. (1968). Observations on nests and nesting behaviour of *Amegilla (Asaropoda)* sp. (Hymenoptera : Apoidea : Anthophorinae). *Aust. J. Zool.* **16**: 709–713 (biology of probably this species); Cardale, J. (1968). Parasites and other organisms associated with nests of *Amegilla* Friese (Hymenoptera : Anthophorinae). *J. Aust. Entomol. Soc.* **7**: 29–34 (probably this species, as host); Cardale, J. (1968). Immature stages of Australian Anthophorinae (Hymenoptera : Apoidea). *J. Aust. Entomol. Soc.* **7**: 35–41 (immature stages of probably this species); Cane, J.H. (1979). The hind tibiotarsal and tibial spur articulations in bees (Hymenoptera : Apoidea). *J. Kansas Entomol. Soc.* **52**: 123–137 (morphology); Hockings, F.D. (1980). *Friends and Foes of Australian Gardens*: (including pests, diseases, parasites and predators). Sydney : Reed, in association with the Society for Growing Australian Plants 151 pp. (illustration); Brooks, R.W. (1988). Systematics and phylogeny of the anthophorine bees (Hymenoptera: Anthophoridae; Anthophorini). *Univ. Kansas Sci. Bull.* **53**: 436–575 (illustration); Houston, T.F. (1991). Ecology and behaviour of the bee *Amegilla (Asaropoda) dawsoni* (Rayment) with notes on a related species (Hymenoptera: Anthophoridae). *Rec. West. Aust. Mus.* **15**: 535–553 (biology).

Amegilla (Asaropoda) calva (Rayment, 1935)

Anthophora calva Rayment, T. (1935). *A Cluster of Bees.* Sixty essays on the life-histories of Australian bees, with specific descriptions of over 100 new species, and an introduction by Professor E.F. Phillips, D.Ph., Cornell University, U.S.A. Sydney : Endeavour Press 752 pp. [712].

Type data: syntypes, ANIC 2♀.
Type locality: Davis Creek, NSW.

Distribution: SE coastal, NSW; known only from type locality.
Ecology: adult—volant; melliferous, solitary.

Amegilla (Asaropoda) cygni (Rayment, 1931)

Anthophora cygni Rayment, T. (1931). Bees in the collections of the Western Australian Museum and the Agricultural Department, Perth. *J. Proc. R. Soc. West. Aust.* **17**: 157–190 [179].
Type data: holotype, WADA ♂.
Type locality: Swan River, WA.

Distribution: SW coastal, WA; known only from type locality.
Ecology: adult—volant; melliferous, solitary.

Amegilla (Asaropoda) dawsoni (Rayment, 1951)

Anthophora dawsoni Rayment, T. (1951). A critical revision of species in the genus *Asaropoda* by new characters. *Mem. Natl Mus. Vict.* **17**: 65–80 [77].
Type data: holotype, NMV ♂.
Type locality: Onslow, WA.

Distribution: SW coastal, NW coastal, W plateau, WA.
Ecology: larva—sedentary : adult—volant; melliferous, solitary, nest gregariously in bare, flat, hard, clay soil, flower visiting record: *Cassia* L. *s.lat.* [Caesalpiniaceae], *Eremophila* R.Br. [Myoporaceae], *Solanum* L. [Solanaceae] and *Trichodesma* R.Br. [Boraginaceae].
References: Michener, C.D. (1965). A classification of the bees of the Australian and South Pacific regions. *Bull. Am. Mus. Nat. Hist.* **130**: 1–362 [217] (biology); Douglas, A.M. (1980). *Our Dying Fauna. A personal perspective on a changing environment.* Perth : Creative Research, in association with Biological Services 170 pp. (biology); Houston, T.F. (1991). Ecology and behaviour of the bee *Amegilla (Asaropoda) dawsoni* (Rayment) with notes on a related species (Hymenoptera: Anthophoridae). *Rec. West. Aust. Mus.* **15**: 535–553 (biology, distribution).

Amegilla (Asaropoda) dentiventris (Rayment, 1951)

Asaropoda dentiventris Rayment, T. (1951). A critical revision of species in the genus *Asaropoda* by new characters. *Mem. Natl Mus. Vict.* **17**: 65–80 [73].
Type data: holotype, NMV ♂.
Type locality: Broadmeadows, VIC.

Distribution: SE coastal, VIC; known only from type locality.
Ecology: adult—volant; melliferous, solitary.

Amegilla (Asaropoda) epaphrodita Brooks, 1988

Amegilla (Asaropoda) epaphrodita Brooks, R.W. (1988). Systematics and phylogeny of the anthophorine bees (Hymenoptera: Anthophoridae; Anthophorini). *Univ.*

Kansas Sci. Bull. **53**: 436–575 [554].
Type data: holotype, ANIC ♀*.
Type locality: 15 km E Mt Cahill, NT.

Distribution: N coastal, NT; only published localities 15 km E Mt Cahill and Burnside.
Ecology: adult—volant; melliferous, solitary.

Amegilla (Asaropoda) grisescens (Rayment, 1931)

Anthophora grisescens Rayment, T. (1931). Bees in the collections of the Western Australian Museum and the Agricultural Department, Perth. *J. Proc. R. Soc. West. Aust.* **17**: 157–190 [181].
Type data: holotype, ANIC ♀.
Type locality: Geraldton, WA.

Distribution: NW coastal, WA; known only from type locality.
Ecology: adult—volant; melliferous, solitary.
Reference: Rayment, T. (1951). A critical revision of species in the genus *Asaropoda* by new characters. *Mem. Natl Mus. Vict.* **17**: 65–80 (illustration).

Amegilla (Asaropoda) houstoni Brooks, 1988

Amegilla (Asaropoda) houstoni Brooks, R.W. (1988). Systematics and phylogeny of the anthophorine bees (Hymenoptera: Anthophoridae; Anthophorini). *Univ. Kansas Sci. Bull.* **53**: 436–575 [555].
Type data: holotype, WAM ♀*.
Type locality: Top of Napier Range, Windjana Gorge, Kimberley Div., WA.

Distribution: N coastal, WA; known only from type locality.
Ecology: adult—volant; melliferous, solitary, flower visiting record: *Trichodesma* R.Br. [Boraginaceae].

Amegilla (Asaropoda) imitata (Rayment, 1951)

Asaropoda imitata Rayment, T. (1951). A critical revision of species in the genus *Asaropoda* by new characters. *Mem. Natl Mus. Vict.* **17**: 65–80 [74].
Type data: holotype, ANIC ♀.
Type locality: NSW.

Distribution: NSW; known only from type locality, exact locality not specified.
Ecology: adult—volant; melliferous, solitary.

Amegilla (Asaropoda) meltonensis (Rayment, 1951)

Asaropoda meltonensis Rayment, T. (1951). A critical revision of species in the genus *Asaropoda* by new characters. *Mem. Natl Mus. Vict.* **17**: 65–80 [74].
Type data: holotype, NMV ♀.
Type locality: Melton, VIC.

Distribution: SE coastal, VIC; known only from type locality.
Ecology: adult—volant; melliferous, solitary, flower visiting record: *Loranthus* Jacq. [Loranthaceae].

Amegilla (Asaropoda) preissi (Cockerell, 1910)

Anthophora preissi Cockerell, T.D.A. (1910). Some Australian bees in the Berlin Museum. *J. N.Y. Entomol. Soc.* **18**: 98–114 [107].
Type data: holotype, ZMB 1405 ♀*.
Type locality: WA.
Anthophora preissi froggatti Cockerell, T.D.A. (1914). Descriptions and records of bees. LXIV. *Ann. Mag. Nat. Hist. (8)***14**: 464–472 [468].
Type data: holotype, BMNH ♀*.
Type locality: Brewarrina, NSW.

Taxonomic decision for synonymy: Brooks, R.W. (1988). Systematics and phylogeny of the anthophorine bees (Hymenoptera: Anthophoridae; Anthophorini). *Univ. Kansas Sci. Bull.* **53**: 436–575 [571].

Distribution: Murray-Darling basin, NSW, WA; only published locality Brewarrina, exact locality in WA not specified.
Ecology: adult—volant; melliferous, solitary.
References: Rayment, T. (1931). Bees in the collections of the Western Australian Museum and the Agricultural Department, Perth. *J. Proc. R. Soc. West. Aust.* **17**: 157–190 (taxonomy); Rayment, T. (1935). *A Cluster of Bees.* Sixty essays on the life-histories of Australian bees, with specific descriptions of over 100 new species, and an introduction by Professor E.F. Phillips, D.Ph., Cornell University, U.S.A. Sydney : Endeavour Press 752 pp. (illustration); Rayment, T. (1951). A critical revision of species in the genus *Asaropoda* by new characters. *Mem. Natl Mus. Vict.* **17**: 65–80 (illustration, as *A[saropoda] preissi froggatti* (Cockerell, 1914)).

Amegilla (Asaropoda) punctata (Rayment, 1931)

Asaropoda punctata Rayment, T. (1931). Bees in the collections of the Western Australian Museum and the Agricultural Department, Perth. *J. Proc. R. Soc. West. Aust.* **17**: 157–190 [182] [a specimen in the ANIC labelled "type" bears a locality which was not given in the original description].
Type data: holotype (probable), whereabouts unknown ♂*.
Type locality: Sydney, NSW.

Distribution: NE coastal, SE coastal, Murray-Darling basin, QLD, NSW, VIC; only published localities Brisbane, Sydney, Marrickville and Gunbower.
Ecology: larva—sedentary : adult—volant; melliferous, solitary, males found clustering on plant stems.
References: Rayment, T. (1935). *A Cluster of Bees.* Sixty essays on the life-histories of Australian bees, with specific descriptions of over 100 new species, and an introduction by Professor E.F. Phillips, D.Ph., Cornell University, U.S.A. Sydney : Endeavour Press 752 pp. (biology, illustration); Rayment, T. (1939). Bees from the high lands of New South Wales and Victoria. *Aust. Zool.* **9**: 263–294 (distribution); Rayment, T. (1951). A critical revision of species in the genus *Asaropoda* by new characters. *Mem. Natl Mus. Vict.* **17**: 65–80 (redescription).

Amegilla (Asaropoda) rhodoscymna (Cockerell, 1905)

Anthophora rhodoscymna Cockerell, T.D.A. (1905). Descriptions and records of bees. IV. *Ann. Mag. Nat. Hist. (7)***16**: 392–403 [395].
Type data: syntypes, BMNH 3♂*.
Type locality: Mackay district, QLD, see Cockerell, T.D.A. (1931). The bees of Australia. *Aust. Zool.* **7**: 34–54 [36].

Distribution: NE coastal, QLD, NSW, WA; only published localities Mackay, Brisbane and Pialba, exact localities in NSW and WA not specified.
Ecology: adult—volant; melliferous, solitary.
References: Cockerell, T.D.A. (1913). Some Australian bees. *Proc. Acad. Nat. Sci. Philad.* **65**: 28–44 (distribution); Cockerell, T.D.A. (1914). Descriptions and records of bees. LX. *Ann. Mag. Nat. Hist. (8)***14**: 1–13 (description of female); Rayment, T. (1931). Bees in the collections of the Western Australian Museum and the Agricultural Department, Perth. *J. Proc. R. Soc. West. Aust.* **17**: 157–190 (distribution); Rayment, T. (1951). A critical revision of species in the genus *Asaropoda* by new characters. *Mem. Natl Mus. Vict.* **17**: 65–80 (illustration).

Amegilla (Asaropoda) rickae (Rayment, 1951)

Asaropoda rickae Rayment, T. (1951). A critical revision of species in the genus *Asaropoda* by new characters. *Mem. Natl Mus. Vict.* **17**: 65–80 [75] [the species description is of a female, called an "allotype"; as the male was not described this female is considered to be the holotype].
Type data: holotype (probable), ANIC ♀.
Type locality: Bolgart, WA.

Distribution: SW coastal, WA; known only from type locality.
Ecology: adult—volant; melliferous, solitary, nest in soil under loose sand.

Amegilla (Asaropoda) rubricata (Rayment, 1951)

Asaropoda rubricata Rayment, T. (1951). A critical revision of species in the genus *Asaropoda* by new characters. *Mem. Natl Mus. Vict.* **17**: 65–80 [76].
Type data: holotype, whereabouts unknown ♂*.
Type locality: Lismore, NSW.
Asaropoda rubricata dentata Rayment, T. (1951). A critical revision of species in the genus *Asaropoda* by new characters. *Mem. Natl Mus. Vict.* **17**: 65–80 [76].
Type data: holotype, ANIC ♂.
Type locality: Sydney, NSW.

Taxonomic decision for synonymy: Brooks, R.W. (1988). Systematics and phylogeny of the anthophorine bees (Hymenoptera: Anthophoridae; Anthophorini). *Univ. Kansas Sci. Bull.* **53**: 436–575 [572].

Distribution: SE coastal, NSW; only published localities Lismore, Parramatta and Sydney.
Ecology: adult—volant; melliferous, solitary, flower visiting record: *Antigonon* Endl. [Polygonaceae].

Amegilla (Asaropoda) rufa (Rayment, 1931)

Asaropoda rufa Rayment, T. (1931). Bees in the collections of the Western Australian Museum and the Agricultural Department, Perth. *J. Proc. R. Soc. West. Aust.* **17**: 157–190 [181] [the species was described from a female from Sydney; Rayment, T. (1951). A critical revision of species in the genus *Asaropoda* by new characters. *Mem. Natl Mus. Vict.* **17**: 65–80 (76) stated that the type was a male from Enoggera, (QLD); as the descriptions do not agree, the male "type" in the ANIC cannot be the holotype].
Type data: holotype (probable), whereabouts unknown ♀*.
Type locality: Enoggera, QLD (as Sydney, NSW in original description).

Distribution: NE coastal, SE coastal, Murray-Darling basin, QLD, NSW, VIC.
Ecology: larva—sedentary : adult—volant; melliferous, solitary, nest in soil, males found clustering on plant stems, flower visiting record: *Eucalyptus* L'Hérit. [Myrtaceae], *Hakea* Schrader [Proteaceae].
References: Rayment, T. (1935). *A Cluster of Bees*. Sixty essays on the life-histories of Australian bees, with specific descriptions of over 100 new species, and an introduction by Professor E.F. Phillips, D.Ph., Cornell University, U.S.A. Sydney : Endeavour Press 752 pp. (biology); Rayment, T. (1939). Bees from the high lands of New South Wales and Victoria. *Aust. Zool.* **9**: 263–294 (biology); Rayment, T. (1951). A critical revision of species in the genus *Asaropoda* by new characters. *Mem. Natl Mus. Vict.* **17**: 65–80 (redescription, biology).

Amegilla (Asaropoda) rufescens (Friese, 1911)

Anthophora rufescens Friese, H. (1911). Zur Bienenfauna Neuguineas und der benachbarten Gebiete (Hym.) (Nachtrag II). *Dtsch. Entomol. Zeit.* **1911**: 448–453 [449].
Type data: holotype, whereabouts unknown ♂*.
Type locality: Mackay, QLD.

Distribution: NE coastal, QLD; known only from type locality.
Ecology: adult—volant; melliferous, solitary.
Reference: Rayment, T. (1951). A critical revision of species in the genus *Asaropoda* by new characters. *Mem. Natl Mus. Vict.* **17**: 65–80 (taxonomy).

Amegilla (Asaropoda) scymna (Gribodo, 1893)

Anthophora scymna Gribodo, G. (1893). Note imenotterologiche. Nota II. Nuovi generi e nuove specie di Imenotteri antofili et osservazioni sopra alcune specie gia conosciute. *Boll. Soc. Entomol. Ital.* **25**: 248–287, 388–428 [389].
Type data: holotype (probable), whereabouts unknown (Gribodo coll.) ♀*.
Type locality: QLD.
Anthophora flava Friese, H. (1911). Zur Bienenfauna Neuguineas und der benachbarten Gebiete (Hym.) (Nachtrag II). *Dtsch. Entomol. Zeit.* **1911**: 448–453 [448].
Type data: holotype, whereabouts unknown ♀*.
Type locality: Fremantle (as Freemantle), WA.

Taxonomic decision for synonymy: Brooks, R.W. (1988). Systematics and phylogeny of the anthophorine bees (Hymenoptera: Anthophoridae; Anthophorini). *Univ. Kansas Sci. Bull.* **53**: 436–575 [572].

Distribution: S Gulfs, SW coastal, NW coastal, QLD, SA, WA; only published localities Adelaide, Waroona, Geraldton (as Champion Bay) and Fremantle, exact locality in QLD not specified.
Ecology: adult—volant; melliferous, solitary.
References: Dalla Torre, K.W. (1896). *Catalogus Hymenopterorum Hucusque Descriptorum Systematicus et Synonymicus.* Apidae (Anthophila). Lipsiae : G. Engelmann Vol. x 643 pp. (as *Podalirius scymnus* (Gribodo, 1893)); Cockerell, T.D.A. (1905). Descriptions and records of bees. IV. *Ann. Mag. Nat. Hist.* (7)**16**: 392–403 (distribution); Cockerell, T.D.A. (1919). Bees in the collection of the United States National Museum. *Proc. U.S. Natl Mus.* **55**: 167–221 (description of male); Cockerell, T.D.A. (1931). The bees of Australia. *Aust. Zool.* **7**: 34–54 (distribution); Rayment, T. (1951). A critical revision of species in the genus *Asaropoda* by new characters. *Mem. Natl Mus. Vict.* **17**: 65–80 (taxonomy, as *Asaropoda flava* (Friese, 1911)).

Amegilla (Asaropoda) sordida (Rayment, 1931)

Anthophora sordida Rayment, T. (1931). Bees in the collections of the Western Australian Museum and the Agricultural Department, Perth. *J. Proc. R. Soc. West. Aust.* **17**: 157–190 [180].
Type data: holotype, ANIC ♂.
Type locality: Geraldton, WA.

Distribution: NW coastal, WA; known only from type locality.
Ecology: adult—volant; melliferous, solitary.

Amegilla (Asaropoda) sordidula (Rayment, 1931)

Anthophora sordidula Rayment, T. (1931). Bees in the collections of the Western Australian Museum and the Agricultural Department, Perth. *J. Proc. R. Soc. West. Aust.* **17**: 157–190 [179].
Type data: holotype, WADA ♂.
Type locality: Swan River, WA.

Distribution: SW coastal, WA; known only from type locality.
Ecology: adult—volant; melliferous, solitary.

Amegilla (Asaropoda) victoriensis (Rayment, 1951)

Asaropoda victoriensis Rayment, T. (1951). A critical revision of species in the genus *Asaropoda* by new characters. *Mem. Natl Mus. Vict.* **17**: 65–80 [77].
Type data: holotype, NMV ♂.
Type locality: Broadmeadows, VIC.

Distribution: SE coastal, VIC; known only from type locality.
Ecology: adult—volant; melliferous, solitary.

Amegilla (Notomegilla) Brooks, 1988

Notomegilla Brooks, R.W. (1988). Systematics and phylogeny of the anthophorine bees (Hymenoptera: Anthophoridae; Anthophorini). *Univ. Kansas Sci. Bull.* **53**: 436–575 [511] [proposed with subgeneric rank in *Amegilla* Friese, 1897]. Type species: *Anthophora aeruginosa* Smith, 1854 by original designation.

Amegilla (Notomegilla) adamsella (Rayment, 1944)

Anthophora adamsella Rayment, T. (1944). A critical revision of species in the *zonata* group of *Anthophora* by new characters (Part I). *Treubia* (Japanese edition) **1**: 1–30 [dated 1942, actual date of issue 1944] [23].
Type data: syntypes (probable), ANIC ♂♀.
Type locality: Edungalba, QLD.

Distribution: NE coastal, QLD; only published localities Edungalba, Proserpine and Mossman.
Ecology: adult—volant; melliferous, solitary.
Reference: Brooks, R.W. (1988). Systematics and phylogeny of the anthophorine bees (Hymenoptera: Anthophoridae; Anthophorini). *Univ. Kansas Sci. Bull.* **53**: 436–575 (subgeneric placement).

Amegilla (Notomegilla) aeruginosa (Smith, 1854)

Anthophora aeruginosa Smith, F. (1854). *Catalogue of Hymenopterous Insects in the Collection of the British Museum.* Part II. Apidae. London : British Museum pp. 199–465 [336].
Type data: syntypes (probable), BMNH ♂♀*.
Type locality: Hunter River, NSW.

Distribution: NE coastal, SE coastal, N coastal, QLD, NSW, WA, NT.
Ecology: adult—volant; melliferous, solitary, flower visiting record: *Solanum* L. [Solanaceae].
References: Dalla Torre, K.W. (1896). *Catalogus Hymenopterorum Hucusque Descriptorum Systematicus et Synonymicus.* Apidae (Anthophila). Lipsiae : G. Engelmann Vol. x 643 pp. (as *Podalirius aeruginosus* (Smith, 1854)); Cockerell, T.D.A. (1905). Descriptions and records of bees. II. *Ann. Mag. Nat. Hist. (7)***16**: 292–301 (taxonomy); Rayment, T. (1944). A critical revision of species in the *zonata* group of *Anthophora* by new characters (Part I). *Treubia* (Japanese edition) **1**: 1–30 [dated 1942, actual date of issue 1944] (taxonomy); Brooks, R.W. (1988). Systematics and phylogeny of the anthophorine bees (Hymenoptera: Anthophoridae; Anthophorini). *Univ. Kansas Sci. Bull.* **53**: 436–575 (subgeneric placement, illustration); Anderson, G.J. & Symon, D. (1988). Insect foragers on *Solanum* flowers in Australia. *Ann. M. Bot. Gard.* **75**: 842–852 (flower record).

Amegilla (Notomegilla) chlorocyanea (Cockerell, 1914)

Anthophora chlorocyanea Cockerell, T.D.A. (1914). Descriptions and records of bees. LXIV. *Ann. Mag. Nat. Hist. (8)***14**: 464–472 [469].

Type data: syntypes (probable), BMNH 2♀.
Type locality: Clare, SA.

Anthophora luteola Rayment, T. (1944). A critical revision of species in the *zonata* group of *Anthophora* by new characters (Part I). *Treubia* (Japanese edition) **1**: 1–30 [dated 1942, actual date of issue 1944] [27].
Type data: syntypes, ANIC ♂♀.
Type locality: Ororoo, SA.

Anthophora tinsleyella Rayment, T. (1944). A critical revision of species in the *zonata* group of *Anthophora* by new characters (Part I). *Treubia* (Japanese edition) **1**: 1–30 [dated 1942, actual date of issue 1944] [29] [a specimen in the ANIC labelled "type" bears a locality which was not given in the original description].
Type data: syntypes, whereabouts unknown ♂♀*.
Type locality: MacIntosh Holding, via Edungalba, QLD.

Taxonomic decision for synonymy: Brooks, R.W. (1988). Systematics and phylogeny of the anthophorine bees (Hymenoptera: Anthophoridae; Anthophorini). *Univ. Kansas Sci. Bull.* **53**: 436–575 [562].

Distribution: NE coastal, SE coastal, Murray-Darling basin, S Gulfs, SW coastal, N coastal, QLD, NSW, VIC, SA, WA, NT.
Ecology: adult—volant; melliferous, solitary, flower visiting record: lavender.
References: Cockerell, T.D.A. (1905). Descriptions and records of bees. IV. *Ann. Mag. Nat. Hist. (7)***16**: 392–403 (as *Anthophora cingulata* (Fabricius, 1775)); Meade-Waldo, G. (1914). Notes on the Apidae (Hymenoptera) in the collection of the British Museum, with descriptions of new species. *Ann. Mag. Nat. Hist. (8)***13**: 45–58 (taxonomy); Cockerell, T.D.A. (1930). Australian bees in the Museum of Comparative Zoology. *Psyche (Camb.)* **37**: 141–154 (taxonomy); Rayment, T. (1944). A critical revision of species in the *zonata* group of *Anthophora* by new characters (Part I). *Treubia* (Japanese edition) **1**: 1–30 [dated 1942, actual date of issue 1944] (taxonomy); Rayment, T. (1953). *Bees of the Portland District.* Victoria : Portland Field Naturalist's Club 39 pp. (flower record).

Amegilla (Notomegilla) grayella (Rayment, 1944)

Anthophora grayella Rayment, T. (1944). A critical revision of species in the *zonata* group of *Anthophora* by new characters (Part I). *Treubia* (Japanese edition) **1**: 1–30 [dated 1942, actual date of issue 1944] [27].
Type data: syntypes, ANIC ♂♀ (♂ is labelled 'type ♀', ♀ is labelled 'allotype ♂').
Type locality: Ororoo, SA.

Distribution: S Gulfs, SA; known only from type locality.
Ecology: adult—volant; melliferous, solitary.
Reference: Brooks, R.W. (1988). Systematics and phylogeny of the anthophorine bees (Hymenoptera: Anthophoridae; Anthophorini). *Univ. Kansas Sci. Bull.* **53**: 436–575 (subgeneric placement).

Amegilla (Notomegilla) jamesi (Rayment, 1944)

Anthophora tinsleyella jamesi Rayment, T. (1944). A critical revision of species in the *zonata* group of *Anthophora* by new characters (Part I). *Treubia* (Japanese edition) **1**: 1–30 [dated 1942, actual date of issue 1944] [30].
Type data: syntypes (probable), ANIC ♂♀.
Type locality: Orroroo, SA.

Distribution: S Gulfs, SA; known only from type locality.
Ecology: adult—volant; melliferous, solitary.
References: Michener, C.D. (1965). A classification of the bees of the Australian and South Pacific regions. *Bull. Am. Mus. Nat. Hist.* **130**: 1–362 [216] (taxonomy); Brooks, R.W. (1988). Systematics and phylogeny of the anthophorine bees (Hymenoptera: Anthophoridae; Anthophorini). *Univ. Kansas Sci. Bull.* **53**: 436–575 (subgeneric placement).

Amegilla (Notomegilla) mewiella (Rayment, 1944)

Anthophora mewiella Rayment, T. (1944). A critical revision of species in the *zonata* group of *Anthophora* by new characters (Part I). *Treubia* (Japanese edition) **1**: 1–30 [dated 1942, actual date of issue 1944] [28].
Type data: syntypes, ANIC ♂♀.
Type locality: Orroroo, SA.

Distribution: Murray-Darling basin, SE coastal, NSW, VIC, SA; only published localities Broken Hill, Silverton, Portland, Orroroo and Black Rock Hills.
Ecology: adult—volant; melliferous, solitary, flower visiting record: lavender, yellow broom, *Loranthus* Jacq. [Loranthaceae].
References: Rayment, T. (1953). *Bees of the Portland District*. Victoria : Portland Field Naturalist's Club 39 pp. (distribution); Brooks, R.W. (1988). Systematics and phylogeny of the anthophorine bees (Hymenoptera: Anthophoridae; Anthophorini). *Univ. Kansas Sci. Bull.* **53**: 436–575 (subgeneric placement).

Amegilla (Notomegilla) murrayi (Rayment, 1944)

Anthophora luteola murrayi Rayment, T. (1944). A critical revision of species in the *zonata* group of *Anthophora* by new characters (Part I). *Treubia* (Japanese edition) **1**: 1–30 [dated 1942, actual date of issue 1944] [28].
Type data: holotype (probable), ANIC ♂.
Type locality: Robertson, NSW.

Distribution: SE coastal, NSW; known only from type locality.
Ecology: adult—volant; melliferous, solitary.
References: Michener, C.D. (1965). A classification of the bees of the Australian and South Pacific regions. *Bull. Am. Mus. Nat. Hist.* **130**: 1–362 [217] (taxonomy); Brooks, R.W. (1988). Systematics and phylogeny of the anthophorine bees (Hymenoptera: Anthophoridae; Anthophorini). *Univ. Kansas Sci. Bull.* **53**: 436–575.

Amegilla (Notomegilla) sybilae (Rayment, 1944)

Anthophora sybilae Rayment, T. (1944). A critical revision of species in the *zonata* group of *Anthophora* by new characters (Part I). *Treubia* (Japanese edition) **1**: 1–30 [dated 1942, actual date of issue 1944] [22].
Type data: syntypes, ANIC ♂♀.
Type locality: McIntosh Holding and Magnetic Is., QLD.

Distribution: NE coastal, QLD; only published localities Mossman, MacIntosh Holding, Edungalba and Magnetic Is.
Ecology: adult—volant; melliferous, solitary.
Reference: Brooks, R.W. (1988). Systematics and phylogeny of the anthophorine bees (Hymenoptera: Anthophoridae; Anthophorini). *Univ. Kansas Sci. Bull.* **53**: 436–575 (subgeneric placement).

Amegilla (Zonamegilla) Popov, 1950

Zonamegilla Popov, V.V. (1950). [On the genus *Amegilla* Friese (Hymenoptera, Apoidea)]. *Entomol. Obozr.* **31**: 257–261 [In Russian] [260] [proposed with subgeneric rank in *Amegilla* Friese, 1897]. Type species: *Apis zonata* Linnaeus, 1758 by original designation.

Extralimital distribution: SE Palaearctic and Oriental Regions, extending E to Solomon Ils, see Brooks, R.W. (1988). Systematics and phylogeny of the anthophorine bees (Hymenoptera: Anthophoridae; Anthophorini). *Univ. Kansas Sci. Bull.* **53**: 436–575 [510].

Amegilla (Zonamegilla) adelaidae (Cockerell, 1905)

Anthophora adelaidae Cockerell, T.D.A. (1905). Descriptions and records of bees. IV. *Ann. Mag. Nat. Hist.* (7)**16**: 392–403 [397].
Type data: holotype, BMNH ♂*.
Type locality: Adelaide River, NT.
Anthophora adelaidae ernesti Rayment, T. (1944). A critical revision of species in the *zonata* group of *Anthophora* by new characters (Part I). *Treubia* (Japanese edition) **1**: 1–30 [dated 1942, actual date of issue 1944] [fig. ix, figs 3 & 4c on p. 25] [*nom. nud.*, Cardale, J.C., this work; name introduced and used only as captions to figures].
Anthophora adelaidae ernesti Rayment, T. (1947). A critical revision of species in the *zonata* group of *Anthophora* by new characters (Part II). *Treubia* **19**: 46–73 [47].
Type data: holotype, ANIC ♂.
Type locality: Edungalba, QLD.

Taxonomic decision for synonymy: Brooks, R.W. (1988). Systematics and phylogeny of the anthophorine bees (Hymenoptera: Anthophoridae; Anthophorini). *Univ. Kansas Sci. Bull.* **53**: 436–575 [559].

Distribution: NE coastal, SE coastal, Murray-Darling basin, SW coastal, NW coastal, N coastal, QLD, NSW, VIC, WA, NT.
Ecology: adult—volant; melliferous, solitary, flower visiting record: *Plectranthus* L'Hérit. [Lamiaceae], *Ricinus* L. [Euphorbiaceae].

References: Rayment, T. (1934). Contributions to the fauna of Rottnest Island. VIII. Apoidea. With description of new species. *J. Proc. R. Soc. West. Aust.* **20**: 201–212 (description of female); Rayment, T. (1939). Bees from the high lands of New South Wales and Victoria. *Aust. Zool.* **9**: 263–294 (distribution); Rayment, T. (1947). A critical revision of species in the *zonata* group of *Anthophora* by new characters (Part II). *Treubia* **19**: 46–73 (taxonomy).

Amegilla (Zonamegilla) asserta (Cockerell, 1926)

Anthophora asserta Cockerell, T.D.A. (1926). Descriptions and records of bees. CXII. *Ann. Mag. Nat. Hist.* *(9)***18**: 216–227 [224].
Type data: holotype, NMV ♂.
Type locality: Lower Ferntree Gully, VIC.

Distribution: SE coastal, NSW, VIC.
Ecology: adult—volant; melliferous, solitary, flower visiting record: *Gladiolus* L. [Iridaceae].
References: Rayment, T. (1944). A critical revision of species in the *zonata* group of *Anthophora* by new characters (Part I). *Treubia* (Japanese edition) **1**: 1–30 [dated 1942, actual date of issue 1944] (illustration); Rayment, T. (1947). A critical revision of species in the *zonata* group of *Anthophora* by new characters (Part II). *Treubia* **19**: 46–73 (taxonomy); Brooks, R.W. (1988). Systematics and phylogeny of the anthophorine bees (Hymenoptera: Anthophoridae; Anthophorini). *Univ. Kansas Sci. Bull.* **53**: 436–575 (subgeneric placement).

Amegilla (Zonamegilla) australis (Rayment, 1944)

Anthophora australis Rayment, T. (1944). A critical revision of species in the *zonata* group of *Anthophora* by new characters (Part I). *Treubia* (Japanese edition) **1**: 1–30 [dated 1942, actual date of issue 1944] [24].
Type data: syntypes, ANIC 3♀.
Type locality: Sandringham, VIC.

Distribution: SE coastal, VIC; known only from type locality.
Ecology: adult—volant; melliferous, solitary, flower visiting record: *Begonia* L. [Begoniaceae], *Dianella* Lam. [Liliaceae].
Reference: Brooks, R.W. (1988). Systematics and phylogeny of the anthophorine bees (Hymenoptera: Anthophoridae; Anthophorini). *Univ. Kansas Sci. Bull.* **53**: 436–575 (subgeneric placement).

Amegilla (Zonamegilla) berylae (Rayment, 1947)

Anthophora berylae Rayment, T. (1947). A critical revision of species in the *zonata* group of *Anthophora* by new characters (Part II). *Treubia* **19**: 46–73 [49].
Type data: holotype (probable), whereabouts unknown ♂*.
Type locality: unknown (possibly Edungalba, QLD, as this species was dedicated to a person at this locality).

Distribution: (NE coastal), QLD; known only from type locality, exact locality unknown.
Ecology: adult—volant; melliferous, solitary.

Reference: Brooks, R.W. (1988). Systematics and phylogeny of the anthophorine bees (Hymenoptera: Anthophoridae; Anthophorini). *Univ. Kansas Sci. Bull.* **53**: 436–575 (subgeneric placement).

Amegilla (Zonamegilla) cingulata (Fabricius, 1775)

Andrena cingulata Fabricius, J.C. (1775). *Systema Entomologiae,* sistens insectorum classes, ordines, genera, species, adiectis synonymis, locis, descriptionibus, observationibus. Korte : Flensburgi et Lipsiae xxvii 832 pp. [378].
Type data: holotype, BMNH (Banks coll.) ♀.
Type locality: Australia (as New Holland).
Anthophora emendata Smith, F. (1879). *Descriptions of New Species of Hymenoptera in the Collection of the British Museum.* London : British Museum xxi 240 pp. [123].
Type data: holotype, BMNH ♂* (described as ♀).
Type locality: Australia.
Anthophora emendata gilberti Cockerell, T.D.A. (1905). Descriptions and records of bees. IV. *Ann. Mag. Nat. Hist.* *(7)***16**: 392–403 [396].
Type data: syntypes, BMNH ♂♀*.
Type locality: QLD.
Anthophora lilacine Cockerell, T.D.A. (1921). Australian bees in the Queensland Museum. *Mem. Qd Mus.* **7**: 81–98 [84].
Type data: holotype, QM ♂*.
Type locality: Kuranda, QLD.

Taxonomic decision for synonymy: Brooks, R.W. (1988). Systematics and phylogeny of the anthophorine bees (Hymenoptera: Anthophoridae; Anthophorini). *Univ. Kansas Sci. Bull.* **53**: 436–575 [562].

Distribution: NE coastal, Murray-Darling basin, SE coastal, S Gulfs, SW coastal, NW coastal, QLD, NSW, VIC, SA, WA.
Ecology: adult—volant; melliferous, solitary, nest gregariously in decomposing sandstone, flower visiting record: mango, tomatoes, *Hypochaeris* L. [Asteraceae], *Ipomoea* L. [Convolvulaceae], *Lantana* L. [Verbenaceae], *Persoonia* Sm. [Proteaceae], *Rosa* L. [Rosaceae].
References: Fabricius, J.C. (1804). *Systema Piezatorum.* Brunsvigae : C. Reichard xiv 439 pp. (as *Megilla cingulata* (Fabricius, 1775)); Sichel, J. (1869). *In* Dours, J.A. Monographie iconographique du genre *Anthophora,* Latr. *Mém. Soc. Linn. N. Fr.* **2**: 5–211 (as *Anthophora zonata cingulata* (Fabricius, 1775)); Dalla Torre, K.W. (1896). *Catalogus Hymenopterorum Hucusque Descriptorum Systematicus et Synonymicus.* Apidae (Anthophila). Lipsiae : G. Engelmann Vol. x 643 pp. (as *Podalirius cingulatus* (Fabricius, 1775)); Friese, H. (1911). Zur Bienenfauna Neuguineas und der benachbarten Gebiete (Hym.) (Nachtrag II). *Dtsch. Entomol. Zeit.* **1911**: 448–453 (taxonomy, as *Anthophora emendata* (Smith, 1879)); Meade-Waldo, G. (1914). Notes on the Apidae (Hymenoptera) in the collection of the British Museum, with descriptions of new species.

Ann. Mag. Nat. Hist. *(8)*13: 45–58 (taxonomy); Cockerell, T.D.A. (1922). Australian bees in the Queensland Museum. *Mem. Qd Mus.* 7: 257–279 (*Anthophora lilacine* emended to *Anthophora lilacina* Cockerell, 1921); Rayment, T. (1935). *A Cluster of Bees.* Sixty essays on the life-histories of Australian bees, with specific descriptions of over 100 new species, and an introduction by Professor E.F. Phillips, D.Ph., Cornell University, U.S.A. Sydney : Endeavour Press 752 pp. (biology); Rayment, T. (1944). A critical revision of species in the *zonata* group of *Anthophora* by new characters (Part I). *Treubia* (Japanese edition) 1: 1–30 [dated 1942, actual date of issue 1944] (illustration, as *Anthophora gilberti* Cockerell, 1905); Rayment, T. (1947). A critical revision of species in the *zonata* group of *Anthophora* by new characters (Part II). *Treubia* 19: 46–73 (taxonomy); Michener, C.D. & Houston, T.F. (1991). Apoidea. pp. 993–1000 *in* CSIRO (sponsor) *The Insects of Australia.* A textbook for students and research workers. Melbourne : Melbourne University Press Vol. II 2nd Edn (illustration).

Amegilla (Zonamegilla) fabriciana (Rayment, 1947)

Anthophora zonata cincta Sichel, J. (1869). *In* Dours, J.A. Monographie iconographique du genre *Anthophora*, Latr. *Mém. Soc. Linn. N. Fr.* 2: 5–211 [58] [junior secondary homonym of *Andrena cincta* Fabricius, 1781].
Type data: holotype (probable), whereabouts unknown (Dours coll.).
Type locality: Australia (as New Holland).

Anthophora fabriciana Rayment, T. (1947). A critical revision of species in the *zonata* group of *Anthophora* by new characters (Part II). *Treubia* 19: 46–73 [53] [*nom. nov.* for *Anthophora zonata cincta* Dours, 1869].

Distribution: SE coastal, NSW; known only from type locality.
Ecology: adult—volant; melliferous, solitary.
References: Meade-Waldo, G. (1914). Notes on the Apidae (Hymenoptera) in the collection of the British Museum, with descriptions of new species. *Ann. Mag. Nat. Hist.* *(8)*13: 45–58 (as *Anthophora cingulata* (Fabricius, 1775)); Rayment, T. (1944). A critical revision of species in the *zonata* group of *Anthophora* by new characters (Part I). *Treubia* (Japanese edition) 1: 1–30 [dated 1942, actual date of issue 1944] (illustration); Brooks, R.W. (1988). Systematics and phylogeny of the anthophorine bees (Hymenoptera: Anthophoridae; Anthophorini). *Univ. Kansas Sci. Bull.* 53: 436–575 (subgeneric placement).

Amegilla (Zonamegilla) ferrisi (Rayment, 1947)

Anthophora ferrisi Rayment, T. (1947). A critical revision of species in the *zonata* group of *Anthophora* by new characters (Part II). *Treubia* 19: 46–73 [73].
Type data: syntypes, ANIC ♂ (number of specimens unknown).
Type locality: Gunbower, VIC.

Distribution: Murray-Darling basin, VIC; known only from type locality.
Ecology: adult—volant; melliferous, solitary.
Reference: Brooks, R.W. (1988). Systematics and phylogeny of the anthophorine bees (Hymenoptera: Anthophoridae; Anthophorini). *Univ. Kansas Sci. Bull.* 53: 436–575 (subgeneric placement).

Amegilla (Zonamegilla) hackeri (Rayment, 1947)

Anthophora hackeri Rayment, T. (1947). A critical revision of species in the *zonata* group of *Anthophora* by new characters (Part II). *Treubia* 19: 46–73 [55].
Type data: syntypes, ANIC ♂♀.
Type locality: Mossman, QLD.

Distribution: NE coastal, QLD; known only from type locality.
Ecology: adult—volant; melliferous, solitary.
Reference: Brooks, R.W. (1988). Systematics and phylogeny of the anthophorine bees (Hymenoptera: Anthophoridae; Anthophorini). *Univ. Kansas Sci. Bull.* 53: 436–575 (subgeneric placement).

Amegilla (Zonamegilla) holmesi (Rayment, 1947)

Anthophora holmesi Rayment, T. (1947). A critical revision of species in the *zonata* group of *Anthophora* by new characters (Part II). *Treubia* 19: 46–73 [56] [a specimen in the ANIC labelled "type" bears a locality which was not given in the original description].
Type data: syntypes (probable), whereabouts unknown ♂♀* (number of specimens unknown).
Type locality: Woollahra (as Woolahra) and Hunters Hill, NSW.

Distribution: SE coastal, NSW; only published localities Woollahra and Hunters Hill.
Ecology: adult—volant; melliferous, solitary.
Reference: Brooks, R.W. (1988). Systematics and phylogeny of the anthophorine bees (Hymenoptera: Anthophoridae; Anthophorini). *Univ. Kansas Sci. Bull.* 53: 436–575 (subgeneric placement).

Amegilla (Zonamegilla) kershawi (Rayment, 1944)

Anthophora kershawi Rayment, T. (1944). A critical revision of species in the *zonata* group of *Anthophora* by new characters (Part I). *Treubia* (Japanese edition) 1: 1–30 [dated 1942, actual date of issue 1944] [21].
Type data: holotype, whereabouts unknown ♂*.
Type locality: Claudie River, QLD.

Distribution: NE coastal, QLD; known only from type locality.
Ecology: adult—volant; melliferous, solitary.

Amegilla (Zonamegilla) longmani (Rayment, 1947)

Anthophora longmani Rayment, T. (1947). A critical revision of species in the *zonata* group of *Anthophora* by new characters (Part II). *Treubia* 19: 46–73 [58] [a specimen in the ANIC labelled "type" bears a locality which was not given in the original description].

Type data: syntypes, whereabouts unknown ♂♀* (number of specimens unknown).
Type locality: Bribie Is., QLD.

Distribution: NE coastal, QLD; known only from type locality.
Ecology: adult—volant; melliferous, solitary.
Reference: Brooks, R.W. (1988). Systematics and phylogeny of the anthophorine bees (Hymenoptera: Anthophoridae; Anthophorini). *Univ. Kansas Sci. Bull.* **53**: 436–575 (subgeneric placement).

Amegilla (Zonamegilla) longula (Rayment, 1947)

Anthophora longula Rayment, T. (1944). A critical revision of species in the *zonata* group of *Anthophora* by new characters (Part I). *Treubia* (Japanese edition) **1**: 1–30 [dated 1942, actual date of issue 1944] [fig. IV on p. 15] [*nom. nud.*, Cardale, J.C., this work; name introduced and used only as caption to figure].
Anthophora longula Rayment, T. (1947). A critical revision of species in the *zonata* group of *Anthophora* by new characters (Part II). *Treubia* **19**: 46–73 [59].
Type data: syntypes, ANIC ♂♀.
Type locality: Orroroo, SA.

Distribution: S Gulfs, SA; known only from type locality.
Ecology: adult—volant; melliferous, solitary.
Reference: Brooks, R.W. (1988). Systematics and phylogeny of the anthophorine bees (Hymenoptera: Anthophoridae; Anthophorini). *Univ. Kansas Sci. Bull.* **53**: 436–575 (subgeneric placement).

Amegilla (Zonamegilla) mimica (Rayment, 1944)

Anthophora adamsella mimica Rayment, T. (1944). A critical revision of species in the *zonata* group of *Anthophora* by new characters (Part I). *Treubia* (Japanese edition) **1**: 1–30 [dated 1942, actual date of issue 1944] [25].
Type data: holotype, whereabouts unknown ♂* (not located in T. Rayment coll. transferred to ANIC).
Type locality: Edungalba, QLD.

Distribution: NE coastal, QLD; known only from type locality.
Ecology: adult—volant; melliferous, solitary.
References: Michener, C.D. (1965). A classification of the bees of the Australian and South Pacific regions. *Bull. Am. Mus. Nat. Hist.* **130**: 1–362 [217] (taxonomy, as *Amegilla (Amegilla) mimica* (Rayment, 1944)); Brooks, R.W. (1988). Systematics and phylogeny of the anthophorine bees (Hymenoptera: Anthophoridae; Anthophorini). *Univ. Kansas Sci. Bull.* **53**: 436–575.

Amegilla (Zonamegilla) murrayensis (Rayment, 1935)

Anthophora murrayensis Rayment, T. (1935). *A Cluster of Bees.* Sixty essays on the life-histories of Australian bees, with specific descriptions of over 100 new species, and an introduction by Professor E.F. Phillips, D.Ph., Cornell University, U.S.A. Sydney : Endeavour Press 752 pp. [363].
Type data: syntypes, ANIC ♂ (number of specimens unknown).
Type locality: Gunbower, VIC.

Distribution: Murray-Darling basin, VIC; known only from type locality.
Ecology: adult—volant; melliferous, solitary, nest gregariously in mud-bricks.
References: Rayment, T. (1939). Bees from the high lands of New South Wales and Victoria. *Aust. Zool.* **9**: 263–294 (described again as new); Rayment, T. (1944). A critical revision of species in the *zonata* group of *Anthophora* by new characters (Part I). *Treubia* (Japanese edition) **1**: 1–30 [dated 1942, actual date of issue 1944] (biology); Rayment, T. (1947). A critical revision of species in the *zonata* group of *Anthophora* by new characters (Part II). *Treubia* **19**: 46–73 (redescription); Brooks, R.W. (1988). Systematics and phylogeny of the anthophorine bees (Hymenoptera: Anthophoridae; Anthophorini). *Univ. Kansas Sci. Bull.* **53**: 436–575 (subgeneric placement).

Amegilla (Zonamegilla) parapulchra (Rayment, 1947)

Anthophora parapulchra Rayment, T. (1944). A critical revision of species in the *zonata* group of *Anthophora* by new characters (Part I). *Treubia* (Japanese edition) **1**: 1–30 [dated 1942, actual date of issue 1944] [5] [*nom. nud.*, Cardale, J.C., this work, name listed without information to distinguish it from other species].
Anthophora parapulchra Rayment, T. (1947). A critical revision of species in the *zonata* group of *Anthophora* by new characters (Part II). *Treubia* **19**: 46–73 [61].
Type data: syntypes, ANIC ♂♀.
Type locality: Hunters Hill, Sydney, NSW.

Distribution: NE coastal, SE coastal, QLD, NSW; known only from type localities.
Ecology: adult—volant; melliferous, solitary.
Reference: Brooks, R.W. (1988). Systematics and phylogeny of the anthophorine bees (Hymenoptera: Anthophoridae; Anthophorini). *Univ. Kansas Sci. Bull.* **53**: 436–575 (subgeneric placement).

Amegilla (Zonamegilla) perasserta (Rayment, 1947)

Anthophora perasserta Rayment, T. (1947). A critical revision of species in the *zonata* group of *Anthophora* by new characters (Part II). *Treubia* **19**: 46–73 [62].
Type data: syntypes, ANIC ♂♀.
Type locality: White Swamp, NSW.

Anthophora perasserta assertiella Rayment, T. (1947). A critical revision of species in the *zonata* group of *Anthophora* by new characters (Part II). *Treubia* **19**: 46–73 [63] [a specimen in the ANIC labelled "type" bears a locality which was not given in the original description].
Type data: syntypes (probable), whereabouts unknown ♂♀*.

Type locality: Orroroo, SA, White Swamp and Cooranbong, NSW and Mackay, QLD.

Taxonomic decision for synonymy: Brooks, R.W. (1988). Systematics and phylogeny of the anthophorine bees (Hymenoptera: Anthophoridae; Anthophorini). *Univ. Kansas Sci. Bull.* **53**: 436–575 [570].

Distribution: NE coastal, Murray-Darling basin, SE coastal, S Gulfs, QLD, NSW, SA; only published localities Edungalba, Mackay, White Swamp, Cooranbong and Orroroo.
Ecology: larva—sedentary : adult—volant; melliferous, solitary, ?nest in soil.
References: Rayment, T. (1944). A critical revision of species in the *zonata* group of *Anthophora* by new characters (Part I). *Treubia* (Japanese edition) **1**: 1–30 [dated 1942, actual date of issue 1944] (?biology); Brooks, R.W. (1988). Systematics and phylogeny of the anthophorine bees (Hymenoptera: Anthophoridae; Anthophorini). *Univ. Kansas Sci. Bull.* **53**: 436–575 (subgeneric placement).

Amegilla (Zonamegilla) perpulchra (Rayment, 1947)

Anthophora perpulchra Rayment, T. (1944). A critical revision of species in the *zonata* group of *Anthophora* by new characters (Part I). *Treubia* (Japanese edition) **1**: 1–30 [dated 1942, actual date of issue 1944] [5] [*nom. nud.*, Cardale, J.C., this work].
Anthophora perpulchra wallaciella Rayment, T. (1944). A critical revision of species in the *zonata* group of *Anthophora* by new characters (Part I). *Treubia* (Japanese edition) **1**: 1–30 [dated 1942, actual date of issue 1944] [10] [*nom. nud.*, Cardale, J.C., this work].
Anthophora perpulchra Rayment, T. (1947). A critical revision of species in the *zonata* group of *Anthophora* by new characters (Part II). *Treubia* **19**: 46–73 [64] [a specimen in the ANIC labelled "type" bears a locality which was not given in the original description].
Type data: syntypes (probable), whereabouts unknown ♂♀*.
Type locality: Woy Woy, NSW.
Anthophora perpulchra wallaciella Rayment, T. (1947). A critical revision of species in the *zonata* group of *Anthophora* by new characters (Part II). *Treubia* **19**: 46–73 [65] [a specimen in the ANIC labelled "type" bears a locality which was not given in the original description].
Type data: syntypes, whereabouts unknown ♂♀*.
Type locality: Robertson, NSW.

Taxonomic decision for synonymy: Brooks, R.W. (1988). Systematics and phylogeny of the anthophorine bees (Hymenoptera: Anthophoridae; Anthophorini). *Univ. Kansas Sci. Bull.* **53**: 436–575 [570].

Distribution: NE coastal, SE coastal, Murray-Darling basin, QLD, NSW.
Ecology: larva—sedentary : adult—volant; melliferous, solitary.
References: Rayment, T. (1944). A critical revision of species in the *zonata* group of *Anthophora* by new characters (Part I). *Treubia* (Japanese edn) **1**: 1–30

[dated 1942, actual date of issue 1944] (biology, as *Anthophora perpulchra wallaciella*; illustrations); Brooks, R.W. (1988). Systematics and phylogeny of the anthophorine bees (Hymenoptera: Anthophoridae; Anthophorini). *Univ. Kansas Sci. Bull.* **53**: 436–575 (subgeneric placement).

Amegilla (Zonamegilla) pulchra (Smith, 1854)

Anthophora pulchra Smith, F. (1854). *Catalogue of Hymenopterous Insects in the Collection of the British Museum.* Part II. Apidae. London : British Museum pp. 199–465 [335] [Brooks, R.W. (1988). Systematics and phylogeny of the anthophorine bees (Hymenoptera: Anthophoridae; Anthophorini). *Univ. Kansas Sci. Bull.* **53**: 436–575 (571), states "In the British Museum the female type of *An[thophora] pulchra* Smith, B.M. Type Hym. 17B666a, is not the type according to D. Baker. The type was apparently repinned and lost and the specimen in its place is *Am[egilla] niveocincta* (Smith)"].
Type data: syntypes (probable), BMNH ♂♀*.
Type locality: Cape Upstart, Moreton Bay, QLD, Hunter River, NSW.

Anthophora townleyella Rayment, T. (1944). A critical revision of species in the *zonata* group of *Anthophora* by new characters (Part I). *Treubia* (Japanese edition) **1**: 1–30 [dated 1942, actual date of issue 1944] [10] [*nom. nud.*, Cardale, J.C., this work].
Anthophora pulchra townleyella Rayment, T. (1947). A critical revision of species in the *zonata* group of *Anthophora* by new characters (Part II). *Treubia* **19**: 46–73 [67].
Type data: syntypes, ANIC ♂♀ (one specimen in ANIC is labelled 'type').
Type locality: Lismore, NSW.

Taxonomic decision for synonymy: Brooks, R.W. (1988). Systematics and phylogeny of the anthophorine bees (Hymenoptera: Anthophoridae; Anthophorini). *Univ. Kansas Sci. Bull.* **53**: 436–575 [571].

Distribution: NE coastal, SE coastal, Murray-Darling basin, S Gulfs, SW coastal, QLD, NSW, VIC, SA, WA.
Ecology: larva—sedentary : adult—volant; melliferous, solitary, nest gregariously in soil, in mortar between bricks and in mud-bricks, females attracted to old nests, males found clustering, flower visiting record: tomatoes, *Hypochaeris* L. [Asteraceae], *Ipomoea* L. [Convolvulaceae], *Leptospermum* Forster & G.Forster [Myrtaceae], *Solanum* L. [Solanaceae].
References: Sichel, J. (1869). *In* Dours, J.A. Monographie iconographique du genre *Anthophora*, Latr. *Mém. Soc. Linn. N. Fr.* **2**: 5–211 (as *Anthophora zonata pulchra* Smith, 1854); Dalla Torre, K.W. (1896). *Catalogus Hymenopterorum Hucusque Descriptorum Systematicus et Synonymicus.* Apidae (Anthophila). Lipsiae : G. Engelmann Vol. x 643 pp. (as *Podalirius pulchra* (Smith, 1854)); Cockerell, T.D.A. (1931). The bees of Australia. *Aust. Zool.* **7**: 34–54 (as synonym of *Anthophora zonata* (Linnaeus, 1758)); Rayment, T. (1935). *A Cluster of Bees.* Sixty essays on the life-histories of Australian bees, with

specific descriptions of over 100 new species, and an introduction by Professor E.F. Phillips, D.Ph., Cornell University, U.S.A. Sydney : Endeavour Press 752 pp. (illustration); Rayment, T. (1944). A critical revision of species in the *zonata* group of *Anthophora* by new characters (Part I). *Treubia* (Japanese edition) **1**: 1–30 [dated 1942, actual date of issue 1944] (biology, as *Anthophora townleyella*; illustration); Rayment, T. (1947). A critical revision of species in the *zonata* group of *Anthophora* by new characters (Part II). *Treubia* **19**: 46–73 (taxonomy); Michener, C.D. (1960). Observations on the behaviour of a burrowing bee (*Amegilla*) near Brisbane, Queensland (Hymenoptera, Anthophorinae). *Qd Nat.* **16**: 63–67 (biology, as *Amegilla salteri* (Cockerell, 1905)); Cardale, J. (1968). Nests and nesting behaviour of *Amegilla (Amegilla) pulchra* (Smith) (Hymenoptera : Apoidea : Anthophorinae). *Aust. J. Zool.* **16**: 689–707 (biology); Cardale, J. (1968). Parasites and other organisms associated with nests of *Amegilla* Friese (Hymenoptera : Anthophorinae). *J. Aust. Entomol. Soc.* **7**: 29–34 (as host); Cardale, J. (1968). Immature stages of Australian Anthophorinae (Hymenoptera : Apoidea). *J. Aust. Entomol. Soc.* **7**: 35–41 (immature stages); Brooks, R.W. (1988). Systematics and phylogeny of the anthophorine bees (Hymenoptera: Anthophoridae; Anthophorini). *Univ. Kansas Sci. Bull.* **53**: 436–575 (subgeneric placement); Houston, T.F. (1991). Ecology and behaviour of the bee *Amegilla (Asaropoda) dawsoni* (Rayment) with notes on a related species (Hymenoptera: Anthophoridae). *Rec. West. Aust. Mus.* **15**: 535–553 (biology); Anderson, G.J. & Symon, D. (1988). Insect foragers on *Solanum* flowers in Australia. *Ann. M. Bot. Gard.* **75**: 842–852 (flower record).

Amegilla (Zonamegilla) salteri (Cockerell, 1905)

Anthophora salteri Cockerell, T.D.A. (1905). Descriptions and records of bees. IV. *Ann. Mag. Nat. Hist. (7)***16**: 392–403 [398].
Type data: holotype, BMNH ♂*.
Type locality: Parramatta, NSW.

Distribution: NE coastal, SE coastal, Murray-Darling basin, QLD, NSW, VIC.
Ecology: larva—sedentary : adult—volant; melliferous, solitary, nest gregariously in hard soil, flower visiting record: *Bignonia* L. [Bignoniaceae].
References: Rayment, T. (1935). *A Cluster of Bees.* Sixty essays on the life-histories of Australian bees, with specific descriptions of over 100 new species, and an introduction by Professor E.F. Phillips, D.Ph., Cornell University, U.S.A. Sydney : Endeavour Press 752 pp. (biology); Rayment, T. (1944). A critical revision of species in the *zonata* group of *Anthophora* by new characters (Part I). *Treubia* (Japanese edition) **1**: 1–30 [dated 1942, actual date of issue 1944] (illustration); Rayment, T. (1947). A critical revision of species in the *zonata* group of *Anthophora* by new

characters (Part II). *Treubia* **19**: 46–73 (taxonomy); Michener, C.D. (1974). *The Social Behaviour of the Bees.* A comparative study. Cambridge : Belknap Press of Harvard University Press 404 pp. (biology); Brooks, R.W. (1988). Systematics and phylogeny of the anthophorine bees (Hymenoptera: Anthophoridae; Anthophorini). *Univ. Kansas Sci. Bull.* **53**: 436–575 (subgeneric placement); Houston, T.F. (1991). Ecology and behaviour of the bee *Amegilla (Asaropoda) dawsoni* (Rayment) with notes on a related species (Hymenoptera: Anthophoridae). *Rec. West. Aust. Mus.* **15**: 535–553 (biology reference transferred to *Amegilla (Zonamegilla) pulchra*, (Smith, 1854)).

Amegilla (Zonamegilla) shafferyella (Rayment, 1947)

Anthophora shafferyella Rayment, T. (1947). A critical revision of species in the *zonata* group of *Anthophora* by new characters (Part II). *Treubia* **19**: 46–73 [70].
Type data: syntypes (probable), whereabouts unknown ♂* (number of specimens unkown).
Type locality: Mossman, QLD.

Distribution: NE coastal, QLD; known only from type locality.
Ecology: adult—volant; melliferous, solitary.
Reference: Brooks, R.W. (1988). Systematics and phylogeny of the anthophorine bees (Hymenoptera: Anthophoridae; Anthophorini). *Univ. Kansas Sci. Bull.* **53**: 436–575 (subgeneric placement).

Amegilla (Zonamegilla) subsalteri (Rayment, 1947)

Anthophora subsalteri Rayment, T. (1947). A critical revision of species in the *zonata* group of *Anthophora* by new characters (Part II). *Treubia* **19**: 46–73 [69].
Type data: holotype, ANIC ♂.
Type locality: Orroroo, SA.

Distribution: S Gulfs, SA; known only from type locality.
Ecology: adult—volant; melliferous, solitary.
Reference: Brooks, R.W. (1988). Systematics and phylogeny of the anthophorine bees (Hymenoptera: Anthophoridae; Anthophorini). *Univ. Kansas Sci. Bull.* **53**: 436–575 (subgeneric placement).

Amegilla (Zonamegilla) thorogoodi (Rayment, 1939)

Anthophora thorogoodi Rayment, T. (1939). Bees from the high lands of New South Wales and Victoria. *Aust. Zool.* **9**: 263–294 [289].
Type data: holotype, ANIC ♂.
Type locality: Proserpine, QLD.

Distribution: NE coastal, SE coastal, QLD, NSW, VIC.
Ecology: adult—volant; melliferous, solitary, nest in a large mudwasp "nest".
References: Rayment, T. (1947). A critical revision

of species in the *zonata* group of *Anthophora* by new characters (Part II). *Treubia* **19**: 46–73 (redescription, distribution); Brooks, R.W. (1988). Systematics and phylogeny of the anthophorine bees (Hymenoptera: Anthophoridae; Anthophorini). *Univ. Kansas Sci. Bull.* **53**: 436–575 (subgeneric placement).

Amegilla (Zonamegilla) walkeri (Cockerell, 1905)

Anthophora walkeri Cockerell, T.D.A. (1905). Descriptions and records of bees. IV. *Ann. Mag. Nat. Hist.* *(7)***16**: 392–403 [396].
Type data: syntypes, BMNH 1♂2♀*.
Type locality: Baudin Is., WA.
Anthophora darwini Cockerell, T.D.A. (1910). Descriptions and records of bees. XXVIII. *Ann. Mag. Nat. Hist. (8)***5**: 409–419 [409].
Type data: holotype, BMNH ♂*.
Type locality: Darwin, NT.

Taxonomic decision for synonymy: Brooks, R.W. (1988). Systematics and phylogeny of the anthophorine bees (Hymenoptera: Anthophoridae; Anthophorini). *Univ. Kansas Sci. Bull.* **53**: 436–575 [575].

Distribution: NE coastal, S Gulfs, SW coastal, N coastal, QLD, SA, WA, NT.
Ecology: adult—volant; melliferous, solitary.
References: Cockerell, T.D.A. (1929). Bees from the Australian region. *Am. Mus. Novit.* **346**: 1–18 (distribution); Rayment, T. (1931). Bees in the collections of the Western Australian Museum and the Agricultural Department, Perth. *J. Proc. R. Soc. West. Aust.* **17**: 157–190 (distribution); Rayment, T. (1947). A critical revision of species in the *zonata* group of *Anthophora* by new characters (Part II). *Treubia* **19**: 46–73 (redescription); Brooks, R.W. (1988). Systematics and phylogeny of the anthophorine bees (Hymenoptera: Anthophoridae; Anthophorini). *Univ. Kansas Sci. Bull.* **53**: 436–575 (subgeneric placement).

Amegilla (Zonamegilla) whiteleyella (Rayment, 1947)

Anthophora whiteleyella Rayment, T. (1947). A critical revision of species in the *zonata* group of *Anthophora* by new characters (Part II). *Treubia* **19**: 46–73 [72].
Type data: holotype, ANIC ♂.
Type locality: Port Macquarie (as Port McQuarie), NSW.

Distribution: SE coastal, NSW; known only from type locality.
Ecology: adult—volant; melliferous, solitary.
Reference: Brooks, R.W. (1988). Systematics and phylogeny of the anthophorine bees (Hymenoptera: Anthophoridae; Anthophorini). *Univ. Kansas Sci. Bull.* **53**: 436–575 (subgeneric placement).

Amegilla (Zonamegilla) zonata (Linnaeus, 1758)

Apis zonata Linnaeus, C. von (1758). *Systema Naturae per Regna tria Naturae, secundum Classes, Ordines, Genera, Species, cum Characteribus, Differentiis, Synonymis,* Locis. Edition X, reformata. Holmiae : Laur. Salvii Tom. I 823 pp. [576].
Type data: holotype (probable), ZIUU *♀.
Type locality: "in Indiis" (Oriental Region), see Day, M.C. (1979). The species of Hymenoptera described by Linnaeus in the genera *Sphex, Chrysis, Vespa, Apis* and *Mutilla. Biol. J. Linn. Soc.* **12**: 45–84 [77] (also states specimen at Museum Ludovica Ulrica is ?holotype).

Distribution: NE coastal, Murray-Darling basin, SW coastal, QLD, NSW, VIC, WA; also New Guinea and Aru.
Ecology: adult—volant; melliferous, solitary, flower visiting record: *Teucrium* L. [Lamiaceae].
References: Smith, F. (1854). *Catalogue of Hymenopterous Insects in the Collection of the British Museum.* Part II. Apidae. London : British Museum pp. 199–465 (as *Anthophora zonata* (Linnaeus, 1758)); Dalla Torre, K.W. (1896). *Catalogus Hymenopterorum Hucusque Descriptorum Systematicus et Synonymicus.* Apidae (Anthophila). Lipsiae : G. Engelmann Vol. x 643 pp. (as *Podalirius zonatus* (Linnaeus, 1758)); Cockerell, T.D.A. (1905). Descriptions and records of bees. IV. *Ann. Mag. Nat. Hist. (7)***16**: 392–403 (taxonomy); Friese, H. (1909). Die Bienenfauna von Neu-Guinea. *Ann. Hist.-Nat. Mus. Natl. Hung.* **7**: 179–288 (distribution); Cockerell, T.D.A. (1910). Descriptions and records of bees. XXVIII. *Ann. Mag. Nat. Hist. (8)***5**: 409–419 (taxonomy); Cockerell, T.D.A. (1929). Bees from the Australian region. *Am. Mus. Novit.* **346**: 1–18 (distribution); Rayment, T. (1934). Contributions to the fauna of Rottnest Island. VIII. Apoidea. With description of new species. *J. Proc. R. Soc. West. Aust.* **20**: 201–212 (distribution); Rayment, T. (1944). A critical revision of species in the *zonata* group of *Anthophora* by new characters (Part I). *Treubia* (Japanese edition) **1**: 1–30 [dated 1942, actual date of issue 1944] (taxonomy); Brooks, R.W. (1988). Systematics and phylogeny of the anthophorine bees (Hymenoptera: Anthophoridae; Anthophorini). *Univ. Kansas Sci. Bull.* **53**: 436–575 (subgeneric placement, listed as being from the Oriental Region only).

Thyreus Panzer, 1806

Thyreus Panzer, G.W.F. (1806). *Kritische Revision der Insektenfaune Deutschlands nach dem System bearbeitet.* Nürnberg : Felssecker Vol. 2 xii 271 pp. [263]. Type species: *Nomada scutellaris* Fabricius, 1781 by monotypy. Compiled from secondary source: Sandhouse, G.A. (1943). The type species of the genera and subgenera of bees. *Proc. U.S. Natl Mus.* **92**(3156): 519–619 [604].

Crocissa Panzer, G.W.F. (1806). *Kritische Revision der Insektenfaune Deutschlands nach dem System bearbeitet.* Nürnberg : Felssecker Vol. 2 xii 271 pp. [263]. Type species: *Nomada scutellaris* Fabricius, 1781 by subsequent designation, see Sandhouse, G.A. (1943). The type species of the genera and subgenera of bees. *Proc. U.S. Natl Mus.* **92**(3156): 519–619 [541].

Crocisa Jurine, L. (1807). *Nouvelle Méthode de Classer les Hyménoptères et les Diptères.* Vol. 1 Hyménoptères.

287

Genève : J.J. Paschoud 319+4 pp. [239]. Type species: *Nomada scutellaris* Fabricius, 1781 by subsequent designation, see Michener, C.D. (1965). A classification of the bees of the Australian and South Pacific regions. *Bull. Am. Mus. Nat. Hist.* **130**: 1–362 [218].

Taxonomic decision for synonymy: Sandhouse, G.A. (1943). The type species of the genera and subgenera of bees. *Proc. U.S. Natl Mus.* **92**(3156): 519–619 [604].

Extralimital distribution: Palaearctic and Oriental Regions, extending E to Solomon Ils, see Michener, C.D. (1965). A classification of the bees of the Australian and South Pacific regions. *Bull. Am. Mus. Nat. Hist.* **130**: 1–362 [218].

Species now known not to occur in Australia: *Thyreus gemmata* (Cockerell, 1911): Solomon Ils (one specimen labelled "Cairns", either the label is incorrect or the specimen was introduced), see Cockerell, T.D.A. (1939). Studies of the Pacific bees in the collection of Bishop Museum (Hymenoptera, Apoidea). *Occ. Pap. Bernice P. Bishop Mus.* **15**: 133–140 [139]; *Thyreus novaehollandiae* (Lepeletier, 1841): Timor (probably) (type described from "Nouvelle Hollande", the label is incorrect), see Lieftinck, M.A. (1962). Revision of the Indo-Australian species of the genus *Thyreus* Panzer (=*Crocisa* Jurine) (Hym., Apoidea, Anthophoridae). Part 3. Oriental and Australian species. *Zool. Verh.* **53**: 1–212 [31].

Thyreus caeruleopunctatus (Blanchard, 1840)

Crocisa caeruleopunctata Blanchard, E. (1840). Hyménoptères. pp. 219-415 *in, Histoire Naturelle des Insectes.* Orthoptères, Névroptères, Hémiptères, Hyménoptères, Lépidoptères et Diptères. Paris : Duménil Vol. 3 [411].
Type data: holotype (probable), MNHP ♂*.
Type locality: Australia (as New Holland).

Crocisa australensis Radoszkowsky, O.I. (1893). Revue des armures copulatrices des mâles des genres : *Crocisa* Jur., *Melecta* Lat., *Pseudomelecta* Rad., *Chrysantheda* Pert., *Mesocheira* Lep., *Aglae* Lep., *Melissa* Smith, *Euglossa* Lat., *Eulema* Lep., *Acanthopus* Klug. *Bull. Soc. Imp. Nat. Moscou (ns)***7**: 163–188 [=Radoszkowski, O.I.] [177].
Type data: holotype, ZMB ♀*.
Type locality: TAS (type locality probably incorrect, as this genus is not known to occur in TAS), see Michener, C.D. (1965). A classification of the bees of the Australian and South Pacific regions. *Bull. Am. Mus. Nat. Hist.* **130**: 1–362 [218].

Taxonomic decision for synonymy: Lieftinck, M.A. (1959). Notes on some eighteenth century bees of the genus *Thyreus* Panzer, with description of a new species (Hymenoptera, Apoidea). *Tijdschr. Entomol.* **102**: 17–34 [34].

Distribution: NE coastal, SE coastal, Murray-Darling basin, S Gulfs, N coastal, N Gulf, QLD, NSW, ACT, VIC, SA, WA, NT; also New Guinea.
Ecology: larva—sedentary : adult—volant; melliferous, solitary, cleptoparasitic on *Amegilla (Zonamegilla) pulchra* (Smith, 1854).

References: Lieftinck, M.A. (1962). Revision of the Indo-Australian species of the genus *Thyreus* Panzer (=*Crocisa* Jurine) (Hym., Apoidea, Anthophoridae). Part 3. Oriental and Australian species. *Zool. Verh.* **53**: 1–212 (redescription, distribution); Cardale, J. (1968). Parasites and other organisms associated with nests of *Amegilla* Friese (Hymenoptera : Anthophorinae). *J. Aust. Entomol. Soc.* **7**: 29–34 (biology); Cardale, J. (1968). Immature stages of Australian Anthophorinae (Hymenoptera : Apoidea). *J. Aust. Entomol. Soc.* **7**: 35–41 (immature stages).

Thyreus lugubris (Smith, 1879)

Crocisa lugubris Smith, F. (1879). *Descriptions of New Species of Hymenoptera in the Collection of the British Museum.* London : British Museum xxi 240 pp. [107].
Type data: holotype, BMNH Hym.17.b.457 ♂ (described as ♀).
Type locality: Australia.

Crocisa quadrinotata Radoszkowsky, O.I. (1893). Revue des armures copulatrices des mâles des genres : *Crocisa* Jur., *Melecta* Lat., *Pseudomelecta* Rad., *Chrysantheda* Pert., *Mesocheira* Lep., *Aglae* Lep., *Melissa* Smith, *Euglossa* Lat., *Eulema* Lep., *Acanthopus* Klug. *Bull. Soc. Imp. Nat. Moscou (ns)***7**: 163–188 [=Radoszkowski, O.I.] [176].
Type data: holotype (probable), whereabouts unknown ♀*.
Type locality: Australia (no locality given in original description), see Meyer, R. (1921). Apidae—Nomadinae. I. Gattung *Crocisa* Jur. *Arch. Naturg.* **87**(A)1: 67–178 [176].

Crocisa turneri Friese, H. (1905). Neue *Crocisa*-Arten der Tropen (Hym.). *Z. Syst. Hymenopterol. Dipterol.* **5**: 2–12 [3].
Type data: lectotype, ZMB ♀*.
Subsequent designation: Lieftinck, M.A. (1962). Revision of the Indo-Australian species of the genus *Thyreus* Panzer (=*Crocisa* Jurine) (Hym., Apoidea, Anthophoridae). Part 3. Oriental and Australian species. *Zool. Verh.* **53**: 1–212 [180].
Type locality: Mackay, QLD.

Crocisa albopicta Cockerell, T.D.A. (1910). Some bees of the genus *Crocisa* from Asia and Australia. *Entomologist* **43**: 216–220 [217].
Type data: holotype, BMNH Hym.17.b.458 ♀.
Type locality: Mackay, QLD.

Taxonomic decision for synonymy: Lieftinck, M.A. (1962). Revision of the Indo-Australian species of the genus *Thyreus* Panzer (=*Crocisa* Jurine) (Hym., Apoidea, Anthophoridae). Part 3. Oriental and Australian species. *Zool. Verh.* **53**: 1–212 [179].

Distribution: NE coastal, SE coastal, QLD, NSW.
Ecology: larva—sedentary : adult- -volant; melliferous, solitary, cleptoparasitic on *Amegilla (Asaropoda)* sp.
References: Rayment, T. (1951). A critical revision of species in the genus *Asaropoda* by new characters. *Mem. Natl Mus. Vict.* **17**: 65–80 (biology); Cardale, J. (1968). Parasites and other organisms associated with nests of *Amegilla* Friese (Hymenoptera : Anthophorinae). *J. Aust. Entomol. Soc.* **7**: 29–34 (bi-

ology); Cardale, J. (1968). Immature stages of Australian Anthophorinae (Hymenoptera : Apoidea). *J. Aust. Entomol. Soc.* **7**: 35–41 (immature stages).

Thyreus macleayi (Cockerell, 1907)

Crocisa albomaculata Smith, F. (1868). Descriptions of aculeate Hymenoptera from Australia. *Trans. Entomol. Soc. Lond.* **1868**: 231–258 [258] [junior secondary homonym of *Apis albomaculata* de Geer, 1778].
Type data: holotype, BMNH Hym.17.b.459 ♀.
Type locality: Champion Bay (Geraldton), WA.

Crocisa macleayi Cockerell, T.D.A. (1907). On a collection of Australian and Asiatic bees. *Bull. Am. Mus. Nat. Hist.* **23**: 221–236 [232].
Type data: holotype, AMNH ♀*.
Type locality: NSW.

Crocisa albovittata Friese, H. (1912). Namensänderungen für einige Apiden (Hym.). *Arch. Naturg.* **78**(A)12: 89 [89] [*nom. nov.* for *Crocisa albomaculata* Smith, 1868].

Crocisa plurinotata Meyer, R. (1921). Apidae—Nomadinae. I. Gattung *Crocisa* Jur. *Arch. Naturg.* **87**(A)1: 67–178 [97].
Type data: holotype, ZMB ♀*.
Type locality: Turkestan (incorrectly labelled, no other specimens of this species collected in central Asia), see Lieftinck, M.A. (1962). Revision of the Indo-Australian species of the genus *Thyreus* Panzer (=*Crocisa* Jurine) (Hym., Apoidea, Anthophoridae). Part 3. Oriental and Australian species. *Zool. Verh.* **53**: 1–212 [200].

Taxonomic decision for synonymy: Lieftinck, M.A. (1962). Revision of the Indo-Australian species of the genus *Thyreus* Panzer (=*Crocisa* Jurine) (Hym., Apoidea, Anthophoridae). Part 3. Oriental and Australian species. *Zool. Verh.* **53**: 1–212 [196].

Distribution: NE coastal, S Gulfs, SW coastal, W plateau, NW coastal, QLD, NSW, SA, WA; exact locality in NSW unknown.
Ecology: adult—volant; melliferous, solitary, cleptoparasitic, probably on *Amegilla*.
Reference: Michener, C.D. (1965). A classification of the bees of the Australian and South Pacific regions. *Bull. Am. Mus. Nat. Hist.* **130**: 1–362 [215] (illustration).

Thyreus nitidulus nitidulus (Fabricius, 1804)

Melecta nitidula Fabricius, J.C. (1804). *Systema Piezatorum.* Brunsvigae : C. Reichard xiv 439 pp. [386].
Type data: lectotype, BMNH ♀*.
Subsequent designation: Lieftinck, M.A. (1959). Revision of the Indo-Australian species of the genus *Thyreus* Panzer (=*Crocisa* Jurine) (Hym., Apoidea, Anthophoridae). Part 2. *Thyreus nitidulus* (Fabricius). *Nova Guinea (ns)***10**: 99–130 [115].
Type locality: probably N Australia or Aru Is. (there is no label on the specimen and the species does not occur on Ambon (Amboina), the locality given in the description), see Lieftinck, M.A. (1959). Revision of the Indo-Australian species of the genus *Thyreus* Panzer (=*Crocisa* Jurine) (Hym., Apoidea, Anthophoridae). Part 2. *Thyreus nitidulus* (Fabricius). *Nova Guinea (ns)***10**: 99–130 [115].

Crocisa lamprosoma Boisduval, J.A. (1835). *Voyage de Découvertes de l'*Astrolabe *exécuté par ordre du Roi, pendant les années 1826-1827-1828-1829, sous le commandement de M.J. Dumont d'Urville.* Faune Entomologique de l'Océan Pacifique, avec l'illustration des insectes nouveaux recueillis pendant le voyage. 2me Partie. Coléoptères et autres Ordres. Paris : J. Tastu vii 716 pp. [653].
Type data: holotype, MNHP ♂*.
Type locality: Vanikoro, Sta Cruz Is. (doubtful locality; *Thyreus nitidulus nitidulus* (Fabricius, 1804) known only from Australia, New Guinea and close islands), see Lieftinck, M.A. (1959). Revision of the Indo-Australian species of the genus *Thyreus* Panzer (=*Crocisa* Jurine) (Hym., Apoidea, Anthophoridae). Part 2. *Thyreus nitidulus* (Fabricius). *Nova Guinea (ns)***10**: 99–130 [117].

Crocisa caeruleifrons Kirby, W.F. (1883). Report on a small collection of Hymenoptera and Diptera from the Timor Laut Islands, formed by Mr. H.O. Forbes. *Proc. Zool. Soc. Lond.* **1883**: 343–346 [343].
Type data: holotype, BMNH Hym.17.b.447 ♀.
Type locality: Tanimbar (as Timor Laut Islands).

Crocisa caeruleifrons darwini Cockerell, T.D.A. (1905). Descriptions and records of bees. I. *Ann. Mag. Nat. Hist.* **(7)16**: 216–225 [219].
Type data: lectotype, BMNH Hym.17.b.448 ♂, paralectotype BMNH ♀.
Subsequent designation: Lieftinck, M.A. (1959). Revision of the Indo-Australian species of the genus *Thyreus* Panzer (=*Crocisa* Jurine) (Hym., Apoidea, Anthophoridae). Part 2. *Thyreus nitidulus* (Fabricius). *Nova Guinea (ns)***10**: 99–130 [115]; Cardale J.C., this work, interprets Lieftinck's incorrect inference of holotype as a lectotype designation (Art. 74, ICZN 1985).
Type locality: Darwin, NT.

Crocisa beatissima Cockerell, T.D.A. (1907). A new bee of the genus *Crocisa*. *Entomol. News* **18**: 46 [46].
Type data: holotype, BMNH Hym.17.b.456 ♀.
Type locality: Adelaide, SA.

Crocisa omissa Cockerell, T.D.A. (1919). The Philippine bees of the families Anthophoridae and Melectidae. *Philipp. J. Sci.* **14**: 195–199 [198].
Type data: holotype, USNM*.
Type locality: Mackay, QLD.

Taxonomic decision for synonymy: Lieftinck, M.A. (1959). Revision of the Indo-Australian species of the genus *Thyreus* Panzer (=*Crocisa* Jurine) (Hym., Apoidea, Anthophoridae). Part 2. *Thyreus nitidulus* (Fabricius). *Nova Guinea (ns)***10**: 99–130 [99]; Lieftinck, M.A. (1962). Revision of the Indo-Australian species of the genus *Thyreus* Panzer (=*Crocisa* Jurine) (Hym., Apoidea, Anthophoridae). Part 3. Oriental and Australian species. *Zool. Verh.* **53**: 1–212 [173].

Distribution: NE coastal, SE coastal, S Gulfs, N coastal, QLD, NSW, SA, NT; also New Guinea and adjacent Ils.
Ecology: larva—sedentary : adult—volant; melliferous, solitary, cleptoparasitic on *Amegilla* spp. (?*Amegilla* (*Zonamegilla*) *pulchra* (Smith, 1854), ?*Amegilla* (*Zonamegilla*) *murrayensis* (Rayment, 1935)).
References: Rayment, T. (1935). *A Cluster of Bees.*

Sixty essays on the life-histories of Australian bees, with specific descriptions of over 100 new species, and an introduction by Professor E.F. Phillips, D.Ph., Cornell University, U.S.A. Sydney : Endeavour Press 752 pp. (biology, as *Crocisa lamprosoma* Boisduval, 1835); Cardale, J. (1968). Parasites and other organisms associated with nests of *Amegilla* Friese (Hymenoptera : Anthophorinae). *J. Aust. Entomol. Soc.* **7**: 29–34 (biology); Michener, C.D. & Houston, T.F. (1991). Apoidea. pp. 993–1000 *in* CSIRO (sponsor) *The Insects of Australia*. A textbook for students and research workers. Melbourne : Melbourne University Press Vol. II 2nd Edn (illustration).

Thyreus quadrimaculatus (Radoszkowski, 1893)

Crocisa quadrimaculata Radoszkowsky, O.I. (1893). Revue des armures copulatrices des mâles des genres : *Crocisa* Jur., *Melecta* Lat., *Pseudomelecta* Rad., *Chrysantheda* Pert., *Mesocheira* Lep., *Aglae* Lep., *Melissa* Smith, *Euglossa* Lat., *Eulema* Lep., *Acanthopus* Klug. *Bull. Soc. Imp. Nat. Moscou (ns)***7**: 163–188 [=Radoszkowski, O.I.] [171].
Type data: syntypes, whereabouts unknown ♂♀*.
Type locality: Australia.

Distribution: SE coastal, S Gulfs, Lake Eyre basin, NSW, SA, NT; only published localities White Swamp, Adelaide and Finke River.
Ecology: adult—volant; melliferous, solitary, cleptoparasitic, probably on *Amegilla*.
Reference: Lieftinck, M.A. (1962). Revision of the Indo-Australian species of the genus *Thyreus* Panzer (=*Crocisa* Jurine) (Hym., Apoidea, Anthophoridae). Part 3. Oriental and Australian species. *Zool. Verh.* **53**: 1–212 (taxonomy).

Thyreus rotundatus (Friese, 1905)

Crocisa rotundata Friese, H. (1905). Neue *Crocisa*-Arten der Tropen (Hym.). *Z. Syst. Hymenopterol. Dipterol.* **5**: 2–12 [4].
Type data: holotype, ZMB ♂*.
Type locality: Mackay, QLD.
Crocisa albifrons Rayment, T. (1931). Bees in the collections of the Western Australian Museum and the Agricultural Department, Perth. *J. Proc. R. Soc. West. Aust.* **17**: 157–190 [172].
Type data: holotype, WAM 29–883 ♀.
Type locality: Landor Station, WA.

Taxonomic decision for synonymy: Lieftinck, M.A. (1962). Revision of the Indo Australian species of the genus *Thyreus* Panzer (=*Crocisa* Jurine) (Hym., Apoidea, Anthophoridae). Part 3. Oriental and Australian species. *Zool. Verh.* **53**: 1–212 [193].

Distribution: NE coastal, NW coastal, QLD, WA; only published localities Mackay and Landor Station, Gascoyne River district.
Ecology: adult—volant; melliferous, solitary, cleptoparasitic, probably on *Amegilla*, flower visiting record: *Loranthus* Jacq. [Loranthaceae].
Reference: Rayment, T. (1935). *A Cluster of Bees*.

Sixty essays on the life-histories of Australian bees, with specific descriptions of over 100 new species, and an introduction by Professor E.F. Phillips, D.Ph., Cornell University, U.S.A. Sydney : Endeavour Press 752 pp. (flower record, as *Crocisa albifrons* Rayment, 1931).

Thyreus rufitarsus (Rayment, 1931)

Crocisa rufitarsus Rayment, T. (1931). Bees in the collections of the Western Australian Museum and the Agricultural Department, Perth. *J. Proc. R. Soc. West. Aust.* **17**: 157–190 [174].
Type data: holotype, WADA ♂.
Type locality: probably WA (description states "locality and collector unknown, as specimen is in collection of WA Dept. of Agriculture, it was probably collected in WA").

Distribution: WA; known only from type locality, exact locality unknown.
Ecology: adult—volant; melliferous, solitary.
Reference: Lieftinck, M.A. (1962). Revision of the Indo-Australian species of the genus *Thyreus* Panzer (=*Crocisa* Jurine) (Hym., Apoidea, Anthophoridae). Part 3. Oriental and Australian species. *Zool. Verh.* **53**: 1–212 (taxonomy).

Thyreus sicarius Lieftinck, 1962

Thyreus sicarius Lieftinck, M.A. (1962). Revision of the Indo-Australian species of the genus *Thyreus* Panzer (=*Crocisa* Jurine) (Hym., Apoidea, Anthophoridae). Part 3. Oriental and Australian species. *Zool. Verh.* **53**: 1–212 [200].
Type data: holotype, WAM 64–39 ♀.
Type locality: WA.

Distribution: W plateau, WA; only published locality Belele Station.
Ecology: adult—volant; melliferous, solitary, cleptoparasitic, probably on *Amegilla*.

Thyreus tinctus (Cockerell, 1905)

Crocisa tincta Cockerell, T.D.A. (1905). Descriptions and records of bees. I. *Ann. Mag. Nat. Hist.* (7)**16**: 216–225 [219].
Type data: lectotype, BMNH Hym.17.b.455 ♀, paralectotype BMNH ♀.
Subsequent designation: Lieftinck, M.A. (1962). Revision of the Indo-Australian species of the genus *Thyreus* Panzer (=*Crocisa* Jurine) (Hym., Apoidea, Anthophoridae). Part 3. Oriental and Australian species. *Zool. Verh.* **53**: 1–212 [174]; Cardale J.C., this work, interprets Lieftinck's incorrect inference of holotype as a lectotype designation (Art. 74, ICZN 1985).
Type locality: Toowoomba, QLD.

Distribution: Murray-Darling basin, QLD; known only from type locality.
Ecology: adult—volant; melliferous, solitary.
Reference: Lieftinck, M.A. (1962). Revision of the Indo-Australian species of the genus *Thyreus* Panzer (=*Crocisa* Jurine) (Hym., Apoidea, Anthophoridae).

Part 3. Oriental and Australian species. *Zool. Verh.* **53**: 1–212 (redescription).

Thyreus waroonensis (Cockerell, 1913)

Crocisa waroonensis Cockerell, T.D.A. (1913). Australian bees. i. A new *Crocisa*, with a list of the Australian species of the genus. *Proc. Linn. Soc. N.S.W.* **37**: 594–595 [594].
Type data: holotype, BMNH Hym.17.b.1198 ♂.
Type locality: Waroona, WA.

Distribution: Murray-Darling basin, S Gulfs, W plateau, SW coastal, NW coastal, Lake Eyre basin, NSW, VIC, SA, WA, NT.
Ecology: larva—sedentary : adult—volant; melliferous, solitary, cleptoparasitic, probably on *Amegilla*, flower visiting record: *Eucalyptus* L'Hérit. [Myrtaceae], *Melaleuca* L. [Myrtaceae].
References: Whitlock, F.L. (1947). Cuckoo bees (*Crocisa*) at Bunbury. *West. Aust. Nat.* **1**: 44–45 (biology), Lieftinck, M.A. (1962). Revision of the Indo-Australian species of the genus *Thyreus* Panzer (=*Crocisa* Jurine) (Hym., Apoidea, Anthophoridae). Part 3. Oriental and Australian species. *Zool. Verh.* **53**: 1–212 (redescription, generic placement).

Incertae sedis

Anthophora cinctofemorata Sichel, J. (1869). *In* Dours, J.A. Monographie iconographique du genre *Anthophora*, Latr. *Mém. Soc. Linn. N. Fr.* **2**: 5–211 [151].
Type data: holotype, whereabouts unknown (Dours coll.) ♂*.
Type locality: Australia (as New Holland).

NOMADINAE

Nomada Scopoli, 1770

Nomada Scopoli, J.A. (1770). *Historico naturalis.* Annus IV. Leipzig : Hilscher 150 pp. [44]. Type species: *Apis ruficornis* Linnaeus, 1758 by subsequent designation, see Curtis, J. (1832). *British Entomology; being illustrations and descriptions of the genera of insects found in Great Britain and Ireland : containing coloured figures from nature of the most rare and beautiful species, and in many instances of the plants upon which they are found.* London : John Curtis Vol. 9 pls 384–433 [pl. 419].

Extralimital distribution: Nearctic, Neotropical, Afrotropical, Palaearctic and Oriental Regions, extending E to Solomon Ils, see Michener, C.D. (1965). A classification of the bees of the Australian and South Pacific regions. *Bull. Am. Mus. Nat. Hist.* **130**: 1–362 [214].

Generic reference: Alexander, B. (1991). *Nomada* phylogeny reconsidered (Hymenoptera: Anthophoridae). *J. Nat. Hist.* **25**: 315–330.

Nomada australensis Perkins, 1912

Nomada australensis Perkins, R.C.L. (1912). Notes, with descriptions of new species, on aculeate Hymenoptera of the Australian Region. *Ann. Mag. Nat. Hist. (8)***9**: 96–121 [116].
Type data: syntypes, BMNH Hym.17.b.574a,b 1♂1♀.
Type locality: Kuranda (as Cairns Kuranda), QLD.

Distribution: NE coastal, QLD; only published localities Kuranda and Mackay.
Ecology: adult—volant; melliferous, solitary, cleptoparasitic, possibly on *Lasioglossum* (Halictidae).
References: Cockerell, T.D.A. (1931). The bees of Australia. *Aust. Zool.* **7**: 34–54 (taxonomy); Michener, C.D. (1965). A classification of the bees of the Australian and South Pacific regions. *Bull. Am. Mus. Nat. Hist.* **130**. 1–362 [215] (illustration).

Nomada rubinii (Rayment, 1930)

Neoceratina rubinii Rayment, T. (1930). New and remarkable bees. *Proc. R. Soc. Vict.* **43**: 42–61 [55].
Type data: holotype, ANIC ♀.
Type locality: Townsville, QLD.

Distribution: NE coastal, QLD; known only from type locality.
Ecology: adult—volant; melliferous, solitary, cleptoparasitic, possibly on *Lasioglossum* (Halictidae).
References: Cockerell, T.D.A. (1931). The bees of Australia. *Aust. Zool.* **7**: 34–54 (taxonomy, probable synonym of *Nomada australensis* Perkins, 1912); Rayment, T. (1935). *A Cluster of Bees.* Sixty essays on the life-histories of Australian bees, with specific descriptions of over 100 new species, and an introduction by Professor E.F. Phillips, D.Ph., Cornell University, U.S.A. Sydney : Endeavour Press 752 pp. (illustration).

XYLOCOPINAE

Braunsapis Michener, 1969

Braunsapis Michener, C.D. (1969). African genera of allodapine bees (Hymenoptera : Anthophoridae : Ceratinini). *J. Kansas Entomol. Soc.* **42**: 289–293 [290].
Type species: *Allodape facialis* Gerstaecker, 1857 by original designation.

Extralimital distribution: Afrotropical, Palaearctic and Oriental Regions, extending E to Solomon Ils, see Reyes, S.G. (1991). Revision of the bee genus *Braunsapis* in the Oriental Region (Apoidea: Xylocopinae: Allodapini). *Univ. Kansas Sci. Bull.* **54**: 179–207 [190].

Braunsapis associata (Michener, 1961)

Allodapula associata Michener, C.D. (1961). Probable parasitism among Australian bees of the genus *Allodapula* (Hymenoptera, Apoidea, Ceratinini). *Ann. Entomol. Soc. Am.* **54**: 532–534 [533].
Type data: holotype, QM T6223 ♀.
Type locality: Mt Edwards, QLD.

Distribution: NE coastal, Murray-Darling basin, QLD, NSW.
Ecology: adult—volant; melliferous, probably cleptoparasitic, found in nests of *Braunsapis unicolor* (Smith, 1854), nest in dead twigs, flower visiting record: *Eucalyptus* L'Hérit. [Myrtaceae].
References: Michener, C.D. & Syed, I.H. (1962). Specific characters of the larvae and adults of *Allodapula* in the Australian region (Hymenoptera : Ceratinini). *J. Entomol. Soc. Qd* **1**: 30–41 (taxonomy); Michener, C.D. (1974). *The Social Behaviour of the Bees*. A comparative study. Cambridge : Belknap Press of Harvard University Press 404 pp. (generic placement).

Braunsapis clarissima (Cockerell, 1929)

Allodape clarissima Cockerell, T.D.A. (1929). Bees from the Australian region. *Am. Mus. Novit.* **346**: 1–18 [15].
Type data: holotype, USNM ♂*.
Type locality: Thursday Is., QLD.

Distribution: NE coastal, QLD; only published localities Thursday Is., near Ayr, Mt Boppy, near Bowen and Yaamba.
Ecology: larva—sedentary : adult—volant; melliferous, nest in dead, dry twigs (*Cassia* L. *s.lat.* [Caesalpiniaceae]), several females in one nest and larvae of various ages are found together, not in separate cells.
References: Cockerell, T.D.A. (1929). Bees from the Australian region. *Am. Mus. Novit.* **346**: 1–18 (description of female, as *Allodape plebeia* Cockerell, 1929); Michener, C.D. & Syed, I.H. (1962). Specific characters of the larvae and adults of *Allodapula* in the Australian region (Hymenoptera : Ceratinini). *J. Entomol. Soc. Qd* **1**: 30–41 (redescription, distribution, as *Allodapula clarissima* (Cockerell, 1929); Michener, C.D. (1962). Biological observations on the primitively social bees of the genus *Allodapula* in the Australian region (Hymenoptera, Xylocopinae). *Insectes Soc.* **9**: 355–373 (biology); Michener, C.D. (1974). *The Social Behaviour of the Bees*. A comparative study. Cambridge : Belknap Press of Harvard University Press 404 pp. (generic placement).

Braunsapis diminuta (Cockerell, 1915)

Allodape diminuta Cockerell, T.D.A. (1915). Descriptions and records of bees. LXV. *Ann. Mag. Nat. Hist.* (8)**15**: 261–269 [266].
Type data: lectotype, USNM ♂*.
Subsequent designation: Michener, C.D. & Syed, I.H. (1962). Specific characters of the larvae and adults of

Allodapula in the Australian region (Hymenoptera : Ceratinini). *J. Entomol. Soc. Qd* **1**: 30–41 [40].
Type locality: Yarrawin, NSW.

Distribution: NE coastal, Murray-Darling basin, N coastal, QLD, NSW, NT.
Ecology: larva—sedentary : adult—volant; melliferous, nest in dead, dry twigs (*Cassia* L. *s.lat.* [Caesalpiniaceae]), several females in one nest and larvae of various ages are found together, not in separate cells, flower visiting record: *Bursaria* Cav. [Pittosporaceae], *Callistemon* R.Br. [Myrtaceae], *Loranthus* Jacq. [Loranthaceae].
References: Cockerell, T.D.A. (1929). Bees from the Australian region. *Am. Mus. Novit.* **346**: 1–18 (taxonomy); Rayment, T. (1935). *A Cluster of Bees*. Sixty essays on the life-histories of Australian bees, with specific descriptions of over 100 new species, and an introduction by Professor E.F. Phillips, D.Ph., Cornell University, U.S.A. Sydney : Endeavour Press 752 pp. (illustration, flower record); Rayment, T. (1946). New bees and wasps—Part II. Describing two black species of *Exoneura*. *Vict. Nat.* **62**: 230–236 (flower record); Michener, C.D. & Syed, I.H. (1962). Specific characters of the larvae and adults of *Allodapula* in the Australian region (Hymenoptera : Ceratinini). *J. Entomol. Soc. Qd* **1**: 30–41 (redescription, biology, as *Allodapula diminuta* Cockerell, 1915); Michener, C.D. (1962). Biological observations on the primitively social bees of the genus *Allodapula* in the Australian region (Hymenoptera, Xylocopinae). *Insectes Soc.* **9**: 355–373 (biology); Michener, C.D. (1974). *The Social Behaviour of the Bees*. A comparative study. Cambridge : Belknap Press of Harvard University Press 404 pp. (generic placement).

Braunsapis minor (Michener and Syed, 1962)

Allodapula minor Michener, C.D. & Syed, I.H. (1962). Specific characters of the larvae and adults of *Allodapula* in the Australian region (Hymenoptera : Ceratinini). *J. Entomol. Soc. Qd* **1**: 30–41 [38].
Type data: holotype, BMNH Hym.17.a.2843 ♀.
Type locality: Mackay, QLD.

Distribution: NE coastal, QLD; known only from type locality.
Ecology: adult—volant; melliferous, solitary, flower visiting record: *Eucalyptus* L'Hérit. [Myrtaceae].
Reference: Michener, C.D. (1974). *The Social Behaviour of the Bees*. A comparative study. Cambridge : Belknap Press of Harvard University Press 404 pp. (generic placement).

Braunsapis nitida (Smith, 1859)

Allodape nitida Smith, F. (1859). Catalogue of hymenopterous insects collected by Mr. A.R. Wallace at the islands of Aru and Key. *J. Linn. Soc. Lond. Zool.* **3**: 132–178 [134].

Type data: holotype (probable), OUM ♀.
Type locality: Aru Is.

Distribution: NE coastal, N coastal, QLD, NT; only published localities Prince of Wales Is., Thursday Is. and Darwin, also Aru Is. and New Guinea.
Ecology: larva—sedentary : adult—volant; melliferous, nest in dead, dry twigs (*Stachys*), several females in one nest and larvae of various ages are found together, not in separate cells.
References: Michener, C.D. & Syed, I.H. (1962). Specific characters of the larvae and adults of *Allodapula* in the Australian region (Hymenoptera : Ceratinini). *J. Entomol. Soc. Qd* **1**: 30–41 (redescription, biology, as *Allodapula nitida* (Smith, 1859)); Michener, C.D. (1962). Biological observations on the primitively social bees of the genus *Allodapula* in the Australian region (Hymenoptera, Xylocopinae). *Insectes Soc.* **9**: 355–373 (biology); Michener, C.D. (1965). A classification of the bees of the Australian and South Pacific regions. *Bull. Am. Mus. Nat. Hist.* **130**: 1–362 [223] (biology, as *Allodapula nitida* (Smith, 1859)); Michener, C.D. (1974). *The Social Behaviour of the Bees*. A comparative study. Cambridge : Belknap Press of Harvard University Press 404 pp. (generic placement).

Braunsapis occidentalis (Michener and Syed, 1962)

Allodapula occidentalis Michener, C.D. & Syed, I.H. (1962). Specific characters of the larvae and adults of *Allodapula* in the Australian region (Hymenoptera : Ceratinini). *J. Entomol. Soc. Qd* **1**: 30–41 [41].
Type data: holotype, WAM 65–732 ♀.
Type locality: Tambrey, near Roebourne, WA.

Distribution: SW coastal, NW coastal, WA; only published localities Tambrey and Mt Jackson.
Ecology: adult—volant; melliferous, flower visiting record: *Chrysogonum* L. [Asteraceae].
Reference: Michener, C.D. (1974). *The Social Behaviour of the Bees*. A comparative study. Cambridge : Belknap Press of Harvard University Press 404 pp. (generic placement).

Braunsapis perkinsiella (Michener and Syed, 1962)

Allodapula perkinsiella Michener, C.D. & Syed, I.H. (1962). Specific characters of the larvae and adults of *Allodapula* in the Australian region (Hymenoptera : Ceratinini). *J. Entomol. Soc. Qd* **1**: 30–41 [37].
Type data: holotype, BMNH Hym.17.a.2842 ♀.
Type locality: Mackay, QLD.

Distribution: NE coastal, QLD.
Ecology: larva—sedentary : adult—volant; melliferous, nest in dead, dry twigs (*Cassia* L. *s.lat.* [Caesalpiniaceae]), several females in one nest and larvae of various ages are found together, not in separate cells, flower visiting record: *Cassia* L. *s.lat.* [Caesalpiniaceae], *Eucalyptus* L'Hérit. [Myrtaceae].
References: Michener, C.D. (1962). Biological observations on the primitively social bees of the genus *Allodapula* in the Australian region (Hymenoptera, Xylocopinae). *Insectes Soc.* **9**: 355–373 (biology); Michener, C.D. (1974). *The Social Behaviour of the Bees*. A comparative study. Cambridge : Belknap Press of Harvard University Press 404 pp. (generic placement).

Braunsapis plebeia (Cockerell, 1929)

Allodape plebeia Cockerell, T.D.A. (1929). Bees from the Australian region. *Am. Mus. Novit.* **346**: 1–18 [15].
Type data: holotype, USNM ♂*.
Type locality: Thursday Is., QLD.

Distribution: NE coastal, QLD; only published localities Thursday Is., Mossman and Edungalba, also New Guinea.
Ecology: larva—sedentary : adult—volant; melliferous, nest in dead, dry twigs (*Stachys*), several females in one nest and larvae of various ages are found together, not in separate cells, flower visiting record: *Plectronia* L. [Rubiaceae].
References: Rayment, T. (1946). New bees and wasps—Part II. Describing two black species of *Exoneura*. *Vict. Nat.* **62**: 230–236 (flower record, as *Allodapula plebeia* (Cockerell, 1929)); Michener, C.D. (1962). Biological observations on the primitively social bees of the genus *Allodapula* in the Australian region (Hymenoptera, Xylocopinae). *Insectes Soc.* **9**: 355–373 (biology); Michener, C.D. & Syed, I.H. (1962). Specific characters of the larvae and adults of *Allodapula* in the Australian region (Hymenoptera : Ceratinini). *J. Entomol. Soc. Qd* **1**: 30–41 (redescription, biology); Michener, C.D. (1965). A classification of the bees of the Australian and South Pacific regions. *Bull. Am. Mus. Nat. Hist.* **130**: 1–362 [223] (biology); Michener, C.D. (1974). *The Social Behaviour of the Bees*. A comparative study. Cambridge : Belknap Press of Harvard University Press 404 pp. (generic placement).

Braunsapis praesumptiosa (Michener, 1961)

Allodapula praesumptiosa Michener, C.D. (1961). Probable parasitism among Australian bees of the genus *Allodapula* (Hymenoptera, Apoidea, Ceratinini). *Ann. Entomol. Soc. Am.* **54**: 532–534 [533].
Type data: holotype, BMNH Hym.17.a.2841 ♀.
Type locality: Mackay, QLD.

Distribution: NE coastal, QLD; known only from type locality.
Ecology: adult—volant; melliferous, probably cleptoparasitic on *Braunsapis simillima* (Smith, 1854), flower visiting record: *Cassia* L. *s.lat.* [Caesalpiniaceae], *Eugenia* L. [Myrtaceae], *Xanthorrhoea* Sm. [Xanthorrhoeaceae].
References: Michener, C.D. & Syed, I.H. (1962). Specific characters of the larvae and adults of *Allodapula* in the Australian region (Hymenoptera : Ceratinini). *J. Entomol. Soc. Qd* **1**: 30–41 (taxonomy); Michener, C.D. (1974). *The Social Behaviour*

of the Bees. A comparative study. Cambridge : Belknap Press of Harvard University Press 404 pp. (generic placement).

Braunsapis simillima (Smith, 1854)

Allodape simillima Smith, F. (1854). *Catalogue of Hymenopterous Insects in the Collection of the British Museum.* Part II. Apidae. London : British Museum pp. 199–465 [229].
Type data: holotype, BMNH Hym.17.b.423 ♀.
Type locality: Macintyre River, NSW.

Distribution: NE coastal, SE coastal, Murray-Darling basin, N coastal, NW coastal, QLD, NSW, WA, NT.
Ecology: larva—sedentary : adult—volant; melliferous, nest in dead, dry twigs (*Leptospermum* Forster & G.Forster [Myrtaceae]), flowering stalks (*Xanthorrhoea* Sm. [Xanthorrhoeaceae]), several females in one nest and larvae of various ages are found together, not in separate cells, flower visiting record: *Acacia* Miller [Mimosaceae], *Angophora* Cav. [Myrtaceae], *Callistemon* R.Br. [Myrtaceae], *Eucalyptus* L'Hérit. [Myrtaceae], *Hibbertia* Andrews [Dilleniaceae], *Jacksonia* Smith [Fabaceae], *Leptospermum* Forster & G.Forster [Myrtaceae], *Leucopogon* R.Br. [Epacridaceae], *Lomatia* R.Br. [Proteaceae], *Loranthus* Jacq. [Loranthaceae], *Melaleuca* L. [Myrtaceae], *Persoonia* Sm. [Proteaceae], *Pultenaea* Sm. [Fabaceae], *Tristania* R.Br. [Myrtaceae], *Velleia* Sm. [Goodeniaceae].
References: Cockerell, T.D.A. (1905). Descriptions and records of bees. II. *Ann. Mag. Nat. Hist. (7)*16: 292–301 (distribution); Cockerell, T.D.A. (1912). Descriptions and records of bees. XLIII. *Ann. Mag. Nat. Hist. (8)*9: 377–387 (description of male); Cockerell, T.D.A. (1929). Bees from the Australian region. *Am. Mus. Novit.* 346: 1–18 (distribution); Rayment, T. (1939). Bees from the high lands of New South Wales and Victoria. *Aust. Zool.* 9: 263–294 (flower record); Rayment, T. (1946). New bees and wasps—Part II. Describing two black species of *Exoneura. Vict. Nat.* 62: 230–236 (flower record, as *Allodapula simillima* (Smith, 1854)); Michener, C.D. (1961). Probable parasitism among Australian bees of the genus *Allodapula* (Hymenoptera, Apoidea, Ceratinini). *Ann. Entomol. Soc. Am.* 54: 532–534 (biology, as *Allodapula simillima* (Smith, 1854)); Michener, C.D. & Syed, I.H. (1962). Specific characters of the larvae and adults of *Allodapula* in the Australian region (Hymenoptera : Ceratinini). *J. Entomol. Soc. Qd* 1: 30–41 (redescription); Michener, C.D. (1962). Biological observations on the primitively social bees of the genus *Allodapula* in the Australian region (Hymenoptera, Xylocopinae). *Insectes Soc.* 9: 355–373 (biology); Michener, C.D. (1965). A classification of the bees of the Australian and South Pacific regions. *Bull. Am. Mus. Nat. Hist.* 130: 1–362 [222, 242] (illustration, flower record); Michener, C.D. (1966). Parasitism among Indoaustralian bees of the genus

Allodapula (Hymenoptera : Ceratinini). *J. Kansas Entomol. Soc.* 39: 705–708 (illustration); Michener, C.D. (1974). *The Social Behaviour of the Bees.* A comparative study. Cambridge : Belknap Press of Harvard University Press 404 pp. (generic placement); Cane, J.H. (1979). The hind tibiotarsal and tibial spur articulations in bees (Hymenoptera : Apoidea). *J. Kansas Entomol. Soc.* 52: 123–137 (morphology).

Braunsapis unicolor (Smith, 1854)

Allodape unicolor Smith, F. (1854). *Catalogue of Hymenopterous Insects in the Collection of the British Museum.* Part II. Apidae. London : British Museum pp. 199–465 [230].
Type data: holotype, BMNH Hym.17.b.424 ♀.
Type locality: Australia (as New Holland).

Distribution: NE coastal, N coastal, QLD, WA, NT; also New Guinea.
Ecology: larva—sedentary : adult—volant; melliferous, nest in dead, dry twigs (*Callistemon* R.Br. [Myrtaceae], *Cassia* L. *s.lat.* [Caesalpiniaceae], *Lantana* L. [Verbenaceae]), flowering stalks (*Xanthorrhoea* Sm. [Xanthorrhoeaceae]), several females in one nest and larvae of various ages are found together, not in separate cells, flower visiting record: *Acacia* Miller [Mimosaceae], *Angophora* Cav. [Myrtaceae], *Callistemon* R.Br. [Myrtaceae], *Eucalyptus* L'Hérit. [Myrtaceae], *Hibbertia* Andrews [Dilleniaceae], *Jacksonia* Smith [Fabaceae], *Leptospermum* Forster & G.Forster [Myrtaceae], *Leucopogon* R.Br. [Epacridaceae], *Melaleuca* L. [Myrtaceae], *Persoonia* Sm. [Proteaceae], *Pultenaea* Sm. [Fabaceae], *Tristania* R.Br. [Myrtaceae], *Velleia* Sm. [Goodeniaceae].
References: Cockerell, T.D.A. (1905). Descriptions and records of bees. II. *Ann. Mag. Nat. Hist. (7)*16: 292–301 (distribution); Friese, H. (1909). Die Bienenfauna von Neu-Guinea. *Ann. Hist.-Nat. Mus. Natl. Hung.* 7: 179–288 (distribution); Cockerell, T.D.A. (1929). Bees from the Australian region. *Am. Mus. Novit.* 346: 1–18 (distribution); Michener, C.D. (1961). Probable parasitism among Australian bees of the genus *Allodapula* (Hymenoptera, Apoidea, Ceratinini). *Ann. Entomol. Soc. Am.* 54: 532–534 (biology, as *Allodapula unicolor* (Smith, 1854)); Michener, C.D. & Syed, I.H. (1962). Specific characters of the larvae and adults of *Allodapula* in the Australian region (Hymenoptera : Ceratinini). *J. Entomol. Soc. Qd* 1: 30–41 (redescription, biology); Michener, C.D. (1962). Biological observations on the primitively social bees of the genus *Allodapula* in the Australian region (Hymenoptera, Xylocopinae). *Insectes Soc.* 9: 355–373 (biology); Michener, C.D. (1965). A classification of the bees of the Australian and South Pacific regions. *Bull. Am. Mus. Nat. Hist.* 130: 1–362 [225, 242] (illustration, flower record); Michener, C.D. (1974). *The Social Behaviour of the Bees.* A

comparative study. Cambridge : Belknap Press of Harvard University Press 404 pp. (generic placement).

Ceratina Latreille, 1802

Clavicera Latreille, P.A. (1802). *Histoire Naturelle des Fourmis et Recueil de Mémoires et d'Observations sur les Abeilles, les Areignées, les Faucheurs et autres Insectes.* Paris : Barrois 445 pp. [432] [*Clavicera* suppressed under the Plenary Powers of the International Commission of Zoological Nomenclature, see International Commission on Zoological Nomenclature (1973). Opinion 1001. *Ceratina* Latreille, (1802–1803) (Insecta, Hymenoptera) : validated under the plenary powers. *Bull. Zool. Nomen.* **30**: 84–85].

Ceratina Latreille, P.A. (1802). *Histoire Naturelle, Générale et Particulière des Crustacés et des Insectes.* Paris : F. Dufart Vol. 3 xii 13+467 pp. [380] [*Ceratina* placed on the Official List of Generic Names in Zoology, see International Commission on Zoological Nomenclature (1973). Opinion 1001. *Ceratina* Latreille, (1802–1803) (Insecta, Hymenoptera) : validated under the plenary powers. *Bull. Zool. Nomen.* **30**: 84–85]. Type species: *Hylaeus albilabris* Fabricius, 1793 (=*Apis cucurbitina* Rossi, 1792) by monotypy.

Taxonomic decision for subgeneric arrangement: Hirashima, Y. (1971). Subgeneric classification of the genus *Ceratina* Latreille of Asia and West Pacific, with comments on the remaining subgenera of the world (Hymenoptera, Apoidea). *J. Fac. Agric. Kyushu Univ.* **16**: 349–375 [349].

Extralimital distribution: Nearctic, Neotropical, Afrotropical, Palaearctic and Oriental Regions, see Hirashima, Y. (1971). Subgeneric classification of the genus *Ceratina* Latreille of Asia and West Pacific, with comments on the remaining subgenera of the world (Hymenoptera, Apoidea). *J. Fac. Agric. Kyushu Univ.* **16**: 349–375.

Ceratina (Neoceratina) Perkins, 1912

Neoceratina Perkins, R.C.L. (1912). Notes, with descriptions of new species, on aculeate Hymenoptera of the Australian Region. *Ann. Mag. Nat. Hist.* (8)**9**: 96–121 [117]. Type species: *Neoceratina australensis* Perkins, 1912 by monotypy.

Extralimital distribution: Palaearctic and Oriental Regions, extending E to Solomon Ils, see Hirashima, Y. (1971). Subgeneric classification of the genus *Ceratina* Latreille of Asia and West Pacific, with comments on the remaining subgenera of the world (Hymenoptera, Apoidea). *J. Fac. Agric. Kyushu Univ.* **16**: 349–375 [362].

Ceratina (Neoceratina) australensis (Perkins, 1912)

Neoceratina australensis Perkins, R.C.L. (1912). Notes, with descriptions of new species, on aculeate Hymenoptera of the Australian Region. *Ann. Mag. Nat. Hist.* (8)**9**: 96–121 [117].
Type data: holotype, BMNH Hym.17.a.2831 ♀.
Type locality: Bundaberg, QLD.

Allodape bribiensis Cockerell, T.D.A. (1914). New Australian bees. *Entomologist* **47**: 197–201 [200].
Type data: holotype, QM T4109 ♀.
Type locality: Bribie Is., QLD.

Taxonomic decision for synonymy: Michener, C.D. & Syed, I.H. (1962). Specific characters of the larvae and adults of *Allodapula* in the Australian region (Hymenoptera : Ceratinini). *J. Entomol. Soc. Qd* **1**: 30–41 [30].

Distribution: NE coastal, SE coastal, Murray-Darling basin, QLD, NSW; also New Guinea and Solomon Ils.

Ecology: larva—sedentary : adult—volant; melliferous, solitary, nest in dead dry pithy stems (weed, *Lantana* L. [Verbenaceae], *Rubus* L. [Rosaceae], *Verbena* L. [Verbenaceae], *Xanthorrhoea* Sm. [Xanthorrhoeaceae]), no evidence of castes or social behaviour, each larva reared in individual, mass-provisioned cell, but several adults may be found in one nest, overwintering, or soon after emergence.

References: Rayment, T. (1935). *A Cluster of Bees.* Sixty essays on the life-histories of Australian bees, with specific descriptions of over 100 new species, and an introduction by Professor E.F. Phillips, D.Ph., Cornell University, U.S.A. Sydney : Endeavour Press 752 pp. (description of male, nest described is not of this species); Michener, C.D. (1962). The genus *Ceratina* in Australia, with notes on its nests (Hymenoptera : Apoidea). *J. Kansas Entomol. Soc.* **35**: 414–421 (biology, as *Ceratina australensis* (Perkins, 1912)); Michener, C.D. (1965). A classification of the bees of the Australian and South Pacific regions. *Bull. Am. Mus. Nat. Hist.* **130**: 1–362 [222] (illustration, as *Ceratina (Ceratina) australensis*); Hirashima, Y. (1971). Subgeneric classification of the genus *Ceratina* Latreille of Asia and West Pacific, with comments on the remaining subgenera of the world (Hymenoptera, Apoidea). *J. Fac. Agric. Kyushu Univ.* **16**: 349–375 (generic placement, distribution).

Exoneura Smith, 1854

Taxonomic decision for subgeneric arrangement: Michener, C.D. (1965). A classification of the bees of the Australian and South Pacific regions. *Bull. Am. Mus. Nat. Hist.* **130**: 1–362 [232].

Exoneura (Exoneura) Smith, 1854

Exoneura Smith, F. (1854). *Catalogue of Hymenopterous Insects in the Collection of the British Museum.* Part II. Apidae. London : British Museum pp. 199–465 [232]. Type species: *Exoneura bicolor* Smith, 1854 by monotypy.

Exoneura (Exoneura) abstrusa Cockerell, 1922

Exoneura abstrusa Cockerell, T.D.A. (1922). Australian bees in the Queensland Museum. *Mem. Qd Mus.* **7**: 257–279 [278].
Type data: holotype, QM T2518 ♂.
Type locality: Brisbane, QLD.

Distribution: NE coastal, SE coastal, QLD, NSW; only published localities Brisbane and Woy Woy.

Ecology: adult—volant; melliferous, nest in dead, dry, woody twigs, two or more adult females may be present in one nest, not all females lay eggs, all immature stages found in the communal chamber, larvae fed progressively.

References: Rayment, T. (1935). *A Cluster of Bees*. Sixty essays on the life-histories of Australian bees, with specific descriptions of over 100 new species, and an introduction by Professor E.F. Phillips, D.Ph., Cornell University, U.S.A. Sydney : Endeavour Press 752 pp. (description of female); Rayment, T. (1951). Biology of the reed-bees. With descriptions of three new species and two allotypes of *Exoneura*. *Aust. Zool.* **11**: 285–313 (illustration).

Exoneura (Exoneura) albopilosa Rayment, 1951

Exoneura albopilosa Rayment, T. (1951). *In* Erickson, R. & Rayment, T. Simple social bees of Western Australia. *West. Aust. Nat.* **3**: 45–59 [51].
Type data: holotype, ANIC ♂.
Type locality: 40 miles S Perth, WA.

Distribution: SW coastal, WA; known only from type locality.
Ecology: adult—volant; melliferous, nest in *Xanthorrhoea* Smith [Xanthorrhoeaceae] stems.

Exoneura (Exoneura) angophorae Cockerell, 1912

Exoneura angophorae Cockerell, T.D.A. (1912). Descriptions and records of bees. XLII. *Ann. Mag. Nat. Hist. (8)***9**: 220–229 [224].
Type data: holotype, USNM ♀*.
Type locality: Sydney, NSW.

Distribution: NE coastal, SE coastal, Murray-Darling basin, QLD, NSW, VIC.
Ecology: larva—sedentary : adult—volant; melliferous, nest in dead, dry stems (*Erythrina, Lantana* L. [Verbenaceae]), flowering stalks (*Xanthorrhoea* Sm. [Xanthorrhoeaceae]), two or more adult females may be present in one nest, not all females lay eggs, all immature stages found in the communal chamber, larvae fed progressively, flower visiting record: *Angophora* Cav. [Myrtaceae].
References: Rayment, T. (1947). Bees from the Victorian Alps. *Vict. Nat.* **64**: 103–107 (distribution); Rayment, T. (1948). New bees and wasps—Part VII. Two undescribed species of *Exoneura*, with notes on recent collectings of several other Exoneurae and the extraordinary appendages of their larvae. *Vict. Nat.* **65**: 85–91 (biology); Rayment, T. (1949). New bees and wasps—Part VIII. A new species of *Exoneura*, with notes on other reed-bees from the Grampians. *Vict. Nat.* **65**: 208–212 (taxonomy); Rayment, T. (1951). Biology of the reed-bees. With descriptions of three new species and two allotypes of *Exoneura*. *Aust. Zool.* **11**: 285–313 (biology); Michener, C.D. (1965). The life cycle and social organization of bees of the genus *Exoneura* and their parasite, *Inquilina* (Hymenoptera : Xylocopinae). *Univ. Kansas Sci. Bull.* **46**: 317–358 (biology); Cane, J.H. & Michener, C.D. (1983). Chemistry and function of mandibular gland products of bees of the genus *Exoneura* (Hymenoptera, Anthophoridae). *J. Chem. Ecol.* **9**: 1525–1531 (taxonomy).

Exoneura (Exoneura) angophorella Rayment, 1948

Exoneura angophorella Rayment, T. (1948). New bees and wasps—Part VII. Two undescribed species of *Exoneura*, with notes on recent collectings of several other Exoneurae and the extraordinary appendages of their larvae. *Vict. Nat.* **65**: 85–91 [85].
Type data: holotype, ANIC ♀.
Type locality: Lane Cove, NSW.

Distribution: SE coastal, NSW; known only from type locality.
Ecology: adult—volant; melliferous, nest in stems of *Lantana* L. [Verbenaceae].
References: Rayment, T. (1949). New bees and wasps—Part VIII. A new species of *Exoneura*, with notes on other reed-bees from the Grampians. *Vict. Nat.* **65**: 208–212 (illustration); Rayment, T. (1951). Biology of the reed-bees. With descriptions of three new species and two allotypes of *Exoneura*. *Aust. Zool.* **11**: 285–313 (illustration).

Exoneura (Exoneura) apposita Rayment, 1949

Exoneura apposita Rayment, T. (1949). New bees and wasps—Part IX. Four undescribed species of *Exoneura*, with notes on their collection, and description of new parasites discovered on the genus. *Vict. Nat.* **65**: 247–254 [248].
Type data: holotype, ANIC ♂.
Type locality: Lane Cove, NSW.

Distribution: SE coastal, NSW; known only from type locality.
Ecology: adult—volant; melliferous, nest in stems of *Lantana* L. [Verbenaceae].

Exoneura (Exoneura) asimillima Rayment, 1951

Exoneura simillima Rayment, T. (1949). New bees and wasps—Part VIII. A new species of *Exoneura*, with notes on other reed-bees from the Grampians. *Vict. Nat.* **65**: 208–212 [208] [junior primary homonym of *Exoneura simillima* Rayment, 1935].
Type data: syntypes (probable), ANIC ♂♀.
Type locality: Cranbourne, VIC.

Exoneura asimillima Rayment, T. (1951). Biology of the reed-bees. With descriptions of three new species and two allotypes of *Exoneura*. *Aust. Zool.* **11**: 285–313 [288] [*nom. nov.* for *Exoneura simillima* Rayment, 1949].

Distribution: SE coastal, NSW, VIC; only published localities Nadgee Nature Reserve, Cranbourne, Grampians and Portland district.
Ecology: larva—sedentary : adult—volant; melliferous, nest in dead, dry pithy stems (sword grass,

Gahnia, Juncus), flowering stalks (*Xanthorrhoea* Sm. [Xanthorrhoeaceae]), two or more adult females may be present in one nest, not all females lay eggs, all immature stages found in the communal chamber, larvae fed progressively, flower visiting record: *Aotus* Smith [Fabaceae], *Arctotheca* Wendl. [Asteraceae], *Bursaria* Cav. [Pittosporaceae], *Epacris* Cav. [Epacridaceae], *Eucalyptus* L'Hérit. [Myrtaceae], *Melaleuca* L. [Myrtaceae].
References: Rayment, T. (1951). Biology of the reed-bees. With descriptions of three new species and two allotypes of *Exoneura*. *Aust. Zool.* **11**: 285–313 [298] (biology); Rayment, T. (1953). *Bees of the Portland District*. Victoria : Portland Field Naturalist's Club 39 pp. (flower record); Sugden, E. (1988). Inside the (secret) societies of native bees. *Aust. Nat. Hist.* **22**: 381–384 (biology); Sugden, E.A. (1989). A semi-natural, manipular observation nest for *Exoneura* spp. and other allodapine bees (Hymenoptera: Anthophoridae). *Pan-Pac. Entomol.* **65**: 17–24 (biology); Sugden, E.A. & Pyke, G.H. (1991). Effects of honey bees on colonies of *Exoneura asimillima*, an Australian native bee. *Aust. J. Ecol.* **16**: 171–181 (biology).

Exoneura (Exoneura) baculifera Cockerell, 1922

Exoneura baculifera Cockerell, T.D.A. (1922). Australian bees in the Queensland Museum. *Mem. Qd Mus.* **7**: 257–279 [276].
Type data: syntypes, QM 5♀ (a female is labelled 'type' and has registration number T2520).
Type locality: [Lamington] National Park, QLD.

Distribution: NE coastal, SE coastal, QLD, NSW, VIC; only published localities Lamington National Park, Woy Woy, Gladesville, Lindfield and Gorae West.
Ecology: larva—sedentary : adult—volant; melliferous, nest in dead, dry stems (on edge of rainforest, of *Erythrina*), in galleries in dry timber, two or more adult females may be present in one nest, not all females lay eggs, all immature stages found in the communal chamber, larvae fed progressively, flower visiting record: *Claoxylon* A. Juss. [Euphorbiaceae], *Leucopogon* R.Br. [Epacridaceae], *Lomatia* R.Br. [Proteaceae].
References: Rayment, T. (1939). Bees from the high lands of New South Wales and Victoria. *Aust. Zool.* **9**: 263–294 (distribution); Rayment, T. (1948). New bees and wasps—Part VII. Two undescribed species of *Exoneura*, with notes on recent collectings of several other Exoneurae and the extraordinary appendages of their larvae. *Vict. Nat.* **65**: 85–91 (biology); Rayment, T. (1953). *Bees of the Portland District*. Victoria : Portland Field Naturalist's Club 39 pp. (distribution); Rayment, T. (1954). New bees and wasps—Part XXII. The altruistic reed-bees, *Exoneura*. *Vict. Nat.* **71**: 13–16 (illustration); Michener, C.D. (1965). A classification of the bees of the Aus-

tralian and South Pacific regions. *Bull. Am. Mus. Nat. Hist.* **130**: 1–362 [243] (flower record); Michener, C.D. (1965). The life cycle and social organization of bees of the genus *Exoneura* and their parasite, *Inquilina* (Hymenoptera : Xylocopinae). *Univ. Kansas Sci. Bull.* **46**: 317–358 (biology); Michener, C.D. (1977). Discordant evolution and the classification of allodapine bees. *Syst. Zool.* **26**: 32–56 (taxonomy).

Exoneura (Exoneura) baxteri Rayment, 1956

Exoneura baxteri Rayment, T. (1956). New species of bees and wasps—Part XXV. *Vict. Nat.* **72**: 173–174 [173].
Type data: holotype, ANIC ♂.
Type locality: Gorae West (Bats Ridges on label), Portland, VIC.

Distribution: SE coastal, VIC; known only from type locality.
Ecology: adult—volant; melliferous, nest in beetle burrows in branch of *Eucalyptus* L'Hérit. [Myrtaceae].

Exoneura (Exoneura) bicincta Rayment, 1935

Exoneura bicincta Rayment, T. (1935). *A Cluster of Bees*. Sixty essays on the life-histories of Australian bees, with specific descriptions of over 100 new species, and an introduction by Professor E.F. Phillips, D.Ph., Cornell University, U.S.A. Sydney : Endeavour Press 752 pp. [731].
Type data: holotype, NMV ♂.
Type locality: Mt William, VIC.

Distribution: SE coastal, Murray-Darling basin, VIC; only published localities Mt William, near Belgrave, Dandenong Ranges and Gorae West.
Ecology: larva—sedentary : adult—volant; melliferous, nest in dead, dry stems (*Rubus* L. [Rosaceae]), in deserted beetle galleries in a beam of dry timber (*Eucalyptus* L'Hérit. [Myrtaceae]), in dead fronds (*Dicksonia*), two or more adult females may be present in one nest, not all females lay eggs, all immature stages found in the communal chamber, larvae fed progressively.
References: Rayment, T. (1951). Biology of the reed-bees. With descriptions of three new species and two allotypes of *Exoneura*. *Aust. Zool.* **11**: 285–313 (illustration); Rayment, T. (1954). New bees and wasps—Part XXII. The altruistic reed-bees, *Exoneura*. *Vict. Nat.* **71**: 13–16 (description of female, biology); Cane, J.H. & Michener, C.D. (1983). Chemistry and function of mandibular gland products of bees of the genus *Exoneura* (Hymenoptera, Anthophoridae). *J. Chem. Ecol.* **9**: 1525–1531 (taxonomy, mandibular gland products); Michener, C.D. (1983). The parasitic Australian allodapine genus *Inquilina* (Hymenoptera, Anthophoridae). *J. Kansas Entomol. Soc.* **56**: 555–559 (as possible host of *Inquilina schwarzi* Michener, 1983); Schwarz, M.P. (1986). Persistent multi-female nests in an Australian allodapine bee, *Exoneura bicolor* (Hymenoptera, An-

thophoridae). *Insectes Soc.* **33**: 258–277 (biology); Schwarz, M.P. (1988). Notes on cofounded nests in three species of social bees in the genus *Exoneura* (Hymenoptera; Anthophoridae). *Vict. Nat.* **105**: 212–215 (biology).

Exoneura (Exoneura) bicolor Smith, 1854

Exoneura bicolor Smith, F. (1854). *Catalogue of Hymenopterous Insects in the Collection of the British Museum.* Part II. Apidae. London : British Museum pp. 199–465 [232] [type locality not resolved].
Type data: holotype (probable), BMNH Hym.17.b.339 ♀.
Type locality: Australia (as New Holland on label, Australia (Swan River), Van Diemens Land in description).

Distribution: Murray-Darling basin, SE coastal, QLD, NSW, VIC, TAS.
Ecology: larva—sedentary : adult—volant; melliferous, nest in dead, dry stems (*Callistemon* R.Br. [Myrtaceae], *Rubus* L. [Rosaceae]), dead fronds (*Dicksonia*), semisocial, two or more adult females may be present in one nest, not all females lay eggs, all immature stages found in the communal chamber, larvae fed progressively, flower visiting record: *Boronia* Sm. [Rutaceae], *Daviesia* Sm. [Fabaceae], *Helichrysum* Miller *s.lat.* [Asteraceae], *Hypochaeris* L. [Asteraceae], *Jacksonia* Smith [Fabaceae], *Pultenaea* Sm. [Fabaceae].
References: Friese, H. (1899). Die Bienengattung *Exoneura* Sm. *Entomol. Nachr.* **25**: 209–211 (description of male); Cockerell, T.D.A. (1929). Bees from the Australian region. *Am. Mus. Novit.* **346**: 1–18 (flower record); Rayment, T. (1935). *A Cluster of Bees.* Sixty essays on the life-histories of Australian bees, with specific descriptions of over 100 new species, and an introduction by Professor E.F. Phillips, D.Ph., Cornell University, U.S.A. Sydney : Endeavour Press 752 pp. (illustration); Michener, C.D. (1963). Division of labour among primitively social bees. *Science* **141**: 434–435 (biology); Michener, C.D. (1965). A classification of the bees of the Australian and South Pacific regions. *Bull. Am. Mus. Nat. Hist.* **130**: 1–362 [243] (flower record); Michener, C.D. (1965). The life cycle and social organization of bees of the genus *Exoneura* and their parasite, *Inquilina* (Hymenoptera : Xylocopinae). *Univ. Kansas Sci. Bull.* **46**: 317–358 (biology); Cane, J.H. (1979). The hind tibiotarsal and tibial spur articulations in bees (Hymenoptera : Apoidea). *J. Kansas Entomol. Soc.* **52**: 123–137 (morphology); Cane, J.II. & Michener, C.D. (1983). Chemistry and function of mandibular gland products of bees of the genus *Exoneura* (Hymenoptera, Anthophoridae). *J. Chem. Ecol.* **9**: 1525–1531 (taxonomy, gland products); Michener, C.D. (1983). The parasitic Australian allodapine genus *Inquilina* (Hymenoptera, Anthophoridae). *J. Kansas Entomol. Soc.* **56**: 555–559 (as host); Schwarz, M.P. (1986). Persistent multi-female nests in an Australian allodapine bee, *Exoneura bicolor*

(Hymenoptera, Anthophoridae). *Insectes Soc.* **33**: 258–277 (biology); Schwarz, M.P. (1987). Intra-colony relatedness and sociality in the allodapine bee *Exoneura bicolor*. *Behav. Ecol. Sociobiol.* **21**: 387–392 (biology); Schwarz, M.P., Scholz, O. & Jensen, G. (1987). Ovarian inhibition among nestmates of *Exoneura bicolor* Smith (Hymenoptera : Xylocopinae). *J. Aust. Entomol. Soc.* **26**: 355–359 (biology); Sugden, E. (1988). Inside the (secret) societies of native bees. *Aust. Nat. Hist.* **22**: 381–384 (biology); Schwarz, M.P. (1988). Notes on cofounded nests in three species of social bees in the genus *Exoneura* (Hymenoptera; Anthophoridae). *Vict. Nat.* **105**: 212–215 (biology); Schwarz, M.P. (1988). Local resource enhancement and sex ratios in a primitively social bee. *Nature* **331**: 346–348 (biology); O'Keefe, K.J. & Schwarz, M.P. (1990). Pheromones are implicated in reproductive differentiation in a primitively social bee. *Naturwissensch.* **77**: 83–86 (biology); Michener, C.D. & Houston, T.F. (1991). Apoidea. pp. 993–1000 *in* CSIRO (sponsor) *The Insects of Australia. A textbook for students and research workers.* Melbourne : Melbourne University Press Vol. II 2nd Edn (illustration); Schwarz, M.P. & Blows, M.W. (1991). Kin association during nest founding in the bee *Exoneura bicolor*: active discrimination, philopatry and familiar landmarks. *Psyche (Camb.)* **98**: 241–250 (biology); Schwarz, M.P. & O'Keefe, K.J. (1991). Cooperative nesting and ovarian development in females of the predominantly social bee *Exoneura bicolor* Smith (Hymenoptera: Anthophoridae) after forced solitary eclosion. *J. Aust. Entomol. Soc.* **30**: 251–255 (biology).

Exoneura (Exoneura) diversipes Cockerell, 1922

Exoneura diversipes Cockerell, T.D.A. (1922). Australian bees in the Queensland Museum. *Mem. Qd Mus.* **7**: 257–279 [277].
Type data: syntypes, QM 3♂ (a male is labelled 'type' and has registration number T2519).
Type locality: [Lamington] National Park, QLD.

Distribution: NE coastal, QLD; known only from type locality.
Ecology: adult—volant; melliferous.

Exoneura (Exoneura) florentiae Rayment, 1939

Exoneura florentiae Rayment, T. (1939). Bees from the high lands of New South Wales and Victoria. *Aust. Zool.* **9**: 263–294 [291].
Type data: holotype, ANIC ♀.
Type locality: Black Sands, Yarra Valley, VIC.

Distribution: SE coastal, VIC; known only from type locality.
Ecology: adult—volant; melliferous, flower visiting record: *Dillwynia* Sm. [Fabaceae].
Reference: Rayment, T. (1951). Biology of the reedbees. With descriptions of three new species and

two allotypes of *Exoneura*. *Aust. Zool.* **11**: 285–313 (illustration).

Exoneura (Exoneura) fultoni Cockerell, 1913

Exoneura fultoni Cockerell, T.D.A. (1913). Some Australian bees. *Proc. Acad. Nat. Sci. Philad.* **65**: 28–44 [31].
Type data: holotype, USNM ♀*.
Type locality: Croydon, VIC.

Distribution: SE coastal, Murray-Darling basin, VIC; only published localities Croydon, Portland and the Grampians.
Ecology: larva—sedentary : adult—volant; melliferous, nest in dead, dry stems (sword grass), two or more adult females may be present in one nest, not all females lay eggs, all immature stages found in the communal chamber, larvae fed progressively, flower visiting record: *Leucopogon* R.Br. [Epacridaceae].
References: Rayment, T. (1949). New bees and wasps—Part VIII. A new species of *Exoneura*, with notes on other reed-bees from the Grampians. *Vict. Nat.* **65**: 208–212 (biology); Rayment, T. (1953). *Bees of the Portland District*. Victoria : Portland Field Naturalist's Club 39 pp. (flower record).

Exoneura (Exoneura) grandis Rayment, 1935

Exoneura grandis Rayment, T. (1935). *A Cluster of Bees*. Sixty essays on the life-histories of Australian bees, with specific descriptions of over 100 new species, and an introduction by Professor E.F. Phillips, D.Ph., Cornell University, U.S.A. Sydney : Endeavour Press 752 pp. [728].
Type data: holotype, ANIC ♀.
Type locality: Caulfield, VIC.

Distribution: SE coastal, VIC; known only from type locality.
Ecology: adult—volant; melliferous.

Exoneura (Exoneura) hackeri Cockerell, 1913

Exoneura angophorae hackeri Cockerell, T.D.A. (1913). Some Australian bees. *Proc. Acad. Nat. Sci. Philad.* **65**: 28–44 [29].
Type data: holotype, QM ♀ (number of specimens unknown, a female is labelled 'type' and has registration number T4114).
Type locality: Sunnybank, Brisbane, QLD.
Exoneura insularis Cockerell, T.D.A. (1914). New Australian bees. *Entomologist* **47**: 197–201 [200].
Type data: holotype, USNM ♀*.
Type locality: Stradbroke Is., QLD.

Taxonomic decision for synonymy: Michener, C.D. (1965). The life cycle and social organization of bees of the genus *Exoneura* and their parasite, *Inquilina* (Hymenoptera : Xylocopinae). *Univ. Kansas Sci. Bull.* **46**: 317–358 [352].

Distribution: NE coastal, QLD.
Ecology: larva—sedentary : adult—volant; melliferous, nest in dead, dry stems (on rainforest margin), two or more adult females may be present in one nest, not all females lay eggs, all immature stages found in the communal chamber, larvae fed progressively, flower visiting record: *Hibbertia* Andrews [Dilleniaceae], *Leptospermum* Forster & G.Forster [Myrtaceae].
References: Cockerell, T.D.A. (1918). Some bees collected in Queensland. *Mem. Qd Mus.* **6**: 112–120 (description of male, subspecies to species); Rayment, T. (1949). New bees and wasps—Part VIII. A new species of *Exoneura*, with notes on other reed-bees from the Grampians. *Vict. Nat.* **65**: 208–212 (taxonomy); Michener, C.D. (1961). A new parasitic genus of Ceratinini from Australia (Hymenoptera : Apoidea). *J. Kansas Entomol. Soc.* **34**: 178–180 (illustration); Michener, C.D. (1963). Division of labour among primitively social bees. *Science* **141**: 434–435 (biology); Michener, C.D. (1965). A classification of the bees of the Australian and South Pacific regions. *Bull. Am. Mus. Nat. Hist.* **130**: 1–362 [243] (flower record).

Exoneura (Exoneura) hamulata Cockerell, 1905

Exoneura hamulata Cockerell, T.D.A. (1905). Descriptions and records of bees. V. *Ann. Mag. Nat. Hist.* (7)**16**: 465–477 [466].
Type data: syntypes, BMNH 2♀ (a female is labelled 'type' and has registration number Hym. 17.b.347).
Type locality: Moss Bay (description gives "Moss Bay, Australia, 13.12.1893 W.W. Froggatt", probably Mosmans Bay, as Froggatt lived in Sydney), NSW.

Distribution: NE coastal, SE coastal, Murray-Darling basin, SW coastal, QLD, NSW, VIC, WA, TAS.
Ecology: larva—sedentary : adult—volant; melliferous, nest in dead, dry stems (*Callistemon* R.Br. [Myrtaceae], *Lantana* L. [Verbenaceae], *Rubus* L. [Rosaceae]), dead fronds (*Dicksonia*), flowering stalks (*Xanthorrhoea* Sm. [Xanthorrhoeaceae]), two or more adult females may be present in one nest, not all females lay eggs, all immature stages found in the communal chamber, larvae fed progressively, flower visiting record: aster, *Leucopogon* R.Br. [Epacridaceae], *Persoonia* Sm. [Proteaceae], *Prasophyllum* R.Br. [Orchidaceae], *Rubus* L. [Rosaceae], *Stylidium* Willd. [Stylidiaceae], *Swainsona* Salisb. [Fabaceae].
References: Cockerell, T.D.A. (1913). Some Australian bees. *Proc. Acad. Nat. Sci. Philad.* **65**: 28–44 (description of male); Rayment, T. (1931). Bees in the collections of the Western Australian Museum and the Agricultural Department, Perth. *J. Proc. R. Soc. West. Aust.* **17**: 157–190 (distribution); Rayment, T. (1946). New bees and wasps—Part III. Another new *Exoneura*; also notes on the biology of *E. hamulata*. *Vict. Nat.* **63**: 63–68 (biology); Rayment, T. (1951). Biology of the reed-bees. With descriptions of three new species and two allotypes of *Exoneura*. *Aust. Zool.* **11**: 285–313 (biology); Rayment, T. (1953). *Bees of the Portland District*. Victoria :

Portland Field Naturalist's Club 39 pp. (flower record); Wakefield, N.A. (1953). Notes on East Gippsland orchids. *Vict. Nat.* **70**: 28 (flower record); Erickson, R. (1958). *Triggerplants*. Perth : Paterson Brokensha 229 pp. (flower record); Syed, I.H. (1963). Comparative studies of larvae of Australian ceratinine bees (Hymenoptera, Apoidea). *Univ. Kansas Sci. Bull.* **64**: 263–280 (larva); Michener, C.D. (1965). A classification of the bees of the Australian and South Pacific regions. *Bull. Am. Mus. Nat. Hist.* **130**: 1–362 [243] (flower record); Michener, C.D. (1973). Size and form of eggs of allodapine bees. *J. Entomol. Soc. S. Afr.* **36**: 281–285 (egg, as *Exoneura hamata*, incorrect subsequent spelling); Michener, C.D. & Scheiring, J.F. (1976). Pupae of allodapine bees (Hymenoptera : Xylocopinae). *J. Aust. Entomol. Soc.* **15**: 63–70 (pupa); Michener, C.D. (1983). The parasitic Australian allodapine genus *Inquilina* (Hymenoptera, Anthophoridae). *J. Kansas Entomol. Soc.* **56**: 555–559 (taxonomy and as host of an *Inquilina*); Cane, J.H. & Michener, C.D. (1983). Chemistry and function of mandibular gland products of bees of the genus *Exoneura* (Hymenoptera, Anthophoridae). *J. Chem. Ecol.* **9**: 1525–1531 (taxonomy); Michener, C.D. & Brooks, R.W. (1984). A comparative study of the glossae of bees (Apoidea). *Contrib. Am. Entomol. Inst.* **22**: 1–73 (glossa).

Exoneura (Exoneura) holmesi Rayment, 1946

Exoneura holmesi Rayment, T. (1946). New bees and wasps—Part I. Notes on the biology of *Exoneurae*, with a specific description. *Vict. Nat.* **62**: 178–184 [181].
Type data: holotype, ANIC ♂.
Type locality: Heathcote, VIC.

Distribution: SE coastal, NSW; known only from type locality.
Ecology: adult—volant; melliferous, nest in gallery in dead *Banksia* L.f. [Proteaceae] branch, flower visiting record: *Leptospermum* Forster & G.Forster [Myrtaceae].
Reference: Rayment, T. (1951). Biology of the reed-bees. With descriptions of three new species and two allotypes of *Exoneura*. *Aust. Zool.* **11**: 285–313 (illustration).

Exoneura (Exoneura) illustris Rayment, 1951

Exoneura illustris Rayment, T. (1951). *In* Erickson, R. & Rayment, T. Simple social bees of Western Australia. *West. Aust. Nat.* **3**: 45–59 [49].
Type data: holotype, ANIC ♂.
Type locality: 40 miles S Perth, WA.

Distribution: SW coastal, WA; known only from type locality.
Ecology: adult—volant; melliferous, nest in dead, dry flowering stalks (*Xanthorrhoea* Sm. [Xanthorrhoeaceae]) two or more adult females may be present in one nest, not all females lay eggs, all immature stages found in the communal chamber,

larvae fed progressively, flower visiting record: *?Eucalyptus* L'Hérit. [Myrtaceae], *?Melaleuca* L. [Myrtaceae].
Reference: Rayment, T. (1956). New species of bees and wasps—Part XXV. *Vict. Nat.* **72**: 173–174 (taxonomy).

Exoneura (Exoneura) incerta Cockerell, 1918

Exoneura hackeri incerta Cockerell, T.D.A. (1918). Some bees collected in Queensland. *Mem. Qd Mus.* **6**: 112–120 [120].
Type data: holotype, QM T4101 ♀.
Type locality: Brisbane, QLD.

Distribution: NE coastal, QLD; known only from type locality.
Ecology: adult—volant; melliferous.
Reference: Michener, C.D. (1965). A classification of the bees of the Australian and South Pacific regions. *Bull. Am. Mus. Nat. Hist.* **130**: 1–362 [226] (taxonomy).

Exoneura (Exoneura) laeta Alfken, 1907

Exoneura pictifrons laeta Alfken, J.D. (1907). Apidae. pp. 259–261 *in* Michaelsen, W. & Hartmeyer, R. (eds) *Die Fauna Südwest-Australiens*. Jena : G. Fischer Bd 1 Lfg 6 [260].
Type data: syntypes (probable), whereabouts unknown ♂*.
Type locality: Mundijong, WA.

Distribution: SW coastal, WA; known only from type locality.
Ecology: adult—volant; melliferous.
References: Rayment, T. (1951). *In* Erickson, R. & Rayment, T. Simple social bees of Western Australia. *West. Aust. Nat.* **3**: 45–59 (taxonomy); Michener, C.D. (1965). A classification of the bees of the Australian and South Pacific regions. *Bull. Am. Mus. Nat. Hist.* **130**: 1–362 [226] (taxonomy).

Exoneura (Exoneura) montana Rayment, 1939

Exoneura montana Rayment, T. (1939). Bees from the high lands of New South Wales and Victoria. *Aust. Zool.* **9**: 263–294 [290].
Type data: syntypes (probable), ANIC ♀ (number of specimens unknown, female specimen labelled 'type').
Type locality: White Swamp, NSW.

Distribution: SE coastal, Murray-Darling basin, NSW, VIC; only published localities White Swamp, Patonga Beach, Brooklyn and Mt Buffalo.
Ecology: larva—sedentary : adult—volant; melliferous, nest in dead, dry stems (*Lantana* L. [Verbenaceae]), (punky cherry wood), two or more adult females may be present in one nest, not all females lay eggs, all immature stages found in the communal chamber, larvae fed progressively, flower visiting record: *Kunzea* Reichb. [Myrtaceae], *Stylidium* Willd. [Stylidiaceae].
References: Rayment, T. (1947). Bees from the Victorian Alps. *Vict. Nat.* **64**: 103–107 (flower re-

cord); Rayment, T. (1948). Some bees from the Victorian Alps. *Vict. Nat.* **65**: 201–202 (flower record); Rayment, T. (1949). New bees and wasps—Part VIII. A new species of *Exoneura*, with notes on other reed-bees from the Grampians. *Vict. Nat.* **65**: 208–212 (distribution); Rayment, T. (1949). New bees and wasps—Part IX. Four undescribed species of *Exoneura*, with notes on their collection, and description of new parasites discovered on the genus. *Vict. Nat.* **65**: 247–254 (biology); Rayment, T. (1954). Incidence of acarid mites on the biology of bees. *Aust. Zool.* **12**: 26–38 (as host); Michener, C.D. (1983). The parasitic Australian allodapine genus *Inquilina* (Hymenoptera, Anthophoridae). *J. Kansas Entomol. Soc.* **56**: 555–559 (taxonomy).

Exoneura (Exoneura) nigrihirta Rayment, 1953

Exoneura nigrihirta Rayment, T. (1953). *Bees of the Portland District.* Victoria : Portland Field Naturalist's Club 39 pp. [38].
Type data: holotype, ANIC ♂.
Type locality: Bats Ridges (Portland district), VIC.

Distribution: SE coastal, VIC; only published localities Portland district.
Ecology: adult—volant; melliferous, nest in dead, dry stems, two or more adult females may be present in one nest, not all females lay eggs, all immature stages found in the communal chamber, larvae fed progressively, flower visiting record: *Leptospermum* Forster & G.Forster [Myrtaceae], *Leucopogon* R.Br. [Epacridaceae].

Exoneura (Exoneura) obliterata Cockerell, 1913

Exoneura angophorae obliterata Cockerell, T.D.A. (1913). Some Australian bees. *Proc. Acad. Nat. Sci. Philad.* **65**: 28–44 [29].
Type data: syntypes (probable), USNM ♀* (number of specimens unknown).
Type locality: Sunnybank, Brisbane, QLD.

Distribution: NE coastal, SE coastal, Murray-Darling basin, QLD, NSW, VIC.
Ecology: larva—sedentary : adult—volant; melliferous, nest in dead, dry reeds, two or more adult females may be present in one nest, not all females lay eggs, all immature stages found in the communal chamber, larvae fed progressively, flower visiting record: *Arctotheca* Wendl. [Asteraceae], *Boronia* Sm. [Rutaceae], *Daviesia* Sm. [Fabaceae], *Helichrysum* Miller *s.lat.* [Asteraceae], *Hibbertia* Andrews [Dilleniaceae], *Jacksonia* Smith [Fabaceae], *Leptospermum* Forster & G.Forster [Myrtaceae], *Leucopogon* R.Br. [Epacridaceae], *Melaleuca* L. [Myrtaceae], *Pultenaea* Sm. [Fabaceae], *Rapistrum* Crantz [Brassicaceae], *Swainsona* Salisb. [Fabaceae], *Wahlenbergia* Roth [Campanulaceae].
References: Rayment, T. (1949). New bees and wasps—Part VIII. A new species of *Exoneura*, with notes on other reed-bees from the Grampians. *Vict.*

Nat. **65**: 208–212 (biology, subspecies to species); Rayment, T. (1953). *Bees of the Portland District.* Victoria : Portland Field Naturalist's Club 39 pp. (flower record); Michener, C.D. (1965). A classification of the bees of the Australian and South Pacific regions. *Bull. Am. Mus. Nat. Hist.* **130**: 1–362 [243] (flower record).

Exoneura (Exoneura) obscura Alfken, 1907

Exoneura pictifrons obscura Alfken, J.D. (1907). Apidae. pp. 259–261 *in* Michaelsen, W. & Hartmeyer, R. (eds) *Die Fauna Südwest-Australiens.* Jena : G. Fischer Bd 1 Lfg 6 [261] [description indicates that type series contained more than one specimen, location of other type(s) unknown].
Type data: syntypes, WAM ♂*.
Type locality: Mundijong, WA.

Distribution: SW coastal, WA; only published localities Mundijong and Rottnest Is.
Ecology: adult—volant; melliferous, nest in dead, dry stems, two or more adult females may be present in one nest, not all females lay eggs, all immature stages found in the communal chamber, larvae fed progressively.
Reference: Rayment, T. (1951). *In* Erickson, R. & Rayment, T. Simple social bees of Western Australia. *West. Aust. Nat.* **3**: 45–59 [50] (taxonomy).

Exoneura (Exoneura) obscuripes Michener, 1963

Exoneura obscuripes Michener, C.D. (1963). New Ceratinini from Australia (Hymenoptera, Apoidea). *Univ. Kansas Sci. Bull.* **44**: 257–261 [260].
Type data: holotype, ANIC ♀.
Type locality: Binna Burra, QLD.

Distribution: NE coastal, QLD; known only from type locality.
Ecology: adult—volant; melliferous, nest in stems of vines in rainforest.
References: Syed, I.H. (1963). Comparative studies of larvae of Australian ceratinine bees (Hymenoptera, Apoidea). *Univ. Kansas Sci. Bull.* **64**: 263–280 (larva); Michener, C.D. (1965). The life cycle and social organization of bees of the genus *Exoneura* and their parasite, *Inquilina* (Hymenoptera : Xylocopinae). *Univ. Kansas Sci. Bull.* **46**: 317–358 (biology); Michener, C.D. (1973). Size and form of eggs of allodapine bees. *J. Entomol. Soc. S. Afr.* **36**: 281–285 (egg).

Exoneura (Exoneura) perpensa Cockerell, 1922

Exoneura perpensa Cockerell, T.D.A. (1922). Australian bees in the Queensland Museum. *Mem. Qd Mus.* **7**: 257–279 [277].
Type data: holotype, QM T2515 ♂.
Type locality: Armidale, NSW.

Distribution: Murray-Darling basin, SE coastal, NSW, VIC; only published localities Armidale, White Swamp and Portland.
Ecology: larva—sedentary : adult—volant; mellifer-

ous, nest in dead, dry stems, two or more adult females may be present in one nest, not all females lay eggs, all immature stages found in the communal chamber, larvae fed progressively, flower visiting record: *Bursaria* Cav. [Pittosporaceae], *Eucalyptus* L'Hérit. [Myrtaceae], *Lomatia* R.Br. [Proteaceae]. References: Rayment, T. (1946). New bees and wasps—Part I. Notes on the biology of *Exoneurae*, with a specific description. *Vict. Nat.* **62**: 178–184 (biology); Rayment, T. (1951). *In* Erickson, R. & Rayment, T. Simple social bees of Western Australia. *West. Aust. Nat.* **3**: 45–59 (taxonomy); Rayment, T. (1953). *Bees of the Portland District.* Victoria : Portland Field Naturalist's Club 39 pp. (distribution).

Exoneura (Exoneura) pictifrons Alfken, 1907

Exoneura pictifrons Alfken, J.D. (1907). Apidae. pp. 259–261 *in* Michaelsen, W. & Hartmeyer, R. (eds) *Die Fauna Südwest-Australiens.* Jena : G. Fischer Bd 1 Lfg 6 [260].
Type data: syntypes, WAM 4796 ♂, WAM 4797 ♂.
Type locality: Mundijong, WA.

Exoneura angophorae occidentalis Cockerell, T.D.A. (1914). New Australian bees. *Entomologist* **47**: 197–201 [200].
Type data: syntypes, BMNH 4♀ (a female is labelled 'type' and has registration number Hym. 17.b.351).
Type locality: Yallingup, WA.

Taxonomic decision for synonymy: Cockerell, T.D.A. (1930). The bees of Australia. *Aust. Zool.* **6**: 137–156, 205–236 [155].

Distribution: SW coastal, WA.
Ecology: larva—sedentary : adult—volant; melliferous, nest in dead, dry flowering stalks (*Xanthorrhoea* Sm. [Xanthorrhoeaceae]), two or more adult females may be present in one nest, not all females lay eggs, all immature stages found in the communal chamber, larvae fed progressively.
References: Cockerell, T.D.A. (1910). Descriptions and records of bees. XXXIII. *Ann. Mag. Nat. Hist.* *(8)***6**: 356–366 (taxonomy); Cockerell, T.D.A. (1931). The bees of Australia. *Aust. Zool.* **7**: 34–54 (distribution, as *Exoneura angophorae occidentalis* Cockerell, 1914); Rayment, T. (1934). Contributions to the fauna of Rottnest Island. VIII. Apoidea. With description of new species. *J. Proc. R. Soc. West. Aust.* **20**: 201–212 (taxonomy); Rayment, T. (1951). *In* Erickson, R. & Rayment, T. Simple social bees of Western Australia. *West. Aust. Nat.* **3**: 45–59 (biology).

Exoneura (Exoneura) punctata Rayment, 1930

Exoneura punctata Rayment, T. (1930). Notes on a collection of bees from Western Australia. *J. Proc. R. Soc. West. Aust.* **16**: 45–56 [55].
Type data: holotype, ANIC ♀.
Type locality: Albany, WA.

Distribution: SW coastal, WA; only published localities Albany and Perth.
Ecology: adult—volant; melliferous, nest in dead, dry stems, two or more adult females may be present in one nest, not all females lay eggs, all immature stages found in the communal chamber, larvae fed progressively.
Reference: Rayment, T. (1931). Bees in the collections of the Western Australian Museum and the Agricultural Department, Perth. *J. Proc. R. Soc. West. Aust.* **17**: 157–190 (distribution).

Exoneura (Exoneura) rhodoptera Cockerell, 1922

Exoneura rhodoptera Cockerell, T.D.A. (1922). Australian bees in the Queensland Museum. *Mem. Qd Mus.* **7**: 257–279 [277].
Type data: holotype, QM T2680 ♀.
Type locality: Stradbroke Is., QLD.

Distribution: NE coastal, QLD; known only from type locality.
Ecology: adult—volant; melliferous.

Exoneura (Exoneura) richardsoni Rayment, 1951

Exoneura richardsoni Rayment, T. (1951). Biology of the reed-bees. With descriptions of three new species and two allotypes of *Exoneura. Aust. Zool.* **11**: 285–313 [288].
Type data: holotype, ANIC ♀.
Type locality: Narre Warren, VIC.

Distribution: SE coastal, VIC; only published localities Narre Warren, near Belgrave, Portland and Dandenong.
Ecology: larva—sedentary : adult—volant; melliferous, nest in dead, dry stems (*Rosa* L. [Rosaceae], *Rubus* L. [Rosaceae]), fronds (*Dicksonia*), two or more adult females may be present in one nest, not all females lay eggs, all immature stages found in the communal chamber, larvae fed progressively, flower visiting record: *Leucopogon* R.Br. [Epacridaceae].
References: Rayment, T. (1953). *Bees of the Portland District.* Victoria : Portland Field Naturalist's Club 39 pp. (as *Exoneura dawsoni* Rayment, 1946); Cane, J.H. & Michener, C.D. (1983). Chemistry and function of mandibular gland products of bees of the genus *Exoneura* (Hymenoptera, Anthophoridae). *J. Chem. Ecol.* **9**: 1525–1531 (mandibular gland products); Michener, C.D. (1983). The parasitic Australian allodapine genus *Inquilina* (Hymenoptera, Anthophoridae). *J. Kansas Entomol. Soc.* **56**: 555–559 (taxonomy); Schwarz, M.P. (1986). Persistent multi-female nests in an Australian allodapine bee, *Exoneura bicolor* (Hymenoptera, Anthophoridae). *Insectes Soc.* **33**: 258–277 (biology); Schwarz, M.P. (1988). Notes on cofounded nests in three species of social bees in the genus *Exoneura* (Hymenoptera; Anthophoridae). *Vict. Nat.* **105**: 212–215 (biology).

Exoneura (Exoneura) robusta Cockerell, 1922

Exoneura robusta Cockerell, T.D.A. (1922). Australian bees in the Queensland Museum. *Mem. Qd Mus.* **7**: 257–279 [275].
Type data: holotype, QM T2516 ♀.
Type locality: [Lamington] National Park, QLD.

Distribution: NE coastal, SE coastal, Murray-Darling basin, QLD, NSW, VIC; only published localities Lamington National Park, Mt Glorious, Lindfield and Mt Buffalo.
Ecology: larva—sedentary : adult—volant; melliferous, nest in dead, dry stems (*Spartium*), two or more adult females may be present in one nest, not all females lay eggs, all immature stages found in the communal chamber, larvae fed progressively, flower visiting record: *Lomatia* R.Br. [Proteaceae], *Oxylobium* Andrews [Fabaceae], *Rubus* L. [Rosaceae], *Stylidium* Willd. [Stylidiaceae].
References: Rayment, T. (1947). Bees from the Victorian Alps. *Vict. Nat.* **64**: 103–107 (flower record); Rayment, T. (1948). New bees and wasps—Part VII. Two undescribed species of *Exoneura*, with notes on recent collectings of several other Exoneurae and the extraordinary appendages of their larvae. *Vict. Nat.* **65**: 85–91 (biology); Michener, C.D. (1963). Division of labour among primitively social bees. *Science* **141**: 434–435 (biology); Michener, C.D. (1965). A classification of the bees of the Australian and South Pacific regions. *Bull. Am. Mus. Nat. Hist.* **130**: 1–362 [243] (flower record).

Exoneura (Exoneura) rufa Rayment, 1935

Exoneura rufa Rayment, T. (1935). *A Cluster of Bees.* Sixty essays on the life-histories of Australian bees, with specific descriptions of over 100 new species, and an introduction by Professor E.F. Phillips, D.Ph., Cornell University, U.S.A. Sydney : Endeavour Press 752 pp. [726].
Type data: holotype, ANIC ♀.
Type locality: Heyington, near Melbourne, VIC.

Distribution: SE coastal, VIC; known only from type locality.
Ecology: adult—volant; melliferous.
Reference: Rayment, T. (1951). Biology of the reed-bees. With descriptions of three new species and two allotypes of *Exoneura*. *Aust. Zool.* **11**: 285–313 (illustration).

Exoneura (Exoneura) subbaculifera Rayment, 1948

Exoneura subbaculifera Rayment, T. (1948). New bees and wasps—Part VII. Two undescribed species of *Exoneura*, with notes on recent collectings of several other Exoneurae and the extraordinary appendages of their larvae. *Vict. Nat.* **65**: 85–91 [86] [a specimen in the ANIC labelled "type" bears a locality which was not given in the original description].
Type data: holotype, whereabouts unknown ♀* (not located

in T. Rayment coll., transferred to ANIC).
Type locality: Lindfield, NSW.

Distribution: Murray-Darling basin, SE coastal, QLD, NSW; only published localities Cunninghams Gap and Lindfield.
Ecology: larva—sedentary : adult—volant; melliferous, nest in dead, dry stems (*Erythrina, Rubus* L. [Rosaceae]), two or more adult females may be present in one nest, not all females lay eggs, all immature stages found in the communal chamber, larvae fed progressively.
References: Rayment, T. (1949). New bees and wasps—Part IX. Four undescribed species of *Exoneura*, with notes on their collection, and description of new parasites discovered on the genus. *Vict. Nat.* **65**: 247–254 (illustration); Syed, I.H. (1963). Comparative studies of larvae of Australian ceratinine bees (Hymenoptera, Apoidea). *Univ. Kansas Sci. Bull.* **64**: 263–280 (larva); Michener, C.D. (1965). The life cycle and social organization of bees of the genus *Exoneura* and their parasite, *Inquilina* (Hymenoptera : Xylocopinae). *Univ. Kansas Sci. Bull.* **46**: 317–358 (biology); Michener, C.D. (1973). Size and form of eggs of allodapine bees. *J. Entomol. Soc. S. Afr.* **36**: 281–285 (egg).

Exoneura (Exoneura) subhamulata Rayment, 1935

Exoneura subhamulata Rayment, T. (1935). *A Cluster of Bees.* Sixty essays on the life-histories of Australian bees, with specific descriptions of over 100 new species, and an introduction by Professor E.F. Phillips, D.Ph., Cornell University, U.S.A. Sydney : Endeavour Press 752 pp. [732].
Type data: holotype, ANIC ♀.
Type locality: Caulfield, VIC.

Distribution: SE coastal, VIC; known only from type locality.
Ecology: adult—volant; melliferous.

Exoneura (Exoneura) tasmanica Cockerell, 1930

Exoneura tasmanica Cockerell, T.D.A. (1930). New Australian bees. *Mem. Qd Mus.* **10**: 37–50 [49].
Type data: holotype, USNM ♂*.
Type locality: Windermere, TAS.

Distribution: TAS; known only from type locality.
Ecology: adult—volant; melliferous.

Exoneura (Exoneura) turneri Cockerell, 1914

Exoneura turneri Cockerell, T.D.A. (1914). New Australian bees. *Entomologist* **47**: 197–201 [199].
Type data: syntypes, BMNH 2♀ (a female specimen is labelled 'type' and has registration number Hym. 17.b.350).
Type locality: Eaglehawk Neck, TAS.

Distribution: TAS; known only from type locality.
Ecology: adult—volant; melliferous.

Exoneura (Exoneura) variabilis Rayment, 1949

Exoneura variabilis Rayment, T. (1949). New bees and wasps—Part IX. Four undescribed species of *Exoneura*, with notes on their collection, and description of new parasites discovered on the genus. *Vict. Nat.* **65**: 247–254 [252].
Type data: syntypes, ANIC ♂ (number of specimens is unknown, a male specimen is labelled type).
Type locality: Narooma, NSW.

Distribution: NE coastal, Murray-Darling basin, SE coastal, QLD, NSW, VIC.
Ecology: larva—sedentary : adult—volant; melliferous, nest in dead, dry stems (*Deeringia* R.Br. [Amaranthaceae], *Hydrangea* L. [Hydrangeaceae], *Lantana* L. [Verbenaceae], *Plectranthus* L'Hérit. [Lamiaceae], *Rubus* L. [Rosaceae]), two or more adult females may be present in one nest, not all females lay eggs, all immature stages found in the communal chamber, larvae fed progressively, flower visiting record: *Bursaria* Cav. [Pittosporaceae], *Erigeron* L. [Asteraceae], *Helichrysum* Miller *s.lat.* [Asteraceae], *Leucopogon* R.Br. [Epacridaceae], *Lomatia* R.Br. [Proteaceae].
References: Syed, I.H. (1963). Comparative studies of larvae of Australian ceratinine bees (Hymenoptera, Apoidea). *Univ. Kansas Sci. Bull.* **64**: 263–280 (larva); Michener, C.D. (1965). The life cycle and social organization of bees of the genus *Exoneura* and their parasite, *Inquilina* (Hymenoptera : Xylocopinae). *Univ. Kansas Sci. Bull.* **46**: 317–358 (biology); Michener, C.D. (1973). Size and form of eggs of allodapine bees. *J. Entomol. Soc. S. Afr.* **36**: 281–285 (egg); Michener, C.D. & Scheiring, J.F. (1976). Pupae of allodapine bees (Hymenoptera : Xylocopinae). *J. Aust. Entomol. Soc.* **15**: 63–70 (pupa); Michener, C.D. (1977). Discordant evolution and the classification of allodapine bees. *Syst. Zool.* **26**: 32–56 (taxonomy); Cane, J.H. & Michener, C.D. (1983). Chemistry and function of mandibular gland products of bees of the genus *Exoneura* (Hymenoptera, Anthophoridae). *J. Chem. Ecol.* **9**: 1525–1531 (taxonomy); Michener, C.D. (1983). The parasitic Australian allodapine genus *Inquilina* (Hymenoptera, Anthophoridae). *J. Kansas Entomol. Soc.* **56**: 555–559 (as host).

Exoneura (Exoneura) ziegleri Rayment, 1935

Exoneura ziegleri Rayment, T. (1935). *A Cluster of Bees.* Sixty essays on the life-histories of Australian bees, with specific descriptions of over 100 new species, and an introduction by Professor E.F. Phillips, D.Ph., Cornell University, U.S.A. Sydney : Endeavour Press 752 pp. [733].
Type data: holotype, ANIC ♂ (described as ♀).
Type locality: Emerald, VIC.

Distribution: SE coastal, VIC; known only from type locality.
Ecology: adult—volant; melliferous, flower visiting

record: *Leptospermum* Forster & G.Forster [Myrtaceae].
Reference: Rayment, T. (1951). Biology of the reed-bees. With descriptions of three new species and two allotypes of *Exoneura*. *Aust. Zool.* **11**: 285–313 (illustration).

Exoneura (Brevineura) Michener, 1965

Brevineura Michener, C.D. (1965). A classification of the bees of the Australian and South Pacific regions. *Bull. Am. Mus. Nat. Hist.* **130**: 1–362 [224] [proposed with subgeneric rank in *Exoneura* Smith, 1854]. Type species: *Exoneura concinnula* Cockerell, 1913 by original designation.

Exoneura (Brevineura) albolineata Cockerell, 1929

Exoneura albolineata Cockerell, T.D.A. (1929). Bees in the Australian Museum collection. *Rec. Aust. Mus.* **17**: 199–243 [241].
Type data: holotype, AM K48338 ♀.
Type locality: Ulong, East Dorrigo, NSW.

Distribution: SE coastal, NSW, VIC; only published localities Ulong (East Dorrigo), Lane Cove, Brooklyn and Dandenong.
Ecology: larva—sedentary : adult—volant; melliferous, nest in dead, dry stems (bramble, *Dahlia* Cav. [Asteraceae], *Hydrangea*, *Lantana* L. [Verbenaceae], *Rosa* L. [Rosaceae]), two or more adult females may be present in one nest, not all females lay eggs, all immature stages found in the communal chamber, larvae fed progressively.
References: Rayment, T. (1948). New bees and wasps—Part VII. Two undescribed species of *Exoneura*, with notes on recent collectings of several other Exoneurae and the extraordinary appendages of their larvae. *Vict. Nat.* **65**: 85–91 (distribution); Rayment, T. (1951). Biology of the reed-bees. With descriptions of three new species and two allotypes of *Exoneura*. *Aust. Zool.* **11**: 285–313 (larva).

Exoneura (Brevineura) aterrima Cockerell, 1916

Exoneura botanica aterrima Cockerell, T.D.A. (1916). A collection of bees from Queensland. *Mem. Qd Mus.* **5**: 197–204 [204].
Type data: holotype, USNM ♀*.
Type locality: Brisbane, QLD.

Distribution: NE coastal, QLD; only published localities Brisbane, Capalaba and Caloundra.
Ecology: larva—sedentary : adult—volant; melliferous, nest in dead, dry flowering stalks (*Xanthorrhoea* Sm. [Xanthorrhoeaceae]), two or more adult females may be present in one nest, not all females lay eggs, all immature stages found in the communal chamber, larvae fed progressively, flower visiting record: *Callistemon* R.Br. [Myrtaceae].
References: Cockerell, T.D.A. (1918). Some bees collected in Queensland. *Mem. Qd Mus.* **6**: 112–120 (description of male); Michener, C.D. (1965). A clas-

sification of the bees of the Australian and South Pacific regions. *Bull. Am. Mus. Nat. Hist.* **130**: 1–362 [242] (flower record); Michener, C.D. (1965). The life cycle and social organization of bees of the genus *Exoneura* and their parasite, *Inquilina* (Hymenoptera : Xylocopinae). *Univ. Kansas Sci. Bull.* **46**: 317–358 (biology).

Exoneura (Brevineura) botanica Cockerell, 1905

Exoneura botanica Cockerell, T.D.A. (1905). Descriptions and records of bees. V. *Ann. Mag. Nat. Hist.* *(7)***16**: 465–477 [465].
Type data: holotype, BMNH Hym.17.b.348 ♀.
Type locality: Botany, NSW.

Distribution: SE coastal, NSW; known only from type locality.
Ecology: adult—volant; melliferous.

Exoneura (Brevineura) brisbanensis Cockerell, 1916

Exoneura brisbanensis Cockerell, T.D.A. (1916). A collection of bees from Queensland. *Mem. Qd Mus.* **5**: 197–204 [204].
Type data: holotype, USNM ♀*.
Type locality: Brisbane, QLD.

Distribution: NE coastal, QLD; only published localities Brisbane, Capalaba, Tamborine and Caloundra.
Ecology: adult—volant; melliferous, nest in dead, dry stems, two or more adult females may be present in one nest, not all females lay eggs, all immature stages found in the communal chamber, larvae fed progressively, flower visiting record: *Alphitonia* Reisseck ex Endl. [Rhamnaceae], *Eucalyptus* L'Hérit. [Myrtaceae].
Reference: Michener, C.D. (1965). A classification of the bees of the Australian and South Pacific regions. *Bull. Am. Mus. Nat. Hist.* **130**: 1–362 [242] (flower record).

Exoneura (Brevineura) clarissima Cockerell, 1915

Exoneura clarissima Cockerell, T.D.A. (1915). Descriptions and records of bees. LXV. *Ann. Mag. Nat. Hist.* *(8)***15**: 261–269 [267].
Type data: holotype, USNM ♂*.
Type locality: Yarrawin, NSW.

Distribution: Murray-Darling basin, NSW; known only from type locality.
Ecology: adult—volant; melliferous.

Exoneura (Brevineura) cliffordiella Rayment, 1953

Exoneura cliffordiella Rayment, T. (1953). *Bees of the Portland District*. Victoria : Portland Field Naturalist's Club 39 pp. [37].
Type data: holotype, ANIC ♀.
Type locality: Gorae West, VIC.

Distribution: SE coastal, VIC; known only from type locality.

Ecology: adult—volant; melliferous, flower visiting record: *Eucalyptus* L'Hérit. [Myrtaceae].

Exoneura (Brevineura) concinnula Cockerell, 1913

Exoneura concinnula Cockerell, T.D.A. (1913). Some Australian bees. *Proc. Acad. Nat. Sci. Philad.* **65**: 28–44 [31].
Type data: holotype, USNM ♀*.
Type locality: NSW.

Distribution: NE coastal, Murray-Darling basin, SE coastal, QLD, NSW, VIC.
Ecology: larva—sedentary : adult—volant; melliferous, nest in galls formed by *Ethon* (Coleoptera : Buprestidae) on plant stems (*Pultenaea* Sm. [Fabaceae]), two or more adult females may be present in one nest, not all females lay eggs, all immature stages found in the communal chamber, larvae fed progressively, flower visiting record: *Angophora* Cav. [Myrtaceae], *Bursaria* Cav. [Pittosporaceae], *Calytrix* Lab. [Myrtaceae], *Jacksonia* Smith [Fabaceae], *Leptospermum* Forster & G.Forster [Myrtaceae].
References: Rayment, T. (1951). Biology of the reed-bees. With descriptions of three new species and two allotypes of *Exoneura*. *Aust. Zool.* **11**: 285–313 (biology); Rayment, T. (1954). Incidence of acarid mites on the biology of bees. *Aust. Zool.* **12**: 26–38 (as host); Syed, I.H. (1963). Comparative studies of larvae of Australian ceratinine bees (Hymenoptera, Apoidea). *Univ. Kansas Sci. Bull.* **64**: 263–280 (larva); Michener, C.D. (1965). A classification of the bees of the Australian and South Pacific regions. *Bull. Am. Mus. Nat. Hist.* **130**: 1–362 [242] (flower record); Michener, C.D. & Scheiring, J.F. (1976). Pupae of allodapine bees (Hymenoptera : Xylocopinae). *J. Aust. Entomol. Soc.* **15**: 63–70 (pupa); Michener, C.D. (1977). Discordant evolution and the classification of allodapine bees. *Syst. Zool.* **26**: 32–56 (taxonomy).

Exoneura (Brevineura) elongata Rayment, 1954

Exoneura elongata Rayment, T. (1954). New bees and wasps—Part XXII. The altruistic reed-bees, *Exoneura*. *Vict. Nat.* **71**: 13–16 [15].
Type data: holotype, ANIC ♀.
Type locality: Gorae West, VIC.

Distribution: SE coastal, VIC; known only from type locality.
Ecology: adult—volant; melliferous.

Exoneura (Brevineura) froggatti Friese, 1899

Exoneura froggatti Friese, H. (1899). Die Bienengattung *Exoneura* Sm. *Entomol. Nachr.* **25**: 209–211 [210].
Type data: holotype, whereabouts unknown ♀*.
Type locality: Thornleigh (as Sydney, Thurmleigh), NSW.

Distribution: SE coastal, Murray-Darling basin, NSW, VIC; only published localities Thornleigh,

Moss Bay (possibly Mosmans Bay), Sydney, Croydon and Grampians.

Ecology: larva—sedentary : adult—volant; melliferous, nest in galls (formed by *Ethon* (Coleoptera : Buprestidae), or in pithy stems of swordgrass, two or more adult females may be present in one nest, not all females lay eggs, all immature stages found in the communal chamber, larvae fed progressively, flower visiting record: *Angophora* Cav. [Myrtaceae].

References: Cockerell, T.D.A. (1905). Descriptions and records of bees. V. *Ann. Mag. Nat. Hist. (7)***16**: 465–477 (distribution); Cockerell, T.D.A. (1912). Descriptions and records of bees. XLII. *Ann. Mag. Nat. Hist. (8)***9**: 220–229 (flower record); Cockerell, T.D.A. (1913). Some Australian bees. *Proc. Acad. Nat. Sci. Philad.* **65**: 28–44 (description of female); Rayment, T. (1949). New bees and wasps—Part VIII. A new species of *Exoneura*, with notes on other reed-bees from the Grampians. *Vict. Nat.* **65**: 208–212 (biology).

Exoneura (Brevineura) gracilis Cockerell, 1918

Exoneura gracilis Cockerell, T.D.A. (1918). Some bees collected in Queensland. *Mem. Qd Mus.* **6**: 112–120 [119].
Type data: holotype, QM T4112 ♀.
Type locality: Brisbane, QLD.

Distribution: NE coastal, QLD; only published localities Brisbane and Capalaba.
Ecology: adult—volant; melliferous, nest in dead, dry stems, two or more adult females may be present in one nest, not all females lay eggs, all immature stages found in the communal chamber, larvae fed progressively, flower visiting record: *Callistemon* R.Br. [Myrtaceae].
Reference: Michener, C.D. (1965). A classification of the bees of the Australian and South Pacific regions. *Bull. Am. Mus. Nat. Hist.* **130**: 1–362 [242] (flower record).

Exoneura (Brevineura) maculata Rayment, 1935

Exoneura maculata Rayment, T. (1935). *A Cluster of Bees.* Sixty essays on the life-histories of Australian bees, with specific descriptions of over 100 new species, and an introduction by Professor E.F. Phillips, D.Ph., Cornell University, U.S.A. Sydney : Endeavour Press 752 pp. [730].
Type data: holotype, ANIC ♀.
Type locality: Seville, VIC.

Distribution: SE coastal, VIC; known only from type locality.
Ecology: adult—volant; melliferous, flower visiting record: *Arctotheca* Wendl. [Asteraceae], *Bursaria* Cav. [Pittosporaceae], *Hypochaeris* L. [Asteraceae].

Exoneura (Brevineura) melaena Cockerell, 1918

Exoneura melaena Cockerell, T.D.A. (1918). Some bees collected in Queensland. *Mem. Qd Mus.* **6**: 112–120 [119].

Type data: holotype, QM T4113 ♀.
Type locality: Caloundra, QLD.

Distribution: NE coastal, QLD; known only from type locality.
Ecology: adult—volant; melliferous.

Exoneura (Brevineura) minutissima Rayment, 1951

Exoneura minutissima Rayment, T. (1951). *In* Erickson, R. & Rayment, T. Simple social bees of Western Australia. *West. Aust. Nat.* **3**: 45–59 [52].
Type data: holotype, ANIC ♀.
Type locality: Bolgart, WA.

Distribution: SW coastal, WA; known only from type locality.
Ecology: adult—volant; melliferous.

Exoneura (Brevineura) nigrofulva Rayment, 1935

Exoneura nigrofulva Rayment, T. (1935). *A Cluster of Bees.* Sixty essays on the life-histories of Australian bees, with specific descriptions of over 100 new species, and an introduction by Professor E.F. Phillips, D.Ph., Cornell University, U.S.A. Sydney : Endeavour Press 752 pp. [729].
Type data: holotype, ANIC ♀.
Type locality: Halls Gap, Grampians, VIC.

Distribution: Murray-Darling basin, VIC; known only from type locality.
Ecology: adult—volant; melliferous, flower visiting record: *Bursaria* Cav. [Pittosporaceae].

Exoneura (Brevineura) nitida Cockerell, 1922

Exoneura nitida Cockerell, T.D.A. (1922). Australian bees in the Queensland Museum. *Mem. Qd Mus.* **7**: 257–279 [275].
Type data: syntypes, QM 1♂4♀ (number of specimens unknown, a female specimen is labelled 'type' and has registration number T2517).
Type locality: Stradbroke Is., QLD.

Distribution: NE coastal, QLD; known only from type locality.
Ecology: adult—volant; melliferous.

Exoneura (Brevineura) normani Rayment, 1948

Exoneura roddiana normani Rayment, T. (1948). New bees and wasps—Part VII. Two undescribed species of *Exoneura*, with notes on recent collectings of several other Exoncurae and the extraordinary appendages of their larvae. *Vict. Nat.* **65**: 85–91 [87].
Type data: syntypes, ANIC 1♂4♀.
Type locality: Lane Cove, NSW.

Distribution: SE coastal, NSW; known only from type locality.
Ecology: adult—volant; melliferous.
Reference: Michener, C.D. (1965). A classification of the bees of the Australian and South Pacific regions. *Bull. Am. Mus. Nat. Hist.* **130**: 1–362 [226] (taxonomy).

Exoneura (Brevineura) parvula Rayment, 1935

Exoneura parvula Rayment, T. (1935). *A Cluster of Bees.* Sixty essays on the life-histories of Australian bees, with specific descriptions of over 100 new species, and an introduction by Professor E.F. Phillips, D.Ph., Cornell University, U.S.A. Sydney : Endeavour Press 752 pp. [727].
Type data: holotype, NMV 1408 ♀.
Type locality: Marysville, VIC.

Distribution: SE coastal, NSW, VIC; only published localities Sydney, Woy Woy and Marysville.
Ecology: adult—volant; melliferous, nest in dead, dry stems, two or more adult females may be present in one nest, not all females lay eggs, all immature stages found in the communal chamber, larvae fed progressively, flower visiting record: *Bursaria* Cav. [Pittosporaceae], *Hypochaeris* L. [Asteraceae].
References: Rayment, T. (1939). Bees from the high lands of New South Wales and Victoria. *Aust. Zool.* **9**: 263–294 (distribution); Rayment, T. (1951). Biology of the reed-bees. With descriptions of three new species and two allotypes of *Exoneura*. *Aust. Zool.* **11**: 285–313 (distribution).

Exoneura (Brevineura) perparvula Rayment, 1948

Exoneura parvula perparvula Rayment, T. (1948). Notes on remarkable wasps and bees. With specific descriptions. *Aust. Zool.* **11**: 238–254 [253].
Type data: holotype, ANIC ♀.
Type locality: Bundeena, NSW.

Distribution: SE coastal, NSW; known only from type locality.
Ecology: adult—volant; melliferous, flower visiting record: *Eucalyptus* L'Hérit. [Myrtaceae].
Reference: Michener, C.D. (1965). A classification of the bees of the Australian and South Pacific regions. *Bull. Am. Mus. Nat. Hist.* **130**: 1–362 [226] (taxonomy).

Exoneura (Brevineura) perplexa Rayment, 1953

Exoneura perplexa Rayment, T. (1953). *Bees of the Portland District.* Victoria : Portland Field Naturalist's Club 39 pp. [38].
Type data: holotype (probable), ANIC ♀.
Type locality: Mt Clay (Gorae West on label), VIC.

Distribution: SE coastal, VIC; known only from type locality.
Ecology: adult—volant; melliferous, flower visiting record: aster, *Leptospermum* Forster & G.Forster [Myrtaceae].

Exoneura (Brevineura) ploratula Cockerell, 1912

Exoneura ploratula Cockerell, T.D.A. (1912). Descriptions and records of bees. XLII. *Ann. Mag. Nat. Hist. (8)***9**: 220–229 [224].
Type data: holotype, USNM ♀*.
Type locality: Sydney, NSW.

Distribution: NE coastal, Murray-Darling basin, SE coastal, QLD, NSW.
Ecology: adult—volant; melliferous, nest in dead, dry stems, two or more adult females may be present in one nest, not all females lay eggs, all immature stages found in the communal chamber, larvae fed progressively, flower visiting record: *Angophora* Cav. [Myrtaceae], *Bursaria* Cav. [Pittosporaceae], *Callistemon* R.Br. [Myrtaceae], *Jacksonia* Smith [Fabaceae], *Xanthorrhoea* Sm. [Xanthorrhoeaceae].
References: Rayment, T. (1939). Bees from the high lands of New South Wales and Victoria. *Aust. Zool.* **9**: 263–294 (distribution); Michener, C.D. (1965). A classification of the bees of the Australian and South Pacific regions. *Bull. Am. Mus. Nat. Hist.* **130**: 1–362 [242] (flower record).

Exoneura (Brevineura) roddiana Rayment, 1946

Exoneura roddiana Rayment, T. (1946). New bees and wasps—Part II. Describing two black species of *Exoneura*. *Vict. Nat.* **62**: 230–236 [230].
Type data: holotype, ANIC ♂.
Type locality: Lane Cove, NSW.

Distribution: SE coastal, Murray-Darling basin, NSW, VIC; only published localities Lane Cove and the Grampians.
Ecology: larva—sedentary : adult—volant; melliferous, nest in dead, dry stems or twigs (reed, *Acacia* Miller [Mimosaceae], *Lantana* L. [Verbenaceae]), two or more adult females may be present in one nest, not all females lay eggs, all immature stages found in the communal chamber, larvae fed progressively, flower visiting record: legume, *Acacia* Miller [Mimosaceae].
References: Rayment, T. (1948). New bees and wasps—Part VII. Two undescribed species of *Exoneura*, with notes on recent collectings of several other Exoneurae and the extraordinary appendages of their larvae. *Vict. Nat.* **65**: 85–91 (biology); Rayment, T. (1949). New bees and wasps—Part VIII. A new species of *Exoneura*, with notes on other reed-bees from the Grampians. *Vict. Nat.* **65**: 208–212 (biology); Rayment, T. (1951). Biology of the reed-bees. With descriptions of three new species and two allotypes of *Exoneura*. *Aust. Zool.* **11**: 285–313 (biology).

Exoneura (Brevineura) rufitarsis Rayment, 1948

Exoneura rufitarsis Rayment, T. (1948). Notes on remarkable wasps and bees. With specific descriptions. *Aust. Zool.* **11**: 238–254 [253] [a specimen in the ANIC labelled "type" bears a locality which was not given in the original description].
Type data: holotype (probable), ANIC ♀.
Type locality: Cranbourne, VIC.

Distribution: SE coastal, VIC; only published localities Cranbourne, Clyde, Gippsland and Dandenong.
Ecology: larva—sedentary : adult—volant; mellifer-

ous, nest in dead, dry stems (wild parsnip, *Viminaria* Smith [Fabaceae]), two or more adult females may be present in one nest, not all females lay eggs, all immature stages found in the communal chamber, larvae fed progressively.
Reference: Rayment, T. (1951). Biology of the reed-bees. With descriptions of three new species and two allotypes of *Exoneura. Aust. Zool.* **11**: 285–313 (description of male, biology).

Exoneura (Brevineura) simillima Rayment, 1935

Exoneura simillima Rayment, T. (1935). *A Cluster of Bees.* Sixty essays on the life-histories of Australian bees, with specific descriptions of over 100 new species, and an introduction by Professor E.F. Phillips, D.Ph., Cornell University, U.S.A. Sydney : Endeavour Press 752 pp. [730].
Type data: holotype, ANIC ♀.
Type locality: Marysville, VIC.

Distribution: SE coastal, Murray-Darling basin, VIC; only published localities Marysville, Portland district and the Grampians.
Ecology: adult—volant; melliferous, nest in dead, dry stems, two or more adult females may be present in one nest, not all females lay eggs, all immature stages found in the communal chamber, larvae fed progressively, flower visiting record: *Leucopogon* R.Br. [Epacridaceae].
References: Rayment, T. (1951). Biology of the reed-bees. With descriptions of three new species and two allotypes of *Exoneura. Aust. Zool.* **11**: 285–313 (illustration, as *Exoneura asimillima*, incorrect subsequent spelling); Rayment, T. (1953). *Bees of the Portland District.* Victoria : Portland Field Naturalist's Club 39 pp. [39] (distribution, correction of spelling of *Exoneura asimillima*).

Exoneura (Brevineura) subexcavata Rayment, 1951

Exoneura subexcavata Rayment, T. (1951). Biology of the reed-bees. With descriptions of three new species and two allotypes of *Exoneura. Aust. Zool.* **11**: 285–313 [287].
Type data: holotype, ANIC ♀.
Type locality: Emerald, VIC.

Distribution: SE coastal, VIC; known only from type locality.
Ecology: adult—volant; melliferous, flower visiting record: *Leptospermum* Forster & G.Forster [Myrtaceae].

Exoneura (Brevineura) tau Cockerell, 1905

Exoneura tau Cockerell, T.D.A. (1905). Descriptions and records of bees. V. *Ann. Mag. Nat. Hist.* (7)**16**: 465–477 [466].
Type data: holotype, BMNH Hym.17.b.349 ♀.
Type locality: Moss Bay (presumably Mosmans Bay), NSW.

Distribution: NE coastal, Murray-Darling basin, SE coastal, QLD, NSW.
Ecology: adult—volant; melliferous, nest in dead, dry stems, two or more adult females may be present in one nest, not all females lay eggs, all immature stages found in the communal chamber, larvae fed progressively, flower visiting record: *Angophora* Cav. [Myrtaceae], *Jacksonia* Smith [Fabaceae], *Leptospermum* Forster & G.Forster [Myrtaceae], *Pultenaea* Sm. [Fabaceae].
References: Cockerell, T.D.A. (1916). A collection of bees from Queensland. *Mem. Qd Mus.* **5**: 197–204 (description of female); Michener, C.D. (1965). A classification of the bees of the Australian and South Pacific regions. *Bull. Am. Mus. Nat. Hist.* **130**: 1–362 [243] (flower record).

Exoneura (Brevineura) xanthoclypeata Rayment, 1935

Exoneura xanthoclypeata Rayment, T. (1935). *A Cluster of Bees.* Sixty essays on the life-histories of Australian bees, with specific descriptions of over 100 new species, and an introduction by Professor E.F. Phillips, D.Ph., Cornell University, U.S.A. Sydney : Endeavour Press 752 pp. [728].
Type data: holotype, ANIC ♂.
Type locality: Halls Gap, Grampians, VIC.

Distribution: Murray-Darling basin, VIC; known only from type locality.
Ecology: adult—volant; melliferous.
Reference: Rayment, T. (1951). Biology of the reed-bees. With descriptions of three new species and two allotypes of *Exoneura. Aust. Zool.* **11**: 285–313 (illustration).

Exoneura (Exoneurella) Michener, 1963

Exoneurella Michener, C.D. (1963). New Ceratinini from Australia (Hymenoptera, Apoidea). *Univ. Kansas Sci. Bull.* **44**: 257–261 [257]. Type species: *Exoneura lawsoni* Rayment, 1946 by original designation.

Exoneura (Exoneurella) eremophila Houston, 1976

Exoneura (Exoneurella) eremophila Houston, T.F. (1976). New Australian allodapine bees (subgenus *Exoneurella* Michener) and their immatures (Hymenoptera : Anthophoridae). *Trans. R. Soc. S. Aust.* **100**: 15–28 [17].
Type data: holotype, SAMA I20961 ♂*.
Type locality: New Kalamurina Homestead, SA.

Distribution: Lake Eyre basin, Murray-Darling basin, W plateau, QLD, NSW, SA, NT.
Ecology: larva—sedentary : adult—volant; melliferous, nest in dead, dry pithy stems (*Crotalaria* L. [Fabaceae], *Myriocephalus* Benth. [Asteraceae]), basically subsocial, each female founding and maintaining her own nest, occasionally two or more females may oviposit and rear brood together in one nest, all immature stages found in the communal chamber,

larvae fed progressively, flower visiting record: *Calandrinia* Kunth [Portulacaceae], *Eremophila* R.Br. [Myoporaceae], *Goodenia* Sm. [Goodeniaceae], *Hakea* Schrader [Proteaceae], *Helichrysum* Miller *s.lat.* [Asteraceae], *Hibiscus* L. [Malvaceae], *Myriocephalus* Benth. [Asteraceae], *Ptilotus* R.Br. [Amaranthaceae], *Scaevola* L. [Goodeniaceae], *Wahlenbergia* Roth [Campanulaceae].
Reference: Houston, T.F. (1977). Nesting biology of three allodapine bees in the subgenus *Exoneurella* Michener (Hymenoptera : Anthophoridae). *Trans. R. Soc. S. Aust.* **101**: 99–113 (biology).

Exoneura (Exoneurella) lawsoni Rayment, 1946

Exoneura lawsoni Rayment, T. (1946). New bees and wasps—Part II. Describing two black species of *Exoneura*. *Vict. Nat.* **62**: 230–236 [230].
Type data: holotype, ANIC ♂.
Type locality: Canberra, ACT.

Distribution: NE coastal, Murray-Darling basin, SE coastal, QLD, NSW, ACT, VIC.
Ecology: larva—sedentary : adult—volant; melliferous, nest in dead, dry pithy stems (*Hydrangea, Verbena* L. [Verbenaceae]), basically subsocial, each female founding and maintaining her own nest, all immature stages found in the communal chamber, larvae fed progressively, flower visiting record: *Wahlenbergia* Roth [Campanulaceae].
References: Michener, C.D. (1963). New Ceratinini from Australia (Hymenoptera, Apoidea). *Univ. Kansas Sci. Bull.* **44**: 257–261 (redescription, generic placement); Syed, I.H. (1963). Comparative studies of larvae of Australian ceratinine bees (Hymenoptera, Apoidea). *Univ. Kansas Sci. Bull.* **64**: 263–280 (larva); Michener, C.D. (1964). The bionomics of *Exoneurella*, a solitary relative of *Exoneura* (Hymenoptera : Apoidea : Ceratinini). *Pac. Insects* **6**: 411–426 (biology); Michener, C.D. (1965). A classification of the bees of the Australian and South Pacific regions. *Bull. Am. Mus. Nat. Hist.* **130**: 1–362 [225] (illustration); Michener, C.D. (1973). Size and form of eggs of allodapine bees. *J. Entomol. Soc. S. Afr.* **36**: 281–285 (egg); Houston, T.F. (1976). New Australian allodapine bees (subgenus *Exoneurella* Michener) and their immatures (Hymenoptera : Anthophoridae). *Trans. R. Soc. S. Aust.* **100**: 15–28 (taxonomy); Michener, C.D. & Scheiring, J.F. (1976). Pupae of allodapine bees (Hymenoptera : Xylocopinae). *J. Aust. Entomol. Soc.* **15**: 63–70 (pupa); Michener, C.D. (1977). Discordant evolution and the classification of allodapine bees. *Syst. Zool.* **26**: 32–56 (larva); Houston, T.F. (1977). Nesting biology of three allodapine bees in the subgenus *Exoneurella* Michener (Hymenoptera : Anthophoridae). *Trans. R. Soc. S. Aust.* **101**: 99–113 (biology); Michener, C.D. & Brooks, R.W. (1984). A comparative study of the glossae of bees (Apoidea). *Contrib. Am. Entomol. Inst.* **22**: 1–73 (glossa).

Exoneura (Exoneurella) setosa Houston, 1976

Exoneura (Exoneurella) setosa Houston, T.F. (1976). New Australian allodapine bees (subgenus *Exoneurella* Michener) and their immatures (Hymenoptera : Anthophoridae). *Trans. R. Soc. S. Aust.* **100**: 15–28 [18].
Type data: holotype, SAMA I20962 ♂*.
Type locality: West Beach, Adelaide, SA.

Distribution: NE coastal, S Gulfs, Murray-Darling basin, QLD, SA.
Ecology: larva—sedentary : adult—volant; melliferous, nest in dead, dry pithy stems (*Euphorbia* L. [Euphorbiaceae], *Foeniculum* Miller [Apiaceae], *Geranium* L. [Geraniaceae]), basically subsocial, each female founding and maintaining her own nest, all immature stages found in the communal chamber, larvae fed progressively, flower visiting record: pigface, *Cakile* Miller [Brassicaceae], *Geranium* L. [Geraniaceae], *Reichardia* Roth [Asteraceae], *Wahlenbergia* Roth [Campanulaceae].
Reference: Houston, T.F. (1977). Nesting biology of three allodapine bees in the subgenus *Exoneurella* Michener (Hymenoptera : Anthophoridae). *Trans. R. Soc. S. Aust.* **101**: 99–113 (biology).

Exoneura (Exoneurella) tridentata Houston, 1976

Exoneura (Exoneurella) tridentata Houston, T.F. (1976). New Australian allodapine bees (subgenus *Exoneurella* Michener) and their immatures (Hymenoptera : Anthophoridae). *Trans. R. Soc. S. Aust.* **100**: 15–28 [19].
Type data: holotype, SAMA I20963 ♂*.
Type locality: Lake Gilles National Park, SA.

Distribution: Murray-Darling basin, S Gulfs, W plateau, NW coastal, SA, WA.
Ecology: larva—sedentary : adult—volant; melliferous, nest in dead, dry, hollowed-out woody twigs (*Heterodendrum* Desf. [Sapindaceae]), semisocial, small colonies with queen and worker castes, all immature stages found in the communal chamber, larvae fed progressively, flower visiting record: *Amyema* Tieghem [Loranthaceae], *Eremophila* R.Br. [Myoporaceae], *Eucalyptus* L'Hérit. [Myrtaceae], *Loranthus* Jacq. [Loranthaceae], *Melaleuca* L. [Myrtaceae], *Myoporum* Banks & Sol. ex G.Forster [Myoporaceae].
References: Houston, T.F. (1977). Nesting biology of three allodapine bees in the subgenus *Exoneurella* Michener (Hymenoptera : Anthophoridae). *Trans. R. Soc. S. Aust.* **101**: 99–113 (biology); Sugden, E. (1988). Inside the (secret) societies of native bees. *Aust. Nat. Hist.* **22**: 381–384 (biology).

Exoneura (Unplaced)

Exoneura marjoriella Rayment, 1949

Exoneura marjoriella Rayment, T. (1949). New bees and wasps—Part IX. Four undescribed species of *Exoneura*, with notes on their collection, and description of new

parasites discovered on the genus. *Vict. Nat.* **65**: 247–254 [251].
Type data: holotype, whereabouts unknown ♂* (not located in T. Rayment coll. transferred to ANIC).
Type locality: Brooklyn, NSW.

Distribution: SE coastal, NSW; known only from type locality.
Ecology: adult—volant; melliferous, nest in dead, dry stems (*Lantana* L. [Verbenaceae]).
Reference: Michener, C.D. (1965). A classification of the bees of the Australian and South Pacific regions. *Bull. Am. Mus. Nat. Hist.* **130**: 1–362 (taxonomy).

Exoneura nigrescens Friese, 1899

Exoneura bicolor nigrescens Friese, H. (1899). Die Bienengattung *Exoneura* Sm. *Entomol. Nachr.* **25**: 209–211 [210].
Type data: syntypes (probable), whereabouts unknown ♂♀*.
Type locality: Sydney, NSW.

Distribution: SE coastal, NSW; known only from type locality.
Ecology: adult—volant; melliferous.
Reference: Michener, C.D. (1965). A classification of the bees of the Australian and South Pacific regions. *Bull. Am. Mus. Nat. Hist.* **130**: 1–362 (taxonomy).

Exoneura rufa Rayment, 1935

Exoneura hamulata rufa Rayment, T. (1935). *A Cluster of Bees*. Sixty essays on the life-histories of Australian bees, with specific descriptions of over 100 new species, and an introduction by Professor E.F. Phillips, D.Ph., Cornell University, U.S.A. Sydney : Endeavour Press 752 pp. [728] [junior primary homonym of *Exoneura rufa* Rayment, 1935: 726; raised to specific rank, Cardale, J.C., this work].
Type data: holotype, whereabouts unknown*.
Type locality: Caulfield, VIC.

Distribution: SE coastal, VIC.
Ecology: adult—volant; melliferous.

Inquilina Michener, 1961

Inquilina Michener, C.D. (1961). A new parasitic genus of Ceratinini from Australia (Hymenoptera : Apoidea). *J. Kansas Entomol. Soc.* **34**: 178–180 [179]. Type species: *Exoneura excavata* Cockerell, 1922 by original designation.

Inquilina excavata (Cockerell, 1922)

Exoneura excavata Cockerell, T.D.A. (1922). Australian bees in the Queensland Museum. *Mem. Qd Mus.* **7**: 257–279 [276].
Type data: holotype, QM T2521 ♀.
Type locality: [Lamington] National Park, QLD.

Exoneura dawsoni Rayment, T. (1946). New bees and wasps—Part III. Another new *Exoneura*; also notes on the biology of *E. hamulata*. *Vict. Nat.* **63**: 63–68 [63].
Type data: holotype, ANIC ♀.
Type locality: Neerim South, VIC.

Exoneura concava Rayment, T. (1949). New bees and wasps—Part IX. Four undescribed species of *Exoneura*, with notes on their collection, and description of new parasites discovered on the genus. *Vict. Nat.* **65**: 247–254 [249].
Type data: holotype, ANIC ♀ (described as ♂).
Type locality: Brooklyn, NSW.

Exoneura angulata Rayment, T. (1951). Biology of the reed-bees. With descriptions of three new species and two allotypes of *Exoneura*. *Aust. Zool.* **11**: 285–313 [287].
Type data: holotype, ANIC ♀.
Type locality: Dandenong, VIC.

Taxonomic decision for synonymy: Michener, C.D. (1983). The parasitic Australian allodapine genus *Inquilina* (Hymenoptera, Anthophoridae). *J. Kansas Entomol. Soc.* **56**: 555–559 [556].

Distribution: NE coastal, SE coastal, Murray-Darling basin, QLD, NSW, VIC.
Ecology: larva—sedentary : adult—volant; melliferous, cleptoparasitic in nests of *Exoneura variabilis* Rayment, 1949, in stems (*Lantana* L. [Verbenaceae], *Olearia* Moench [Asteraceae]), all immature stages found in the communal chamber, larvae fed progressively, flower visiting record: *Leptospermum* Forster & G.Forster [Myrtaceae].
References: Rayment, T. (1949). New bees and wasps—Part IX. Four undescribed species of *Exoneura*, with notes on their collection, and description of new parasites discovered on the genus. *Vict. Nat.* **65**: 247–254 (biology); Michener, C.D. (1961). A new parasitic genus of Ceratinini from Australia (Hymenoptera : Apoidea). *J. Kansas Entomol. Soc.* **34**: 178–180 (redescription, generic placement); Syed, I.H. (1963). Comparative studies of larvae of Australian ceratinine bees (Hymenoptera, Apoidea). *Univ. Kansas Sci. Bull.* **64**: 263–280 (larva); Michener, C.D. (1965). The life cycle and social organization of bees of the genus *Exoneura* and their parasite, *Inquilina* (Hymenoptera : Xylocopinae). *Univ. Kansas Sci. Bull.* **46**: 317–358 (biology); Michener, C.D. & Scheiring, J.F. (1976). Pupae of allodapine bees (Hymenoptera : Xylocopinae). *J. Aust. Entomol. Soc.* **15**: 63–70 (pupa); Michener, C.D. & Brooks, R.W. (1984). A comparative study of the glossae of bees (Apoidea). *Contrib. Am. Entomol. Inst.* **22**: 1–73 (glossa).

Inquilina schwarzi Michener, 1983

Inquilina schwarzi Michener, C.D. (1983). The parasitic Australian allodapine genus *Inquilina* (Hymenoptera, Anthophoridae). *J. Kansas Entomol. Soc.* **56**: 555–559 [558].
Type data: holotype, ANIC ♀.
Type locality: Brooklyn, NSW.

Distribution: SE coastal, NSW, VIC; only published localities Brooklyn and Dandenong Ranges.
Ecology: adult—volant; melliferous, cleptoparasitic in nests of *Exoneura bicolor* Smith, 1854, ?*E. bicincta* Rayment, 1935, ?*E. hamulata* Cockerell,

1905, all immature stages found in the communal chamber, larvae fed progressively.

Lestis Lepeletier and Serville, 1828

Lestis Lepeletier, A.L.M. & Serville, A. (1828). *In* Latreille, P.A., Lepeletier, A.L.M., Serville, A. & Guérin-Méneville, F.E. *Encyclopédie Méthodique.* Tome x. Histoire Naturelle. Entomologie, ou Histoire Naturelle des Crustacés, des Arachnides et des Insectes. Paris : Agasse 832 pp. [799]. Type species: *Apis bombylans* Fabricius, 1775 by subsequent designation, see International Commission on Zoological Nomenclature (1963). Opinion 657. *Lestis* Lepeletier & Serville, 1828 (Insecta, Hymenoptera) : designation of a type-species under the plenary powers. *Bull. Zool. Nomen.* **20**: 181–182 [81].

Lestis aeratus Smith, 1851

Lestis aeratus Smith, F. (1851). Notes on the habits of Australian Hymenoptera. *Trans. Entomol. Soc. Lond. (ns)***1**: 179–181 [180].
Type data: syntypes, OUM 3♂♂2♀.
Type locality: Australia.

Distribution: NE coastal, SE coastal, Murray-Darling basin, S Gulfs, QLD, NSW, VIC, SA, (TAS).
Ecology: larva—sedentary : adult—volant; melliferous, nest, usually communally, in dead, dry flowering stalks (*Xanthorrhoea* Sm. [Xanthorrhoeaceae]), twigs (*Casuarina* L. [Casuarinaceae]), each larva in individual, mass-provisioned cell, flower visiting record: *Leptospermum* Forster & G.Forster [Myrtaceae], *Leucopogon* R.Br. [Epacridaceae].
References: Smith, F. (1854). *Catalogue of Hymenopterous Insects in the Collection of the British Museum.* Part II. Apidae. London : British Museum pp. 199–465 (record from TAS); Cockerell, T.D.A. (1930). The bees of Australia. *Aust. Zool.* **6**: 137–156, 205–236 (distribution); Rayment, T. (1935). *A Cluster of Bees.* Sixty essays on the life-histories of Australian bees, with specific descriptions of over 100 new species, and an introduction by Professor E.F. Phillips, D.Ph., Cornell University, U.S.A. Sydney : Endeavour Press 752 pp. (biology); Rayment, T. (1953). *Bees of the Portland District.* Victoria : Portland Field Naturalist's Club 39 pp. (as *Lestis aerata,* unnecessary emendation); Michener, C.D. (1965). A classification of the bees of the Australian and South Pacific regions. *Bull. Am. Mus. Nat. Hist.* **130**: 1–362 [227] (illustration); Winston, M. L. (1979). The proboscis of the long-tongued bees: a comparative study. *Univ. Kansas Sci. Bull.* **51**: 631–667 (proboscis); Michener, C.D. & Brooks, R.W. (1984). A comparative study of the glossae of bees (Apoidea). *Contrib. Am. Entomol. Inst.* **22**: 1–73 (glossa); Houston, T.F. (1992). Biological observations of the Australian green carpenter bees, genus *Lestis* (Hymenoptera: Anthophoridae: Xylocopini). *Rec. West. Aust. Mus.* **15**: 785–798 (biology).

Lestis australensis (W. Kirby, 1819)

Xylocopa australensis Kirby, W. (1819). A description of several new species of insects collected in New Holland by Robert Brown, Esq. F.R.S. Lib. Linn. Soc. *Trans. Linn. Soc. Lond.* **12**: 454–482 [477].
Type data: holotype (probable), whereabouts unknown ♂*.
Type locality: Australia (as New Holland).

Distribution: Australia; known only from type locality, exact locality unknown.
Ecology: adult—volant; melliferous, solitary.
Reference: Hurd, P.D., Jr & Moure, J.S. (1963). A classification of the large carpenter bees (Xylocopini) (Hymenoptera : Apoidea). *Univ. Calif. Publ. Entomol.* **29**: 1–365 (generic placement).

Lestis bombylans (Fabricius, 1775)

Apis bombylans Fabricius, J.C. (1775). *Systema Entomologiae,* sistens insectorum classes, ordines, genera, species, adiectis synonymis, locis, descriptionibus, observationibus. Korte : Flensburgi et Lipsiae xxvii 832 pp. [386].
Type data: holotype, BMNH (Banks coll.) ♀.
Type locality: Australia (as New Holland).
Lestis bombiliformis Froggatt, W.W. (1896). The entomology of the grass-trees (*Xanthorrhoea*). *Proc. Linn. Soc. N.S.W.* **21**: 74–87 [81] [incorrect subsequent spelling for *Lestis bombylans* (Fabricius, 1775); name not available].
Taxonomic decision for synonymy: Michener, C.D. (1965). A classification of the bees of the Australian and South Pacific regions. *Bull. Am. Mus. Nat. Hist.* **130**: 1–362 [228].

Distribution: NE coastal, SE coastal, Murray-Darling basin, QLD, NSW, VIC.
Ecology: larva—sedentary : adult—volant; melliferous, nest, usually communally, in dead, dry wood (*Acacia* Miller [Mimosaceae], *Banksia* L.f. [Proteaceae], *Casuarina* L. [Casuarinaceae], *Eucalyptus* L'Hérit. [Myrtaceae], *Leptospermum* Forster & G.Forster [Myrtaceae], *Tristania* R.Br. [Myrtaceae]), flowering stalks (*Xanthorrhoea* Sm. [Xanthorrhoeaceae]), each larva in individual, mass-provisioned cell, flower visiting record: *Baeckea* L. [Myrtaceae], *Eucalyptus* L'Hérit. [Myrtaceae], *Hibbertia* Andrews [Dilleniaceae], *Leucopogon* R.Br. [Epacridaceae], *Melaleuca* L. [Myrtaceae], *?Xanthorrhoea* Sm. [Xanthorrhoeaceae].
References: Smith, F. (1851). Notes on the habits of Australian Hymenoptera. *Trans. Entomol. Soc. Lond. (ns)***1**: 179–181 (taxonomy); McKeown, K.C. (1918). Notes on the habits of (*Lestis bombylans*), the carpenter bee of the grass-trees. *Aust. Nat.* **4**: 21–25 (biology); Hacker, H. (1918). Entomological contributions. *Mem. Qd Mus.* **6**: 106–111 pls 31–32 (biology); Rayment, T. (1935). *A Cluster of Bees.* Sixty essays on the life-histories of Australian bees, with specific descriptions of over 100 new species, and an introduction by Professor E.F. Phillips, D.Ph., Cornell University, U.S.A. Sydney : Endeavour Press

752 pp. (biology); Cockerell, T.D.A. (1939). Studies of the Pacific bees in the collection of Bishop Museum (Hymenoptera, Apoidea). *Occ. Pap. Bernice P. Bishop Mus.* **15**: 133–140 (distribution); McKeown, K.C. (1945). *Australian Insects. An Introductory Handbook.* Sydney : Royal Zoological Society of N.S.W. 2nd edn 303 pp. (biology); Rayment, T. (1954). Incidence of acarid mites on the biology of bees. *Aust. Zool.* **12**: 26–38 (as host); Cane, J.H. (1979). The hind tibiotarsal and tibial spur articulations in bees (Hymenoptera : Apoidea). *J. Kansas Entomol. Soc.* **52**: 123–137 (morphology); Fain, A. (1982). *Sennertia* Oudemans (Acari, Chaetodactylidae) on Australian bees. *Trans. R. Soc. S. Aust.* **106**: 67–70 (as host); Houston, T.F. (1992). Biological observations of the Australian green carpenter bees, genus *Lestis* (Hymenoptera: Anthophoridae: Xylocopini). *Rec. West. Aust. Mus.* **15**: 785–798 (biology).

Lestis gibbonsi Cockerell, 1929

Lestis aerata gibbonsi Cockerell, T.D.A. (1929). Bees in the Australian Museum collection. *Rec. Aust. Mus.* **17**: 199–243 [240].
Type data: holotype, AM K57725 ♂.
Type locality: [Royal] National Park, NSW.

Distribution: SE coastal, NSW; known only from type locality.
Ecology: adult—volant; melliferous.

Lestis violascens Cockerell, 1905

Lestis aerata violascens Cockerell, T.D.A. (1905). Notes on some bees in the British Museum. *Trans. Am. Entomol. Soc.* **31**: 309–364 [323].
Type data: holotype (probable), BMNH ♂.
Type locality: Australia.
Lestis bombylans violacea Rayment, T. (1939). Bees from the high lands of New South Wales and Victoria. *Aust. Zool.* **9**: 263–294 [293] [incorrect subsequent spelling for *Lestis violascens* Cockerell, 1905; name not available].

Taxonomic decision for synonymy: Michener, C.D. (1965). A classification of the bees of the Australian and South Pacific regions. *Bull. Am. Mus. Nat. Hist.* **130**: 1–362 [293].

Distribution: SE coastal, Murray-Darling basin, NSW; only published localities Woods Reef (Barraba), Bingera and White Swamp.
Ecology: adult —volant; melliferous.
Reference: Rayment, T. (1954). Incidence of acarid mites on the biology of bees. *Aust. Zool.* **12**: 26–38 (as host).

Xylocopa Latreille, 1802

Xilocopa Latreille, P.A. (1802). *Histoire Naturelle des Fourmis et Recueil de Mémoires et d'Observations sur les Abeilles, les Areignées, les Faucheurs et autres Insectes.* Paris : Barrois 445 pp. [431] [*Xilocopa* suppressed under the Plenary Powers of the International Commission of Zoological Nomenclature, see International Commission on Zoological Nomenclature (1965). Opinion 743. *Xylocopa* Latreille, [1802–1803] (Insecta, Hymenoptera): validated under the plenary powers. *Bull. Zool. Nomen.* **22**: 178–179].

Xylocopa Latreille, P.A. (1802). *Histoire Naturelle, Générale et Particulière des Crustacés et des Insectes.* Paris : F. Dufart Vol. 3 xii 13+467 pp. [379] [placed on the Official List of Generic Names in Zoology (Name No. 1687), Opinion 743, see International Commission on Zoological Nomenclature (1965). Opinion 743. *Xylocopa* Latreille, [1802–1803] (Insecta, Hymenoptera): validated under the plenary powers. *Bull. Zool. Nomen.* **22**: 178–179].
Type species: *Apis violacea* Linnaeus, 1758 by subsequent designation, see Westwood, J.O. (1840). Synopsis of the genera of British Insects. pp. 1–158 *in* Westwood, J.O. *An Introduction to the Modern Classification of Insects; founded on the natural habits and corresponding organisation of the different families.* London : Longman Vol. 2 [86].

Taxonomic decision for subgeneric arrangement: Michener, C.D. (1965). A classification of the bees of the Australian and South Pacific regions. *Bull. Am. Mus. Nat. Hist.* **130**: 1–362 [228].

Extralimital distribution: Palaearctic Region, see Hurd, P.D., Jr & Moure, J.S. (1963). A classification of the large carpenter bees (Xylocopini) (Hymenoptera : Apoidea). *Univ. Calif. Publ. Entomol.* **29**: 1–365 [188].

Generic reference: Gerling, D., Velthuis, H.H.W. & Hefetz, A. (1989). Bionomics of the large carpenter bees of the genus *Xylocopa*. *Ann. Rev. Entomol.* **34**: 163–190.

Xylocopa (Koptortosoma) Gribodo, 1894

Koptortosoma Gribodo, G. (1894). Note imenotterologiche. Nota II, continuazione. *Boll. Soc. Entomol. Ital.* **26**: 76–136, 262–314 [271]. Type species: *Apis aestuans* Linnaeus, 1758 by subsequent designation, see Vitzthum, H.G. (1930). Acarologische Beobachtungen. *Zool. Jb. Abt. Syst.* **59**: 281–350 [314].

Orbitella Maa, T.-C. (as Tsing-chao Ma) (1938). The Indian species of the genus *Xylocopa* Latr. (Hymenoptera). *Rec. Ind. Mus.* **40**: 265–329 [270] [proposed with subgeneric rank in *Xylocopa* Latreille, 1802; junior homonym of *Orbitella* Douville, 1915 (Protozoa)]. Type species: *Xylocopa confusa* Pérez, 1901 by original designation.

Maiella Michener, C.D. (1942). Taxonomic observations on bees with descriptions of new genera and species (Hymenoptera, Apoidea). *J. N.Y. Entomol. Soc.* **50**: 273–282 [282] [*nom. nov.* for *Orbitella* Maa, 1938].

Euryapis Sandhouse, G.A. (1943). The type species of the genera and subgenera of bees. *Proc. U.S. Natl Mus.* **92**(3156): 519–619 [551] [*nom. nov.* for *Orbitella* Maa, 1938].

Taxonomic decision for synonymy: Hurd, P.D., Jr & Moure, J.S. (1963). A classification of the large carpenter bees (Xylocopini) (Hymenoptera : Apoidea). *Univ. Calif. Publ. Entomol.* **29**: 1–365 [267].

Extralimital distribution: S Palaearctic, Afrotropical and Oriental Regions, extending E to Bismarck

Archipelago, see Michener, C.D. (1965). A classification of the bees of the Australian and South Pacific regions. *Bull. Am. Mus. Nat. Hist.* **130**: 1–362 [228].

Species now known not to occur in Australia: *Xylocopa bryorum* (Fabricius, 1775): Malaysian (type described from "Nova Hollandia", the label is incorrect), see Lieftinck, M.A. (1957). The identity of some Fabrician types of bees (Hymenoptera, Apoidea) 1B. *Proc. K. Ned. Akad. Wet. (C)***60**: 441–450; *Xylocopa muscaria* (Fabricius, 1775): South America (type described from "Nova Hollandia", the label is incorrect), see Hurd, P.D., Jr & Moure, J.S. (1963). A classification of the large carpenter bees (Xylocopini) (Hymenoptera : Apoidea). *Univ. Calif. Publ. Entomol.* **29**: 1–365; *Xylocopa simillima* Smith, 1854: South America (type described from "Australia", the label is incorrect), see Hurd, P.D., Jr & Moure, J.S. (1963). A classification of the large carpenter bees (Xylocopini) (Hymenoptera : Apoidea). *Univ. Calif. Publ. Entomol.* **29**: 1–365.

Xylocopa (Koptortosoma) aruana Ritsema, 1876

Xylocopa aruana Ritsema, C. (1876). Acht nieuwe oost-indische *Xylocopa*-Soorten. *Tijdschr. Entomol.* **19**: 177–185 [178].
Type data: syntypes, RMNH 7♀*.
Type locality: Aru Is.

Distribution: NE coastal, N Gulf, Murray-Darling basin, SE coastal, S Gulfs, N coastal, QLD, NSW, VIC, SA, WA, NT; also New Guinea and Aru.
Ecology: larva—sedentary : adult—volant; melliferous, nest in dead, dry wood (*Capparis* L. [Capparaceae], *Eucalyptus* L'Hérit. [Myrtaceae]), each larva in individual, mass-provisioned cell, flower visiting record: wisteria, *Acacia* Miller [Mimosaceae], *Crotalaria* L. [Fabaceae], *Eucalyptus* L'Hérit. [Myrtaceae], *Passiflora* L. [Passifloraceae], *Solanum* L. [Solanaceae].
References: Rayment, T. (1935). *A Cluster of Bees.* Sixty essays on the life-histories of Australian bees, with specific descriptions of over 100 new species, and an introduction by Professor E.F. Phillips, D.Ph., Cornell University, U.S.A. Sydney : Endeavour Press 752 pp. (biology, as *Xylocopa (Mesotrichia) bryorum* (Fabricius, 1775)); Rayment, T. (1939). Bees from the high lands of New South Wales and Victoria. *Aust. Zool.* **9**: 263–294 (biology, as *Xylocopa (Mesotrichia) bryorum* (Fabricius, 1775)); Rayment, T. (1954). Incidence of acarid mites on the biology of bees. *Aust. Zool.* **12**: 26–38 (as host, as *Xylocopa (Mesotrichia) bryorum* (Fabricius, 1775)); Lieftinck, M.A. (1957). Revision of the carpenter-bees (*Xylocopa* Latr., subgenus *Maiella* Michener) of the Papuan region (Hymenoptera, Apoidea). *Nova Guinea (ns)***8**: 325–376 (taxonomy, previously recorded as *Xylocopa aestuans* (Linnaeus, 1758), *Xylocopa bryorum* (Fabricius, 1775), *Xylocopa confusa* (Pérez, 1901), *Xylocopa dimidiata* (Lepeletier,

1841)); Hurd, P.D., Jr & Moure, J.S. (1963). A classification of the large carpenter bees (Xylocopini) (Hymenoptera : Apoidea). *Univ. Calif. Publ. Entomol.* **29**: 1–365 (generic placement); Michener, C.D. (1965). A classification of the bees of the Australian and South Pacific regions. *Bull. Am. Mus. Nat. Hist.* **130**: 1–362 (illustration); Houston, T.F. (1974). Notes on the behaviour of an Australian carpenter bee, genus *Xylocopa* Latr. (Hymenoptera : Xylocopinae). *Aust. Entomol. Mag.* **2**: 36–38 (biology); Fain, A. (1982). *Sennertia* Oudemans (Acari, Chaetodactylidae) on Australian bees. *Trans. R. Soc. S. Aust.* **106**: 67–70 (as host, as *Mesotrichia bryorum* (Fabricius, 1775)); Goebel, R.L. (1986). Australian native bees. *Qd Agric. J.* **112**: 285–286 (biology, as *Xylocopa bryorum* (Fabricius, 1775)); Anderson, G.J. & Symon, D. (1988). Insect foragers on *Solanum* flowers in Australia. *Ann. M. Bot. Gard.* **75**: 842–852 (flower record).

Xylocopa (Koptortosoma) disconota Friese, 1914

Xylocopa disconota Friese, H. (1914). Die Bienenfauna von Java. *Tijdschr. Entomol.* **57**: 1–61 [61].
Type data: holotype, ZMB ♀*.
Type locality: Redlynch (as Redlynck), Cairns, QLD.

Distribution: NE coastal, QLD; only published localities Cairns, Redlynch, Kuranda and Cape York.
Ecology: adult—volant; melliferous.
References: Lieftinck, M.A. (1957). Revision of the carpenter-bees (*Xylocopa* Latr., subgenus *Maiella* Michener) of the Papuan region (Hymenoptera, Apoidea). *Nova Guinea (ns)***8**: 325–376 (redescription); Hurd, P.D., Jr & Moure, J.S. (1963). A classification of the large carpenter bees (Xylocopini) (Hymenoptera : Apoidea). *Univ. Calif. Publ. Entomol.* **29**: 1–365 (generic placement).

Xylocopa (Koptortosoma) nigroclypeata Rayment, 1935

Xylocopa bryorum nigroclypeata Rayment, T. (1935). *A Cluster of Bees.* Sixty essays on the life-histories of Australian bees, with specific descriptions of over 100 new species, and an introduction by Professor E.F. Phillips, D.Ph., Cornell University, U.S.A. Sydney : Endeavour Press 752 pp. [725].
Type data: holotype, ANIC ♀.
Type locality: Wyndham, WA.

Distribution: N coastal, WA; known only from type locality.
Ecology: adult—volant; melliferous.
References: Lieftinck, M.A. (1957). Revision of the carpenter-bees (*Xylocopa* Latr., subgenus *Maiella* Michener) of the Papuan region (Hymenoptera, Apoidea). *Nova Guinea (ns)***8**: 325–376 (taxonomy, as *Xylocopa (Mesotrichia) bryorum nigroclypeata* Rayment, 1935); Hurd, P.D., Jr & Moure, J.S. (1963). A classification of the large carpenter bees (Xylocopini) (Hymenoptera : Apoidea). *Univ. Calif.*

Publ. Entomol. **29**: 1–365 (generic placement, subspecies to species).

Xylocopa (Koptortosoma) parvula Rayment, 1935

Xylocopa bryorum parvula Rayment, T. (1935). *A Cluster of Bees.* Sixty essays on the life-histories of Australian bees, with specific descriptions of over 100 new species, and an introduction by Professor E.F. Phillips, D.Ph., Cornell University, U.S.A. Sydney : Endeavour Press 752 pp. [725].
Type data: holotype, ANIC ♀.
Type locality: Wyndham, WA.

Distribution: N coastal, WA; known only from type locality.
Ecology: adult—volant; melliferous.
References: Lieftinck, M.A. (1957). Revision of the carpenter-bees (*Xylocopa* Latr., subgenus *Maiella* Michener) of the Papuan region (Hymenoptera, Apoidea). *Nova Guinea (ns)***8**: 325–376 (taxonomy, as *Xylocopa (Mesotrichia) bryorum parvula* Rayment, 1935); Hurd, P.D., Jr & Moure, J.S. (1963). A classification of the large carpenter bees (Xylocopini) (Hymenoptera : Apoidea). *Univ. Calif. Publ. Entomol.* **29**: 1–365 (generic placement, subspecies to species).

Xylocopa (Koptortosoma) wallabia Lieftinck, 1957

Xylocopa (Maiella) wallabia Lieftinck, M.A. (1957). Revision of the carpenter-bees (*Xylocopa* Latr., subgenus *Maiella* Michener) of the Papuan region (Hymenoptera, Apoidea). *Nova Guinea (ns)***8**: 325–376 [369].
Type data: holotype, ZMA ♂*.
Type locality: Burnett River, QLD.

Distribution: NE coastal, QLD; only published localities Burnett River and Charters Towers.
Ecology: adult—volant; melliferous.
Reference: Hurd, P.D., Jr & Moure, J.S. (1963). A classification of the large carpenter bees (Xylocopini) (Hymenoptera : Apoidea). *Univ. Calif. Publ. Entomol.* **29**: 1–365 (generic placement).

Xylocopa (Koptortosoma) xerophila Lieftinck, 1957

Xylocopa (Maiella) xerophila Lieftinck, M.A. (1957). Revision of the carpenter-bees (*Xylocopa* Latr., subgenus *Maiella* Michener) of the Papuan region (Hymenoptera, Apoidea). *Nova Guinea (ns)***8**: 325–376 [371].
Type data: holotype, ANIC ♂.
Type locality: Brocks Creek, NT.

Distribution: N coastal, NT; known only from type locality.
Ecology: adult—volant; melliferous.
Reference: Hurd, P.D., Jr & Moure, J.S. (1963). A classification of the large carpenter bees (Xylocopini) (Hymenoptera : Apoidea). *Univ. Calif. Publ. Entomol.* **29**: 1–365 (generic placement).

APIDAE

INTRODUCTION

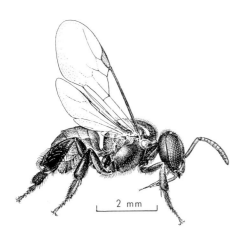

Trigona essingtoni   [by M. Quick]

The Apidae is a family of long-tongued bees and includes all the highly social bees. They live in large colonies, with morphologically differentiated female castes (Michener 1974). The features that set this family apart as the most specialised of the Apoidea (Michener 1979, 1990) are the highly developed social behaviour and the corbicula—the pollen-carrying area on the hind legs of females (Michener *et al.* 1978).

The family is divided into four subfamilies, two of which, Bombinae and Euglossinae, do not occur naturally in Australia. The first introductions of European species of Bombinae, the bumblebees, into Australia to aid in the pollination of introduced plants, were unsuccessful (Young 1967). In 1992, however, an established population of *Bombus terrestris* (Linnaeus, 1758), was discovered in Tasmania. The Euglossinae are native to tropical America.

Meliponinae are small (3–5 mm), native honeybees. They are also called stingless bees or sugar bag bees (Michener 1965, 1990). The subfamily occurs in tropical and southern subtropical areas throughout the world. In Australia, they are found mainly in the north and only two species occur as far southwards as the Sydney area (Wagner & Briscoe 1983; Dollin & Dollin 1986). Adults nest in pre-existing cavities, such as tree hollows, crevices among rocks or in managed hives (Michener 1961; Wille 1983; Heard 1988). The nests are constructed from cerumen, a mixture of secreted wax and resin (Milborrow *et al.* 1987). Flower visiting records are given in Michener (1965) and Armstrong (1979).

The subfamily Apinae has a cosmopolitan distribution (Ruttner 1987). In Australia, it is represented only by the introduced *Apis mellifera*, the honeybee, which is found over most of the continent and in Tasmania (Ruttner 1976; Rhodes 1988). Honeybees construct large nests of wax which may be exposed or may be concealed in pre-existing cavities (Winston 1987).

References

Armstrong, J.A. (1979). Biotic pollination mechanisms in the Australian flora—a review. *N.Z. J. Bot.* **17**: 467–508

Dollin, A. & Dollin, L. (1986). Tracing aboriginal apiculture of Australian native bees in the far north-west. *Australas. Beekpr* **88**: 118–122

Heard, T.A. (1988). Propagation of hives of *Trigona carbonaria* Smith (Hymenoptera: Apidae). *J. Aust. Entomol. Soc.* **27**: 303–304

Michener, C.D. (1961). Observations on the nests and behavior of *Trigona* in Australia and New Guinea (Hymenoptera, Apidae). *Am. Mus. Novit.* **2026**: 1–46

Michener, C.D. (1965). A classification of the bees of the Australian and South Pacific regions. *Bull. Am. Mus. Nat. Hist.* **130**: 1–362

Michener, C.D. (1974). *The Social Behaviour of the Bees.* A comparative study. Cambridge : Belknap Press of Harvard University Press 404 pp.

Michener, C.D. (1979). Biogeography of the bees. *Ann. Mo. Bot. Gdn* **66**: 277–347

Michener, C.D. (1990). Classification of the Apidae (Hymenoptera). *Univ. Kansas Sci. Bull.* **54**: 75–164

Michener, C.D., Winston, M.L. & Jander, R. (1978). Pollen manipulation and related activities and structures in bees of the family Apidae. *Univ. Kansas Sci. Bull.* **51**: 575–601

Milborrow, B.V., Kennedy, J.M. & Dollin A. (1987). Composition of wax made by the Australian stingless bee *Trigona australis. Aust. J. Biol. Sci.* **40**: 15–25

Rhodes, J.W. (ed.) (1988). *Bee Keeping in the Year 2000.* Second Australian and International Beekeeping Congress. Surfers Paradise, Gold Coast, Queensland, Australia. July 21–26, 1988. Brisbane : Dept Primary Industries 288 pp.

Ruttner, F. (1976). Isolated populations of honeybees in Australia. *J. Apic. Res.* **15**: 97–104

Ruttner, F. (1987). *Biogeography and taxonomy of honeybees.* Berlin : Springer 284 pp.

Wagner, A.E. & Briscoe, D.A. (1983). An absence of enzyme variability within two species of *Trigona* (Hymenoptera). *Heredity* **50**: 97–103

Wille, A. (1983). Biology of the stingless bees. *Ann. Rev. Ent.* **28**: 41–64

Winston, M.L. (1987). *The biology of the honey bee.* Cambridge : Harvard University Press 281 pp.

Young, L. (1967). *The Melody Lingers On.* Biography of Tarlton Rayment. Melbourne : Hawthorne Press 123 pp.

APINAE

Apis Linnaeus, 1758

Taxonomic decision for subgeneric arrangement: Michener, C.D. (1965). A classification of the bees of the Australian and South Pacific regions. *Bull. Am. Mus. Nat. Hist.* **130**: 1–362 [231].

Apis (Apis) Linnaeus, 1758

Apis Linnaeus, C. von (1758). *Systema Naturae per Regna tria Naturae, secundum Classes, Ordines, Genera, Species, cum Characteribus, Differentiis, Synonymis, Locis.* Edition X, reformata. Holmiae : Laur. Salvii Tom. I 823 pp. [343]. Type species: *Apis mellifica* Linnaeus, 1761 (=*Apis mellifera* Linnaeus, 1758) by subsequent designation, see Latreille, P.A. (1810). *Considérations Générales sur*
l'Ordre Naturel des Animaux Composant les Classes des Crustacès, des Arachnides, et des Insectes; avec un Tableau Méthodique de leurs Genres, Disposés en Familles. Paris : F. Schoell 444 pp. [439].

Extralimital distribution: Palaearctic, Afrotropical and Oriental Regions; introduced into all parts of the world, see Michener, C.D. (1990). Classification of the Apidae (Hymenoptera). *Univ. Kansas Sci. Bull.* **54**: 75–164 [140].

Apis (Apis) mellifera Linnaeus, 1758

Honeybee

Apis mellifera Linnaeus, C. von (1758). *Systema Naturae per Regna tria Naturae, secundum Classes, Ordines, Genera, Species, cum Characteribus, Differentiis,*

Synonymis, Locis. Edition X, reformata. Holmiae : Laur. Salvii Tom. I 823 pp. [343].
Type data: lectotype, LS worker*.
Subsequent designation: Day, M.C. (1979). The species of Hymenoptera described by Linnaeus in the genera *Sphex, Chrysis, Vespa, Apis* and *Mutilla*. *Biol. J. Linn. Soc.* **12**: 45–84 [67].
Type locality: Europe.

Apis aenigmaticus Rayment, T. (1925). A new species of honey-bee. *Austral. Beekpr* **XXVII**: 67–69 [67] [species name based on drawing of comb constructed by insect, and hearsay description of insect, no evidence that either combs or specimens exist].
Type locality: Gippsland, VIC.

Apis trigona Rayment, T. (1925). A new species of honey-bee. *Austral. Beekpr* **XXVII**: 67–69 [69] [*nom. nud.*, Cardale, J.C., this work, name only and without description or illustration].

Taxonomic decision for synonymy: Michener, C.D. (1965). A classification of the bees of the Australian and South Pacific regions. *Bull. Am. Mus. Nat. Hist.* **130**: 1–362 [232].

Distribution: cosmopolitan, introduced into all regions of Australia.
Ecology: larva—sedentary : adult—volant; melliferous, social insects, living in large colonies, with female reproductive and worker castes, nests of wax and resin, exposed, or in cavities such as hives or in trees, flower visiting record: probably all angiosperms and nectar and pollen producing plants.
References: For general literature on apiculture see specialist journals, *e.g. Journal of Apiculture* and *Australasian Beekeeper* which deal almost exclusively with *Apis mellifera*. For literature on the effect of bee venom on humans see medical literature, *e.g.* Southcott, R.V. (1988). Some harmful Australian insects. *Med. J. Aust.* **149**: 656–662; Piek, T. (ed.) (1986). *Venoms of the Hymenoptera*. Biochemical, pharmacological and behavioural aspects. London : Academic Press 570 pp. A selection of recent and/or Australian references include: Blake, S.T. & Roff, C. (1958). *The Honey Flora of South-eastern Queensland*. Brisbane : Dept. Agriculture & Stock 199 pp. (plants of importance to beekeepers); Ruttner, F. (1976). Isolated populations of honeybees in Australia. *J. Apic. Res.* **15**: 97–104 (populations in Kangaroo Is. and Tasmania); Vithanage, V. & Ironside, D.A. (1986). The insect pollinators of *Macadamia* and their relative importance. *J. Aust. Inst. Agric. Sci.* **52**: 155–160 (pollination); Seeley, T.D. (1985). *Honeybee Ecology*: a study of adaptation in social life. Monographs in Behavior and Ecology. Princeton : Princeton University Press x 201 pp. (ecology); Hornitzky, M.A.Z. (1987). Prevalence of virus infections of honeybees in eastern Australia. *J. Apic. Res.* **26**: 181–185 (diseases); Moezel, P.G. van der, Delfs, J.C., Pate, J.S., Loneragan, W.A. & Bell, D.T. (1987). Pollen selection by honeybees in shrublands of the northern sandplains of Western Australia. *J. Apic. Res.* **26**: 224–232 (flower records); Ruttner, F.

(1987). *Biogeography and taxonomy of honeybees.* Berlin : Springer 284 pp. (taxonomy); Winston, M.L. (1987). *The biology of the honey bee.* Cambridge : Harvard University Press 281 pp. (biology); Rhodes, J. W. (ed.) (1988). *Bee Keeping in the Year 2000*. Second Australian and International Beekeeping Congress. Surfers Paradise, Gold Coast, Queensland, Australia. July 21–26, 1988. Brisbane : Dept Primary Industries 288 pp. (papers on recent research); Velthuis, H.H.W. (1990). The biology and the economic value of the stingless bees, compared to the honeybees. *Apiacta* **25**: 68–74 (biology); Alexander, B.A. (1991). Phylogenetic analysis of the genus *Apis* (Hymenoptera: Apidae). *Ann. Entomol. Soc. Am.* **84**: 137–149 (taxonomy); Vaughton, G. (1992). Effectiveness of nectarivorous birds and honeybees as pollinators of *Banksia spinulosa* (Proteaceae). *Aust. J. Ecol.* **17**: 43–50 (pollination).

BOMBINAE

Bombus Latreille, 1802

Bombus Latreille, P.A. (1802). *Histoire Naturelle des Fourmis et Recueil de Mémoires et d'Observations sur les Abeilles, les Areignées, les Faucheurs et autres Insectes.* Paris : Barrois 445 pp. [437]. Type species: *Apis terrestris* Linnaeus, 1758 by monotypy.

Extralimital distribution: Holoarctic, Neotropical and Oriental Regions; introduced into all warmer parts of the world, see Michener, C.D. (1990). Classification of the Apidae (Hymenoptera). *Univ. Kansas Sci. Bull.* **54**: 75–164 [147].

Generic references: Richards, O.W. (1968). The subgeneric division of the genus *Bombus* Latreille (Hymenoptera : Apidae). *Bull. Br. Mus. (Nat. Hist.) Entomol.* **22**: 209–276; Williams, P.H. (1985). A preliminary cladistic investigation of relationships among the bumble bees (Hymenoptera, Apidae). *Syst. Entomol.* **10**: 239–255.

Bombus terrestris (Linnaeus, 1758)

Apis terrestris Linnaeus, C. von (1758). *Systema Naturae per Regna tria Naturae, secundum Classes, Ordines, Genera, Species, cum Characteribus, Differentiis, Synonymis, Locis.* Edition X, reformata. Holmiae : Laur. Salvii Tom. I 823 pp. [578].
Type data: lectotype, LS ♀*.
Subsequent designation: Day, M.C. (1979). The species of Hymenoptera described by Linnaeus in the genera *Sphex, Chrysis, Vespa, Apis* and *Mutilla*. *Biol. J. Linn. Soc.* **12**: 45–84.
Type locality: Europe.

Distribution: introduced into TAS; established in the Hobart area (first record at Battery Point in February 1992, subsequent records from Glenorchy, Lindisfarne and Collinsvale; P.B. McQuillan & T.D.

Semmens pers. comm. 1993), species native to Pal-aearctic Region, introduced and established in New Zealand since 1885.

Ecology: larva—sedentary : adult—volant; melliferous, social insects, living in colonies, with female reproductive and worker castes, nests of wax in pre-existing cavities in ground (in Europe, usually in abandoned nests of small rodents).

References: Sladen, F.W.L. (1912). *The humble-bee. Its life-history and how to domesticate it: with descriptions of all the British species of Bombus and Psithyrus.* London : Macmillan 238 pp. (biology, p.158 states (incorrectly) 'It [*Bombus terrestris*] has also been acclimatized in Australia'); Rayment, T. (1935). *A Cluster of Bees.* Sixty essays on the life-histories of Australian bees, with specific descriptions of over 100 new species, and an introduction by Professor E.F. Phillips, D.Ph., Cornell University, U.S.A. Sydney : Endeavour Press 752 pp. [505] (as *Bremus terrestris* (Linnaeus, 1758)); Holm, S.N. (1966). The utilization and management of bumble bees for red clover and alfalfa seed production. *Ann. Rev. Entomol.* **11**: 155–182 (management for seed production); Alford, D.V. (1975). *Bumblebees.* London : Davis-Poynter 352 pp. (taxonomy, biology); Donovan, B.J. & Wier, S.S. (1978). Development of hives for field population increase, and studies on the life cycles of the four species of introduced bumble bees in New Zealand. *N.Z. J. Agric. Res.* **21**: 733–756 (biology); Donovan, B.J. (1980). Interactions between native and introduced bees in New Zealand. *N.Z. J. Ecol.* **3**: 104–116 (biology); Donovan, B.J. (1990). Selection and importation of new pollinators to New Zealand. *N.Z. Entomol.* **13**: 26–32 (biology).

MELIPONINAE

Austroplebeia Moure, 1961

Austroplebeia Moure, J.S. (1961). A preliminary supra-specific classification of the Old World meliponine bees (Hymenoptera, Apoidea). *Studia Entomol. (ns)*4: 181–242 [195]. Type species: *Trigona cassiae* Cockerell, 1910 by original designation.

Extralimital distribution: New Guinea (Papua New Guinea), see Michener, C.D. (1990). Classification of the Apidae (Hymenoptera). *Univ. Kansas Sci. Bull.* **54**: 75–164 [133].

Austroplebeia australis (Friese, 1898)

Trigona australis Mocsáry, S. (1898). *In* Friese, H. Die *Trigona*-Arten Australiens. *Természetr. Füz.* **21**: 427–431 [430].
Type data: syntypes, SMNS workers*.
Type locality: Central Australia.

Distribution: NE coastal, SE coastal, Murray-Darling basin, QLD, NSW.

Ecology: larva—sedentary : adult—volant; melliferous, social insects, living in large colonies, with female reproductive and worker castes, nests of wax and resin (and pollen), in trunks of small (average diameter 18 cm) living trees, flower visiting record: *Alphitonia* Reisseck ex Endl. [Rhamnaceae], *Angophora* Cav. [Myrtaceae], *Callistemon* R.Br. [Myrtaceae], *Eucalyptus* L'Hérit. [Myrtaceae], *Melaleuca* L. [Myrtaceae], *Rapistrum* Crantz [Brassicaceae], *Swainsona* Salisb. [Fabaceae], *Wahlenbergia* Roth [Campanulaceae].

References: Hockings, H.J. (1884). Notes on two Australian species of *Trigona*. *Trans. Entomol. Soc. Lond.* **1884**: 149–157 (biology, under aboriginal name "kootchar"); Rayment, T. (1932). The stingless bees of Australia. 6. The finding of a new species. *Vict. Nat.* **49**: 104–107 (taxonomy); Michener, C.D. (1961). Observations on the nests and behavior of *Trigona* in Australia and New Guinea (Hymenoptera, Apidae). *Am. Mus. Novit.* **2026**: 1–46 (biology, as *Trigona (Plebeia) australis* Friese, 1898); Moure, J.S. (1961). A preliminary supra-specific classification of the Old World meliponine bees (Hymenoptera, Apoidea). *Studia Entomol. (ns)*4: 181–242 (generic placement); Michener, C.D. (1965). A classification of the bees of the Australian and South Pacific regions. *Bull. Am. Mus. Nat. Hist.* **130**: 1–362 (illustration, flower record, as *Trigona (Plebeia) australis* Friese, 1898); Michener, C.D. (1974). *The Social Behaviour of the Bees.* A comparative study. Cambridge : Belknap Press of Harvard University Press 404 pp. (biology); McKenzie, E. (1975). Growing up with aborigines. *Qd Nat.* **21**: 46–51 (honey); Wagner, A. & Dollin, L. (1982). Probing the mysteries of the N.S.W. native bees. *Australas. Beekpr* **83**: 157–161 (biology, distribution); Wagner, A.E. & Briscoe, D.A. (1983). An absence of enzyme variability within two species of *Trigona* (Hymenoptera). *Heredity* **50**: 97–103 (genetic variability); Goebel, R.L. (1986). Australian native bees. *Qd Agric. J.* **112**: 285–286 (biology); Milborrow, B.V., Kennedy, J.M. & Dollin A. (1987). Composition of wax made by the Australian stingless bee *Trigona australis*. *Aust. J. Biol. Sci.* **40**: 15–25 (biochemistry); Michener, C.D. (1990). Classification of the Apidae (Hymenoptera). *Univ. Kansas Sci. Bull.* **54**: 75–164 (illustration).

Austroplebeia cassiae (Cockerell, 1910)

Trigona cassiae Cockerell, T.D.A. (1910). New and little-known bees. *Trans. Am. Entomol. Soc.* **36**: 199–249 [247].
Type data: holotype, BMNH Hym.17.b.1137 worker.
Type locality: Mackay, QLD.

Distribution: NE coastal, QLD; only published localities Mackay, Caloundra and Brisbane.

Ecology: larva—sedentary : adult—volant; melliferous, social insects, living in large colonies, with female reproductive and worker castes, nests of wax and resin, flower visiting record: *Cassia* L. *s.lat.* [Caesalpiniaceae], *Eucalyptus* L'Hérit. [Myrtaceae]. References: Rayment, T. (1932). The stingless bees of Australia. 2. The architecture. *Vict. Nat.* **48**: 203–212 (biology); Rayment, T. (1935). *A Cluster of Bees.* Sixty essays on the life-histories of Australian bees, with specific descriptions of over 100 new species, and an introduction by Professor E.F. Phillips, D.Ph., Cornell University, U.S.A. Sydney : Endeavour Press 752 pp. (biology); Michener, C.D. (1961). Observations on the nests and behavior of *Trigona* in Australia and New Guinea (Hymenoptera, Apidae). *Am. Mus. Novit.* **2026**: 1–46 (as synonym of *Trigona (Plebeia) australis* Friese, 1898); Moure, J.S. (1961). A preliminary supra-specific classification of the Old World meliponine bees (Hymenoptera, Apoidea). *Studia Entomol. (ns)***4**: 181–242 (generic placement); Michener, C.D. (1990). Classification of the Apidae (Hymenoptera). *Univ. Kansas Sci. Bull.* **54**: 75–164 (illustration).

Austroplebeia cincta (Mocsáry, 1898)

Trigona cincta Mocsáry, S. (1898). *in* Friese, H. Die *Trigona*-Arten Australiens. *Természetr. Füz.* **21**: 427–431 [431].
Type data: holotype (probable), MNH worker*.
Type locality: Madang (as Friedrich Wilhelmshafen), New Guinea.

Distribution: N Australia (no locality specified); also in New Guinea.
Ecology: larva—sedentary : adult—volant; melliferous, social insects, living in large colonies, with female reproductive and worker castes, nests of wax and resin in living or dead trunks of large (diameter 35 cm or more) trees.
References: Rayment, T. (1932). The stingless bees of Australia. 6. The finding of a new species. *Vict. Nat.* **49**: 104–107 (taxonomy); Michener, C.D. (1961). Observations on the nests and behavior of *Trigona* in Australia and New Guinea (Hymenoptera, Apidae). *Am. Mus. Novit.* **2026**: 1–46 (biology, as *Trigona (Plebeia) cincta* Mocsary, 1898); Moure, J.S. (1961). A preliminary supra-specific classification of the Old World meliponine bees (Hymenoptera, Apoidea). *Studia Entomol. (ns)***4**: 181–242 (generic placement); Michener, C.D. (1974). *The Social Behaviour of the Bees.* A comparative study. Cambridge : Belknap Press of Harvard University Press 404 pp. (Australian record); Michener, C.D. (1990). Classification of the Apidae (Hymenoptera). *Univ. Kansas Sci. Bull.* **54**: 75–164 (generic placement).

Austroplebeia cockerelli (Rayment, 1930)

Trigona cockerelli Rayment, T. (1930). New and remarkable bees. *Proc. R. Soc. Vict.* **43**: 42–61 [57].
Type data: holotype, ANIC worker.
Type locality: Borroloola, NT.

Distribution: N Gulf, NT; known only from type locality.
Ecology: adult—volant; melliferous, social insects, living in large colonies, with female reproductive and worker castes, nests of wax and resin, flower visiting record: turpentine tree, *Cassia* L. *s.lat.* [Caesalpiniaceae], *Eucalyptus* L'Hérit. [Myrtaceae].
References: Rayment, T. (1932). The stingless bees of Australia. 6. The finding of a new species. *Vict. Nat.* **49**: 104–107 (taxonomy); Rayment, T. (1935). *A Cluster of Bees.* Sixty essays on the life-histories of Australian bees, with specific descriptions of over 100 new species, and an introduction by Professor E.F. Phillips, D.Ph., Cornell University, U.S.A. Sydney : Endeavour Press 752 pp. (illustration, flower record); Moure, J.S. (1961). A preliminary supra-specific classification of the Old World meliponine bees (Hymenoptera, Apoidea). *Studia Entomol. (ns)***4**: 181–242 (generic placement); Michener, C.D. (1965). A classification of the bees of the Australian and South Pacific regions. *Bull. Am. Mus. Nat. Hist.* **130**: 1–362 (as *Trigona (Plebeia) cockerelli* Rayment, 1930).

Austroplebeia essingtoni (Cockerell, 1905)

Trigona essingtoni Cockerell, T.D.A. (1905). Descriptions and records of bees. I. *Ann. Mag. Nat. Hist. (7)***16**: 216–225 [220].
Type data: syntypes, BMNH 2 workers (one labelled 'type' and has registration number Hym.17.b.1138).
Type locality: Port Essington, NT.

Distribution: N coastal, NW coastal, NT, WA.
Ecology: adult—volant; melliferous, social insects, living in large colonies, with female reproductive and worker castes, nests of wax and resin.
References: Rayment, T. (1932). The stingless bees of Australia. 6. The finding of a new species. *Vict. Nat.* **49**: 104–107 (taxonomy); Rayment, T. (1953). The distribution of the bee genus, *Trigona*. *West. Aust. Nat.* **4**: 22–23 (distribution); Moure, J.S. (1961). A preliminary supra-specific classification of the Old World meliponine bees (Hymenoptera, Apoidea). *Studia Entomol. (ns)***4**: 181–242 (generic placement, description of male); Michener, C.D. (1965). A classification of the bees of the Australian and South Pacific regions. *Bull. Am. Mus. Nat. Hist.* **130**: 1–362 (as *Trigona (Plebeia) essingtoni* Cockerell, 1905); Evans, H.E. & Matthews, R.W. (1973). Systematics and nesting behavior of Australian *Bembix* sand wasps (Hymenoptera, Sphecidae). *Mem. Am. Entomol. Inst.* **20**: 1–387 (as prey); Evans, H.E., Evans, M.A. & Hook, A. (1982). Observations on the nests and prey of Australian *Bembix* sand wasps (Hymenoptera : Sphecidae). *Aust. J. Zool.* **30**: 71–80 (as prey, illustration); Michener, C.D. (1990). Classification of the Apidae (Hymenoptera). *Univ. Kansas Sci. Bull.* **54**: 75–164 (generic placement, illustration);

Michener, C.D. & Houston, T.F. (1991). Apoidea. pp. 993–1000 *in* CSIRO (sponsor) *The Insects of Australia.* A textbook for students and research workers. Melbourne : Melbourne University Press Vol. II 2nd Edn (illustration).

Austroplebeia ornata (Rayment, 1932)

Trigona cockerelli ornata Rayment, T. (1932). The stingless bees of Australia. 6. The finding of a new species. *Vict. Nat.* **49**: 104–107 [107].
Type data: syntypes, NMV worker, ♂.
Type locality: Cape York, QLD.

Distribution: NE coastal, QLD; known only from type locality.
Ecology: adult—volant; melliferous, social insects, living in large colonies, with female reproductive and worker castes, nests of wax and resin.
References: Rayment, T. (1935). *A Cluster of Bees.* Sixty essays on the life-histories of Australian bees, with specific descriptions of over 100 new species, and an introduction by Professor E.F. Phillips, D.Ph., Cornell University, U.S.A. Sydney : Endeavour Press 752 pp. (described again as new); Moure, J.S. (1961). A preliminary supra-specific classification of the Old World meliponine bees (Hymenoptera, Apoidea). *Studia Entomol. (ns)***4**: 181–242 (generic placement); Michener, C.D. (1965). A classification of the bees of the Australian and South Pacific regions. *Bull. Am. Mus. Nat. Hist.* **130**: 1–362 (as *Trigona (Plebeia) ornata* Rayment, 1932).

Austroplebeia percincta (Cockerell, 1929)

Trigona cincta percincta Cockerell, T.D.A. (1929). Bees in the Australian Museum collection. *Rec. Aust. Mus.* **17**: 199–243 [242].
Type data: syntypes (probable), ZMB 4 workers*.
Type locality: Finke River, Hermannsburg, NT.

Distribution: Lake Eyre basin, NT; known only from type locality.
Ecology: adult—volant; melliferous, social insects, living in large colonies, with female reproductive and worker castes, nests of wax and resin.
References: Cockerell, T.D.A. (1910). New and little-known bees. *Trans. Am. Entomol. Soc.* **36**: 199–249 (as *Trigona cincta* Mocsáry, 1898); Rayment, T. (1932). The stingless bees of Australia. 6. The finding of a new species. *Vict. Nat.* **49**: 104–107 (taxonomy); Michener, C.D. (1961). Observations on the nests and behavior of *Trigona* in Australia and New Guinea (Hymenoptera, Apidae). *Am. Mus. Novit.* **2026**: 1–46 (as *Trigona (Plebeia) percincta* Cockerell, 1929); Moure, J.S. (1961). A preliminary supra-specific classification of the Old World meliponine bees (Hymenoptera, Apoidea). *Studia Entomol. (ns)***4**: 181–242 (generic placement).

Austroplebeia symei (Rayment, 1932)

Trigona symei Rayment, T. (1932). The stingless bees of Australia. 6. The finding of a new species. *Vict. Nat.* **49**: 104–107 [106].
Type data: holotype, ANIC worker.
Type locality: N QLD.

Distribution: QLD; known only from type locality, exact locality not known.
Ecology: adult—volant; melliferous, social insects, living in large colonies, with female reproductive and worker castes, nests of wax and resin, flower visiting record: *Dendrobium* Sw. [Orchidaceae].
References: Rayment, T. (1935). *A Cluster of Bees.* Sixty essays on the life-histories of Australian bees, with specific descriptions of over 100 new species, and an introduction by Professor E.F. Phillips, D.Ph., Cornell University, U.S.A. Sydney : Endeavour Press 752 pp. (described again as new); MacPherson, K. & Rupp, H.M.R. (1936). Further notes on orchid pollination. *N. Qd Nat.* **4**(43): 25–26 (flower record); Moure, J.S. (1961). A preliminary supra-specific classification of the Old World meliponine bees (Hymenoptera, Apoidea). *Studia Entomol. (ns)***4**: 181–242 (generic placement); Michener, C.D. (1965). A classification of the bees of the Australian and South Pacific regions. *Bull. Am. Mus. Nat. Hist.* **130**: 1–362 (as *Trigona (Plebeia) symei* Rayment, 1932).

Austroplebeia websteri (Rayment, 1932)

Trigona websteri Rayment, T. (1932). The stingless bees of Australia. 6. The finding of a new species. *Vict. Nat.* **49**: 104–107 [105].
Type data: holotype, ANIC worker.
Type locality: Wyndham, WA.

Distribution: N coastal, WA; known only from type locality.
Ecology: larva—sedentary : adult—volant; melliferous, social insects, living in large colonies, with female reproductive and worker castes, nests of wax and resin.
References: Rayment, T. (1935). *A Cluster of Bees.* Sixty essays on the life-histories of Australian bees, with specific descriptions of over 100 new species, and an introduction by Professor E.F. Phillips, D.Ph., Cornell University, U.S.A. Sydney : Endeavour Press 752 pp. (taxonomy); Moure, J.S. (1961). A preliminary supra-specific classification of the Old World meliponine bees (Hymenoptera, Apoidea). *Studia Entomol. (ns)***4**: 181–242 (generic placement); Michener, C.D. (1965). A classification of the bees of the Australian and South Pacific regions. *Bull. Am. Mus. Nat. Hist.* **130**: 1–362 (as *Trigona (Plebeia) websteri* Rayment, 1932).

Trigona Jurine, 1807

Trigona Jurine, L. (1807). *Nouvelle Méthode de Classer les Hyménoptères et les Diptères.* Vol. 1 Hyménoptères. Genève : J.J. Paschoud 319+4 pp. [245]. Type species: *Apis* amalthea Fabricius, 1793 (=*Apis amalthea* Olivier, 1789) by subsequent designation, see Latreille, P.A. (1810). *Considérations Générales sur l'Ordre Naturel des Animaux Composant les Classes des Crustacès, des Arachnides, et des Insectes;* avec un Tableau Méthodique de leurs Genres, Disposés en Familles. Paris : F. Schoell 444 pp. [439].

Taxonomic decision for subgeneric arrangement: Michener, C.D. (1990). Classification of the Apidae (Hymenoptera). *Univ. Kansas Sci. Bull.* **54**: 75–164 [119].

Extralimital distribution: Neotropical Region, see Michener, C.D. (1990). Classification of the Apidae (Hymenoptera). *Univ. Kansas Sci. Bull.* **54**: 75–164 [127].

Trigona (Heterotrigona) Schwarz, 1939

Heterotrigona Schwarz, H.F. (1939). The Indo-Malayan species of *Trigona*. *Bull. Am. Mus. Nat. Hist.* **76**: 83–141 [96] [proposed with subgeneric rank in *Trigona* Jurine, 1807]. Type species: *Trigona itama* Cockerell, 1918 by original designation.

Platytrigona Moure, J.S. (1961). A preliminary supra-specific classification of the Old World meliponine bees (Hymenoptera, Apoidea). *Studia Entomol. (ns)* **4**: 181–242 [203]. Type species: *Trigona planifrons* Smith, 1864 by original designation.

Lophotrigona Moure, J.S. (1961). A preliminary supra-specific classification of the Old World meliponine bees (Hymenoptera, Apoidea). *Studia Entomol. (ns)* **4**: 181–242 [205]. Type species: *Trigona canifrons* Smith, 1857 by original designation.

Tetragonula Moure, J.S. (1961). A preliminary supra-specific classification of the Old World meliponine bees (Hymenoptera, Apoidea). *Studia Entomol. (ns)* **4**: 181–242 [206]. Type species: *Trigona iridipennis* Smith, 1857 by original designation.

Tetragonilla Moure, J.S. (1961). A preliminary supra-specific classification of the Old World meliponine bees (Hymenoptera, Apoidea). *Studia Entomol. (ns)* **4**: 181–242 [210]. Type species: *Trigona atripes* Smith, 1857 by original designation.

Geniotrigona Moure, J.S. (1961). A preliminary supra-specific classification of the Old World meliponine bees (Hymenoptera, Apoidea). *Studia Entomol. (ns)* **4**: 181–242 [212]. Type species: *Trigona thoracica* Smith, 1857 by original designation.

Odontotrigona Moure, J.S. (1961). A preliminary supra-specific classification of the Old World meliponine bees (Hymenoptera, Apoidea). *Studia Entomol. (ns)* **4**: 181–242 [213]. Type species: *Trigona haematoptera* Cockerell, 1919 by original designation.

Tetrigona Moure, J.S. (1961). A preliminary supra-specific classification of the Old World meliponine bees (Hymenoptera, Apoidea). *Studia Entomol. (ns)* **4**: 181–242 [213]. Type species: *Trigona apicalis* Smith, 1857 by original designation.

Trigonella Sakagami, D.F. (1975). Stingless bees (excl. *Tetragonula*) from the continental southeast Asia in the collection of the Bernice P. Bishop Museum, Honolulu. Jour. Fac. Sci. Hokkaido Univ. Ser. VI, Zool. **20**: 49–76 [57]. Type species: *Trigona moorei* Schwarz, 1939 by

monotypy. Compiled from secondary source: Michener, C.D. (1990). Classification of the Apidae (Hymenoptera). *Univ. Kansas Sci. Bull.* **54**: 75–164.

Taxonomic decision for synonymy: Michener, C.D. (1990). Classification of the Apidae (Hymenoptera). *Univ. Kansas Sci. Bull.* **54**: 75–164 [126].

Extralimital distribution: Oriental Region, extending E to Solomon Ils, see Michener, C.D. (1990). Classification of the Apidae (Hymenoptera). *Univ. Kansas Sci. Bull.* **54**: 75–164 [127].

Species now known not to occur in Australia: *Trigona (Heterotrigona) canifrons* Smith, 1857: Borneo (incorrectly attributed to Australia), see Michener, C.D. (1965). A classification of the bees of the Australian and South Pacific regions. *Bull. Am. Mus. Nat. Hist.* **130**: 1–362 [231].

Trigona (Heterotrigona) carbonaria Smith, 1854

Trigona carbonaria Smith, F. (1854). *Catalogue of Hymenopterous Insects in the Collection of the British Museum.* Part II. Apidae. London : British Museum pp. 199–465 [414].
Type data: holotype, BMNH Hym.17.b.1136 worker.
Type locality: Australia.

Trigona angophorae Cockerell, T.D.A. (1912). Descriptions and records of bees. XLII. *Ann. Mag. Nat. Hist.* (8)**9**: 220–229 [225].
Type data: holotype, BMNH Hym.17.b.1139 worker.
Type locality: Sydney, NSW.

Taxonomic decision for synonymy: Cockerell, T.D.A. (1930). The bees of Australia. *Aust. Zool.* **6**: 137–156, 205–236 [150].

Distribution: NE coastal, SE coastal, Murray-Darling basin, N coastal, QLD, NSW, WA; also in New Guinea.

Ecology: larva—sedentary : adult—volant; melliferous, social insects, living in large colonies, with female reproductive and worker castes, nests of wax and resin in trunks of large (average diameter 55 cm), dead or alive, standing trees, or in specially constructed boxes, flower visiting record: fruit trees, sunflowers, *Ageratum* L. [Asteraceae], *Alocasia* (Schott) G. Don [Araceae], *Angophora* Cav. [Myrtaceae], *Banksia* L.f. [Proteaceae], *Callistemon* R.Br. [Myrtaceae], *Claoxylon* A. Juss. [Euphorbiaceae], *Cupaniopsis* Radlk. [Sapindaceae], *Daviesia* Sm. [Fabaceae], *Dendrobium* Sw. [Orchidaceae], *Eucalyptus* L'Hérit. [Myrtaceae], *Hibbertia* Andrews [Dilleniaceae], *Jacksonia* Smith [Fabaceae], *Leptospermum* Forster & G.Forster [Myrtaceae], *Melaleuca* L. [Myrtaceae], *Melastoma* L. [Melanstomataceae], *Nymphaea* L. [Nymphaeaceae], *Oxylobium* Andrews [Fabaceae], *Persoonia* Sm. [Proteaceae], *Podolepis* Labill. [Asteraceae], *Pultenaea* Sm. [Fabaceae], *Rubus* L. [Rosaceae], *Telopea* R.Br. [Proteaceae], *Xanthorrhoea* Sm. [Xanthorrhoeaceae].

References: Smith, F. (1863). Exhibitions etc. *Proc. Entomol. Soc. Lond. (3)*1: 171, 174, 181 (biology); Hockings, H.J. (1884). Notes on two Australian species of *Trigona. Trans. Entomol. Soc. Lond.* 1884: 149–157 (biology, under aboriginal name "karbi"); Friese, H. (1912). Zur Bienenfauna von Neu-Guinea und Oceania. *Mitt. Zool. Mus. Berl.* 6: 93–96 (distribution); Cockerell, T.D.A. (1929). Bees in the Queensland Museum. *Mem. Qd Mus.* 9: 298–323 (taxonomy); Rayment, T. (1932). The stingless bees of Australia. 2. The architecture. *Vict. Nat.* 48: 203–212 (biology); Rayment, T. (1932). The stingless bees of Australia. 6. The finding of a new species. *Vict. Nat.* 49: 104–107 (taxonomy); Rayment, T. (1935). *A Cluster of Bees.* Sixty essays on the life-histories of Australian bees, with specific descriptions of over 100 new species, and an introduction by Professor E.F. Phillips, D.Ph., Cornell University, U.S.A. Sydney : Endeavour Press 752 pp. (biology); Michener, C.D. (1961). Observations on the nests and behavior of *Trigona* in Australia and New Guinea (Hymenoptera, Apidae). *Am. Mus. Novit.* 2026: 1–46 (biology, as *Trigona (Tetragona) carbonaria* Smith, 1854); Moure, J.S. (1961). A preliminary supra-specific classification of the Old World meliponine bees (Hymenoptera, Apoidea). *Studia Entomol. (ns)*4: 181–242 (as *Tetragonula carbonaria* (Smith, 1854)); Rayment, T. (1961). A tiny bee (*Trigona carbonaria*) and a very large flower (*Telopea*). *Proc. R. Zool. Soc. N.S.W.* 1958–59: 96–97 (biology); Michener, C.D. (1965). A classification of the bees of the Australian and South Pacific regions. *Bull. Am. Mus. Nat. Hist.* 130: 1–362 (flower record, as *Trigona (Tetragona) carbonaria* Smith, 1854); Evans, H.E. & Matthews, R.W. (1973). Systematics and nesting behavior of Australian *Bembix* sand wasps (Hymenoptera, Sphecidae). *Mem. Am. Entomol. Inst.* 20: 1–387 (as prey); Michener, C.D. (1974). *The Social Behaviour of the Bees.* A comparative study. Cambridge : Belknap Press of Harvard University Press 404 pp. (biology); McKenzie, E. (1975). Growing up with aborigines. *Qd Nat.* 21: 46–51 (honey); Anderson, D. & Gibbs, A. (1982). Viruses and Australian native bees. *Australas. Beekpr* 83: 131–134 (biology); Wagner, A. & Dollin, L. (1982). Probing the mysteries of the N.S.W. native bees. *Australas. Beekpr* 83: 157–161 (biology); Evans, H.E., Evans, M.A. & Hook, A. (1982). Observations on the nests and prey of Australian *Bembix* sand wasps (Hymenoptera : Sphecidae). *Aust. J. Zool.* 30: 71–80 (as prey); Hawkeswood, T.J. (1983). Pollination and fruit production of *Cupaniopsis anacardioides* (A. Rich.) Radlkf. (Sapindaceae) at Townsville, North Queensland. 1. Pollination and floral biology. *Vict. Nat.* 100: 12–20 (flower record); Shaw, D.E. & Cantrell, B.K. (1983). A study of the pollination of *Alocasia macrorrhiza* (L.) G. Don (Araceae) in southeast Queensland. *Proc. Linn. Soc.*

N.S.W. 106: 323–335 (flower record); Wagner, A.E. & Briscoe, D.A. (1983). An absence of enzyme variability within two species of *Trigona* (Hymenoptera). *Heredity* 50: 97–103 (genetic variability); Goebel, R.L. (1986). Australian native bees. *Qd Agric. J.* 112: 285–286 (biology, illustration); Milborrow, B.V., Kennedy, J.M. & Dollin A. (1987). Composition of wax made by the Australian stingless bee *Trigona australis. Aust. J. Biol. Sci.* 40: 15–25 (resin collection); Fain, A. & Heard, T.A. (1987). Description and life cycle of *Cerophagus trigona* spec. nov. (Acari, Acaridae), associated with the stingless bee *Trigona carbonaria* Smith in Australia. *Bull. Inst. R. Sci. Nat. Belg. Entomol.* 57: 197–202 (biology); Heard, T.A. (1988). Propagation of hives of *Trigona carbonaria* Smith (Hymenoptera: Apidae). *J. Aust. Entomol. Soc.* 27: 303–304 (biology); Slater, A.T. & Calder, D.M. (1988). The pollination biology of *Dendrobium speciosum* Smith: a case of false advertising? *Aust. J. Bot.* 36: 145–158 (pollination); Michener, C.D. (1990). Classification of the Apidae (Hymenoptera). *Univ. Kansas Sci. Bull.* 54: 75–164 (generic placement, illustration).

Trigona (Heterotrigona) clypearis Friese, 1908

Trigona laeviceps clypearis Friese, H. (1908). Hymenoptera. II. Apidae. Nova Guinea. pp. 353–359 pl. XV *in* Wichmann, A. *Résultats de L'Expedition Scientifique Néerlandaise à la Nouvelle Guinée en 1903.* Leiden : E.J. Brill [358].
Type data: syntypes (probable), whereabouts unknown, workers*.
Type locality: Maniki (as Manikion) and Wendesi, New Guinea.

Trigona wybenica Cockerell, T.D.A. (1929). Bees in the Queensland Museum. *Mem. Qd Mus.* 9: 298–323 [300].
Type data: holotype, USNM worker*.
Type locality: Thursday Is., QLD.

Taxonomic decision for synonymy: Moure, J.S. (1961). A preliminary supra-specific classification of the Old World meliponine bees (Hymenoptera, Apoidea). *Studia Entomol. (ns)*4: 181–242 [209].

Distribution: NE coastal, QLD; also in New Guinea.
Ecology: larva—sedentary : adult—volant; melliferous, social insects, living in large colonies, with female reproductive and worker castes, nests of wax and resin, in dead timber, in various house cavities.
References: Rayment, T. (1932). The stingless bees of Australia. 6. The finding of a new species. *Vict. Nat.* 49: 104–107 (taxonomy, as *Trigona wybenica* Cockerell, 1929); Michener, C.D. (1961). Observations on the nests and behavior of *Trigona* in Australia and New Guinea (Hymenoptera, Apidae). *Am. Mus. Novit.* 2026: 1–46 (biology, as *Trigona (Tetragona) wybenica* Cockerell, 1929); Michener, C.D. (1974). *The Social Behaviour of the Bees.* A comparative study. Cambridge : Belknap Press of Harvard University Press 404 pp. (biology); Wagner, A. & Dollin, L. (1982). Swarming in Australian na-

tive bees—help solve the mystery! *Australas. Beekpr* **84**: 34–38 (biology, as *Trigona wybenica* Cockerell, 1929); Wagner, A. & Dollin, L. (1982). North Queensland's native bees—the little Aussie battlers. *Australas. Beekpr* **84**: 70–72 (biology, as *Trigona wybenica* Cockerell, 1929); Dollin, L. & Dollin, A. (1983). Honeymooning in far north Queensland with Australian native bees. *Australas. Beekpr* **85**: 104–107 (biology, as *Trigona wybenica* Cockerell, 1929); Michener, C.D. (1990). Classification of the Apidae (Hymenoptera). *Univ. Kansas Sci. Bull.* **54**: 75–164 (generic placement).

Trigona (Heterotrigona) hockingsi Cockerell, 1929

Trigona carbonaria hockingsi Cockerell, T.D.A. (1929). Bees from the Australian region. *Am. Mus. Novit.* **346**: 1–18 [8].
Type data: syntypes, workers (a specimen is labelled 'type' and has the registration number Hy/3722).
Type locality: Cape York, QLD.

Distribution: NE coastal, N Gulf, N coastal, QLD, NT.
Ecology: larva—sedentary : adult—volant; melliferous, social insects, living in large colonies, with female reproductive and worker castes, nests of wax and resin (fresh oil-based paint and putty from buildings may be used), in tree cavities, underground or in house cavities, flower visiting record: *Dendrobium* Sw. [Orchidaceae].
References: Cockerell, T.D.A. (1929). Bees in the Queensland Museum. *Mem. Qd Mus.* **9**: 298–323 (biology); Rayment, T. (1932). The stingless bees of Australia. 6. The finding of a new species. *Vict. Nat.* **49**: 104–107 (taxonomy); Rayment, T. (1935). *A Cluster of Bees.* Sixty essays on the life-histories of Australian bees, with specific descriptions of over 100 new species, and an introduction by Professor E.F. Phillips, D.Ph., Cornell University, U.S.A. Sydney : Endeavour Press 752 pp. (taxonomy); MacPherson, K. & Rupp, H.M.R. (1936). Further notes on orchid pollination. *N. Qd Nat.* **4**(43): 25–26 (flower record, as *Trigona kockingsi*, incorrect spelling); Michener, C.D. (1961). Observations on the nests and behavior of *Trigona* in Australia and New Guinea (Hymenoptera, Apidae). *Am. Mus. Novit.* **2026**: 1–46 (biology); Moure, J.S. (1961). A preliminary supra-specific classification of the Old World meliponine bees (Hymenoptera, Apoidea). *Studia Entomol. (ns)***4**: 181–242 (as *Tetragonula hockingsi* (Cockerell, 1929)); Michener, C.D. (1974). *The Social Behaviour of the Bees.* A comparative study. Cambridge : Belknap Press of Harvard University Press 404 pp. (biology); Levitt, D. (1981). *Plants and People:* aboriginal uses of plants on Groote Eylandt. Canberra : Institute of Aboriginal Studies 166 pp. (aboriginal use); Michener, C.D. (1981). Paint for nest construction. *Bee World* **62**: 34. (biology); Wagner, A. & Dollin, L. (1982). Swarming in Aus-

tralian native bees—help solve the mystery! *Australas. Beekpr* **84**: 34–38 (biology); Wagner, A. & Dollin, L. (1982). North Queensland's native bees— the little Aussie battlers. *Australas. Beekpr* **84**: 70–72 (biology); Dollin, L. & Dollin, A. (1983). Honeymooning in far north Queensland with Australian native bees. *Australas. Beekpr* **85**: 104–107 (biology); Michener, C.D. (1990). Classification of the Apidae (Hymenoptera). *Univ. Kansas Sci. Bull.* **54**: 75–164 (generic placement).

Trigona (Heterotrigona) laeviceps Smith, 1858

Trigona laeviceps Smith, F. (1858). Catalogue of the hymenopterous insects collected at Sarawak, Borneo; Mount Ophir, Malacca; and at Singapore, by A.R. Wallace. *J. Proc. Linn. Soc. Lond. Zool.* **2**: 42–130 [51] [type locality not resolved].
Type data: holotype, BMNH Hym.17.b.1184 worker.
Type locality: Mt Ophir (on label), Singapore (in description).

Distribution: NE coastal, N coastal, QLD, NT; only published localities Cape York, Thursday Is., Gordonvale and Adelaide River, also in New Guinea and SE Asia.
Ecology: larva—sedentary : adult—volant; melliferous, social insects, living in large colonies, with female reproductive and worker castes, nests of wax and resin.
References: Cockerell, T.D.A. (1905). Descriptions and records of bees. I. *Ann. Mag. Nat. Hist.* (7)**16**: 216–225 (as *Trigona canifrons* Smith, 1857); Cockerell, T.D.A. (1922). Australian bees in the Queensland Museum. *Mem. Qd Mus.* **7**: 257–279 (distribution); Cockerell, T.D.A. (1929). Bees from the Australian region. *Am. Mus. Novit.* **346**: 1–18 (distribution); Cockerell, T.D.A. (1930). The bees of Australia. *Aust. Zool.* **6**: 137–156, 205–236 (taxonomy); Rayment, T. (1932). The stingless bees of Australia. 6. The finding of a new species. *Vict. Nat.* **49**: 104–107 (taxonomy); Moure, J.S. (1961). A preliminary supra-specific classification of the Old World meliponine bees (Hymenoptera, Apoidea). *Studia Entomol. (ns)***4**: 181–242 (as *Tetragonula laeviceps* (Smith, 1857)); Michener, C.D. (1965). A classification of the bees of the Australian and South Pacific regions. *Bull. Am. Mus. Nat. Hist.* **130**: 1–362 (as *Trigona (Tetragona) laeviceps* Smith, 1857); Wille, A. (1977). A general review of the fossil stingless bees. *Rev. Biol. Trop.* **25**: 43–46 (as synonym); Sakagami, S.F. (1978). *Tetragonula* stingless bees of the Continental Asia and Sri Lanka (Hymenoptera, Apidae). *J. Fac. Sci. Hokkaido Univ. Ser. VI, Zool.* **21**: 165–247 (taxonomy); Dollin, L. & Dollin, A. (1983). Honeymooning in far north Queensland with Australian native bees. *Australas. Beekpr* **85**: 104–107 (biology); Sakagami, S.F., Inoue, T. & Yamane, S. (1983). Nest architecture and colony composition of the Sumatran stingless bee *Trigona laeviceps*.

Kontyu **51**: 100–111 (biology); Sakagami, S.F., Yamane, S. & Inoue, T. (1983). Oviposition behavior of two southeast Asian stingless bees, *Trigona (Tetragonula) laeviceps* and *T. (T.) pagdeni*. *Kontyu* **51**: 441–457 (biology); Salmah, S., Inoue, T. & Sakagami, S.F. (1984). Relationship between age sequence and pigmentation in the stingless bee *Trigona (Tetragonula) laeviceps*. *J. Apic. Res.* **23**: 55–58 (biology); Inoue, T., Sakagami, S.F., Salmah, S. & Nukmal, N. (1984). Discovery of successful absconding in the stingless bee *Trigona (Tetragonula) laeviceps*. *J. Apic. Res.* **23**: 136–142 (biology); Inoue, T., Sakagami, S.F., Salmah, S. & Yamane, S. (1984). The process of colony multiplication in the Sumatran stingless bee *Trigona (Tetragonula) laeviceps*. *Biotropica* **16**: 100–111 (biology); Michener, C.D. (1990). Classification of the Apidae (Hymenoptera). *Univ. Kansas Sci. Bull.* **54**: 75–164 (generic placement).

Trigona (Heterotrigona) mellipes Friese, 1898

Trigona mellipes Mocsáry, S. (1898). *In* Friese, H. Die *Trigona*-Arten Australiens. *Természetr. Füz.* **21**: 427–431 [429].

Type data: syntypes, ZMB 1 worker 1♂* (A. Dollin pers. comm.).

Type locality: Central Australia (as S. Australia in description), see Friese, H. (1909). Die Bienenfauna von Neu-Guinea. *Ann. Hist.-Nat. Mus. Natl. Hung.* **7**: 179–288 [276].

Distribution: N coastal, N Gulf, WA, NT.

Ecology: adult—volant; melliferous, social insects, living in large colonies, with female reproductive and worker castes, nests of wax and resin.

References: Rayment, T. (1932). The stingless bees of Australia. 6. The finding of a new species. *Vict. Nat.* **49**: 104–107 (taxonomy, as *Trigona melipes* incorrect subsequent spelling); Michener, C.D. (1965). A classification of the bees of the Australian and South Pacific regions. Bull. Am. Mus. Nat. Hist. **130**: 1–362 (as *Trigona (Tetragona) mellipes* Friese, 1898); Michener, C.D. (1990). Classification of the Apidae (Hymenoptera). *Univ. Kansas Sci. Bull.* **54**: 75–164 (generic placement).

APPENDIX I

ABBREVIATIONS AND SYMBOLS

ACT	Australian Capital Territory
alt.	altitude
Art.	Article
Bd	Band
E	east, eastern
ed./eds	editor/editors
edn	edition
emend.	emendation
fasc.	fascicule
fig./figs	figure/figures
ft	feet
ICZN	International Code of Zoological Nomenclature
Is./Ils	Island/Islands
km	kilometre
Lfg	Lieferung
livr.	livraison
m	metre
ms	manuscript
Mt/Mtn/Mts	Mount/Mountain/Mountains
N	north, northern
Nat.	Natural
Natl	National
no.	number
nom. nov.	*nomen novum* (new replacement name)
nom. nud.	*nomen nudum* (not an available name)
nov. comb.	*nova combinatio* (new combination)
ns	new series
NSW	New South Wales
NT	Northern Territory
p./pp.	page/pages
pl./pls	plate/plates
pt/pts	part/parts
QLD	Queensland
S	south, southern
SA	South Australia
ser.	series
sp./spp.	species
TAS	Tasmania
Tom.	Tome/Tomus
var.	variety
Verl.	Verlag
VIC	Victoria
Vol.	Volume
W	west, western
WA	Western Australia
[*name*]	square brackets enclosing a valid or available name indicate a qualification of the use of that name in the context in which it appears.
*	appears only with reference to type specimen information and indicates that the author has not seen the specimen(s).
♂	male(s)
♀	female(s)

APPENDIX II

MUSEUM ACRONYMS

AM	Australian Museum, Sydney, Australia
AMNH	American Museum of Natural History, New York, USA
ANIC	Australian National Insect Collection, CSIRO, Canberra, Australia
BMNH	British Museum (Natural History), London, England
BPBM	Bernice P. Bishop Museum, Honolulu, USA
CAS	California Academy of Science, San Francisco, USA
DEIB	Deutsches Entomologisches Institut, Eberswalde, Germany
HNHM	Hungarian Natural History Museum, Budapest, Hungary
LS	Linnaean Society, London, England
MCZ	Museum of Comparative Zoology, Harvard University, Cambridge, USA
MNH	Musei Nationalis Hungarici, Budapest, Hungary
MNHP	Muséum National d'Histoire Naturelle, Paris, France
NHMW	Naturhistorisches Museum, Wien, Austria
NHRM	Naturhistoriske Riksmuseum, Stockholm, Sweden
NMV	Museum of Victoria, Melbourne, Australia
OUM	Hope Department Entomology, Oxford University, Oxford, England
QM	Queensland Museum, Brisbane, Australia
RMNH	Rijksmuseum van Natuurlijke Historie, Leiden, Netherlands
SAMA	South Australian Museum, Adelaide, Australia
SMNS	Staatliches Museum für Naturkunde, Stuttgart, Germany
USNM	US National Museum, Smithsonian Institution, Washington DC, USA
WADA	Western Australia Department of Agriculture, Perth, Australia
WAM	Western Australia Museum, Perth, Australia
ZIUU	Uppsala Universitets Zoologiska Museum, Uppsala, Sweden
ZMA	Universiteit van Amsterdam, Amsterdam, Holland
ZMB	Museum für Naturkunde an der Universität Humbold zu Berlin, Berlin, Germany
ZMK	Zoologisches Museum der Universität Kiel, Kiel, Germany

APPENDIX III

TAXONOMIC DECISIONS MADE IN THIS WORK

Note: Taxonomic decisions are by J.C. Cardale, except for a new replacement name by T.F. Houston.

New Replacement Name
Euryglossa (Callohesma) tibialis Cardale (for *Euryglossa (Callohesma) tuberculata* Exley, 1974)
Hylaeus (Prosopisteron) simplus Houston, T.F. (for *Hylaeus (Prosopisteron) simplex* Michener, 1965)

Nomina nuda
Anthophora adelaidae ernesti Rayment, 1944
Anthophora duttiella Rayment, 1944
Anthophora engganensis Rayment, 1944
Anthophora engannensis Rayment, 1946
Anthophora longula Rayment, 1944
Anthophora parapulchra Rayment, 1944
Anthophora perpulchra Rayment, 1944
Anthophora perpulchra wallaciella Rayment, 1944
Anthophora townleyella Rayment, 1944
Anthophora sybilae glauca Rayment, 1944
Apis trigona Rayment, 1925
Euryglossa nigrocyanea Rayment, 1935
Exoneura roddi Rayment, 1949
Exoneura subholmesi Rayment, 1949
Halictus darlingensis Rayment, 1954
Halictus paradimorphus Rayment, 1955
Hylaeus dorothae Erickson, 1951
Hylaeus nigrojugata Rayment, 1951
Hylaeus nigrojugatus Rayment, 1954
Paracolletes paradoxus Rayment, 1955
Prosopis ruficornis Rayment, 1929

New Status Assignments
Exoneura rufa Rayment, 1935 as species

Emendation
Halictus elliottii Rayment, 1929 (for *elliotii*)

Corrections to Type Designations
Cladocerapis persooniae Rayment, 1950
Crocisa caeruleifrons darwini Cockerell, 1905
Crocisa tincta Cockerell, 1905
Euryglossa calliopsella Cockerell, 1910
Euryglossa ephippiata punctata Rayment, 1939
Euryglossella nothula Cockerell, 1922
Halictus flindersi Cockerell, 1905
Halictus williamsi Cockerell, 1930
Hyleoides zonalis albocincta Cockerell, 1909
Lamprocolletes obscurus Smith, 1853
Meroglossa chiropterina Cockerell, 1930
Meroglossa deceptor Perkins, 1912

Meroglossa decipiens Perkins, 1912
Meroglossa sculptissima Cockerell, 1910
Paracolletes marginatus Smith, 1879
Prosopis albipes Friese, 1924
Prosopis chalybaea Friese, 1924
Prosopis elegans Smith, 1853
Prosopis metallicus Smith, 1862
Prosopis nigropersonata Cockerell, 1910
Prosopis nubilosella Cockerell, 1910
Prosopis obscuriceps Friese, 1924
Prosopis violacea Smith, 1853
Stilpnosoma piceum Friese, 1924
Turnerella pachycephala Cockerell, 1929
Turnerella semiflava Cockerell, 1929

TAXONOMIC INDEX

COMMON NAME INDEX

PUBLICATION DATES OF PREVIOUS VOLUMES

Volume 1 29 November 1983
Amphibia & Reptilia
by H.G. Cogger, E.E. Cameron & H.M. Cogger

Volume 2 22 May 1985
Hymenoptera (Part 1)
Formicoidea by R.W. Taylor & D.R. Brown
Vespoidea & Sphecoidea by Josephine Cardale

Volume 3 9 September 1985
Arachnida (Part 1)
Mygalomorphae by B.Y. Main
Araneomorphae (Part) by Valerie T. Davies with Lycosidae by R.J. McKay
Pseudoscorpionida, Amblypygi & Palpigradi by M.S. Harvey

Volume 4 22 April 1987
Coleoptera
Archostemata, Myxophaga & Adephaga (Part)
by J.F. Lawrence, B.P. Moore, J.E. Pyke & T.A. Weir

Volume 5 13 April 1988
Mammalia
by J.L. Bannister, J.H. Calaby, L.J. Dawson, J.K. Ling, J.A. Mahoney,
G.M. McKay, B.J. Richardson, W.D.L. Ride & D.W. Walton

Volume 6 23 December 1988
Ephemeroptera by I. Campbell
Megaloptera by G. Theischinger & W.W.K. Houston
Odonata by W.W.K. Houston & J.A.L. Watson
Plecoptera by F.B. Michaelis & C.M. Yule
Trichoptera by A. Neboiss

Volume 7 30 June 1989
Pisces (Part 1)
Petromyzontidae to Carangidae
by J.R. Paxton, D.F. Hoese, G.R. Allen & J.E. Hanley

Volume 8 30 Jan 1992
Non-Marine Mollusca
by B.J. Smith

Volume 9 22 June 1992
Coleoptera: Scarabaeoidea
by G. Cassis, W.W.K. Houston, T.A. Weir & B.P. Moore